SILVER BURDETT & GINN PHYSICAL SCIENCE

Experience the excellence.

REVIEWER'S GUIDE*

MOTIVATION

An Interactive Approach

• Illustrations and text ignite student curiosity and interest, which leads to active learning and understanding. See pages T4-T5, T6-T7, T10-T11, 193, 336.

• Up-to-date coverage of contemporary and basic topics relates physical science to current events and to students' everyday lives. See pages T12-T13, 36, 179, 335, 512.

• Activities allow all students to experience the excitement of making scientific discoveries through their own investigations. See pages T4-T5, T10-T11, 140, 196, 337.

UNDERSTANDING

A Variety of Paths to Student Success

• Objectives in every section increase comprehension by giving students clear goals and a purpose for reading. See pages T6, 12, 256, 450.

• Illustrations interact so closely with the text that they serve as context clues to the understanding of key terms and concepts. See pages T6-T7, 178, 378, 510.

• Study skills are consistently developed by a variety of study aids throughout the program. See pages T6-T7, T20-T21, 526-527, SG105.

CRITICAL THINKING

Problem Solving and Decision Making

• Interactive questions throughout the text require students to use skills ranging from observing, sequencing, and comparing to predicting, inferring, and hypothesizing. See pages T8-T9, T24-T25, 15, 37, 114, 424.

• Literal to more challenging questions after each section and chapter build skills from retention to reasoning. See pages T8-T9, 150–151, 220, 300-301, 348.

• A problem-solving *Puzzler* in each chapter intrigues students' interest. See pages T8-T9, 144, 200, 396, 456.

• *Issues and Technology* focuses on graph-reading, map-reading, and decision-making skills. See pages 275-277, 569-571.

• *Physical Science Skills Handbook* at the back of the text develops interpretive and analytical skills by investigating a variety of phenomena relating to physical science. See pages T12, 579-591.

• Thinking skills are identified and additional suggestions for developing these skills are given in the teacher's marginal notes. See pages TE8, TE178, TE 362.

ACTIVE LEARNING

From Observation to Experimentation

• The text begins with a two-chapter unit that focuses on the process, the skills, and the tools for obtaining knowledge in the physical sciences. See pages viii-49.

• Skills and content are developed simultaneously through student interaction with the text and illustrations. See pages 14, 69, 109, 231, 282, 372, 552.

• Active learning experiences build science process skills from simple observation and measurement exercises to problem-solving activities and open-ended projects. See pages T10-T11, 15, 210, 340, 527, 563.

• Activities in the Student Text and investigations in the Laboratory Manual offer flexibility for accommodating a variety of classroom situations and student needs. See pages T10-T11, T20-T21, 305, 448, LM7-10, LM65-66.

ENRICHMENT

Making Physical Science Relevant

• Students are kept up to date on the latest research findings, technological developments, and career opportunities. See pages T12-T13, 50, 352, 475, 568.

• Biographies and high-interest feature articles help students experience the human dimension of physical science. See pages T12-T13, 274, 519-521.

• Students are given opportunities to evaluate information and to make decisions on issues of current concern. See pages T13, 569-571.

ACHIEVEMENT

Reinforcing and Evaluating Student Progress

• Multilevel questions after each section and each chapter measure students' attainment of objectives and application of critical-thinking skills. See pages T14-T15, 67, 128-129, 192, 211, 454, 458-459.

• *Review and Skill Masters* and the testing program evaluate student progress at varying degrees of mastery—from basic facts and skills to higher-level concepts and critical-thinking skills. See pages T14-T15, RSM23-28, TM13-16, TM89-98.

TEACHER SUPPORT

Planning Ahead

• *Chapter Planning Guide* correlates program components at a glance, and include an activity materials list and reduced copy masters. See pages T16-T17, 105a-105d, 157a-157d.

• A consistent three-step teaching plan in the extended margins provides a wealth of resources for both the new and experienced teacher. See pages T18-T19, TE62-67, TE197-201, TE286-289.

FLEXIBILITY

Meeting Individual Needs

• Self-contained units can be taught in any sequence. See page T2.

• Comprehensive content plus a consistent emphasis on thinking and process skills makes the program suitable for a variety of teaching and learning styles. See pages T8-T9.

• A well-organized variety of program components makes it easy to provide for a wide range of individual differences in student abilities, interests, and learning styles. See pages T3, T14-T15, T20-T21.

*Explanation of Page References
T—Teacher Edition Front Matter
TE—Teacher Edition of Student Text
SG—Study Guide
LM—Laboratory Manual
RSM—Review and Skill Masters
TM—Test Masters
Nonlabeled Pages—Student Text

SILVER BURDETT & GINN

PHYSICAL SCIENCE

TABLES OF CONTENTS

TEACHER EDITION

STUDENT EDITION

See pp. ii-vii for detailed Table of Contents.

PROGRAM COMPONENTS	FORMAT			
Student Text	Hardcover			
Teacher Edition	Hardcover			
Teacher Resource Package	Three-ring binder			

	IN TEACHER RESOURCE PACKAGE*	BLACKLINE MASTER	SPIRIT MASTER	CONSUMABLE TEXT AND TEACHER EDITION
Review and Skill Masters	✔	✔	✔	
Laboratory Manual	✔	✔		✔
Study Guide	✔	✔		✔
Test Masters	✔	✔	✔	
Science Olympics	✔	✔	✔	
The Invention Convention	✔	✔	✔	
Safety Handbook	✔	✔		
Posters	✔			
Color Transparencies	✔			
Transparency Masters	✔	✔		
Computer Test Bank Software		✔		

*Blackline master form only

PHYSICAL SCIENCE

MOTIVATION: An Interactive Approach

Lively, informative text and striking illustrations work together to involve students in fascinating explorations of physical science.

1 **Interactive questions** throughout each chapter spark students' involvement with the text and illustrations.

2 **Up-to-date information** on the study of magnetic fields in the human body helps make students aware of the relevance of physical science to their own lives.

SCIENCE & TECHNOLOGY

2 **O**rgans in the human body have magnetic fields, just as the earth or a horseshoe magnet has a magnetic field. The most common source of magnetism in the body is electric currents generated naturally by muscles and nerves. The heart and brain produce the most current.

New technology has provided better detectors for the tiny magnetic fields produced by organs. One of the newest and most sensitive detectors is known as SQUID. This name stands for "superconducting quantum interference device."

Much of the research done with SQUID on human magnetism is centered on the brain. Electric currents in the brain produce magnetic fields. When these fields are sensed by SQUID, they produce charts called

magnetoencephalograms, or MEG's. The MEG's sense small sources of activity in the brain. Thus, MEG's can define individual sources of electrical activity clearly. This can give doctors information to help diagnose brain disorders.

Epilepsy is one illness that is being better diagnosed with the help of MEG's. A person with epilepsy has disrupted electrical rhythms in the brain. MEG's help locate where in the brain the cause of the epilepsy is.

BTI Biomagnetic Technologies, Inc.

ACIDS, BASES, AND SALTS

Hydronium ions form in acid solutions. Acids are sometimes defined as substances that produce hydronium ions. However, it is the release of hydrogen ions that determines the behavior of acids. It is more convenient to discuss reactions of acids in terms of hydrogen ions.

Table 8-1 lists some common acids. Notice that all of these acids contain hydrogen. Acids also contain one or more nonmetals, such as chlorine. Acids usually do not contain metals.

When an acid dissolves in water, some of the units may not dissociate. Thus some acids produce more H^+ ions than do others. A *strong acid* is an acid that releases many hydrogen ions in water. Strong acids dissociate completely. Nitric acid, HNO_3, is a strong acid and dissociates as shown below.

$$HNO_3(aq) \rightarrow H^+(aq) + NO_3^-(aq)$$

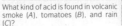

Table 8-1 *Common Acids*

Name of Acid	Chemical Formula	Source
Acetic acid	CH_3COOH	Vinegar
Ascorbic acid (vitamin C)	$(CH_2COOH)_2COHCOOH$	Tomatoes, citrus fruits, vegetables
Carbonic acid	H_2CO_3	Rain water, soft drinks
Hydrochloric acid	HCl	Gastric juice in stomach
Sulfurous acid	H_2SO_3	Acid rain, volcanic smoke

Figure 8-1

What kind of acid is found in volcanic smoke (*A*), tomatoes (*B*), and rain (*C*)?

186

Students experience the excitement of making discoveries and decisions, thinking creatively, and solving problems.

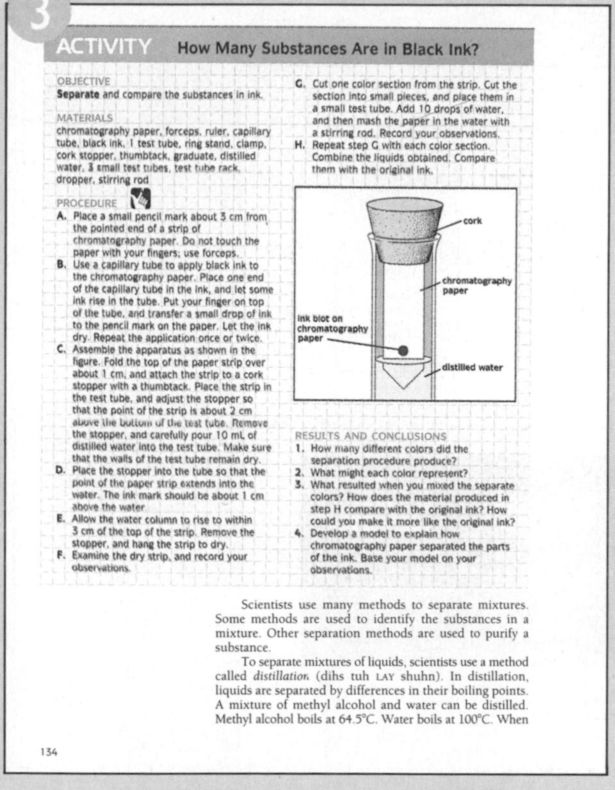

ACTIVITY   How Many Substances Are in Black Ink?

OBJECTIVE
Separate and compare the substances in ink.

MATERIALS
chromatography paper, forceps, ruler, capillary tube, black ink, 1 test tube, ring stand, clamp, cork stopper, thumbtack, graduate, distilled water, 3 small test tubes, test tube rack, dropper, stirring rod

PROCEDURE
A. Place a small pencil mark about 3 cm from the pointed end of a strip of chromatography paper. Do not touch the paper with your fingers; use forceps.
B. Use a capillary tube to apply black ink to the chromatography paper. Place one end of the capillary tube in the ink, and let some ink rise in the tube. Put your finger on top of the tube, and transfer a small drop of ink to the pencil mark on the paper. Let the ink dry. Repeat the application once or twice.
C. Assemble the apparatus as shown in the figure. Fold the top of the paper strip over about 1 cm, and attach the strip to a cork stopper with a thumbtack. Place the strip in the test tube, and adjust the stopper so that the point of the strip is about 2 cm above the bottom of the test tube. Remove the stopper, and carefully pour 10 mL of distilled water into the test tube. Make sure that the walls of the test tube remain dry.
D. Place the stopper into the tube so that the point of the paper strip extends into the water. The ink mark should be about 1 cm above the water.
E. Allow the water column to rise to within 3 cm of the top of the strip. Remove the stopper, and hang the strip to dry.
F. Examine the dry strip, and record your observations.

G. Cut one color section from the strip. Cut the section into small pieces, and place them in a small test tube. Add 10 drops of water, and then mash the paper in the water with a stirring rod. Record your observations.
H. Repeat step G with each color section. Combine the liquids obtained. Compare them with the original ink.

cork

chromatography paper

ink blot on chromatography paper

distilled water

RESULTS AND CONCLUSIONS
1. How many different colors did the separation procedure produce?
2. What might each color represent?
3. What resulted when you mixed the separate colors? How does the material produced in step H compare with the original ink? How could you make it more like the original ink?
4. Develop a model to explain how chromatography paper separated the parts of the ink. Base your model on your observations.

Scientists use many methods to separate mixtures. Some methods are used to identify the substances in a mixture. Other separation methods are used to purify a substance.

To separate mixtures of liquids, scientists use a method called *distillation*. (dihs tuh LAY shuhn). In distillation, liquids are separated by differences in their boiling points. A mixture of methyl alcohol and water can be distilled. Methyl alcohol boils at 64.5°C. Water boils at 100°C. When

134

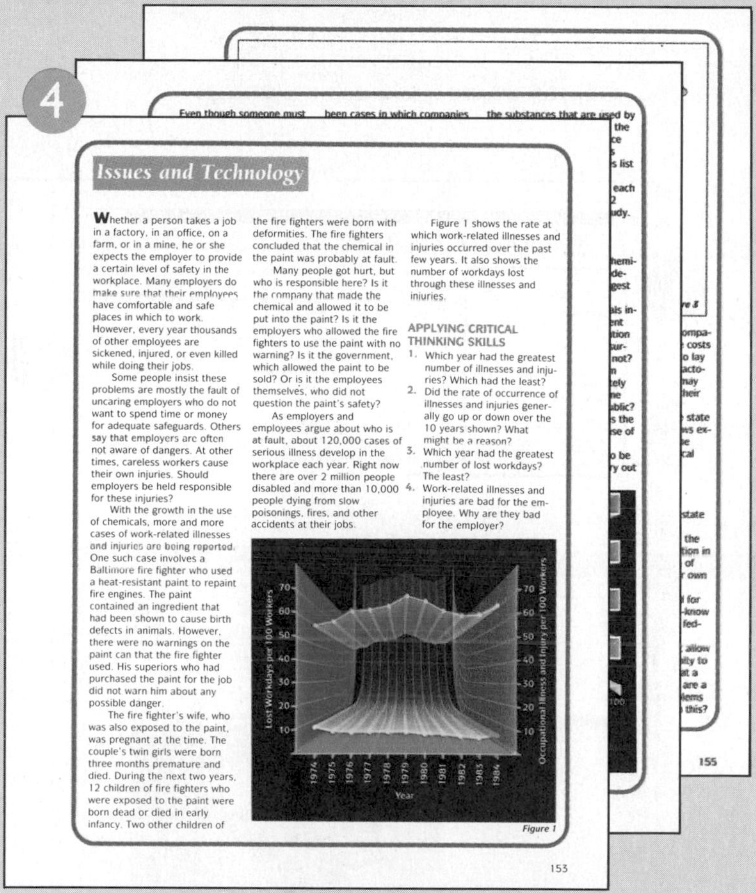

Issues and Technology

Even though someone must   been cases in which companies   the substances that are used by

Whether a person takes a job in a factory, in an office, on a farm, or in a mine, he or she expects the employer to provide a certain level of safety in the workplace. Many employers do make sure that their employees have comfortable and safe places in which to work. However, every year thousands of other employees are sickened, injured, or even killed while doing their jobs.

Some people insist these problems are mostly the fault of uncaring employers who do not want to spend time or money for adequate safeguards. Others say that employers are often not aware of dangers. At other times, careless workers cause their own injuries. Should employers be held responsible for these injuries?

With the growth in the use of chemicals, more and more cases of work-related illnesses and injuries are being reported. One such case involves a Baltimore fire fighter who used a heat-resistant paint to repaint fire engines. The paint contained an ingredient that had been shown to cause birth defects in animals. However, there were no warnings on the paint can that the fire fighter used. His superiors who had purchased the paint for the job did not warn him about any possible danger.

The fire fighter's wife, who was also exposed to the paint, was pregnant at the time. The couple's twin girls were born three months premature and died. During the next two years, 12 children of fire fighters who were exposed to the paint were born dead or died in early infancy. Two other children of

the fire fighters were born with deformities. The fire fighters concluded that the chemical in the paint was probably at fault.

Many people got hurt, but who is responsible here? Is it the company that made the chemical and allowed it to be put into the paint? Is it the employers who allowed the fire fighters to use the paint with no warning? Is it the government, which allowed the paint to be sold? Or is it the employees themselves, who did not question the paint's safety?

As employers and employees argue about who is at fault, about 120,000 cases of serious illness develop in the workplace each year. Right now there are over 2 million people disabled and more than 10,000 people dying from slow poisonings, fires, and other accidents at their jobs.

Figure 1 shows the rate at which work-related illnesses and injuries occurred over the past few years. It also shows the number of workdays lost through these illnesses and injuries.

APPLYING CRITICAL THINKING SKILLS
1. Which year had the greatest number of illnesses and injuries? Which had the least?
2. Did the rate of occurrence of illnesses and injuries generally go up or down over the 10 years shown? What might be a reason?
3. Which year had the greatest number of lost workdays? The least?
4. Work-related illnesses and injuries are bad for the employee. Why are they bad for the employer?

Figure 1

153

Activities in each chapter allow students to make their own discoveries of concepts developed in the text.

Decision-making activities on high-interest contemporary issues help prepare students to live in an increasingly scientific and technological society.

Science Olympics gives students opportunities to solve problems the way scientists solve them—by forming their own hypotheses and designing experiments to test their ideas.

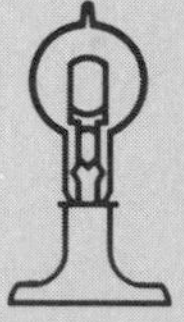

The Invention Convention encourages students to demonstrate their problem-solving and creative-thinking skills by inventing a new product or process which may become a local winner and an entry in Silver Burdett & Ginn's international competition.

PHYSICAL SCIENCE

UNDERSTANDING: A Variety of Paths to Student Success

Text, illustrations, and study aids interact with each other to make concepts understandable.

1 **Section objectives** aid comprehension by giving students a clearly defined, attainable purpose for reading.

2 **Key terms** focus students' attention on bold-faced vocabulary words in the text that are essential to understanding.

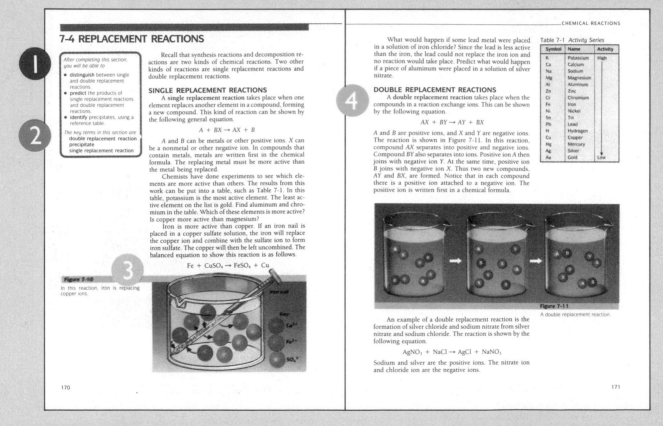

7-4 REPLACEMENT REACTIONS

After completing this section, you will be able to

- **distinguish** between single and double replacement reactions.
- **predict** the products of single replacement reactions and double replacement reactions.
- **identify** precipitates, using a reference table.

The key terms in this section are
double replacement reaction
precipitate
single replacement reaction

Recall that synthesis reactions and decomposition reactions are two kinds of chemical reactions. Two other kinds of reactions are single replacement reactions and double replacement reactions.

SINGLE REPLACEMENT REACTIONS

A **single replacement reaction** takes place when one element replaces another element in a compound, forming a new compound. This kind of reaction can be shown by the following general equation.

$$A + BX \rightarrow AX + B$$

A and B can be metals or other positive ions. X can be a nonmetal or other negative ion. In compounds that contain metals, metals are written first in the chemical formula. The replacing metal must be more active than the metal being replaced.

Chemists have done experiments to see which elements are more active than others. The results from this work can be put into a table, such as Table 7-1. In this table, potassium is the most active element. The least active element on the list is gold. Find aluminum and chromium in the table. Which of these elements is more active? Is copper more active than magnesium?

Iron is more active than copper. If an iron nail is placed in a copper sulfate solution, the iron will replace the copper ion and combine with the sulfate ion to form iron sulfate. The copper will then be left uncombined. The balanced equation to show this reaction is as follows.

$$Fe + CuSO_4 \rightarrow FeSO_4 + Cu$$

Figure 7-10
In this reaction, iron is replacing copper ions.

Key
Cu^{2+}
Fe^{2+}
SO_4^{2-}

170

CHEMICAL REACTIONS

What would happen if some lead metal were placed in a solution of iron chloride? Since the lead is less active than the iron, the lead could not replace the iron ion and no reaction would take place. Predict what would happen if a piece of aluminum were placed in a solution of silver nitrate.

DOUBLE REPLACEMENT REACTIONS

A **double replacement reaction** takes place when the compounds in a reaction exchange ions. This can be shown by the following equation.

$$AX + BY \rightarrow AY + BX$$

A and B are positive ions, and X and Y are negative ions. The reaction is shown in Figure 7-11. In this reaction, compound AX separates into positive and negative ions. Compound BY also separates into ions. Positive ion A then joins with negative ion Y. At the same time, positive ion B joins with negative ion X. Thus two new compounds, AY and BX, are formed. Notice that in each compound there is a positive ion attached to a negative ion. The positive ion is written first in a chemical formula.

Figure 7-11
A double replacement reaction.

An example of a double replacement reaction is the formation of silver chloride and sodium nitrate from silver nitrate and sodium chloride. The reaction is shown by the following equation.

$$AgNO_3 + NaCl \rightarrow AgCl + NaNO_3$$

Sodium and silver are the positive ions. The nitrate ion and chloride ion are the negative ions.

Table 7-1 *Activity Series*

Symbol	Name	Activity
K	Potassium	High
Ca	Calcium	
Na	Sodium	
Mg	Magnesium	
Al	Aluminum	
Zn	Zinc	
Cr	Chromium	
Fe	Iron	
Ni	Nickel	
Sn	Tin	
Pb	Lead	
H	Hydrogen	
Cu	Copper	
Hg	Mercury	
Ag	Silver	
Au	Gold	Low

171

3 **Interaction** builds a concept three ways: in the text, in the illustration, and in the caption.

4 **Vocabulary development** is built in—not added on. *Key terms* are phonetically respelled whenever appropriate and contextually defined at their first appearance. *Word parts* in the margins build lasting fluency by defining scientific prefixes, suffixes, and root words.

Concepts are developed, reinforced, and extended in a variety of ways to help all students experience successful learning.

Another example of a double replacement reaction is the formation of hydrogen sulfide gas. Iron sulfide reacts with hydrochloric acid. The products of the reaction are iron chloride and hydrogen sulfide. Study the following balanced equation. Identify the positive and negative ions in this reaction.

$$FeS + 2HCl \rightarrow FeCl_2 + H_2S$$

In some reactions one of the products is not soluble and is called a precipitate. A **precipitate** (prih SIHP uh tayt) is a solid material that is formed in a chemical reaction and that separates from the solution. Precipitates tend to sink to the bottom of the reaction container.

A table of solubilities is used to determine whether a precipitate will form in a chemical reaction. Look at Table 7-2, which gives the solubilities of different compounds in water. According to the table, aluminum chloride is soluble. Therefore it will not form a precipitate. Silver chloride, however, is not soluble. It will form a precipitate.

Figure 7-12 shows lead nitrate reacting with sodium iodide. The products are lead iodide and sodium nitrate. The reaction can be shown as follows.

$$Pb(NO_3)_2 + 2NaI \rightarrow PbI_2 + 2NaNO_3$$

The yellow precipitate formed is lead iodide.

Figure 7-12
Lead iodide forms a yellow precipitate, and sodium nitrate remains dissolved.

Table 7-2 *Solubilities in Water*

S = Soluble
P = Partially Soluble
I = Insoluble

	Bromide	Carbonate	Chloride	Hydroxide	Nitrate	Phosphate	Sulfate
Aluminum	S	–	S	S	S	I	S
Barium	S	P	S	S	S	I	I
Calcium	S	P	S	S	S	P	P
Copper II	S	–	S	I	S	I	S
Iron II	S	P	S	I	S	I	S
Iron III	S	–	S	I	S	P	P
Magnesium	S	P	S	I	S	P	S
Potassium	S	S	S	S	S	S	S
Silver	I	I	I	–	S	I	P
Sodium	S	S	S	S	S	S	S
Zinc	S	P	S	I	S	I	S

172

ACTIVITY — What Are the Types of Chemical Reactions?

OBJECTIVE
Distinguish between different types of chemical reactions, using experimental data.

MATERIALS
safety goggles, lab apron, graduate, water, bromthymol blue, 3 test tubes, test-tube rack, drinking straw, copper (II) sulfate solution, zinc strip, barium chloride solution, potassium sulfate solution

PROCEDURE
A. Wear safety goggles and a lab apron throughout this activity.
B. Draw a data table like the one shown.
C. Measure 10 mL of water into a test tube. Add 5 drops of bromthymol blue.
D. Using a clean drinking straw, gently blow into the solution. Record your observations in the data table.
E. Measure 10 mL of copper (II) sulfate ($CuSO_4$) solution, and pour the solution into a test tube. Rinse the graduate with water.
F. Place a zinc strip into the solution.
G. After 5 to 10 minutes, examine the zinc. Record your observations.
H. Measure 5 mL of barium chloride ($BaCl_2$) solution, and pour the solution into a test tube. Rinse the graduate with water.
I. Measure 5 mL of potassium sulfate (KSO_4) solution. Add this solution to the barium chloride solution in the test tube. Record your observations.

Reactants	Observations
$CaOH_2$, CO_2	
PbO	
Zn, $CuSO_4$	

RESULTS AND CONCLUSIONS
1. What evidence is there that chemical reactions took place?
2. Write a balanced equation for each chemical reaction.
3. Which reaction(s) produced a precipitate?
4. Identify each type of reaction that occurred. Explain your answer.

REVIEW
1. Identify each of the following as a single replacement reaction or a double replacement reaction.
   a. $Mg + H_2SO_4 \rightarrow MgSO_4 + H_2$
   b. $KI + AgNO_3 \rightarrow KNO_3 + AgI$
   c. $HCl + NaOH \rightarrow H_2O + NaCl$
   d. $Al + FeCO_2 \rightarrow AlCO_3 + Fe$
2. Complete and balance each of the following equations.
   a. $K + AlCl_3 \rightarrow$
   b. $NaBr + AgNO_3 \rightarrow$
   c. $AlBr_3 + Ca(OH)_2 \rightarrow$
   d. $FeCl_3 + Na_3PO_4 \rightarrow$
3. Identify any precipitates in the equations given in questions 1 and 2.

CHALLENGE Predict which of the following reactions would occur. Write a balanced equation for each reaction that would occur.
   a. $Al + CuSO_4 \rightarrow$
   b. $Cu + AlCl_3 \rightarrow$
   c. $Zn + AgNO_3 \rightarrow$
   d. $Ag + ZnCl_2 \rightarrow$

---

5 Interactive questions get students involved in observing illustrations and consulting the text to arrive at the answer.

6 Activities provide concrete reinforcement and extension of concepts developed in the text.

7 Multilevel questions after each section measure students' mastery of objectives and challenge students to apply concepts to new situations.

8 A Study Guide page for each section asks direct-recall questions to help students as they read, thus providing thorough and specific reinforcement of basic facts and concepts. The Study Guide is ideal as additional review, or can be used with lower-level students as an alternative to the text questions.

Name _____ Date _____

7-4 Replacement Reactions
PAGES 170-173

The following exercise will help you with your reading of this section. Work independently and at your own pace.

1. What is a single replacement reaction? Give one example.

2. What is a double replacement reaction? Give one example.

Refer to Table 7-1 on page 171. Answer the following questions.

3. Which of the elements is least active and most active?

4. Which of the elements is more active, copper _____

5. What is a pre___

PHYSICAL SCIENCE

CRITICAL THINKING: Problem Solving and Decision Making

Students are given opportunities to solve problems and to make decisions relevant to familiar situations and issues affecting their lives.

1 **Opportunities for decision making** based on a variety of data in the text are consistently provided. These experiences make students aware of important scientific issues and help them develop skills they will need as tomorrow's adult decision makers.

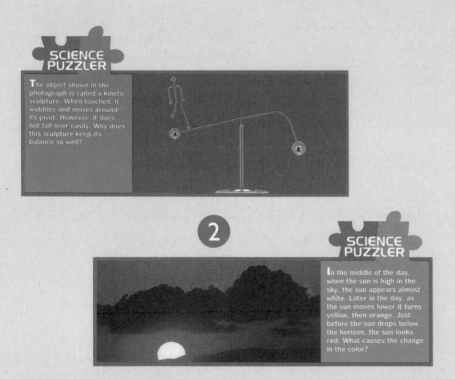

SCIENCE PUZZLER

The object shown in the photograph is called a kinetic sculpture. When touched, it wobbles and moves around its pivot. However, it does not fall over easily. Why does this sculpture keep its balance so well?

2

SCIENCE PUZZLER

In the middle of the day, when the sun is high in the sky, the sun appears almost white. Later in the day, as the sun moves lower it turns yellow, then orange. Just before the sun drops below the horizon, the sun looks red. What causes the change in the color?

2 **Illustrated Puzzlers** offer students fascinating side trips to explore problem-solving situations related to the content of each chapter.

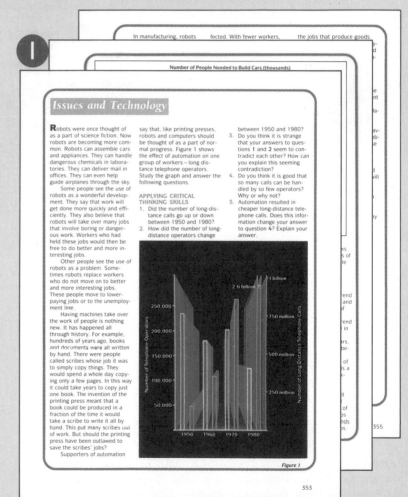

Issues and Technology

Robots were once thought of as a part of science fiction. Now robots are becoming more common. Robots can assemble cars and appliances. They can handle dangerous chemicals in laboratories. They can deliver mail in offices. They can even help guide airplanes through the sky.

Some people see the use of robots as a wonderful development. They say that work will get done more quickly and efficiently. They also believe that robots will take over many jobs that involve boring or dangerous work. Workers who had held these jobs would then be free to do better and more interesting jobs.

Other people see the use of robots as a problem. Sometimes robots replace workers who do not move on to better and more interesting jobs. These people move to lower-paying jobs or to the unemployment line.

Having machines take over the work of people is nothing new. It has happened all through history. For example, hundreds of years ago, books and documents were all written by hand. There were people called scribes whose job it was to simply copy things. They would spend a whole day copying only a few pages. In this way it could take years to copy just one book. The invention of the printing press meant that a book could be produced in a fraction of the time it would take a scribe to write it all by hand. This put many scribes out of work. But should the printing press have been outlawed to save the scribes' jobs?

Supporters of automation say that, like printing presses, robots and computers should be thought of as a part of normal progress. Figure 1 shows the effect of automation on one group of workers — long distance telephone operators. Study the graph and answer the following questions.

APPLYING CRITICAL THINKING SKILLS

1. Did the number of long-distance calls go up or down between 1950 and 1980?
2. How did the number of long-distance operators change between 1950 and 1980?
3. Do you think it is strange that your answers to questions **1** and **2** seem to contradict each other? How can you explain this seeming contradiction?
4. Do you think it is good that so many calls can be handled by so few operators? Why or why not?
5. Automation resulted in cheaper long-distance telephone calls. Does this information change your answer to question **4**? Explain your answer.

Figure 1

353

Number of People Needed to Build Cars (thousands)

In manufacturing, robots   fected. With fewer workers,   the jobs that produce goods.

355

Questions after each section and chapter provide ongoing reinforcement and extension of critical-thinking skills.

3 **Challenge/Critical-Thinking Masters** in the Review and Skill Masters found in the Teacher Resource Package offer additional opportunities for the practice of higher-level thinking skills—such as making predictions and working with variables.

After each section:

4 **Challenge** questions that encourage the use of critical-thinking skills are included in each Section Review.

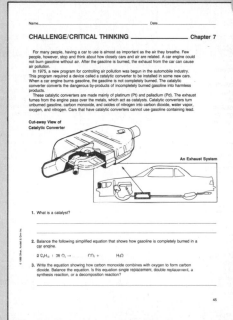

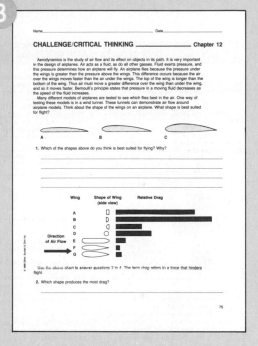

After each chapter:

5 **Application/Critical Thinking** questions ask students to use problem-solving skills and to synthesize information in the text.

6 **Extension** topics invite students to explore chapter concepts beyond the text through library research and/or hands-on projects.

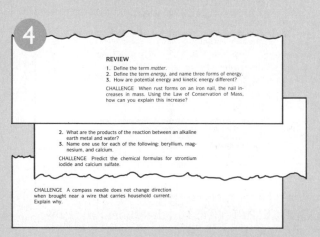

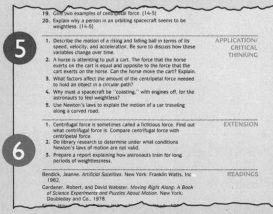

PHYSICAL SCIENCE

ACTIVE LEARNING: From Observation to Experimentation

Students are given opportunities to solve problems the way scientists solve them—by active investigation and discovery.

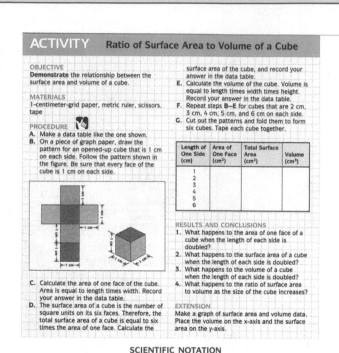

ACTIVITY Ratio of Surface Area to Volume of a Cube

OBJECTIVE
Demonstrate the relationship between the surface area and volume of a cube.

MATERIALS
1-centimeter-grid paper, metric ruler, scissors, tape

PROCEDURE
A. Make a data table like the one shown.
B. On a piece of graph paper, draw the pattern for an opened-up cube that is 1 cm on each side. Follow the pattern shown in the figure. Be sure that every face of the cube is 1 cm on each side.

C. Calculate the area of one face of the cube. Area is equal to length times width. Record your answer in the data table.
D. The surface area of a cube is the number of square units on its six faces. Therefore, the total surface area of a cube is equal to six times the area of one face. Calculate the surface area of the cube, and record your answer in the data table.
E. Calculate the volume of the cube. Volume is equal to length times width times height. Record your answer in the data table.
F. Repeat steps B–E for cubes that are 2 cm, 3 cm, 4 cm, 5 cm, and 6 cm on each side.
G. Cut out the patterns and fold them to form six cubes. Tape each cube together.

Length of One Side (cm)	Area of One Face (cm²)	Total Surface Area (cm²)	Volume (cm³)
1			
2			
3			
4			
5			
6			

RESULTS AND CONCLUSIONS
1. What happens to the area of one face of a cube when the length of each side is doubled?
2. What happens to the surface area of a cube when the length of each side is doubled?
3. What happens to the volume of a cube when the length of each side is doubled?
4. What happens to the ratio of surface area to volume as the size of the cube increases?

EXTENSION
Make a graph of surface area and volume data. Place the volume on the x-axis and the surface area on the y-axis.

SCIENTIFIC NOTATION
Physical scientists often use very large numbers or very small numbers. For example, the diameter of the sun is 1,390,000,000 m. To simplify large numbers, scientists write them as multiples of ten. In the example above, the seven zeros show that 139 has been multiplied by 10 seven times. This multiplication can be shown as a power of 10, written as 10^7. In **scientific notation**, a number is written as the product of a coefficient (koh uh FIHSH uhnt) between 1 and 10 and a power of ten. The number that indicates the power of ten is called an exponent (EHK spoh-nuhnt). The diameter of the sun is written as 1.39×10^9. The coefficient 1.39 shows the significant digits in the

40

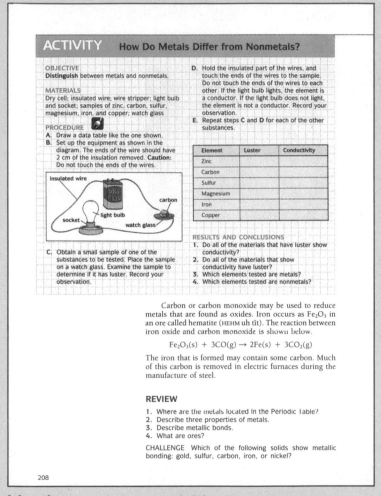

ACTIVITY How Do Metals Differ from Nonmetals?

OBJECTIVE
Distinguish between metals and nonmetals.

MATERIALS
Dry cell; insulated wire; wire stripper; light bulb and socket; samples of zinc, carbon, sulfur, magnesium, iron, and copper; watch glass

PROCEDURE
A. Draw a data table like the one shown.
B. Set up the equipment as shown in the diagram. The ends of the wire should have 2 cm of the insulation removed. **Caution:** Do not touch the ends of the wires.

C. Obtain a small sample of one of the substances to be tested. Place the sample on a watch glass. Examine the sample to determine if it has luster. Record your observation.

D. Hold the insulated part of the wires, and touch the ends of the wires to the sample. Do not touch the ends of the wires to each other. If the light bulb lights, the element is a conductor. If the light bulb does not light, the element is not a conductor. Record your observation.
E. Repeat steps C and D for each of the other substances.

Element	Luster	Conductivity
Zinc		
Carbon		
Sulfur		
Magnesium		
Iron		
Copper		

RESULTS AND CONCLUSIONS
1. Do all of the materials that have luster show conductivity?
2. Do all of the materials that show conductivity have luster?
3. Which elements tested are metals?
4. Which elements tested are nonmetals?

Carbon or carbon monoxide may be used to reduce metals that are found as oxides. Iron occurs as Fe_2O_3 in an ore called hematite (HEHM uh tīt). The reaction between iron oxide and carbon monoxide is shown below.

$$Fe_2O_3(s) + 3CO(g) \rightarrow 2Fe(s) + 3CO_2(g)$$

The iron that is formed may contain some carbon. Much of this carbon is removed in electric furnaces during the manufacture of steel.

REVIEW
1. Where are the metals located in the Periodic Table?
2. Describe three properties of metals.
3. Describe metallic bonds.
4. What are ores?

CHALLENGE Which of the following solids show metallic bonding: gold, sulfur, carbon, iron, or nickel?

208

Paper-and-pencil activities in the student text give students active learning experiences with skills that range from taking and recording measurements to making and testing predictions.

Hands-on science activities in the student text provide concept reinforcement and skills development. Simple-to-perform activities built right into the text chapters use commonly available materials.

Students progress through the entire hierarchy of science process skills.

Three levels of problem solving...

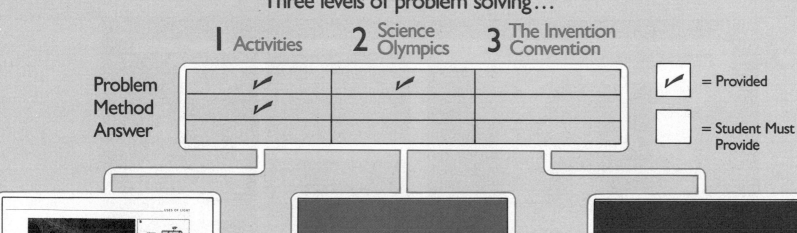

	1 Activities	**2** Science Olympics	**3** The Invention Convention
Problem	✔	✔	
Method	✔		
Answer			

✔ = Provided

☐ = Student Must Provide

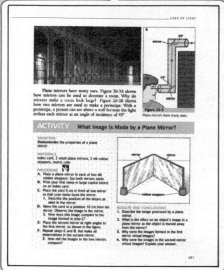

1. Activities Activities in each chapter allow students to discover for themselves important concepts developed in the text. Students are given a problem to solve and step-by-step procedures to follow. Questions guide students to the answers.

2. Science Olympics Problem solving becomes more open-ended in Science Olympics. Given problems to solve, students must design their own experiments to find the answers.

3. The Invention Convention This completely open-ended project stresses creative thinking as well as scientific problem solving. Students must identify a problem, develop their own methods for solving it, and invent an original solution.

PHYSICAL SCIENCE

ENRICHMENT: Making Physical Science Relevant

Students comprehend the relevance of the physical sciences to the world around them—and to their own lives.

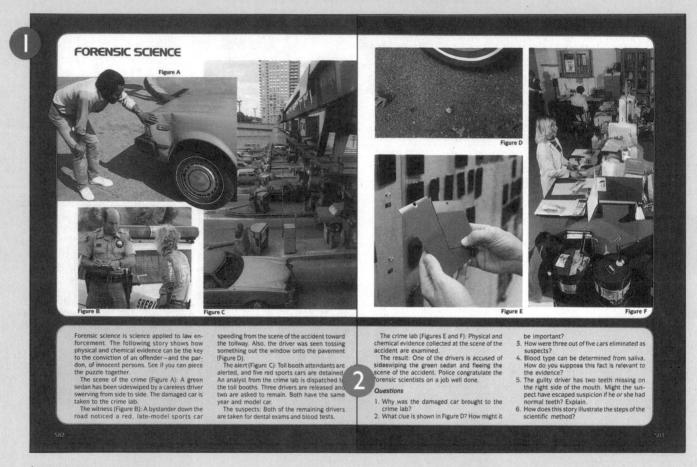

FORENSIC SCIENCE

Figure A

Figure B

Figure C

Figure D

Figure E

Figure F

Forensic science is science applied to law enforcement. The following story shows how physical and chemical evidence can be the key to the conviction of an offender—and the pardon, of innocent persons. See if you can piece the puzzle together.

The scene of the crime (Figure A): A green sedan has been sideswiped by a careless driver swerving from side to side. The damaged car is taken to the crime lab.

The witness (Figure B): A bystander down the road noticed a red, late-model sports car speeding from the scene of the accident toward the tollway. Also, the driver was seen tossing something out the window onto the pavement (Figure D).

The alert (Figure C): Toll booth attendants are alerted, and five red sports cars are detained. An analyst from the crime lab is dispatched to the toll booths. Three drivers are released and two are asked to remain. Both have the same year and model car.

The suspects: Both of the remaining drivers are taken for dental exams and blood tests.

The crime lab (Figures E and F): Physical and chemical evidence collected at the scene of the accident are examined.

The result: One of the drivers is accused of sideswiping the green sedan and fleeing the scene of the accident. Police congratulate the forensic scientists on a job well done.

Questions

1. Why was the damaged car brought to the crime lab?
2. What clue is shown in Figure D? How might it be important?
3. How were three out of five cars eliminated as suspects?
4. Blood type can be determined from saliva. How do you suppose this fact is relevant to the evidence?
5. The guilty driver has two teeth missing on the right side of the mouth. Might the suspect have escaped suspicion if he or she had normal teeth? Explain.
6. How does this story illustrate the steps of the scientific method?

582

583

1 Physical Science Skills Handbook uses a variety of high interest topics to develop interpretive and analytical skills related to each unit. This reference is bound into the back of the text.

2 Critical-thinking questions get students actively involved using forensic science to solve a crime.

Up-to-date content keeps students interested in learning and well-informed for decision making.

(3) Science in Careers provides descriptions and educational requirements for a variety of career opportunities available in the expanding fields of physical science.

(4) Biographies of outstanding science contributors enhance the human interest of the physical sciences and provide role models that students can emulate.

Science in Careers

You may think of your neighborhood drugstore as the place to buy school supplies or magazines. But the most important function of a pharmacy, or drugstore, is selling medicine.

Pharmacists provide the medicine specified in a doctor's or dentist's prescription. Usually the medicine is measured and put into a labeled container. The label includes directions and cautions to the patient. The pharmacist must keep an accurate record of each prescription. Pharmacists working in drugstores also help customers select medicines that do not require a prescription.

In addition to working in drugstores, pharmacists may work in hospitals or clinics. Pharmacists earn a five- or six-year college degree in pharmacy. They must then pass a test to be licensed. If you are interested in this career, you should take courses in biology and chemistry in high school.■

Pharmacist

Although pottery is an ancient craft, an understanding of physical science is helpful to the potter. Knowing the physical properties of various clays and paints enables the potter to produce the desired effect.

There are several different techniques of pottery-making. Many potters use a potter's wheel, a large heavy disc that spins as the potter works. The potter throws the wet clay on the center of the rotating wheel. By firmly pressing his or her hands on this spinning mass of clay, the potter gradually shapes an object.

Potters often work alone as independent craftworkers. They may sell their wares at craft shows and shops. Potters go to art school or work as an apprentice. If you are interested in becoming a potter, you should take crafts and fine arts courses in high school.■

Potter

People in Science

Dr. Stephen Hawking is a theoretical physicist. He is famous for having proposed the existence of black holes before they were found by astronomers.

Dr. Hawking had theorized that a black hole forms when a large star grows old and stops producing energy. Its gravity causes the star to shrink and compress. As it compresses, the gravitational pull increases. Finally, not even light can escape from the black hole.

Like other theoretical physicists, Dr. Hawking makes his

Dr. Stephen Hawking, Physicist

predictions by using his imagination and mathematical calculations. But in some ways Dr. Hawking is different from others. He is almost completely paralyzed by a progressive nerve disease. Dr. Hawking is unable to write and his speech is so weak that he needs an interpreter to translate what he says. Yet Dr. Hawking prefers not to concentrate on his physical limitations. Instead he sees his illness as something that forces him to focus on basic physics, freeing him from distractions.■

152

SCIENCE & TECHNOLOGY

(5)

Controlling fusion is like trying to bottle the sun. The two biggest problems are creating a plasma at very high temperatures and then holding the plasma long enough for it to react. In a container with ordinary walls, the highly charged plasma particles would lose their energy as they touched the walls. The plasma would cool.

The solution to these problems might be a tokamak like the one shown here. The tokamak is a device that produces a powerful magnetic field around the plasma. The magnetic field confines the plasma without absorbing energy from the plasma.

In experiments with tokamaks, only a few fusion reactions have been created. Right now much more energy is put into making the reactions occur than is being produced by the fusion reactions themselves.

Scientists and engineers are designing new tokamaks. New models are expected to release more power than the amount of energy put into the reacting particles.

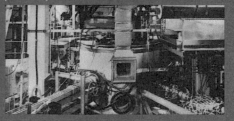

(5) Interesting new information about nuclear energy heightens students' interest while expanding their understanding of concepts developed in the text.

DO YOU KNOW?

(6)

Gold has been used to fix teeth since the time of ancient civilizations. The Etruscans were probably the first people to use gold for dental work. The Etruscans lived during the sixth century B.C., along what is now the western shore of Italy. They were experts at working with iron, bronze, and gold. A goldsmith's shop often would be visited by doctors and their patients. Here, false teeth were fitted to the patient.

The replacement tooth would be attached to the patient's own teeth by means of strips of gold. The gold strips were placed around the teeth on either side of

the gap left by the missing tooth. A replacement tooth was placed into the gap and held in place by rivets. Sometimes the tooth that was lost would be put back in place. In other cases, an animal tooth would be used. Sometimes a replacement

tooth was made completely of gold.

Gold is still used in dentistry today. Cheaper alloys from other metals have been developed, but no substitute has matched gold. The long history of gold in dentistry is likely to continue.

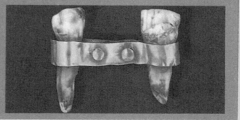

(6) Fascinating sidelights pique students' curiosity and expand their understanding of chapter concepts.

PHYSICAL SCIENCE

ACHIEVEMENT: Reinforcing and Evaluating Student Progress

Evaluation and reinforcement are provided for ALL students at ALL times for ALL levels of understanding.

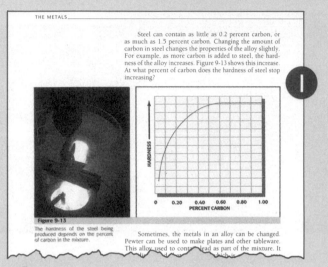

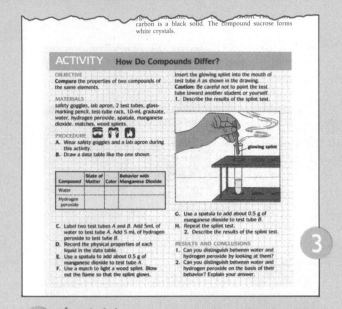

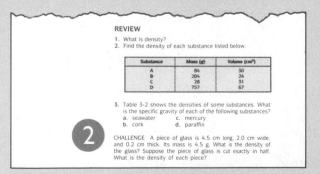

1 Ongoing assessment of students' understanding comes from interactive questions within the text that ask students to find information in a graph, chart, map, or other illustration.

3 Activities in each chapter offer the teacher opportunities to evaluate student mastery of science skills. As alternative approaches to concepts developed in the text, activities are also ideal for reteaching and reinforcement.

2 Varying levels of understanding are measured by each Section Review. A series of literal questions is followed by a Challenge question that requires students to apply concepts and to think critically.

Evaluation aids include:

REVIEW AND SKILL MASTERS

consisting of four different kinds of worksheets for each chapter:
• **Vocabulary Review**
• **Chapter Review**
• **Skill**
• **Challenge/Critical Thinking**
See pages T20-T21.

STUDY GUIDE

One page of literal-level, short-answer questions for each chapter section provides full coverage of essential information.

Evaluative materials ranging from literal questions to library research projects are at your command to chart each student's course for success.

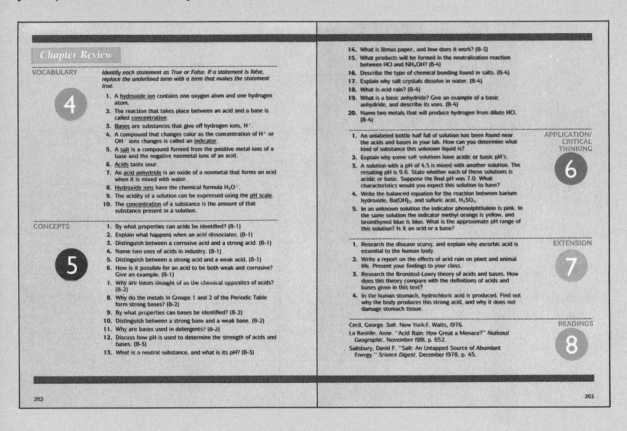

4 **Vocabulary exercises** are provided to reinforce and/or assess students' retention of key terms introduced in the chapter.

5 **Concepts** checks on basic understanding of chapter content.

6 **Application/ Critical Thinking** requires students to synthesize information in the text. Inferring, hypothesizing, predicting, and problem solving are among the skills reinforced.

7 **Extension** requires students to obtain information from the library, from hands-on investigations, or from other sources outside the text.

8 **A reading list** helps students pursue topics that excite their interest.

Two comprehensive yet flexible TESTING PROGRAM approaches

• Criterion-referenced TESTS consisting of a four-page test for each chapter, a midterm, and final test. Questions range from direct-recall to problem solving.

• A COMPUTER TEST BANK consisting of 3500 criterion-referenced test items. Questions can be edited, added, and previewed on screen. Tests can also be generated automatically according to the number and type of questions you request.

PHYSICAL SCIENCE

CHAPTER PLANNING GUIDE: A Timesaving Organizer

The Teacher Edition Chapter Planning Guide is your blueprint for success.

1 **Section and Activity** This overview of the chapter's organization makes it easy for you to choose the content and the activities you wish to use with your students.

2 **Reinforcement and Evaluation** These entries help you quickly locate a variety of items for determining different levels of mastery: *Review* (literal recall), *Challenge* and *Puzzler* (critical thinking, problem solving), and *Test* (all levels).

3 **Review and Skill Masters** Four kinds of copy master worksheet pages are correlated to chapter pages in the Student Text.

4 **Other Components in Teacher Resource Package** Laboratory Manual and Study Guide are correlated to the Student Text.

5 **Materials** Activities are easy to plan with the aid of this chart, which helps you organize all materials.

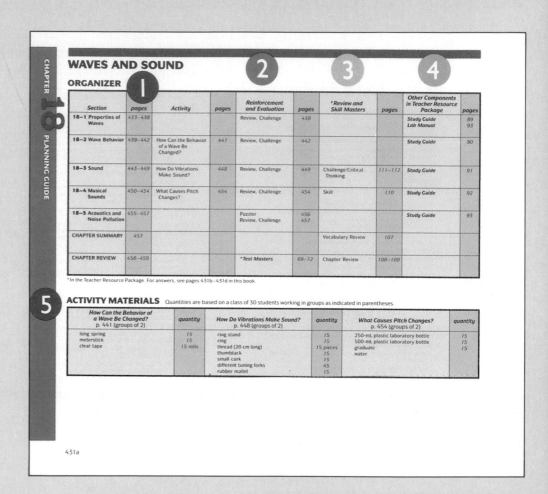

CHAPTER 18 PLANNING GUIDE

WAVES AND SOUND
ORGANIZER

Section	pages	Activity	pages	Reinforcement and Evaluation	pages	*Review and Skill Masters	pages	Other Components in Teacher Resource Package	pages
18–1 Properties of Waves	433–438			Review, Challenge	438			Study Guide / Lab Manual	89 / 93
18–2 Wave Behavior	439–442	How Can the Behavior of a Wave Be Changed?	441	Review, Challenge	442			Study Guide	90
18–3 Sound	443–449	How Do Vibrations Make Sound?	448	Review, Challenge	449	Challenge/Critical Thinking	111–112	Study Guide	91
18–4 Musical Sounds	450–454	What Causes Pitch Changes?	454	Review, Challenge	454	Skill	110	Study Guide	92
18–5 Acoustics and Noise Pollution	455–457			Puzzler / Review, Challenge	456 / 457			Study Guide	93
CHAPTER SUMMARY	457					Vocabulary Review	107		
CHAPTER REVIEW	458–459			*Test Masters	69–72	Chapter Review	108–109		

*In the Teacher Resource Package. For answers, see pages 431b–431d in this book.

ACTIVITY MATERIALS
Quantities are based on a class of 30 students working in groups as indicated in parentheses.

How Can the Behavior of a Wave Be Changed? p. 441 (groups of 2)	quantity	How Do Vibrations Make Sound? p. 448 (groups of 2)	quantity	What Causes Pitch Changes? p. 454 (groups of 2)	quantity
long spring	15	ring stand	15	250-mL plastic laboratory bottle	15
meterstick	15	ring	15	500-mL plastic laboratory bottle	15
clear tape	15 rolls	thread (20 cm long)	15 pieces	graduate	15
		thumbtack	15	water	
		small cork	15		
		different tuning forks	45		
		rubber mallet	15		

431a

Whether you're a new or an experienced physical science teacher, you'll enjoy saving time with this well-organized Teacher Edition.

For your convenience and reference, the Review and Skill Masters and Test Masters are displayed with answers in place.

Review and Skill Masters
Reduced copy masters help you select the kinds of worksheets best suited to your students' needs.

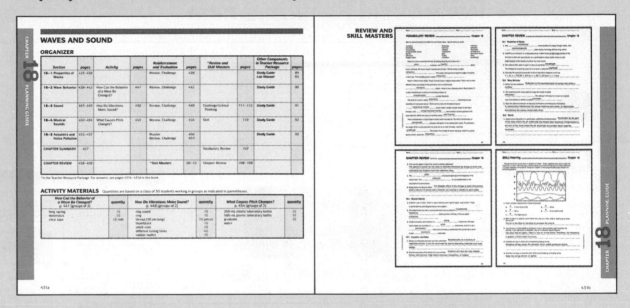

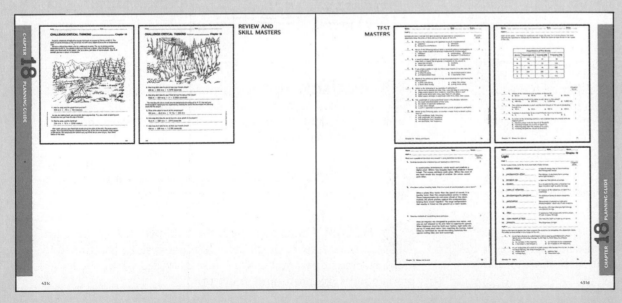

Test Masters
This four-part test on each chapter enables you to evaluate students at specific levels of skill and understanding. The choice is yours.

A THREE-STEP PLAN: For Your Teaching Success

A consistent plan for teaching each section follows three proven steps to success: <u>Motivation</u>, <u>Concept Development</u>, and <u>Review and Reinforcement</u>.

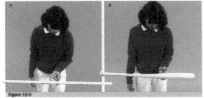

Objectives and Vocabulary Expectations of student performance and science terms important to the achievement of these goals are clearly stated at the beginning of each section.

1 Motivation A concrete experience, a demonstration, or a class discussion gets students actively involved with the section topic before they open their books.

2 Concept Development These strategies for guiding students' progress through the section are available for your use while your class is in session.

a Teaching Tips Suggestions for enhancing the development of section topics include information and hints for piquing students' interest, expanding their understanding, and guiding their discussions.

b Background Additional information for the teacher amplifies the text and supports instruction.

c Activity Integrated with the total plan for teaching the section, Activity notes include process skills list, time allotment, teaching tips, and answers. Also provided when needed: preparation suggestions and safety tips.

A variety of helpful annotations are clearly visible in the margins and conveniently positioned for immediate use as needed.

d **Enrichment** High-interest, optional projects usually involve research beyond the text.

e **Answers** to interactive questions appear only in the Teacher Edition.

f **Thinking Skills** Special feature boxes identify important skills developed in the text and suggest additional exercises for reinforcing these skills.

3 **Review and Reinforcement** For closure, criterion-referenced Review Questions tie back to section objectives, and critical-thinking Challenge questions extend section topics. Answers to these questions are provided in the margins. Follow-up assignments in the Review and Skill Masters are suggested. Test Masters are referenced at the end of each chapter.

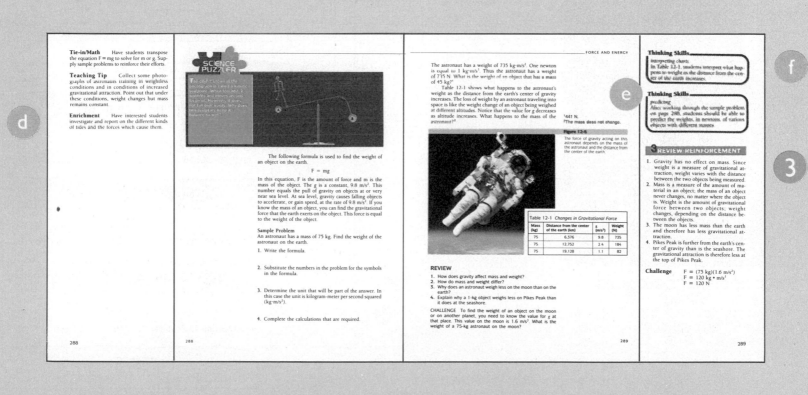

PHYSICAL SCIENCE

FLEXIBILITY: Meeting Individual Needs

Because different students have different learning needs...
the TEACHER RESOURCE PACKAGE
meets your teaching needs.

Chapter opener photograph
stimulates class discussion.

INTRODUCTION TO PHYSICAL SCIENCE

CHAPTER

1

Have you ever tried to fly a kite? The shape and weight of a kite are very important. A kite should be wide enough to "catch the wind." Its tail must be long enough to keep the kite upright but not so long that it makes the kite too heavy to fly. Studying physical science can help you understand the forces that keep a kite flying. It can help you design experiments to improve the performance of a kite or some other object.

- *What forces are involved in flying a kite?*
- *How does a scientist study these forces?*
- *Are the same forces involved in the flight of other objects?*

1-1 WHAT IS PHYSICAL SCIENCE?

Have you ever wondered what causes a rainbow or why the sky is blue? Perhaps you have an interest in electricity or electronics. You may be interested in the laser and its uses, or you may wish to know how a camera or a computer works. Have you ever wondered why some materials differ from others? For example, what is the difference between the safety glass used in eyeglasses and the kind of glass used in tableware? Have you noticed that on some nights the moon seems to have a halo around it? Can you explain why this happens? Your questions about objects and events in the world around you are questions of science.

Science is a method of obtaining knowledge about nature. Nature is the earth, space, nonliving things, and living things. Science has many branches, including life science, earth science, and physical science.

Science is older than recorded history. Ancient people saw events around them in nature. They noticed that the weather changes from day to day and from season to season. There is a pattern to these changes. People learned to make predictions based on these patterns. Predicting changes in the seasons probably helped these people survive. Modern scientists continue to study patterns and make predictions.

After completing this section, you will be able to

- **define** the term *science*.
- **name** the two major branches of physical science.
- **compare** science and technology.

The key terms in this section are
physical science
science
technology

scientia (knowledge)

NOTE
Many terms in science have their origins in other languages, including Latin and Greek. The foreign word parts and their meanings are listed in the margin for many of the science terms in this book. Use the word parts to help you understand the meanings of the science terms.

5

Name _____ Date _____

How Can Safety Be Promoted in the Physical Science Laboratory?

LABORATORY MANUAL

Name_____ Date_____

SKILL/Measuring _____ Chapter 1

SKILL

Name_____ Date_____

CHALLENGE/CRITICAL THINKING _____ Chapter 1

CHALLENGE/CRITICAL THINKING

Name _____ Date _____

1-1   What is Physical Science?
PAGES 3-6

STUDY GUIDE

Name_____ Date_____

CHAPTER REVIEW _____ Chapter 1

CHAPTER REVIEW

Name_____ Date_____

VOCABULARY REVIEW _____ Chapter 1

VOCABULARY REVIEW

Name_____ Date_____ Score_____
_____ Chapter 1

Introduction to Physical Science

TESTS

A variety of options are available at all points of the program for meeting a wide range of individual needs.

TEACHER RESOURCE PACKAGE

Chapter-Related Components

Unit-Related Components

For each section:

REVIEW AND SKILL MASTERS

Vocabulary Review
Additional vocabulary practice is provided by a variety of exercises, including puzzles.

Chapter Review
Two pages of questions provide feedback on students' attainment of section objectives.

Skill
These worksheets build a wide range of skills needed for success in science—including language skills as well as basic thinking and process skills.

Challenge/Critical Thinking
Problem-solving situations presented on these copy masters offer additional opportunities for the practice of higher-level thinking skills.

STUDY GUIDE
Direct-recall questions keyed to each chapter section provide thorough and specific coverage of basic facts and concepts.

LABORATORY MANUAL
Keyed to the chapters in the text, the Manual offers teachers the option of giving their students experiences with formally structured, fully developed laboratory investigations offering greater challenge than the activities in the text.

TESTS
These criterion-referenced tests ask direct-recall questions, problem-solving questions, and essay questions to evaluate attainment of chapter goals and competence in a wide range of skills. A four-page test for each chapter may be used in selected parts to assess specific levels of understanding.

SAFETY HANDBOOK
Several exercises and a test ensure that students are properly instructed in the use of safety symbols, guidelines, and practices in the laboratory. This component should ideally be used at the beginning of the school year.

SCIENCE OLYMPICS
These strategies and activities stress higher-level thinking and science skills. Students are asked to collect, analyze, and evaluate information as well as to design and conduct independent experiments.

POSTERS
Six full-color posters—one per unit—use illustrations from the text to increase student motivation and to reinforce unit concepts.

COLOR TRANSPARENCIES
Two full-color transparencies for each unit in the text allow you to illustrate key concepts.

TRANSPARENCY MASTERS
Twelve blackline masters—two for each unit in the text—allow you to illustrate key concepts.

Yearly Activity

THE INVENTION CONVENTION
This activity provides your students an opportunity to practice science skills by inventing a new product or process. Teachers' instructions and necessary forms are included.

RESEARCH AND FIELD TESTING

The initial steps in the development of Silver Burdett & Ginn's Junior High School Science Series involved the gathering of information from science educators across the country. The information was gathered in two ways: through a questionnaire sent to junior high school science teachers and through a series of focus meetings held with teachers and science supervisors around the country. Information was sought on the following points.

1. The types of materials being used in the classrooms.
2. The strengths and weaknesses of existing programs.
3. Preferences in the sequencing of topics and in the depth of coverage.
4. The types of features and ancillary materials that would be most useful to science teachers at the junior high school level.

The teachers and supervisors were also asked to react to ideas that Silver Burdett & Ginn was considering for inclusion in the new program.

With the information obtained, the authors and editors developed outlines for each program in the series. The actual development of the textbooks and ancillary materials then began.

To assist the authors and editors in developing the program, two groups of consultants were selected to review the materials. One group of consultants reviewed the materials for educational soundness and appropriateness. The other group reviewed the material to ensure that is was accurate, complete, and up-to-date.

As each chapter was completed, it was field-tested by classroom teachers. Results of such field testing were used to modify the program to improve its usefulness to students and teachers.

We would like to thank the teachers, supervisors, and consultants whose criticisms and evaluations contributed to the development of this program.

BASIC PHYSICAL SCIENCE PROGRAM

SILVER BURDETT & GINN PHYSICAL SCIENCE presents content in a flexible format. You can customize the program in a variety of ways to meet your time requirements and teaching needs.

The sections shown in the chart provide minimal coverage of physical science. This suggested core program allows you to concentrate your instruction on essential concepts, facts, and skills. It can also be used as a complete physical science program for a one-semester course. The remaining sections in each chapter contain valuable material that can be included in your teaching if time permits.

The sequence of the units — The Nature of Matter, Changes in Matter, Forces and Energy, Energy at Work, and Energy Sources — is a logical sequence to teaching physical science. However, the units dealing with forces and energy, Units Four, Five, and Six, can be covered before the units dealing with chemistry, Units Two and Three.

Units	Chapters	Sections
The Study of Physical Science	1 Introduction to Physical Science 2 Skills of Physical Science	1-1, 1-2, 1-3 2-1, 2-2, 2-4
The Nature of Matter	3 Properties of Matter 4 Atomic Structure 5 Compounds 6 Mixtures	3-1, 3-2, 3-3, 3-5 4-2, 4-3, 4-4, 4-5 5-1, 5-2, 5-3, 5-4 6-1, 6-2, 6-4
Changes in Matter	7 Chemical Reactions 8 Acids, Bases, and Salts 9 Metals 10 Nonmetals and Metalloids	7-1, 7-5 8-1, 8-2 9-1 10-1
Forces and Energy	12 Force and Energy 13 Work and Machines 14 Motion	12-1, 12-2, 12-4 13-1, 13-2 14-1, 14-2, 14-3, 14-4
Energy at Work	15 Heat 16 Electricity 17 Magnetism 18 Waves and Sound 19 Light 20 Uses of Light	15-1, 15-2, 15-5 16-1, 16-2, 16-4 17-1, 17-2 18-1, 18-2, 18-3 19-1, 19-2, 19-3, 19-4 20-1, 20-2
Energy Sources	21 Nuclear Energy 22 Energy Resources	21-1, 21-3, 21-4 22-1, 22-2, 22-3, 22-4, 22-5

THINKING SKILLS IN SILVER BURDETT & GINN PHYSICAL SCIENCE

The development of thinking skills commences at birth and continues throughout life. Development of these skills should be a major goal of the instructional program in all content areas. Instruction in science and all other content areas is interrelated with reading instruction. Just as sound reading instruction introduces higher-level thinking skills, science instruction should provide opportunities for students to analyze, synthesize, and evaluate information. (See pages T8–T11 for examples of skill development in the program.)

Student Text

The use of photographs and art in SILVER BURDETT & GINN PHYSICAL SCIENCE correlates directly with the text to explain, support, or extend the material presented. Diagrams and magnifications help clarify and define many terms and ideas. Captions contain concise, informative statements about the figures. Charts and tables give students a clearer understanding of the topic. In-text questions direct the student's attention to the illustrations and get students involved in practicing skills while using the text.

Activities throughout the book involve students in hands-on application of science process skills.

At the junior high level, students are increasingly capable of applying problem-solving skills to new situations. The SILVER BURDETT & GINN PHYSICAL SCIENCE program has been specially designed to help students develop and use critical-thinking skills. Questions requiring problem solving can be found in the Challenge question for every section and the Science Puzzler feature in every chapter. The Application/Critical Thinking and Extensions sections at the end of each chapter provide additional opportunities to use higher-level thinking skills.

The Issues and Technology feature at the end of each unit presents a current issue in science and requires that students analyze and evaluate data. Students then use critical-thinking skills to suggest possible solutions.

The Physical Science Skills Handbook at the end of the book consists of brief discussions on a variety of phenomena relating to physical science, with corresponding questions that require students to use a range of thinking skills.

Teacher Edition

Teacher notes titled "Thinking Skills," found in the teaching plan for each section, identify specific thinking skills needed in understanding concepts. In addition, a strategy to reinforce the thinking skill is provided.

The process skills for each activity are identified and range from basic to higher-level skills.

In the Teacher Resource Package

● **Review and Skill Masters**

Vocabulary Review masters reinforce new terms and develop word skills.

Skill masters develop basic science skills through a variety of exercises.

Challenge/Critical Thinking masters help better students develop higher-level critical-thinking and problem-solving skills.

● **Laboratory Manual**

Thirty-five investigations provide the opportunity for students to perform in-depth studies of physical science topics. For each lab, the process skills and laboratory techniques required are listed. A handy reference of laboratory techniques is provided at the end of the manual.

● **Science Olympics**

The challenging activities allow all students to develop higher-level thinking and problem-solving skills.

● **The Invention Convention**

This component provides an excellent opportunity for students to exercise creative-thinking and problem-solving skills, as well as a wide range of science skills as they develop their own inventions.

Thinking Skills identified in
SILVER BURDETT & GINN PHYSICAL SCIENCE

● classifying	● inferring
● sequencing	● hypothesizing
● comparing	● interpreting diagrams
● predicting	● interpreting graphs
● identifying cause and effect	● interpreting charts

Process Skills identified in the activities
SILVER BURDETT & GINN PHYSICAL SCIENCE

● observing	● hypothesizing
● measuring	● interpreting diagrams
● classifying	● interpreting graphs
● sequencing	● interpreting charts
● comparing	● interpreting data
● predicting	● designing experiments
● identifying cause and effect	● recording data
● inferring	● graphing data

SAFETY IN THE SCIENCE CLASSROOM

Safety was a primary concern in the design and development of the SILVER BURDETT & GINN PHYSICAL SCIENCE textbook. Performance of the activities in this book poses no danger if procedures are followed as outlined and warning statements are adhered to. Students should be helped to understand that the practice of safety is an important laboratory procedure. Through instruction and example, you can convey safety habits to your students.

General Classroom Safety

Every activity should begin with a discussion of safe procedures. Before each activity, demonstrate the proper use of the materials to be used. Make sure that the procedures are clear to the students. Wear required safety equipment when performing activities and insist that students do the same.

Students should not wear loose hair or loose clothing while working near an open flame. Flammable materials should be kept a safe distance from an open flame. Work tables should be kept clean, dry, and uncluttered at all times. Caution students to follow each of the steps in the activity in the order that they are presented and to resist the temptation to take shortcuts.

During activities, move about the room and keep watch for potentially hazardous situations. Discourage physical play and practical jokes. All activities should be done with your approval. Students should always work under adult supervision.

Cleanup

At the end of each class period, the room should be cleaned, straightened, and made safe for the next class. Instruct students in cleanup procedures before starting any activity. Provide separate containers for paper trash and broken glass. Direct students to unplug all electrical equipment at the end of the class period. Make sure that all materials are properly stored.

Storage

Keep all chemicals in a locked storage area that is accessible only to authorized persons. Each time a chemical is used, take an inventory of the remaining supply and see that this material is replaced as needed. Once chemicals have been removed from their storage containers, unused portions should be discarded. Never return unused chemicals to their storage containers for further use. Store large containers near floor level. Make sure that storage shelves are raised at the front to prevent containers from slipping off shelves.

For suggested shelf storage patterns, refer to *School Science Laboratories: A Guide to Some Hazardous Substances,* U.S. Product Safety Commission, Washington, D.C., 1984. You can obtain this publication from the U.S. Consumer Product Safety Commission, Room 412 — EX-O, Washington, D.C. 20207.

Check local and state regulations regarding the storage of flammable substances. The National Fire Protection Association recommends that flammable liquids be stored in vented, flame-resistant cabinets. Never store flammable liquids in a refrigerator. Never store food in a laboratory refrigerator.

Classroom Organization

Each classroom that functions as a laboratory should contain a smoke alarm, a fire extinguisher, a fire blanket, a phone or intercom to the office, and an eyewash station. Show students how to use this equipment properly, and hold periodic drills on the use of the equipment. Fire drill regulations and a chart outlining emergency procedures should be posted prominently in the laboratory.

Arrange furniture and equipment in the classroom to minimize accidents. Maintain wide, clear aisles to prevent tripping. Set up supply stations throughout the room so that students are not crowded into certain areas of the room when they line up for supplies. Do not allow students to set personal belongings near activity materials.

Laboratory Glassware

Handling laboratory glassware can be dangerous unless proper safety precautions are observed. Cuts from chipped or cracked glassware and burns from hot glassware are common accidents associated with school laboratories. Examine glassware frequently for cracks and chips. Such glassware should be immediately discarded. Glass tubing with sharp ends should be smoothed by fire polishing. Caution students to always allow hot glassware to cool on a hot pad for several minutes before handling.

Great care is required when inserting glass tubing into a stopper. Lubricate both the stopper hole and the tubing. Wrap the tubing in several layers of toweling. Then work the tubing gently into the stopper with a twisting motion. Do not leave tubing in a stopper any longer than necessary. Remove tubing in the same manner used to insert it. When tubing is difficult to remove, it is often necessary to cut the stopper.

Safety Symbols

Silver Burdett & Ginn science materials use safety symbols to alert students to possible hazards. For example, the hand safety symbol appears whenever there is danger of students cutting their hands or fingers with a sharp instrument. Many of these symbols appear in the activities in this textbook. The safety symbols are displayed and explained below. Make sure that students understand the symbols before they begin their laboratory work.

The ten safety symbols that are used in the activities in this book are shown in Appendix 3, on page 576 of the pupil's text. Have students turn to this page. Then review the symbols and their meanings with the students.

The **hand safety** symbol appears when there is a danger of cuts caused by glassware, scalpels, or other potentially sharp laboratory tools or equipment.

The **noxious fumes** symbol appears when chemicals or combinations of chemicals are capable of causing noxious fumes.

The **electrical safety** symbol appears whenever students should exhibit care in handling electrical equipment.

The **plant safety** symbol appears whenever the investigation requires handling plants with sharp edges or thorns.

The **animal safety** symbol appears whenever live animals are studied. It is meant to protect both the student and the animal.

The **radioactive** symbol appears when radioactive materials are present.

The **water safety** symbol appears whenever students will be outdoors near bodies of water.

The **body protection** symbol appears whenever chemicals, acids, or stains can cause damage to clothing. A laboratory apron should be worn in these instances.

The **fire safety** symbol appears to remind students to exhibit caution when working with Bunsen burners or hot plates. This is intended as protection from the equipment itself and also as a warning to avoid burns when handling heated materials and their containers.

The **explosion** symbol appears as a reminder to students to follow directions when working with chemicals that could be explosive if misused.

The **eye safety** symbol appears when safety goggles should be worn and when there is a possibility of danger to eyes.

The **gas safety** symbol appears as a reminder to students to be careful when using the Bunsen burner and to check that the gas outlet is turned off when it is not in use.

The **poison** symbol appears when substances in an investigation could be poisonous if ingested.

MEETING THE NEEDS OF A WIDE RANGE OF STUDENTS

The SILVER BURDETT & GINN PHYSICAL SCIENCE program has been developed to meet the needs of a wide range of student abilities. Although the basic text is geared toward the average learner, many features have been designed to accommodate the needs of the slow learner and the academically gifted learner. A variety of teaching and management strategies can be used with mainstreamed and language minority students.

Slow Learners

These students can become frustrated and lose interest in learning unless their course of study is structured. These features of the program are aids toward a successful learning experience.

- In-text questions focus students' attention on the illustrations, thus acting as context clues to the understanding of concepts.

- Vocabulary terms are in boldface type and many of them are phonetically respelled. Word parts help students build vocabulary skills.

- Objectives and key terms at the beginning of every section give students a clear purpose for reading.

- Text activities with step-by-step procedures guide students and provide concrete experiences to help reinforce basic concepts.

- Review questions at the end of every section test the section objectives and provide a checkpoint to evaluate mastery of concepts.

- The Chapter Summary identifies the main ideas in each section and lists all key terms in the chapter.

- The Chapter Review includes Vocabulary and Concepts sections that test recall of definitions and basic facts.

- The Study Guide, which accompanies the Student Text, provides exercises to guide students as they read each section of the chapter.

Academically Gifted Learners

Students of this caliber often experience frustration unless challenged with new learning experiences. Many features in the program have been designed to meet their special needs.

- At the end of every section, a Challenge question is posed, requiring higher-level thinking skills.

- An illustrated Science Puzzler with every chapter challenges students to use problem-solving skills in arriving at an answer.

- The Chapter Review includes an Application/Critical Thinking section, which requires students to apply concepts to new situations. Extensions offer research and activity ideas. The Readings list gives current titles on related chapter topics.

- Issues and Technology requires students to interpret data and use decision-making skills on topics of current concern.

- The Physical Science Skills Handbook provides enrichment in a variety of topics relating to the units and requires the use of critical-thinking skills.

- Challenge/Critical Thinking masters in the Review and Skill Masters require students to use higher-level thinking skills.

- The Laboratory Manual offers a range of more sophisticated investigations.

- Science Olympics, specially designed for the academically gifted student, offers enriching exercises that challenge students' abilities.

- The Invention Convention — the ultimate in creative thinking and problem solving — encourages students to invent an original product or process.

The Mainstreamed Learner

Aside from the range of students with varying abilities, students with special needs can also experience successful learning in the classroom. Students with learning disabilities can be integrated, or "mainstreamed," into the classroom after assessing whether they can be expected to achieve educational goals in the classroom in spite of their handicaps. Many of these students compare favorably with other students in their curiosity and enjoyment of science.

A number of management strategies can be employed in enabling these special students to achieve their individual potential. Your teaching of mainstreamed students should be based on what they can do, not on what they cannot do. Recommendations here are general management strategies for use in mainstreaming the following types of special students.

Management Strategies

The emotionally handicapped:
- Clearly define class rules.
- Provide a highly structured environment.
- Reward appropriate behaviors and try to ignore inappropriate behaviors.
- Be consistent.
- Intervene and redirect a student before a conflict arises.

The learning disabled:
- Clearly define expectations.
- Utilize a multisensory approach to learning.
- Provide a highly structured environment.
- Offer hands-on activities and concrete experiences.
- Avoid excess stimuli.

The mentally retarded:
- Give concrete and clear explanations.
- Repeat activities when necessary and provide additional activities as reinforcement.
- Utilize a variety of manipulative materials.
- Provide frequent reassurance.

The deaf or hearing impaired:
- Seat the student in the front of the room.
- Face the student when speaking.
- Use films with captions whenever possible.
- Provide visual aids.

The visually impaired:
- Seat the student in the front of the room.
- Assign another student to assist in projects.
- Provide hands-on experience and three-dimensional diagrams.
- Encourage the student to touch materials whenever possible.
- Consult with the resource room teacher for special teaching aids.

The orthopedically handicapped:
- Consult with the student's physical therapist to identify the student's limitations and potential mobility.
- Adapt the physical environment to provide appropriate space and/or support, according to the abilities and the disabilities of the student.

The health impaired:
- Consult with the school nurse and the special education teacher to discuss the student's abilities and limitations.

The Language Minority Learner

Providing instruction to language minority students in their native language is often difficult. However, the teacher can be instrumental in helping these students be successful within a monolingual class. Language minority students are positively affected when acceptance and respect for their culture and language is demonstrated.

Language minority students who understand, speak, read, and write little or no English will need additional support and explanation from the teacher in order to understand the concepts covered in the text. Science, in particular, poses the greatest difficulty for langue minority students because of the technical vocabulary presented in the curriculum. Meeting the needs of these students without native language support can be done in two ways. (1) The teacher can help the student understand the concepts being taught. (2) The teacher can create an optimal environment for the language minority student to experience success by alleviating some of the frustrations and anxieties of the student.

Strategies for Making Concepts Understandable

1. Include the students' background and interests in the learning process.

2. Personalize instruction by making use of the students' experiences, ideas, and opinions.

3. Begin the lesson by clearly identifying the objective of the lesson.

4. Simplify the language of the concept to be learned without diluting the concept.

5. Use a variety of materials such as visuals, manipulatives, props, and so on to help provide a context in which new concepts are taught.

6. Summarize important concepts by providing a brief review at the end of each class period.

7. Write the important concepts on the blackboard or a chart in outline form.

8. Simplify the language of presentation.
   - Speak slowly and articulate clearly. Be conscious of your intonation and volume. Pause between sentences to help students in their listening comprehension.
   - Avoid using contractions such as *I'll, won't, can't, I'd.*
   - Use simple but complete sentences. If necessary, simplify and restate topics.
   - When introducing words in boldfaced type, use pictures, gestures, and props.
   - Use simple vocabulary that is likely to be understandable to the student. Avoid using slang words and idioms.
   - Minimize the use of pronouns; use the term instead. Example: Solar energy is a potential source for heating buildings. Thus, solar energy (it) could save thousands of dollars in heating costs every year.

9. When evaluating the language minority student, use questioning strategies appropriate to the students' competence in English. Ask a range of questions from those requiring lower-level skills to those requiring critical-thinking skills.
   - For students who speak little or no English, use questions that only require a response such as pointing or picking up an object.
   - For students who speak some English, use either/or questions and questions that require single-word answers.
   - Use fill-in-the-blank questions with a single word missing. Example: (Water) and air are renewable resources.

Creating an Optimal Environment for Learning

1. Accept any language the student uses but without any overt correction. Correct the student for science content but not for language content. According to experts, the practice of correcting speech errors is ineffective and actually harms progress in language acquisition.

2. Do not force a student to respond until the student is willing.

3. Have a reader who is fluent in English tape the textbook onto cassettes or read the text to the student.

4. Assign each language minority student a peer with whom to study. The peer can be a speaker of the student's native language or one who is willing to sponsor the student.

5. Modify evaluation techniques to match the strategies used in the instruction. Essay-type tests are difficult and will not be indicative of the students' content knowledge.

Consultant — Rosita Apodaca, Director of Bilingual Education, Dallas Independent School District, Dallas, Texas

MATERIALS

Nonconsumable Materials

Material	Quantity	Page
balance	30	92, 96, 140, 176, 234, 240, 270, 291, 368
balance and masses	15	16, 71
ball, pith with silk cord attached	15	385
ball, table-tennis	15	343
beads, glass	100	92
beaker	30	67
beaker, 100-mL	15	210
beaker, 150-mL	75	189
beaker, 200-mL	15	18
beaker, 250-mL	60	124, 145, 180, 198, 234, 265, 291, 367, 563
beaker, 400-mL	15	240
beaker, 50-mL	120	196
beaker, small	10	75
bend, glass	15	297
board, inclined plane	15	314, 340
book (same thickness)	105	314
bottle, 250-mL plastic laboratory	15	454
bottle, 500-mL plastic laboratory	15	454
bulb, miniature light	45	399
Bunsen burner	30	22, 75, 210, 234, 270
can, overflow	15	291
carbon	15 samples	208
cart, small	15	337, 340
Celsius thermometer	30	18, 67, 145, 176, 363, 367, 368, 553, 563
clamp	30	35, 134, 531
clamp, burette	30	234, 240
clamp, extension	15	321
clamp, lever	15	317
clamp, ring	15	297
clamp, test-tube	15	265
clock with second hand	15	67, 367
coil, wire	1 roll	420
compass, drawing	30	102
compass, small	15	416
copper	15 samples	208
cork	15	297
cork, small	15	448
cylinder, 100-mL graduated	15	71
cylinder, 50-mL graduated	10	248

Material	Quantity	Page
dime	15	16
dish, evaporating	15	270
dropper	30	75, 134, 196, 265
dry cell	30	124, 208, 399
dry cell (1.5 volts)	15	416
electroscope	15	390
flashlight, small	15	464
flask, 100-mL Florence	30	563
flask, 250-mL	30	270, 297
flask, Erlenmeyer 50-mL	15	180
forceps	30	16, 134, 176
fork, different tuning	45	448
funnel	15	198
galvanometer	15	420
gas-collecting trough	10	248
Geiger counter	6	531
glass plate, cobalt	15	210
glass, magnifying	15	495
graduate	30	134, 173, 176, 210, 265, 270, 454, 563
graduate, 10-mL	30	108, 140, 145, 217
graduate, 100-mL	30	15, 189, 196, 198, 363, 368
graduate, 25-mL	15	180
holder, magnet	15	412
holder, mass	15	340
holder, test-tube	10	75
hot plate	15	18, 67, 145, 265, 297, 367
iron	15 samples	208
iron filings	60 g	240
isotope models	15	96
lab apron	30	18, 22, 67, 75, 108, 124, 134, 140, 145, 173, 176, 180, 189, 196, 198, 210, 217, 234, 248, 265, 270, 563
lamp, incandescent	15	22
lens, convex	15	495
light bulb and socket	30	124, 208
magnesium	15 samples	208
magnet, bar	30	412, 420
mallet, rubber	15	448
marker	30	102
mass, 1-kg	15	321
mass, 10-g	90	340

MATERIALS

Nonconsumable Materials

Material	Quantity	Page
mass, 100-g	30	317, 337
mass, 5-g	90	340
masses, slotted gram	10	35
meterstick	30	35, 305, 314, 317, 321, 340, 441
microscope, illuminated pocket (30x)	15	476
mirror, small	15	469
mirror, small plane	30	490
mortar and pestle	15	140
needle, dissecting	15	287
needle, platinum	15	210
nichrome wire with handle	15	22
nickel	30	16, 92
object, metal	15	291
object, rectangular solid	15	15
objects	variety	71
pencil	30	102
pennies	200	527
penny	30	16, 92
plate, pie	15	502
protractor	15	469
pulley with hook	45	321
punch, hole	15	464
quarter	15	92
rack, test-tube	15	367
ring	30	270, 448
rod, glass	30	385, 390
rod, glass-stirring	30	18, 198, 234
rod, hard rubber	15	390
rod, rubber	15	385
rod, stirring	30	134, 145, 270, 368
ruler	15	134
ruler, metric	30	15, 40, 45, 71, 102, 180, 240, 287, 337, 412, 464, 469, 490, 495, 502, 531
safety goggles	30	18, 22, 67, 75, 108, 124, 140, 145, 173, 176, 180, 189, 196, 198, 210, 217, 234, 248, 265, 270, 367, 563
scale, spring	30	291, 305, 314, 321
scissors	30	40, 102, 180, 217, 337, 502
screwdriver	15	399

Material	Quantity	Page
sinker, lead	15	287
sockets, miniature	45	399
spatula	30	108, 140, 234
spectroscope, grating	1	22
splints, wood	10	248
spring, long	15	441
spring, steel	10	35
stand, ring	30	35, 134, 234, 240, 270, 297, 321, 337, 385, 448, 527
stopper, cork	15	134
stopper, one-hole rubber	30	67, 248, 297
stopper, rubber	30	140, 176, 270
stopper, slit rubber	15	464, 469, 490
striker	30	22, 75, 210, 234, 270
student molecular kit	15	259
sulfur	15 samples	208
support, lever	15	317
switch	15	399
test tube	120	75, 108, 134, 140, 145, 173, 176, 210, 217, 234, 240, 248, 265, 367
test tube, large	30	67
test tube, small	45	134
thumbtack	15	134
thumbtacks	1 box	297, 448
timer	1	180
tongs	30	75, 563
tube, capillary	15	134
tube, sealed iodine	10	75
tubing, glass (40 cm long)	10 pieces	248
tubing, rubber (50 cm long)	10 pieces	248
watch glass	15	208
watch with second hand	15	367
watch, stop	15	340
water bath	10	248
weight hanger	10	35
wire stripper	30	124, 208
wire, (45 cm long)	45 pieces	399
wire, copper	60 cm	217
wire, insulated	18 m	124, 208
wire, insulated copper (50 cm long)	15 pieces	416
wood	30 blocks	305
zinc	15 samples	208
zinc metal	15 pieces	217

MATERIALS

Consumable Materials

Material	Quantity	Page
acetic acid	405 mL	189, 265
alcohol, amyl	75 mL	265
alcohol, ethyl	75 mL	265
alcohol, methyl	37.5 mL	265
alcohol, rubbing	3.75 L	124
ammonia	275 mL	196
ammonium chloride	45 g	176
baking soda	2 boxes	124, 248
balloon	15	343
barium chloride solution	75 mL	173
box, shoe	60	287, 527, 553
box, shoe with lid	15	502
bromthymol blue	30 mL	198
butyric acid	30 mL	265
calcium chloride solution	100 mL	22
calcium hydroxide solution (limewater)	150 mL	173
calcium oxide	150 g	198
card, index	90	464, 490
cardboard (12 cm x 6 cm long)	13 pieces	553
cardboard (20 cm x 5 cm long)	15 pieces	337
cardboard (30 cm x 30 cm)	15 pieces	469
cardboard, heavy (21.5 cm x 28 cm)	15 pieces	416
chalk	15 pieces	340
charcoal, powdered	30 g	234
cloth, silk	30 pieces	385, 390
cloth, wool	15 pieces	385
Cobalt-60 source		531
comics, newspaper color	15 sheets	476
copper (II) oxide	15 g	234
copper (II) sulfate	30 g	140
copper (II) sulfate solution	300 mL	173, 217
cotton	3 boxes	563
cup, plastic foam	60	363, 368
detergent, liquid laundry	275 mL	196
filings, iron	50 g	412
foil, small strip of aluminum	15 strips	385
fur, animal	15 pieces	390
glycerine	1 tube	67
hydrochloric acid	1225 mL	180, 189, 196, 198, 210, 248
hydrochloric acid, dilute	15 mL	75
hydrogen peroxide	4 L	108, 124, 248, 18, 368

Material	Quantity	Page
ice		
ink, black	15 bottles	134
juice, lemon	650 mL	189, 196
line, fishing	15 m	343
lithium chloride solution	130 mL	22, 210
lithium nitrate solution	30 mL	210
lubricant	1 tube	67
magnesium ribbon	30 cm	180
manganese dioxide	60 g	108, 248
matches, wooden	11 boxes	108, 248
olive oil	90 mL	270
paper	165 sheets	102, 412
paper towels	15 sheets	270
paper, 1-cm grid graph	30 sheets	40
paper, 12-cm long chromatography	15 sheets	134
paper, filter	15 sheets	198
paper, graph	15 sheets	340
	30 sheets	45
paper, pH	60 strips	198
paper, wax	1 box	502
paper, white	45 sheets	464, 469, 495
paradichlorobenzene (moth balls)	1-lb box	367
paraffin	1 box	67
pencil, colored	30	45
pencil, glass-marking	30	108, 124, 140, 189, 196, 210, 248, 265, 469, 502
pin, straight		
poster board	30	102
potassium chloride solution	30 mL	210
potassium nitrate	100 g	145
potassium nitrate solution	30 mL	210
potassium sulfate solution	75 mL	173
red cabbage indicator solution	60 mL	196
salicylic acid	30 mL	265
salt, table	2 boxes	75, 124
sodium chloride	45 g	270
sodium chloride solution	30 mL	210
sodium hydroxide pellets	225	176
sodium hydroxide solution	555 mL	196, 198, 270
sodium nitrate solution	30 mL	210
soil, dark	17 kg	553
Solution A containing 0.1 m of barium nitrate	30 mL	75
Solution B containing 0.1 m of sodium chromate	30 mL	75

MATERIALS

Consumable Materials

Material	Quantity	Page
Solution C containing 0.1 m of iron chloride	30 mL	75
Solution D containing 0.1 m of potassium thiocyanate	30 mL	75
splint, wood	15	108
steel wool	1 box	75
straw, drinking	45	173, 198, 343
string (30 cm long)	30 pieces	287, 291
string (40 cm long)	15 pieces	297
string (50 cm long)	60 pieces	305, 314, 317, 340
string (70 cm long)	15 pieces	321
strontium chloride solution	100 mL	22
sugar	1-lb box	124
sulfuric acid	402.5 mL	189, 265
tape, clear	30 rolls	40, 102, 441, 502
tape, masking	30 rolls	248, 337, 343, 416, 553
tea	275 mL	196
thread (20 cm long)	15 pieces	448
unknown solution containing one or more lithium, sodium, or potassium ions	30 mL	210
vinegar	100 mL	248
vinegar, white	275 mL	196
water, distilled		124, 134, 140, 145, 176, 196, 198
water, hot tap		363, 563
water, ice		563
water, soda	375 mL	189
water, tap		15, 18, 67, 75, 108, 145, 270, 363, 454
wrap, clear plastic	1 roll	553
zinc strip	15	173
zinc sulfate solution	150 mL	217
zinc, mossy	60 g	75, 189, 248

Bibliography

Chapter 1

Ardley, Neil. *Making Metric Measurements,* New York: Franklin Watts, 1983.

Asimov, Isaac. *Measure of the Universe,* New York: Harper and Row, 1983.

McCorduck, Pamela. "The Conquering Machine." *Science 84,* November 1984, p. 131.

Reich, Leonard S. "From Edison's Wastebasket." *Science 84,* November 1984, p. 73.

Townes, Charles H. "Harnessing Light." *Science 84,* November 1984, p. 153.

*Klein, H. Arthur. *World of Measurements,* New York: Simon & Schuster, 1974.

Chapter 2

Cromer, Alan. *Physics for the Life Sciences,* New York: McGraw-Hill, 1974.

Harper, P. *The Timetable of Technology.* New York: Hearst Books, 1982.

Lu, Cary. "Micros Get Graphic." *High Technology,* March 1986, p. 18.

Measuring and Computing, New York: Arco Publishing Co., Inc., 1984.

Woodruff, Bobby J. *Terms, Tables, and Skills for the Physical Sciences,* Morristown, N.J.: Silver Burdett Co., 1966.

Chapter 3

Apfel, Necia. *It's All Elementary,* New York: Lothrop, Lee, and Shepard Books, 1985.

Gunston, Bill. *Water,* Morristown, N.J.: Silver Burdett Co., 1982.

Trefil, James. "Matter vs. Antimatter." *Science 81,* September 1981, p. 66.

Walton, Alan J. *Three Phases of Matter,* New York: Oxford University Press, 1983.

*Goodstein, David L. *States of Matter,* New York: Dover Publications, 1985.

Chapter 4

Asimov, Isaac. *How Did We Find Out About Atoms?* New York: Walker and Co., 1976.

Asimov, Isaac. *Inside the Atom.* New York: Abelard-Schuman, 1974.

Gallant, Roy A. *Explorers of the Atom,* Garden City, N.Y.: Doubleday and Company, 1974.

Mebane, Robert. *Adventures with Atoms and Molecules,* Hillside, N.J.: Enslow Publishers, 1985.

Neubauer, Alfred. *Chemistry Today,* New York: Arco Books, Inc., 1983.

Quigg, Chris. "Elementary Particles and Forces." *Scientific American,* April 1985, p. 84.

Chapter 5

Bershad, Carol and Deborah Bernick. *Body-Works: The Kid's Guide to Food and Physical Fitness.* New York: Random House, Inc., 1981.

Considine, Dougle M. (ed.) *Encyclopedia of Chemistry,* New York: Van Nostrand Reinhold Company, 1984.

Neubauer, Alfred. *Chemistry Today,* New York: Arco Books, 1983.

Weis, Malcolm E. *Why Glass Breaks, Rubber Bends, and Glue Sticks.* New York: Harcourt, Brace, Jovanovich Inc., 1979.

Chapter 6

Dickinson, E. *Colloids in Food.* New York: Elsevier, 1982.

Holden, Alan, and Phylis Morrison. *Crystals and Crystal Growing.* Cambridge, Mass.: MIT Press, 1982.

Murrell, J.N., and E.A. Boucher. *Properties of Liquids and Solutions,* New York: Wiley, 1982.

Updegraffe, Imelda, and Robert Updegraffe. *Seas and Oceans.* New York: Penguin, 1983.

*Moore, Walter J. *Basic Physical Chemistry,* Englewood Cliffs, N.J.: Prentice-Hall, Inc., 1983.

*Nielson, Lawrence. *Predicting the Properties of Mixtures,* New York: Dekker, Inc., 1978.

Chapter 7

Angier, Natalie. "Hazards of a Toxic Wasteland." *Time,* December 17, 1984, p. 32.

Chishom, J., and M. Lynnington. *Chemistry,* Tulsa, Oklahoma: EDC Publishing, 1983.

Choppin, Gregory. *Chemistry,* Morristown, N.J.: Silver Burdett Co., 1982.

Parker, Sybil (ed.) *McGraw-Hill Dictionary of Chemistry,* N.Y.: McGraw-Hill Book Co., Inc., 1984.

Chapter 8

Cecil, George. *Salt.* New York: Franklin Watts, 1976.

Drago, Russell S. *Acids and Bases,* Lexington, Mass.: D.C. Heath and Company, 1968.

La Bastille, Anne. "Acid Rain: How Great a Menace." *National Geographic,* November 1981, p. 652.

Pearson, R.G. (ed.) *Hard and Soft Acids and Bases,* N.Y.: Van Nostrand Reinhold, 1973.

Salisbury, David F. "Salt: An Untapped Source of Abundant Energy." *Science Digest,* December 1978, p. 45.

Chapter 9

Haines, Gail Kay. *The Elements,* New York: Franklin Watts, Inc., 1972.

Kear, Bernard H. "Advanced Metals." *Scientific American,* October 1986, p. 158.

Kerrod, Robin. *Metals.* Morristown, N.J.: Silver Burdett Co., 1982.

Noble Metals, Morristown, New Jersey: Silver Burdett Co., 1983.

Siberner, J. "New Factor in Salt." *Science News,* December 10, 1983, p. 372.

"Sodium Bicarb Use Questioned." *Science News,* May 18, 1985, p. 311.

"A Tungsten Coat for Silicon." *Science News,* March 16, 1985, p. 173.

*Levi, Primo. *The Periodic Table,* New York: Schocken Books, 1984.

Chapter 10

Bardeen, John. "To a Solid State." *Science 84,* October 1984, p. 143.

"The Carbon Story." *Science 85,* October 1985, p. 54.

Milne, Lorus J. and Margery Milne. *Nature's Great Carbon Cycle,* Boston, Mass.: Atheneum, 1983.

Morgan, Diana. "How Does Fluoride Fight Tooth Decay?" *Science 84,* December 1984, p. 27.

Richardson, Stephen H. and others. "Antique Diamonds." *Current Science,* October 1984, p. 6.

Chapter 11

Baer, Eric. "Advanced Polymers." *Scientific American,* October 1986, p. 178.

Charney, Ted. *Organic Compounds,* New York: Richard Rosen Press, 1976.

Cobb, Vicki. *Gases,* New York: Franklin Watts, Inc., 1970.

Cohen, Bernard (ed.) *Laws of Gases,* New York: Ayer Company, 1981.

Peterson, I., "Conducting a New Polymer into Batteries." *Science News,* November 24, 1984, p. 326.

"Polymer Power." *Scientific American,* November 1984, p. 72.

Chapter 12

Ardley, Neil and Eric Laithwaithe. *Force and Strength,* New York: Franklin Watts, Inc., 1984.

Asimov, Isaac. *How Did We Find Out About Energy?,* New York: Avon Books, 1981.

Berger, Melvin. *Energy,* New York: Franklin Watts, Inc., 1983.

Galligan, Mary. "In Solar Village, Sunshine Is Put in Harness." *US News and World Report,* February 11, 1985, p. 72.

Kakela, Peter. "Low Head Hydropower for Local Use." *Environment,* January/February 1985, p. 31.

Schefter, Jim. "Solar Power, Cheaper Than Coal, Oil, Gas." *Popular Science,* February 1985, p. 77.

Chapter 13

Bargo, Michael. "All Gear Steering." *Popular Science,* July 1985, p. 60.

Brown, Stuart. "World's Most Advanced Bike." *Popular Science,* February 1985, p. 95.

Hames, Peter. *Story of the Wheel,* Sussex, England: Wayland Publishers, 1978.

James, Elizabeth. *Simple Facts of Simple Machines,* New York: Lothrop, Lee, and Shepard Co., 1975.

Machines, Power and Transportation, New York. Arco Publishing, Inc., 1984.

Chapter 14

Ardley, Neil and Eric Laithwaithe, *Making Things Move,* New York: Franklin Watts, Inc., 1984.

Bendick, Jeane. *Artificial Satellites,* New York: Franklin Watts, Inc., 1982.

Gardener, Robert and David Webster. *Moving Right Along: A Book of Science Experiments and Puzzles About Motion.* New York: Doubleday and Co., 1978.

Hancock, Ralph. *Understanding Movement.* Morristown, N.J.: Silver Burdett Co., 1985.

Smith, Howard E., Jr. *Balance It!* New York: Four Winds, 1982.

Chapter 15

Adler, Irving. *Hot and Cold.* New York: John Day and Co., 1975.

Bittman. M. "Keep Heat Inside with Outside Insulation." *Popular Science,* October 1984, p. 100.

Kentzer, Michael. *Heat.* (Young Scientist Series). Morristown, N.J.: Silver Burdett Co.

Nelson, R. "A Look Inside the Super-engines." *Popular Mechanics,* February 1984, p. 80.

Whyman, *Kathryn.* Heat and Energy. New York: Franklin Watts, Inc., 1986.

Chapter 16

Ardley, Neil and Eric Laithwaithe. *Discovering Electricity.* New York: Franklin Watts, Inc., 1984.

Cooper, Alan. *Visual Science Electricity.* Morristown, N.J.: Silver Burdett Co., 1983.

Gutnik, Martin J. *Electricity: From Faraday to Solar Generators.* New York.: Franklin Watts, Inc., 1986.

Leon, George. *The Electricity Story: 2500 Years of Discoveries and Experiments.* New York: Arco Publishing, 1983.

Math, Irwin. *Wires and Watts: Understanding and Using Electricity.* New York: Charles Scribner's Sons, 1981.

Vogt, Gregory. *Electricity and Magnetism.* New York: Franklin Watts, Inc., 1985.

*Fowler, Richard. *Electricity: Principles and Applications,* New York: McGraw-Hill, Inc., 1984.

Chapter 17

Adler, David. *Amazing Magnets.* Mahwah, N.J.: Troll, 1983.

Branley, Franklyn M. *The Electromagnetic Spectrum,* New York: Thomas Y. Crowell, 1979.

Chaudhari, Praveen. "Electronic and Magnetic Materials," *Scientific American,* October 1986, p. 136.

Math, Irwin. *Wires and Watts,* New York: Charles Scribner's Sons, 1981.

Stansell, John. *Discovering Communications.* London: Sceptre Books, Ltd., 1983.

Vogt, Gregory. *Electricity and Magnetism,* New York: Franklin Watts, Inc., 1985.

Chapter 18

Ardley, Neil and Eric Laithwaithe. *Sound and Music,* New York: Franklin Watts, Inc., 1984.

Buckley, R. *Oscillations and Waves,* Accord, Mass.: International Publication Service, Inc., 1985.

Kettlekamp, Larry. *Magic of Sound,* New York: William Morrow and Co., 1982.

Knight, David C. *Silent Sound: The World of Ultrasonics.* New York: Morrow, Williams and Co., Inc., 1980.

Ruby, D.J. "Visible Wind (Doppler Acoustic Sounder)." *Popular Science,* November 1983, p. 103.

Chapter 19

Branley, Franklyn. *Color — From Rainbows to Lasers,* New York: Thomas Y. Crowell, 1978.

Brou, Philippe. "Colors of Things," *Scientific American,* September 1986, p. 84.

Cole, K.C. *Facets of Light, Images and Things that Glow in the Dark,* San Francisco, Calif.: The Exploratorium, 1980.

Johnson, P.C. "Secrets of Color Underwater," *Outdoor Life,* January 1985, p. 32.

Levin, Edith. *Penetrating Beam, Reflections on Light,* New York: Richard Rosen Press, 1978.

Morris, Richard. *Light,* New York: Bobbs-Merrill Co., Inc., 1979.

Peterson, Ivars. "Pigment Processing for Cave Paintings," *Science News,* June 2, 1984, p. 348.

Sight, Light and Color., New York: Arco Publishing, Inc., 1984.

White, Jack R. *Invisible World of the Infrared,* New York: Dodd, Mead and Co., 1984.

Chapter 20

Lewis, Bruce. *What Is a Laser?* New York: Dodd, Mead and Co., 1979.

Rowell, J.M. "Photonic Materials." *Scientific American,* October 1986, p. 147.

Shuford, R.S. "An Introduction to Fiber Optics." *Byte,* January 1985, p. 197.

Sight, Light and Color. New York: Arco Publishing Co., Inc., 1984.

Thomsen, D.E. "Catching On to a Light Wave," *Science News,* February 2, 1985, p. 76.

Thomsen, D.E. "More Heroes of Optical Communications." *Science News,* March 2, 1985, p. 134.

Waldman, Gary. *Introduction to Light.* Hillside, N.J.: Enslow, 1983.

Wenyon, Michael. *Understanding Holography.* New York: Arco Publishing, Inc., 1985.

Chapter 21

Craxton, R. Stephen. "Progress in Laser Fusion." *Scientific American,* August 1986, p. 68.

Epstein, S.S. and Carl Pope. "Hazardous Wastes in America." San Francisco, Calif.: Sierra, 1983.

Lampton, Christopher. *Fusion: The Eternal Flame,* New York: Franklin Watts, Inc., 1982.

Ligtman, A. "Weighing the Odds." *Science 83,* December 1983, p. 10.

Moché, Dinah. *Radiation.* New York: Franklin Watts, Inc., 1979.

"Physicists Create a New Element." *Science 82,* December 1982, p. 7.

Pringle, Laurence. *Radiation.* Hillside, N.J.: Enslow Publishers, 1983.

Chapter 22

Branley, Franklyn. *Feast or Famine? The Energy Future.* New York: Thomas Y. Crowell, 1980.

Berger, Melvin. *Energy.* New York: Franklin Watts, Inc., 1983.

Claassen, Richard S. "Materials for Energy Utilization." *Scientific American,* October 1986, p. 103.

Energy, Forces and Resources. New York: Arco Publishing Co., Inc., 1984.

"Energy Resources, A Special Report." *National Geographic,* February 1981.

Gadler, Steve J., and Wendy Adamson. *Sun Power: Facts About Solar Energy.* Minneapolis, Minn.: Lerner, 1978.

Naar, John. *The New Wind Power.* New York: Penguin, 1982.

Palz, W. *Wind Energy.* Higham, Mass.: Kluwer Academic, 1983.

Sander, Leonard. "Power from the Sea." *Scientific American,* January 1987, p. 86.

Smith, Norman F. *Energy Isn't Easy.* New York: Putnam's, 1984.

SILVER BURDETT & GINN
PHYSICAL SCIENCE

Series Authors

Peter Alexander, Ph.D.
Professor of Biology and Computer Science
St. Peter's College
Jersey City, New Jersey

Marilyn Fiegel, Ed.D.
District Science Coordinator
West Seneca Central Schools
West Seneca, New York

Steven K. Foehr
Teacher of Science
Wickford Middle School
North Kingstown, Rhode Island

Anne F. Harris
Environmental Scientist
Black and Veatch, Engineers/Architects
Kansas City, Missour

Joseph G. Krajkovich, Ed.D.
Supervisor of Science
Edison Twp. Board of Education
Edison, New Jersey

Kenneth W. May
Chairperson, Science Department
Camden Central School
Camden, New York

Nicholas Tzimopoulos, Ph.D.
Director of Science
Sleepy Hollow High School
North Tarrytown, New York

Rita K. Voltmer, Ph.D.
Assistant Professor of Science Education
Miami University
Oxford, Ohio

SILVER BURDETT & GINN
MORRISTOWN, NJ • NEEDHAM, MA
Atlanta, GA • Cincinnati, OH • Dallas, TX • Menlo Park, CA • Northfield, IL

Content Reviewers

Edmund Bertschinger, Ph.D.
Assistant Professor of Physics
Massachusetts Institute of Technology
Cambridge, Massachusetts

Edward Booker, Ph.D.
Professor of Chemistry
Texas Southern University
Houston, Texas

Stephen J. Hawkes, Ph.D.
Professor of Chemistry
Oregon State University
Corvallis, Oregon

Pan Papacosta, Ph.D.
Assistant Professor of Physics
Stetson University
Deland, Florida

Stephen Riter, Ph.D.
Professor of Electrical Engineering
   and Computer Science
University of Texas at El Paso
El Paso, Texas

Barbara A. Wilson, Ph.D.
Supervisor of Optoelectronic Materials
   Research Group
AT&T Bell Laboratories
Murray Hill, New Jersey

Teacher Reviewers

Michael M. Athey
Instructional Supervisor
Berkeley County Schools
Martinsburg, West Virginia

William E. Beggs
Secondary Science Supervisor
Pinellas County Schools
Largo, Florida

Eugene L. Chiappetta, Ph.D.
Professor in Curriculum and Instruction
University of Houston — University Park
Houston, Texas

Fern Ione Cleary
Chairperson, Science Department
Seminole Middle School
Seminole, Florida

Mary Ann Esquibel
District Science Coordinator
Albuquerque Public Schools
Albuquerque, New Mexico

Michael H. Farmer
Chairperson, Science Department
Riverside High School
Greer, South Carolina

William W. Farran
Science Teacher
Taft Middle School
Albuquerque, New Mexico

Warner E. Freeman
Department Instructional Specialist, Science
Martin Luther King, Jr. High School
Berkeley, California

Joyce Gibson
Chairperson, Science Department
Babb Junior High School
Forest Park, Georgia

Anne Brink Hair
Chairperson, Science Department
Northview Middle School
Indianapolis, Indiana

Roger W. Hamm, Ph.D.
Lecturer of Education
California State University — San Bernardino
San Bernardino, California

Quincy T. Hathorn
Science Specialist
Memphis City Schools
Memphis, Tennessee

Rod Shriwise
Science Division Coordinator
Milburn Junior High School
Shawnee Mission, Kansas

Frances E. Starks
Chairperson, Science Department
Prairie Hills Junior High School
Markham, Illinois

About the Cover
The front cover shows hot air balloons floating in the air. Diagrams showing the
behavior of the air in the balloons are shown on the back cover. See Chapter 12,
Section 12-3, and Chapter 15, Sections 15-4 and 15-5, for more information on
why the balloons rise and fall.

Contents

Activities

Unit 1

THE STUDY OF PHYSICAL SCIENCE

UNIT OVERVIEW

Chapter 1 discusses the major branches of physical science, the scientific method, measurement in science, and the use of tools in science.

Chapter 2 introduces the concepts of matter and energy. It also reviews math and graph skills useful in physical science, as well as safe laboratory techniques.

Unit One

THE STUDY OF PHYSICAL SCIENCE

Modern physical scientists study matter and energy and their interactions. Nearly every facet of industry relies on the physical sciences. Computer technology, communications, transportation, and manufacturing are just a few of the industries that make use of research in the physical sciences. Scientists use many tools and many skills. As you read this unit, you will learn about the tools and skills of the physical scientists. You will also learn how to perform laboratory activities safely. ■

▲ *These tubes are filled with gases that give off light when electricity passes through them.*

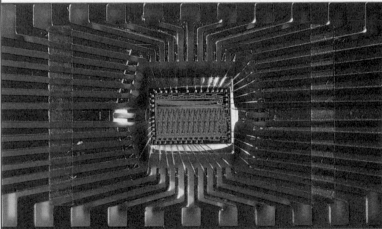

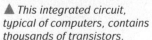
▲ *This integrated circuit, typical of computers, contains thousands of transistors.*

▶ *Line engraving of an air pump used by Robert Boyle in the seventeenth century.*

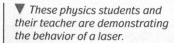

▼ These physics students and their teacher are demonstrating the behavior of a laser.

▶ This is a computer model of a protein. Computer models are useful in chemistry research.

▼ A nineteenth-century engraving of Sir Isaac Newton dispersing sunlight through a prism.

▲ A loadstone, which is a natural magnet, was mounted in this brass carrier. It was used during the eighteenth century to find north.

Sections appearing in red provide coverage of basic topics in this unit. See page T23.

INTRODUCTION TO PHYSICAL SCIENCE

ORGANIZER

Section	pages	Activity	pages	Reinforcement and Evaluation	pages	*Review and Skill Masters	pages	Other Components in Teacher Resource Package	pages
1—1 What Is Physical Science?	3–6			Puzzler Review, Challenge	5 6			Study Guide	5
1—2 The Scientific Method	7–11			Review, Challenge	11	Challenge/Critical Thinking	9–10	Study Guide Lab Manual	6 1
1—3 Units of Measurement	12–18	How Is Volume Measured? How Is Mass Measured? How Is Temperature Measured	15 16 18	Review, Challenge	18	Skill	8	Study Guide Lab Manual	7 5
1—4 Tools of the Physical Scientist	19–23	How Is a Spectroscope Used?	22	Review, Challenge	23			Study Guide	8
CHAPTER SUMMARY	23					Vocabulary Review	5		
CHAPTER REVIEW	24–25			*Test Masters	1–4	Chapter Review	6–7		

*In the Teacher Resource Package. For answers, see pages 1b—1d in this book.

ACTIVITY MATERIALS   Quantities are based on a class of 30 students working in groups as indicated in parentheses.

How Is Volume Measured? p. 15 (groups of 2)	quantity	How Is Mass Measured? p. 16 (groups of 2)	quantity	How Is Temperature Measured? p. 18 (groups of 2)	quantity	How Is a Spectroscope Used? p. 22 (groups of 2)	quantity
metric ruler	15	balance and masses	15	safety goggles	30	safety goggles	30
100—mL graduate	15	forceps	15	Celsius thermometer	15	Bunsen burner	15
water		coins — dime, nickel, penny	15 each	200-mL beaker	15	striker	15
rectangular solid object	15			ice		nichrome wire with handle	15
				water		calcium chloride solution	100 mL
				hot plate	15	lithium chloride solution	100 mL
				glass stirring rod	15	strontium chloride solution	100 mL
				lab apron	30	incandescent lamp	15
						grating spectroscope	1
						lab apron	30

REVIEW AND SKILL MASTERS

VOCABULARY REVIEW _____ Chapter 1

Use the clues to complete the puzzle and find the term in the boxes.

1. h y p o t h e s i s
2. t e c h n o l o g y
3. t h e o r y
4. s c i e n c e
5. e x p e r i m e n t
6. c o n c l u s i o n
7. o b s e r v a t i o n
8. k i l o g r a m
9. s p e c t r o s c o p e
10. s c i e n t i f i c l a w
11. l i t e r
12. m e t e r
13. s c i e n t i f i c m e t h o d
14. d e g r e e c e l s i u s
15. n e w t o n

1. A possible answer to a question, based on known facts
2. Applying scientific knowledge to improve the quality of human life
3. A hypothesis that has been tested and supported
4. A method of obtaining knowledge about nature
5. A controlled situation designed to test a hypothesis
6. A statement that tells if the data supports the hypothesis
7. An examination of something in nature
8. The SI unit of mass
9. A tool that separates light into different colors
10. A general statement that describes some pattern in nature (two words)
11. A unit of volume
12. The SI unit of length
13. The way that scientists gather information and test ideas (two words)
14. Unit of temperature used in science (two words)
15. A unit of force

CHAPTER REVIEW _____ Chapter 1

1-1 What is Physical Science?

1. Describe the two major branches of physical science.
   Chemistry is the study of matter and the changes that matter undergoes. Physics is the study of energy and the relationship between matter and energy.

2. Give two examples that highlight the difference between science and technology.
   Answers will vary but may include the following. Learning about the nature of fire is science. Learning to control and use fire is technology. Studying the behavior of light is science. Using this knowledge to make optical fibers is technology.

1-2 The Scientific Method

1. What is the scientific method? The scientific method is the way scientists gather information and test ideas.

2. What is an observation? An observation is more than just seeing. It is an examination of something in nature.

3. What is a hypothesis and how is it related to a theory?
   A hypothesis is a possible answer to the question. After a hypothesis has been tested and supported many times, it is considered to be a theory.

4. What is an experiment? An experiment is a controlled procedure that tests a hypothesis. It usually contains a control group and an experimental group.

CHAPTER REVIEW (Continued) _____ Chapter 1

1-3 Units of Measurement

1. Why do scientists need a standard set of measurements?
   The description of any measurement must have a clear meaning to another person.

2. Name four units of measurement and the quantity that each represents.
   The meter is a unit of length, the liter a unit of volume, the kilogram a unit of mass, and the degree Celsius a unit of temperature.

3. What is the difference between mass and weight? Mass is a measure of the amount of matter in an object. Weight is a measure of the force of gravity on an object.

1-4 Tools of Physical Science

1. Describe what a barometer is used for. A barometer is used to measure air pressure and is useful in weather forecasting.

2. A Crookes tube is used with electric current to study the behavior of charged particles

3. A pH meter measures the acidity of a substance.

4. What does a spectroscope do? A spectroscope separates light given off by heated elements into different colors.

5. Give examples of how computers are used in physical science.
   Computers are useful in every field of science and do more than just process information. They can do mathematical operations much quicker than humans can. Robot computers can handle dangerous materials. Computers can be sent into space to gather information. (Many possible answers.)

SKILL/Measuring _____ Chapter 1

You are an astronaut and have returned to Earth with a sample of moon rock. To begin your study of the moon rock, you decide to learn more about its properties. Study the three drawings below and answer the following questions.

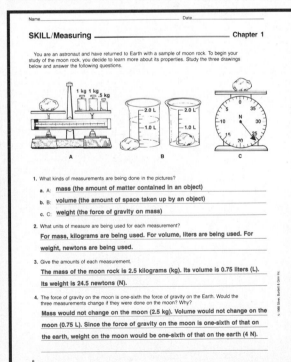

A   B   C

1. What kinds of measurements are being done in the pictures?
   a. A: mass (the amount of matter contained in an object)
   b. B: volume (the amount of space taken up by an object)
   c. C: weight (the force of gravity on mass)

2. What units of measure are being used for each measurement?
   For mass, kilograms are being used. For volume, liters are being used. For weight, newtons are being used.

3. Give the amounts of each measurement.
   The mass of the moon rock is 2.5 kilograms (kg). Its volume is 0.75 liters (L). Its weight is 24.5 newtons (N).

4. The force of gravity on the moon is one-sixth the force of gravity on the Earth. Would the three measurements change if they were done on the moon? Why?
   Mass would not change on the moon (2.5 kg). Volume would not change on the moon (0.75 L). Since the force of gravity on the moon is one-sixth of that on the earth, weight on the moon would be one-sixth of that on the earth (4 N).

CHAPTER 1 PLANNING GUIDE

REVIEW AND SKILL MASTERS

Name_____ Date_____

CHALLENGE/CRITICAL THINKING _____ Chapter 1

On a camping trip in the mountains, you notice that your food is taking much longer than normal to cook. Most of the foods you brought on your camping trip are freeze-dried foods that require boiling, and you find that you must almost double the normal cooking time to reach the desired result. While you wait for supper to be ready, you decide to design an experiment to help you find out why your food is taking so long to cook!

1. Check which observations would be useful in designing your experiment.

a. __X__ You didn't have this problem last week when you camped at the seashore.

b. _____ Freeze-dried foods taste awful no matter how they're cooked.

c. __X__ Increasing cooking time cooked the food adequately.

d. __X__ You're cooking at a much higher altitude than usual.

e. _____ The scenery is much nicer in the mountains.

f. __X__ The air pressure is lower at high altitudes.

9

Name_____ Date_____

CHALLENGE/CRITICAL THINKING (Continued) _____ Chapter 1

2. Given the observations you checked above, what hypothesis would be appropriate to your experiment?

Answers will vary, but should include: Water appears to boil at a lower

temperature at higher altitudes than at lower altitudes.

3. Here is your experiment. Fill in the blanks.

Control group: **Finding the boiling point of water at sea level.**

Experimental group _____: Finding the boiling point of water at 10,000 m.

Variable _____: Air pressure (altitude).

4. You boil water five different times at sea level and at 10,000 m. What conclusion would you make from the following data?

Test	Boiling Point At Sea Level (°C)	Boiling Point At 10,000 m (°C)
1	100.0	96.9
2	100.0	97.0
3	100.0	96.5
4	100.0	97.1
5	100.0	97.0

You could conclude that water boils at a lower temperature at higher altitudes.

5. A statement of a pattern in nature is a scientific law. A scientific law sometimes bears the name of the scientist who first identifies it. Using your own name, state the scientific law that could result from your experiment.

(Student's name) _____ Law states that:

Students' answers will vary, but should include the following idea: The boiling

point of a liquid changes with altitude (air pressure).

10

1c

TEST MASTERS

Page 1

Name_____ Date_____ Score_____

Chapter 1

Introduction to Physical Science

PART 1

In the space below, write the term that each phrase defines.

Chapter Goal

1. physical science — The study of matter and energy — 1
2. newton — The SI unit of force — 4
3. theory — A hypothesis that has been tested and supported many times — 2
4. scientific method — The logical plan that scientists use to gather information and test ideas about nature — 2
5. technology — The application of scientific knowledge in an effort to improve the quality of human life — 1
6. meter — The SI unit of length — 4
7. spectroscope — A scientific tool that separates light into different colors and is used to identify different substances — 5
8. experiment — A controlled procedure designed to test a hypothesis — 2
9. kilogram — The SI unit of mass — 4

PART 2

Choose the term or phrase that best answers the question or completes the statement. Write the letter of that choice in the space at the left.

c 1. An object that is moved from an area of high gravity to an area of low gravity will most likely experience a change in: 3
   a. mass.   b. volume.   c. weight.   d. length.

a 2. To identify the elements that make up a piece of rock, a physical scientist would most likely use a: 5
   a. spectroscope.   b. barometer.   c. meterstick.   d. Crooke's tube.

Page 2

Name_____ Date_____ Score_____

PART 2

Choose the term or phrase that best answers the question or completes the statement. Write the letter of that choice in the space at the left.

Chapter Goal

c 3. Which of the following would a scientist use to measure the mass of a pencil? 3
   a. barometer   b. spectroscope   c. balance   d. thermometer

a 4. Which of the following units would a scientist use to measure the volume of the water in a pond? 4
   a. kiloliter   b. decimeter   c. milligram   d. nanometer

d 5. Which of the following would be used to measure the length of a baseball bat? 3
   a. thermometer   b. balance   c. graduate   d. meterstick

b 6. A scientist wants to determine if a type of yeast will make a cake rise. The scientist bakes one cake with the yeast and one cake without the yeast. Which of the following is the variable in this experiment? 2
   a. the scientist   c. the cake with the yeast
   b. the yeast   d. the cake without the yeast

a 7. A scientist develops a new airplane fuel. To test how much energy the fuel contains, the scientist will most likely use a: 5
   a. calorimeter.   c. chromatograph.
   b. Crooke's tube.   d. pH meter.

c 8. When the mercury in the tube of a barometer is falling, it most likely means that changes are occurring in the: 5
   a. gases in the tube.   c. air pressure around the tube.
   b. temperature of the mercury.   d. pH of the mercury.

d 9. Which of the following would be an example of technology? 1
   a. observing a rainbow after a storm
   b. explaining why crystals sparkle
   c. learning about the nature of fire
   d. producing a medicine from a plant

a 10. Which of the following would a chemist be most likely to study? 1
   a. the amount of acid in a liquid
   b. the movement of the gears of a bicycle
   c. the angle of light in a prism
   d. the speed of wind in a wind tunnel

a 11. Which of the following would be used to measure the volume of a liquid? 3
   a. graduate   b. balance   c. meterstick   d. spring scale

---

Page 3

Name_____ Date_____ Score_____

PART 3

Look at the diagram. Then read the questions that follow. Choose the term or phrase that best answers the question or completes the statement. Write the letter of that choice in the space at the left.

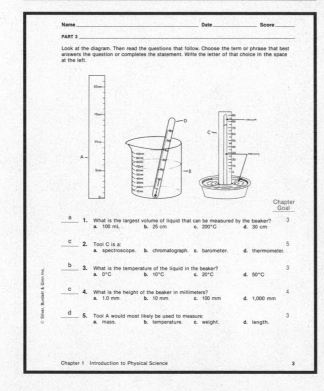

Chapter Goal

a 1. What is the largest volume of liquid that can be measured by the beaker? 3
   a. 100 mL   b. 25 cm   c. 200°C   d. 30 cm

c 2. Tool C is a: 5
   a. spectroscope.   b. chromatograph.   c. barometer.   d. thermometer.

b 3. What is the temperature of the liquid in the beaker? 3
   a. 0°C   b. 10°C   c. 20°C   d. 50°C

c 4. What is the height of the beaker in millimeters? 4
   a. 1.0 mm   b. 10 mm   c. 100 mm   d. 1,000 mm

d 5. Tool A would most likely be used to measure: 3
   a. mass.   b. temperature.   c. weight.   d. length.

Page 4

Name_____ Date_____ Score_____

PART 4

Read each question or direction and answer it using complete sentences.

Chapter Goal

1. Why is it important to have standard units of measurement in science? 3

   Scientists need to be able to make measurements quickly and accurately. They also need to be able to understand measurements made by other scientists so that experiments can be duplicated, and so the results of experiments have a clear meaning. Therefore, it is important for scientists to be able to compare the measurements they make in the laboratory with a defined standard unit that has the same meaning to scientists all over the world.

2. Describe ways in which computers can be used in physical science. 5

   Computers can be used to collect data or to do mathematical operations much faster than humans can do them. Computers work with robots, handling dangerous materials. They also test sample materials and help analyze data. A computer can be linked to a spectroscope and used to identify substances.

3. Describe the four main processes of the scientific method. 2

   In the scientific method, a scientist makes an observation of something in nature. The scientist may also do research to learn more about a subject. Observations lead to questions that become the topic of scientific study. The scientist forms a hypothesis, a possible answer to a question. After a hypothesis has been formed, it is tested by making further observations or by doing an experiment. During an experiment, the scientist makes measurements and records results that are called data. At the end of the experiment, the scientist draws a conclusion from the data. The conclusion tells whether or not the data support the hypothesis.

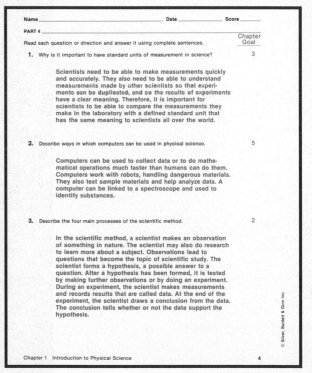

CHAPTER 1 PLANNING GUIDE

1d

1

INTRODUCTION TO PHYSICAL SCIENCE

The questions in the CHAPTER TEST are based on these Chapter Goals.

1. Distinguish between science and technology, and identify the branches of physical science.
2. Explain the processes involved in the scientific method.
3. Explain why measurement is important; describe some tools of measurement.
4. Describe the International System of Measurement and the units used in science.
5. Describe the tools and techniques of the physical scientist.

INTRODUCTION TO PHYSICAL SCIENCE

Have you ever tried to fly a kite? The shape and weight of a kite are very important. A kite should be wide enough to "catch the wind." Its tail must be long enough to keep the kite upright but not so long that it makes the kite too heavy to fly. Studying physical science can help you understand the forces that keep a kite flying. It can help you design experiments to improve the performance of a kite or some other object.

- *What forces are involved in flying a kite?*
- *How does a scientist study these forces?*
- *Are the same forces involved in the flight of other objects?*

1-1 WHAT IS PHYSICAL SCIENCE?

Have you ever wondered what causes a rainbow or why the sky is blue? Perhaps you have an interest in electricity or electronics. You may be interested in the laser and its uses, or you may wish to know how a camera or a computer works. Have you ever wondered why some materials differ from others? For example, what is the difference between the safety glass used in eyeglasses and the kind of glass used in tableware? Have you noticed that on some nights the moon seems to have a halo around it? Can you explain why this happens? Your questions about objects and events in the world around you are questions of science.

Science is a method of obtaining knowledge about nature. Nature is the earth, space, nonliving things, and living things. Science has many branches, including life science, earth science, and physical science.

Science is older than recorded history. Ancient people saw events around them in nature. They noticed that the weather changes from day to day and from season to season. There is a pattern to these changes. People learned to make predictions based on these patterns. Predicting changes in the seasons probably helped these people survive. Modern scientists continue to study patterns and make predictions.

After completing this section, you will be able to

- **define** the term *science*.
- **name** the two major branches of physical science.
- **compare** science and technology.

The key terms in this section are
physical science
science
technology

scientia (knowledge)

NOTE
Many terms in science have their origins in other languages, including Latin and Greek. The foreign word parts and their meanings are listed in the margin for many of the science terms in this book. Use the word parts to help you understand the meanings of the science terms.

Have students make observations about the photograph. Ask students why it is important to have the kites made of lightweight material. Students should be aware that wind is necessary to keep the kites in the air. Ask students what characteristics the kites in the photograph have in common.
- What forces are involved in flying a kite? (Wind, gravity, and the individual pulling on the string.)
- How does a scientist study these forces? (By making observations, performing experiments, and arriving at a conclusion.)
- Are the same forces involved in the flight of other objects? (Yes.)

1-1 WHAT IS PHYSICAL SCIENCE?
pages 3–6

OBJECTIVES
Refer to pupil page 3.

VOCABULARY
Key terms: physical science, science, technology
Other terms: chemistry, physics

1 MOTIVATION

Since physical science is the study of matter and energy, you can intrigue and motivate your students with the help of an inexpensive photoelectric cell and tiny rotor. As light (energy) strikes the matter of the photoelectric cell, there is a flow of electrons (matter and energy). This electric current spins a motor, which turns the rotor (another form of energy). Allow students to shield the photoelectric cell from the light and note what happens.

Thinking Skills

predicting
Students observe patterns of change in nature and then use those patterns to make predictions. Display calendar sheets showing the phases of the moon for two consecutive months. Have students look for a pattern, and then ask them to predict what day of the next month the moon will be full, new, at first quarter, and at third quarter.

Background   Physical science is the most basic and all-inclusive of the sciences. It is concerned with matter and energy and their interactions. Matter is any substance that occupies space and has weight. The amounts of space and weight can be extremely small, as in the case of a subatomic particle, or extremely large, as in the case of an entire galaxy. Energy is the ability to do work. There are many forms of energy. Electricity, heat, and light are all forms of energy.

Teaching Tip   Knowledge of physical science is important in many occupations. Discuss with students why it is important for the following people to have a knowledge of physical science: teachers, doctors, politicians, engineers, lawyers, foresters, farmers, cooks, dancers, contractors, business executives, and assembly-line workers.

Background   The ancient Greek philosopher Aristotle (384 B.C.–322 B.C.) noticed that when light was admitted into a dark room through a small opening, an inverted image formed on the opposite wall. Using this scientific discovery, an Italian technologist of the fifteenth century built a large dark box with a tiny hole in it to form such images. It was called a *camera obscura,* from the Latin words for "dark chamber." Over the centuries, camera obscuras were used to study light, to view partial eclipses of the sun safely, and to aid artists in making sketches.

Physical science is the study of matter and energy. The two major branches of physical science are chemistry and physics. *Chemistry* is the study of matter and the changes that matter undergoes. *Physics* is the study of the many forms of energy. It is also the study of the relationship between energy and matter. Physical science can help you understand many things that you see or do. Chemistry can explain how baking soda makes a cake rise or why a volcano adds to acid rain. A knowledge of chemistry can help you decide what type of fertilizer you should add to your lawn or garden.

Physics can explain how the gears of a bicycle work or why hot air balloons rise. Look at Figure 1-1. Using the laws of physics makes it possible for you to lift someone or something heavier than yourself.

Figure 1-1

The laws of physics make it possible for a small person to lift a larger one.

Many physical scientists are involved in basic research. They search for knowledge for its own sake. Many physical scientists in basic research do their work in universities or government laboratories.

Other physical scientists work in the area of applied research. They set out to solve a particular problem, using the knowledge, tools, and techniques of science.

Most chemists and physicists work in laboratories, but some work in unusual places. The wind tunnel shown in Figure 1-2 is used to test the strength of airplane parts or the shape of a car. A physicist will study the results of wind tunnel tests. These tests may lead to changes in the design of the car or plane.

Figure 1-2
Testing designs in a wind tunnel.

techno- (skill)
-logy (study of)

Sometimes people confuse the meanings of *science* and *technology* (tehk NAHL uh jee). In fact when many people use the word *science* they really mean *technology*. As you have just seen, science is the study of the natural world. Scientists gather knowledge about the natural world. **Technology** is applying scientific knowledge in an effort to improve the quality of human life. Many of the scientists who work in applied research can be thought of as working in the field of technology.

Technology may be as old as science. When ancient people first used fire, they were using technology. They learned to apply a knowledge of fire to keep warm, to cook food, and to keep dangerous animals away. Learning about the nature of fire is *science*. Learning to control and use fire is *technology*.

SCIENCE PUZZLER

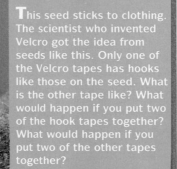

This seed sticks to clothing. The scientist who invented Velcro got the idea from seeds like this. Only one of the Velcro tapes has hooks like those on the seed. What is the other tape like? What would happen if you put two of the hook tapes together? What would happen if you put two of the other tapes together?

Background　　A good example of the interplay between science and technology is provided by the discovery of light-sensitive materials and the subsequent development of photography. In 1727, chemist Johann Schulze discovered that certain silver salts darkened when exposed to light and that the degree of darkening depended on the intensity of the light and the time of exposure. Nearly 100 years later, Joseph Nicephore Niepce combined the discoveries of Aristotle and Schulze. Niepce coated one wall of a camera obscura with silver salts and thus produced a permanent image. In 1839, as the great technology of photography was born, Louis Daguerre refined this discovery and developed a process for making photographs on silver-plated sheets of copper.

Puzzler　　The other tape is made of loops. Two hooked tapes put together do not hold; two looped tapes put together do not hold.

Tie-in/Language Arts　　Have students research the meanings of the following prefixes: *astro-, electro-, geo-, photo-,* and *thermo-*. Then have students describe the work of each of the following scientists: astrophysicist, electrochemist, geophysicist, photochemist, and thermochemist.

1. The observation and investigation of natural phenomena.
2. The study of matter and energy; chemistry and physics.
3. Both science and technology frequently involve observation, experimentation, and testing.
4. Science is primarily concerned with obtaining knowledge. Scientists ask why things happen. Technology is the application of knowledge for the purpose of solving problems and developing useful products. Technologists ask how discoveries can be put to use.

Challenge   This type of technology produces products that are helpful to people, and it may be very important if other sources of the product become unavailable.

Physicists have studied the behavior of light to find out why diamonds and other crystals sparkle. From these studies, scientists have learned how to control the path of a beam of light. This knowledge has been used to make optical fibers like the ones shown in Figure 1-3. This technology allows people to use light to send messages.

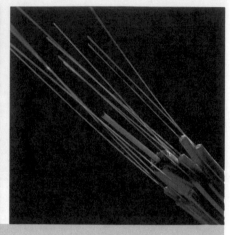

Figure 1-3

Telephone messages are carried on fibers like these.

Research on the properties of simple chemicals has led to the development of very complex chemicals, like plastics. Plastics technology has produced many useful things. However, making plastic produces wastes that cause pollution. Many plastic containers and wrappings are thrown away every day, resulting in large amounts of garbage. As new technologies are developed, people must be aware of problems that could be caused. Someday you may be making decisions about balancing the advantages and disadvantages of a new technology. Studying science can help prepare you to make these decisions.

REVIEW

1. What is science?
2. What is physical science, and what are the two major branches of physical science?
3. How are science and technology similar?
4. How does technology differ from science?

CHALLENGE   Research in chemistry has made it possible for scientists to take a natural substance and make it in the laboratory. Insulin is a chemical needed by people who have a kind of diabetes. Synthetic insulin is now available. How does this kind of technology benefit people?

1-2 THE SCIENTIFIC METHOD

Scientists around the world and in every field of science have the same goal. They seek information and answers to questions. The **scientific method** is the way that scientists gather information and test ideas. The scientific method is not one set of steps to follow like those in a recipe for a cake. It is a logical plan for solving a puzzle. Scientists apply their knowledge and experiences to the puzzles of nature. When you use your knowledge and experience in an attempt to solve a problem in a logical way, you are using the scientific method. The scientific method has four key processes: making observations, forming a hypothesis, doing experiments, and drawing a conclusion.

An **observation** is an examination of something in nature. Observing is more than seeing. It requires attention to details. It is a skill that requires patience and practice. You may have observed that a rainbow forms when the sun comes out suddenly after a rainstorm. But how closely have you observed rainbows? Are the same colors always there? Are the colors always in the same order?

After completing this section, you will be able to

- **describe** the scientific method.
- **contrast** hypothesis and theory.

The key terms in this section are
conclusion   scientific law
experiment   scientific
hypothesis   method
observation   theory

observare (to watch)

Figure 1-4

A rainbow appears when light passes through droplets of water in the air.

Observations lead to questions that become the topic of scientific study. After scientists ask a question, they try to find out what is already known about the question. They search through the journals and papers written by other scientists. The task of searching for information is usually done by computer. Computers can be linked to huge libraries of information that are called data bases. A computer can be used to search the data bases for a topic.

1-2 THE SCIENTIFIC METHOD
pages 7–11

OBJECTIVES
Refer to pupil page 7.

VOCABULARY
Key terms: conclusion, experiment, hypothesis, observation, scientific law, scientific method, theory
Other terms: data, variable

1 MOTIVATION

Display a large beaker partially filled with water and a dish containing several ice cubes and one clear cube of halite (rock salt) that looks like an ice cube. Do not describe the materials to students. Have students describe what they see as you place each cube, one at a time, in the water. (All cubes except the halite will float.) Then ask students to write a question based on their observations. Have several students read their questions. Explain that questions such as these can be the basis of scientific study.

2 CONCEPT DEVELOPMENT

Teaching Tip   Discuss with students the meaning of the phrase, "reinventing the wheel." Lead students to understand how this phrase demonstrates the need for doing library and database research before undertaking an experiment.

Enrichment   Arrange a lesson in the library, and have the librarian show students how to use the card catalogue, various indexes, and other means of locating information. Assign each student a physical science topic, and have each develop a list of the library's resources on that topic. Introduce students to the *Readers' Guide to Periodical Literature* (or the abridged edition) and, if it is available, the General Science Index.

Figure 1-5

Prisms produce patterns of color.

Scientists may find the answer to their question in the information they read. Sometimes their library research helps scientists restate their question more clearly.

Once a question is stated clearly, the scientist can form a hypothesis (hī PAHTH uh sihs). A **hypothesis** is a possible answer to a question. Forming a hypothesis requires careful thought and skill. You might have observed that a "rainbow" forms when light passes through a glass prism (PRIH zuhm). You might think that some characteristic of the glass causes the rainbow to form. Suppose a scientist forms the hypothesis that a rainbow forms when light passes through a thick piece of glass.

After a hypothesis has been formed, it is tested. A hypothesis can be tested by making further observations or by doing an experiment. An **experiment** is a controlled procedure designed to test a hypothesis. An experiment usually has two parts, or groups. One part is called the control, or the control group. The other part is called the experimental group. Figure 1-6 shows the control group for an experiment that tests the hypothesis given above.

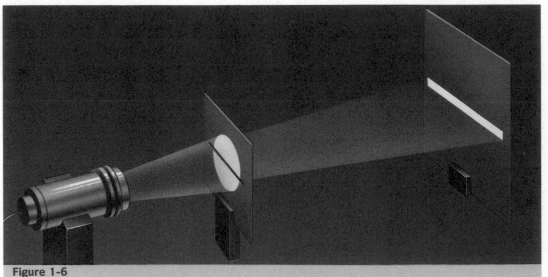

Figure 1-6

In this control group, no object has been placed in the path of the light.

The experimental group differs from the control group in one factor or condition. The factor that makes the experimental group different from the control group is called the *variable*. When the experiment is completed, the experimental group is compared with the control group. The scientist can then decide if, and how, the variable affects the experiment.

In the control group a beam of light would shine directly on a screen. Figure 1-7 shows the experimental group. In this group a beam of light would pass through a square piece of glass and then strike the screen. The distance between the light source and the screen, and the strength of the light source, would be the same in both groups. The piece of glass would be the variable.

The results of an experiment are called *data*. Sometimes data may describe what happened. At other times data may include measurements that were made. In this experiment, the data would be what the scientist saw on the screen. In both groups, ordinary white light would be seen. No rainbow would be produced.

At the end of an experiment, a scientist draws a conclusion from the data. A **conclusion** is a statement that tells if the data support the hypothesis. In the experiment with light, the conclusion would be that the hypothesis is not supported by the data.

What happens when a hypothesis is not supported by the results of an experiment? The scientist may try the

concludere (to close)

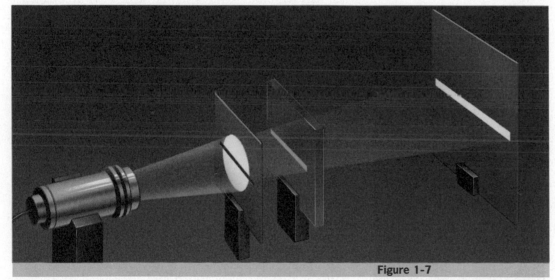

Figure 1-7

In this experimental group a glass square has been placed in the path of the light.

experiment again or may plan a new experiment to test the hypothesis. If the results again do not support the hypothesis, the scientist may then suggest another hypothesis. Scientists do not always come up with the correct idea the first time around. But testing a wrong hypothesis is not a waste of time. New information can be gained whenever an experiment is done.

Background   Sir Isaac Newton did the original experiment with light and a prism in 1666 to test his hypothesis that white light contains the colors of the spectrum. Newton's experiment was simple. He allowed a beam of sunlight to enter a dark room. He placed a clear glass prism in the path of the light. Light emerging from the prism was separated into color bands. Newton then placed a second prism, held upside down, in the path of the colored light. Bands of colored light entered the second prism and emerged as a beam of white light. As a result of this experiment, Newton provided an explanation for the observed behavior of light passing through a prism.

Demonstration   Demonstrate Newton's prism experiment described in the *Background* section above. Make sure that the room is dark, and align the prisms as described.

Thinking Skills

designing experiments
Students list several problems that could be solved by using the scientific method. Select a few problems that involve physical science, and have students design an experiment for each. Have them follow the sequence described on page 8 of their text—the clear statement of the question, the formation of the hypothesis, the design of an experiment to test the hypothesis, and the review of experimental data. Stress the need for a control group and a variable group.

Teaching Tip   Emphasize the difference between the use of the word *theory* in everyday life and its meaning in science.

Review and Skill Masters

CHALLENGE/CRITICAL THINKING, pages 9–10. See page 1b in this book for answers.

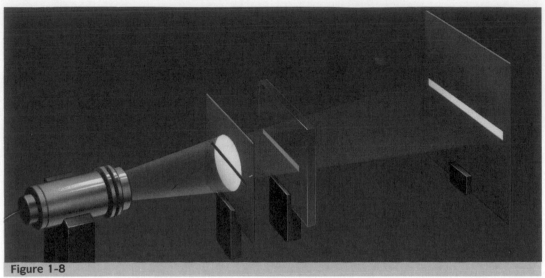

Figure 1-8

In this control group a glass square has been placed in the path of the light.

Figure 1-9

Prisms can be many different shapes and sizes.

For a new hypothesis, a scientist might suggest that the angle of the prism causes light to make a rainbow. To test this hypothesis, the scientist would set up a new experiment. The control group is shown in Figure 1-8. Again, all factors except one would be the same in both groups. The only difference would be the variable being tested. That variable would be the angled shape of the prism as shown in Figure 1-10. If the scientist wanted to try different prisms, they could be tested one at a time. But there would always be a control to provide a comparison.

This time the data would show that the light source with the square glass produced white light. The light source with the angled glass produced a rainbow. Thus the hypothesis would be supported by the data.

What happens when a hypothesis is supported by the data? The scientist usually repeats the experiment to check the results. The scientist may then publish the results, to share the information with other scientists. Other scientists may also check the results of the experiments.

Other scientists may test a hypothesis again. A hypothesis that has been tested and supported many times is called a **theory** (THEE uh ree). A theory helps scientists explain the behavior of something in nature. A theory also is the basis for further experiments. Theories may be changed as new information is gained. If an accurate observation does not fit a theory, that theory is reviewed. The observation may lead to the development of a new theory. You may have heard the word *theory* being used to describe

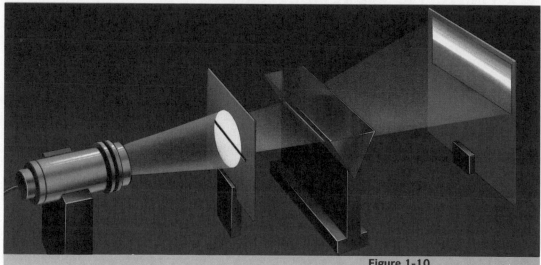

Figure 1-10

In this experimental group a prism has been placed in the path of the light.

an unsupported idea. This is different from the scientific meaning of the word. In science a theory is an idea that has been supported by many experiments.

A **scientific law** is a general statement that describes some pattern in nature. A law may be in words or in a mathematical form. For example, Snell's Law states that light rays bend as they pass from one substance to another. This law can be used to calculate the angle at which a prism will bend light rays.

A theory serves as a basis for explaining a law. Experiments like the one shown above have contributed to light theory. This theory explains why light rays bend according to Snell's Law.

The discoveries and breakthroughs in science are a result of the work of many people over many years. The body of knowledge called science is never final. New facts and new concepts are always being introduced. New questions and new methods provide new data that require the formation of new theories.

REVIEW

1. What are the processes of the scientific method?
2. How do observations differ from data?
3. How are a hypothesis and a conclusion related?
4. What is the difference between a hypothesis and a theory?

CHALLENGE Design an experiment to find out at what temperature milk remains unspoiled for the longest time.

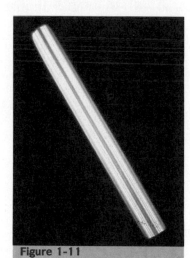

Figure 1-11

Snell's Law says that light rays bend as they pass from one layer of this glass to another.

Background Progress in science rarely takes place in a rigid, step-by-step fashion. A law may precede a theory, for example. Snell's law (from Willebrord Snell, 1591–1626) states that light rays bend as they pass from one substance to another. Several later theories were formulated by Christian Huygens (1690), Sir Isaac Newton (1704), Thomas Young (1801), Augustin Jean Fresnel (1815), and James Clerk Maxwell (1873), to explain why and how this happens.

3 REVIEW/REINFORCEMENT

1. Observation, hypothesis, experiment, conclusion.
2. An observation is the examination of something in nature; data are the result of an experiment and may include measurements.
3. A hypothesis is a possible answer to a question. A conclusion is a statement that indicates whether the data support the hypothesis.
4. A theory is a hypothesis that has been tested and supported many times.

Challenge Place equal amounts of milk in several cooling devices (such as refrigerators) set at different temperatures ranging from slightly cold (15°C) to very cold (2°C). By noting the amount of time it takes for spoilage to occur in each case, you can determine the temperature at which milk will remain unspoiled for the longest time. Odor and appearance can be used to decide when spoilage has occurred.

1-3 UNITS OF MEASUREMENT

pages 12–18

1-3 UNITS OF MEASUREMENT

OBJECTIVES

Refer to pupil page 12.

VOCABULARY

Key terms: degree Celsius, kilogram, liter, meter, newton

Other terms: balance, meniscus, metric system

1 MOTIVATION

Introduce body-based length measurements, such as the cubit (the length from the elbow to the end of the longest finger) and the span (the length from the tip of the thumb to the tip of the little finger when the hand is fully extended). Have several students make measurements of door widths, desk-top lengths, and bookcase heights by using these units. Then compare their measurements. Ask the students if these measurements are standard for all people. Discuss the problems that could arise from their use.

After completing this section, you will be able to

- **explain** the need for standard measurements.
- **name** the units used to measure length, mass, temperature, and time.
- **measure** mass, volume, and temperature by using appropriate tools.

The key terms in this section are
degree Celsius   **meter**
kilogram   **newton**
liter

Even from the earliest times, people have needed to make measurements. In the past some measurements were based on human features and common objects or materials. For example, the yard, a measurement of length first used in England in the fifteenth century, was defined as the distance between the king's nose and the tip of his middle finger when his arm was extended. Thus the length of one yard was different from time to time, depending on who the monarch was. The inch was defined as the length of three barleycorns. Like arms, barleycorns vary in length. Thus the lengths of an inch and a yard varied and were not easy to duplicate.

Scientists need a standard system of measurement. When a scientist describes the length of an object, that description should have a clear meaning to any other person. Thus, length or any other measurement must be compared to a defined standard. In the late 1700s a group of scientists gathered to come up with a uniform system of measurement. The group chose a unit called the **meter** as the standard unit of length. They defined the meter as the length equal to 1/10,000,000 of the distance from the North Pole to the Equator. The symbol used for the meter is m. The system of measurement based on the meter is called the *metric system*.

Figure 1-12

The first standard for a meter was a distance on the earth.

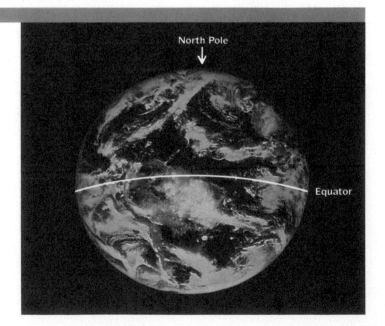

Table 1-1 *Units of Measurement*

Measurement	Unit	Symbol
length	meter	m
volume	liter	L
mass	kilogram	kg
force	newton	N
temperature	degree Celsius	°C
time	second	s

When you describe an object as being three meters long, you are comparing its length to the length of the standard meter. The first standard for the meter was a metal bar stored in France. The modern standard for a meter is based on the distance light travels in a fraction of a second.

Many countries keep a metal mass like the one shown in Figure 1-13 as a standard. The standard for the kilogram is a mass that is made of platinum and iridium. Notice that the standard is kept under two glass covers. These covers protect the metal against chemical changes that might affect the mass of the metal.

In 1960 a modern system of units was adopted by international agreement. It is known as the International System of Units, or SI, from the French *Le Système International d'Unites*. The SI units are easy to use because they are based on mutiples of ten. Each SI base unit can be multiplied or divided by ten. Prefixes are used to show how many times the base unit is multiplied or divided. The prefix is added to the name of the base unit. When symbols are used, the symbol for the prefix is written before the symbol for the base unit. Table 1-2 shows some of the prefixes used to express SI measurements. How many meters are there in a kilometer (km)?[1]

Figure 1-13

The standard kilogram is made of platinum and iridium.

[1]There are 1000 m in 1 km.

Table 1-2 *Metric Prefixes*

Prefix	Symbol	Meaning
mega-	M	1,000,000
kilo-	k	1000
deci-	d	1/10
centi-	c	1/100
milli-	m	1/1000
micro-	μ	1/1,000,000
nano-	n	1/1,000,000,000

2 CONCEPT DEVELOPMENT

Background   The actual measurement of the meter was made along the meridian that passes through Paris, France.

Background   The international standard of mass is a cylinder of platinum-iridium metal stored at the International Bureau of Weights and Measures in Sevres, France. The United States has a copy of the standard at the National Bureau of Standards, near Washington, D.C.

Thinking Skills

interpreting data
Refer students to Table 1-2. Ask them to convert 14,500 m into kilometers and 0.007 g into milligrams. As a second exercise, ask students to convert 13,200 ft into miles and 0.35 lb into ounces. Ask what advantages students see in the SI units.

Figure 1-14

How wide is this stamp?[5]

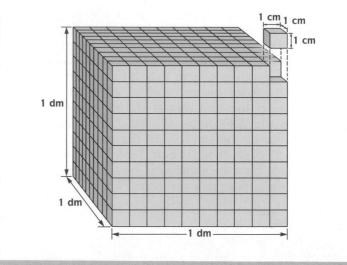

Figure 1-15

One cubic decimeter (dm^3) is equal to one liter.

The SI unit of length is the meter (m). The common tool for measuring length is the meterstick. A meterstick can be marked in decimeter (dm), centimeter (cm), or millimeter (mm) divisions. Some objects are much too small to be measured in centimeters or millimeters. Objects such as the parts of a cell are measured in tiny units called nanometers. One nanometer is equal to one billionth of a meter. What is the symbol for a nanometer?[1]

Some distances are too large to be measured in meters. Instead they are measured in kilometers. A kilometer is a distance equal to 1000 meters. Kilometers are used to measure long distances, such as those between locations on earth.

Volume is the amount of space an object takes up. The measure of volume is based on the measure of length. Volume can be measured in cubic meters (m^3). A cubic meter is the volume of a cube that is 1 m long on each edge. Similar units of volume are the cubic centimeter (cm^3), and the cubic decimeter (dm^3). The volume of the cube shown in Figure 1-15 is found by multiplying length times width times height.

The **liter** is a unit of volume. One liter (L) is equal to the volume of a cube that measures 10 cm on each edge. How many cubic centimeters are in the 1-L cube shown in Figure 1-15?[2] One commonly used fraction of the liter is the milliliter (mL). How many milliliters are in 1 L?[3] How many cubic centimeters are there in 1 mL?[4]

[1] nm.
[2] $1000 \text{ cm}^3 = 1 \text{ L}$.
[3] $1000 \text{ mL} = 1 \text{ L}$.
[4] $1 \text{ cm}^3 = 1 \text{ mL}$.
[5] 3 cm.

ACTIVITY   How Is Volume Measured?

OBJECTIVE
Determine the volume of a regular solid by measurement and by displacement.

MATERIALS
regular solid, metric ruler, 100-mL graduate, water

PROCEDURE
A. Draw a data table like the one shown.
B. Measure the length, width, and height of a solid. Record the data in the data table.
C. Calculate the volume of the solid by finding the product of the length, the width, and the height (V = l x w x h).
D. Fill a graduate with water to the 20-mL mark. Remember to read the bottom of the meniscus. Record in the data table the volume of the water.

E. Carefully place the solid into the water in the graduate. Record the new volume in the data table. The change in the volume of the water equals the volume of the solid.

Measurement	Amount
Length
Width
Height
Volume	
Volume of water
Volume of water and solid
Volume of solid	

RESULTS AND CONCLUSIONS
1. How do the volumes compare?
2. If you had an irregularly shaped stone, could you determine its volume in both ways? Explain your answer.

ACTIVITY 30 minutes

PROCESS SKILLS
measuring, recording data

Preparation   Students will need a regular solid, a 100-mL graduate, a metric ruler, and water. Select solids that will fit easily into the cylinder and that have a volume of at least 2 cm^3.

Teaching Tip   Remind students to place the graduate on a flat surface, to bend down so that the meniscus is at eye level, and read the bottom of the meniscus.

Answers to Results and Conclusions
1. Same.
2. No; it is difficult to get the dimensions of an irregularly shaped solid. Only displacement could be used.

A graduated cylinder, or graduate, can be used to measure volume. Graduates usually are marked in milliliters. Notice in Figure 1-16 that the surface of the liquid curves upward at the sides of the graduate. This curved surface is called a *meniscus* (muh NIHS kuhs).The shape of the meniscus depends on the nature of the liquid in the graduate. To read a graduate, view it with the liquid's surface at eye level. Read the mark that lines up with the bottom of the meniscus. What is the volume of the liquid in the graduate in Figure 1-16?[1]

[1]20 mL.

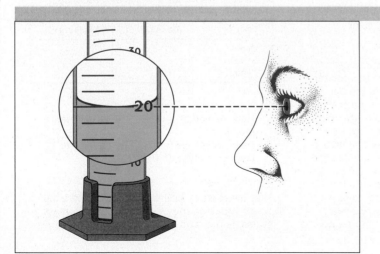

Figure 1-16
Read the volume by looking at the bottom of the meniscus.

ACTIVITY 30 minutes

PROCESS SKILLS
measuring, interpreting data, predicting

Preparation Students will need a balance, masses, forceps, a dime, a nickel, and a penny; they will need a dime, quarter, and half dollar for the *Extension*.

Answers to Procedure

Coin	Mass (g)	Mass (mg)
Dime	2.28	2280.
Nickel	5.0	5000.
Penny	2.1	2100.

Answers to Results and Conclusions
1. 20 dimes.
2. 200 nickels.

Extension
1. *10 cents;* *25 cents;* *50 cents.*
   2.28 g 5.59 g 11.21 g
2. Almost the same.

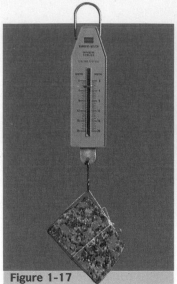

Figure 1-17

A spring scale (*left*) and a double-pan balance (*right*).

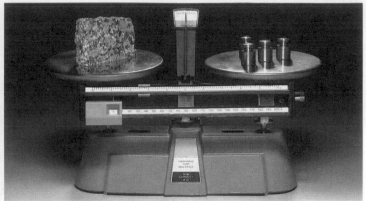

Mass is a measure of the amount of matter in an object. The SI unit of mass is the **kilogram** (kg). The kilogram is a fairly large unit. A baseball bat has a mass of about 1 kg. Scientists often use a smaller unit of mass, the gram (g). One gram is equal to one thousandth of a kilogram. A small paper clip has a mass of about 1 g. The mass of an object is measured using a tool called a *balance*. A balance like the one shown in Figure 1-17 compares the mass of an object with known masses.

ACTIVITY How Is Mass Measured?

OBJECTIVE
Measure the masses of three different coins.

MATERIALS
balance and masses, forceps, 3 coins

PROCEDURE
A. Draw a data table like the one shown.
B. Examine the balance. Notice the pointer and the scale in the center of the balance. The long line at the center of the scale is the zero point. When the pans are empty the pointer should line up with the zero point. If the pointer does not line up use the adjustment knob to zero the balance.
C. Place a dime on the left pan. Use forceps to add masses to the right pan until the pointer lines up with the zero point. Your balance may have one or more small masses on the arm, or beam, to be used in finding the mass. Record the mass of the dime in grams and in milligrams.
D. Repeat step **C** for a nickel and a penny.

Coin	Mass (g)	Mass (mg)
Dime		
Nickel		
Penny		

RESULTS AND CONCLUSIONS
1. How many dimes would it take to balance ten nickels?
2. How many nickels would be needed to balance a mass of 1 kg?

EXTENSION
Find the mass of a dime, a quarter, and a half-dollar. Make a ratio of value in cents to mass in grams. Is the ratio the same for all these coins?

Teaching Tip   Ask students what units are common to both the metric system and the customary system of measurement in the United States. (The second, minute, hour.) Students may want to offer ideas as to why this is so. Interested students can be encouraged to research the development of time measurement.

Enrichment   Students should enjoy converting their weight first to a mass measurement in kilograms, then to a weight measurement in newtons. The conversions are

$$\text{mass in kg} = \frac{\text{weight in lb}}{2.2}$$

weight in newtons = (mass in kg)(9.8).

Figure 1-18

An astronaut has less weight on the moon but has the same mass.

People often refer to mass and weight as though they were the same thing. Mass is a measure of the amount of matter in an object. Weight is a measure of the gravitational force on an object. Weight is usually measured using a scale, such as the one shown in Figure 1-17. The weight of an object may vary depending on where the object is, but the mass of an object does not vary.

The SI unit of force is called the **newton** (N). At sea level an object with a mass of 1 kg has a weight of 9.8 N. On the earth a person with a mass of 90 kg has a weight of 882 N. Figure 1-18 shows an astronaut on earth and on the moon. On the moon this person would have the same mass, but because the moon's gravity is about one sixth the strength of the earth's gravity, this person's weight would be only 147 N.

Time is the interval between two events. Measurements of time are needed to describe how objects move. The SI unit of time is the second (s). You are familiar with measuring time with clocks and watches. Stop watches used in laboratories and at sporting events can measure time in hundredths or thousandths of a second.

PROCESS SKILLS
measuring, recording data, interpreting data

Preparation Students will need safety goggles, a Celsius thermometer, a 200-mL beaker, crushed ice, water, a hot plate, and a glass stirring rod.

Safety Tip Wear safety goggles throughout this activity, and tie back loose clothing and long hair. Make sure hot-plate wires are out of the way, and do not touch the beaker after placing it on the hot plate.

Answers to Procedure
1. Answers may vary; for commonly available thermometers, −50°C; Answers may vary; for commonly available thermometers, +110°C.

Answers to Results and Conclusions
1. No.
2. Answers will vary.
3. Probably not; explanations may include variations in the mass of the ice cubes and different settings on the hot plates.

③ REVIEW/REINFORCEMENT

1. They must collect data accurately and share the data with other scientists.
2. Meter—length; kilogram—mass; degree Celsius—temperature; second—time.
3. Balance.
4. Newton.

Challenge *Centi-* is Latin for "hundred"; *grade* is from the Latin *gradus,* which means "step" or "degree." The Celsius scale is a centigrade (100-step) scale; there are 100 *Celsius* degrees between the freezing and boiling points of water at sea level. The name *Celsius* is appropriate for this scale because Swedish astronomer Anders Celsius (1701–1744) invented the centigrade thermometer in 1742.

ACTIVITY How Is Temperature Measured?

OBJECTIVE
Practice using a thermometer.

MATERIALS
safety goggles, Celsius thermometer, 200-mL beaker, ice, water, hot plate, glass stirring rod

PROCEDURE
A. Wear safety goggles during this activity.
B. Draw a data table like the one shown. List time in two-minute intervals from 0 to 20 minutes.
C. Examine a Celsius thermometer.
   1. What is the lowest temperature it can measure? the highest?
D. Place 2 ice cubes in a beaker. Add enough water to half fill the beaker. Record the temperature of this mixture. Enter this temperature at time 0 minutes.
E. Place the beaker of ice water on a hot plate. Heat the water at a steady rate, stirring it with a glass stirring rod. Record the temperature of the water every 2 minutes. Hold the thermometer so that the bulb is in the water but not touching the sides or bottom of the beaker. Continue for 20 minutes.

Time (min)	Temperature (°C)
0	
2	
4	

RESULTS AND CONCLUSIONS
1. Did the temperature change by the same amount during each 2-minute interval?
2. Predict the temperature of the water if you had heated it for 22 minutes.
3. Compare your highest temperature with that of two other laboratory groups. Were the final temperatures all the same? Suggest a reason for your answer.

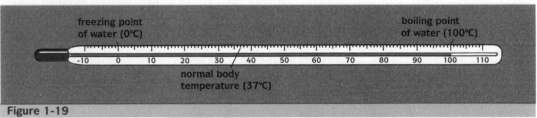

Figure 1-19

A Celsius thermometer.

¹0°C; 100°C.

Temperature is a measure of how hot or cold an object is. A unit of temperature used in science is the **degree Celsius** (°C). Look at the thermometer shown in Figure 1-19. What is the freezing point of water? What is the boiling point?¹The interval between the two points is divided into 100 equal units called degrees Celsius.

REVIEW

1. Why do physical scientists need to make measurements?
2. Name four units of measurement.
3. What tool do you need to measure mass?
4. What is the unit of force called?

CHALLENGE The Celsius scale was sometimes called the centigrade scale. Why was this name appropriate?

1-4 TOOLS OF THE PHYSICAL SCIENTIST

Accurate measurements are important in science. Physical scientists have developed many tools to make measurements. Many of the most useful tools are simple ones like a barometer.

The barometer is a tool for measuring air pressure. You have heard weather forecasters describing air pressure as rising, falling, or holding steady. Changes in air pressure indicate changes in the weather. Changes in air pressure can have an effect on an experiment. Thus it is important for a scientist to know the air pressure at any time.

Many barometers use a tube of mercury, like the one shown in Figure 1-20. Air pressure pushes down on the mercury in the dish with enough force to hold up 76 cm of mercury in the tube. The space above the mercury in the tube is a vacuum. A vacuum is an area where there is no matter. In the vacuum there is no air pressure to push the mercury down.

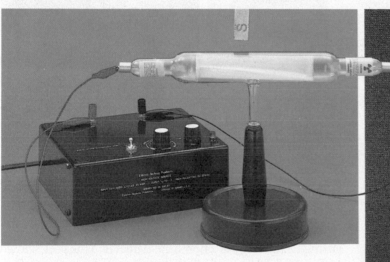

A pump can be used to remove air from a container. There would be a vacuum in the container. Tubes that have been partially emptied of air have helped scientists explain the behavior and properties of matter. Figure 1-20 also shows a Crookes tube. It is a sealed tube with just a small amount of gases inside. By passing an electric current through a Crookes tube, scientists can study the behavior of charged particles. Much of our understanding of matter comes from experiments with tools like the Crookes tube. Studies with Crookes tubes led to the development of television picture tubes.

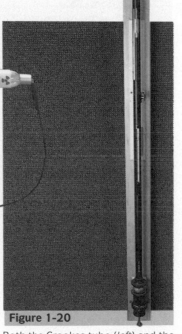

Figure 1-20

Both the Crookes tube (*left*) and the barometer (*right*) contain vacuums.

OBJECTIVES
Refer to pupil page 19.

VOCABULARY
Key term: spectroscope
Other terms: amino acids, Calorie

1 MOTIVATION

Start a class discussion about the tools used to do familiar tasks. Describe the evolution of some of these tools. For example, before the advent of word processors, typewriters were commonly used; before typewriters, writing was done by hand. Other examples for discussion include the computer (calculator, adding machine, abacus) and the microwave oven (convection oven, coal oven, coals, fire).

2 CONCEPT DEVELOPMENT

Teaching Tip Have students measure the diameter of the wire in a paper clip by using a centimeter ruler and a micrometer. Have them compare each measurement and then select the better tool for this ·task.

Background The first barometer was developed by Evangelista Torricelli (1608–1647). Torricelli filled a glass tube with mercury and inverted it in a basin of mercury. The mercury level in the tube was 76 cm. Torricelli concluded that the "weight" of the air was pushing down on the mercury in the basin with enough force to hold up 76 cm of mercury. (**Caution:** Do not allow students to attempt this demonstration. Mercury is a toxic substance.)

comparing

Have students compare how accurate the tools used to measure the following must be: the duration of a school day and the duration of a race; the length of the classroom and the thickness of a sheet of paper; the capacity of a bathtub and the capacity of a thimble.

Enrichment   Arrange to take students to a hospital or university laboratory for instruction on the equipment used there.

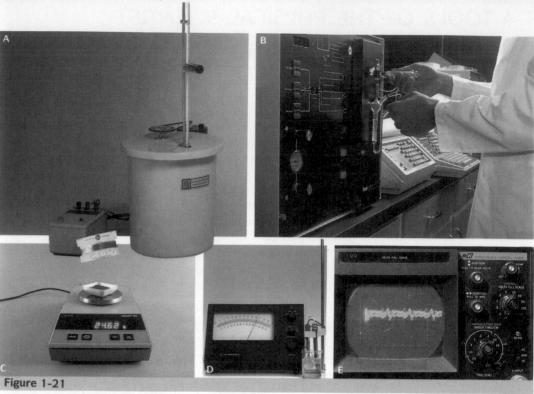

Figure 1-21

A bomb calorimeter (A), a chromatograph (B), a balance (C), a pH meter (D), and an oscilloscope (E)

Some scientific tools use display screens that are like television picture tubes. The oscilloscope (uh SIHL uh skohp) is a tool that displays data in a wave pattern. Sometimes an oscilloscope is linked to a printer that can make a drawing of the wave pattern. Hospitals use tools like oscilloscopes to monitor the heart rate or breathing rate of a patient.

Chemists are interested in the changes that take place in matter. One of the tools these scientists use in measuring heat energy is a bomb calorimeter. This tool, shown in Figure 1-21, measures the amount of heat given off or absorbed during a chemical change. Calorimeters are used to measure the energy contained in food and fuels. The energy content in substances can be measured in units called calories.

The calorie is a very small unit. Foods contain a large amount of energy. The kilocalorie is a larger unit used to measure the energy content in foods. How many calories are there in one kilocalorie?[1] When food labels show the calorie content of food, they often use the term *Calorie*. The Calorie with a capital *C* is equal to one kilocalorie.

[1]1000.

Another tool used by chemists is the pH meter. The pH of a substance indicates the acidity of the substance. This information has many practical uses. For example, many industrial processes can take place only at certain pH levels. Scientists, doctors, and technicians in many fields of work need the information that can be supplied by pH meters.

Physical scientists also use complex tools that require a great deal of skill in their use. A tool called a chromatograph is used to test the makeup of proteins. This tool separates a protein into smaller units called *amino acids*. A protein may contain hundreds of these units. The pattern produced by the amino acids helps a scientist identify a protein.

The computer is a tool used by many scientists. Computers are used in every field of science. They are more than just information processors. Computers sent into space collect data and transmit these data back to the earth. Computers in hospital laboratories test samples from patients. The results of many tests can be compared and analyzed quickly. Thus, computers help doctors make diagnoses. In laboratories and factories computers can be used with robots to handle dangerous materials. Computers can solve mathematical problems in a fraction of the time it would take humans to do the work.

Background   Computers are being used to create three dimensional models of objects and to predict the behavior of many systems. They are also being used to simulate events that have never been witnessed—such as the formation of the solar system—based on current information in the fields of physics and chemistry.

Demonstration   If you have access to a computer, demonstrate the use of computers in experimentation. Hook up a simple experiment to the computer, using the appropriate interfacing equipment, and run the experiment for the class.

SCIENCE & TECHNOLOGY

Supercomputers in use today can handle up to 800 million operations per second. It's hard to believe that computers would ever need to solve a problem faster than that. Yet, scientists are working to find ways to make computers work faster.

As long as they are organized the way they are now, computers will probably not be able to work any faster. A modern computer approaches a problem in the same way the first computers did—step by step. All operations involved in solving a problem are done one at a time. The answer to each step must be sent to the computer's memory before the next step can begin.

To increase the speed of a computer, scientists are finding ways to make it handle several steps at one time. In the future, computers may contain as many as a thousand processors. Different processors will work on parts of a problem all at once. This teamwork approach is called parallel processing. It should help scientists solve problems that used to take too long, even on a computer.

PROCESS SKILLS
observing, comparing

Preparation   Reduce the light in the room to a level bright enough for students to be able to see safely what they are doing but dim enough for them to be able to identify the colors of the emitted light. Provide beakers of dilute HCl so that students can clean their nichrome wire loops.

Safety Tip   Wear safety goggles throughout this activity. Tie back loose clothing and long hair.

Teaching Tip   Have students clean the nichrome wire loop between each test by dipping the loop in dilute HCl and then heating it in the edge of the burner flame. If students have difficulty identifying the colors, check their procedure or reduce the level of light in the room.

Answers to Procedure
1. Orange red.
2. Crimson.
3. Bright red.
4. Light is separated into its component colors, resulting in a continuous spectrum.
5. The color lines are in different places in the band of color for each material.

Answers to Results and Conclusions
1. No.
2. Observing the flames with your eyes does not let you distinguish between the materials, but observing them through the grating spectroscope does.

ACTIVITY   How Is a Spectroscope Used?

OBJECTIVE
Demonstrate the use of a physical science tool to study some properties of matter.

MATERIALS
safety goggles, Bunsen burner, striker, nichrome wire with handle, calcium chloride solution, lithium chloride solution, strontium chloride solution, incandescent lamp, grating spectroscope

PROCEDURE
A. Wear safety goggles during this activity.
B. Light a Bunsen burner. Place a small amount of calcium chloride solution on the loop of a nichrome wire. Hold the loop in the flame of the burner.
   1. What color do you see?
C. Repeat step **B**, using lithium chloride.
   2. What color do you see?
D. Repeat step **B**, using strontium chloride solution.
   3. What color do you see?
E. Look at a lighted incandescent lamp through the grating spectroscope.
   4. Describe what you see.
F. Repeat step **B**, using the grating spectroscope to observe the material being heated. Test each of the solutions in this manner.
   5. Describe what you see for each solution tested.

RESULTS AND CONCLUSIONS
1. Can you distinguish between the samples by viewing the flames with your eyes alone?
2. How do the colors you saw in steps **B**, **C**, and **D** compare with the observations made using the spectroscope?

Computers can be linked to other tools and be programmed to operate them. A tool called a **spectroscope** (SPEHK truh skohp) separates light into different colors. Each element gives off a different combination of colors when it is heated. A computer linked to a spectroscope can be used to identify a substance. The pattern of colors produced by the spectroscope can be compared to the patterns in the computer's memory.

Figure 1-22

These are the color patterns produced by calcium (*top*), lithium (*middle*), and barium (*bottom*).

New supercomputers can do more things and do things faster than ordinary computers. For example, in 1978 a computer solved a complex mathematical problem in 500 hours. In 1985 a supercomputer took only 19 minutes to solve the same problem.

REVIEW

1. Name two simple tools used by the physical scientist.
2. What is a spectroscope?
3. Describe two uses of computers in physical science.

CHALLENGE Suppose you have a mixture of substances. How might a computer linked to a spectroscope identify the different substances in the mixture if the computer memory contains only the patterns of pure substances?

CHAPTER SUMMARY

The main ideas in this chapter are listed below. Read these statements before you answer the Chapter Review questions.

- Science is a method of gaining knowledge about the earth, space, nonliving things, and living things. (1-1)

- Physical science is the study of matter and energy. (1-1)

- Technology is applying knowledge gained from science in an attempt to improve the quality of human life. (1-1)

- Scientists are problem solvers. They use the scientific method to gather information and test ideas. (1-2)

- Four key processes of the scientific method are making observations, forming a hypothesis, doing experiments, and drawing a conclusion. (1-2)

- An experiment is a controlled procedure designed to test a hypothesis. (1-2)

- Experiments use two groups—a control group and an experimental group. The factor that makes these groups different is the variable factor. (1-2)

- A hypothesis that is tested and supported many times is called a theory. (1-2)

- A scientific law is a statement that describes some pattern that can be observed in nature. (1-2)

- Scientists use a standard form of measurement so that they can share information without confusion. (1-3)

- The meter is a unit of length. (1-3)

- The liter and cubic centimeter are units of volume. (1-3)

- The kilogram is a unit of mass. (1-3)

- A newton is a unit of force. (1-3)

- The second is a unit of time. (1-3)

- The degree Celsius is a unit of temperature. (1-3)

- Physical scientists rely on accurate measurements for their data. They have developed many tools to aid them with these measurements. (1-4)

- A widely used tool in science today is the computer. (1-4)

The key terms in this chapter are listed below. Use each term in a sentence that shows the meaning of the term.

conclusion	kilogram	observation	scientific method
degree Celsius	liter	physical science	spectroscope
experiment	meter	science	technology
hypothesis	newton	scientific law	theory

1. Accept all reasonable answers.
2. A tool for separating light into different colors.
3. Accept all reasonable answers.

Challenge The patterns of colors produced by the spectroscope can be compared to those in the computer's memory.

Review and Skill Masters

VOCABULARY REVIEW, page 50.
See page 1c in this book for answers.

VOCABULARY

1. f	8. e
2. j	9. d
3. o	10. b
4. h	11. l
5. k	12. g
6. n	13. a
7. c	14. i

CONCEPTS

1. Science is a method of gaining knowledge of nature, and technology is the application of knowledge.
2. Chemistry and physics. Chemistry is the study of matter and the changes that matter undergoes. Physics is the study of the many forms of energy and the relationship between energy and matter.
3. Accept all reasonable answers.
4. Observations lead to questions that can be used to form a hypothesis; observations are also used to test a hypothesis.
5. The experimental group has one variable that the control group does not have.
6. The purpose of an experiment is to test a hypothesis.
7. The experiment may be done again or a new hypothesis may be formed.
8. A hypothesis becomes a theory after it has been tested and proven correct many times.

Review and Skill Masters

CHAPTER REVIEW, pages 6–7.
See page 1c in this book for answers.

24

Chapter Review

VOCABULARY

Write the letter of the term that best matches the definiton. Not all the terms will be used.

1. A unit of volume
2. The study of matter and energy
3. A hypothesis that is tested and supported many times
4. The SI unit of force
5. The method of obtaining knowledge about nature
6. The use of scientific knowledge in an effort to improve life
7. A test of a hypothesis
8. A unit of mass
9. A possible answer to a question
10. A unit of temperature
11. A statement that describes some pattern in nature
12. A unit of length
13. A statement of the results of an experiment
14. An examination of something in nature

a. conclusion
b. degree Celsius
c. experiment
d. hypothesis
e. kilogram
f. liter
g. meter
h. newton
i. observation
j. physical science
k. science
l. scientific law
m. scientific method
n. technology
o. theory

CONCEPTS

1. Explain how science and technology are related. Explain how they are different. (1-1)
2. What are the two major branches of physical science? Describe each (1-1)
3. Give an example of a product that was developed as the result of technology. (1-1)
4. How are observations related to hypotheses? (1-2)
5. How are the control group and experimental group in an experiment different? (1-2)
6. What is the purpose of an experiment as part of the scientific method? (1-2)
7. What happens in the scientific method when the conclusion does not support the hypothesis? (1-2)
8. When could a hypothesis be named a theory? (1-2)

9. Why is it necessary for scientists to have a standard system of measurement? (1-3)

10. What are the units used to measure mass, length, temperature, and time? (1-3)

11. Name four prefixes that scientists use with the SI units, and give the meaning of each of these prefixes. (1-3)

12. How are weight and mass different? (1-3)

13. What is a meniscus? Where does a meniscus occur? (1-3)

14. What tool is used to measure temperature? (1-3)

15. What is the function of a barometer? (1-4)

16. Name two special tools used by chemists and tell what each measures. (1-4)

17. Why are computers so useful in science? (1-4)

---

1. The label on a box of cereal shows that the mass of the contents is 1.5 kg. How many grams and how many milligrams of cereal are in the box?

2. The distance between two cities is 250,000 m. How many kilometers is this distance equal to?

3. What tool would you use to measure 60 mL of water? How many cubic centimeters is this volume equal to?

4. If the length of a table is 2.15 m and the length of another table is 131 cm, what is the combined length of the two tables if they are together?

EXTENSION

1. Do library research on the various careers in physical science, and prepare a report on the educational background needed for one of these careers.

2. Read about the experiments of Alexander Graham Bell, to see how he used the scientific method.

3. Use reference materials to find out more about the development of the metric system.

4. Many outstanding scientists have won the Nobel Prize. Find out what this prize is, and when it was first awarded.

READINGS

McCorduck, Pamela. "The Conquering Machine." *Science 84*, November 1984, p. 131.

Reich, Leonard S. "From Edison's Wastebasket." *Science 84*, November 1984, p.73.

Townes, Charles H. "Harnessing Light." *Science 84*, November 1984, p. 153.

---

9. So that scientists all over the world can communicate clearly with each other.

10. Mass—kilogram; length—meter; temperature—degree Celsius; time—second.

11. Answers will vary, depending on those chosen; see Table 1-2 for correct responses.

12. Mass is a measure of the quantity of matter, and weight is a measure of the gravitational force on mass.

13. The curved surface of a liquid; occurs at the top of a column of liquid in a graduate.

14. Thermometer.

15. To measure air pressure.

16. Accept all reasonable answers.

17. Accept all reasonable answers.

APPLICATION/CRITICAL THINKING

1. 1500 g; 1,500,000 mg.

2. 250 km.

3. 100-mL graduate; 60 cm^3.

4. 3.46 m.

Test Masters

CHAPTER TEST, pages 1—4.
See page 1d in this book for answers.

SKILLS OF PHYSICAL SCIENCE

ORGANIZER

Section	pages	Activity	pages	Reinforcement and Evaluation	pages	*Review and Skill Masters	pages	Other Components in Teacher Resource Package	pages
2–1 Understanding Basic Ideas	27–29			Review, Challenge	29			Study Guide Lab Manual	9 7
2–2 Displaying Data	30–36	How Much Will a Spring Stretch?	35	Puzzler Review, Challenge	33 36	Challenge/Critical Thinking	15–16	Study Guide Transparency	10
2–3 Using Mathematics	37–41	Ratio of Surface Area to Volume of a Cube	40	Review, Challenge	41	Skill	14	Study Guide Lab Manual	11 11
2–4 Laboratory Safety	42–46	Safety in the Laboratory	45	Review, Challenge	46			Study Guide Poster	12
CHAPTER SUMMARY	47					Vocabulary Review	11		
CHAPTER REVIEW	48–49			*Test Masters	5–8	Chapter Review	12–13		

*In the Teacher Resource Package. For answers, see pages 25b–25d in this book.

ACTIVITY MATERIALS Quantities are based on a class of 30 students working in groups as indicated in parentheses.

How Much Will a Spring Stretch? p. 35 (groups of 3)	quantity	Ratio of Surface Area to Volume of a Cube p. 40 (groups of 1)	quantity	Safety in the Laboratory p. 45 (groups of 1)	quantity
meterstick	10	1-cm grid graph paper	30 sheets	graph paper	30 sheets
ring stand	10	metric ruler	30	metric ruler	30
clamp	20	scissors	30	colored pencil	30
steel spring	10	clear tape	30 rolls		
weight hanger	10				
slotted gram masses	10				

REVIEW AND SKILL MASTERS

Name_____ Date_____

VOCABULARY REVIEW — Chapter 2

Match the definition in column A with the correct term in column B.

Column A

- **J** 1. Stored energy.
- **B** 2. A push or a pull.
- **H** 3. A measure of the amount of matter.
- **E** 4. The energy of motion.
- **I** 5. Anything that has mass and takes up space.
- **G** 6. States that mass is neither created nor destroyed.
- **C** 7. A display of data.
- **F** 8. States that energy is neither created nor destroyed.
- **A** 9. Means to obtain values beyond those known.

Column B

A. extrapolation
B. force
C. graph
D. interpolation
E. kinetic energy
F. Law of Conservation of Energy
G. Law of Conservation of Mass
H. mass
I. matter
J. potential energy

Use the terms **accuracy**, **measurement**, **scientific notation**, and **significant digits** to complete the following paragraph.

An observation that has numerical value is called **measurement**. How close a measured value comes to a true value is called **accuracy**. When reading a measurement, a scientist looks at a number's **significant digits**. In the system of **scientific notation** numbers are expressed as products of a number between 1 and 10 multiplied by a power of 10.

© 1988 Silver, Burdett & Ginn Inc.

11

Name_____ Date_____

CHAPTER REVIEW — Chapter 2

2-1 Understanding Basic Ideas

1. How are the terms matter and mass related? **Mass is a measure of the amount of matter contained in any object.**

2. Use the motion of a child on a swing to describe potential energy, kinetic energy, and the Law of Conservation of Energy. **As the swing rises, it gains potential, or stored, energy, which gives an object the potential to do work. During the downswing, this potential energy converts to kinetic energy, or the energy of motion. No energy is lost in this conversion. It is simply changed from one form to another. This illustrates the Law of Conservation of Energy.**

3. How are matter and energy related? **Matter and energy can be changed from one form to another.**

2-2 Displaying Data

1. List and describe two methods that use a graph to interpret data and make predictions. **By interpolation, which is a way of estimating values of a function between two known values. By extrapolation, which is a way of predicting by projecting existing data beyond that which is already shown on the graph.**

2-3 Using Mathematics

1. How are numbers that result from direct counting different from numbers that result from measuring devices? **Numbers resulting from direct counting are exact. Numbers expressing measurement are never exact.**

© 1988 Silver, Burdett & Ginn Inc.

12

Name_____ Date_____

CHAPTER REVIEW (Continued) — Chapter 2

2. Note the following measurement: 3.14159265 cm
   a. Which are the significant digits? **All of them.**
   b. Which are the certain digits? **3.1415926**
   c. Which are the doubtful digits? **The last digit, 5.**

3. Write the following number using scientific notation: 6,400,000,000,000,000,000
   6.4×10^{18}

2-4 Laboratory Safety

1. List a few items of safety equipment you should be familiar with before you begin work in a science laboratory. **Answers will vary but may include fire extinguishers, safety showers, eye washes, fire blankets, protective clothing, and safety goggles.**

2. What are some safety precautions you should take before you begin work in a science laboratory? **Answers may vary but may include: read every step of the activity you will be doing; learn the location and use of fire extinguishers, safety showers, eye washes, fire blankets, and any other safety equipment in the lab; wear protective clothing; know how to safely use the equipment listed in the activity.**

3. Describe the correct method for lighting a Bunsen burner. **Before lighting the burner, be sure that the tubing is securely attached at both ends and has no cracks or holes. Make sure the burner is in good condition and check that the striker will make a spark. Turn on the gas, hold the striker at the top of the burner, and make a spark.**

© 1988 Silver, Burdett & Ginn Inc.

13

Name_____ Date_____

SKILL/Making Mathematical Conversions — Chapter 2

Physical scientists may record measurements in different forms, such as whole numbers, fractions, decimals, and scientific notation. The chart below shows the same measurement written in four different forms. Change each number to fraction, decimal, and scientific notation forms. Convert all length measurements to meters. Convert all mass measurements to kilograms. The first row is completed for you.

ORIGINAL NUMBER	FRACTION	DECIMAL	SCIENTIFIC NOTATION
1 cm	1/100 m	0.01 m	1×10^{-2} m
26 cm	26/100 m	0.26 m	2.6×10^{-1} m
792 cm	792/100 m	7.92 m	7.9×10^{0} m
1,668 cm	1,668/100 m	16.68 m	1.7×10^{1} m
5.8×10^{6} cm	5,800,000/100 m	58,000.0 m	5.8×10^{4} m
1 mm	1/1,000 m	0.001 m	1.0×10^{-3} m
83 mm	83/1,000 m	0.083 m	8.3×10^{-2} m
514 mm	514/1,000 m	0.514 m	5.1×10^{-1} m
6,722 mm	6,722/1,000 m	6.722 m	6.7×10^{0} m
9.6×10^{3} mm	9,600/1,000 m	9.600 m	9.6×10^{0} m
3.7×10^{5} mm	370,000/1,000 m	370.0 m	3.7×10^{2} m
5.8 km	5,800/1 m	5,800 m	5.8×10^{3} m
391.8 km	391,800/1 m	391,800 m	3.9×10^{5} m
3,123.9 km	3,123,900/1 m	3,123,900.0 m	3.1×10^{6} m
1 g	1/1,000 kg	0.001 kg	1.0×10^{-3} kg
413 g	413/1000 kg	0.413 kg	4.1×10^{-1} kg
7,198 g	7,198/1,000 kg	7.198 kg	7.2×10^{0} kg

© 1988 Silver, Burdett & Ginn Inc.

14

Name_____ Date_____

CHALLENGE/CRITICAL THINKING _____ Chapter 2

A fortune in stolen diamonds lured Sir James back to the Hickman mansion. The police and other insurance investigators had given up on finding the thief. But Sir James had one thought trapped in his mind. The diamonds had to be taken by one of the four people who lived on the estate.

Sir James drove up the driveway to the gardens. "Somewhere there is a clue," he thought. He quietly got out of the car and walked over to the rose bed. He paused for a moment, then crossed the path directly behind the garden. A very straight, lone willow sapling stood at the south edge of the garden.

At that moment he heard the sound of footsteps on the gravel pathway. Quickly, he hoisted himself up into a nearby tree. The leaves were thick but he could still view the ground surrounding the willow.

Sir James could see a person's shadow. The shadow started at the base of the willow and reached to the near edge of the garden. It bent down, dug, and removed a small bag from the dirt. Immediately, the shadow left.

Sir James jumped down from the tree. He took his tape measure from his pocket and measured the willow. "Exactly two meters," he muttered. Then he measured the shadow of the willow. "Fifty centimeters," he wrote in his little black book. Next, he measured from the base of the willow to the near edge of the garden. He recorded 40 centimeters in his book.

Quickly, he walked to the mansion. He measured and recorded the heights of everyone.

Mr. Jonathan Hickman III	(JH 3)	180 cm
Mrs. Veronica Hickman	(VH)	150 cm
Mr. Jonathan Hickman IV	(JH 4)	190 cm
Mrs. Mae Jones-Hickman	(MJ-H)	160 cm

1. Why did Sir James measure the shadow length and the height of the tree?

Sir James measured the shadow length and the height of the tree in order to

set a standard to compare measurements (proportion).

2. How are interpolation and extrapolation used in measurement?

Interpolation and extrapolation are used in measurement to find information

between and beyond values that are known.

3. Plot and label the height of each suspect using a vertical line and initials on the graph. Then, plot the shadow length and the height of the willow using a **W**. Draw a line from 0,0 through the point marked **W**.

15

Name_____ Date_____

CHALLENGE/CRITICAL THINKING (Continued) _____ Chapter 2

4. What does the point (0,0) represent?

The point (0,0) represents an object that is flat (height=0) and thus will not

cast a shadow (shadow length=0).

5. What does the line from (0,0) through the point marked **W** represent?

The line from (0,0) through the point marked W represents the shadow length

for all heights from 0 cm to 240 cm.

6. A nearby flag pole has a height of 220 cm. What is its shadow length?

Its shadow length is 55 cm.

7. Sir James has a shadow length of 42.5 cm. What is his height?

Sir James has a height of 170 cm.

8. Who is the thief? How do you know?

Mrs. Mae Jones-Hickman is the thief. She is the only person whose height

casts a shadow length of 40 cm.

16

TEST MASTERS

Top-left sheet:

Name _____ Date _____ Score _____

Chapter 2

Skills of Physical Science

PART 1

In the space below, write the term that each phrase defines.

Chapter Goal

1. **significant digits** — The numbers in a measurement that a scientist reads and estimates on a scale — 3

2. **interpolation** — A way of using a graph to find information between values that are known — 2

3. **potential energy** — Energy that is stored — 1

4. **extrapolation** — A means of using a graph to obtain values for quantities beyond those that are known — 2

5. **scientific notation** — A way of expressing numbers in which scientists write a number as the product of a coefficient between 1 and 10 and a power of 10 — 4

6. **accuracy** — The degree of closeness between a measured value and a true value — 3

7. **mass** — A measure of the amount of matter in an object — 1

PART 2

Choose the term or phrase that best answers the question or completes the statement. Write the letter of that choice in the space at the left.

_a_ 1. What is the correct way to write 53,000 in scientific notation? — 4
a. 5.3×10^4 b. 5.3×10^3 c. 0.53×10^4 d. 0.53×10^5

_c_ 2. The device used to make a spark to light a gas flame is called a: — 5
a. test tube.   b. hot plate.   c. striker.   d. Bunsen burner.

_d_ 3. Which of the following numbers would a scientist be most likely to write in scientific notation? — 4
a. 0.8   b. 6.7   c. 3000   d. 23,900,000

_d_ 4. One difference between energy and matter is that only matter can be: — 1
a. created.   b. destroyed.   c. changed.   d. touched.

Chapter 2   Skills of Physical Science   5

Top-right sheet:

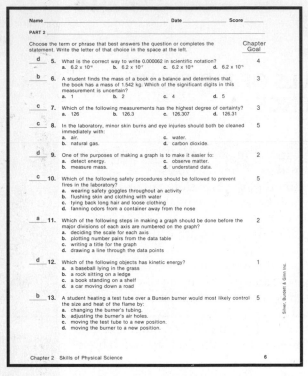

Name _____ Date _____ Score _____

PART 2

Choose the term or phrase that best answers the question or completes the statement. Write the letter of that choice in the space at the left.

Chapter Goal

_d_ 5. What is the correct way to write 0.000062 in scientific notation? — 4
a. 6.2×10^5 b. 6.2×10^{-7} c. 6.2×10^4 d. 6.2×10^{-5}

_b_ 6. A student finds the mass of a book on a balance and determines that the book has a mass of 1.542 kg. Which of the significant digits in this measurement is uncertain? — 3
a. 1   b. 2   c. 4   d. 5

_c_ 7. Which of the following measurements has the highest degree of certainty? — 3
a. 126   b. 126.3   c. 126.307   d. 126.31

_c_ 8. In the laboratory, minor skin burns and eye injuries should both be cleaned immediately with: — 5
a. air.   b. natural gas.   c. water.   d. carbon dioxide.

_d_ 9. One of the purposes of making a graph is to make it easier to: — 2
a. detect energy.   b. measure mass.   c. observe matter.   d. understand data.

_c_ 10. Which of the following safety procedures should be followed to prevent fires in the laboratory? — 5
a. wearing safety goggles throughout an activity
b. flushing skin and clothing with water
c. tying back long hair and loose clothing
d. fanning odors from a container away from the nose

_a_ 11. Which of the following steps in making a graph should be done before the major divisions of each axis are numbered on the graph? — 2
a. deciding the scale for each axis
b. plotting number pairs from the data table
c. writing a title for the graph
d. drawing a line through the data points

_d_ 12. Which of the following objects has kinetic energy? — 1
a. a baseball lying in the grass
b. a rock sitting on a ledge
c. a book standing on a shelf
d. a car moving down a road

_b_ 13. A student heating a test tube over a Bunsen burner would most likely control the size and heat of the flame by: — 5
a. changing the burner's tubing.
b. adjusting the burner's air holes.
c. moving the test tube to a new position.
d. moving the burner to a new position.

Chapter 2   Skills of Physical Science   6

Bottom-left sheet:

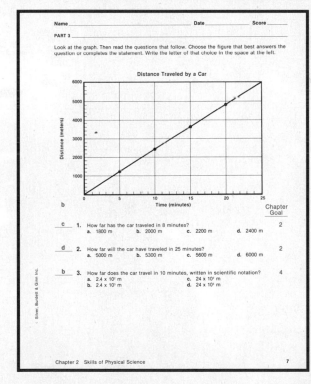

Name _____ Date _____ Score _____

PART 3

Look at the graph. Then read the questions that follow. Choose the figure that best answers the question or completes the statement. Write the letter of that choice in the space at the left.

Distance Traveled by a Car

(graph: Distance (meters) vs. Time (minutes))

Chapter Goal

_c_ 1. How far has the car traveled in 8 minutes? — 2
a. 1800 m   b. 2000 m   c. 2200 m   d. 2400 m

_d_ 2. How far will the car have traveled in 25 minutes? — 2
a. 5000 m   b. 5300 m   c. 5600 m   d. 6000 m

_b_ 3. How far does the car travel in 10 minutes, written in scientific notation? — 4
a. 2.4×10^3 m   b. 2.4×10^5 m   c. 24×10^2 m   d. 24×10^3 m

Chapter 2   Skills of Physical Science   7

Bottom-right sheet:

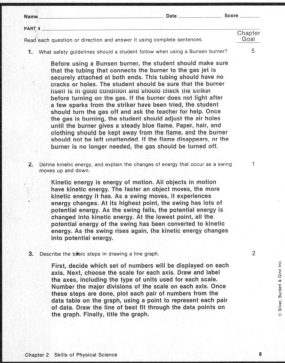

Name _____ Date _____ Score _____

PART 4

Read each question or direction and answer it using complete sentences.

Chapter Goal

1. What safety guidelines should a student follow when using a Bunsen burner? — 5

   Before using a Bunsen burner, the student should make sure that the tubing that connects the burner to the gas jet is securely attached at both ends. This tubing should have no cracks or holes. The student should be sure that the burner itself is in good condition and should check the striker before turning on the gas. If the burner does not light after a few sparks from the striker have been tried, the student should turn the gas off and ask the teacher for help. Once the gas is burning, the student should adjust the air holes until the burner gives a steady blue flame. Paper, hair, and clothing should be kept away from the flame, and the burner should not be left unattended. If the flame disappears, or the burner is no longer needed, the gas should be turned off.

2. Define kinetic energy, and explain the changes of energy that occur as a swing moves up and down. — 1

   Kinetic energy is energy of motion. All objects in motion have kinetic energy. The faster an object moves, the more kinetic energy it has. As a swing moves, it experiences energy changes. At its highest point, the swing has lots of potential energy. As the swing falls, the potential energy is changed into kinetic energy. At the lowest point, all the potential energy of the swing has been converted to kinetic energy. As the swing rises again, the kinetic energy changes into potential energy.

3. Describe the basic steps in drawing a line graph. — 2

   First, decide which set of numbers will be displayed on each axis. Next, choose the scale for each axis. Draw and label the axes, including the type of units used for each scale. Number the major divisions of the scale on each axis. Once these steps are done, plot each pair of numbers from the data table on the graph, using a point to represent each pair of data. Draw the line of best fit through the data points on the graph. Finally, title the graph.

Chapter 2   Skills of Physical Science   8

CHAPTER **2** PLANNING GUIDE

25d

2

SKILLS OF PHYSICAL SCIENCE

The questions in the CHAPTER TEST are based on these Chapter Goals.

1. Identify the properties of matter, and distinguish between potential energy and kinetic energy.
2. Explain how graphs are constructed and used.
3. Explain the importance of accurate measurement and the use of significant digits.
4. Describe scientific notation and how it is used.
5. Describe safety guidelines, equipment, and techniques for a physical science laboratory.

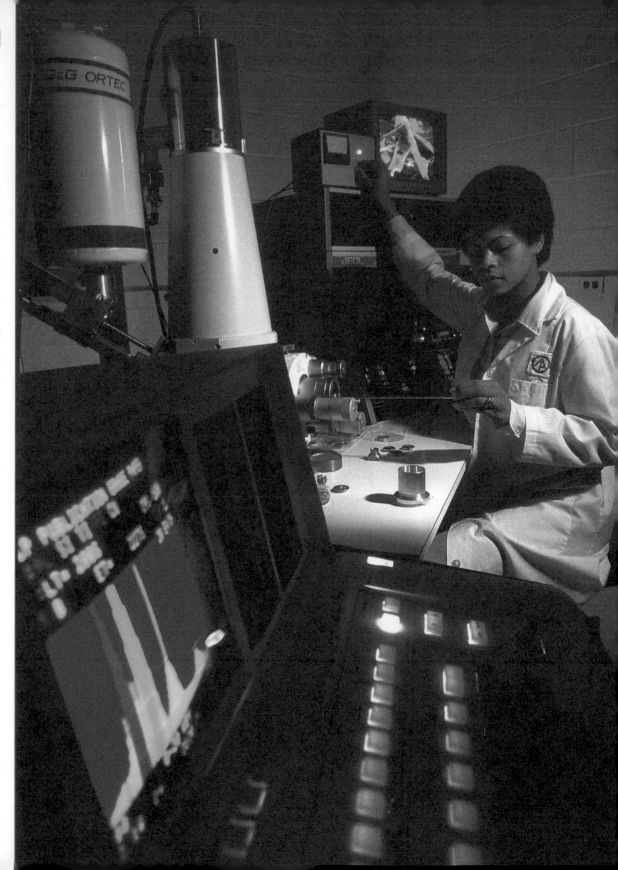

SKILLS OF PHYSICAL SCIENCE

Scientists like the one shown in the photograph collect data when they do experiments. Scientists spend much of their time organizing and analyzing data. Many scientists use computers to help with these tasks. A computer can solve mathematical problems more quickly than a human can. A computer can display data in many different kinds of charts and graphs.

- *What kinds of charts and graphs are used to display data?*
- *In addition to data from experiments, what other kinds of information might you want to show in a chart or a graph?*

2-1 UNDERSTANDING BASIC IDEAS

The concept of energy is a central idea in physics and chemistry. It links these sciences to all other sciences. Energy and matter make up the universe. Matter is the material in the universe and energy is the mover of this material. Matter is acted upon by forces in the universe. Scientists explain most of what they study in terms of matter, energy, and force. Understanding and using these basic concepts is an important skill in physical science.

MATTER

Matter is anything that has mass and takes up space. **Mass** is a measure of the amount of matter in an object. Each type of matter has characteristics that can help you identify it. A characteristic that helps to distinguish one kind of matter from another is called a *property*. Some properties of matter are color, odor, hardness, density, melting point, and boiling point.

Most matter on earth exists in three states: solid, liquid, and gas. Matter can be changed from one state to another. For example, ice, which is water in the solid state, can be melted and changed to the liquid state. The amount of matter always remains the same during such changes. Melting 100 g of ice produces 100 g of water.

After completing this section, you will be able to

- **define** the term *matter*.
- **distinguish** between potential and kinetic energy.

The key terms in this section are
energy
force
kinetic energy
Law of Conservation of Energy
Law of Conservation of Mass
mass
matter
potential energy

Refer students to the chapter opening photograph. Ask them what the scientist is doing. Ask students why computers are valuable tools for scientists. The introductory questions are for discussion purposes.

- What kinds of charts and graphs are used to display data? (Data can be displayed on line graphs, bar graphs, or pie graphs.)
- In addition to data from experiments, what other kinds of information might you want to show in a chart or graph? (Charts or graphs can be used to make predictions, show comparisons, or simplify complex experiments.)

2-1 UNDERSTANDING BASIC IDEAS
pages 27–29

OBJECTIVES
Refer to pupil page 27.

VOCABULARY
Key terms: energy, force, kinetic energy, Law of Conservation of Energy, Law of Conservation of Mass, mass, matter, potential energy
Other term: property

1 MOTIVATION

Set up a hand generator and attach the generator to a light bulb. Turn the generator so the bulb lights. Ask students what has occurred to create electricity. Have them list the forms of energy that were used to light the bulb. Then have students make a list of the forms of energy used to pick up an object.

2 CONCEPT DEVELOPMENT

Background   Energy in its many forms causes everything that happens. The sun's radiant energy provides the heat that warms the earth's land masses and oceans. The energy that a person uses to lift an object comes from the food that the person eats. In the human body, chemical energy from food is changed into heat and into mechanical energy used to move muscles and to perform other body functions. The change of one kind of matter into another is always accompanied by a change from one form of energy to another.

Thinking Skills

comparing
Students learn that the mass of a substance is conserved when it undergoes a physical change. Have students fill a graduate with ice cubes and find the mass. Set the graduate aside until the ice melts. Have students find the mass again. Have them compare the two masses and verify if the Law of Conservation of Mass is shown in this activity.

Teaching Tip   To demonstrate a change from potential energy to kinetic energy, drop a rubber ball. Ask students to describe the change from potential energy to kinetic energy that occurs as the ball falls.

Figure 2-1

Work is done when a force moves through a distance.

en- (in)
ergon (work)

[1] The student putting books on the higher shelf is doing more work.

Figure 2-2

A solar-powered calculator

Matter can go through many kinds of changes. But in each change, the total amount of matter remains the same. If you burn 12 g of carbon in 32 g of oxygen, you get 44 g of carbon dioxide gas. The **Law of Conservation of Mass** states that mass cannot be created or destroyed.

ENERGY

Matter can be seen and touched. Energy cannot be seen or touched. You can see the effects of energy. For example, when an object is moved, energy is used. **Energy** is defined as the ability to do work. When you lift an object, you are doing work. The higher you lift the object, or the heavier the object is, the more work you do. Look at Figure 2-1. Which student is doing more work?[1] Work is any process in which matter is moved by the action of a force. A **force** is a push or a pull.

Energy can exist in several forms. Heat, light, sound, and electricity are forms of energy. Solar cells change light energy into electrical energy. Electrical energy can be changed into sound energy. The solar-powered calculator shown in Figure 2-2 makes a sound when each key is touched.

All forms of energy can be discussed in terms of two types of energy. **Potential energy** is stored energy. Stored energy gives an object the potential to do work. **Kinetic energy** is energy of motion. Any object in motion has kinetic energy and is able to do work. The faster an object moves, the more kinetic energy it has.

You probably have observed energy being changed from one form to another. Look at Figure 2-3. The child in the swing is going through energy changes. The person pushing the child uses energy to do the work of moving the swing. As the swing rises, it gains potential energy. During the downward swing the potential energy is changed into energy of motion, or kinetic energy. At the lowest point the potential energy of the swing has been converted to kinetic energy. As the swing continues to move, it rises as the kinetic energy is changed into potential energy. No energy is lost. It is simply changed from one form to another. The **Law of Conservation of Energy** states that energy cannot be created or destroyed. It may be changed from one form to another, but the total amount of energy never changes.

Matter and energy are closely related. The two conservation laws can be combined into one law. The Law of Conservation of Mass and Energy states that matter and energy cannot be created or destroyed. Matter and energy are interchangeable.

Figure 2-3

Energy can be changed from one form to another.

REVIEW

1. Define the term *matter*.
2. Define the term *energy*, and name three forms of energy.
3. How are potential energy and kinetic energy different?

CHALLENGE When rust forms on an iron nail, the nail increases in mass. Using the Law of Conservation of Mass, how can you explain this increase?

Teaching Tip   Use the automobile as an example of conversions of various forms of energy. For example, stored chemical energy in the battery converts to electrical energy (introduced when the ignition key is turned on). The electrical energy converts to mechanical kinetic energy when the starting motor cranks the engine. Electricity flows to the spark plugs and ignites the gasoline and air mixture. Mechanical kinetic energy moves the car.

Tie-in/Language Arts   Have students research the meaning of the following prefixes and then list some forms of energy that use the prefixes: *thermo-*; *geo-*; *photo-*; *hydro-*.

3 REVIEW/REINFORCEMENT

1. Matter is anything that has mass and takes up space.
2. Energy is defined as the ability to do work; the forms of energy named will vary but may include radiant, electrical, chemical, atomic, nuclear, and mechanical.
3. Potential energy is stored energy, and kinetic energy is energy of motion.

Challenge   The iron in the nail did not increase in mass; however, moist oxygen in the air combined with the iron nail to increase the nail's mass.

2-2 DISPLAYING DATA

OBJECTIVES
Refer to pupil page 30.

VOCABULARY
Key terms: extrapolation, graph, interpolation
Other terms: atmospheres, dependent variable, independent variable, x-axis, y-axis

---

1 MOTIVATION

Daily newspapers report the high and low temperatures of major cities in this country and around the world. Have students collect data on the high or low temperature of several cities for one day. Let students select the cities they would like to compare. Have them prepare a data table with the high or low temperature for each city on that day. Then have them construct a bar graph of the same data, with the temperatures on the x-axis and the names of the cities on the y-axis. This should be done as a class, on the chalkboard. Ask students to compare the temperature of the different cities for the same day by using the data table and the bar graph. Students should realize that it is easier to make comparisons by using the graph.

2 CONCEPT DEVELOPMENT

Background   There are certain assumptions that should be taken into consideration regarding the data presented in Table 2-1. The temperature of the ice is 0°C, and the system is insulated. In addition, it should be noted that the water temperatures presented in the table have been rounded to the nearest degree.

After completing this section, you will be able to

- **construct** a graph.
- **use** the processes of interpolation and extrapolation.

The key terms in this section are
extrapolation
graph
interpolation

---

[1]Use a thermometer.

graphe (to draw)

You will make many observations in physical science. Some observations will tell you about such properties of matter as color, odor, shape, and texture. To make these observations, you will need only your senses. You will also make observations with the aid of tools such as the thermometer, the balance, and the metric ruler.

Some of the observations that you can make with your senses can be made more accurately if you use tools. You can measure the volume of liquids with a graduate, the mass of solids and liquids with a balance, and temperature changes with a thermometer. For example, suppose you place 100 mL of water in a glass and add one gram of ice. You can feel the glass and sense that it is colder than it was before the ice was added. When you add one more gram of ice, you can sense that the glass of water becomes even colder. How could you tell exactly how cold the glass of water is?[1]

Suppose the water temperature is 20°C before any ice was added. One gram of ice would lower the temperature to 19°C. A second gram of ice would lower the temperature to 18°C. You could continue to describe the data in this way, but it would be hard to understand. To make data easy to read, scientists organize data in tables. Table 2-1 shows the results of an experiment in which ice was added to 100 mL of water.

Table 2-1 *The Effect of Ice on Water Temperature*

Total Mass of Ice Used (g)	Temperature of Water (°C)
0	20
1	19
2	18
3	17
4	16
5	15

MAKING GRAPHS

The results of an experiment can often be presented in a graph. A **graph** is a display of data. When presented in a graph, information may be easier to read and easier to understand. Graphs can also be used to make predictions. Graphs can be drawn in many ways. The kind of graph used most often in science is the line graph. A line graph shows the relationship between two sets of numbers.

The graph in Figure 2-4 displays the data shown in Table 2-1. The amount of ice added to the water is shown on the horizontal line of the graph. The horizontal line is called the *x-axis*. The temperature of the water is shown on the vertical line of the graph. This vertical line is called the *y-axis*. Notice that all the divisions on an axis are equal. Each division on the x-axis is equal to 0.20 g. Each division on the y-axis is equal to 1°C.

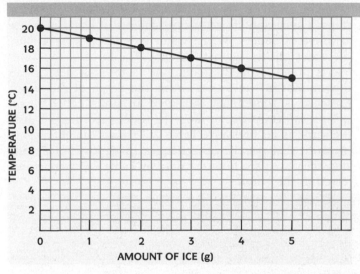

Figure 2-4

The effect of ice on the temperature of water.

Knowing how to draw a graph is an important skill. A graph should be neat and easy to read. You should always use a sharp pencil to get a fine line. The following are the basic steps in drawing a line graph.

1. Decide which set of numbers will be displayed on each axis.
2. Decide what the scale of each axis will be. Choose scales that are easy to plot and easy to read. It is not necessary to use the same scale for both axes. But on each axis all spaces must have the same value. Choose scales so that the graph fills as much of the sheet as possible, but be sure the axes will fit on the paper.
3. Draw and label the axes. For each axis, include the unit in which it is expressed.
4. Number the major divisions on the graph paper according to the chosen scales. Place the numbers outside the axes. Each scale can start at zero. However, there are cases where starting at zero is not practical. In such cases, start at a value just below the smallest number to be graphed.

Teaching Tip   Tell students that in many cases, one of the variables may have values beginning much higher than zero. In these cases the first value can be used as the origin.

Tie-in/Math   Have students use Figure 2-4 to determine the change in water temperature for each 3-g change in the mass of ice.

Enrichment Students are always concerned about grades that are curved. To enhance the concept of graphing, group and graph a set of grades. Show how the curve can be used to determine individual performances in relation to the performance of other students.

Review and Skill Masters

CHALLENGE/CRITICAL THINKING, pages 15–16. See page 25c in this book for answers.

5. Plot on the graph each pair of numbers from the data table. Represent each pair of data with a point.
6. Draw the line of best fit through the data points on the graph. If the points do not fall in a straight line, draw the best or most probable smooth line or curve through the points. Try to draw the line so that there are equal numbers of points above and below the line.
7. Title the graph.

The graph in Figure 2-6 was drawn by following these steps. This graph shows measurements of water pressure at different depths. When water is held back by a dam, the water pushes against the dam. The force of the water exerts pressure on the dam. The factor that determines the amount of water pressure is the depth of the water. Pressure is sometimes measured in units called *atmospheres* (atm). At the surface, the water pressure is 1 atm, the same as air pressure. Table 2-2 shows the changes in pressure that occur with changes in depth. Follow the steps below to see how the data in Table 2-2 were transferred to the graph.

Table 2-2 *Water Pressure*

Depth (m)	Pressure (atm)
0	1
20	3
40	5
60	7
80	9
100	11
120	13

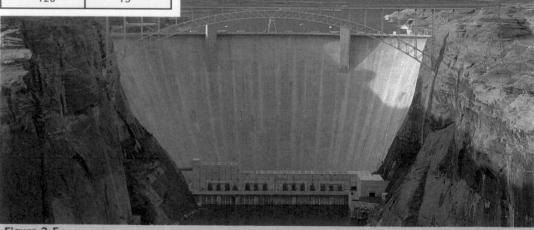

Figure 2-5

The water exerts pressure on the dam.

1. Decide which set of numbers will be displayed on each axis. The y-axis shows the *dependent variable*. These numbers depend on, or are the result of, the way an experiment is carried out. In this case the pressure exerted by the water depends on how deep the water is. The x-axis shows the *independent variable*. Depth does not depend on pressure. Thus, depth is shown on the x-axis, and pressure is shown on the y-axis.

2. Decide what the scale of each axis will be. A depth of 20 m is represented by 4 squares on the x-axis. Each square on the y-axis stands for 1 atm.
3. Draw and label the axes. Notice that these labels match the headings on the columns of the data table.
4. Number the divisions on each axis. Notice that only 20-m intervals are marked. Amounts between these points are not marked.
5. Plot on the graph each pair of numbers from the data table. At a depth of 0 m, the water pressure is 1 atm. To plot this point, find the 0-m mark on the x-axis. Find 1 atm on the y-axis. Follow the line up from the 0-m mark until it crosses the line for 1 atm. The intersection of these lines is marked with a point. Continue plotting points in this manner.
6. Draw the line of best fit through the data points. In this case, the line of best fit is a straight line. Small variations often are found in data. However, you should not bend the line to touch every point. These data show a steady increase in pressure, and thus, they should be represented by a straight line.
7. Title the graph.

When you look at the graph, you can see that as the depth of water increases, the pressure it exerts increases. This increase happens at a steady rate. Is it easier to see this pattern in a data table or in a graph? [1]

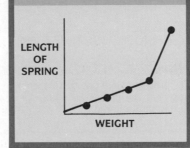

[1]A graph.

Figure 2-6

The effect of depth on water pressure.

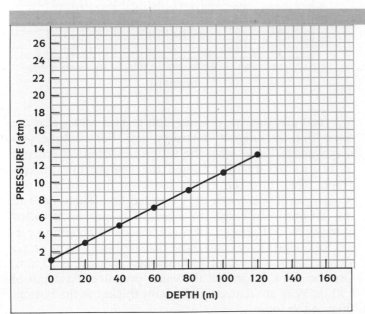

Thinking Skills

graphing data
Have students use the following data to prepare a graph of a runner's distance record.

Week	Distance ran
1	2 miles
2	3 miles
3	5 miles
4	5 miles
5	7 miles
6	8 miles
7	10 miles
8	13 miles
9	14 miles

Puzzler   The suspended weight must be great enough to stretch the spring beyond its elastic limit.

Transparency

The Teacher Resource Package includes a color transparency and a black-line master of Figures 2-6 and 2-7. You may wish to use these in your discussion of graphing.

USING GRAPHS

After the graph has been completed, it can be used to find out other information. Imagine, for example, that you want to know the pressure at a depth of 45 m. Table 2-2 does not list this information. But by using the graph, you can find an approximate answer. On the graph in Figure 2-7, find 45 m on the x-axis and then move upward until you reach the line. Next move across to the y-axis and read the pressure. The process just described is called interpolation. **Interpolation** is a way of finding information between values that are known. At a depth of 45 m, the water pressure is 5.5 atm. What is the water pressure at a depth of 85 m?[1]

inter- (between)

[1]9.5 atm.

Figure 2-7

The process of interpolation is shown in green. The process of extrapolation is shown in red.

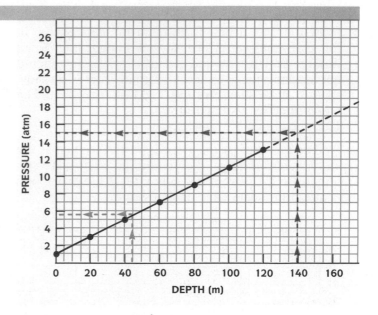

You can also use a line graph to find values that are not within the range of measured data. For example, you may want to know what the water pressure is at a depth of 140 m. To do this, extend the straight line on this graph. Then find the 140-m mark on the x-axis. Move upward until you reach the extended line. Then move to the left until you reach the y-axis. This process is called extrapolation. **Extrapolation** is a means of obtaining values for quantities beyond those that are known. The graph shows that at a depth of 140 m, water pressure is 15 atm. Use the graph to predict the water pressure at a depth of 150 m.[2] Why are dams usually built thicker at the bottom than at the top?[3]

[2]16 atm.
[3]Water pressure increases with depth, so dams are thickest at the bottom to withstand the greater pressure.

ACTIVITY   How Much Will a Spring Stretch?

OBJECTIVE
Draw a graph of the behavior of a spring that is subjected to varying forces.

MATERIALS
meterstick, ring stand, clamp, ring, steel spring, weight hanger, slotted gram masses

PROCEDURE
A. Draw a data table like the one shown.
B. Clamp a meterstick to a ring stand, as shown in the figure. Hang a spring from the ring, and hang a weight hanger from the bottom of the spring.
C. Note the reading on the meterstick at the bottom of the spring. Record this reading in the data table.
D. Place a slotted 50-g mass on the weight hanger. Note the reading on the meterstick at the bottom of the spring. Record this reading in the data table.
E. Find the total change in length of the spring by subtracting the reading in step **C** from your last reading. Record this change in the table.
F. Repeat steps **D** and **E** with 100-g, 150-g, 200-g, and 250-g masses.
G. A mass of 1000 g weighs about 10 N. Convert the masses you used to newtons by multiplying the mass by 10N/1000g. Follow this example:

$$50 \text{ g} \times \frac{10 \text{ N}}{1000 \text{ g}} = 0.5 \text{ N}$$

Record the weights in the data table.
H. Set up a graph with weight (in N) on the x-axis and the total change in the length of the spring (in cm) on the y-axis. The scale on the x-axis should extend from 0 N to 3.0 N. The scale on the y-axis should extend from 0 cm to a length greater than the last length you measured.
I. Plot the data on the graph.

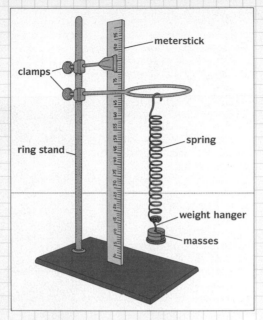

meterstick

clamps

ring stand

spring

weight hanger

masses

RESULTS AND CONCLUSIONS
1. Describe the line on your graph.
2. Extrapolate to predict the total change in length of the spring if a mass of 300 g were suspended from the spring.
3. Interpolate to find the total change in the length of the spring if a mass of 175 g were suspended from the spring.
4. What does the graph tell you about the relationship between force and the stretch of a spring?

EXTENSION
Set up a similar experiment using a heavy rubber band. Then repeat the experiment using two such rubber bands. Plot the data for each of the experiments on the same graph, and compare the results.

Total Mass of Slotted Masses (g)	Weight (N)	Reading of Meterstick (cm)	Total Change in Length of Spring (cm)
0	0		–
50			
100			
150			
200			
250			

ACTIVITY 30 minutes

PROCESS SKILLS
measuring, recording data, graphing data, predicting

Preparation   None required.

Background   Weight is the measure of the gravitational force on an object. It is measured in newtons (N). Mass is the measure of the quantity of matter in an object. It is measured in kilograms. At sea level an object that has a mass of 1 kg weighs 10 N. A mass of 100 g weighs 1 N.

Teaching Tip   In step **G**, remind students why they are multiplying the masses by 10 N/1000 g. Students will recall that an object with a mass of 1 kg, or 1000 g, weighs 10 N, or in other words, there are 10 N per 1000 g. Work out step **G** on the chalkboard with students so they will understand the logic behind the calculations.

Answers to Results and Conclusions
1. The line on the graph is a straight line that passes through the origin.
2. Answers will vary, depending on the gauge of the spring used, but the stretch distance will be in the same proportion to the applied force as shown on the graph.
3. Answers will vary, depending on the gauge of the spring used, but the stretch distance will be in the same proportion to the applied force as shown on the graph.
4. The amount of stretching varies directly with the force producing the stretching.

Extension   Answers will vary, depending on the materials used. All curves should be straight lines displaced because increasing the number of bands diminishes the stretch.

1. A graph is a pictorial display of data that allows scientists to see relationships among the data.
2. Interpolation is a way of obtaining values for quantities that are known. Extrapolation is a way of obtaining values for quantities beyond those that are known.
3. The number of books will be shown on the *x*-axis. Force will be shown on the *y*-axis. The line between the *x* and *y* axes will be a straight line sloping upward from left to right.
4. The force for 5 books is 0.75 N; a force of 1.8 N will push a stack of 12 books.

Challenge   The graph will still be a straight line sloping upward from left to right, but the slope will be less than in question **3**.

DO YOU KNOW?

Computers can produce line graphs, bar graphs, and pie charts quickly. They use colors and shading to show information. However, sharpness has always been a problem on computer-drawn graphs. This is because the lines are made up of hundreds of dots called pixels. Lines formed from pixels tend to have fuzzy edges. Now systems are being developed to improve the clarity of computer-drawn graphs.

Even with new improvements, computers still do not show enough clear detail to represent some scientific data. For these graphs, a plotter may be used. When hooked up to a computer, this device draws graphs, charts, and other figures. A plotter draws with black or colored pens. Some can draw as quickly as 38 cm per second. Desk-top plotters have become fairly inexpensive and are now available to everyday users.

Computers and plotters still cannot match the accuracy of the hand. A fuzzy line or tiny inkblot can change the meaning of a graph. To show scientific data many scientists prefer to draw graphs by hand.

ELEMENT PROPERTIES
ALL LAYERS

There are many uses of line graphs in physical science. For example, you can plot the mass of objects in terms of their volumes. You might plot how the volume of a gas changes with changes in temperature. Such graphs allow you to see the simple relationships between the two factors being plotted on the graph. Such relationships are very important in the formation of scientific laws.

REVIEW

Number of Books	Force (N)
2	0.3
4	0.6
6	0.9
8	1.2

1. What is the purpose of a graph?
2. Distinguish between the processes of interpolation and extrapolation.
3. The data shown are the results of an experiment in which stacks of books were pushed across a floor. As the number of books on the stack increased, the force needed to push them also increased. Draw a graph to display these data.
4. Use your graph from question **3** to find the amount of force needed to move five books. Extend the graph to find the number of books that could be pushed by a force of 1.8 N.

CHALLENGE Predict how your graph from question **3** would change if the floor were polished so that less force was needed to slide the books.

2-3 USING MATHEMATICS

Knowledge in science is based on accurate observations. A **measurement** is an observation that has a numerical value. When you measure a physical quantity, you compare it with a standard quantity called a unit. For example, if you measure an object's length as 1.78 m, you are using the meter as the unit of comparison. Saying that the object's length is 1.78 is incomplete. This statement could mean 1.78 yards, feet, decimeters, or meters. Every measurement must be expressed by a number and a unit.

There are many tools for taking measurements. Many of these, such as the metric ruler, thermometer, barometer, and graduate, are marked with a scale. The scale is marked to give readings in appropriate units.

ACCURACY

In making any measurement, you want to be as accurate as possible. **Accuracy** is the degree of closeness between a measured value and a true value. Accuracy depends on using good techniques and highly accurate tools. Look at the timers shown in Figure 2-8. Which would give the race results with greater accuracy?[1]

When scientists record a measurement, they note how certain it is. They indicate this certainty by the way they write the number. In a measurement the numbers that a scientist reads and estimates on a scale are called **significant digits**. These include all the certain digits and one doubtful digit. The doubtful digit is based on the observer's estimate of a fraction of the smallest division on a scale.

After completing this section, you will be able to

- **explain** how significant digits express the accuracy of a measurement.
- **use** scientific notation.

The key terms in this section are
accuracy
measurement
scientific notation
significant digits

accuratus (done with care)

[1]The digital timer is more accurate.

Figure 2-8
Races like this are carefully timed.

OBJECTIVES
Refer to pupil page 37.

VOCABULARY
Key terms: accuracy, measurement, scientific notation, significant digits

1 MOTIVATION

Have students bring in measuring cups from home, and ask students to determine the accuracy of these cups. To stress the importance of standardization, provide a set of measuring cups to be used as a standard, and have students compare the accuracy of other sets of measuring cups with the standard.

2 CONCEPT DEVELOPMENT

Background   Measurement is a method of expressing knowledge in a form that is standard. Observations expressed in terms of numerical values (quantitative data) are less ambiguous and, therefore, usually much more valuable than qualitative observations such as "large" or "small."

Demonstration   Demonstrate the value of accuracy by using two balances of varying accuracy limits to determine the mass of several objects.

Teaching Tip   Remind students that the metric system allows for standardization and that its use simplifies communication and trade with other nations.

Enrichment   Have students use a triple-beam balance and a double-pan balance, to determine the mass of the same objects, for the purpose of comparing results.

Thinking Skills

measuring
Have students measure 10 mL of water in a graduate and determine its mass with two different balances—one accurate to 0.1 g, and the other accurate to 0.01 g. Have students compare the degree of accuracy in terms of significant digits.

If you count the number of students in your class, there is no uncertain value in the number you get. There may be, say, exactly 25 students in your science class. Also, there is no uncertainty in the number of centimeters in one meter. By definition, 100 centimeters equals one meter. Numbers that result from direct counting or defined values are exact numbers.

Numbers that result from measuring devices are never exact. In Figure 2-9 the length of a book is being measured with a meterstick marked in centimeters. The end of the book falls between the 23-cm and 24-cm marks. You can be certain about the first two digits in the length—the 2 and the 3—but the third digit is doubtful. A reasonable estimate of the book's end position might be 0.6 of the distance between the 23-cm and 24-cm marks. Thus the length of the book to three significant digits is 23.6 cm. But the third number might be any number from 5 to 7, depending on the observer.

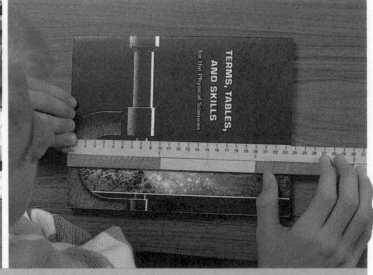

Figure 2-9

This measurement includes two certain digits and one doubtful digit.

In any number the last significant digit is uncertain. If the meterstick shown in Figure 2-9 were marked in tenths of a centimeter, you might measure the book as 23.57 cm long. Now there are four significant digits. Three digits are certain and one is uncertain.

Scientists often repeat their measurements several times to be sure that the numbers are accurate. Suppose you want to test the strength of a kind of wire used in a piano. You would hang weights from a piece of the wire and keep adding weights until the wire breaks. If you repeat this test with several pieces of wire you might have some variation in your data. Which number should you use? The best number to use would be an average of all the numbers you record.

Table 2-3 shows the results of an experiment to test the strength of wire. The average was calculated by adding all of the measurements and then dividing the total by the number of measurements used.

Figure 2-10

The stronger the wire, the more weight it can hold.

Table 2-3 *Strength of a Wire*

Wire	Weight (N)
1	1730
2	1720
3	1700
4	1740
5	1710
Average	1720

RATIOS

A ratio shows a relationship between two quantities. For example, the speed of a car is measured in kilometers per hour, km/h. If a car is driven 80 km in one hour, the speed would be written as 80 km/h. If another car is driven the same distance in two hours, the speed would be written as 80 km/2 h, or 40 km/h.

Writing numbers in ratio form makes it easy to compare data. If a car was driven 301 km in 3.5 h, it would be difficult to compare this speed with the speed of another car. However, by dividing 301 km by 3.5 h, you can write the speed of this car as 86 km/h. Which of the cars listed in Table 2-4 traveled fastest?[1]

[1]Car 3 traveled fastest.

Table 2-4 *Speeds of Cars*

Car	Distance (km)	Time (h)	Speed (km/h)
1	80	1	80
2	80	2	40
3	301	3.5	86

Tie-in/Math   Have students do arithmetic operations with numbers expressed in scientific notation.

PROCESS SKILLS
measuring, recording data, comparing

Preparation   None required.

Answers to Results and Conclusions

1. The area of one face of a cube is quadrupled when the length of each side is doubled.
2. It is multiplied by 4.
3. It is multiplied by 8.
4. As the size of the cube increases, the volume increases at a greater rate than does the surface area. As a result, the ratio of surface area to volume decreases.

Extension   Volume will be shown on the *x*-axis. Surface area will be shown on the *y*-axis. The graph has the following coordinates plotted: (1,6) (8,24) (27,54) (64,96) (125,150) (216,216)

ACTIVITY   Ratio of Surface Area to Volume of a Cube

OBJECTIVE
Demonstrate the relationship between the surface area and volume of a cube.

MATERIALS
1-centimeter-grid paper, metric ruler, scissors, tape

PROCEDURE
A. Make a data table like the one shown.
B. On a piece of graph paper, draw the pattern for an opened-up cube that is 1 cm on each side. Follow the pattern shown in the figure. Be sure that every face of the cube is 1 cm on each side.

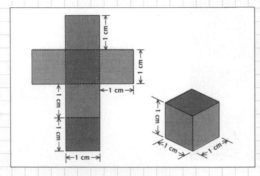

C. Calculate the area of one face of the cube. Area is equal to length times width. Record your answer in the data table.
D. The surface area of a cube is the number of square units on its six faces. Therefore, the total surface area of a cube is equal to six times the area of one face. Calculate the surface area of the cube, and record your answer in the data table.
E. Calculate the volume of the cube. Volume is equal to length times width times height. Record your answer in the data table.
F. Repeat steps **B–E** for cubes that are 2 cm, 3 cm, 4 cm, 5 cm, and 6 cm on each side.
G. Cut out the patterns and fold them to form six cubes. Tape each cube together.

Length of One Side (cm)	Area of One Face (cm²)	Total Surface Area (cm²)	Volume (cm³)
1			
2			
3			
4			
5			
6			

RESULTS AND CONCLUSIONS
1. What happens to the area of one face of a cube when the length of each side is doubled?
2. What happens to the surface area of a cube when the length of each side is doubled?
3. What happens to the volume of a cube when the length of each side is doubled?
4. What happens to the ratio of surface area to volume as the size of the cube increases?

EXTENSION
Make a graph of surface area and volume data. Place the volume on the x-axis and the surface area on the y-axis.

SCIENTIFIC NOTATION
Physical scientists often use very large numbers or very small numbers. For example, the diameter of the sun is 1,390,000,000 m. To simplify large numbers, scientists write them as multiples of ten. In the example above, the seven zeros show that 139 has been multiplied by 10 seven times. This multiplication can be shown as a power of 10, written as 10^7. In **scientific notation**, a number is written as the product of a coefficient (koh uh FIHSH uhnt) between 1 and 10 and a power of ten. The number that indicates the power of ten is called an exponent (EHK spohnuhnt). The diameter of the sun is written as 1.39×10^9. The coefficient 1.39 shows the significant digits in the

original number. The exponent 9 tells you that the coefficient is multiplied by 10 nine times. In other words, 10^9 stands for nine decimal places after the decimal point of the coefficient.

A number much smaller than 1 and expressed in scientific notation will have a negative exponent. The sun contains many helium atoms. Each of these atoms has a diameter of 0.000000000244 m. This number would be written as 2.44×10^{-10}. The exponent -10 tells you that the coefficient must be divided by 10 ten times. In other words, 10^{-10} stands for ten decimal places in front of the decimal point of the coefficient.

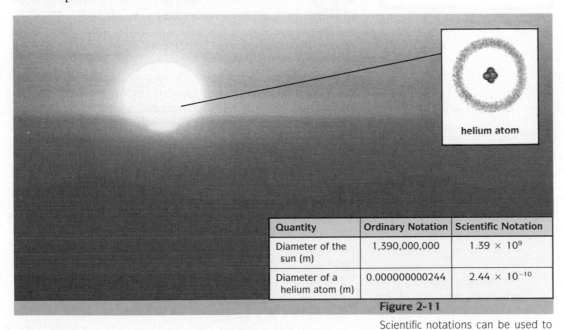

helium atom

Quantity	Ordinary Notation	Scientific Notation
Diameter of the sun (m)	1,390,000,000	1.39×10^9
Diameter of a helium atom (m)	0.000000000244	2.44×10^{-10}

Figure 2-11

Scientific notations can be used to express numbers that are very large or very small.

REVIEW

1. How do measurements differ from other observations?
2. A penny is found to have a mass of 2.09 g. How many digits in this measurement are certain?
3. Round off the mass of the penny in question **2** to two significant digits. Round off this mass to one significant digit.
4. Express each of the following numbers in scientific notation.
   a. 0.0369   **c.** 15   **e.** 29.6
   b. 205.7   **d.** 0.000401   **f.** 0.12

CHALLENGE To add a group of numbers in scientific notation, you must change them so that they are all multiplied by the same power of ten. Add the following numbers: 1.0×10^2; 6.5×10^1; 3.7×10^3.

1. Measurements have numerical values that are compared to standard units.
2. Two.
3. 2.1 g; 2 g.
4. a. 3.69×10^{-2}.
   b. 2.057×10^2.
   c. 1.5×10^1.
   d. 4.01×10^{-4}.
   e. 2.96×10^1.
   f. 1.2×10^{-1}.

Challenge $0.1 \times 10^3 + 0.065 \times 10^3 + 3.7 \times 10^3 = 3.865 \times 10^3$

Review and Skill Masters

SKILL, page 14.
See page 25b in this book for answers.

2-4 LABORATORY SAFETY

pages 42–46

2-4 LABORATORY SAFETY

OBJECTIVES
Refer to pupil page 42.

1 MOTIVATION

Have students think about accidents that could occur at a summer camp, at the beach, at school, or on the highway. On the chalkboard, list the causes of each, and have students suggest ways in which each accident could be prevented. Compare any appropriate ideas with the rules that apply in a laboratory setting.

After completing this section, you will be able to

- **list** general safety guidelines for the physical science laboratory.
- **list** laboratory safety equipment.
- **describe** the technique for lighting and adjusting a Bunsen burner.

The activities that you perform in the laboratory can be an important part of your study of physical science. The physical science laboratory is a safe area to conduct activities if you are careful and use common sense.

Someone driving a car must pay attention to the road and be ready to act in case of an emergency. The driver cannot be careless. The same is true when doing an experiment. You must pay attention to what you are doing at all times. You must be prepared before you begin an activity. You should read the entire activity before you do it. When reading the activity, pay special attention to any caution statement in the activity. Know the rules for behavior that apply while performing an experiment.

Most accidents in the physical science laboratory result from carelessness. Accidents can happen in the laboratory, just as they can happen in the kitchen, on the sports field, in the swimming pool, or on the highway. But accidents can be prevented. Professional football players would not enter a game without wearing protective equipment. Drivers take lessons and pass tests to be sure that they can handle an automobile safely. In the same way, you need to know the safety guidelines for your activities in the physical science laboratory.

The laboratory is a place for scientific work. There should be no fooling around, pushing, or running. Do not eat or drink anything in the laboratory. Never smell or taste anything in the laboratory unless directed to do so by your teacher. When you are directed to smell something, fan the odor toward your nose, as shown in Figure 2-12. Why should you not inhale fumes directly?[1]

[1]Fumes could have an unpleasant odor or could be harmful in large amounts.

Figure 2-12

This is the correct method for smelling fumes. Smell chemicals only when directed to do so.

Poster

The Teacher Resource Package includes a poster that shows safety symbols and safe laboratory practices. You may wish to display this poster in your classroom.

Know the emergency procedures and fire drill regulations. Learn the location and use of fire extinguishers, safety showers, eye washes, fire blankets, and any other safety equipment in the lab. Report any accident to the teacher immediately. Flush with water any minor skin burns and chemical spills on skin, clothes, or lab benches. If any substances get into your eye, flush the eye with water, using an eyewash.

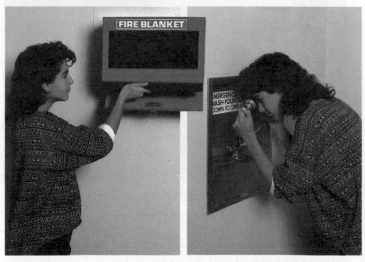

Do only those activities assigned to you or your group, and use only the equipment and materials assigned. Read all labels before using a chemical. You should not work in the laboratory unless your teacher is present. There should always be someone with you, in case you need help in an emergency.

It is important to keep your work area clean. Put away any books or notebooks that you will not be using during an activity. At the end of an activity, clean your work area and dispose of materials as directed by your teacher. Wash your hands when you have finished your work in the laboratory.

You should read every step of an activity before you begin to do any work in the laboratory. Look for safety cautions and be prepared to follow them. Wear safety goggles when the activity directs you to do so. It is best to wear the goggles throughout the activity. Even if you are doing a procedure that may not require safety goggles, your neighbor may not be on the same step. If you keep the goggles on for the entire period, you will be sure of your safety.

Figure 2-13

Laboratory safety equipment.

Background   A laboratory is only as safe as its least safe person. It is the responsibility of each person in the laboratory to practice agreed-upon safety measures. Teachers must set examples for safety and find ways to ensure that each lab participant behaves appropriately. Check with your department chairperson about state and local safety regulations and about first-aid and emergency procedures.

Teaching Tip   Have students prepare skits in which they act out procedures to be followed in case of laboratory accidents. Make sure students explain where the appropriate kinds of safety equipment are located and how to use the equipment. Have the class judge each skit on its adequacy in imparting the proper safety education. Quiz students on the proper safety procedures.

Enrichment Have students assist you in the development of safety rules. Have students keep the rules handy in their notebook. From time to time, ask them to demonstrate the use of safety devices such as a fire blanket and fire extinguisher.

Teaching Tip Safety procedures are a part of all scientific investigations; they must be stressed throughout the year, not isolated in a single teaching unit.

Figure 2-14

What safety rules is this student following?[1]

[1]Wearing goggles and apron; tying back long hair; keeping work area neat.

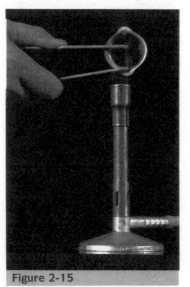

Figure 2-15

Use a striker to light a burner.

Wear protective clothing when you are directed to do so. Long hair and loose clothing should be tied back, especially when you are working with an open flame.

An important reason for reading an activity before beginning work is that you should know what materials and techniques are needed. If you do not understand any part of the directions, ask your teacher for help before you start the activity. You will learn some new techniques as you do the activities in the book. Some techniques will be used more often than others.

In some activities you will need to heat substances. A hot plate can be used in many activities, but sometimes a Bunsen burner is needed. A Bunsen burner uses natural gas for fuel. Always be sure that the tubing that connects the burner to the gas jet is securely attached at both ends. Also check to be certain that the hose has no cracks or holes. Check to see that the burner is in good condition.

Natural gas will begin to burn if it is exposed to a spark. A striker is a device used to light a gas flame by making a spark. Before you turn on the gas, check that the striker will make a spark. When you are ready to light the burner, turn on the gas, hold the striker at the top of the burner, and make a spark. If the gas does not light after a few sparks have been tried, turn off the gas and check the striker. Ask your teacher for assistance in adjusting the striker or the gas.

ACTIVITY   Safety in the Laboratory

OBJECTIVE
Identify and **locate** safety equipment and emergency exits in the laboratory.

MATERIALS
graph paper, metric ruler, colored pencil

PROCEDURE
A. Draw a scale diagram of the laboratory. Include the location of furniture, cabinets, wall units, windows, and doors. Label each object.
B. Make a list of all safety equipment in the laboratory. Mark their locations on your diagram, using a different symbol for each one. Make a key of the symbols on the diagram.
C. Use symbols to show the locations of all electrical outlets and gas outlets.
D. Mark the position of your lab station.
E. Use a colored pencil to map out the quickest and safest emergency route from your lab station to the hallway.

RESULTS AND CONCLUSIONS
1. How many doors are in the laboratory?
2. According to your emergency exit plan, how many other lab stations would you pass as you leave the room?
3. Does the laboratory contain any fire extinguishers? If so, how many are there, and what do they contain?

ACTIVITY 25 minutes

PROCESS SKILLS
observing, making diagrams

Preparation You may want to discuss step *B* with students and decide with them the symbols they will use. This will provide uniformity and make location of equipment easier. The same symbols should be used as labels on the safety equipment.

Teaching Tip Encourage students to keep their completed diagrams in their notebook, to be referred to when necessary.

Answers to Results and Conclusions
1. Answers will vary.
2. Answers will vary.
3. All laboratories should contain at least one fire extinguisher. The fire extinguisher will most likely contain carbon dioxide.

The mixture of gas and air going into the Bunsen burner determines the size and heat of the flame. You can control the amount of gas being burned by adjusting the lever on the gas jet. You can control the amount of air going into the burner by changing the size of the air holes at the base of the burner. As gas moves through the burner, it does not leak out through these holes. Instead, it draws in air from the room. Adjust the air holes until you have a steady blue flame that does not waver. The flame shown in Figure 2-16A is not adjusted properly, so it is not steady. The flame shown in Figure 2-16B is adjusted properly. It will provide even, reliable heat.

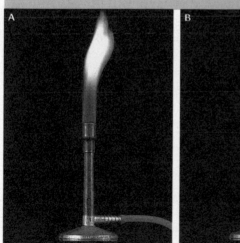
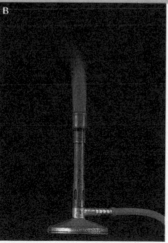

Figure 2-16

Incorrectly adjusted flame (*A*). Correctly adjusted flame (*B*).

Background   The eight most common accidents that take place in the classroom laboratory are burns, cuts, fainting, fire, foreign matter in eyes, poisoning, severe bleeding, and spills on skin. Familiarize students with the best method of handling each of these accidents.

Demonstration   Demonstrate the appropriate techniques for the safe use of a Bunsen burner and other heating devices that will be used in the laboratory.

Enrichment   Ask students what they should do if they discover that an air-gas mixture has accumulated in an oven because of a faulty pilot light or because the gas was turned on accidently.

Thinking Skills

comparing
Have students compare the flame of a Bunsen burner with that of a candle. How are they alike? How are they different?

3 REVIEW/REINFORCEMENT

1. Because any number of accidents can happen, and someone should be present in case help is needed.
2. By adjusting the air holes until you have a steady blue flame that does not waver.
3. To be familiar with the rules of behavior that apply while performing the experiment, and to be familiar with any caution statements.

Challenge   The material spilled could be flammable; the material spilled could release toxic fumes that are flammable; you may become occupied with the cleanup, which might cause the Bunsen burner's flame to go out allowing gas to escape into the classroom.

46

When an activity requires the use of a Bunsen burner, you must be very careful. Keep papers, hair, and clothing away from the flame. Never leave the burner unattended. If the flame blows out, turn off the gas immediately. When you no longer need to use the burner, turn off the gas and the flame will go out.

Figure 2-17

The correct method for heating a test tube. Never point a test tube at yourself or anyone else.

In some activities you will be directed to heat a test tube in the flame of a Bunsen burner. To do this, use a test-tube holder to position the test tube in the tip of the flame. The test tube should be kept at an angle, as shown in Figure 2-17. Move the test tube up and down through the flame so that the whole length is heated. If you heat only the bottom, the test tube could boil over. As you heat a test tube, do not look directly into it. Never point a test tube at anyone. Why is this important?[1]

[1]If the test tube boils over, the contents could burn someone.

REVIEW

1. Why should you not work in the laboratory alone?
2. How is the flame of a Bunsen burner adjusted?
3. Give two reasons why an activity should be read before work begins.

CHALLENGE If you spill a substance on yourself or on your work area while your Bunsen burner is on, your lab partner should turn off the burner immediately. Give three reasons why it is important to do so.

46

CHAPTER SUMMARY

The main ideas in this chapter are listed below. Read these statements before you answer the Chapter Review questions.

- Matter is anything that has mass and takes up space. (2-1)

- Properties are characteristics that help to distinguish one kind of matter from another. (2-1)

- The Law of Conservation of Mass states that in physical and chemical changes, mass is neither created nor destroyed. (2-1)

- Energy is the ability to do work. The two types of energy are potential energy and kinetic energy. (2-1)

- The Law of Conservation of Energy states that energy cannot be created or destroyed but may be changed from one form to another. (2-1)

- The Law of Conservation of Matter and Energy states that matter and energy are interchangeable. (2-1)

- A graph is a display of data. Graphs can be used for both interpolation and extrapolation. (2-2)

- Interpolation is a way of finding information between values that are known. (2-2)

- Extrapolation is a means of obtaining values for quantities beyond those that are known. (2-2)

- Accuracy is the degree of closeness between a measured value and the true value of some quantity. (2-3)

- Significant digits are the numbers that a scientist reads and estimates in a measurement. (2-3)

- It is important to read and follow all directions in an activity, especially safety instructions. (2-4)

- Many activities will include instructions to use safety goggles and other safety equipment. (2-4)

- Before a Bunsen burner is lighted, the gas connections, the burner itself, and the striker should be checked for leaks or damage. (2-4)

- When heating a test tube over a flame, do not point the test tube at yourself or anyone else. (2-4)

The key terms in this chapter are listed below. Use each term in a sentence that shows the meaning of the term.

accuracy	interpolation	matter
energy	kinetic energy	measurement
extrapolation	Law of Conservation of Energy	potential energy
force	Law of Conservation of Mass	scientific notation
graph	mass	significant digits

Review and Skill Masters

VOCABULARY REVIEW, page 11.
See page 25b in this book for answers.

VOCABULARY

1. interpolation
2. graph
3. matter
4. kinetic energy
5. extrapolation
6. energy
7. potential energy
8. accuracy
9. mass
10. scientific notation
11. Law of Conservation of Energy
12. measurement

CONCEPTS

1. Density, melting point, boiling point, color, odor, hardness.
2. Work is any process in which matter is moved by the action of a force.
3. Potential energy gives an object the potential to do work. Any object in motion has kinetic energy and is able to do work.
4. Energy from food is stored in the muscles, to be used later to do work.
5. Matter and energy are interchangeable.
6. A graph allows you to see relationships in the data that can be used to make predictions.
7. The dependent variable represents the numbers that depend on or are the result of the way in which the experiment is carried out. The independent variable represents numbers that do not depend on the way in which the experiment is carried out.
8. Because you can obtain values for quantities beyond those that are known and see the relationship between two factors.

Review and Skill Masters

CHAPTER REVIEW, pages 12–13.
See page 25b in this book for answers.

Chapter Review

VOCABULARY

1. A way of obtaining values for quantities between known values is called _____ .
2. A/An _____ is a visual display of data.
3. Anything that takes up space and has mass is called _____ .
4. Energy of motion is called _____ .
5. _____ is a means of obtaining values for quantities beyond those that are known.
6. _____ is the ability to do work.
7. _____ is stored energy.
8. The degree of closeness between measured values and the true values is the _____ of the data.
9. The amount of matter in an object is called its _____ .
10. _____ is a way of expressing very large or very small numbers so they are easier to work with.
11. The _____ states that energy cannot be created or destroyed but can be changed from one form to another.
12. An observation that has a numerical value assigned to it is called a/an _____ .

CONCEPTS

1. List three properties that help to distinguish one kind of matter from another. (2-1)
2. How are force and work related? (2-1)
3. How are kinetic energy and potential energy related? (2-1)
4. Why can food be described as containing potential energy? (2-1)
5. Why is it possible to combine the Law of Conservation of Mass and the Law of Conservation of Energy into one law? (2-1)
6. How is a graph different from a data table? (2-2)
7. How is the dependent variable different from the independent variable on a graph? (2-2)
8. Why is extrapolation useful? (2-2)
9. Why is the last digit in a measurement usually not accurate? (2-3)
10. Round off each of the following numbers to three significant digits. (2-3)
    a. 9.7647   **b.** 23.546   **c.** 358.72
11. Express the following numbers in scientific notation. (2-3)
    a. 0.000017   **b.** 175,800,000,000

12. Name three pieces of safety equipment in a laboratory. (2-4)
13. What device is used to light a Bunsen burner? (2-4)
14. What precautions should be taken in the laboratory when working with an open flame? (2-4)
15. Why should test tubes that are being heated always be tilted away from anyone in the laboratory? (2-4)

APPLICATION/ CRITICAL THINKING

1. Describe the energy changes in a baseball from the time it is hit by a bat to the time it hits the ground in the outfield.
2. In the activity in Section 2-3, you determined the surface area and the volume of several cubes. What is the ratio of surface area to volume of a cube that measures 6 cm on each side? How many cubes with a side of 6 cm would it take to build a cube with a side of 12 cm? What is the ratio of surface area to volume of this new cube?
3. Would interpolation or extrapolation of data on a graph be more reliable? Why?
4. The data in the following table represent the relationship between the volume and temperature of a gas. Draw a graph of this data, with temperature on the x-axis. What is the volume of the gas at 5°C? What would be the volume of the gas at 50°C?

Temperature (°C)	Volume (L)
0	10.0
10	10.4
20	10.7
30	11.1
40	11.5

EXTENSION

1. Do research on the different types of fire extinguishers and their special uses. What type of fire extinguisher is found in your lab?
2. Look up the Occupational Safety and Health Administration (OSHA). Find out why this government agency was formed.
3. Do library research on Bernoulli's principle. What does this principle have to do with the air control on a Bunsen burner?

READINGS

Harper, P. *The Timetable of Technology*. New York: Hearst Books, 1982.

Lu, Cary. "Micros Get Graphic." *High Technology*, March 1986, p. 18.

Woodruff, Bobby J. *Terms, Tables, and Skills for the Physical Sciences*. Morristown, N.J.: Silver Burdett Co., 1966.

9. Because it is based on the observer's estimated fraction of the smallest division on a scale.
10. **a.** 9.76. **b.** 23.5. **c.** 359.
11. **a.** 1.7×10^{-5}. **b.** 1.758×10^{11}.
12. Fire extinguisher, fire blanket, safety shower, eye wash.
13. Striker.
14. Long hair and loose clothing should be tied back, and safety goggles should be worn.
15. The test tube should be tilted so that the contents will be evenly heated. The test tube should be pointed away from people so that if it does boil over, the contents will not burn someone.

APPLICATION/CRITICAL THINKING

1. The ball acquires potential energy from the moving bat; the potential energy is transformed into the kinetic energy of the moving ball; the kinetic energy of the moving ball is transformed into a small amount of heat energy (from friction) as the ball moves through the air and into more heat energy (from friction) and sound energy when the ball hits the ground.
2. 1:1; 8; 1:2.
3. If the curve on the graph is a straight line, both interpolation and extrapolation will give reliable results. If the curve is not a straight line, extrapolation is not as reliable as interpolation.
4. 10.2L; 11.8L.

Test Masters

CHAPTER TEST, pages 5–8.
See page 25d in this book for answers.

Science in Careers

A physicist is a scientist who studies matter and energy. There are many areas in physics, and most physicists become experts in just one. For example, some physicists study light and other types of radiation. Other physicists study the nuclei of atoms.

Nuclear physicists may perform experiments and use equipment such as nuclear reactors and particle accelerators. Other physicists do not run experiments but instead do complex calculations and formulate hypotheses. The main tool for this type of research is usually the computer.

Many physicists conduct research and teach at universities. Others design and test products in private industry.

Most research jobs in physics require an advanced degree, usually a Ph.D. If you are interested in being a physicist, you should take courses in physics and chemistry in high school.■

Physicist

In the past most of the products that people used were made by the people themselves or by craftworkers. Each product was checked as it was made.

Today most products are factory-made. Often there are too many products to check that each one is without flaws. However, by checking a portion of the products, it is possible to find and correct defects.

Testing products is the job of a quality-control technician.

The tests may be complex, or they may be as simple as seeing that a light will turn on and off.

A quality-control technician must have a high school diploma and may also need a two-year college certificate. On-the-job training is also provided. Most of these jobs are in private industry. If you are interested in being a quality-control technician, you should take courses in shop in high school.■

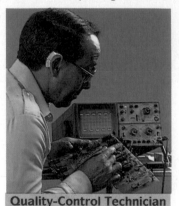
Quality-Control Technician

People in Science

Dr. Chien-Shiung Wu, Physicist

Scientific research can be compared to working on a jigsaw puzzle. Several different researchers may contribute to the solution of complex problems. Dr. Chien-Shiung Wu contributed the missing piece of information in just such a problem.

For many years, scientists had believed that beta particles flew off in random directions from the nuclei of radioactive atoms. A beta particle is a high-speed electron that is emitted as a radioactive element decays. Then, two young scientists, Dr. Lee and Dr. Yang, theorized that beta particles were emitted not in random directions but in specific patterns. But their theory lacked proof.

Dr. Lee and Dr. Yang took their problem to Dr. Wu, who was known for her experimental work. Dr. Wu designed and performed the crucial experiment that proved Dr. Lee and Dr. Yang's theory to be correct.

Dr. Wu has received many honors for her work. Today she is a professor emeritus at Columbia University.■

Issues and Technology

Some people would like to make the metric system the standard system of measurement in the United States. They want to replace the English system of measurement — feet, pounds, and gallons — in use now. The metric system is easier to use and many people in the world already use it. Many people in the United States do not want to change to metric: they say it would be confusing and costly.

One reason some people want to get rid of the English system is because it is so complex, with its many different units. The complexities come from the fact that this system is very old. Like people now, people long ago needed ways to measure everyday things like the size of fields or the weight of things they sold. But they only had very simple ways to make these measurements. Monarchs often set standards of measurement for their kingdoms. The system of measurement based on inches, feet, and pounds is called the English system because English monarchs defined many of the units used.

Some English measuring units were based on the bodies of monarchs. The inch, for instance, was orginally the width of the monarch's finger. A cup was the amount of liquid held in the monarch's drinking cup.

Other units were based on simple measuring methods available then. The size of the acre, a unit of area, was defined as the amount of land that a team of oxen could plow in a day.

The English system was just one of *many* old systems of

Roman Standards of Measurement

1 Roman foot

1 Roman pace
1000 paces = 1 Roman mile

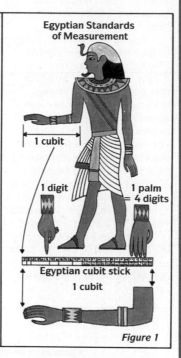

Egyptian Standards of Measurement

1 cubit

1 digit

1 palm = 4 digits

Egyptian cubit stick
1 cubit

Figure 1

measurement. But most of them no longer exist. Figure 1 shows some early Egyptian and Roman units of measurement and their sources. Notice the drawing of the cubit stick. Although early measurement standards were based on body parts, measuring tools were available.

APPLYING CRITICAL THINKING SKILLS

1. What are most of these units of measurement based on?
2. Are any of the units we now use similar to these old measurements?
3. Suppose a unit of measurement were based on the width of the knee and everyone could use his or her own knee as a ruler. Would there be any problems? Suppose each President were to base

measurements only on his or her own body? What would happen when a new President was elected?

When the French developed the metric system in the late 1700s, it was a major change. The metric system was based on simple and exact standards that could be used everywhere. That way, everyone would always measure things in the same way.

The basic unit of metric length, the meter, was set at 1/10,000,000 the distance from the equator to the North Pole. The basic unit of mass, the gram, was the weight of a cube of water 0.01 m on a side. The basic unit of volume, the liter, was the amount that would fit in a container 0.1 m on a side.

The following thinking skills will be applied in answering questions.
- *Interpreting* data.
- *Comparing* ancient systems of measurement with the English system of measurement.
- *Predicting* the effects of having a system of measurement that could change every four or eight years.

Answers to questions
1. Most of these measurements are based on parts of the human body.
2. The English measurement known as the foot is similar to an old standard unit of measurement.
3. Students' answers will vary. If each person used his or her own body as a standard for measurement, there would be no consistency in measurements. It would be impossible to communicate regarding the size of any object, to purchase standard parts for equipment, or to carry on scientific research as we know it. If standard units were based on each President in office, the standard would change every four or eight years. This change would cause great confusion and expense.

The following thinking skills will be applied in answering questions.
- *Relating* the English system of measurement to the metric system.
- *Comparing* English units with metric units.
- *Predicting* the effects of changing to the metric system.

Answers to questions

1. A sweater or light jacket would be appropriate outdoor clothing at 10°C.
2. Average room temperature is about 20°C.
3. At 100 kilometers per hour, you would be speeding in a 55-miles-per-hour zone. At 100 kilometers per hour, you would be traveling at 62 miles per hour.
4. If the car's odometer were in metric units, the odometer would advance faster than if it were in miles.
5. A liter is larger than a quart. If the United States were to use metric units, milk could still be sold in the same size containers that are used now. The amount of milk in a quart container would simply be less than one liter. In time the size of milk cartons could be changed to hold exactly one liter.
6. Answers will vary.

The same prefixes are used with all unit names. For example, *milli-* means "one thousandth," *centi-* means "one hundredth," and *deci-* means "one tenth."

People who want to change to the metric system say the simplicity of this system makes it easy to use. They point out that because of the strange way the English system came about, its units have very complicated relationships with one another. For instance, in English volume units there are 3 teaspoons in a tablespoon, 16 tablespoons in a cup, and 2 cups in a pint. If you wanted to know how many teaspoons are in a pint, you would need to do a bit of arithmetic.

There are no such complexities in the metric system. Every unit is found by multiplying or dividing by 10 or a multiple of 10.

Even though the metric system is easier to use for mathematical conversions, people who do not want to switch point out that the change to metric would still take a long time to get used to. Certain ways in which people deal with measurement become instinctive. For instance, if someone says a shelf is 3 feet long or that it is 70°F outside, you probably have a pretty good idea of what that means. Getting that same familiarity with metric units will take time. Figure 2 compares English and metric measurements.

APPLYING CRITICAL THINKING SKILLS

1. The temperature outside is 10°C. What kind of outdoor clothing would be appropriate for this type of weather?
2. In degrees Celsius, what would be the average room temperature inside your house?
3. If you were driving at 100 kilometers per hour and the speed limit was 55 miles per hour, would you be speeding?
4. The odometer of a car shows the distance the car has been driven. If your car's odometer were in metric units, would the total number of kilometers driven advance faster or slower than would the total number of miles?
5. Is a liter larger or smaller than a quart? If the United States were to use metric units, do you think the sizes of milk cartons would be changed? What would you suggest?
6. Would changing to the metric system be difficult for you? Why or why not?

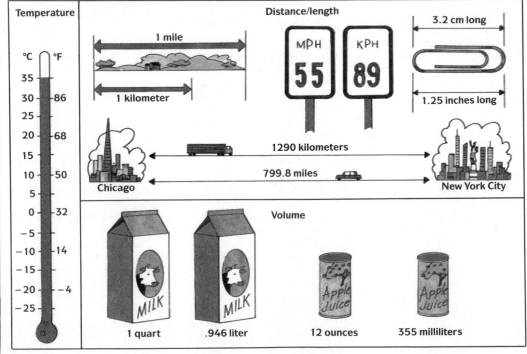

Figure 2

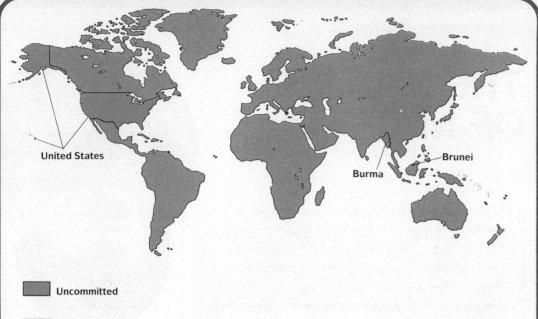

United States

Burma

Brunei

■ Uncommitted

■ Metric or committed to metric

Figure 3

Keeping the English system is costing the United States a lot of money. Many American companies must trade with other nations to sell goods. However, some people in countries that use the metric system do not want to buy products based on the English system. The spare parts and the tools needed to fix machinery made according to the English system do not match those made according to the metric system. Thus, American-made products do not match products made in other countries. Converting one product to match another is an expensive process. This is a barrier in selling American products abroad—and many American jobs depend on producing goods to sell abroad.

The American business community has started to take this matter in hand. Your microwave oven, your car, your typewriter, your computer, and many other things around you may have already quietly gone metric. This is because American businesses find it too expensive to make English-measurement products for America and metric ones for overseas. American companies like General Motors, Kodak, IBM, and Caterpillar have already converted or are in the process of doing so.

If you look carefully, you can see that metric *is* creeping slowly into your life. New cars have speedometers marked in miles per hour and kilometers per hour. Some road signs show distances in both miles and kilometers. Soft-drink bottles often have their contents listed in liters and in quarts. Some cameras use 35-mm film.

As far back as 1866, the United States Congress passed a law saying Americans *could* use the metric system. However, only scientists adopted it. In 1975, President Gerald Ford signed legislation creating the Metric Board to help Americans make the transition from the English system to metric. That board was eliminated in 1982 without accomplishing its goal.

Figure 3 shows which countries use metric and which countries still use the English system or some other system.

APPLYING CRITICAL THINKING SKILLS

1. The United States is one country that does not use the metric system. How many other countries do not use it?
2. Is the United States in the majority or minority in not using the metric system?
3. Does it surprise you that so few countries are not using the metric system? Why or why not?
4. Do you think other people in the world find it strange that the United States still uses the English system? Explain your answer.

The following thinking skills will be applied in answering questions.
- *Interpreting* data.
- *Hypothesizing* reasons why the metric system is widely used.
- *Drawing conclusions* about the use of the metric system in most countries other than the United States.

Answers to questions
1. Two other countries, Brunei and Burma, do not use the metric system.
2. With only two other countries not using the metric system, the United States is part of a very small minority.
3. Some students may respond that they are surprised that more countries are not using the same system of measurement as that used by the United States, since the United States is a leader in technology and industry. However, the metric system is widely used because it is simple. Once the metric system became widely established, more and more countries began to use it.
4. Many people in other countries may find it strange that the United States still uses the English system of measurement. The metric system has long been the standard system used by scientists.

Unit 2

THE NATURE OF MATTER

UNIT OVERVIEW

Chapter 3 describes the states of matter and some physical properties and chemical properties of matter. It also compares physical changes and chemical changes.

Chapter 4 reviews several models of the atom, including the current model of the atom. The use of symbols and the Periodic Table are also included.

Chapter 5 discusses the nature of compounds and compares ionic compounds and covalent compounds.

Chapter 6 describes kinds of mixtures, with an emphasis on solutions. Suspensions and colloids are compared with solutions.

Unit Two

THE NATURE OF MATTER

*M*atter can exist in several physical states. On the earth most matter exists as either a solid, a liquid, or a gas. There are many kinds of substances. The physical state of a substance depends on what the substance is as well as the temperature and the pressure of the surrounding area. In this unit you will study the various properties of matter. You will learn about the atomic structure of some elements and how they form compounds and mixtures. ■

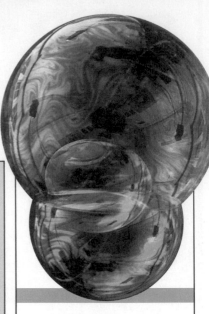

▲ Soap bubbles are made of a mixture.

▲ Gold is an element that has been valued throughout history.

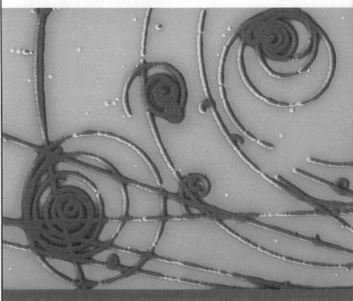

◀ These spiral tracks show the paths of charged particles given off by an atom.

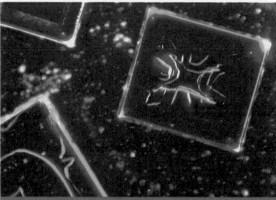

▶ *Sodium chloride, or salt, is a compound that forms crystals. This photograph shows sodium chloride crystals magnified over 100 times.*

▼ *This woodcut was made in 1496. The corners show the four elements believed to exist at the time — earth, air, fire, and water.*

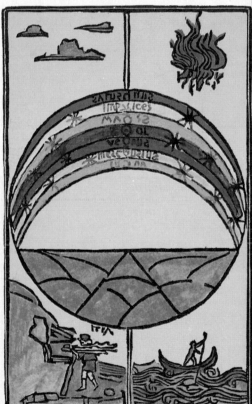

▲ *Different compounds form different crystal shapes. This is a quartz crystal.*

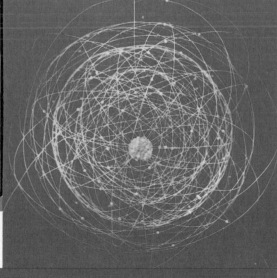

▶ *A model of what an atom of uranium might look like.*

Sections appearing in red provide coverage of basic topics in this unit. See page T23.

PROPERTIES OF MATTER

ORGANIZER

Section	pages	Activity	pages	Reinforcement and Evaluation	pages	*Review and Skill Masters	pages	Other Components in Teacher Resource Package	pages
3—1 What Is Matter?	57–59			Review, Challenge	59			Study Guide	13
3—2 States of Matter	60–61			Review, Challenge	61			Study Guide Transparency	14
3—3 Physical Properties	62–67	Does Sample Size Affect Freezing Point?	67	Puzzler Review, Challenge	63 67			Study Guide	15
3—4 Density and Specific Gravity	68–72	How Is Density Determined?	71	Review, Challenge	72	Skill	20–21	Study Guide Lab Manual	16 15
3—5 Physical Changes and Chemical Changes	73–76	Do Chemical and Physical Changes Differ?	75	Review, Challenge	76	Challenge/Critical Thinking	22	Study Guide	17
CHAPTER SUMMARY	77					Vocabulary Review	17		
CHAPTER REVIEW	78–79			*Test Masters	9–12	Chapter Review	18–19		

*In the Teacher Resource Package. For answers, see pages 55b–55d in this book.

ACTIVITY MATERIALS Quantities are based on a class of 30 students working in groups as indicated in parentheses.

Does Sample Size Affect Freezing Point? p. 67 (groups of 2)	quantity	How Is Density Determined? p. 71 (groups of 2)	quantity	Do Chemical and Physical Changes Differ? p. 75 (groups of 3)	quantity
lab apron	30	balances and masses	15	safety goggles	30
safety goggles	30	metric ruler	15	lab apron	30
paraffin	1 box	100-mL graduated cylinder	15	sealed iodine tube	10
large test tube	30	variety of objects	15	Bunsen burner	10
beaker	30			striker	10
water				steel wool	1 box
hot plate	15			table salt	1 box
Celsius thermometer	15			tap water	
one-hole rubber stopper	15			mossy zinc	25 g
clock with second hand	1			dilute hydrochloric acid	15 mL
glycerine or lubricant	1 tube			test-tube holder	10
				test-tube rack	10
				test tube	50
				dropper	20
				small beaker	10
				tongs	10
				Solution A containing 0.1 m of barium nitrate	30 mL
				Solution B containing 0.1 m of sodium chromate	30 mL
				Solution C containing 0.1 m of iron chloride	30 mL
				Solution D containing 0.1 m of potassium thiocyanate	30 mL

REVIEW AND SKILL MASTERS

Name_____ Date_____

VOCABULARY REVIEW _____ Chapter 3

Match the definition in Column A with the term in Column B. Not all terms are used.

Column A

E 1. A substance made up of two or more elements combined chemically

W 2. The tendency of liquids to form a skin at the surface

A 3. A solid whose particles lack a regular, repeating order

I 4. The mass per unit volume of a substance

L 5. The state of matter that does not have a definite shape or volume

N 6. Anything that has mass and takes up space

F 7. The temperature at which a gas changes to a liquid

S 8. A hot gas of electrically charged particles

C 9. A change that produces one or more kinds of matter that are different from those present before the change

G 10. A chemical change that occurs when a metal combines with substances in the environment

M 11. The state of matter that has a definite volume but not a definite shape

J 12. A substance that cannot be made into simpler substances by ordinary means

O 13. The temperature at which a solid becomes a liquid

V 14. The direct change from a solid to a gas

D 15. The ability of a substance to undergo or resist chemical changes

K 16. The temperature at which a liquid changes to a solid

H 17. A solid whose particles are arranged in a regular, repeating three-dimensional pattern

U 18. A ratio between the density of a substance and the density of water

Column B

A. amorphous solid
B. boiling point
C. chemical change
D. chemical property
E. compound
F. condensation point
G. corrosion
H. crystalline solid
I. density
J. element
K. freezing point
L. gas
M. liquid
N. matter
O. melting point
P. mixture
Q. physical change
R. physical property
S. plasma
T. solid
U. specific gravity
V. sublimation
W. surface tension

17

Name_____ Date_____

CHAPTER REVIEW _____ Chapter 3

3-1 What Is Matter?

1. Define the term matter. **Matter is anything that has mass and takes up space.**

2. Compare elements, compounds, and mixtures. **Elements are substances that cannot be broken down into simpler substances by ordinary means. Compounds are made up of two or more elements chemically combined. Mixtures are made up of two or more kinds of matter that keep their own properties.**

3-2 States of Matter

1. List the four states of matter and give the properties of each.
Solids have a definite shape and volume. Liquids flow and do not have a definite shape but have a definite volume. Gases do not have a definite volume or shape and mix easily. Plasma contains particles that are shaking violently at very high temperatures.

2. How does a liquid become a gas? **When a liquid is heated, energy is added to its particles causing them to move faster and further apart. The particles gain energy and can overcome the forces of attraction that held them together in the liquid state. The liquid becomes a gas.**

3-3 Physical Properties

1. Name three physical properties of liquids. **Three physical properties of liquids are viscosity (their resistance to flow), surface tension, and cohesion.**

18

Name_____ Date_____

CHAPTER REVIEW (Continued) _____ Chapter 3

2. List four physical properties of solids. **Four physical properties of solids are malleability, brittleness, hardness, and tensile strength.**

3. Give two examples of how physical properties can determine how a substance is used.
Drill bits are made from diamonds because they are the hardest of natural substances. Metals with elasticity are used to make coils and springs.

3-4 Density and Specific Gravity

1. What is the formula to find the density of a substance?
The formula to find the density of a substance is density = mass ÷ volume.

2. What is the density of a substance that has a mass of 36.9 g and a volume of 3.0 cm³?
12.3 g/cm³.

3. What is specific gravity? **Specific gravity is a ratio between the density of a substance and the density of water.**

4. Water expands as it freezes. Explain how this is different from the general trend of solids having higher densities than liquids. **As water freezes and expands, its volume increases but not its mass, giving it a lower density than liquid water.**

3-5 Physical Changes and Chemical Changes

1. In a ___**physical**___ change, the appearance of matter changes but the properties and makeup remain the same. In a ___**chemical**___ change, one or more kinds of matter are present after the change that were not present before.

2. Label the following as physical or chemical changes.

a. Melting **physical change**

b. Rusting **chemical change**

c. Sublimation **physical change**

d. Burning **chemical change**

19

Name_____ Date_____

SKILL/Classification _____ Chapter 3

Scientists define matter as anything that occupies space and has mass. These two properties of matter are incorporated into a ratio called density. Density is often used to identify substances. If the density of a substance is compared to the density of water, the ratio that results is called specific gravity. Specific gravity is often used to determine if a substance will float or sink in water. If the specific gravity of a substance is less than 1.0, the substance will float in water. If the specific gravity of a substance is greater than 1.0, the substance will sink. The following equations are used in computing density and specific gravity.

$$D = M \div V \qquad V = M \div D \qquad M = V \times D$$

In the formulas, D stands for density (g/cm³), M stands for mass (g), and V stands for volume (cm³).

$$\text{specific gravity} = \frac{\text{density of substance}}{\text{density of water}}$$

1. In order to determine the density of a substance, which formula should be used if the values for mass and volume are known?
The formula that should be used is D = M ÷ V.

2. In order to determine the mass of a substance, which formula should be used if the values for volume and density are known?
The formula that should be used is M = V × D.

3. If the specific gravity of a substance is known, how could the density of that substance be determined?
The density of the substance could be determined by using the following formula: specific gravity = density of substance ÷ density of water.

4. Assume that the specific gravity of water is 1.0. Will the following substances float or sink in water?

a. oil, Specific gravity = 0.90 **float**

b. lead, Specific gravity = 11.3 **sink**

c. cork, Specific gravity = 0.24 **float**

d. ice, Specific gravity = 0.92 **float**

e. iron, Specific gravity = 7.9 **sink**

20

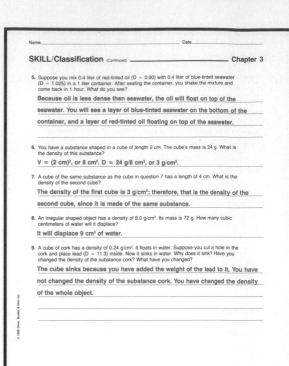

Name_____ Date_____

SKILL/Classification (Continued) _____ Chapter 3

5. Suppose you mix 0.4 liter of red-tinted oil (D = 0.90) with 0.4 liter of blue-tinted seawater (D = 1.025) in a 1 liter container. After sealing the container, you shake the mixture and come back in 1 hour. What do you see?

   Because oil is less dense than seawater, the oil will float on top of the

   seawater. You will see a layer of blue-tinted seawater on the bottom of the

   container, and a layer of red-tinted oil floating on top of the seawater.

6. You have a substance shaped in a cube of length 2 cm. The cube's mass is 24 g. What is the density of this substance?

   V = (2 cm)³, or 8 cm³. D = 24 g/8 cm³, or 3 g/cm³.

7. A cube of the same substance as the cube in question 7 has a length of 4 cm. What is the density of the second cube?

   The density of the first cube is 3 g/cm³; therefore, that is the density of the

   second cube, since it is made of the same substance.

8. An irregular shaped object has a density of 8.0 g/cm³. Its mass is 72 g. How many cubic centimeters of water will it displace?

   It will displace 9 cm³ of water.

9. A cube of cork has a density of 0.24 g/cm³. It floats in water. Suppose you cut a hole in the cork and place lead (D = 11.3) inside. Now it sinks in water. Why does it sink? Have you changed the density of the substance cork? What have you changed?

   The cube sinks because you have added the weight of the lead to it. You have

   not changed the density of the substance cork. You have changed the density

   of the whole object.

Name_____ Date_____

CHALLENGE/CRITICAL THINKING _____ Chapter 3

A glass tumbler has a maximum volume of 250 cm³. Two hundred forty grams (240 g) of water and a ten-gram (10 g) ice cube are added to the tumbler. The ice cube floats and, in doing so, displaces a mass of water equal to its own mass.

1. Water has a density of 1 g/cm³. What is the volume of the water?   **240 cm³**

2. Ice has a density of 0.917 g/cm³. What is the volume of the ice?   **10.9 cm³**

3. What is the mass of water displaced by the ice?   **10 g**

4. What is the volume of water displaced by the ice?   **10 cm³**

5. What is the volume of the part of the ice cube that is above the water?   **0.9 cm³**

6. What is the level of water in the tumbler in cubic centimeters?   **250 cm³**

7. Will water overflow the rim of the tumbler? Why or why not?

   No. The ice displaces a volume equal to 10 grams of water.

8. Half of the ice melts into water. Describe the water level in terms of cubic centimeters.

   The level remains at 250 cm³.

9. The last half of the ice melts into water. Describe the water level in terms of cubic centimeters.

   The level remains at 250 cm³.

10. What kind of change occurred when the ice melted to water?

    A physical change occurred.

11. What happened to the volume of the ice when it melted to water?

    The volume of the ice changed from 10.9 to 10 cm³.

12. Describe another experiment that would illustrate density.

    Students' answers will vary.

TEST MASTERS

Properties of Matter

PART 1

In the space below, write the term that each phrase defines.

Chapter Goal

1. **physical change** — A type of change in which the appearance of matter changes but its properties and makeup remain the same — 5

2. **solid** — The state of matter that has a definite volume and a definite shape — 2

3. **condensation point** — The temperature at which a gas changes to a liquid — 3

4. **matter** — The general name for anything that has mass and takes up space — 1

5. **density** — The mass per unit volume of a substance — 4

6. **specific gravity** — A ratio between the density of a substance and the density of water — 4

7. **physical properties** — The characteristics of matter that can be measured and observed without changing the makeup of the substance — 3

8. **chemical change** — A type of change that produces one or more kinds of matter that are different from those present before the change — 5

9. **plasma** — The state of matter that is a gas of electrically charged particles shaking violently at very high temperatures — 2

10. **compound** — The general name for a substance that is made up of two or more elements combined chemically — 1

PART 2

Choose the term or phrase that best answers the question or completes the statement. Write the letter of that choice in the space at the left.

a 1. The particles of a compound are most strongly held together when it is in the state of a: — 2
   a. solid.   b. liquid.   c. gas.   d. plasma.

c 2. Which of the following would be classified as an element? — 1
   a. air   b. water   c. oxygen   d. granite

© Silver, Burdett & Ginn Inc.

Choose the term or phrase that best answers the question or completes the statement. Write the letter of that choice in the space at the left.

Chapter Goal

c 3. The particles of salt and the particles of water in the ocean are attracted to each other by: — 3
   a. sublimation.   b. condensation.   c. adhesion.   d. cohesion.

c 4. A scientist does an experiment at 20°C using metal that has a density of 12.0 g/cm³, water that has a density of 1.0 g/cm³, and oxygen that has a density of .0014 g/cm³. What is the specific gravity of the metal used? — 4
   a. 6.0   b. 10.0   c. 12.0   d. 20.0

d 5. A scientist discovers that a substance is malleable and has a high tensile strength. The substance is most likely a: — 3
   a. gas.   b. plasma.   c. liquid.   d. solid.

b 6. A certain material contains three kinds of matter and has properties that vary from one point in the material to another. The material should be classified as: — 1
   a. an element.   b. a mixture.   c. a compound.   d. a substance.

b 7. An object that has a mass of 12 g and a volume of 3 cm³ has a density of: — 4
   a. 1 g/cm³.   b. 4 g/cm³.   c. 6 g/cm³.   d. 9 g/cm³.

c 8. Which of the following is a chemical change? — 5
   a. the melting of wax   c. the corroding of silver
   b. the breaking of glass   d. the evaporation of water

a 9. Which of the following involves only physical changes? — 5
   a. subliming snow   c. digesting food
   b. rusting iron   d. burning wood

d 10. Which of the following would cause a solid to change to a gas? — 2
   a. arranging the particles in a repeating pattern
   b. increasing the attraction between the particles
   c. bringing the particles closer together
   d. adding heat energy to the particles

© Silver, Burdett & Ginn Inc.

Look at the table. Then read the questions that follow. Choose the term or phrase that best answers the question or completes the statement. Write the letter of that choice in the space at the left.

Name	Melting Point (°C)	Density (g/cm³)
Potassium	62	0.86
Potassium chloride	770	1.98
Chlorine	−101	0.0032
Magnesium	649	1.74
Magnesium oxide	2,852	3.58
Oxygen	−219	0.0014
Water	0	1.00

Chapter Goal

b 1. What is the specific gravity of magnesium? — 4
   a. 0.174   b. 1.74   c. 17.4   d. 174

a 2. At what temperature does chlorine freeze? — 3
   a. −101°C   b. 1.98°C   c. 62°C   d. 776°C

a 3. At 50°C, what state of matter does potassium exist in? — 2
   a. solid   b. liquid   c. gas   d. plasma

c 4. Which substance is a solid at 2000°C? — 1
   a. potassium chloride   c. magnesium oxide
   b. water   d. oxygen

d 5. Which of the following substances on the chart would undergo a change of state at 649°C? — 2
   a. potassium   c. chlorine
   b. potassium chloride   d. magnesium

© Silver, Burdett & Ginn Inc.

Read each question or direction and answer it using complete sentences.

Chapter Goal

1. Describe the characteristics of mixtures. — 1

   A mixture is made up of varying amounts of two or more kinds of matter that can be separated by physical means. These different types of matter keep their own properties. Some mixtures have the same composition and properties throughout the sample. In other mixtures the composition and properties vary from one point in the mixture to another.

2. What are the differences between physical changes and chemical changes? — 5

   In a physical change, the appearance of matter changes but its properties and makeup remain the same. A physical change does not involve a change of one kind of matter into another. A chemical change produces one or more kinds of matter that are different from those present before the change. A chemical change usually releases or absorbs more energy than a physical change.

3. Explain why a solid melts when it is heated. — 2

   The particles in a solid are held very closely together by strong forces of attraction. When the solid is heated, energy is added to its particles. This energy causes the particles to move faster and faster. As the particles gain more energy, they move fast enough to overcome the forces of attraction. Thus, the solid loses its shape and melts.

© Silver, Burdett & Ginn Inc.

CHAPTER 3 PLANNING GUIDE

55d

3

PROPERTIES OF MATTER

The questions in the CHAPTER TEST are based on these Chapter Goals.

1. Describe characteristics of matter, and distinguish among elements, compounds, and mixtures.
2. Describe characteristics of the four states of matter, and identify changes of state.
3. Describe physical properties of matter.
4. Calculate density, and compare the densities of different substances and states of matter.
5. Distinguish between physical changes and chemical changes, and give examples of each.

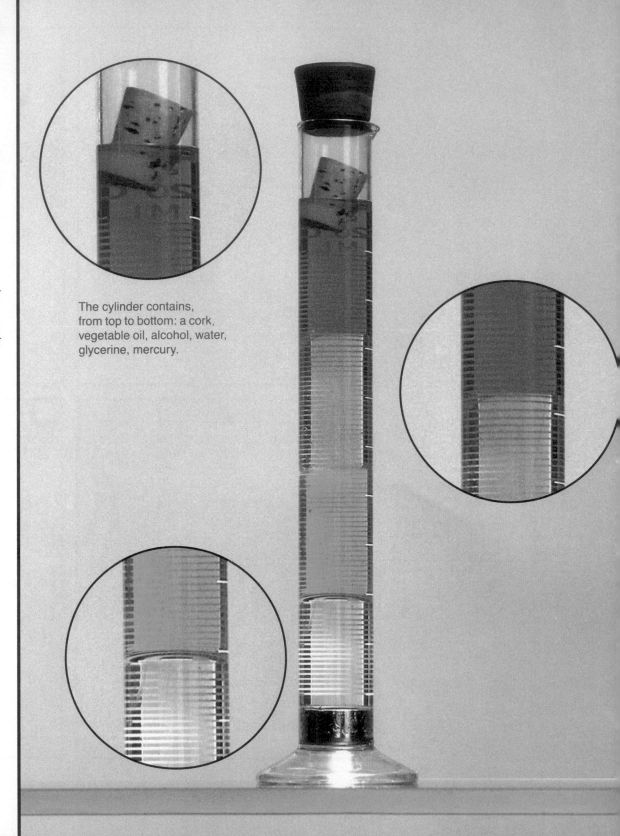

The cylinder contains, from top to bottom: a cork, vegetable oil, alcohol, water, glycerine, mercury.

PROPERTIES OF MATTER

This photograph shows several examples of matter. Most are liquids and one is a solid. Although they are all in the same container, they have not mixed together. Each kind of matter has stayed separate from the rest.

Each kind of matter has its own set of characteristics, or properties. One of these properties, density, has kept these layers of matter from mixing.

- *What other properties of matter can you name?*
- *Do the properties of a substance change if the substance changes from a liquid to a solid?*
- *How do scientists study the properties of matter?*
- *How can properties be used to identify a sample of matter?*

3-1 WHAT IS MATTER?

Matter is easier to describe than to define. It is the stuff that makes up all objects. You and all of the things around you—other people, the air, this book, water, trees, flowers, buildings, the sun—are made of matter. **Matter** is anything that has mass and takes up space. *Mass* is a measure of the amount of matter in an object.

Each of the many kinds of matter has characteristics that help to identify it. A property is a characteristic that distinguishes one substance from another. Some examples of properties are color, odor, ability to dissolve, and the temperature at which a substance melts or boils. Other properties describe the way one kind of matter can combine with other kinds of matter.

Any sample of matter may be classified into one of two groups. Matter is either a substance or a mixture. A *substance* is a particular kind of matter, all samples of which have the same makeup and properties. Gold, silver, water, salt, and sugar are examples of substances. A substance may be thought of as a pure sample of matter because all particles in the sample are the same.

> After completing this section, you will be able to
>
> - **define** the term *matter*.
> - **compare** and **identify** elements, compounds, and mixtures.
>
> *The key terms in this section are*
> compound   matter
> element   mixture

Background   Matter can also be defined in terms of inertia. In other words, matter is anything that has mass, occupies space, and exhibits the property of inertia. Inertia is the resistance of matter to a change in motion.

Background   Weight is the force with which an object is attracted by the earth's gravitational field. Mass is a measure of the quantity of matter in a body. A sample of matter has the same mass anywhere in the universe, but its weight is different at different places in the universe because of different gravitational attraction.

Teaching Tip   Tell students that volume is the amount of space occupied by a certain amount of matter.

Teaching Tip   Students are aware that an element is a substance that cannot be made into simpler substances by ordinary means such as heating, cooling, or crushing. Tell students that nuclear changes are not considered to be ordinary means, even though some radioactive decay occurs naturally.

Enrichment   Have students make an inventory of household products, such as health aids (vitamins, over-the-counter medicines), cleaning products, and home repair and maintenance products (paints, rust preventors, caulk). Have students read the label of each product. Have them prepare a chart of their findings that includes categories such as recommendations for storage, safety precautions, and shelf life. Have students use the chart to determine whether any of the products in their homes are stored improperly or have outlived their shelf lives.

componere (put together)

[1]Hydrogen and oxygen are gases at room temperature. Water is a liquid at room temperature.

There are two kinds of substances: elements and compounds. An **element** is a substance that cannot be made into simpler substances by ordinary means such as heating, cooling, or crushing. Gold and silver are examples of elements. At present scientists know of 109 elements. About 90 of these come from natural sources. The rest have been made in the laboratory. All matter is made up of elements, either alone or in combination.

A **compound** is a substance that is made up of two or more elements chemically combined. Water, salt, and sugar are all compounds. Each compound has its own properties, which can be used to identify it. Compounds keep their properties during some changes. For example, when water is heated or cooled, it remains water. But compounds can be changed into their elements. Water can be broken down into its parts—hydrogen and oxygen. How are the properties of these elements different from the properties of water?[1]

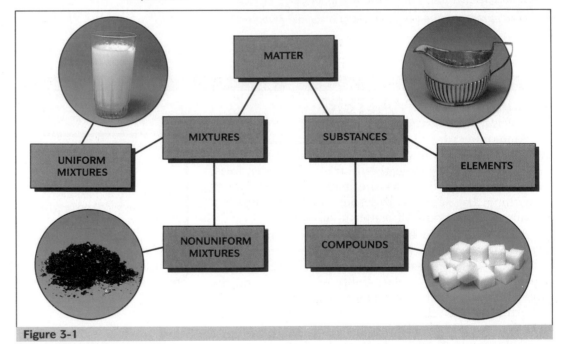

Figure 3-1

How are mixtures different from compounds? [2]

[2]Mixtures are combined physically; compounds are combined chemically

Most samples of matter are mixtures. Air, brass, salt water, ice cream, and vegetable soup all are examples of mixtures. A **mixture** is a combination of two or more kinds of matter that can be separated by physical means. Each kind of matter in a mixture can be found in any amount. The different kinds of matter keep their own properties.

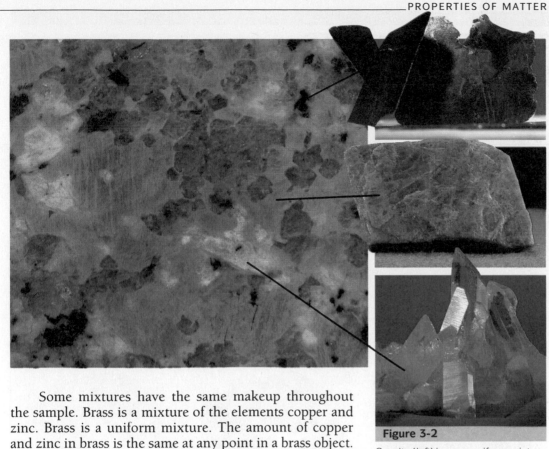

Figure 3-2

Granite (*left*) is a nonuniform mixture that contains mica (*top*), feldspar (*middle*), and quartz (*bottom*).

Some mixtures have the same makeup throughout the sample. Brass is a mixture of the elements copper and zinc. Brass is a uniform mixture. The amount of copper and zinc in brass is the same at any point in a brass object. The skim milk shown in Figure 3-1 is a uniform mixture. Would you expect whole milk to be a uniform mixture?[1]

Not all mixtures are uniform. In some mixtures the composition and properties vary from one point in the mixture to another. An example of a mixture that is not uniform is the rock called granite. Look at Figure 3-2. The sample of granite shown is a mixture that contains quartz, feldspar, and mica. Each of these substances can be seen in the sample of granite.

[1]No. Whole milk contains fat, which might not be evenly distributed in the mixture.

REVIEW

1. What two characteristics do all samples of matter have in common?
2. What is the difference between an element and a compound?
3. Which of the following mixtures could be described as uniform: concrete, gasoline, milk, or raisin bread?

CHALLENGE How might you separate a mixture of iron filings and salt?

classifying
Display different samples of matter, such as sand in water, salt water, brass, copper wire, zinc wire, water, and sugar. Have students classify each sample as an element, compound, or mixture.

3 REVIEW/REINFORCEMENT

1. All matter has mass and takes up space.
2. An element is a substance that cannot be made into simpler materials by ordinary means. A compound is a substance that is made up of two or more elements chemically combined.
3. Gasoline, milk.

Challenge Iron filings can be separated from salt by using a magnet. They can also be separated from salt by dissolving the mixture in water and then filtering, which leaves the iron filings on the filter paper.

3-2 STATES OF MATTER
pages 60–61

1 MOTIVATION

Ask students if mass is lost during a change of state. Have them explain their reasoning. Then place some water in a container, and determine the mass of the container and the water. Place the container in a freezer overnight. The next day determine the mass of the ice, and have students compare it with the mass of the container and water before it was frozen. Allow students to draw conclusions.

2 CONCEPT DEVELOPMENT

Background If enough energy is added to a molecular substance, the molecules separate into atoms. Then the atoms come apart, forming a "gas" of free electrons and ions or nuclei. This gas is the fourth state of matter, known as plasma. The plasma state is not common on the earth, but the ionized gas in flourescent lamps is a plasma.

Teaching Tip When comparing solid, liquid, and gas states, write the differences in their properties on the chalkboard. Compare the degree of order in the structure of the three states, with solid state being the most ordered. Tell students that most differences in the properties of the three states are due to the differences in the distances between their particles.

After completing this section, you will be able to

- **list** and **compare** the four states of matter.
- **describe** the events that occur in a change of state.

The key terms in this section are
amorphous solid   liquid
crystalline solid   plasma
gas   solid

a- (without)
morphe (shape)
[1]Butter is an amorphous solid. Sugar is a crystalline solid.

Matter is found in four forms, or states: solid, liquid, gas, and plasma. How can you tell one state of matter from another? Each state of matter has certain properties. A **solid** has a definite shape and takes up a definite volume. As shown in Figure 3-3, the particles in a solid are very close together. They are held together by strong forces of attraction. The particles in matter are always in motion. In a solid, the particles vibrate but do not move around.

Solids are divided into two major groups—crystalline (KRIHS tuh lihn) solids and amorphous (uh MOR fuhs) solids. A **crystalline solid** is a solid whose particles are arranged in a regular, repeating, three-dimensional pattern. Salt, ice, and diamonds are crystalline solids. An **amorphous solid** is a solid whose particles lack a regular, repeating order. In an amorphous solid the particles are jumbled together. Some examples of amorphous solids are glass and wax. What kinds of solids are butter and sugar?[1]

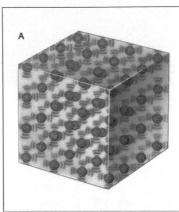 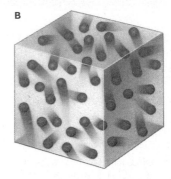 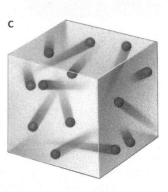

Figure 3-3

Most matter on earth exists as a solid (*A*), a liquid (*B*), or a gas (*C*).

A **liquid** has a definite volume but not a definite shape. As in solids, the particles in liquids are held together by forces of attraction. But the forces between particles in liquids are not strong enough to hold the liquids in definite shapes. Thus, a liquid will flow and take the shape of its container.

A **gas** does not have a definite shape or volume. A gas expands to fill and take the shape of its container. The particles of gases are very far apart compared to those of liquids and solids. The forces between the particles are very weak. Gas particles move quickly and collide with one another often. As a result, gases mix together easily.

DO YOU KNOW?

Most of the matter in the universe is in the plasma state. Stars, including the sun, are glowing masses of plasma. The sun sends out clouds of plasma, called the solar winds.

When these clouds of plasma reach the earth, they collide with air particles in the upper atmosphere. This causes the formation of colored lights called auroras. Auroras at the North Pole are called the Northern Lights.

Matter in the plasma state may be used to produce energy in the future. Plasma is very difficult to contain and study in a laboratory. The Northern

Lights are giving scientists a chance to learn more about plasma. If scientists can learn more about the behavior of plasma in nature, they may be able to learn how to control plasma under laboratory conditions.

Matter is not usually found in the plasma state on the earth, although plasma may exist under some experimental conditions. Scientists estimate that more than 90 percent of the matter in the universe is plasma. The sun and other stars, which contain most of the matter in the universe, are in the plasma state. The particles of plasma are shaking violently at very high temperatures, making **plasma** a hot gas of electrically charged particles.

Substances can be changed from one state to another. Recall that particles in matter are held together by forces of attraction. These forces give a solid its definite shape. When you heat a solid, you are adding energy to its particles. This energy causes the particles to move faster and farther apart. As the particles gain more energy, they move fast enough to overcome the forces of attraction. Thus the solid melts and it loses its shape. If enough heat energy is added to a liquid, the liquid will change to the gas state. What happens to a liquid as it changes to a solid?[1]

[1]The liquid loses energy, and its particles move more slowly.

REVIEW

1. Name the four states of matter.
2. Name the forms of matter that have no definite shape.
3. How does the space between particles of a solid change when the solid becomes a liquid?

CHALLENGE Suggest a reason for the fact that matter is not usually found in the plasma state on the earth.

3-3 PHYSICAL PROPERTIES

pages 62–67

OBJECTIVES
Refer to pupil page 62.

VOCABULARY
Key terms: boiling point, condensation point, freezing point, melting point, physical properties, surface tension

Other terms: adhesion, brittleness, cohesion, elasticity, hardness, malleable, tensile strength, viscosity

1 MOTIVATION

Create a display showing different elements and compounds by placing samples of copper, sulfur, iron, copper sulfate, and iron sulfide into different vials. Ask students to identify some physical properties of each element or compound. Ask students if they can identify the elements and the compounds by their properties.

3-3 PHYSICAL PROPERTIES

After completing this section, you will be able to

- **list** some examples of physical properties.
- **describe** practical uses of physical properties.

The key terms in this section are
boiling point
condensation point
freezing point
melting point
physical properties
surface tension

Physical properties are characteristics of matter that can be measured and observed without changing the makeup of the substance. Color, taste, odor, and melting temperature are familiar physical properties. The physical properties of a kind of matter remain the same regardless of the shape, form, or amount of that matter. For example, think of an iron nail. Its mass is 12 g, and it is rod-shaped. If the nail is broken into two pieces, each piece has a mass of less than 12 g. However, the nail is still the same kind of matter—iron.

When talking about physical properties of matter, the conditions under which the properties are determined should be stated. For example, iron could be described as a solid with a silvery color. This description is correct for iron at room temperature. It is not correct for iron at the temperature in a blast furnace. The physical properties of matter often vary with temperature, pressure, and state.

PROPERTIES OF LIQUIDS

Some liquids resist flow more than others. A liquid's resistance to flow is called *viscosity* (vihs KAHS uh tee). Liquids such as water flow easily and have low viscosities. Some liquids, such as heavy oils, have high viscosities. These liquids flow slowly. Motor oil, which lubricates the moving parts of an engine, is rated by viscosity. An oil should have a viscosity that is high enough to lubricate the engine but not so high that it does not flow through

Figure 3-4

The viscosity of oil changes as the temperature changes.

the engine. As you can see in Figure 3-4, the viscosity of a liquid changes with temperature. Viscosity becomes less and the liquid flows more freely as the temperature rises. As the engine runs, the temperature of the oil rises, and the viscosity decreases. The driver must use an oil with the correct viscosity rating for the running temperature of the car's engine.

Recall that there are forces of attraction between the particles in a sample of matter. These forces exist in all directions within a liquid. At the surface of the liquid, however, the forces do not exist in all directions. As you can see in Figure 3-5, surface particles are acted on by forces of attraction from below but not from above. The surface particles also attract each other. As a result the surface particles are pulled inward and close together, forming a "skin" on the surface of the liquid. The tendency of a liquid to form a skin at the surface is called **surface tension**. The surface tension of water makes it possible for certain insects to stand on top of pond water.

The attraction between particles of the same substance is called *cohesion* (koh HEE zhuhn). The cohesion of the particles in the water contributes to surface tension. If you add soap to water, particles of the soap get between particles of water. Some of the soap particles will be attracted to the water particles. This attraction between particles of different substances is called *adhesion* (ad HEE-zhuhn). The soap particles break up the cohesion within the water, and surface tension decreases. Could an insect stand on the surface of soapy water?[1]

[1]No. There would not be enough surface tension to hold up the insect.

Figure 3-5

The cohesion of the particles in the water causes the property of surface tension.

Background   All measurable physical properties of matter fall into two distinct categories: extensive physical properties, and intensive physical properties. Extensive physical properties depend on how much matter is being considered. Properties such as mass, length, and volume are extensive. Values for extensive properties can be added together. For example, the total volume of water in two beakers is the sum of the volume of water in each of the two beakers. Intensive physical properties do not depend on the amount of matter being considered. Color, melting point, boiling point, and density are intensive physical properties. For example, water will freeze at 0°C regardless of the amount of water.

Background   Substances can exist as solids, liquids, and gases at the same time under appropriate conditions. For example, water exists in all three phases at 0.01°C and a pressure of 0.006 atm (standard atmosphere).

Puzzler   The cohesion between mercury atoms is greater than the adhesion between mercury atoms and the graduate, so the mercury forms the dome-shaped meniscus.

Background   The degree of surface tension depends on the amount of energy in the intermolecular forces. Liquids that possess strong intermolecular forces have a strong surface tension. Water molecules form hydrogen bonds between each other and have strong intermolecular force; as a result, a strong surface tension is created.

Teaching Tip   Have students list the physical properties of some common substances, such as water, ice, salt, sugar, olive oil, salt water, air, and sand. Then ask students to list the similarities and differences between the substances.

Demonstration   Demonstrate the properties of malleability, brittleness, and tensile strength. For malleability, use a hammer to pound a small ball of copper into a flat mass. For brittleness, break a sulfur rod. For tensile strength, add slotted weights to each of two or three wires of equal gauge and length until one or more of the wires break.

PROPERTIES OF SOLIDS

Solids also show a variety of properties. Some solids are *malleable* (MAL ee uh buhl). They can be hammered into very thin sheets. Copper and gold, for example, are malleable. A rubber band can be stretched by pulling. When the pulling stops, the rubber band goes back to its original shape. Since it stretches and then returns to its original shape, a rubber band shows the property of *elasticity* (ih las TIHS uh tee). Elasticity also gives objects, such as the balls shown in Figure 3-6, the ability to bounce. Aluminum, copper, and steel also are somewhat elastic.

Figure 3-6

Objects that bounce show the property of elasticity.

Some substances, such as sulfur, cannot be hammered into thin sheets or drawn into wires. Sulfur shows the property of *brittleness*. It breaks if it is hammered. Many solids show a physical property known as *hardness*. Hardness is the ability to resist being scratched. Diamond is the hardest substance in nature. Graphite, which is used in pencil "lead," is one of the softest.

The physical property called *tensile* (TEHN suhl) *strength* describes how well a solid resists breaking under tension. If a copper wire and a steel wire of the same thickness are pulled with great force, the copper wire will break first. The steel wire has a higher tensile strength than does copper wire.

CHANGE OF STATE

The temperatures at which changes of state take place are physical properties. The temperature at which a solid becomes a liquid is called the **melting point**. If a melted substance is cooled, it will change back into the solid state. This reverse change is called freezing. The temperature at which a liquid freezes is called the **freezing point**. The freezing point and the melting point of a substance are the same. For water, this temperature at sea level is 0°C. When ice is warmed to 0°C, it begins to melt. As more heat is added to ice at 0°C, more and more of the ice melts. Until all of the ice melts, the temperature remains at 0°C. Both the solid and liquid states of water exist at this temperature. The temperature will begin to rise only after all of the ice is melted.

The melting point and freezing point of a substance are physical properties that help to identify substances. Table 3-1 shows the melting and freezing points of a few substances. The melting and freezing points of different kinds of matter vary because the strength of the forces between particles varies from one kind of matter to another. Oxygen has a low melting point because the forces between the particles of oxygen are weak. On the other hand, iron has a high melting point. The forces between iron particles are very strong.

A liquid can change to a gas state by evaporation or boiling. Evaporation takes place at the surface of any liquid in an open container. Boiling takes place all through the liquid. Bubbles form, rise, and burst on the surface. The temperature at which a liquid boils at sea level is the **boiling point** for that liquid. Table 3-1 shows the boiling

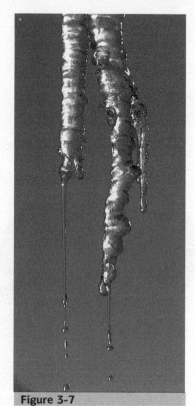

Figure 3-7

Water can exist as both a solid and a liquid at 0°C.

Thinking Skills

predicting

Have students predict the melting points of crushed ice and margarine. Have one group of students place some crushed ice in a test tube, and have another group place some margarine in another test tube. Place a thermometer in each test tube, and have students immerse the test tubes in a beaker of hot water. Have students record the temperature in 30-second intervals and then graph temperature (*x*-axis) versus time (*y*-axis). Ask them to compare the results with their predictions. Ask students to explain the plateau in each graph.

Table 3-1 *Change of State*

Substance	Melting/Freezing Points (°C)	Boiling/Condensation Points (°C)
Water	0	100
Aluminum	658	2467
Copper	1080	2595
Iron	1530	3000
Lead	328	1740
Helium	−272	−269
Mercury	−39	357
Oxygen	−219	−184
Hydrogen	−259	−252
Sulfur dioxide	−73	−10

Background The heat energy absorbed during a change of state, such as from a solid to a liquid, involves the particles adjusting themselves to conditions required for the new phase. The plateau produced on a graph of temperature change during a change of state indicates that the average kinetic energy of the particles is constant.

Tie-in/Social Studies The aim of the alchemists of the Middle Ages was to produce gold from base metals. Many of the advances in early chemistry were a direct result of alchemists' experiments. Encourage interested students to research alchemy and share their findings with the class.

points of several substances. Water, which melts at 0°C, is a liquid between 0°C and 100°C. The temperature of boiling water is 100°C. The water vapor produced is also 100°C. After all the water is boiled away, continued heating of the water vapor would cause its temperature to rise.

Condensation is the reverse of boiling. When a gas is cooled, it loses energy, and its particles move more slowly. If cooling continues, the gas loses enough energy to change to a liquid. The temperature at which a gas changes to a liquid is called the **condensation point**. Water vapor, which has been formed by boiling water, can be condensed into liquid water. What is the temperature of the water vapor when it condenses?[1] The boiling point and condensation point of a substance are the same.

[1]100°C.

Figure 3-8

Matter can be used in many ways, including steel saw blades (A), diamond drill bits (B), and steel bridge cables (C).

[2]Hardness (A) and (B). Tensile strength (C).

Knowledge of the physical properties of matter helps people choose ways to use matter. Drill bits are made from diamonds. Steel wires support the weight of huge bridges. Elastic metals are used to make springs for scales, furniture, and other objects. Metals with a low melting point are used in fire sprinkler systems. Metals with a high melting point are used to carry electricity. Look at the ways in which matter is being used in Figure 3-8. What properties are useful in these objects?[2]

ACTIVITY — Does Sample Size Affect Freezing Point?

OBJECTIVE
Compare the freezing points of two different masses of a substance.

MATERIALS
safety goggles, two 250-mL beakers, water, hot plate, paraffin, 2 large test tubes, thermometer inserted into a split cork, clock or watch with second hand

PROCEDURE
A. Wear safety goggles during this activity.
B. Draw a data table like the one shown.
C. Place a beaker half full of water on a hot plate, and heat the water.
D. Fill a test tube one-fourth full with paraffin.
E. Place the test tube in the hot water bath. When the paraffin has melted, remove the test tube from the water bath.
F. Carefully insert a split cork and thermometer. The bulb of the thermometer should be covered by the liquid. Be sure that the scale of the thermometer can be seen through the opening in the cork.

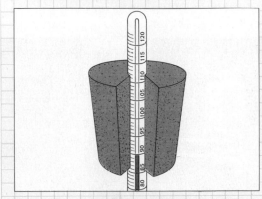

G. Fill another beaker half full of cold water. Place the test tube in the cold water bath.
H. Record the temperature of the paraffin every minute. Continue for 5 minutes after the liquid has become solid.
I. Place the test tube back in the hot water bath. When the solid has melted, remove the stopper and thermometer.
J. Repeat steps **E** through **I** using a test tube one-half full with paraffin.
K. Prepare a full-page graph. Plot the temperature in °C along the y-axis and time along the x-axis. Use a solid line to graph the data for the smaller amount. Use a dashed line to graph the data for the larger amount.

Time (minutes)	Temperature of small amount (°C)	Temperature of large amount (°C)
1		
2		
3		
4		
5		
6		
7		
8		
9		
10		

RESULTS AND CONCLUSIONS
1. What was the freezing point of the smaller sample?
2. What was the freezing point of the larger sample?
3. Does the freezing point of a substance depend on the mass of the sample?

REVIEW

1. List four physical properties.
2. What is surface tension?
3. How is a substance's melting point related to its freezing point?
4. How is evaporation different from boiling?

CHALLENGE Look at Table 3-1 on page 65. At 20°C, what is the state of matter of each of the substances listed in the table?

ACTIVITY 35 minutes

PROCESS SKILLS
measuring, recording data, graphing data, interpreting data

Preparation Insert a thermometer into a split cork that has a small wedge cut out of it for each group that will perform the activity.

Safety Tip Caution students to handle hot test tubes carefully. Students must wear safety goggles during this activity.

Answers to Results and Conclusions
1. 49°C–63°C. (Note: The actual freezing point will depend on the kind of paraffin wax used.)
2. 49°C–63°C.
3. No, the freezing point of a substance does not depend on the mass of the sample.

3 REVIEW/REINFORCEMENT

1. Melting point, freezing point, boiling point, viscosity, malleability, tensile strength, and so on.
2. It is the tendency of a liquid to form a "skin" at the surface. Surface particles are acted on by forces of attraction from below and from each side, causing particles to be drawn inward and close together but not upward.
3. The melting point and freezing point of a substance is the same temperature.
4. Evaporation takes place at the surface of any liquid in an open container. Boiling takes place all through the liquid.

Challenge The state of matter of each substance at 20°C: water—liquid; aluminum—solid; copper—solid; iron—solid; lead—solid; helium—gas; mercury—liquid; oxygen—gas; hydrogen—gas; sulfur dioxide—gas.

3-4 DENSITY AND SPECIFIC GRAVITY

pages 68–72

OBJECTIVES
Refer to pupil page 68.

VOCABULARY
Key terms: density, specific gravity

1 MOTIVATION

Fill one 250-mL beaker three-quarters full with water and another 250-mL beaker three-quarters full with rubbing alcohol. Ask students to observe the liquids in the beakers. Then carefully drop ice cubes of similar size into each beaker. Again, ask students to make careful observations. The ice cube in the water floats because the density of ice is less than the density of water. But rubbing alcohol is less dense than ice, so the ice sinks in the beaker that contains rubbing alcohol. As the ice in the alcohol melts, the overall density of the liquid mixture increases, and the ice rises a bit. Ask students to explain their observations.

2 CONCEPT DEVELOPMENT

Background Density, which is the ratio of mass to volume, is an intensive physical property. The mass of 1000 cm³ of water at 4°C and normal atmospheric pressure is almost exactly 1 kg. Under these conditions, water exhibits its maximum density: 1.00 g/cm³.

After completing this section, you will be able to

- **calculate** the density of a substance.
- **compare** densities of different substances.
- **compare** densities of different states of matter.

The key terms in this section are
density   specific gravity

densus (thick)

¹The smaller block is more dense.

Figure 3-9

Substances with the same mass and different volumes have different densities.

Which has more mass, one kilogram of bricks or one kilogram of feathers? The correct answer is that they both have the same mass. One kilogram of a substance has the same mass as one kilogram of any other substance.

Which has a greater volume, one kilogram of bricks or one kilogram of feathers? The answer leads to a very important property of matter. One kilogram of feathers occupies a much larger volume than one kilogram of bricks. The relationship between the mass and volume of a substance is very useful in science.

Density (DEHN suh tee) is a measure of how closely the mass of a substance is packed into a given volume. **Density** is the mass per unit volume of a substance. It is a ratio and it does not depend on sample size. As volume increases, mass increases. The ratio is always the same. Because different kinds of matter have different densities, the density of a substance can be used to help identify that substance. Figure 3-9 shows two different kinds of wood. Notice that these blocks of wood have the same mass. However, one block of wood has a larger volume. Which block of wood is more dense?¹

The density of a sample of matter is found by measuring its mass and volume and then dividing the mass by the volume. The formula to find the density of a substance is written as follows.

$$D = \frac{M}{V}$$

In the formula, D stands for density, M stands for mass, and V stands for volume.

Sample Problem

Find the density of a sample of a substance. The sample has a volume of 2.00 cm³ and a mass of 38.6 g.

1. Write the formula.

$$D = \frac{M}{V}$$

2. Substitute the numbers in the problem for the symbols in the formula.

$$D = \frac{38.6 \text{ g}}{2.00 \text{ cm}^3}$$

3. Determine the unit that will be part of the answer. In this case the unit is g/cm³, which is read as "grams per cubic centimeter."

$$D = \frac{38.6}{2.00} \text{ g/cm}^3$$

4. Complete the calculations that are required. In this example, 38.6 divided by 2.00 equals 19.3.

$$D = 19.3 \text{ g/cm}^3$$

As you can see, the unit used to express density is g/cm³. For example, the density of water is written as 1.0 g/cm³. Table 3-2 shows the densities of several substances. Which substance has the same density as the substance in the sample problem?[1]

Figure 3-10

A cork and a rubber stopper. Which object has more mass?[2]

NOTE:
Throughout this book there are sample problems like the one shown here. The lines printed in blue show how to solve the problem.

[1]Gold.
[2]The rubber stopper has more mass than the cork.

Table 3-2 *Densities of Some Common Materials at 20°C.*

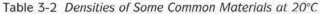

Substance	Density (g/cm³)	Substance	Density (g/cm³)
Platinum	21.4	Seawater	1.025
Gold	19.3	Water	1.00
Mercury	13.6	Ice	0.92
Lead	11.3	Oil	0.90
Silver	10.5	Paraffin	0.87
Copper	8.9	Gasoline	0.7
Brass	8.5	Wood (oak)	0.7
Iron	7.9	Wood (pine)	0.4
Steel	7.8	Cork	0.24
Aluminum	2.7	Oxygen	0.0014
Marble	2.7	Air	0.0013
Rubber	1.1	Helium	0.0002

Enrichment

Distribute bottles containing different liquids to which food coloring has been added. Include some of the following liquids: water, vegetable oil, alcohol, glycerine, corn syrup. Ask students to place equal amounts of each liquid into one large test tube and make observations. Have students stopper the test tube and shake it. Allow the contents of the test tube to settle for a few minutes, and then ask students to make observations. Ask students to explain their observations. (The liquids will settle at different levels according to their densities; the liquids that are less dense will rise.)

Review and Skill Masters

SKILL, page 20.
See page 55b in this book for answers.

Figure 3-11
The density of the iceberg is less than the density of the seawater.

Most kinds of matter expand when their temperatures rise and contract when their temperatures drop. Thus, density changes with temperature.

Gases are less dense than liquids and solids. Air bubbles in the water in a fish tank move upward and escape. A coin sinks in water. The solid states of matter generally have higher densities than do liquids. One exception to this pattern is water. Unlike other liquids, water expands as it freezes. How does Figure 3-11 demonstrate that ice is less dense than liquid water?[1]

¹The iceberg is floating.

The relationship between mass and volume has several useful applications. For example, wearing a life jacket while in a boat decreases a person's overall density. The decreased density makes it easier for a person to stay afloat. The life jacket increases the body's volume but adds very little mass.

A submarine changes depth as water is removed or added to its ballast tanks. When water is removed from the tanks, the submarine loses mass. It floats higher in the water. When water is added to the tanks, the submarine gains mass. It sinks lower in the water because its density is greater.

It is useful to compare the density of a substance to the density of water. **Specific gravity** is a ratio between the density of a substance and the density of water. The formula for calculating specific gravity is as follows.

$$\text{specific gravity} = \frac{\text{density of substance}}{\text{density of water}}$$

ACTIVITY   How Is Density Determined?

OBJECTIVE
Calculate the densities of several objects.

MATERIALS
several solid objects, balance and masses, metric ruler, 100-mL graduate, water

PROCEDURE

A. Draw a data table like the one shown.
B. Measure the mass of each of the objects. Record this information in the data table.
C. Measure the length, width, and height of the regular objects. Record this data.
D. Calculate the volume of each regular object by multiplying length × width × height.
E. Find the volume of each irregular object by using water displacement.
F. Compute the density of each object, using the following formula.

$$D = \frac{M}{V}$$

Record your answers in the data table.

RESULTS AND CONCLUSIONS

1. What was the densest sample you tested?
2. What was the least dense sample?
3. Did more than one sample have the same density? If so, do you think they are the same kind of matter?

Object	Mass (g)	Length (cm)	Width (cm)	Height (cm)	Volume (cm³)	Density (g/cm³)
Regular Object						
Irregular Object		–	–	–		

Sample Problem
What is the specific gravity of steel?

1. Write the formula.

$$\text{specific gravity} = \frac{\text{density of substance}}{\text{density of water}}$$

2. Substitute the numbers in the problem for the symbols in the formula. Find the density of each substance in Table 3-2.

$$\text{specific gravity} = \frac{7.8 \text{ g/cm}^3}{1.0 \text{ g/cm}^3}$$

3. Determine the unit that will be part of the answer. In this case the same unit is in the numerator and the denominator of the equation. The units will therefore cancel each other. Thus, specific gravity is not represented by a unit.

$$\text{specific gravity} = \frac{7.8}{1.0}$$

4. Complete the calculations that are required.

$$\text{specific gravity} = 7.8$$

The specific gravity of steel is 7.8. What is the specific gravity of platinum?[1]

[1] 21.4.

PROCESS SKILLS
measuring, recording data, comparing, interpreting data

Preparation   Before assigning irregular solids to be measured by displacement, make sure that they will fit into the graduates that will be used.

Teaching Tip   Tell students to make very careful measurements. Inform students that small errors in the measurements of dimensions of the regular objects can result in larger errors in volume and, thus, in density.

Teaching Tip   When making measurements with a metric ruler, always start at some point other than the end of the ruler.

Teaching Tip   A small wad of absorbent cotton can be placed in the bottom of the graduate as a cushion. Once the cotton soaks up some water, air bubbles will not be a problem.

Answers to Results and Conclusions
1. Answers will vary, depending on the samples chosen.
2. Answers will vary, depending on the samples chosen.
3. Samples with the same density are not necessarily the same kind of matter; another property should be considered to be certain that the samples are the same kind of matter.

Background   Hydrometers are used to measure the sugar content in maple syrup and the strength of car battery acid. Hydrometers are also used in hospitals to measure the specific gravity of urine, one source of information about a patient's health.

Tie-in/Social Studies   Have students research how Archimedes, a Greek mathematician and inventor, discovered density.

3 REVIEW/REINFORCEMENT

1. Density is the mass per unit volume of a substance. It is a measure of how closely the mass of a substance is packed into a given volume.
2. a. 2.8 g/cm^3 c. 0.9 g/cm^3
   b. 8.5 g/cm^3 d. 11.3 g/cm^3
3. a. seawater

   $$\frac{1.025 \text{ g/cm}^3}{1.00 \text{ g/cm}^3} = 1.025$$

   b. cork

   $$\frac{0.24 \text{ g/cm}^3}{1.00 \text{ g/cm}^3} = 0.24$$

   c. mercury

   $$\frac{13.6 \text{ g/cm}^3}{1.00 \text{ g/cm}^3} = 13.6$$

   d. paraffin

   $$\frac{0.87 \text{ g/cm}^3}{1.00 \text{ g/cm}^3} = 0.87$$

Challenge

Volume $= (4.5 \text{ cm})(2.0 \text{ cm})(0.2 \text{ cm})$
   $= 1.8 \text{ cm}^3$
Mass $= 4.5 \text{ g}$
Density of glass $= \dfrac{4.5 \text{ g}}{1.8 \text{ cm}^3} = 2.5 \text{ g/cm}^3$

The density of each half is 2.5 g/cm^3, since sample size does not affect density.

Figure 3-12

A hydrometer is used to measure the density of a liquid.

Specific gravity is often used to describe liquids. The specific gravity of a liquid can be measured with a device called a hydrometer. A hydrometer is a sealed tube with a weight in the bottom and markings along its side. The hydrometer is floated in a liquid. It floats high in a dense liquid and floats lower in a less dense liquid. The specific gravity is determined by the mark at the surface of the liquid. What is the specific gravity of the salt water in the aquarium shown in Figure 3-12?[1]

[1] 1.025.

REVIEW

1. What is density?
2. Find the density of each substance listed below.

Substance	Mass (g)	Volume (cm³)
A	84	30
B	204	24
C	28	31
D	757	67

3. Table 3-2 shows the densities of some substances. What is the specific gravity of each of the following substances?
   a. seawater   c. mercury
   b. cork   d. paraffin

CHALLENGE   A piece of glass is 4.5 cm long, 2.0 cm wide, and 0.2 cm thick. Its mass is 4.5 g. What is the density of the glass? Suppose the piece of glass is cut exactly in half. What is the density of each piece?

3-5 PHYSICAL CHANGES AND CHEMICAL CHANGES

The evaporation of water, the melting of wax, the dissolving of salt in water, and the breaking of glass are physical changes. In each case, no new matter is formed. Matter is changed from one state to another in evaporation and melting. Two kinds of matter are mixed when salt is dissolved in water. Matter is changed in size and shape when glass is broken. A **physical change** is one in which the appearance of matter changes but its properties and makeup remain the same. A physical change does not involve a change of one kind of matter into another.

Although water and ice look different, they are the same kind of matter. The water can be frozen and then melted again. Melting is a physical change. Boiling is also a physical change.

Most solids melt when heated. However, some solids change directly to a gas without melting. The direct change from solid to gas is known as **sublimation** (suhb luh MAY-zhuhn). Moth balls, ice, snow, and solid carbon dioxide sublime. Solid air fresheners release their odors by the process of sublimation.

Figure 3-13 shows the results of two different kinds of changes. Both the bat and the ashes started as a piece of a tree. The bat is the result of a physical change. But how were the ashes produced? New substances are produced when wood burns. There are ashes, which had not been there before. Smoke is given off. Odors are present that were not present before. Burning produces chemical changes in matter.

> *After completing this section, you will be able to*
> - **give examples** of physical changes.
> - **give examples** of chemical changes.
> - **distinguish** between physical changes and chemical changes.
>
> *The key terms in this section are*
> chemical change
> chemical property
> corrosion
> physical change
> sublimation

Figure 3-13

Wood can be changed physically (*left*) or chemically (*right*).

3-5 PHYSICAL CHANGES AND CHEMICAL CHANGES
pages 73–76

OBJECTIVES
Refer to pupil page 73.

VOCABULARY
Key terms: chemical change, chemical property, corrosion, physical change, sublimation

1 MOTIVATION

Ask students to name all the physical changes and chemical changes that they observe during a day. Guide students to name as many changes as possible that can be seen by a variety of supporting evidence such as color change, heat absorption or release, precipitate formation, and gas release. You may want to continue the discussion by providing a list of the physical and chemical changes that occur in the human body, the home, or school.

2 CONCEPT DEVELOPMENT

Background   All matter can undergo physical changes. Water, whether a solid, liquid, or gas, always has the same composition. Yet some physical properties of matter change with physical changes. For example, the density of solid water (ice) is different from that of liquid water.

Background   Sublimation is used in the preparation of dehydrated foods. Freeze-dried products are produced by placing frozen food in a vacuum at a very low pressure, usually 1 mm Hg. The frozen water in the food sublimes, and the food loses much of its original weight.

Enrichment   Give students two vials containing mixtures—one a salt solution, and the other, fine iron filings in vegetable oil. Provide students with safety goggles, an alcohol burner, an evaporating dish, tongs, a small aluminum dish, and a magnet. Ask them to separate the components by appropriate physical means. Have students write a description of what they did and why.

Background   All chemical changes require some energy to begin. The smallest amount of energy needed to start a chemical change is called activation energy. It may be heat energy or some other kind of energy. Some chemical changes need only a small amount of activation energy; others need much larger amounts.

Background   During a physical change in state, a rise in temperature is used to supply the energy needed to cause the particles to move apart and enter a new state, such as from solid to liquid or liquid to gas. A decrease in temperature reduces the energy and causes the particles to come closer together, favoring the change from gas to liquid or liquid to solid. Physical changes in state are also affected by an increase or decrease in pressure.

Thinking Skills

identifying cause and effect
Students are asked to observe physical changes and identify the causes. Have students take three ice cubes of equal size and place each on a watch glass. Then tell students to place a slotted mass of 1 g or 2 g on one ice cube and a mass of 2 g or 4 g on a second ice cube. They should not place a weight on the third ice cube. Have students make careful observations and explain their observations in terms of cause and effect.

A **chemical change** is a change that produces one or more kinds of matter that are different from those present before the change. Iron rust is made of oxygen and iron. Rust is not the same as the matter from which it formed. Thus the formation of iron rust is a chemical change.

Every time you cook an egg, you are causing changes. Breaking the egg is a physical change. If you scramble the egg, you are causing another physical change. As the egg cooks, a chemical change takes place.

When you eat the egg, another series of physical and chemical changes begins. The egg is broken down by grinding and cutting, which are physical changes. It is changed chemically by enzymes in digestive juices. Thus, digestion is a series of chemical and physical changes.

Figure 3-14

Which of these changes are physical changes?[1]

[1]Breaking the egg and scrambling the egg are physical changes.

Physical and chemical changes often differ in the amount of energy each uses. A chemical change usually releases or absorbs much more energy than does a physical change. For example, breaking down 1.0 g of water into hydrogen and oxygen requires forty times more energy than does the melting of 1.0 g of ice.

Different kinds of matter can undergo different kinds of chemical changes. The ability of a substance to undergo or resist chemical changes is called a **chemical property**. When iron is placed in some acids, a chemical change causes hydrogen gas to be released. The ability to cause this change is a chemical property of iron. When gold is placed in acid, no chemical change takes place. Thus, iron and gold differ in this property.

ACTIVITY — Do Chemical and Physical Changes Differ?

OBJECTIVE
Classify changes as chemical or physical.

MATERIALS
safety goggles; lab apron; sealed iodine tube; test-tube holder; Bunsen burner; striker; steel wool; tongs; 4 test tubes; glass-marking pencil; test-tube rack; water; wood splint; salt; dilute HCl; mossy zinc; solutions A, B, C, and D; 4 droppers

PROCEDURE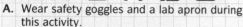

A. Wear safety goggles and a lab apron during this activity.
B. Draw a data table like the one shown.
C. Read each direction carefully. Make observations before, during, and after the change. Enter all observations in the data table.

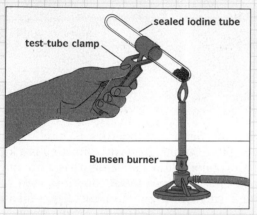

- **sealed iodine tube**
- **test-tube clamp**
- **Bunsen burner**

D. Hold an iodine tube in a test-tube holder, and gently heat the bottom of the tube over the flame of a Bunsen burner. Be careful to keep the top of the tube cool. Allow the tube to cool before putting it away.
E. Hold a small piece of steel wool with tongs. Place the steel wool into the flame. Remove the steel wool from the flame. Set it aside to cool.
F. Label four test tubes *1* through *4*. Place the test tubes in a test-tube rack.
G. Add water to a depth of about 1 cm to test tube *1*. Using a wood splint, add a small amount of salt.
H. **Caution:** Acids can burn your eyes, skin, and clothing. Add dilute HCl to a depth of about 1 cm to test tube *2*. Add a small piece of mossy zinc.
I. In test tube *3*, mix 5 drops of solution A and 2 drops of solution B. Use a different dropper for each solution.
J. In test tube *4*, mix 5 drops of solution C and 2 drops of solution D. Use a different dropper for each solution.

RESULTS AND CONCLUSIONS
1. Which procedure(s) produced a physical change?
2. What observation(s) indicate that a physical change took place?
3. Which procedure(s) produced a chemical change?
4. What observation(s) indicate that a chemical change took place?

Procedure	Observation Before Change	Observation During Change	Observation After Change	Type of Change
Heating iodine				
Heating steel wool				
Combining water and salt				
Combining HCl and mossy zinc				
Combining solutions A and B				
Combining solutions C and D				

ACTIVITY 30 minutes

PROCESS SKILLS
observing, measuring, recording data, comparing, classifying

Preparation   Prepare the solutions for steps I and J as follows: For solution A, 0.1M $Ba(NO_3)_2$, dissolve 26.1 g barium nitrate in water, and dilute to make 1 L of solution. For solution B, 0.1M Na_2CrO_4, dissolve 16.0 g of sodium chromate in water, and dilute to make 1 L of solution. For solution C, 0.1M $FeCl_3$, dissolve 27.0 g of iron(III) chloride hexahydrate in 50 mL of 6M HCl, and dilute with water to make 1 L of solution. For solution D, 0.1M KCNS, dissolve 9.7 g of potassium thiocyanate in water, and dilute to make 1 L of solution.

Safety Tip   Tell students to keep safety goggles on during the entire activity. Caution students to handle hot objects carefully.

Answers to Results and Conclusions
1. Step **D, E, G.**
2. On heating, iodine changes to a gas, through sublimation; salt in water dissolves; but can be obtained back by evaporation; heating steel wool makes it glow but not burn.
3. **H, I, J.**
4. Gas formation; formation of a yellow solid; formation of a deep red solution.

Review and Skill Masters

CHALLENGE/CRITICAL THINKING, page 22.
See page 55c in this book for answers.

3 REVIEW/REINFORCEMENT

1. The evaporation of water, the melting of ice, the melting of a candle, and the breaking of glass.
2. The rusting of iron, the burning of wood, the toasting of bread, and the tarnishing of silverware.
3. A physical change is one in which the appearance of matter changes but the properties and composition of it remain the same. A chemical change is one that produces one or more kinds of matter that are different from those present before the change.

Challenge Physical change—melting of wax; chemical change—burning of wick.

Figure 3-15

Restoring the Statue of Liberty.

Knowledge of chemical properties is important in using materials. For example, iron rusts. Rusting is a kind of corrosion. **Corrosion** (kuh ROH zhuhn) is a chemical change that takes place when a metal combines with substances around it, such as oxygen. Iron rust flakes off after it forms. As a result, rusting continues on the newly exposed surface. Buildings, bridges, and other structures made of iron must be painted or protected in some other way to prevent rusting.

Metal structures that have not been protected may become corroded. Pollution can cause corrosion. Millions of dollars were raised to restore the Statue of Liberty after corrosion had damaged it.

REVIEW

1. Describe two physical changes.
2. Describe two chemical changes.
3. How do chemical changes and physical changes differ?

CHALLENGE Identify one physical change and one chemical change that take place as a candle burns.

CHAPTER SUMMARY

The main ideas in this chapter are listed below. Read these statements before you answer the Chapter Review questions.

- Matter is anything that has mass and takes up space. (3-1)

- An element is a substance that cannot be changed into simpler substances by ordinary means. (3-1)

- A compound is a substance made up of two or more elements chemically combined. The elements in a compound are always present in definite proportions. (3-1)

- A mixture is made up of two or more kinds of matter, each keeping its own properties. (3-1)

- Matter has four states: solid, liquid, gas, and plasma. (3-2)

- Solids are classified as crystalline or amorphous solids. (3-2)

- Matter in the plasma state is a hot, electrically charged gas. (3-2)

- Physical properties are characteristics of matter that can be measured and observed without changing the makeup of the substance. (3-3)

- Physical properties include color, odor, melting point, and boiling point. (3-3)

- Density is the mass per unit volume of a substance. The unit used to express density is g/cm^3. (3-4)

- The specific gravity of a substance is a ratio between the density of a substance and the density of water. (3-4)

- Physical changes may change the appearance of matter but not its makeup. Physical changes include melting and boiling. (3-5)

- Sublimation is the direct change of a solid to a gas without going through the liquid state. (3-5)

- Chemical changes produce new substances that differ in appearance and makeup from the original substances. (3-5)

- Corrosion is a chemical change that occurs when a metal combines with substances around it. (3-5)

The key terms in this chapter are listed below. Use each term in a sentence that shows the meaning of the term.

amorphous solid	density	physical change
boiling point	element	physical properties
chemical change	freezing point	plasma
chemical property	gas	solid
compound	liquid	specific gravity
condensation point	matter	sublimation
corrosion	melting point	surface tension
crystalline solid	mixture	

Review and Skill Masters

VOCABULARY REVIEW, page 17.
See page 55b in this book for answers.

VOCABULARY
1. melting point
2. element
3. compound
4. density
5. mixture
6. specific gravity
7. sublimation
8. matter
9. crystalline solid
10. corrosion
11. plasma

CONCEPTS
1. Substance and mixture.
2. Compounds are made up of two or more elements chemically combined.
3. In a uniform mixture the makeup is the same throughout the sample. In a mixture that is not uniform, the composition and properties vary from point to point.
4. Solid—iron, copper; liquid—water, milk; gas—air, oxygen.
5. Plasma state; on the sun and other stars in the universe.
6. In a crystalline solid the particles are arranged in a regular, repeating, three dimensional pattern. In an amorphous solid the particles lack a regular, repeating order.
7. When you heat a solid, you add energy to its particles, causing the particles to move faster and farther apart. As the particles gain more energy, they move fast enough to overcome the forces of attraction between particles. Thus the solid melts and loses its shape. The liquid flows and takes the shape of its container. If enough energy is added to a liquid, the liquid will change to the gaseous state. The particles of gases are very far apart compared with those of solids and liquids.
8. Viscosity, boiling point, surface tension, freezing point.
9. Melting point, malleability, hardness, elasticity, tensile strength, brittleness.

Review and Skill Masters

CHAPTER REVIEW, page 18.
See page 55b in this book for answers.

78

Chapter Review

VOCABULARY

Use the key terms from this chapter to complete the following sentences correctly .

1. The temperature at which a solid becomes a liquid is called the _____ .
2. A substance that cannot be made into simpler substances by ordinary means is called a/an _____ .
3. A/An _____ results when new substances are formed from the combination of two or more different elements.
4. _____ is the mass per unit volume of a substance.
5. A/An _____ is the combination of two or more substances, with each keeping its own properties.
6. The ratio between the density of a substance and the density of water is called _____ .
7. _____ is a change from the solid state directly to the gas state.
8. Anything that has mass and takes up space is called _____ .
9. A/An _____ is a solid whose particles are arranged in a regular, repeating, three-dimensional pattern.
10. _____ is the chemical change that takes place when a metal combines with oxygen or other substances around it.
11. The _____ state of matter is a hot, electrically charged gas.

CONCEPTS

1. Into what two groups is matter classified? (3-1)
2. What is the relationship between elements and compounds? (3-1)
3. How does a uniform mixture differ from a mixture that is not uniform? (3-1)
4. What are the three states of matter that normally exist on the earth? Give one example of each. (3-2)
5. What is the state of matter not normally found on earth? Where is this matter found? (3-2)
6. Compare the particle arrangements in crystalline and amorphous solids. (3-2)
7. What happens to the particles in a substance as it changes state? (3-2)
8. List three physical properties of liquids. (3-3)
9. List three physical properties of solids. (3-3)
10. What is the relationship between boiling point and condensation point? (3-3)

11. If a substance has a high density, what is known about its mass in relation to its volume? (3-4)

12. Find the density of each of the following substances. (3-4)

Substance	Mass (g)	Volume (cm³)
A	386	20
B	84	8
C	12	50

13. Use Table 3-2 to identify each substance in question 12. (3-4)

14. Find the specific gravity of each substance in question 12. (3-4)

15. What is the difference between density and specific gravity? (3-4)

16. What tool is used to measure the specific gravity of a liquid? Explain how it is used. (3-4)

17. Label each of the following as a physical change or a chemical change. (3-5)
    a. burning wood
    b. breaking a window
    c. exploding firecraker
    d. burning sulfur

APPLICATION/
CRITICAL
THINKING

1. Two substances have the same melting and boiling points. You want more evidence to determine whether the two substances are the same or not. What other properties would you investigate?

2. A student has two blocks with the same volume. One block is made of wood and the other of cork. The density of the wood is 0.7 g/cm³. The density of cork is 0.24 g/cm³. How many times heavier than the cork block is the wood block?

3. Crystalline solids are usually harder than amorphous solids. Suggest a reason for this difference.

4. What properties would you look for in choosing substances to make a tennis ball? Would you look for the same properties in choosing substances to make a baseball?

5. Baking a cake involves both chemical and physical changes. Describe some of the changes that take place as a cake bakes. Classify these changes as chemical or physical.

EXTENSION

1. Do research on the Brenell test. Find out how it is used in the laboratory.

2. The tensile strength of a fiber in a spider's web is as great as that of some metals. Find out how tensile strength is measured, and what unit is used to express it.

READINGS

Gunston, Bill. *Water*. Morristown, N.J.: Silver Burdett, 1982.

Trefil, James. "Matter vs. Antimatter." *Science 81*, September 1981, p.66.

---

10. Condensation is the reverse of boiling. The boiling point and condensation point of a substance are the same point.

11. The mass is large in relation to its volume.

12. Density of A is 19.3 g/cm³; density of B is 10.5 g/cm³; density of C is 0.24 g/cm³.

13. A is gold, B is silver, and C is cork.

14. The specific gravity of A is 19.3, of B is 10.5, and of C is 0.24.

15. Density is the mass per unit volume of a substance. Specific gravity is a ratio between the density of a substance and the density of water.

16. Hydrometer; the hydrometer is floated in a liquid, and the specific gravity is determined by the mark at the surface of the liquid.

17. a. Chemical   c. Chemical
    b. Physical   d. Chemical

APPLICATION/CRITICAL THINKING

1. Determine the densities of the two materials. Determine the chemical properties of the two materials.

2. $\dfrac{\text{Density of wood}}{\text{Density of cork}} = \dfrac{0.7 \text{ g/cm}^3}{0.24 \text{ g/cm}^3} = 2.92$
   Thus, the wood cube is 2.92 times heavier than the cork cube.

3. The forces of attraction between the particles in a crystalline solid are much greater than those in an amorphous solid.

4. For a tennis ball—elasticity and tensile strength; for a baseball—elasticity, hardness, and tensile strength.

5. The actual baking of the cake causes chemical changes, but the rising of the cake is a physical change caused by the chemical change in which CO_2 is given off.

Test Masters

CHAPTER TEST, page 9.
See page 55d in this book for answers.

ATOMIC STRUCTURE

ORGANIZER

Section	pages	Activity	pages	Reinforcement and Evaluation	pages	*Review and Skill Masters	pages	Other Components in Teacher Resource Package	pages
4—1 Early Models of the Atom	81–86			Review, Challenge	86			Study Guide Transparency	18
4—2 The Structure of the Atom	87–89			Review, Challenge	89			Study Guide Lab Manual	19 17
4—3 How Atoms Differ	90–94	How Can Masses Be Compared?	92	Puzzler Review, Challenge	93 94			Study Guide	20
4—4 How Atoms Are Represented	95–97	How Do Isotopes Differ?	96	Review, Challenge	97			Study Guide	21
4—5 The Periodic Table	98–103	How Is the Periodic Table Arranged?	102	Review, Challenge	103	Skill Challenge/Critical Thinking	26–27 28	Study Guide Poster	22
CHAPTER SUMMARY	103					Vocabulary Review	23		
CHAPTER REVIEW	104–105			*Test Masters	13–16	Chapter Review	24–25		

*In the Teacher Resource Package. For answers, see pages 79b–79d in this book.

ACTIVITY MATERIALS
Quantities are based on a class of 30 students working in groups as indicated in parentheses.

How Can Masses Be Compared? p. 92 (groups of 2)	quantity	How Do Isotopes Differ? p. 96 (groups of 2)	quantity	How Is the Periodic Table Arranged? p. 102 (groups of 1)	quantity
balance	15	isotope models	15	pencil or marker	30
nickel	15	balance	15	unlined paper	30 sheets
glass beads	100			drawing compass	30
penny	15			metric ruler	30
quarter	15			scissors	30
				clear tape	30 rolls
				poster board	30

REVIEW AND SKILL MASTERS

Name_____ Date_____

VOCABULARY REVIEW _____ Chapter 4

Fill in the blanks to find the name of the person who made the first model of the atom.

1. m o d e l
2. e l e c t r o n
3. a t o m
4. i s o t o p e s
5. a t o m i c   n u m b e r
6. g r o u p
7. p e r i o d
8. n e u t r o n
9. n u c l e u s
10. m a s s   n u m b e r

1. A scientist's way to explain something that cannot be seen or understood by relating it to something that can be seen

2. The particle in the atom that has a negative charge

3. The smallest particle of an element that has the properties of that element

4. Atoms of the same element but with different numbers of neutrons

5. A number equal to the number of protons in the nucleus of an atom (two words)

6. A vertical column in the Periodic Table made up of elements that have similar chemical properties

7. The horizontal row in the Periodic Table

8. The particle in the atom that has no charge

9. The part of the atom that has most of the mass of the atom

10. The sum of the protons and neutrons in an atom (two words)

23

Name_____ Date_____

CHAPTER REVIEW _____ Chapter 4

4-1 Early Models of the Atom

1. What is the smallest particle of an element that has the properties of that element?
   An atom.

2. Bohr thought that electrons moved in _____ paths _____, rather than whirling around the nucleus in a random way. He also thought that _____ electrons _____ could move from one energy level to another.

3. Why are models used in science? Many ideas in science cannot be seen. Models help scientists to understand and explain such ideas.

4-2 The Structure of the Atom

1. Name the three particles found in an atom and the location of each in the electron cloud model. The proton and the neutron are located in the nucleus; the electrons are found in the electron clouds around the nucleus.

2. State the electric charge of each of the three kinds of particles in the atom.
   A proton has a positive charge; a neutron has no electrical charge; an electron has a negative charge.

4-3 How Atoms Differ

1. Define atomic number and mass number in terms of an atom's particles.
   The atomic number of an element is the number of protons in the nucleus. Mass number is the sum of the protons and neutrons in an atom.

2. How many electrons are held in the first through third energy levels?
   The first energy level can hold up to 2 electrons, the second level can hold up to 8 electrons, and the third energy level can hold up to 18 electrons.

24

Name_____ Date_____

CHAPTER REVIEW (Continued) _____ Chapter 4

4-4 How Atoms Are Represented

1. What is a chemical symbol? It is notation of one or two letters that represents an element.

2. Identify the element that each of the following symbols represents.
   a. C carbon
   b. H hydrogen
   c. Na sodium
   d. N nitrogen

3. Sketch the electron arrangement of aluminum, atomic number 13.

4-5 The Periodic Table

1. Describe the organization of the Periodic Table in terms of groups and periods of elements.
   The vertical columns in a Periodic Table are called groups. The elements of each group have similar chemical properties. The horizontal rows are called periods. The elements in a period have the same number of energy levels.

2. Locate the following elements in the Periodic Table and complete the chart below.

ELEMENT	SYMBOL	ATOMIC NUMBER	GROUP	PERIOD
Oxygen	O	8	16	2
Iron	Fe	26	8	4
Helium	He	2	18	1

25

Name_____ Date_____

SKILL/Interpreting a Table _____ Chapter 4

Chemists have fully described at least 103 of the elements in the Periodic Table. The Periodic Table shown below has a zigzag line that separates the metals from the nonmetals. Metals are shiny and are good conductors of heat and electricity. Nonmetals are dull and are poor conductors of heat and electricity. The nonmetals in Group 18 are called the noble gases because they do not take part in chemical reactions.

Some of the elements that touch the zigzag line in the Periodic Table have some of the properties of metals and some of the properties of nonmetals. These elements are called metalloids.

Look at the Periodic Table shown below and answer the following questions.

Periodic Table of Elements

*Atomic masses appearing in parentheses are those of the most stable known isotopes.
**No names have been given and no mass data is available.

26

Name_____ Date_____

SKILL/Interpreting a Table (Continued) _____ Chapter 4

1. Elements with three or fewer outer electrons usually are __metals_____

2. Elements with five or more outer electrons usually are __nonmetals_____

3. __Metalloids_____ are located along a zigzag line in the Periodic Table.

4. Metalloids have some properties of _____metals_____ and some
   properties of __nonmetals__

5. In which group of the Periodic Table are the noble gases? Are they metals or nonmetals?
   __The noble gases are in Group 18 of the Periodic Table. They are nonmetals.__

6. Examine the Periodic Table on the previous page and then classify the elements listed
   below as a metal, nonmetal, noble gas, or metalloid. Write the correct letter in front of each
   element.

   A — Metal
   B — Nonmetal
   C — Noble gas
   D — Metalloid

   a. __A__ Sodium (Na)   k. __B__ Carbon (C)
   b. __A__ Copper (Cu)   l. __A__ Calcium (Ca)
   c. __A__ Iron (Fe)   m. __A__ Lithium (Li)
   d. __D__ Polonium (Po)   n. __B__ Nitrogen (N)
   e. __B__ Sulfur (S)   o. __B__ Fluorine (F)
   f. __C__ Argon (Ar)   p. __D__ Arsenic (As)
   g. __D__ Silicon (Si)   q. __D__ Boron (B)
   h. __B__ Chlorine (Cl)   r. __B__ Bromine (Br)
   i. __C__ Neon (Ne)   s. __A__ Magnesium (Mg)
   j. __B__ Oxygen (O)   t. __C__ Xenon (Xe)

© 1989 Silver, Burdett & Ginn Inc.

27

Name_____ Date_____

CHALLENGE/CRITICAL THINKING _____ Chapter 4

The table below shows part of the Periodic Table. The atomic numbers of some elements are
shown. Use the chart to find the periodic pattern of increase in atomic numbers within each
group and answer the questions that follow.

	Group 13	Group 14	Group 15	Group 16	Group 17	Group 18
Period 2	5	6	7	8	9	10
Period 3	13	14	15	16	17	18
Period 4	31	32	33	34	35	36
Period 5	49	50	51	52	53	54

1. Look at the atomic numbers of the elements in Group 13. What is the increase in atomic
   number from Period 2 to Period 3? __8__

2. Look at the atomic numbers of the elements in Group 13. What is the increase in atomic
   number from Period 3 to Period 4? __18__

3. Look at the atomic numbers of the elements in Group 13. What is the increase in atomic
   number from Period 4 to Period 5? __18__

4. This same pattern continues for Groups 14-18. Use this periodic pattern to fill in the atomic
   numbers for the blank boxes in the sample Periodic Table above.

5. The periodic pattern changes slightly in different parts of the Periodic Table. Find the other
   patterns of change for Groups 1, 2, and 10.
   __In Group 1, the pattern is 2, 8, 8, 18, 18, 32. In Group 2, the pattern is 8, 8, 18,__
   __18, 32. In Group 10, the pattern is 18, 32.__

© 1989 Silver, Burdett & Ginn Inc.

28

REVIEW AND
SKILL MASTERS

TEST MASTERS

Name _____ **Date** _____ **Score** _____

Chapter 4

Atomic Structure

PART 1

In the space below, write the term that each phrase defines.

			Chapter Goal
1.	**atom**	The smallest particle of an element that has the properties of that element	1
2.	**chemical symbol**	A notation of one or two letters that represents an element	4
3.	**mass number**	The sum of the protons and neutrons in the nucleus of an atom	3
4.	**periodic law**	The statement that says that the properties of the elements repeat in a regular way if the elements are arranged by increasing atomic number	5
5.	**atomic mass unit**	The unit that is one-twelfth the mass of a carbon-12 atom	3
6.	**neutron**	A particle with no charge, found in an atom's nucleus	2
7.	**group**	A vertical column of the Periodic Table, made up of elements that have similar chemical properties	5
8.	**model**	A tool scientists use to try to explain something that they cannot see or understand by relating it to something that they do see or understand	1
9.	**electron**	The negatively charged particle in the atom	2

PART 2

Choose the term or phrase that best answers the question or completes the statement. Write the letter of that choice in the space at the left.

b 1. Neutral atoms have an electrical charge of:
a. −1.   b. 0.   c. +1.   d. +2.   `2`

c 2. Which of the following is the chemical symbol for germanium?
a. Ger   b. gm   c. Ge   d. GE   `4`

Chapter 4   Atomic Structure   **13**

Name _____ **Date** _____ **Score** _____

PART 2

Choose the term or phrase that best answers the question or completes the statement. Write the letter of that choice in the space at the left.

Chapter Goal

b 3. In an atom that has 6 electrons, how many energy levels contain these electrons?
a. 1   b. 2   c. 3   d. 4   `4`

d 4. The expression "2Ca" represents two:
a. electrons.   b. compounds.   c. protons.   d. atoms.   `4`

a 5. In the Periodic Table, elements increase in both mass and number of energy levels from:
a. top to bottom.   c. left to right.
b. bottom to top.   d. right to left.   `5`

c 6. The mass number of an atom depends in part on the number of:
a. electrons.   c. neutrons.
b. energy levels.   d. electron clouds.   `3`

c 7. All models of the atom before the 20th century were based on the belief in:
a. neutral particles.   c. indivisible atoms.
b. charged particles.   d. moving electrons.   `1`

a 8. One of the differences between a proton and an electron is that an electron has a greater:
a. range of motion.   c. mass.
b. electrical charge.   d. density.   `2`

a 9. Isotopes of an element differ in their:
a. mass numbers.   c. freezing points.
b. electrical charges.   d. atomic numbers.   `3`

d 10. Bohr's changes in Rutherford's model of the atom involved the:
a. structure of the nucleus.
b. number of particles.
c. electrical charges of particles.
d. motion of electrons.   `1`

d 11. Which of the following is always true about any two elements in the same period?
a. They have different numbers of energy levels.
b. They have similar chemical properties.
c. The element to the left has more electrons.
d. The element to the right has more protons.   `5`

14   Chapter 4   Atomic Structure

Name _____ **Date** _____ **Score** _____

PART 3

Look at the diagram. Then read the questions that follow. Choose the term or phrase that best answers the question or completes the statement. Write the letter of that choice in the space at the left.

Chapter Goal

c 1. How many protons are contained in the nucleus of the atom shown in the diagram?
a. 2   b. 7   c. 9   d. 10   `2`

d 2. What is the mass number of this atom?
a. 9   b. 12   c. 17   d. 19   `3`

b 3. The atomic model shown is most like the model proposed by:
a. Democritus.   b. Bohr.   c. Dalton.   d. Thomson.   `1`

a 4. What is the correct representation of the isotope shown?
a. $^{19}_{9}F$ b. $^{10}_{7}F$ c. $^{9}_{10}F$ d. $^{17}_{10}F$ `4`

c 5. The atom shown is classified as a:
a. metal.   b. metalloid.   c. nonmetal.   d. silicon.   `5`

Chapter 4   Atomic Structure   **15**

Name _____ **Date** _____ **Score** _____

PART 4

Read each question or direction and answer it using complete sentences.

Chapter Goal

1. What were the main points of Dalton's atomic theory?   `1`

   1. All matter is made up of tiny particles called atoms that cannot be split into smaller particles.
   2. Atoms cannot be created or destroyed.
   3. All atoms of the same element have the same properties, and atoms of different elements have different properties.
   4. Atoms of different elements combine to form new substances.

2. Describe the electron cloud model of the atom.   `2`

   According to the electron cloud model of the atom, electrons are moving very rapidly in regions of space around the nucleus. These regions of space are called electron clouds. There are several types of electron clouds, each with its own shape. There is a good chance of finding a particular electron in an electron cloud.

3. Describe energy levels of electrons.   `3`

   Electrons are found in definite paths around the nucleus called energy levels. Energy levels can be thought of as rings and are referred to by numbers. For example, Level 1 is closest to the nucleus and is the smallest in diameter. Each energy level can hold a certain number of electrons.

16   Chapter 4   Atomic Structure

CHAPTER 4 PLANNING GUIDE

79d

4

ATOMIC STRUCTURE

The questions in the CHAPTER TEST are based on these Chapter Goals.

1. Explain how models are used in science, explain what a model is, and describe early models of the atom.
2. Describe the structure of atoms and the electron cloud model of the atom.
3. Relate atomic number, mass number, and atomic mass units to atomic structure.
4. List the symbols of some elements, and interpret diagrams of atoms.
5. Relate the organization of the Periodic Table to atomic structure and the characteristics of elements.

ATOMIC STRUCTURE

The streaks of light in this photograph are the images produced by the lights of moving cars. These streaks of light show you where the cars were going when the photograph was taken. Look more closely at the photograph. You cannot see the cars. But the streaks of light provide evidence that the cars were there. Scientists cannot see the tiny particles that make up matter, but they have evidence indicating that these particles exist.

- *What evidence is there that matter is made of particles?*
- *How do scientists collect this evidence?*

4-1 EARLY MODELS OF THE ATOM

One of the central ideas in science is that matter is made up of small particles. Imagine taking a pure sample of an element, such as gold, and cutting it in half. Then cut it in half again, and again. Imagine that you are able to cut each smaller piece in half. You would finally have a piece so tiny that it could not be divided further and still be gold. That piece is called an atom. An **atom** is the smallest particle of an element that has the properties of that element.

MODELS IN SCIENCE

Our concept of the atom is an example of a scientific model. In science a **model** is a means by which scientists try to explain something that they cannot see or understand by relating it to something that they do see or understand. Scientists use models to describe things that they cannot observe directly. There are many scientific models for very small things, like the atom. There also are scientific models for things so huge that they cannot be seen in total. For example, many models of the universe have been proposed. Scientists use models as tools. Ideas and comparisons are mental models. A useful model can help a scientist predict and explain data.

After completing this section, you will be able to

- **define** the term *atom*.
- **state** the function of a model in science.
- **describe** early models of the atom.

The key terms in this section are
atom   model

Have students read the introductory paragraph and make observations about the photograph. Ask the students why the streaks of light are evidence that cars are present. Emphasize that scientists have made many discoveries about atoms without ever seeing an atom. Ask students if they can think of other examples of situations that prove the existence of something that cannot be seen.

- What evidence is there that matter is made of particles? (Results of experiments that show energy being released from invisible particles of matter.)
- How do scientists collect this evidence? (By studying the physical and chemical properties of matter and sharing the information.)

4-1 EARLY MODELS OF THE ATOM
pages 81–86

OBJECTIVES
Refer to pupil page 81.

VOCABULARY
Key terms: atom, model
Other terms: alpha particles, electrons, nucleus

1 MOTIVATION

The evaporation of water is an example of how scientists can visualize the invisible by using a model. Have students give examples of their experiences with evaporation. List their examples on the chalkboard. Generate a discussion by asking students to describe what they think is happening when liquids evaporate. Ask why a puddle evaporates more quickly when the sun is out. Also ask why they feel a chill when coming out of a swimming pool. Finally, ask why water evaporates from a teapot more quickly if the burner is set for high heat.

Background   Democritus' model of the atom is an example of an intuitive model. Models such as those made by Dalton and Rutherford are examples of models based on experiments.

Teaching Tip   Remind students that models are used to explain things that cannot be seen and are also used as tools for further scientific inquiry. As knowledge is acquired, models may be revised, changed, or discarded. From Democritus to Dalton to Thomson to Rutherford to Bohr, atomic models have evolved and have helped scientists increase their understanding of matter and the interactions of matter and energy.

Figure 4-1 shows three types of models used in science. The scale replica of the space shuttle shows the three dimensional object. The diagram of the shuttle is a model that shows how the shuttle is built. The equation is a mental model that tells the speed needed for the shuttle to escape the earth's gravity. With these models a scientist would not have to see the shuttle to understand how it works. With models of the atom, scientists are able to understand how atoms behave without seeing them. Many scientists have developed models of the atom.

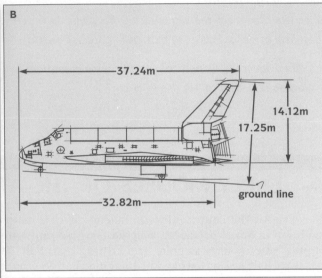

Figure 4-1

Scientists use many models, including a scale replica (*A*), a diagram (*B*), and an equation (*C*).

$$V = \sqrt{2g_{o}r_{o}} \sqrt{\frac{h}{r_{o} + h}}$$

DEMOCRITUS

A Greek philosopher named Democritus (dih MAHK-ruht uhs) lived over 2000 years ago. He was the first person to form a model of the atom. Like all educated people of his time, Democritus did not experiment. He observed nature. From his observations he formed a mental model of matter. He reasoned that all matter is made up of small, indivisible particles. In fact the word *atom* comes from the Greek word *atomos,* which means "indivisible." Democritus also thought that atoms of different substances differ in size and shape and that there is a different kind of atom for every substance.

DALTON

In the early 1800s an English schoolteacher named John Dalton studied Democritus' model of the atom. Dalton formed his model after collecting data about chemical reactions and behavior of gases. Dalton's idea is known as the atomic theory. The main points of this theory can be stated as follows:

- All matter is made up of tiny particles called atoms that cannot be split into smaller particles.
- Atoms cannot be created or destroyed.
- All atoms of the same element have the same properties, and the atoms of different elements have different properties.
- Atoms of different elements can combine to form new substances.

THOMSON

Experiments done in the 1900s led to changes in Dalton's model. J. J. Thomson, a British physicist, showed that atoms contain particles with a negative electrical charge. He called these particles *electrons*. Thomson knew that atoms have no charge. Therefore, he reasoned that atoms must also contain a positive charge. The postive charge would "cancel" the charge of the negative particles. Thomson's model described the atom as a positively charged sphere in which negative particles were scattered. The electrons in Thomson's model were like raisins in a pudding or seeds in a pomegranate.

NOTE:
For further information about electrical charges, see pages 383–385.

[1] The model shows electrons scattered throughout the atom. The pomegranate has seeds scattered throughout the fruit.

Background   Sir Joseph John Thomson (1856–1940) discovered electrons by studying the flow of electricity through gases in near-vacuum tubes containing two electrodes. He noticed that electricity, which is a flow of negative charges, traveled in straight lines from the cathode electrode to the anode electrode. Thomson showed that these rays consisted of small negative particles moving at high speeds and that the ratio of the charge to the mass of the particles was about 2000 times greater than the already known charge-to-mass ratio for a hydrogen atom. This ratio of charge to mass for the negative particles was found to be the same regardless of the gas used in the discharge tube. It was concluded that the particles were universal constituents of matter, and they were given the name *electrons*.

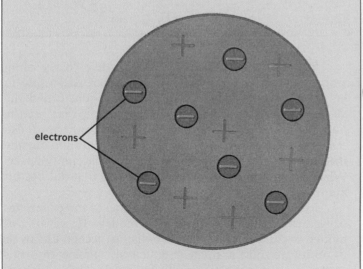

electrons

Figure 4-2

How does Thomson's model of the atom resemble a pomegranate?[1]

Background   Ernest Rutherford (1871–1937) and his coworkers studied the effects of a stream of alpha particles (He^{2+}) directed at a thin foil of gold metal. A special arrangement of screens and microscopes enabled them to observe that almost all of the alpha particles passed directly through the foil; very few were deflected on passage, and of these, a small number were deflected at large angles. Rutherford concluded that all of the positive charge and most of the mass of an atom are concentrated in a very small space at the center of the atom; he called that space the *nucleus*.

Thinking Skills

predicting
Students have studied the results of Rutherford's experiment and how he concluded that most of the atom is empty space. Have students predict the results of the same experiment if Thomson's model of the atom is used instead of Rutherford's.

Thinking Skills

interpreting diagrams
Have students compare Figure 4-2 with Figure 4-4. Encourage students to discuss the changes in the model of the atom.

RUTHERFORD

In 1911, Ernest Rutherford, a physicist from New Zealand, added to the understanding of the atom. He knew that some substances give off positively charged particles called *alpha particles*. When these particles were aimed at a piece of gold foil, most of them passed through the foil and hit the screen behind it. But Rutherford was surprised to see that a few of the particles bounced back when they hit the foil. What caused this bouncing?

Shooting alpha particles at gold foil was like throwing marbles at a net. Most marbles would go through. Only marbles that hit the net would bounce off. Like the net, the atom is mostly empty space.

Figure 4-3

Rutherford's experiment showed that most of the atom is empty space.

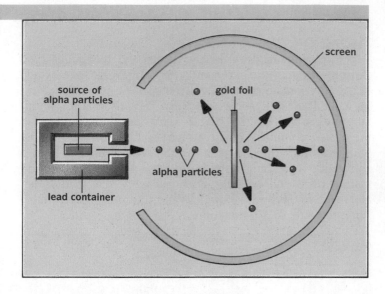

Rutherford said that all of the positive charge of an atom is in a very small point in its center. According to his model the atom has a tiny positive core called the *nucleus* (NOO klee uhs). An alpha particle that hit the nucleus of an atom would bounce back. Rutherford also said that electrons in the atom are whirling around outside the nucleus and that most of the atom is empty space. What would happen to an alpha particle that did not hit a nucleus?[1]

Rutherford's model explained some of the properties of elements better than did other models. However, this model was difficult for some scientists to accept. Electrons in orbits around the nucleus, much like planets in orbits around the sun, were impossible to explain. Unlike planets,

[1]It would continue to move without changing direction.

charged particles in motion were known to give off energy. So it seemed that electrons must lose energy as they speed around the nucleus, and that they would eventually fall into it.

BOHR

Niels Bohr was a young Danish physicist working in Rutherford's laboratory. He knew that under certain conditions, atoms give off energy. Under different conditions, atoms absorb energy. In 1913, Bohr suggested changes in the Rutherford model of the atom to explain these observations.

According to the Bohr model, the electrons in an atom are not whirling around the nucleus in a random way. Instead, electrons move in paths. Each path is a certain distance from the nucleus. Compare Bohr's model to a bookcase, as shown in Figure 4-4. Just as each shelf is a certain distance from the floor, each path is a certain distance from the nucleus. Also, the distance between one path and the next is not the same for each path, just as the shelves in some bookcases are not the same distance from each other. The paths in which electrons circle the nucleus are called energy levels. Electrons are found in energy levels, not between them, just as books are found on bookcase shelves, not floating between shelves.

Background   Niels Bohr (1885–1962) attempted to account for the radiation emitted by hydrogen gas when excited by an electric discharge. Bohr postulated that the electron in a hydrogen atom could move only in particular circular orbits now known as energy levels. When the hydrogen atom was subjected to an electric discharge, the atom was given energy. The electron might absorb this energy and move to a higher energy state or orbit. Furthermore, Bohr suggested that when the electron fell from a higher energy level to a lower energy level, the atom emitted energy in the form of electromagnetic radiation. Bohr was able to calculate the energies of such orbits.

Figure 4-4

According to Bohr's model of the atom, electrons are located in specific energy levels like shelves in a bookcase.

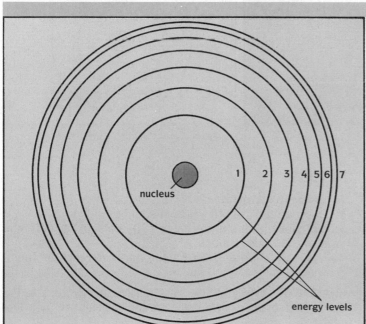

Transparency

The Teacher Resource Package includes a color transparency and a black-line master of Figures 4-4 and 4-6. You may wish to use these in your discussion of atomic models.

Teaching Tip   The atom is hard to visualize in terms of its dimensions. Share the following analogies with your students. If water molecules were enlarged to the size of golf balls, a glass of water would be the size of the earth. If the nucleus of an average atom were enlarged to the size of a tennis ball and placed in the center of the United States, the electrons that move about the nucleus would be spread out to Alaska. If the hydrogen nucleus were enlarged to the size of a tennis ball, its electron would be about 3.2 km from the nucleus.

Tie-in/Social Studies   Have students list historical developments that occurred during the time in which the development of atomic structure was taking place.

3 REVIEW/REINFORCEMENT

1. An atom is the smallest particle of an element that retains the properties of that element.
2. Scientists use models to describe things that cannot be observed directly or completely.
3. Democritus reasoned that all matter is made up of small, indivisible particles. Bohr's model described atoms as having a positively charged nucleus surrounded by negatively charged electrons in specific orbits.
4. Thomson's model described the atom as a positively charged solid sphere in which negatively charged particles were scattered like seeds in a pomegranate. In Rutherford's model of the atom, all of the positive charge was concentrated in the nucleus, and the negative particles were whirling around the nucleus.

Challenge   Scientists thought that as the electrons spiraled about the nucleus, they would give off energy and eventually collapse into the nucleus.

Electrons in each energy level have a definite amount of energy. The farther the energy level from the nucleus, the greater the energy of the electrons there. Bohr said that electrons can move from one energy level to another. Adding energy to an atom moves an electron to an energy level that is farther from the nucleus. When an electron moves to a level that is closer to the nucleus, the atom gives off energy. When the plastic shown in Figure 4-5 is exposed to light, one or more electrons move to a higher energy level. When electrons fall back to their lower level, light energy is given off. Thus, the Bohr model explains why some objects glow in the dark.

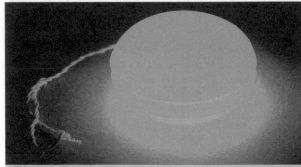
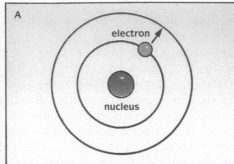
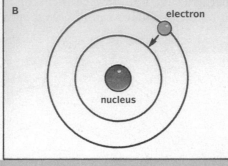

Figure 4-5

Electrons can absorb energy (A) and then release it (B). What happens to the plastic after all electrons have returned to lower levels?[1]

[1]When all electrons have returned to lower levels, no more energy will be given off and the object will stop glowing.

REVIEW

1. Define the term *atom*.
2. Describe the use of models in science.
3. Describe the differences between Democritus' model of the atom and Bohr's model.
4. How is Rutherford's model of the atom different from Thomson's model?

CHALLENGE   Why did scientists think that electrons in the Rutherford model would fall into the nucleus as they lost energy?

4-2 THE STRUCTURE OF THE ATOM

In 1926, Erwin Schrodinger, an Austrian physicist, proposed a new model of the atom. His model is shown in Figure 4-6. It is often called the electron cloud model. According to this model, electrons are moving very rapidly in regions of space around the nucleus. These regions of space are called electron clouds. This model describes several types of electron clouds, each of which has its own shape. An electron cloud is a region of space in which there is a good chance of finding a particular electron in an atom.

The electron cloud model is very complex. Remember that a model is a tool. For many calculations, scientists work with the Bohr model because it is a useful tool.

Figure 4-6

The electron cloud model of the atom.

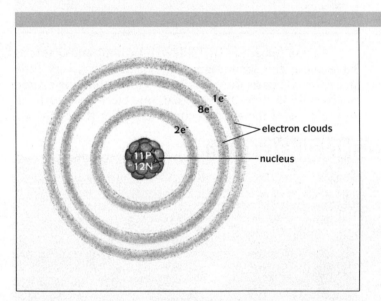

THE PARTS OF THE ATOM

The current model of the atom includes a tiny nucleus with negatively charged particles in electron clouds around the nucleus. The **nucleus** is the part of the atom that has most of the mass of the atom, and that has a positive charge. The positively charged particle in the atom is called the **proton**. The negatively charged particle in the atom is called the **electron**. Scientists call the charge of one proton $1+$. One electron has an equal but opposite charge of $1-$. In a neutral atom there are the same number of protons and electrons. Thus the positive and negative charges are balanced.

protos (first)
electr- (electric)
-on (particle)

OBJECTIVES
Refer to pupil page 87.

VOCABULARY
Key terms: electron, neutron, nucleus,
proton

1 MOTIVATION

An electron occupies a region of space around the nucleus of an atom. A good way to present this idea is to compare an electron cloud with the fuzzy sphere of a propeller in motion. Use a working propeller, such as an electric fan, to generate a discussion of the three-dimensional electron cloud. (**Caution:** Do not allow students to put their fingers near the fan blades.) Ask students how an electron cloud is like the fuzzy sphere of a propeller in motion. Also ask how the fuzzy sphere of a propeller in motion is different from an electron in orbit in Bohr's model.

2 CONCEPT DEVELOPMENT

Background   Schrodinger's model of the atom is based on the idea that the electron exhibits wavelike characteristics. Schrodinger was able to postulate complex mathematical equations whose solutions (called *wave functions*) can be manipulated to provide a measure of the probability of locating an electron in a given region of space. An understanding of how these equations are solved is not necessary to understand the concept of electron clouds. The electron cloud that represents the lowest energy level is spherically shaped. The type of electron cloud that represents the next energy level is represented by a dumbbell-shaped region.

Thinking Skills

comparing

Have students observe the electron cloud model in Figure 4-6 and compare it with Bohr's model in Figure 4-4. Ask students to give reasons why it is easier to use Bohr's model in studying chemistry and physics.

Demonstration   Have one or two students demonstrate the attraction and repulsion of rods of glass rubbed with silk and rods of hard rubber rubbed with fur. Glass rods become positively charged (electrons are removed by the silk) and repel each other. Hard rubber rods become negatively charged (electrons are acquired from the fur) and also repel each other. A glass rod rubbed with silk and a rubber rod rubbed with fur attract each other. Discussion should center on the presence or absence of electrons in each case.

Demonstration   To demonstrate that cathode-ray particles are negatively charged, borrow a cathode-ray tube from the high school physics department, and show the effect a magnet has on a beam of electrons. Depending on the position of the magnet, the beam is deflected downward or upward. If the beam is deflected downward, reversing the position of the poles of the magnet would cause the beam to be deflected upward. Based on their observations, students should be able to conclude that the cathode rays are composed of negatively charged particles.

Thinking Skills

predicting

Students understand that atoms have three particles. They also understand that a neutral atom has an equal number of protons and electrons. Have students predict what the charge would be on an atom that lost an electron.

This description of the atom is not yet complete. Like charges are known to repel each other. If all the positively charged particles—the protons—are found in the nucleus, why don't they repell each other?

Rutherford hypothesized that there is another kind of particle in the nucleus. These particles separate the positive charges and keep them from repelling each other. James Chadwick, one of Rutherford's students, found evidence for the existence of this other particle, called the neutron (NOO trahn). The **neutron** is a particle with no charge, found in an atom's nucleus.

Table 4-1 *The Three Particles in Atoms*

Particle	Relative Mass	Charge	Location
Proton	1	+1	Nucleus
Neutron	1	0	Nucleus
Electron	1/1836	−1	Outside nucleus

As you can see from Table 4-1, protons and neutrons have about the same mass. The electron has very little mass, by comparison. It has been shown that one proton is about 1836 times heavier than one electron. Nearly all of the mass of the atom is concentrated in the nucleus.

SCIENCE & TECHNOLOGY

You know that all matter is made up of atoms and that atoms are made up of protons, neutrons, and electrons. But are these particles made up of still smaller particles?

Scientists think that a few kinds of basic particles make up protons, neutrons, and electrons. One basic particle is a quark. Scientists believe that an atom's neutrons and protons are made of different kinds of quarks.

Studying objects as tiny as these particles requires massive equipment. A particle accelerator, like the one shown in the photograph, is used to study subatomic particles. Particles travel through a circular path and gain speed. From here, the particles follow a straight path until they collide with atomic nuclei. These collisions break apart the nuclei into subatomic particles.

THE SIZE OF THE ATOM

A mental model can help you picture the relative size of parts of an atom. Imagine an atom the size of a large football stadium like the one shown in Figure 4-7. Its nucleus would have the volume of a small marble in the center of the field. The electrons would be like mosquitoes buzzing around in the stands.

But atoms are not the size of stadiums. In fact it is difficult to imagine the size of an atom. The period at the end of this sentence could hold 10^{18} atoms.

The simplest atom is the common hydrogen atom. It has 1 proton, no neutrons, and 1 electron. The most complex atom known today has 109 protons, 157 neutrons, and 109 electrons. In the next section you will examine the differences between atoms of different elements.

Figure 4-7

If an atom were as large as a football stadium, its nucleus would be the size of a marble.

REVIEW

1. Describe the electron cloud model.
2. Name the three particles found in atoms, and give the charge of each.
3. What particles are found in the nucleus, and how are they alike?

CHALLENGE An atom of lead has 82 protons and 118 neutrons in its nucleus. What might happen to an atom that has 118 protons and 82 neutrons in its nucleus?

Teaching Tip Present additional analogies in reference to the size of the atom. To help students visualize how dense the nucleus is, tell them that 1.0 cm³ of nuclear material has been calculated to have a mass of 130 million tons. Also tell them that based on calculations by Rutherford and others, the diameter of the atom is over 100,000 times that of the nucleus. This suggests that if the nucleus of the hydrogen atom were enlarged to the size of a tennis ball, the diameter of the entire atom would be about 6.4 km. This analogy may help students visualize that the atom is mostly empty space.

3 REVIEW/REINFORCEMENT

1. According to the electron cloud model, electrons are moving very rapidly in regions of space about the nucleus. An electron cloud is the region of space in which there is a good chance of finding a given electron in an atom.
2. The atom is made up of protons, which have a positive charge $(1+)$; electrons, which have a negative charge $(1-)$; and neutrons, which are neutral (0 charge).
3. The particles in the nucleus are the proton and the neutron. They both have about the same mass.

Challenge An atom with 118 protons in its nucleus would not be lead. The number of protons in the nucleus of an atom determines the atomic number and, thus, the characteristics of the element. The number of neutrons determines the isotope of the element. If an element with 118 protons and 82 neutrons in its atomic nucleus were possible, it would be unstable.

4-3 HOW ATOMS DIFFER

OBJECTIVES
Refer to pupil page 90.

VOCABULARY
Key terms: atomic mass, atomic mass unit, atomic number, isotopes, mass number

1 MOTIVATION

A good way to present the idea that isotopes differ in mass is to demonstrate the Thomson and F.W. Aston studies of positive beams. Borrow a neon gas discharge tube from the high school physics department and show that two beams result from the deflection produced by a magnetic field. The amount of deflection indicates the mass of the ions. The heavier ions are deflected less than are the lighter ions because it takes a greater force to move a heavier object. Thomson and Aston found that the two beams corresponded to the masses of 20 amu and 22 amu, two isotopes of neon (atomic mass 20.183 amu).

After completing this section, you will be able to

- **relate** the terms *atomic number* and *mass number* to particles in the atom.
- **describe** the atomic mass unit and its use.
- **compare** the number of electrons in energy levels.

The key terms in this section are
atomic mass
atomic mass unit
atomic number
isotopes
mass number

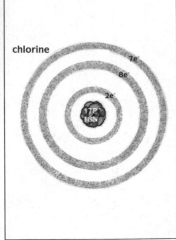

[1]Yes.

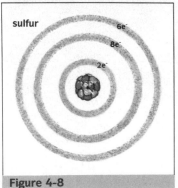

Figure 4-8

How do atoms of chlorine and atoms of sulfur differ?[2]

[2]The chlorine atom has one more proton, one more electron, and two more neutrons than the sulfur atom has.

You may wonder how there can be so many different substances when all substances are made of atoms, all of which are made up of the same kinds of particles. The key is the number of protons.

ATOMIC NUMBER

The number of protons in the nucleus of an atom of an element is the **atomic number** of the element. The atomic number is a unique property of an element. For example, the element hydrogen has an atomic number of 1. All atoms of hydrogen have one proton, and any atom that has just one proton is a hydrogen atom. The atomic number of the element helium is 2. All helium atoms have two protons in their nucleus. The element lithium has an atomic number of 3. Are all atoms that have only three protons lithium atoms?[1]

When you know the number of protons in an atom, you also know the number of electrons in a neutral atom. If an atom is neutral, the number of positive charges is balanced by the number of negative charges. Thus the number of protons equals the number of electrons. Each element has its own number of protons and number of electrons. Each element has its own set of properties. For example, sulfur has 16 protons and 16 electrons. Chlorine has 17 protons and 17 electrons. Under the same conditions, sulfur is a yellow solid and chlorine is a greenish-yellow gas.

MASS NUMBER

Another important term used to describe atoms is mass number. **Mass number** is the sum of the protons and neutrons in an atom. Except for common hydrogen, all atoms contain both protons and neutrons. The number of neutrons in an atom can be found by subtracting the atomic number from the mass number.

number of neutrons = mass number − atomic number

For example, the mass number of chlorine is 35. The atomic number of chlorine is 17. So the number of neutrons in an atom of chlorine is 18.

The atomic number, mass number, and number of neutrons are whole numbers. The number of protons gives an element its identity and also contributes to its mass. The number of neutrons contributes only to the mass of the atom.

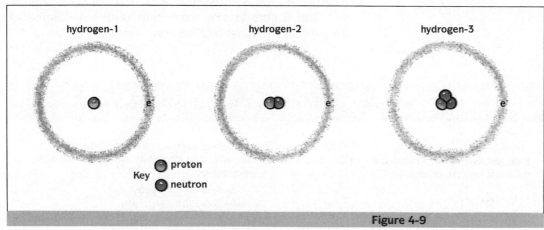

hydrogen-1   hydrogen-2   hydrogen-3

Key
⬤ proton
⬤ neutron

Figure 4-9

There are three isotopes of the element hydrogen.

All atoms of the same element have the same number of protons, but they may have different mass numbers. Atoms of the same element have different mass numbers because they have different numbers of neutrons. Atoms of the same element with different numbers of neutrons are called **isotopes** (ī soh tohps). Three isotopes of hydrogen occur in nature. They are sometimes called hydrogen-1, hydrogen-2, and hydrogen-3. They all have the properties of hydrogen. Each has one proton. The 1, 2, and 3 refer to the mass number of each isotope. As you can see in Figure 4-9, hydrogen-1 has one proton and no neutrons. Hydrogen-2 has one proton and one neutron. Hydrogen-3 has one proton and two neutrons. How many electrons does each isotope have?[1]

iso- (same)
topos (place)

[1]Each isotope has one electron.

Background   A scale of relative masses of atoms was established in 1961. It is based on the assignment of exactly 12.000 amu as the mass of the carbon-12 isotope (the most abundant isotope of carbon). The atomic mass of an atom can be measured by comparing it with the mass of a carbon-12 atom. For example, titanium has an atomic mass of 47.9, which is almost four times the mass of the carbon atom. Hydrogen, with a mass of 1, has 1/12 the mass of the carbon-12 isotope.

Teaching Tip   Show students how to determine the atomic mass of an element when given the natural percent abundance and atomic masses of the isotopes of the element. To calculate the atomic mass of an element, multiply the atomic mass for each isotope by the fraction representing the percent abundance for that isotope; then add the results for all isotopes. For example, the atomic mass of nitrogen is calculated from the following data.

Isotope	Atomic Mass (amu)	Natural Percent Abundance
Nitrogen	14.003	99.63
Nitrogen	15.000	0.37

Atomic mass of nitrogen =
(14.003 amu) (0.9963) + (15.00 amu) (0.0037) =
13.985 amu + 0.056 amu = 14.007 amu

Figure 4-10

This pile of coal contains seven isotopes of carbon.

All isotopes of any element have the chemical properties of that element. There are seven isotopes of the element carbon. All atoms of these isotopes have 6 protons and 6 electrons. The number of neutrons varies from 4 to 10. The properties of an element are determined by the number of protons and electrons in the atoms of that element. Thus the chemical properties of the carbon in the coal shown in Figure 4-10 can be studied without stating which of the isotopes is involved.

ATOMIC MASS

The actual mass of a single atom is very small. For example, one atom of hydrogen-1 has a mass of 1.67×10^{-24} g. Such small numbers are not easy to work with. Scientists use an atomic mass scale. This scale compares all atomic masses to that of one atom. This atom is the most common isotope of carbon, carbon-12. Each atom of carbon-12 has been assigned a mass of exactly 12 atomic mass units. One **atomic mass unit** (amu) is defined as one-twelfth the mass of a carbon-12 atom.

ACTIVITY   30 minutes

PROCESS SKILLS
measuring, comparing, interpreting data

Preparation   Each student team will need a double-pan balance, a set of coins, and glass beads.

Teaching Tip   Remind students to zero the balance before they begin.

Answers to Procedure   Answers will vary, depending on the kind of beads used.

Answers to Results and Conclusions
1. Penny.
2. Doubled.
3. The mass units of the model are much larger than the mass units of the atomic mass scale, but the structures of both scales are similar in that an arbitrary standard is used as a reference.

ACTIVITY   How Can Masses Be Compared?

OBJECTIVE
Determine a relative mass unit and use it to measure masses of objects.

MATERIALS
balance, nickel, glass beads, penny, quarter

PROCEDURE
A. Prepare a data table like the one shown.
B. Place a nickel on the left pan of a balance. Add enough glass beads to the right pan to balance the nickel.
C. Record the number of beads whose mass equals that of the nickel.
D. Repeat step **B**, using a penny. Record the number of beads whose mass equals that of the penny.
E. Repeat step **B**, using a quarter. Record the number of beads whose mass equals that of the quarter.
F. Make the coin whose mass is neither the heaviest nor the lightest your standard. Give your standard a whole-number value.

G. Calculate the relative mass of the other coins in standard units, using the following expression.

$$\frac{\text{mass of coin (in beads)}}{\text{mass of standard (in beads)}} \times \text{standard value}$$

Coin	Number of Beads	Relative Mass

RESULTS AND CONCLUSIONS
1. Which coin was your standard?
2. What would happen to the value of the relative mass of the heaviest coin if you doubled the value assigned to the standard coin?
3. How does this model compare with the atomic mass scale?

4-4 HOW ATOMS ARE REPRESENTED

People who do not speak the same language often have trouble communicating with each other. The world's scientists speak the languages of their countries. When they talk with one another, they also speak "the language of science."

CHEMICAL SYMBOLS

Scientists have developed a language of symbols to stand for the elements. A **chemical symbol** is a notation of one or two letters that represent an element. As you can see in Table 4-3, the first letter of each symbol is a capital letter. If a second letter is used, it is always a lower-case letter. A symbol may be the first letter of the name of the element, as the letter *C* is used for carbon. Calcium also begins with the letter *C*, so a second letter is added. Find the symbol for calcium in Table 4-3.[1]

The symbol of an element also represents the atoms of the element. When you write B, the symbol for boron, it stands for both the element boron and one atom of boron. Thus 2B represents two atoms of boron. What does 3K stand for?[2]

[1]Ca.

[2]Three atoms of potassium.

Table 4-3 *Symbols of Elements with Atomic Numbers 1–20*

Element	Symbol	Atomic Number
Hydrogen	H	1
Helium	He	2
Lithium	Li	3
Beryllium	Be	4
Boron	B	5
Carbon	C	6
Nitrogen	N	7
Oxygen	O	8
Fluorine	F	9
Neon	Ne	10
Sodium	Na	11
Magnesium	Mg	12
Aluminum	Al	13
Silicon	Si	14
Phosphorous	P	15
Sulfur	S	16
Chlorine	Cl	17
Argon	Ar	18
Potassium	K	19
Calcium	Ca	20

OBJECTIVES
Refer to pupil page 95.

VOCABULARY
Key term: chemical symbol

1 MOTIVATION

Use the introductory paragraph of this section to generate a discussion about the necessity of having standard chemical symbols. You might include in the discussion other symbols and their meanings, for example, the symbols for male and female, dollars and cents, arithmetic operations, and various road signs.

2 CONCEPT DEVELOPMENT

Background   Although Bohr's model of the atom is useful, it does not predict the energy values for the spectrum of atoms containing more than one electron. However, Bohr's model does predict that electrons exist in energy levels. Schrodinger's electron cloud model (quantum model) is widely accepted as a more realistic representation of an atom. But Bohr's model is particularly useful for making certain types of qualitative predictions, especially for elements up to atomic number 20.

Teaching Tip   Ask students to identify elements that make up objects in their possession, at home, and in the classroom. Have students write the symbols and draw models of atoms of these elements. Undoubtedly, gold, copper, and silver will be identified. Suggest the idea of energy sublevels to account for electron arrangements in such elements.

comparing

Students compare atomic model diagrams in determining properties of elements. Supply students with drawings of Bohr's models of Li, Na, K, Ne, Ar, and Kr. Have students compare the structures and group these elements according to similarities. Refer students to Table 4-3 and Figure 4-13.

ACTIVITY   20 minutes

PROCESS SKILLS
measuring, comparing, inferring, hypothesizing

Preparation   Prepare models of isotopes of 16 g, 17 g, and 18 g, using plastic foam balls or plastic eggs, tape, and small masses. Label each isotope model in some way so that you can identify each and students can distinguish between isotopes. Student teams will need one of each model and a pan balance.

Teaching Tip   Remind students to zero the balance before beginning, and review the definition of *isotope*.

Answers to Procedure
1. All look the same but appear to have different masses.
2. $_8^{16}X$ $_8^{17}X$ $_8^{18}X$.

Answers to Results and Conclusions
1. $_8^{18}X$.
2. $_8^{16}X$.
3. Oxygen.

ACTIVITY   How Do Isotopes Differ?

OBJECTIVE
Determine the masses of models representing the three isotopes of an element.

MATERIALS
isotope models, balance

PROCEDURE
A. Examine each isotope model.
 1. Do the models differ in any way?
B. Determine and record the mass of each model.

C. The atomic number of the isotopes is 8. Let X be the symbol of this element, and let 1 g = 1 amu.
 2. Write the symbol for each isotope of X.

RESULTS AND CONCLUSIONS
1. Which is the isotope with the largest atomic mass?
2. Which isotope has the smallest atomic mass?
3. What real element could the model isotopes represent?

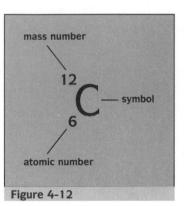

Figure 4-12

This symbol stands for carbon-12.

[1]Carbon-13 has one more neutron than carbon-12 has.

The names of the 109 known elements have many origins. Some are named after scientists. Einsteinium (īn-STĪ nee uhm) is named for Albert Einstein. Some elements are named after places. Californium (kal uh FOR nee uhm) is named after the state of California. Sometimes a symbol does not seem to relate to the name of an element. The symbol for sodium is Na. But the Latin name for sodium is natrium and the symbol comes from that name.

Recall that isotopes are atoms of a given element that differ in mass number. Scientists represent isotopes with the symbol of the element and a superscript and subscript. As you can see in Figure 4-12, the superscript is a small raised number that shows the mass number, and the subscript is a small lowered number that shows the atomic number. For example, $_6^{12}C$ represents carbon-12, an isotope of carbon which has a mass number of 12. Another isotope of carbon is $_6^{13}C$. This isotope has a mass number of 13. How do these two carbon atoms differ?[1]

DRAWING MODELS OF ATOMS

All electrons are the same. They have the same mass and charge. You cannot tell one electron from another. But the number of electrons and the way in which they are arranged in an atom are important. Electrons are located in energy levels around the nucleus. One way to draw a model of an atom is shown in Figure 4-13. The small circle represents the nucleus. The P^+ stands for protons, and the N, neutrons. The circles around the nucleus represent the energy levels. The e^- stands for electrons and their negative charge. To draw a model of hydrogen, place one proton in the sphere representing the nucleus. Place one electron in the first energy level. To

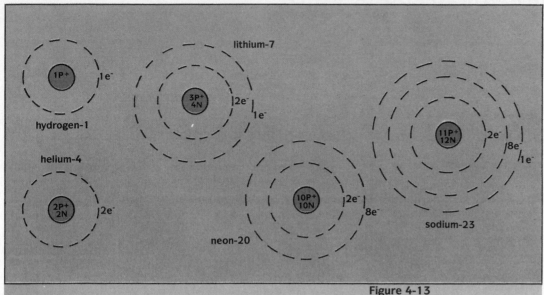

Figure 4-13

These models show how atoms differ.

draw a model of helium, add one proton to the hydrogen nucleus and add one electron to the first energy level. To complete the model of helium, add two neutrons to its nucleus. An atom of lithium has three protons, four neutrons, and three electrons. Notice that the third electron is placed in the second energy level. Remember, the first energy level can hold only two electrons.

If you continue to add one proton, one electron, and the correct number of neutrons at each step, the second energy level will soon hold eight electrons. This occurs with the element neon. Two of neon's ten electrons are in the first energy level, and eight are in the second. Add another proton, another electron, and two neutrons to make the sodium atom. Notice that the new electron goes into the third energy level. You could continue this process until you have many more models. Describe a model of an atom of magnesium-24.[1]

[1]It would show 12 protons, 12 neutrons, and 12 electrons.

REVIEW

1. Name the element that each of the following symbols represents: Na, N, Al, P, K.
2. What are the symbols of the three hydrogen isotopes?
3. Sketch the energy levels of the atoms with atomic numbers 10 and 12.

CHALLENGE How many protons, neutrons, and electrons are there in an atom of uranium-238?

3 REVIEW/REINFORCEMENT

1. Sodium, nitrogen, aluminum, phosphorus, and potassium.
2. ^1_1H, ^2_1H, ^3_1H.
3. Check students' sketches.

Challenge 92 protons, 92 electrons, and 146 neutrons.

4-5 THE PERIODIC TABLE

OBJECTIVES
Refer to pupil page 103.

VOCABULARY
Key terms: group, period, periodic law, Periodic Table

---

1 MOTIVATION

Introduce students to early classifications of elements by Johann Dobereiner and John Newlands. Point out that Mendeleev is given the most credit for the organization of the Periodic Table because he planned his table carefully. Point out the placement of certain elements according to properties rather than increasing atomic mass. List several common elements on the chalkboard. Ask students how they would classify these elements. Write the responses on the chalkboard. Ask students what problems, if any, could occur with their classification system. Ask students to suggest other ways to group and classify elements.

After completing this section, you will be able to

- **describe** the organization of the Periodic Table.
- **locate** an element in the Periodic Table, given its atomic number.
- **distinguish** between periods and groups of elements in the Periodic Table.

The key terms in this section are

group   periodic law
period   Periodic Table

As scientists learned about elements, they noticed that certain elements have similar properties. For example, sodium, lithium, and potassium all conduct electricity and react strongly with water. Fluorine and chlorine are both gases that combine with sodium and other elements.

MENDELEEV'S PERIODIC TABLE

As more and more elements were discovered, scientists needed to organize the information they had about elements. In 1869, Dmitri Mendeleev (mehn deh LAY ehf), a Russian chemist, published a Periodic Table of the 63 elements known at that time. He arranged the elements in rows according to atomic mass. He also grouped the elements into seven columns based on similar chemical and physical properties. When the elements are arranged by increasing atomic mass, the properties of the elements repeat in a pattern.

Table 4-4 *Mendeleev's Periodic Table*

I	II	III	IV	V	VI	VII	VIII
H = 1							
Li = 7	Be = 9	B = 11	C = 12	N = 14	O = 16	F = 19	
Na = 23	Mg = 24	Al = 27	Si = 28	P = 31	S = 32	Cl = 35	
K = 39	Ca = 40	? = 44	Ti = 50	V = 51	Cr = 52	Mn = 55	Fe = 56, Co = 59, Ni = 59
Cu = 63	Zn = 65	? = 68	? = 72	As = 75	Se = 78	Br = 80	
Rb = 81	Sr = 87	Y = 88	Zr = 90	Nb = 94	Mo = 96	? = 100	Ru = 104, Rh = 104, Pd = 104
Ag = 108	Cd = 112	In = 113	Sn = 118	Sb = 122	Te = 128	I = 127	
Cs = 133	Ba = 137	? = 137	Ce = 138				

Table 4-4 shows the arrangement of part of Mendeleev's Periodic Table. Notice that he had some question marks in his table. He believed that the elements that would fit into these spaces would be discovered one day. He also predicted the properties of the "missing" elements. Mendeleev called one of these elements eka-silicon. It is now called germanium. Some properties of this element are shown in Table 4-5. How do the predicted properties compare with the real properties?[1]

[1]They are very similar.

Table 4-5 *Properties of Germanium*

Property	Predicted by Mendeleev	Observed Experimentally
Atomic mass	72	72.6
Density (g/mL)	5.5	5.47
Color	Dirty gray	Grayish white
Compound formed with oxygen	EsO_2	GeO_2
Density of oxygen compound	4.7	4.703
Compound formed with chlorine	$EsCl_4$	$GeCl_4$
Density of chlorine compound	1.9	1.887
Boiling point of chlorine compound	Below 100°C	86°C

Figure 4-14

Mendeleev predicted that germanium would be discovered.

A Periodic Table based on atomic mass was not perfect. For example, the atomic mass of tellurium is greater than that of iodine. Listed by increasing atomic mass, iodine would be placed ahead of tellurium. But tellurium resembles the elements sulfur and selenium, and iodine does not. Mendeleev broke his "rule" of increasing atomic mass, and positioned these elements by their properties. Thus, he placed tellurium before iodine.

When Mendeleev did his work, protons had not yet been discovered. In 1913, a young British physicist named Henry Moseley (MOH slh lee) discovered a connection between the properties of atoms and their number of protons. The properties of elements repeat in a pattern if the elements are arranged by increasing atomic number.

THE MODERN PERIODIC TABLE

With a few exceptions, atomic mass increases in the same order as atomic number. In the modern **Periodic Table**, elements are arranged in order of increasing atomic number. The **periodic law** states that the properties of the elements repeat in a regular way if the elements are arranged by increasing atomic number.

Different forms of the Periodic Table have been proposed over the years. The newest form is shown on pages 100-101. The vertical columns are called groups or families. A **group** is made up of elements that have similar chemical properties. The elements in any one group behave alike chemically because they have the same number of electrons in their outer energy levels.

2 CONCEPT DEVELOPMENT

Background   The modern Periodic Table is one of the most important and useful tools in science. The elements are arranged systematically, so that elements having like properties occur in related positions—in horizontal or vertical sequences. This arrangement allows us to see and understand variations of properties of elements in periods and groups as the elements relate to each other. The electron arrangements in energy levels help to explain why atoms combine the way they do.

Teaching Tip   On the chalkboard, draw the electron arrangements of the elements in Group 1 in a column. Draw the electron arrangements of the elements in the second period horizontally. Ask students to note the similarities and differences in the arrangements of electrons within a group and within a period.

Tie in/Social Studies   Ask students to investigate the historical events that occurred during Mendeleev's lifetime (1804–1907) in his native land of Russia.

Review and Skill Masters

SKILL, pages 26–27.
See page 79b–c in this book for answers.

Background Most countries have been using the Roman numerals I to VIII followed by an A or a B to label the columns in the Periodic Table. However, the A or B part of the label is used differently by different countries. In the United States the A designation indicates that the column contains main group elements and the B designation indicates that the column contains elements in the transition series. In European countries, however, the opposite designations are used. This causes problems in communication among scientists as well as in the reporting and publishing of chemical information throughout the world. To avoid such confusion, the International Union of Pure & Applied Chemistry has recommended doing away with the A and B designations and simply numbering the columns of the Periodic Table from 1 to 18 in Arabic numbers, beginning at the left. This is now the recommendation of the American Chemical Society, also.

The numbering system used in the Pupil Edition for the families of elements in the Periodic Table of elements is the new system recommended by the American Chemical Society. The older system is included in the Periodic Table in the Teacher Edition for those teachers who prefer that system. Teachers may choose to acquaint students with the older system if they wish.

The American Chemical Society has also accepted the recommendation of the International Union of Pure & Applied Chemistry to change the terms *lanthanide series* and *actinide series* to *lanthanoid series* and *actinoid series*. We have included both nomenclatures in the Teacher Edition.

Poster

The Teacher Resource Package includes a poster that shows the Periodic Table of elements. You may wish to display this poster in your classroom.

Periodic Table of Elements

IA 1	IIA 2	IIIB 3	IVB 4	VB 5	VIB 6	VIIB 7	VIIIB 8	9
1 1.0 **H** Hydrogen								
3 6.9 **Li** Lithium	4 9.0 **Be** Beryllium							
11 22.9 **Na** Sodium	12 24.3 **Mg** Magnesium							
19 39.1 **K** Potassium	20 40.0 **Ca** Calcium	21 44.9 **Sc** Scandium	22 47.9 **Ti** Titanium	23 50.9 **V** Vanadium	24 51.9 **Cr** Chromium	25 54.9 **Mn** Manganese	26 55.8 **Fe** Iron	27 58.9 **Co** Cobalt
37 85.4 **Rb** Rubidium	38 87.6 **Sr** Strontium	39 88.9 **Y** Yttrium	40 91.2 **Zr** Zirconium	41 92.9 **Nb** Niobium	42 95.9 **Mo** Molybdenum	43 (99)* **Tc** Technetium	44 101.0 **Ru** Ruthenium	45 102.9 **Rh** Rhodium
55 132.9 **Cs** Cesium	56 137.3 **Ba** Barium	Lanthanide Series†	72 178.4 **Hf** Hafnium	73 180.9 **Ta** Tantalum	74 183.8 **W** Tungsten	75 186.2 **Re** Rhenium	76 190.2 **Os** Osmium	77 192.2 **Ir** Iridium
87 (223)* **Fr** Francium	88 (226)* **Ra** Radium	Actinide Series‡	104 (259)* **Unq** Unnilquadium	105 **Unp** Unnilpentium	106 **Unh** Unnilhexium	107 **	108 **	109 **

Transition Elements

57 138.9 **La** Lanthanum	58 140.1 **Ce** Cerium	59 140.9 **Pr** Praseodymium	60 144.2 **Nd** Neodymium	61 (147)* **Pm** Promethium	62 150.3 **Sm** Samarium	63 151.9 **Eu** Europium
89 (227)* **Ac** Actinium	90 232.0 **Th** Thorium	91 (231)* **Pa** Protactinium	92 238.0 **U** Uranium	93 (237)* **Np** Neptunium	94 (242)* **Pu** Plutonium	95 (243)* **Am** Americium

† **Lanthanide Series**
Lanthanoid Series

‡ **Actinide Series**
Actinoid Series

*Atomic masses appearing in parentheses are those of the most stable known isotopes.

These elements occur in nature, and are solids at room temperature (20°C).

These elements occur in nature, and are liquids at room temperature (20°C).

These elements occur in nature, and are gases at room temperature (20°C).

These elements do not occur in nature, and have been produced in laboratories.

		IIIA 13	IVA 14	VA 15	VIA 16	VIIA 17	VIIIA 18
							2 4.0 **He** Helium
IB	IIB	5 10.8 **B** Boron	6 12.0 **C** Carbon	7 14.0 **N** Nitrogen	8 15.9 **O** Oxygen	9 18.9 **F** Fluorine	10 20.1 **Ne** Neon
10 11 12		13 26.9 **Al** Aluminum	14 28.0 **Si** Silicon	15 30.9 **P** Phosphorus	16 32.0 **S** Sulfur	17 35.4 **Cl** Chlorine	18 39.9 **Ar** Argon

28 58.7 **Ni** Nickel	29 63.5 **Cu** Copper	30 65.3 **Zn** Zinc	31 69.7 **Ga** Gallium	32 72.5 **Ge** Germanium	33 74.9 **As** Arsenic	34 78.9 **Se** Selenium	35 79.9 **Br** Bromine	36 83.8 **Kr** Krypton
46 106.4 **Pd** Palladium	47 107.8 **Ag** Silver	48 112.4 **Cd** Cadmium	49 114.8 **In** Indium	50 118.6 **Sn** Tin	51 121.7 **Sb** Antimony	52 127.6 **Te** Tellurium	53 126.9 **I** Iodine	54 131.3 **Xe** Xenon
78 195.0 **Pt** Platinum	79 196.9 **Au** Gold	80 200.5 **Hg** Mercury	81 204.3 **Tl** Thallium	82 207.1 **Pb** Lead	83 208.9 **Bi** Bismuth	84 (210)* **Po** Polonium	85 (210)* **At** Astatine	86 (222)* **Rn** Radon

64 157.2 **Gd** Gadolinium	65 158.9 **Tb** Terbium	66 162.5 **Dy** Dysprosium	67 164.9 **Ho** Holmium	68 167.2 **Er** Erbium	69 168.9 **Tm** Thulium	70 173.0 **Yb** Ytterbium	71 174.9 **Lu** Lutetium
96 (247)* **Cm** Curium	97 (247)* **Bk** Berkelium	98 (251)* **Cf** Californium	99 (254)* **Es** Einsteinium	100 (257)* **Fm** Fermium	101 (258)* **Md** Mendelevium	102 (255)* **No** Nobelium	103 (256)* **Lr** Lawrencium

* *No names have been given and no mass data is available.

Atomic masses based on C-12 = 12.0000

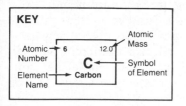

KEY

Atomic Number → 6   12.0 ← Atomic Mass

C ← Symbol of Element

Element Name → **Carbon**

Background   Elements can be classified as metals, nonmetals, and metalloids, based on their properties. Metals occupy the left side and center of the Periodic Table. The lanthanide and actinide elements are also considered to be metals. Nonmetals occupy the right side of the Periodic Table. Metalloids, such as silicon and germanium, are found along the heavy black zigzag line on the right side of the table.

Background   On the basis of systematic study by Mendeleev of the properties of the elements, the periodic law was formulated. The periodic law states: *The properties of the elements are periodic functions of their atomic numbers.*

Background   As more and more elements were discovered during the nineteenth century, chemists began to look for patterns in the properties of elements. Such patterns would show relationships among elements, allowing them to be grouped in various ways. In 1829, J. W. Dobereiner made an attempt to arrange the elements in a table according to their atomic weights. This was forty years before Mendeleev's periodic table.

sequencing
Students learn that the Periodic Table is arranged in order of increasing atomic number. On the chalkboard, list several elements. Have students use the Periodic Table to find each element. Have them list the atomic number and atomic mass for each element. Then have them arrange these elements in order.

ACTIVITY 45 minutes

PROCESS SKILLS
sequencing, inferring, hypothesizing, interpreting diagrams

Preparation Each student will need a pencil, marker, unlined paper, compass, metric ruler, scissors, glue or tape, and poster board. It might be efficient to form groups to share these materials.

Safety Tip If glue is used, make sure that the room is well ventilated. Caution students to handle scissors with care.

Teaching Tip Instruct students to follow the procedures carefully. Review the meaning of the terms *diameter* and *radius*.

Answers to Results and Conclusions
1. Eight groups.
2. Three periods.
3. The atom with atomic number 19 will be placed in the fourth period below the atom with atomic number 11 because they both have one electron in their outermost energy levels.

Review and Skill Masters

CHALLENGE/CRITICAL THINKING, page 28. See page 79c in this book for answers.

ACTIVITY   How Is the Periodic Table Arranged?

OBJECTIVE
Construct atomic model drawings and use them to make a Periodic Table.

MATERIALS
pencils, unlined paper, drawing compass, metric ruler, scissors, tape, poster board

PROCEDURE
A. Cut out 8-cm squares of paper.
B. On each piece of paper, make a drawing to serve as a model of an atom. Follow the style in Figure 4-13 to draw each of the atoms listed in the table.
C. For each drawing, represent the nucleus as a circle 1.0 cm in diameter. Use the atomic number and the mass number to determine the number of protons and neutrons in the nucleus of each atom. Indicate these numbers on each diagram.
D. Show the correct number of electrons in each atom by placing them in the proper energy levels. Make the first energy level a dashed circle 3.0 cm in diameter.
E. Make the second energy level a dashed circle 5.0 cm in diameter. Make the third level a dashed circle 6.0 cm in diameter.
F. Arrange the models on your desk, in order of increasing atomic number.
G. Look at the drawings. Arrange them in a table so that each column contains atoms with similar features. Mount the squares on the poster board in this arrangement.

Atomic Number	Mass Number	Atomic Number	Mass Number
1	1	10	20
2	4	11	23
3	7	12	24
4	9	13	27
5	11	14	28
6	12	15	31
7	14	16	32
8	16	17	35
9	19	18	40

RESULTS AND CONCLUSIONS
1. How many groups does your periodic table have?
2. How many periods does your periodic table have?
3. Where would you place an atom with an atomic number of 19 and a mass number of 39? Explain your answer.

Elements with three or fewer outer electrons are metals. Metals are usually shiny and good conductors of heat. All elements in groups 1 through 12, and some in Groups 13, 14, and 15 are metals. Elements with five or more outer electrons usually are nonmetals. Nonmetals are dull and do not conduct heat. All elements in Groups 17 and 18, and some in Groups 13 through 16 are nonmetals. Notice the zigzag line in the Periodic Table. Elements that border this line are metalloids. Metalloids show some properties of metals and some properties of nonmetals.

Each horizontal row in the Periodic Table is called a **period**. Elements in a period are not alike. They have different properties because each has a different number of outer electrons. Elements in a period have the same number of energy levels. Each element in Group 18 has a complete outer energy level.

The Periodic Table is a useful tool. It shows the atomic number and the atomic mass of each element. Find the atomic number and the atomic mass of boron.[1]

[1]The atomic number is 5. The atomic mass is 10.8.

REVIEW

1. How does Moseley's arrangement of the elements in the Periodic Table differ from that of Mendeleev's?
2. Name the elements represented by each of the following atomic numbers: 6, 7, 12, 17, 30.
3. How are members of a group similar? How are members of a period similar?

CHALLENGE Give the symbol and name of the element that occupies each of the following positions in the Periodic Table: Period 3, Group 15; Period 2, Group 16; Period 5, Group 16.

CHAPTER SUMMARY

The main ideas in this chapter are listed below. Read these statements before you answer the Chapter Review questions.

- Matter is made up of small particles called atoms. An atom is the smallest particle of an element that has the properties of that element. (4-1)
- Scientists use models to explain something that they cannot see or understand by relating it to something that they do see or understand. (4-1)
- An atom has a tiny positive core called the nucleus. Electrons are negatively charged particles outside the nucleus. (4-1)
- Electrons move in regions of space called electron clouds. (4-2)
- The proton is a positively charged particle found in the nucleus of an atom. The neutron is a particle with no charge, found in the nucleus of an atom. (4-2)
- The atomic number of an element is the number of protons in the nucleus. The mass number is the sum of the protons and neutrons in an atom. (4-3)

- Atoms of the same element with different numbers of neutrons are isotopes. (4-3)
- One atomic mass unit (amu) is defined as one-twelfth the mass of a carbon-12 atom. The atomic mass is the mass of an atom in relation to the carbon-12 atom. (4-3)
- In the Bohr model, electrons are found in paths called energy levels. (4-3)
- A chemical symbol is a notation of one or two letters that stand for the name of an element. (4-4)
- The modern Periodic Table is an arrangement of the elements by increasing atomic number. (4-5)
- Vertical columns of the Periodic Table are called groups. Elements in a group have similar chemical properties. (4-5)
- Horizontal rows in the Periodic Table are periods. Elements in a period have the same number of energy levels. (4-5)

The key terms in this chapter are listed below. Use each term in a sentence that shows the meaning of the term.

atom	chemical symbol	mass number	period
atomic mass	electron	model	periodic law
atomic mass unit	group	neutron	Periodic Table
atomic number	isotopes	nucleus	proton

1. Moseley arranged the elements according to increasing atomic numbers. Mendeleev arranged them by increasing atomic mass.
2. Carbon, oxygen, magnesium, chlorine, zinc.
3. Groups run from top to bottom, and periods from left to right, on the Periodic Table. Members of a given group exhibit similar chemical properties. Members of a period have the same number of energy levels.

Challenge P—phosphorus; O—oxygen, Te—tellurium.

VOCABULARY

1. True	7. True
2. True	8. False; neutrons
3. False; group	9. False; electron
4. True	10. True
5. False; periods	11. False; atomic mass
6. True	12. True

CONCEPTS

1. All matter is made of tiny particles called atoms which cannot be split into smaller particles. Atoms cannot be created or destroyed. Atoms of the same element have the same properties, and atoms of different elements have different properties. Atoms of different elements combine to form new substances.
2. Because of Rutherford's findings.
3. The atom is composed of a tiny positive nucleus with electrons whirling around it.
4. The electrons in an atom move in paths outside the nucleus, and each path is a certain distance from the nucleus; distances between paths are not the same.
5. It gives off energy.
6. Electrons are moving very rapidly around the nucleus, in regions of space called electron clouds.

Review and Skill Masters

CHAPTER REVIEW, pages 24–25.
See page 79b in this book for answers.

Chapter Review

VOCABULARY

Identify each statement as True or False. If a statement is false, replace the underlined term with a term that makes the statement true.

1. The <u>nucleus</u> of an atom is composed of protons and neutrons and is the part of the atom that has most of the mass of the atom.
2. The orderly arrangement of elements according to their atomic number makes up the <u>Periodic Table</u>.
3. A <u>period</u> is made up of elements that have similar chemical properties.
4. The <u>atomic number</u> of an element is equal to the number of protons.
5. The horizontal rows of the Periodic Table are called <u>groups</u>.
6. Atoms of the same element that have different numbers of neutrons are called <u>isotopes</u>.
7. The smallest particle of an element that has the properties of that element is called an <u>atom</u>.
8. <u>Electrons</u> are particles found in the nucleus that have an electrical charge of zero.
9. The <u>neutron</u> is a negatively charged particle that is located outside of the nucleus.
10. The <u>periodic law</u> states that the properties of the elements repeat in a pattern if the elements are arranged by increasing atomic number.
11. The mass of an atom in relation to the carbon-12 atom is called the <u>mass number</u>.
12. A <u>model</u> is a scientist's way of explaining something that cannot be seen or understood by relating it to something that can be seen or understood.

CONCEPTS

1. What are the main points of Dalton's atomic theory? (4-1)
2. Why was Thomson's model of the atom discarded? (4-1)
3. What conclusion did Rutherford reach from his research about the atom? (4-1)
4. Neils Bohr suggested changes in Rutherford's model. What were the changes? (4-1)
5. What happens when an electron moves to an energy level closer to the nucleus? (4-1)
6. How was Schrodinger's model of the atom different from Bohr's model? (4-2)

7. List and give the location of each particle in the atom. (4-2)

8. How is the atomic mass of an element calculated? (4-3)

9. Give the greatest number of electrons that can be found in each of the first four energy levels. (4-3)

10. Which electrons have the most effect on the properties of an element? (4-3)

11. Compare the masses of the particles of an atom. (4-3)

12. How many protons does each of the following elements have: helium, oxygen, sodium, potassium? (4-3)

13. Some elements are named for a scientist or a location. Give an example of each. (4-4)

14. Give the symbols for nitrogen, neon, and sodium. (4-4)

15. How many protons, neutrons, and electrons are there in an atom of lead-207? (4-4)

16. Sketch the electron arrangement of a carbon atom. (4-4)

17. How are the atoms arranged in the modern Periodic Table? (4-5)

18. What elements in the Periodic Table have properties similar to those of carbon? (4-5)

APPLICATION/CRITICAL THINKING

1. Would it be possible for someone to discover a new element which would be placed between carbon and nitrogen on the Periodic Table? Explain your answer.

2. Which elements in the Periodic Table are not placed in the order of Mendeleev's periodic law?

3. How many neutrons are there in each of the following isotopes?

a. $^{3}_{1}H$ b. $^{4}_{2}He$ c. $^{31}_{15}P$ d. $^{23}_{11}Na$ e. $^{80}_{35}Br$

4. How does a scientific model differ from models such as a toy airplane used by children?

EXTENSION

1. Do library research on Rutherford's gold-foil experiment. How did he locate the paths of alpha particles?

2. The hydrogen isotopes have the same chemical properties. Do research to find out if they have the same physical properties.

READINGS

Asimov, Isaac. *How Did We Find Out About Atoms?* New York: Walker and Co., 1976.

Quigg, Chris. "Elementary Particles and Forces." *Scientific American,* April, 1985, p. 84.

---

7. Protons and neutrons are located in the nucleus, and electrons, outside the nucleus.

8. The atomic mass is calculated by multiplying the isotopic mass for each isotope by the fraction representing the percent abundance for that isotope and then adding the results for all isotopes found in a natural sample of that element.

9. 2, 8, 18, 32.

10. Electrons in the outermost energy level.

11. The masses of a proton and a neutron are the same; the mass of an electron is 1/1836 that of a proton.

12. 2, 8, 11, 19.

13. Es (Einsteinium) for Einstein, Cf (Californium) for California.

14. N, Ne, Na.

15. 82 protons, 82 electrons, 125 neutrons.

16. Check students' drawings.

17. According to their increasing atomic numbers.

18. Si, Ge, Sn, Pb.

APPLICATION/CRITICAL THINKING

1. No, because the atomic number of an element must always be a whole number. There is no whole number between 6 (carbon) and 7 (nitrogen).

2. K, Ar, Ni, Co, I, Te.

3. 2, 2, 16, 12, 45.

4. A toy airplane model and other models encountered in everyday life are based on objects that can be seen and measured. In science, models often represent things that cannot be seen or are too large to observe in total.

Test Masters

CHAPTER TEST, pages 13–16.
See page 79d in this book for answers.

COMPOUNDS

ORGANIZER

Section	pages	Activity	pages	Reinforcement and Evaluation	pages	*Review and Skill Masters	pages	Other Components in Teacher Resource Package	pages
5–1 What Is a Compound?	107–109	How Do Compounds Differ?	108	Review, Challenge	109			Study Guide Lab Manual	23 21
5–2 Symbols and Formulas	110–114			Review, Challenge	114			Study Guide	24
5–3 Ionic Compounds	115–121			Review, Challenge	121			Study Guide	25
5–4 Covalent Compounds	122–124	What Compounds Conduct Electricity?	124	Review, Challenge	124	Skill	56–57	Study Guide Lab Manual	26 25
5–5 Molecular Mass and Formula Mass	125–127			Puzzler Review, Challenge	126 127	Challenge/Critical Thinking	58	Study Guide	27
CHAPTER SUMMARY	127					Vocabulary Review	29		
CHAPTER REVIEW	128–129			*Test Masters	17–20	Chapter Review	30–31		

*In the Teacher Resource Package. For answers, see pages 105b–105d in this book.

ACTIVITY MATERIALS   Quantities are based on a class of 30 students working in groups as indicated in parentheses.

How Do Compounds Differ? p. 108 (groups of 2)	quantity	What Compounds Conduct Electricity? p. 124 (groups of 3)	quantity		quantity
safety goggles	30	dry cell	10		
lab apron	30	insulated wire	9 m		
test tube	15	wire stripper	10		
glass-marking pencil	15	light bulb and socket	10		
test-tube rack	15	250-mL beaker	60		
10-mL graduate	15	glass-marking pencil	10		
water		table salt	1 box		
hydrogen peroxide	75 mL	sugar	1 lb box		
manganese dioxide	7.5 g	baking soda	1 box		
wooden matches	30	distilled water			
wood splints	15	hydrogen peroxide	3.75 L		
spatula	15	rubbing alcohol	3.75 L		
		safety goggles	30		
		lab apron	30		

REVIEW AND SKILL MASTERS

VOCABULARY REVIEW _____ Chapter 5

Unscramble and define the following terms.

1. poconmdu   compound—a pure substance made up of two or more elements that are chemically joined

2. cmlhieac ndob   chemical bond—the force that holds particles of matter together

3. nio   ion—a charged particle or an atom that does not have the same number of protons as electrons

4. cltevano mpdcooun   covalent compound—a compound that contains covalent bonds

5. eomcuell   molecule—the smallest unit of any covalent substance that can exist alone and still show the properties of that substance

6. noici dnob   ionic bond—a force of attraction between oppositely charged ions

7. llemorcau msas   molecular mass—the sum of the atomic masses of all atoms in a molecule

8. cvlentao ndbo   covalent bond—a bond in which electrons are shared between atoms

9. mufaorl sams   formula mass—the sum of the atomic masses of the atoms present in a formula unit of ions

10. sbsupctri   subscript—a small lowered number that shows the proportion of elements in a compound

11. cmchalei lfroamu   chemical formula—a group of symbols that shows the makeup of a compound

12. iinco dnocmpou   ionic compound—a compound that contains ionic bonds

© 1988 Silver, Burdett & Ginn Inc.

29

CHAPTER REVIEW _____ Chapter 5

5-1   What is a Compound?

1. Define compound and give two examples.   A compound is a pure substance made up of two or more elements that are chemically joined. For example, water and salt are compounds.

2. Describe how compounds and elements are related.   A compound is made up of two or more elements that are chemically joined. Different combinations of elements can produce millions of compounds. Each compound contains certain elements in definite proportions.

5-2   Symbols and Formulas

1. What is a chemical formula?   A chemical formula is a group of symbols that shows the makeup of a compound.

2. Name the compounds given below.

   a. $NaCl$ Sodium chloride

   b. CO_2 Carbon dioxide

   c. $CuCl$ Copper (I) chloride

   d. BaF_2 Barium fluoride

   e. H_2SO_4 Hydrogen sulfate

   f. $Mg(OH)_2$ Magnesium hydroxide

5-3   Ionic Compounds

1. How do ions form?   When a neutral atom loses or gains electrons, it forms a charged particle called an ion. An ion has unequal numbers of protons and electrons.

© 1988 Silver, Burdett & Ginn Inc.

30

CHAPTER REVIEW (Continued) _____ Chapter 5

2. What is an ionic bond and how is it formed?   An ionic bond is a force of attraction between oppositely charged ions. It forms as positive and negative ions attract each other.

3. Give two properties of ionic compounds.   Answers will vary. All ionic compounds form some kind of lattice structure. They also have high melting points and high boiling points.

5-4   Covalent Bonds

1. Describe how a covalent bond forms using hydrogen as an example.   A covalent bond forms when electrons are shared between atoms. In a hydrogen molecule, each of two hydrogen atoms shares its one electron with the other hydrogen atom.

2. What are two properties of covalent compounds?   Answers will vary. Covalent compounds do not form lattice structures. They have low melting points and low boiling points.

5-5   Molecular Mass and Formula Mass

1. Define molecular mass and formula mass.   Molecular mass is the sum of the atomic masses of all atoms in a molecule. Formula mass is the sum of the atomic masses of the atoms present in a unit of ions.

2. Using the Periodic Table in your book, find the molecular mass of carbon dioxide.
   CO_2: C = 12 amu, O = 16 amu; 12 amu + 2(16) amu = 44 amu

© 1988 Silver, Burdett & Ginn Inc.

31

SKILL/Using Mathematics for Classification _____ Chapter 5

Compounds can be divided into two groups: those in which electrons were transferred, *ionic* compounds, and those in which electrons were shared, *covalent* compounds. To make this distinction more easily understood, American chemist Linus Pauling devised a simple mathematical process.

First Pauling defined the term electronegativity as the ability to attract an electron. He gave elements values from 4 to 0.6. A high number shows a tendency to receive electrons, which is a property of nonmetals. A low number indicates a tendency to give off electrons, which is a property of metals.

Then Pauling selected compounds with only two elements and computed the difference between their electronegativity values. The ionic compounds have a difference greater than 1.7, and the covalent compounds have a difference less than 1.7.

Using Pauling's system and the table below, classify the following compounds as either an ionic compound or a covalent compound. Write ionic or covalent and the difference between electronegativity values after each compound.

H 2.1						
Li 1.0	Be 1.5	B 2.0	C 2.5	N 3.0	O 3.5	F 4.0
Na 0.9	Mg 1.2	Al 1.5	Si 1.8	P 2.1	S 2.5	Cl 3.0
K 0.8	Ca 1.0	Ga 1.6	Ge 1.8	As 2.0	Se 2.4	Br 2.8
Rb 0.8	Sr 1.0	In 1.7	Sn 1.8	Sb 1.9	Te 2.1	I 2.5
Cs 0.7	Ba 0.9	Tl 1.8	Pb 1.8	Bi 1.9	Po 2.0	At 2.2
Fr 0.6						

1. Francium fluoride (FrF)   Ionic: Fr 0.6, F 4.0, difference 3.4

2. Cesium chloride (CsCl)   Ionic: Cs 0.7, Cl 3.0, difference 2.3

3. Hydrogen bromide (HBr)   Covalent: H 2.1, Br 2.8, difference 0.7

4. Magnesium oxide (MgO)   Ionic: Mg 1.2, O 3.5, difference 2.3

5. Calcium sulfide (CaS)   Covalent: Ca 1.0, S 2.5, difference 1.5

6. Aluminum phosphide (AlP)   Covalent: Al 1.5, P 2.1, difference 0.6

© 1988 Silver, Burdett & Ginn Inc.

32

CHAPTER **5** PLANNING GUIDE

Name_____ Date_____

CHALLENGE/CRITICAL THINKING _____ Chapter 5

Every compound has properties that help to identify it. Among these properties are molecular mass and formula mass, and the type of bonds the compound has. Suppose your science teacher has given you three containers. Each container contains a different white, solid compound: **A**, **B**, and **C**. These compounds are potassium chloride (KCl), sodium chloride (NaCl), and glucose ($C_6H_{12}O_6$). None of the containers is labeled. You are allowed to perform experiments with each compound and you may ask one question. Using your knowledge of compounds and with the help of the table below, you must figure out what the three compounds are.

NOTE: Most compounds that contain carbon have covalent bonds. Most compounds that do not contain carbon have ionic bonds.

Atomic Mass of Selected Elements (amu)

C = 12.0	K = 39.1
Cl = 35.5	Na = 23.0
H = 1.0	O = 16.0

1. You begin your investigation by deciding to determine the melting point of the three substances. What will this tell you in determining if the bonds in the compound are covalent or ionic?

   A covalent compound generally has a lower melting point than that of an ionic compound.

2. You attempt to determine the melting point of your three compounds. **A** melts at about 150 °C. You cannot heat **B** or **C** to the melting point. What does this tell you about the probable bond structures of **A**, **B**, and **C**?

   A probably has covalent bonds. B and C probably have ionic bonds.

3. You decide to further test this hypotheses by conducting an experiment to find out if any of these substances conduct electricity when dissolved in water. How will that help you determine if the compound has covalent bonds or ionic bonds?

   Most compounds that have covalent bonds do not conduct electricity when dissolved in water. Most compounds that have ionic bonds do conduct electricity when dissolved in water.

33

Name_____ Date_____

CHALLENGE/CRITICAL THINKING (Continued) _____ Chapter 5

4. **A** does not conduct electricity. **B** and **C** do conduct electricity. Does this support your hypothesis formed in question 2? Why or why not?

   Yes, it supports the hypothesis. Since A does not conduct electricity and has a lower melting point than B or C, A probably has covalent bonds. Since B and C do conduct electricity and have high melting points, they probably have ionic bonds.

5. What compound is **A**? How do you know? **Compound A is glucose because it is a covalent compound that does not conduct electricity and has a lower melting point.**

6. Does compound **A** have a formula mass or a molecular mass? Why?

   Compound A has a molecular mass. This is because glucose is a molecule.

7. Now you must determine which compounds are **B** and **C**. You decide that your one question will be: "What is the formula mass of **B**?" Why did you choose that as your question?

   Although sodium chloride and potassium chloride look similar, their formula masses are not equal. This question was chosen because using the formula mass of B, you can compute which compound B is.

8. Determine the formula mass for KCl.

   The formula mass for KCl is 39.1 amu + 35.5 amu = 74.6 amu.

9. Determine the formula mass for NaCl.

   The formula mass for NaCl is 23.0 amu + 35.5 amu = 58.5 amu.

10. Your teacher tells you that the formula mass of **B** is 74.6 amu. What compound is **B**? What compound is **C**?

    Compound B is potassium chloride. Compound C is sodium chloride.

34

TEST MASTERS

Quarter 1 (page 17)

Chapter 5

Compounds

PART 1

In the space below, write the term that each phrase defines.

Chapter Goal

1.	**formula mass**	The sum of the atomic masses of the atoms present in a unit of ions	5
2.	**ionic bond**	A bond formed by a force of attraction between oppositely charged ions	3
3.	**compound**	A pure substance made up of two or more elements that are chemically joined in definite proportions	1
4.	**covalent bond**	A bond in which electrons are shared between atoms	4
5.	**chemical formula**	A group of symbols that shows the makeup of a compound	2
6.	**molecule**	The smallest unit of any covalent substance that can exist alone and still show the properties of that substance	4
7.	**ion**	A charged particle	3
8.	**molecular mass**	The sum of the atomic masses of all atoms in a molecule	5
9.	**subscript**	A small lowered number that is used in a chemical formula to show the proportion of elements in a compound	2

PART 2

Choose the term or phrase that best answers the question or completes the statement. Write the letter of that choice in the space at the left.

c 1. The atomic mass of phosphorus (P) is 31 amu. The atomic mass of chlorine (Cl) is 36 amu. What is the molecular mass of PCl_3? 5
   a. 67 amu   b. 129 amu   c. 139 amu   d. 201 amu

d 2. What is the chemical formula for Dinitrogen trioxide? 2
   a. N_3O_2 b. NO_3 c. N_3O d. N_2O_3

Chapter 5 Compounds   17

Quarter 2 (page 18)

PART 2

Choose the term or phrase that best answers the question or completes the statement. Write the letter of that choice in the space at the left.

Chapter Goal

b 3. A scientist combines hydrogen, oxygen, and sodium to make lye. Which of these four substances is a compound? 1
   a. hydrogen   b. lye   c. oxygen   d. sodium

c 4. In an experiment, a student places 1 g of sucrose in a beaker of ice water and 1 g of sucrose in a beaker of boiling water. The sucrose in each beaker will most likely have a different: 1
   a. melting point.   c. temperature.
   b. boiling point.   d. density.

a 5. A compound that is made when two atoms share electrons most likely: 4
   a. forms a molecule.   c. contains ionic bonds.
   b. conducts electricity.   d. builds a lattice.

b 6. When sodium ions (Na^{1+}) are attracted to sulfide ions (S^{2-}), the compound that is formed has the formula: 3
   a. $2NaS$.   b. Na_2S.   c. NaS_2.   d. NaS^{2-}.

c 7. What is the chemical name for the compound with the formula $MgCl_2$? 2
   a. magnesium chlorite   c. magnesium chloride
   b. magnesium chlorate   d. magnesium chlorine

d 8. Carbon monoxide, CO, and carbon dioxide, CO_2, have different properties because each contains a different: 1
   a. number of carbon atoms.   c. type of element.
   b. kind of oxygen atom.   d. proportion of elements.

a 9. Two oxygen atoms are most likely to share electrons between atoms because sharing electrons allows the atoms to: 4
   a. gain a stable outer electron structure.
   b. develop a strong ionic bond.
   c. become an ion.
   d. form a repeating lattice pattern.

a 10. A calcium atom can form a Ca^{2+} ion. A hydroxide group can form an OH^{1-} ion. Which of the following would form the ionic compound calcium hydroxide, $Ca(OH)_2$? 3
   a. Two hydroxide groups each gain one electron from the calcium atom.
   b. One hydroxide group gains two electrons from the calcium atom.
   c. One calcium atom gains one electron from the hydroxide groups.
   d. Two calcium atoms gain one electron from one hydroxide group.

c 11. Molecular mass and formula mass are similar because both represent the mass of the smallest: 5
   a. atom that makes up an element.
   b. element that makes up a molecule.
   c. unit that makes up a compound.
   d. ion that makes up an atom.

Chapter 5 Compounds   18

Quarter 3 (page 19)

PART 3

Look at the charts. Then read the questions that follow. Choose the term or phrase that best answers the question or completes the statement. Write the letter of that choice in the space at the left.

Ions	
Name	Ion
Potassium	K^{1+}
Ammonium	NH_4^{1+}
Bicarbonate	HCO_3^{1-}
Sodium	Na^{1+}
Nitrate	NO_3^{1-}
Hydroxide	OH^{1-}
Barium	Ba^{2+}
Sulfate	SO_4^{2-}
Carbonate	CO_3^{2-}
Aluminum	Al^{3+}
Phosphate	PO_4^{3-}

Atomic Masses of Various Elements	
Element	Atomic Mass
K	39.1 amu
N	14.0 amu
H	1.0 amu
C	12.0 amu
O	16.0 amu
Ba	137.3 amu
S	32.1 amu
P	31.0 amu
Al	27.0 amu

Chapter Goal

a 1. What is the correct formula for the ionic compound potassium sulfate? 3
   a. K_2SO_4 b. KSO_4 c. $K(SO_4)_2$ d. KSO_2

c 2. What is the molecular mass of the compound that has the formula C_2H_4? 5
   a. 16 amu   b. 25 amu   c. 28 amu   d. 48 amu

d 3. What is the correct formula for the ionic compound aluminum nitrate? 3
   a. $AlNO_3$ b. $Al_3(NO_3)$ c. $Al_3(NO_3)_2$ d. $Al(NO_3)_3$

b 4. What is the name of the compound that has the formula $NaNO_3$? 2
   a. Ammonium carbonate   c. Nitrate ammonium
   b. Sodium nitrate   d. Sodium carbonate

c 5. What is the formula mass of the compound that has the formula KNO_3? 5
   a. 69.1 amu   b. 91.1 amu   c. 101.1 amu   d. 207.3 amu

Chapter 5 Compounds   19

Quarter 4 (page 20)

PART 4

Read each question or direction and answer it using complete sentences.

Chapter Goal

1. How do covalent bonds form? Distinguish between single, double, and triple covalent bonds. 4

   A covalent bond forms when electrons are shared between atoms. By forming covalent bonds, atoms form a stable outer electron structure. A covalent bond in which one pair of electrons is shared is called a single covalent bond. When the atoms share two pairs of electrons, the bond is called a double covalent bond. In some cases, the atoms in a bond share three pairs of electrons. These bonds are called triple covalent bonds.

2. How do ionic bonds form? 3

   An ionic bond forms when a positive ion is attracted to a negative ion. When an ionic bond forms, one atom gains the electron or electrons lost by another atom. The atom that gains electrons becomes a negative ion, and the atom that loses electrons becomes a positive ion.

3. What is the difference between an element and a compound? 1

   The 109 elements are the basic building blocks of all matter. Each element contains only one kind of atom, and each element has unique properties. A compound is a pure substance made up of two or more elements that are chemically joined in definite proportions. The makeup and properties of a compound do not change, but compounds do not look or act like the elements that form them. Each compound has its own chemical and physical properties.

Chapter 5 Compounds   20

5

COMPOUNDS

The questions in the CHAPTER TEST are based on these Chapter Goals.

1. Identify properties of compounds, and distinguish between compounds and elements.
2. Identify the parts of chemical formulas, and name compounds when given their formula.
3. Explain how ions and ionic bonds are formed, and describe properties of ionic compounds.
4. Explain how covalent bonds form, and describe properties of covalent compounds.
5. Distinguish between molecular mass and formula mass, and calculate molecular mass.

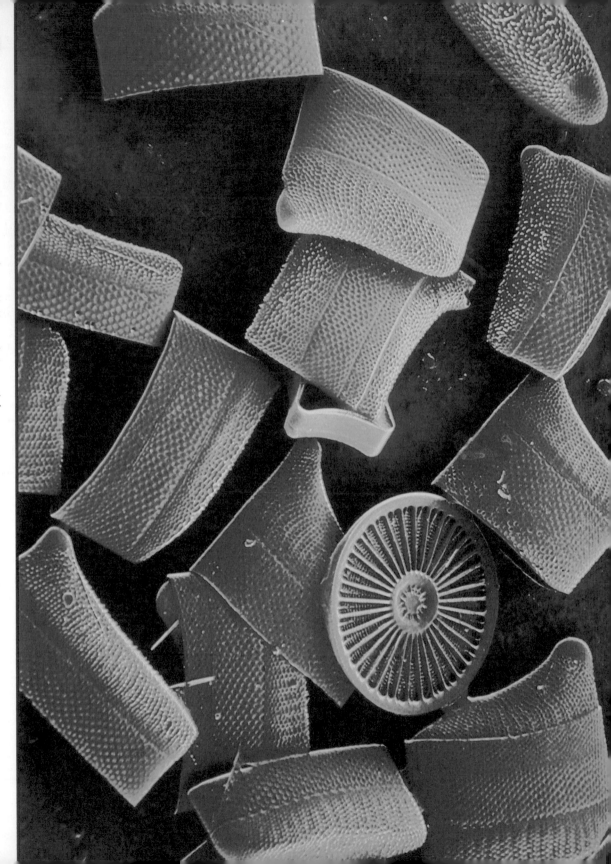

5-3 IONIC COMPOUNDS

Chemical bonds are the forces that hold particles of matter together. The atoms of hydrogen and oxygen in water are held together by bonds.

To understand how bonds form, consider the elements that do not usually form bonds. The elements in Group 18 of the Periodic Table are called the noble gases. These elements are very stable. That is, under normal conditions they do not form chemical bonds. All noble gases have a complete outer energy level. They are stable because of this electron arrangement.

Other atoms do not have a complete outer energy level. These atoms share, give up, or gain electrons to have a stable electron arrangement like that of the noble gases. In the process of changing their electron arrangement, atoms form chemical bonds.

IONS

Many atoms gain or lose electrons and end up with the same number of outer electrons as a noble gas. When a neutral atom loses or gains electrons, it becomes a charged particle. A charged particle is called an **ion**. In an ion the number of protons and the number of electrons are not equal. If there are more protons than electrons the ion will have a positive charge. If there are more electrons than protons the ion will have a negative charge.

Usually, metals lose electrons and nonmetals gain electrons. When a neutral sodium atom loses one electron, it becomes a positive sodium ion. As you can see in Figure 5-7, it still has 11 protons in the nucleus but now has only 10 electrons. The sodium ion has a charge of $1+$. It is written as Na^{1+}.

After completing this section, you will be able to

- **describe** how ions form.
- **explain** how an ionic bond is formed.
- **describe** the properties of ionic compounds.

The key terms in this section are
chemical bond
ion
ionic bond
ionic compound

NOTE:
In the example given here, sodium becomes an ion with a $1+$ charge, shown as Na^{1+}. In future chapters, ions with a charge of 1 will show only the sign of the charge, as in Na^+. The number 1 is understood, but not written.

Figure 5-7

A neutral sodium atom loses one electron to become a sodium ion, Na^{1+}.

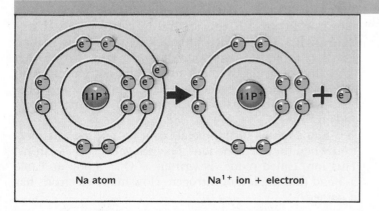

Na atom Na^{1+} ion + electron

OBJECTIVES
Refer to pupil page 115.

VOCABULARY
Key terms: chemical bond, ion, ionic bond, ionic compound
Other terms: electron dot diagram, formula unit, lattice, polyatomic ions

1 MOTIVATION

Perform the following demonstration to generate an interest in bonding and chemical combination. Wear safety goggles and have students do the same during the demonstration. Perform the demonstration in a well-ventilated area, preferably under a hood. Place 20 mL of a well-combined 1:1 mixture of powdered aluminum and powdered iodine on a large ceramic pad. Make a small depression in the top of the pile, and add two drops of water. A vigorous reaction occurs almost immediately. Ask students to comment on the procedure used to obtain the reaction. Ask them to name the compound formed. (Aluminum iodide.)

2 CONCEPT DEVELOPMENT

Background   Bonds are the forces that hold atoms and ions together to form molecules and crystals. The type of bonding within molecules also determines the forces between molecules. The state of matter—whether it is solid, liquid, or gas—depends on bonding forces. The physical shapes of molecules—whether they are spherical, rigid, or flat—are a result of the kinds of bonds that the molecules form.

Teaching Tip   Explain that atoms are stable when they have complete outer energy levels and that atoms with incomplete outer energy levels tend to complete them to achieve stability.

Some atoms lose more than one electron. For example, magnesium loses two electrons resulting in an electron structure like that of neon. The charge resulting from the loss of two electrons is $2+$. The magnesium ion is written as Mg^{2+}. Aluminum loses three electrons and has a charge of $3+$. How would you write the symbol for the aluminum ion?[1]

Some elements do not always lose the same number of electrons. These elements can form more than one type of ion, depending on the number of electrons that are lost. Copper forms an ion with a $1+$ charge when one electron is lost. When two electrons are lost, the charge is $2+$. Recall that copper compounds have names that include a Roman numeral. This numeral indicates the charge of the ion in the compound. Thus copper (I) chloride contains Cu^{1+} ions, and copper (II) chloride contains Cu^{2+} ions. Look at Table 5-4. What are the charges on the two kinds of iron ions?[2]

Table 5-4 *Common Positive Ions*

1+ Ions	2+ Ions	3+ Ions
Cesium Cs^{1+}	Barium Ba^{2+}	Aluminum Al^{3+}
Copper (I) Cu^{1+}	Cadmium Cd^{2+}	Iron (III) Fe^{3+}
Lithium Li^{1+}	Calcium Ca^{2+}	
Sodium Na^{1+}	Copper (II) Cu^{2+}	
Potassium K^{1+}	Iron (II) Fe^{2+}	

Table 5-5 *Common Negative Ions*

1− Ions	2− Ions	3− Ions
Bromide Br^{1-}	Oxide O^{2-}	Nitride N^{3-}
Chloride Cl^{1-}	Sulfide S^{2-}	Phosphide P^{3-}
Fluoride F^{1-}		
Iodide I^{1-}		
Astatide At^{1}		

When a neutral atom gains an electron, it becomes a negative ion. For example, a chlorine atom can gain one electron and become an ion. The ion of chlorine has an outer electron structure like that of an atom of argon. The ion has 17 protons, like the neutral chlorine atom. But as shown in Figure 5-8, this ion has 18 electrons. Its charge is $1-$. This ion is called the chloride ion and is written as Cl^{1-}. Table 5-5 lists some negative ions. Notice that the name of a negative ion has a different ending than does the name of the neutral atom. When one atom becomes negatively charged, the name of the ion formed ends in *-ide*.

Some atoms of nonmetals gain more than one electron when they become ions. Oxygen gains two electrons. This ion, called oxide, is written as O^{2-}. Look at Table 5-5 and find the ion of nitrogen. How many electrons has it gained?[3]

[1] Al^{3+}.
[2] The iron (II) ion has a $2+$ charge. The iron (III) ion has a $3+$ charge.
[3] Three.

Teaching Tip   Let students make a set of flashcards for the information in Tables 5-4, 5-5, and 5-6 (name on one side, and symbol for the ion or formula for the polyatomic ion on the other). Have students use the cards to memorize the information.

Background   In 1916, G.N. Lewis, an American chemist, wrote an article titled "The Atom and the Molecule." This article formed the basis of the modern theory of valence.

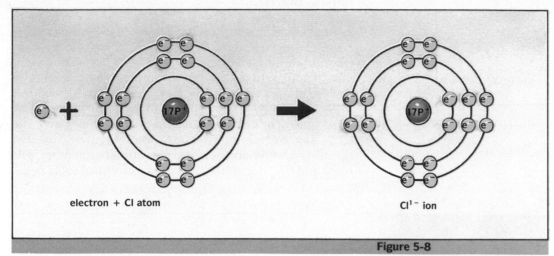

Figure 5-8

electron + Cl atom Cl^{1-} ion

A neutral chlorine atom gains one electron to become a chloride ion, Cl^{1-}.

There are some atoms that are joined together in a group and have a charge. These atoms stay together as a group and behave like one charged atom. Groups of atoms that have a charge are called *polyatomic* (pah lee uh TAHM-ihk) *ions*. Find the ammonium ion and the chlorate ion in Table 5-6. What is the charge of each?[1]

In studying bonds, scientists are interested in the outer electrons of atoms or of ions. Scientists often use electron dot diagrams to show outer electrons. An *electron dot diagram* consists of an element's symbol surrounded by dots. These dots stand for the electrons in the outer energy level. For example, the sodium atom has one electron in its outer energy level. Its electron dot diagram is Na•. An atom of magnesium has two outer electrons. It is shown as Mg:. The electron dot diagrams for atoms of the elements in the second row of the Periodic Table are shown in Figure 5-9. Notice that only outer electrons are shown. What pattern do you notice in these diagrams?[2]

Table 5-6 *Polyatomic Ions*

Name	Ion
Acetate	CH_3COO^{1-}
Ammonium	NH_4^{1+}
Bicarbonate	HCO_3^{1-}
Carbonate	CO_3^{2-}
Chlorate	ClO_3^{1-}
Hydroxide	OH^{1-}
Phosphate	PO_4^{3-}
Sulfate	SO_4^{2-}

Figure 5-9

Electron dot diagrams show the number of outer electrons in each atom.

[1]The ammonium ion has a 1+ charge. The chlorate ion has a 1− charge.

[2]Each atom has one more electron than does the atom to its left.

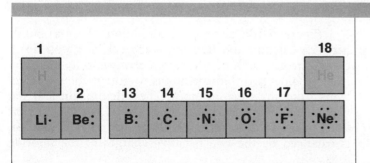

Background Explain to students that nonmetals tend to form negative ions and that metals tend to form positive ions. The differences in the ionic charges create strong electrostatic attractive forces, causing non-metals and metals to form ionic bonds.

Background The attractive forces between the positive nucleus and the unshared electrons help atoms obtain the stable outer electron arrangement. When atoms combine chemically, the strength of their attraction for electrons determines whether they lose, gain, or share electrons.

IONIC BONDS

Some atoms tend to lose one or more electrons to form positive ions. Other atoms tend to gain one or more electrons to form negative ions. Ions that have opposite charges are attracted to each other. An **ionic bond** is a force of attraction between oppositely charged ions. A sodium atom loses its outer level electron and becomes a sodium ion Na^{1+}. A chlorine atom gains the electron lost by sodium. The chlorine atom has become a negative ion, Cl^{1-}. This electron transfer is shown in Figure 5-10A. The resulting positive and negative ions attract each other. The Na^{1+} and Cl^{1-} form NaCl. These ions form an ionic bond.

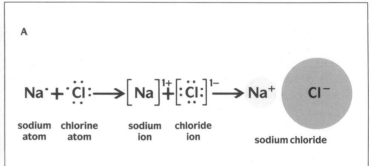

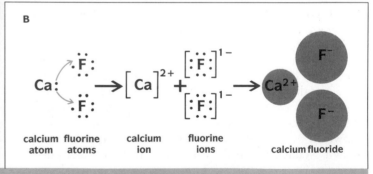

Figure 5-10

The formation of sodium chloride, NaCl (*A*). The formation of calcium fluoride, CaF_2 (*B*).

Figure 5-10*B* shows the formation of ionic bonds between calcium and fluorine. Each calcium atom loses two electrons. Each fluorine atom can gain only one electron. It takes two fluorine atoms to accept the two electrons from the calcium atom. The calcium ion and the two fluoride ions form calcium fluoride, CaF_2. Notice that CaF_2 has no charge. The 2+ charge on the calcium ion is balanced by the two negative charges of the fluoride ions.

IONIC COMPOUNDS

An **ionic compound** is one that contains ionic bonds. The charges on the ions determine the ratio of ions in the compound. The formula shows this ratio.

If the two ions have equal but opposite charges, no subscripts are needed, because the ions are present in a one-to-one ratio, as in NaCl. If the charges are not equal, the formula for the ionic compound must contain subscripts. Determining the correct formula of an ionic compound involves the following three steps.

1. Write the symbols of the ions in the compound next to each other. Write the positive ion first and include the charge on each ion.
2. Cross over the numbers of the charges but not the + or − sign, and write the numbers as subscripts. The charge on the positive ion will be the subscript of the negative ion. The charge on the negative ion will be the subscript of the positive ion.
3. Write the formula of the compound, showing the subscripts but not the charges. If any subscript is 1, you do not need to write it.

Sample Problem

Write the formula for aluminum oxide.

1. Write the symbols of the ions in the compound. The positive ion, Al^{3+}, should be written first.

$$Al^{3+}O^{2-}$$

2. Cross over the numbers of the charges, and write the numbers as subscripts. The 3 from the aluminum ion is the subscript for oxygen. The 2 from the oxide ion is the subscript for aluminum.

$$Al^{3+}_2O^{2-}_3$$

3. Write the formula of the compound, showing the subscripts but not the charges.

$$Al_2O_3$$

To check that a formula has been written correctly, multiply the charge on an ion by the subscript for that ion. Two Al^{3+} ions have a total charge of $6+$. Three O^{2-} ions have a total charge of $6-$. Because these charges are equal but opposite, they balance each other, and the compound is neutral.

$$2(Al^{3+}) + 3(O^{2-}) = 0$$
$$(6+) + (6^-) = 0$$

Figure 5-11

Altnough a ruby is red and a sapphire is blue, both contain the compound aluminum oxide.

Background   The reaction between a metal such as sodium and a nonmetal such as chlorine is highly exothermic. Energy is needed to remove the outer electron from a sodium atom. The chlorine atom releases some energy when it accepts the electron. A large amount of energy is released when a sodium ion and a chloride ion come together to form the sodium chloride crystal.

Teaching Tip   Make sure that students are aware that a sodium atom does not donate its electron freely.

Teaching Tip   Show students a model of the structure of ordinary table salt. Explain the crystalline pattern, and show the sites of the sodium and chloride ions that make up the cube.

Enrichment   Have students construct models of several ionic compounds, and display them in the classroom.

Enrichment   Have students determine the correct formulas for several compounds, such as iron (II) oxide (FeO) and ammonium phosphate $((NH_4)_3 PO_4)$, by making use of Tables 5-4, 5-5, and 5-6.

Teaching Tip   Stress the idea that a compound is electrically neutral, that is, the sum of the total positive charge and the total negative charge is zero.

Sample Problem

Write the formula for barium chlorate.

1. Write the symbols of the ions in the compound.

$$Ba^{2+}ClO_3{}^{1-}$$

2. Cross over the numbers of the charges, and write them as subscripts. Remember that the chlorate ion is treated like a single atom. To show that the subscript refers to the group of atoms in the chlorate ion, parentheses are used around the symbol for the chlorate ion.

$$Ba^{2+}{}_1 (ClO_3{}^{1-})_2$$

3. Write the formula of the compound, showing the subscripts but not the charges. Recall that the subscript 1, for barium, is understood and not written.

$$Ba(ClO_3)_2$$

Check the formula by multiplying the charge on each ion by its subscript. The overall charge should be 0.

   The smallest repeating unit in an ionic compound is called the *formula unit*. The formula unit consists of two or more oppositely charged ions. As you can see in Figure 5-12, ionic compounds are more than just simple pairs of ions. First, a sodium ion, Na^{1+}, and a chloride ion, Cl^{1-}, attract each other and form the formula unit Na^+Cl^-. Next, two Na^+Cl^- units join. Then, more Na^+Cl^- units join. The compound continues to build up, in a repeating pattern and in all directions. Thus, a three-dimensional crystal of sodium chloride is formed. This orderly repeating pattern of units is known as *lattice*. All ionic compounds form some kind of lattice structure.

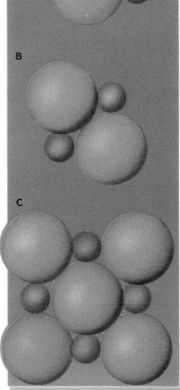

Figure 5-12

In the crystals of an ionic compound, such as sodium chloride, the ions are arranged in a lattice pattern.

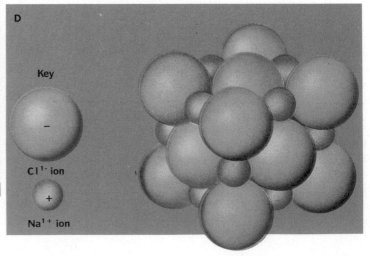

Key

−

Cl^{1-} ion

+

Na^{1+} ion

Ionic bonds are very strong. Because of these strong bonds, ionic compounds have high melting points and high boiling points. Ionic compounds are usually brittle. Their crystals can be broken apart along smooth, flat surfaces.

As solids, ionic compounds do not conduct electricity. However, if they are melted or dissolved in water, ionic compounds do conduct electricity. When an ionic solid is melted or dissolved in water, its lattice structure is destroyed. Thus its ions are able to flow and carry a charge.

Figure 5-13

These crystals are potassium dichromate, $K_2Cr_2O_7$. When they dissolve, they release potassium ions, K^{1+}, and dichromate ions, $Cr_2O_7^{2-}$.

REVIEW

1. How is an ion different from the neutral atom from which it forms?
2. What is an ionic bond?
3. What are some of the properties of ionic compounds?
4. Write the correct formula for each of the following ionic compounds.
   a. magnesium chloride
   b. lithium bromide
   c. barium hydroxide
   d. copper (II) acetate
   e. calcium phosphate
   f. ammonium sulfate

CHALLENGE Consider the elements lithium (Li), sodium (Na), potassium (K), and rubidium (Rb) in Group 1 of the Periodic Table. They all have one electron in the outer energy level, and they all form an ion with a charge of 1+. Rubidium gives up its electron to form a positive ion much more easily than does any of the others. Potassium gives up its one electron more easily than do the rest. Sodium gives up its electron more easily than does lithium. Suggest an explanation for these differences.

3 REVIEW/REINFORCEMENT

1. An ion is a charged particle, and the neutral atom has no charge.
2. An ionic bond is a force of attraction between oppositely charged ions.
3. The bonds in ionic compounds are very strong. Ionic compounds are very stable and have a high melting point and a high boiling point. These compounds are usually brittle and do not conduct electricity as solids, but they conduct electricity when melted or dissolved in water.
4. a. $MgCl_2$.
   b. $LiBr$.
   c. $Ba(OH)_2$.
   d. $Cu(CH_3COO)_2$.
   e. $Ca_3(PO_4)_2$.
   f. $(NH_4)_2SO_4$.

Challenge Although all have one electron in the outer energy level, going down the group from Li to Rb, the outer electron is much farther from the nucleus. The attraction of the positive nucleus for the outermost electron decreases as the distance between them increases. Thus, the farther the outer electron is from the nucleus, the more easily the electron is given up.

5-4 COVALENT BONDS

OBJECTIVES
Refer to pupil page 122.

VOCABULARY
Key terms: covalent bond, covalent compound, molecule
Other terms: double covalent bond, single covalent bond, triple covalent bond

1 MOTIVATION

Chemists are interested in the way covalent molecules are joined together and the kinds of properties that result from these covalent bonds. Use molecular model kits, either purchased or teacher-made, to show students how to build the covalent molecule of CH_4.

$$\begin{array}{c} H \\ | \\ H\text{-}C\text{-}H \\ | \\ H \end{array}$$

Ask them to build covalent molecules of C_2H_6, C_3H_8, and C_4H_{10}. Ask students which atoms are attached to which, and in what way. Ask students how the atoms in a molecule are arranged with respect to one another.

2 CONCEPT DEVELOPMENT

Background A simple covalent compound is produced when neither atom involved in the bond formation tends to produce a positive ion. As two atoms approach each other, their nuclei attract electrons of the approaching atom. When two atoms form a covalent bond, each of the atoms contributes an electron, which results in a shared pair. Thus each atom acquires a stable outer electron arrangement like that of a noble gas.

5-4 COVALENT COMPOUNDS

After completing this section, you will be able to

- **explain** how a covalent bond forms.
- **describe** properties of covalent compounds.

The key terms in this section are
covalent bond
covalent compound
molecule

Sometimes atoms form bonds by sharing electrons. A bond in which electrons are shared between atoms is called a **covalent** (koh VAY lehnt) **bond.** By forming covalent bonds, atoms form a stable outer electron structure. The simplest substance in which atoms form a covalent bond is hydrogen gas, H_2. A hydrogen atom has one electron and must gain an electron to have the stable structure of the noble gas helium. Each of two hydrogen atoms shares its one electron with the other hydrogen atom. Thus a covalent bond is formed. The shared pair of electrons gives each hydrogen atom two electrons. A unit, such as H:H or H_2, that contains a covalent bond is known as a molecule.

A **molecule** is the smallest unit of any covalent substance that can exist alone and still show the properties of that substance. A molecule may be formed by two or more atoms of the same element. As you can see in Figure 5-14, a molecule of the element phosphorus is made up of four atoms of phosphorous. The formula for phosphorus is P_4. The formula for sulfur is S_8. How many sulfur atoms are there in one sulfur molecule?[1]

[1]Eight.

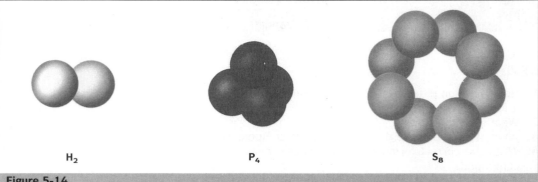

H_2 P_4 S_8

Figure 5-14

Molecules of hydrogen, phosphorus, and sulfur all contain covalent bonds.

A molecule also may be formed from two or more atoms of different elements, as in water, H_2O. How does a water molecule form? An oxygen atom has six electrons in its outer energy level. Thus, it needs two electrons to have a full outer energy level and a stable electron structure. A hydrogen atom needs one more electron to have a stable electron structure. As you can see in Figure 5-15, the oxygen atom shares one of its electrons with one hydrogen atom and another electron with the other hydrogen atom. Each hydrogen atom shares its electron with the oxygen atom. This sharing gives the oxygen atom eight electrons in its outer level. Each hydrogen atom has two electrons in its outer level. The resulting molecule has two covalent bonds. Compounds that contain covalent bonds are called **covalent compounds**.

NOTE
The ball-and-stick models shown in this book represent the arrangement of atoms and bonds in molecules.

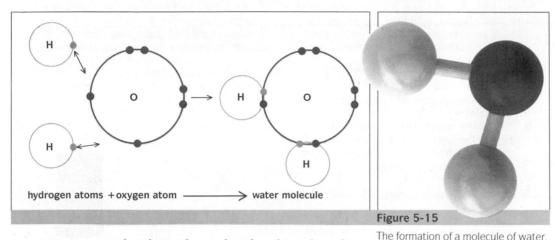

hydrogen atoms + oxygen atom ———————➤ water molecule

Figure 5-15

The formation of a molecule of water.

In a water molecule, each covalent bond involves the sharing of one pair of electrons. Such bonds are called *single covalent bonds*. Look at the diagram of carbon dioxide in Figure 5-16. The carbon atom forms covalent bonds with each oxygen atom. In each bond the carbon atom shares two pairs of electrons with the oxygen atom. Such a bond is known as a *double covalent bond*. Count all the electrons around the carbon atom in CO_2. You see that by forming a double covalent bond with each oxygen atom, the carbon atom has an outer energy level with eight electrons. This gives it a stable outer electron structure. Count the electrons around each of the oxygen atoms. Does each of these atoms have a stable outer electron structure?[1]

Nitrogen gas makes up 78 percent of the earth's atmosphere. Its formula is N_2. A molecule of N_2 is shown in Figure 5-16. How many pairs of electrons do the atoms in each N_2 molecule share?[2] The bond between the nitrogen atoms in nitrogen gas is called a *triple covalent bond*.

Substances that contain covalent bonds show different properties than do ionic substances. Covalent compounds do not form a lattice structure. Covalent compounds generally have low melting and boiling points. At room temperature ionic compounds are solid. Under the same conditions, some covalent compounds are solid while others are in the liquid or gas state.

[1]Yes. [2]Three.

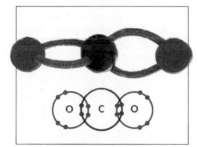

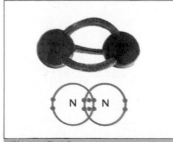

Figure 5-16

Molecules of carbon dioxide, CO_2, (*top*) and nitrogen, N_2, (*bottom*).

123

ACTIVITY 35 minutes

PROCESS SKILLS
observing, recording observations, comparing, classifying

Preparation   None required.

Safety Tip   Emphasize that students should wear safety goggles and a lab apron during the entire activity. Caution students not to touch the ends of the wires.

Answers to Results and Conclusions
1. Table salt in water, and baking soda in water.
2. Table salt and baking soda.
3. Sugar, hydrogen peroxide, and rubbing alcohol.

---

③ REVIEW/REINFORCEMENT

1. A covalent bond forms when two atoms share electrons.
2. A molecule is the smallest unit of any covalent substance that can exist alone and still show the properties of that substance.
3. An atom is the smallest particle of an element that can combine chemically. A molecule is the smallest particle of a covalent element or compound that can exist alone and still show the properties of that substance.
4. Covalent compounds generally have a low melting point and a low boiling point. At room temperature, covalent compounds may be solids, liquids, or gases. For the most part, these compounds do not conduct electricity.

Challenge   Each atom of chlorine shares one of its outer energy-level electrons in the chlorine molecule, Cl_2. In the oxygen molecule, O_2, each oxygen atom shares two of its outer energy-level electrons. Thus the chlorine molecule forms a single covalent bond, and the oxygen molecule forms a double covalent bond.

124

ACTIVITY   What Compounds Conduct Electricity?

OBJECTIVE
Classify compounds, based on their ability to conduct electricity.

MATERIALS
safety goggles, lab apron, dry cell, insulated wire, wire stripper, light bulb and socket, six 250-mL beakers, glass-marking pencil, table salt, sugar, baking soda, distilled water, hydrogen peroxide, rubbing alcohol

PROCEDURE
A. Wear safety goggles and a lab apron during this activity.
B. Set up the equipment as shown in the figure. The ends of the wire should have 2 cm of insulation removed. **Caution:** Do not touch the ends of the wires.
C. Label six beakers *A–F*.
D. Place table salt in beaker *A*, to a depth of about 0.5 cm.
E. Hold the insulated part of the wires, and touch the ends of the wires to the salt. If the light bulb lights, the compound conducts electricity. If the light bulb does not light, the compound does not conduct electricity. Record all observations.
F. Place sugar in beaker *B*, to a depth of about 0.5 cm. Repeat the test for conducting electricity.
G. Place baking soda in beaker *C*, to a depth of about 0.5 cm. Repeat the test for conducting electricity.
H. Add enough distilled water to beakers *A*, *B*, and *C* to half fill them. Swirl each gently to mix. Half fill beaker *D* with distilled water.
I. Test distilled water for conducting electricity.
J. Repeat the test for conducting electricity with each mixture. Rinse the ends of the wires in distilled water after each test.
K. Half fill beaker *E* with hydrogen peroxide. Repeat the test for conducting electricity. Rinse the ends of the wires.
L. Half fill beaker *F* with rubbing alcohol. Repeat the test for conducting electricity. Rinse the ends of the wires.

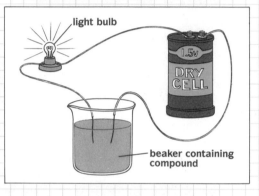

light bulb

beaker containing compound

RESULTS AND CONCLUSIONS
1. Which substances conducted electricity?
2. Which substances are ionic compounds?
3. Which substances are covalent compounds?

Another difference between ionic and covalent compounds is that most covalent compounds do not conduct electricity. Ionic compounds form ions when they dissolve, but covalent compounds do not. When a covalent compound dissolves, its molecules remain bonded. Thus there are no charged particles to carry an electrical charge.

REVIEW

1. How does a covalent bond form?
2. Define the term *molecule*.
3. What is the difference between an atom and a molecule?
4. State two properties of covalent compounds.

CHALLENGE Predict how two chlorine atoms bond to form a chlorine molecule, Cl_2. Predict how two oxygen atoms bond to form an oxygen molecule, O_2.

124

5-5 MOLECULAR MASS AND FORMULA MASS

A symbol may stand for atoms of an element or for the atomic mass of an atom. The atomic mass of hydrogen, H, is 1 amu. However, hydrogen is found in nature as H_2. Because H_2 is a molecule, scientists speak of the *molecular mass* of H_2. **Molecular mass** is equal to the sum of the atomic masses of all atoms in a molecule. Thus, for H_2, the molecular mass is equal to twice its atomic mass, or 2 amu. To find the molecular mass of any substance, use the following steps.

1. Write the chemical formula for the compound.
2. Count the number of atoms of each element in the compound.
3. Look up the atomic mass of each of these elements.
4. Find the total mass that each element contributes to the compound. To do this, multiply the atomic mass of each element by the number of atoms of that element in the compound.
5. Add the total masses of each element from step 4.

Sample Problem
Find the molecular mass of water.

1. Write the chemical formula for the compound.

$$H_2O$$

2. Count the number of atoms of each element in the compound. Water contains two hydrogen atoms and one oxygen atom.

$$2H \qquad 1O$$

3. Look up the atomic mass of each of these elements. Use the Periodic Table in Appendix 1, pages 572-573 to find the atomic masses.

$$H = 1 \text{ amu} \qquad O = 16 \text{ amu}$$

4. Find the total mass of each element in the compound.

$$2H = 2(1 \text{ amu}) = 2 \text{ amu}$$
$$1O = 1(16 \text{ amu}) = 16 \text{ amu}$$

5. Add the total masses of each element in the compound.

$$2 \text{ amu} + 16 \text{ amu} = 18 \text{ amu}$$

The molecular mass of the compound water is 18 amu. Use the model shown in Figure 5-17 to find the molecular mass of methane.[1]

After completing this section, you will be able to
- **distinguish** between molecular mass and formula mass.
- **calculate** the molecular mass of a compound.
- **calculate** the formula mass of a compound.

The key terms in this section are
formula mass
molecular mass

[1]The molecular mass of methane is 18 amu.

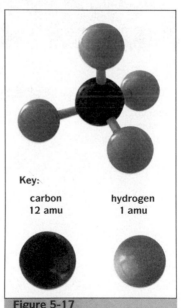

Key:

carbon
12 amu

hydrogen
1 amu

Figure 5-17

A model of methane, CH_4.

5-5 MOLECULAR MASS AND FORMULA MASS

pages 125–127

OBJECTIVES
Refer to pupil page 125.

VOCABULARY
Key terms: formula mass, molecular mass

1 MOTIVATION

Perform the following demonstrations for students. Have them examine the substances both before and after the reactions. Measure the mass of each substance before the reaction and the mass after the reaction. Demonstration 1: Mix 7.0 g of iron and 4.0 g of sulfur, and place the mixture in a crucible. Heat with a Bunsen burner until the reaction is complete. The mass of the iron sulfide should be about 10.9 g. Ask students to compare the mass before and after the demonstration. Demonstration 2: Place 13.0 g of zinc in a second crucible and heat the zinc for several minutes until the zinc reacts completely. The mass of the zinc oxide produced should be about 16.2 g. Ask students why the mass of the zinc is greater after the reaction. (Oxygen combined with the zinc.) Ask them how information obtained in these demonstrations can be used to determine chemical formulas and formula masses.

2 CONCEPT DEVELOPMENT

Background   In the laboratory, mass is measured in gram units, not in atomic mass units. The symbol of an element may sometimes represent one atomic mass unit. Thus, the symbol H may represent 1 amu or 1 g; the symbol C may represent 12 amu or 12 g. However, the mass of one hydrogen atom is not 1 g, nor is the mass of one carbon atom 12 g.

Puzzler The formula mass of hydrated copper sulfate minus the formula mass of copper sulfate equals the total mass of water in hydrated copper sulfate.

$$250 \text{ amu} - 160 \text{ amu} = 90 \text{ amu}$$

Because each water molecule equals 18 amu, 90 amu divided by 18 equals 5 molecules of water. These 5 molecules are attracted to one unit of copper sulfate to make hydrated copper sulfate.

Tie-in/Math Have students calculate the formula mass of $CaSO_4$ (136.1 amu); $(NH_4)_2SO_4$ (132.1 amu); $KMnO_4$ (158 amu); $CuCl_2$ (134.5 amu); and $CuSiF_6$ (205.6 amu).

Enrichment Have students construct models of chloroform ($CHCl_3$), nitrogen dioxide (NO_2), xenon tetrafluoride (XeF_4), copper(II) chloride ($CuCl_2$), and sodium hydroxide ($NaOH$).

Thinking Skills

interpreting data
Students interpret data presented in Figure 5-17 to find molecular mass. Have them compare the amounts of grams for the same number of formula units or molecules of each of these compounds: $NaCl$ (58.4 amu); H_2O (18 amu); CCl_4 (153.8 amu); $C_6H_{12}O_6$ (180 amu). Ask students to explain why the same number of particles of these different compounds have different masses. (Particles do not have the same mass unless they are the same kind of particles; the mass depends on what kinds of particles make up each compound.)

Review and Skill Masters
CHALLENGE/CRITICAL THINKING, pages 33–34. See page 105c in this book for answers.

SCIENCE PUZZLER

Each copper sulfate unit can attract a certain number of water molecules. As this happens, the pale crystals become bright blue. The formula mass of copper sulfate without water is 160 amu. With the water, the formula mass is 250 amu. How many water molecules are attracted to one unit of copper sulfate?

Ionic compounds do not contain individual molecules. Instead they are made up of oppositely charged ions. The formulas written for ionic compounds represent the simplest units that make up the compounds. The mass of an ionic compound is referred to as the formula mass. **Formula mass** is the sum of the atomic masses of the atoms present in a unit of ions. The formula mass of an ionic compound is found by following the steps given for finding the molecular mass of a covalent compound.

Sample Problem
Find the formula mass of sodium carbonate.

1. Write the chemical formula for the compound.

$$Na_2CO_3$$

2. Count the number of atoms of each element in the compound.

$$2Na \quad 1C \quad 3O$$

3. Look up the atomic mass of each of these elements.

$$Na = 23 \text{ amu} \quad C = 12 \text{ amu} \quad O = 16 \text{ amu}$$

4. Find the total mass of each element.

$$2Na = 2(23 \text{ amu}) = 46 \text{ amu}$$
$$1C = 1(12 \text{ amu}) = 12 \text{ amu}$$
$$3O = 3(16 \text{ amu}) = 48 \text{ amu}$$

5. Add the total masses of the elements.

$$46 \text{ amu} + 12 \text{ amu} + 48 \text{ amu} = 106 \text{ amu}$$

Figure 5-18

Sodium carbonate, Na_2CO_3, is mined as soda ash.

REVIEW

1. Compare and contrast molecular mass and formula mass.
2. Find the molecular mass of each of the following.
   a. NO_2 **b.** HF   **c.** H_2O_2 **d.** CCl_4
3. Find the formula mass of each of the following.
   a. KF   **b.** Na_2O **c.** MgO   **d.** $CaSO_4$

CHALLENGE   There are two different compounds that contain copper and oxygen. The formula mass of one of these compounds is 79.5 amu. The formula mass of the other compound is 143.0 amu. Write the formula for each compound.

CHAPTER SUMMARY

The main ideas in this chapter are listed below. Read these statements before you answer the Chapter Review questions.

- A compound is a pure substance made up of two or more elements that are chemically joined. (5-1)
- The proportion of elements in a compound does not change. (5-1)
- A chemical formula is used to show the makeup of a compouund. (5-2)
- A subscript is a small lowered number that stands for the proportion of elements in a compound. (5-2)
- Chemical bonds are forces that hold particles of matter together. (5-3)
- When an atom gains or loses an electron, the atom becomes a charged particle called an ion. (5-3)

- An ionic bond is a force of attraction between oppositely charged ions. (5-3)
- Ionic bonds form when atoms gain or lose electrons. (5-3)
- Covalent bonds are formed when atoms share electrons. (5-4)
- A molecule is the smallest unit of any covalent substance that can exist alone and still show the properties of that substance. (5-4)
- The sum of the atomic masses of all atoms in a molecule is called the molecular mass. (5-5)
- The sum of the atomic masses of the atoms present in a unit of ions is called the formula mass. (5-5)

The key terms in this chapter are listed below. Use each term in a sentence that shows the meaning of the term.

chemical bond	covalent bond	ion	molecular mass
chemical formula	covalent compound	ionic bond	molecule
compound	formula mass	ionic compound	subscript

1. Molecular mass refers to the mass of covalent compounds; it is equal to the sum of the atomic masses of atoms in the molecule. Formula mass refers to the mass of ionic compounds; it is equal to the sum of the atomic masses of the atoms present in a unit of ions.
2. **a.** 45.8 amu.
   b. 19.9 amu.
   c. 33.8 amu.
   d. 153.6 amu.
3. **a.** 58.0 amu.
   b. 61.7 amu.
   c. 40.2 amu.
   d. 135.6 amu.

Challenge
a.
$$+\begin{array}{r} Cu\ 63.5\ amu \\ O\ 15.9\ amu \\ \hline 79.4\ amu \end{array}$$
Formula: CuO

b.
$$-\begin{array}{r} 143.0\ amu \\ 79.5\ amu \\ \hline 63.5\ amu \end{array}$$
, the mass of one copper atom
Formula: Cu_2O

Review and Skill Masters

VOCABULARY REVIEW, page 29.
See page 105b in this book for answers.

VOCABULARY

1. ions
2. molecular mass
3. chemical bonds
4. chemical formula
5. covalent compound
6. compound
7. subscript
8. molecule
9. ionic bond
10. covalent bond

CONCEPTS

1. The elements in a compound lose the properties they exhibited when they were uncombined. Compounds do not look like or act like the elements that form them.
2. **a.** 1 C, 2 O. **b.** 2 H, 1 C, 3 O. **c.** 12 C, 22 H, 11 O. **d.** 1 C, 4 H. **e.** 1 Cu, 2 Cl. **f.** 1 K, 1 Br.
3. **a.** Sodium hydroxide. **b.** Phosphorus trichloride. **c.** Potassium chlorate. **d.** Calcium oxide. **e.** Barium chloride. **f.** Aluminum sulfate.
4. A potassium atom loses its outer level electron and becomes a potassium ion, K^+. A bromine atom gains the electron lost by the potassium and becomes a negative ion, Br^-. The resulting positive and negative ions attract each other; the K^+ and Br^- form KBr.
5. A sodium ion has a charge of 1^+; it has 11 protons and 10 electrons. A sodium atom has no charge; it has 11 protons and 11 electrons.
6. *Molecules* refers to units of covalently bonded substances. Sodium chloride is made up of units of ions.
7. Ionic bond; compounds with ionic bonds have a high melting point and conduct electricity when in the molten state or when dissolved in water.
8. Ionic compounds conduct electricity when they are melted, because their lattice structure is destroyed and the ions formed are able to flow and to carry a charge.

Review and Skill Masters

CHAPTER REVIEW, pages 30–31.
See page 105b in this book for answers.

128

Chapter Review

VOCABULARY

Use the key terms from this chapter to complete the following sentences correctly.

1. Atoms become charged particles called _____ when an electron is gained or lost.
2. The sum of the atomic masses of all atoms in a molecule is called the _____.
3. _____ are the forces that hold particles of matter together.
4. A/An _____ is a group of symbols that shows the makeup of a compound.
5. A compound that contains covalent bonds is called a/an _____.
6. A pure substance made of two or more elements that are chemically joined is called a/an _____.
7. The number that shows the proportion of elements in a chemical formula is a/an _____.
8. A/An _____ is the smallest part of a covalent substance that has the properties of that substance.
9. A/An _____ is the force of attraction between oppositely charged ions.
10. The bond formed by the sharing of electrons between two atoms is called a/an _____.

CONCEPTS

1. How are elements and compounds related? (5-1)
2. How many atoms of each element are present in each of these compounds? (5-2)
   a. CO_2
   b. H_2CO_3
   c. $C_{12}H_{22}O_{11}$
   d. CH_4
   e. $CuCl_2$
   f. KBr
3. Name each of the following compounds. (5-2)
   a. NaOH
   b. PCl_3
   c. $KClO_3$
   d. CaO
   e. $BaCl_2$
   f. $Al_2(SO_4)_3$
4. Describe how the ionic bond in potassium bromide is formed. (5-3)
5. What is the difference between a sodium ion and a sodium atom? (5-3)
6. What is wrong with the expression "a molecule of sodium chloride"? (5-3)
7. A white solid has a high melting point and a high boiling point. When it is melted, this compound conducts electricity. What kind of bond is found in this compound? Explain your answer. (5-3)

128

8. Explain why ionic compounds can conduct electricity when they are melted but not when they are solids. (5-3)

9. Write a formula for each of the following compounds. (5-3)
   a. sodium iodide
   b. potassium phosphate
   c. barium chlorate
   d. calcium carbonate
   e. copper (II) fluoride
   f. sodium nitrate

10. What is the difference between a covalent bond and an ionic bond? (5-3, 5-4)

11. What is the difference between a hydrogen atom and a hydrogen molecule? (5-4)

12. Compare single, double, and triple covalent bonds. (5-4)

13. A compound is a gas at room temperature. It does not conduct electricity. What kind of bonds are found in this compound? Explain your answer. (5-4)

14. Find the molecular mass of each of the following. (5-5)
    a. C_2H_6 b. $C_6H_{12}O_6$ c. CH_2Cl_2 d. C_4H_9OH

15. Find the formula mass of each of the following. (5-5)
    a. KF   b. $Cu(NO_3)_2$ c. $Be(OH)_2$ d. PbI_2

---

1. Suppose scientists have found two new elements, X and Y, that have not been given names yet. These elements have the following electron dot diagrams.

   ·Ẍ: ·Ÿ:

   Predict the kind of bonds that form when each of these elements combines with hydrogen.

2. Write the formula for each compound formed in question 1.

3. Compare oxygen atoms, ions, and molecules.

---

1. The noble gases have been made to react and form a few compounds. Do library research to find out what these compounds are and how they are formed.

2. In addition to the type of bonds, the shape of a molecule determines the properties of a molecule. Find out how scientists have determined the shapes of molecules.

3. Look up the term *electronegativity,* and explain how electronegativity can help to determine the type of chemical bonds that exist in a compound.

Bershad, Carol, and Deborah Bernick. *Body-Works: The Kid's Guide to Food and Physical Fitness.* New York: Random House, Inc., 1981.

Weis, Malcolm E. *Why Glass Breaks, Rubber Bends, and Glue Sticks.* New York: Harcourt Brace Jovanovich, Inc., 1979.

9. a. NaI. b. K_3PO_4. c. $Ba(ClO_3)_2$. d. $CaCO_3$. e. CuF_2. f. $NaNO_3$.

10. In a covalent bond the electrons between the atoms forming the bond are shared. In an ionic bond, one atom transfers one or more of its electrons to the other atom. The bond results from the attraction of the ions formed as a result of the electron transfer.

11. A hydrogen atom has one electron and can lose or gain an electron; a hydrogen molecule is made up of two hydrogen atoms, each sharing its electron with the other.

12. In single covalent bonds, atoms share one electron pair; in double covalent bonds, atoms share two electron pairs; in triple covalent bonds, atoms share three electron pairs.

13. The compound contains covalent bonds. There are no charged particles to carry a charge.

14. a. 30 amu. b. 180 amu. c. 85 amu. d. 74 amu.

15. a. 58.0 amu. b. 186.9 amu. c. 42.8 amu. d. 460.9 amu.

APPLICATION/CRITICAL THINKING

1. Both elements would form covalent bonds.
2. H_2X, YH_3.
3. An oxygen atom has 8 protons in the nucleus and 8 electrons outside the nucleus; an oxygen ion has 8 protons and 10 electrons outside the nucleus, thus having a charge of 2^-; an oxygen molecule is made up of two atoms of oxygen covalently bonded.

Test Masters

CHAPTER TEST, pages 17–20.
See page 105d in this book for answers.

MIXTURES

ORGANIZER

Section	pages	Activity	pages	Reinforcement and Evaluation	pages	*Review and Skill Masters	pages	Other Components in Teacher Resource Package	pages
6–1 Kinds of Mixtures	131–135	How Many Substances Are in Black Ink?	134	Review, Challenge	135	Challenge/Critical Thinking	39–40	Study Guide	28
6–2 Making Solutions	136–140	How Can the Rate of Solution Be Changed?	140	Review, Challenge	140	Skill	38	Study Guide	29
6–3 Properties of Solutions	141–146	How Does Temperature Affect Solubility?	145	Puzzler Review, Challenge	144 146			Study Guide Lab Manual	30 29
6–4 Suspensions and Colloids	147–149			Review, Challenge	149			Study Guide Lab Manual	31 33
CHAPTER SUMMARY	149					Vocabulary Review	35		
CHAPTER REVIEW	150–151			*Test Masters	21–24	Chapter Review	36–37		

*In the Teacher Resource Package. For answers, see pages 129b–129d in this book.

ACTIVITY MATERIALS Quantities are based on a class of 30 students working in groups as indicated in parentheses.

How Many Substances Are in Black Ink? p. 134 (groups of 2)	quantity	How Can the Rate of Solution Be Changed? p. 140 (groups of 2)	quantity	How Does Temperature Affect Solubility? p. 145 (groups of 2)	quantity
lab apron	30	lab apron	30	safety goggles	30
12-cm long chromatography paper	15 sheets	spatula	15	lab apron	30
forceps	15	safety goggles	30	250-mL beaker	15
ruler	15	copper (II) sulfate	30 g	hot plate	15
capillary tube	15	balance	15	Celsius thermometer	15
black ink	15 bottles	mortar and pestle	15	potassium nitrate	100 g
test tube	15	test tube	30	test tube	15
ring stand	15	glass-marking pencil	15	10-mL graduate	15
clamp	15	10-mL graduate	15	distilled water	
cork stopper	15	distilled water		stirring rod	15
thumbtack	15	rubber stopper	30	tap water	
graduate	15	test-tube rack	15		
distilled water					
small test tube	45				
test-tube rack	15				
dropper	15				
stirring rod	15				

REVIEW AND SKILL MASTERS

Name_____ Date_____

VOCABULARY REVIEW _____ Chapter 6

Many chemistry terms are derived from Latin and Greek words. Listed below are nine words about mixtures. The Latin (L.) or Greek (Gr.) origin of each word or word part is given in parentheses. Explain what each term means, based on its origin.

1. heterogeneous mixture (Gr., *heteros*, other, different; Gr., *genos*, kind; L., *mixtus*, to mix)
   A heterogeneous mixture is a mixture that differs from point to point.

2. homogeneous mixture (Gr., *homos*, same; Gr., *genos*, kind; L., *mixtus*, to mix)
   A homogeneous mixture is a mixture that is the same throughout.

3. saturated solution (L., *satur*, full; L., *solutus*, dissolve) **A saturated solution is a solution in which all the solute it can hold has been dissolved.**

4. solubility (L., *solubilis*, to loosen, dissolve) **Solubility is the amount of solute that will dissolve in a given amount of solvent at a given temperature.**

5. solute (L., *solutus*, dissolve) **A solute is the substance that is dissolved in a solution.**

6. solvent (L., *solvens*, loosen) **A solvent is the substance in a solution that dissolves or loosens another substance.**

7. supersaturated solution (L., *super*, over; L., *satur*, full; L., *solutus*, dissolve)
   A supersaturated solution is a solution that has more dissolved solute than normal at a given temperature.

8. suspension (L., *sus*, up; L., *pendere*, to cause to hang, weigh) **A suspension is a mixture in which particles of a substance temporarily hang in a liquid.**

9. unsaturated solution (Gr., *un*, not; L., *satur*, full; L., *solutus*, dissolve)
   An unsaturated solution is a solution in which more solute can be dissolved.

35

Name_____ Date_____

CHAPTER REVIEW _____ Chapter 6

6-1 Kinds of Mixtures

1. How are the properties of mixtures and pure substances different? **The properties of mixtures depend upon the properties of their parts and vary from sample to sample. The properties of pure substances are constant.**

2. Classify the following mixtures as homogeneous or heterogeneous: brass, soil, seawater, blood. **Homogeneous: brass, seawater; heterogeneous: soil, blood.**

6-2 Making Solutions

1. Contrast a solute and a solvent. **In a solution, the solute is the substance present in the smaller amount and the solvent is the substance present in the greater amount.**

2. How does salt, an ionic solute, dissolve in water? **When salt is placed in water, the negative oxygen ends of water attract the positive sodium ions and the positive hydrogen ends of water attract the negative chloride ions.**

3. Name three factors that affect the rate of solution. **The rate of solution is affected by the size of the solute particles, the shaking or stirring of the mixture, and the temperature of the solution.**

6-3 Properties of Solutions

1. Describe two factors that affect the solubility of a gas. **The solubility of a gas decreases as temperature rises. Solubility increases as pressure increases.**

36

Name_____ Date_____

CHAPTER REVIEW (Continued) _____ Chapter 6

2. How do saturated, unsaturated, and supersaturated solutions differ? **A saturated solution has dissolved all the solute it can at a given temperature. An unsaturated solution can dissolve more solute. A supersaturated solution has dissolved more solute than is normal for a given temperature.**

3. How does adding solute particles affect the boiling and freezing points of water? **Adding solute particles to water raises the boiling point and lowers the freezing point.**

6-4 Suspensions and Colloids

1. Give two properties of suspensions and colloids. **Answers will vary. Suspensions have large clusters of particles that can be filtered. Colloids have particles that scatter light; these particles do not separate on standing and cannot be separated by filtering.**

2. Contrast particle size in solutions, suspensions, and colloids. **A solution has very small particles, such as atoms and molecules, that cannot be seen. A suspension has large clusters of particles, such as rocks and soil, that can be seen. A colloid has particles larger than solution particles but smaller than suspension particles, such as soot in the air.**

3. What are two examples of suspensions and colloids? **Examples will vary. Salad dressing and muddy water are suspensions; smoke and eggwhite are colloids.**

37

Name_____ Date_____

SKILL/Interpreting a Graph _____ Chapter 6

Milk is an example of a mixture. The milk that cows produce is called raw milk. It is a heterogeneous mixture of water and milk solids. Raw milk is made into a homogeneous mixture that is sold as whole milk. This change involves five steps: separation, pasteurization, homogenization, fortification, and packaging. Study the diagram and graph and answer the questions below.

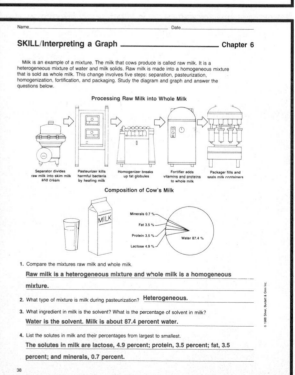

Processing Raw Milk into Whole Milk

Separator divides raw milk into skim milk and cream

Pasteurizer kills harmful bacteria by heating milk

Homogenizer breaks up fat globules

Fortifier adds vitamins and proteins to whole milk

Packager fills and seals milk containers

Composition of Cow's Milk

Minerals 0.7 %
Fat 3.5 %
Protein 3.5 %
Lactose 4.9 %
Water 87.4 %

1. Compare the mixtures raw milk and whole milk.
   Raw milk is a heterogeneous mixture and whole milk is a homogeneous mixture.

2. What type of mixture is milk during pasteurization? **Heterogeneous.**

3. What ingredient in milk is the solvent? What is the percentage of solvent in milk?
   Water is the solvent. Milk is about 87.4 percent water.

4. List the solutes in milk and their percentages from largest to smallest.
   The solutes in milk are lactose, 4.9 percent; protein, 3.5 percent; fat, 3.5 percent; and minerals, 0.7 percent.

38

129b

Name_____ Date_____

CHALLENGE/CRITICAL THINKING _____ Chapter 6

It is possible that the world could run out of its limited supply of petroleum used to produce gasoline. Another source of energy is ethyl alcohol, or ethanol, a colorless, flammable liquid. Automobile and truck engines can use a mixture of 10 percent ethanol and 90 percent gasoline, called gasohol. The gasohol mixture may be more efficient and produce less pollution than does pure gasoline.

Ethanol can be produced from corn using a two-step process. First, corn is fermented by growing yeast cells. Then, the fermented solution is distilled.

Currently, most of the corn grown in the United States is used only to feed cattle, not to make ethanol. However, the corn by-products of the process of making ethanol can still be fed to cattle with only a very small loss in nutrient value.

An experimental farm produced a 10,000 liter mixture containing 5 percent ethanol and 95 percent water. Study the diagram below and answer the following questions.

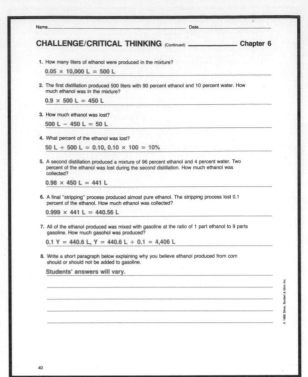

① 95 % water
5 % ethanol

② 95 % water
5 % ethanol

90 % ethanol
10 % water

First Distillation

③ 90 % ethanol
10 % water

96 % ethanol
4 % water

Lost
2 % ethanol

Lost
0.1 % ethanol

④ 99.9 % ethanol

Second Distillation   **Stripping**

© 1989 Silver, Burdett & Ginn Inc.

39

Name_____ Date_____

CHALLENGE/CRITICAL THINKING (Continued) _____ Chapter 6

1. How many liters of ethanol were produced in the mixture?

$0.05 \times 10,000$ L = 500 L

2. The first distillation produced 500 liters with 90 percent ethanol and 10 percent water. How much ethanol was in the mixture?

0.9×500 L = 450 L

3. How much ethanol was lost?

500 L − 450 L = 50 L

4. What percent of the ethanol was lost?

50 L ÷ 500 L = 0.10, 0.10×100 = 10%

5. A second distillation produced a mixture of 96 percent ethanol and 4 percent water. Two percent of the ethanol was lost during the second distillation. How much ethanol was collected?

0.98×450 L = 441 L

6. A final "stripping" process produced almost pure ethanol. The stripping process lost 0.1 percent of the ethanol. How much ethanol was collected?

0.999×441 L = 440.56 L

7. All of the ethanol produced was mixed with gasoline at the ratio of 1 part ethanol to 9 parts gasoline. How much gasohol was produced?

0.1 Y = 440.6 L, Y = 440.6 L ÷ 0.1 = 4,406 L

8. Write a short paragraph below explaining why you believe ethanol produced from corn should or should not be added to gasoline.

Students' answers will vary.

_____
_____
_____
_____

© 1989 Silver, Burdett & Ginn Inc.

40

TEST MASTERS

Mixtures

PART 1

Chapter
Goal

In the space below, write the term that each phrase defines.

1. **supersaturated solution** A solution that has more dissolved solute than is normal for a given temperature — 4

2. **suspension** A heterogeneous mixture in which particles of a substance are temporarily mixed in a liquid — 5

3. **solute** The substance that is present in the smaller amount in a solution — 2

4. **homogeneous mixture** A mixture whose makeup is the same throughout — 1

5. **solvent** The substance that is present in the greater amount in a solution — 2

6. **heterogeneous mixture** A mixture whose makeup differs from point to point throughout — 1

7. **colloid** A mixture whose properties are in between those of a solution and a suspension — 5

8. **solubility** The amount of solute that will dissolve in a given amount of solvent at a given temperature — 3

9. **unsaturated solution** A solution in which more solute can be dissolved — 4

PART 2

Choose the term or phrase that best answers the question or completes the statement. Write the letter of that choice in the space at the left.

d 1. Which of the following would most likely be used to distinguish one substance from another? — 3
   a. temperature   b. mass   c. weight   d. solubility

b 2. Which of the following would reduce the solubility of a solid in a liquid? — 3
   a. an increase in the temperature of the solution
   b. a decrease in the temperature of the solution
   c. an increase in the pressure of the solution
   d. a decrease in the pressure of the solution

Choose the term or phrase that best answers the question or completes the statement. Write the letter of that choice in the space at the left.

d 3. The solubility of lithium chloride at 20°C is 83 g per 100 g of water. Which of the following solutions is a supersaturated solution of lithium chloride? — 4
   a. 80 g in 100 g of water at 20°C   c. 83 g in 100 g of water at 60°C
   b. 83 g in 100 g of water at 20°C   d. 85 g in 100 g of water at 20°C

c 4. The solubility of a gas in a liquid would most likely be increased by an increase in the: — 3
   a. amount of the solute.   c. pressure over the solvent.
   b. temperature of the solution.   d. density of the solute.

a 5. Which term describes an alloy? — 2
   a. solid solution   c. aqueous solution
   b. heterogeneous mixture   d. compound

c 6. Suspensions differ from colloids, because only in suspensions do the particles: — 5
   a. scatter light.   c. form visible clusters.
   b. produce positive ions.   d. contain molecules.

d 7. Colloids are similar to solutions in part because, in both, the particles: — 5
   a. form heterogeneous mixtures.   c. separate upon filtering.
   b. occur in visible clusters.   d. remain mixed upon standing.

c 8. A pure substance is different from a mixture because all samples of a pure substance have the same: — 1
   a. shape.   c. freezing point.
   b. quantity.   d. temperature.

d 9. Heating helps speed up the rate of solution in part by: — 2
   a. increasing the surface area of the solute.
   b. decreasing the motion of particles.
   c. increasing the number of polar molecules.
   d. increasing the motion of particles.

b 10. A difference between mixtures and compounds is that, in a mixture, the: — 1
   a. atoms combine in definite proportions.
   b. substances keep their own properties.
   c. elements develop new physical properties.
   d. compounds combine to form new elements.

d 11. In a solution, boiling point elevation is caused by an increase in the: — 4
   a. energy of the solvent particles.
   b. size of the solute particles.
   c. mass of the solvent particles.
   d. number of the solute particles.

Look at the graph. Then read the questions that follow. Choose the term or phrase that best answers the question or completes the statement. Write the letter of that choice in the space at the left.

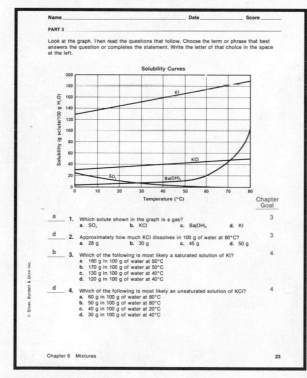

Solubility Curves

a 1. Which solute shown in the graph is a gas? — 3
   a. SO₂   b. KCl   c. Ba(OH)₂   d. KI

d 2. Approximately how much KCl dissolves in 100 g of water at 80°C? — 3
   a. 28 g   b. 30 g   c. 45 g   d. 50 g

b 3. Which of the following is most likely a saturated solution of KI? — 4
   a. 180 g in 100 g of water at 50°C
   b. 170 g in 100 g of water at 50°C
   c. 130 g in 100 g of water at 40°C
   d. 120 g in 100 g of water at 40°C

d 4. Which of the following is most likely an unsaturated solution of KCl? — 4
   a. 60 g in 100 g of water at 80°C
   b. 50 g in 100 g of water at 80°C
   c. 40 g in 100 g of water at 20°C
   d. 30 g in 100 g of water at 40°C

Read each question or direction and answer it using complete sentences.

1. Describe how polar substances dissolve. — 2

   Solutes dissolve when the attraction between solute particles and solvent particles is greater than the attraction between solute particles alone. For example, when a polar solute is placed in a polar solvent such as water, solute ions are attracted to the positive and negative ends of the polar water molecules.

2. What factors affect solubility? How do these factors affect the solubility of different types of solutes? — 3

   Temperature affects the solubility of solids, liquids, and gases. The solubility of solids and liquids increases as temperature increases. The solubility of gases decreases as temperature increases, because, at higher temperatures, gas particles gain energy and escape from solution. Pressure does not affect the solubility of solids and liquids. However, pressure does affect the solubility of gases. More gas dissolves in a liquid when pressure over the liquid increases.

3. How are solutions, colloids, and suspensions similar, and how are they different?

   Solutions, colloids, and suspensions are all types of mixtures. In solutions and colloids, the particles in the mixture are not visible. In a suspension, the particles are visible either with the unaided eye or a magnifier. In solutions, the particles in the mixture are ions, atoms, or molecules. In suspensions, the particles occur in large clusters. In solutions and colloids, particles cannot be separated by filtering, and they will not settle out on standing. In suspensions, particles can be separated by filtering and will settle out. Colloids have properties in between those of a solution and a suspension. Like suspensions, colloids scatter light (Tyndall effect). Solution particles do not scatter light.

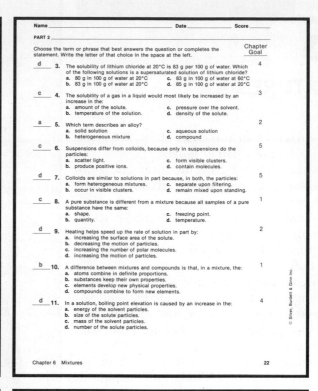

CHAPTER **6** PLANNING GUIDE

6

MIXTURES

The questions in the CHAPTER TEST are based on these Chapter Goals.

1. Distinguish between mixtures and pure substances, and classify mixtures as homogeneous or heterogeneous.
2. Describe the characteristics and parts of a solution and how solutions form; recognize factors that affect the rate of solution.
3. Discuss the factors that affect solubility.
4. Compare saturated, unsaturated, and supersaturated solutions, and explain how solute particles affect boiling point and freezing point.
5. Identify properties of different types of suspensions and colloids, and distinguish between solutions, suspensions, and colloids.

MIXTURES

Have you ever seen water color or oil paintings in a museum? Paint is a mixture of different substances. The color of the paint depends on the type and amount of substances the artist mixes together. The photograph shows an artist's palette with paints on it. How many colors are there? Notice how different colors form when two or more paints mix.

The palette is also a mixture. But the compounds in the palette are different from those in the paint. Therefore the palette has different properties than the paint does.

- *What are some common mixtures?*
- *How are mixtures used?*
- *What are the properties of mixtures?*

6-1 KINDS OF MIXTURES

Any sample of matter can be classified as a pure substance or a mixture. A pure substance is either an element or a compound. A **mixture** is made up of two or more substances that can be separated by physical means. Air is a mixture of oxygen, nitrogen, carbon dioxide, other gases, and water. Gasoline is a mixture that may contain from a few to almost 200 different substances. Most samples of matter are mixtures.

The makeup and properties of pure substances are constant. For example, all water molecules contain two hydrogen atoms for each oxygen atom. Pure water freezes at 0°C whether you have a drop or a tubful.

The properties of a mixture depend upon the properties of its parts. Brass, for example, is a solid mixture of copper, a yellow-red metal, and zinc, a silvery-white metal. Brass made mostly from copper is red-gold. Brass containing at least 50 percent zinc is white.

The properties of mixtures can vary from sample to sample. For example, a mixture made of half a spoonful of sugar in one cup of water has different properties than

After completing this section, you will be able to

- **distinguish** between mixtures and pure substances.
- **classify** mixtures as homogeneous or heterogeneous.

The key terms in this section are
heterogeneous mixture
homogeneous mixture
mixture

Have students read the introductory paragraph. Explain to them that mixtures play an important role in their daily lives. Ask students to list some mixtures that they come in contact with daily. Have them identify some of the parts of the mixtures. Ask students how mixtures of the same substances can vary.

- What are some common mixtures? (Air, blood, gasoline, milk, brass.)
- How are mixtures used? (Mixtures are used in most everyday situations, such as breathing, running an automobile, putting in dental fillings, and making alloys.)
- What are the properties of mixtures? (The properties of mixtures depend upon the properties of their parts.)

6-1 KINDS OF MIXTURES
pages 131–135

OBJECTIVES
Refer to pupil page 131.

VOCABULARY
Key terms: heterogeneous mixture, homogeneous mixture, mixture
Other terms: solutions, distillation

1 MOTIVATION

Display several mixtures, such as baking soda, sugar, and instant coffee, in water. Also display mixtures of flour and talc, in water. Ask students to describe the differences between the mixtures. Dissolve some iron (III) chloride in a beaker of water, and, in a second beaker, mix some dirt and water. Filter both mixtures. (The soil can be separated by filtering, but the iron (III) chloride cannot be separated in this way.) Explain to students that filtering is one way to separate some mixtures. Ask students how they would separate the iron (III) chloride from the water.

2 CONCEPT DEVELOPMENT

Background   Generally, a mixture has three characteristics. First, a mixture consists of two or more substances. Second, these substances can be mixed in different proportions. Third, each substance in a mixture keeps most of its own properties.

Teaching Tip   Explain that mixtures that have distinct regions are heterogeneous. Provide samples of granite, and have students observe the various distinct regions of the minerals mica, quartz, and feldspar. Oil and water is another heterogeneous mixture that is easily observed.

Teaching Tip   Prepare three solutions of CuSO₄ of varying concentrations (1 g CuSO₄ per 100 mL of water; 5 g per 100 mL; 10 g per 100 mL). The varying shades of blue will show that the physical properties of mixtures can vary from sample to sample.

Teaching Tip   Have students make a list of household products, foods, and jewelry. On the chalkboard make a chart that includes four categories in which these products can be placed: Elements, Compounds, Heterogeneous Mixtures, and Homogeneous Mixtures. Have students classify their listed items into these categories.

a mixture of two spoonfuls of sugar in one cup of water. Every drop of mixture from the second cup contains more sugar than every drop of mixture from the first cup. Thus, the sugar mixture in the second cup is sweeter than that in the first cup.

In some mixtures the different substances can be seen easily. One example is a mixture of sand and water. The sand is seen in distinct regions in the mixture. A mixture of sand and water does not have the same makeup throughout the mixture. Instead, it differs from one point to another. A mixture whose makeup differs from point to point is called a **heterogeneous** (heht uhr uh JEE nee-uhs) **mixture**.

hetero- (another)
-genos (kind)

Figure 6-1

Each of these mixtures contains more than one substance.

homo- (same)
-genos (kind)

[1]The candlestick and the orange gelatin are homogeneous mixtures. The other samples are heterogeneous mixtures.

Some mixtures do not differ from point to point. Their makeup is the same throughout. A mixture whose makeup is the same throughout is called a **homogeneous** (hoh muh JEE nee uhs) **mixture**. Seawater and brass are both homogeneous mixtures. Homogeneous mixtures are also called *solutions*. Which of the samples in Figure 6-1 are heterogeneous mixtures? Which are homogeneous mixtures?[1]

SCIENCE & TECHNOLOGY

When a tunnel is dug, there is always a danger that it might cave in or flood. To prevent such problems engineers use a variety of techniques to stabilize the ground around the tunnel. This is especially important when tunnels are built in soft, water-logged areas. First, deep holes are drilled into the ground that is about to be dug out. Then a stabilizer is injected into these holes. The stabilizer spreads through cracks in the ground and hardens around the tunnel.

Many manufacturers now make stabilizers to order. First the manufacturers analyze ground conditions around a tunnel; then they produce a mixture best suited to improving the

ground around that particular tunnel.

One mixture used to stabilize tunnels is called shotcrete. This mixture is used to cover the inside of a tunnel. Shotcrete is made up of cement, sand, water, and other materials that can be sprayed onto the inner

surface of the tunnel. Manufacturers have been trying to improve the mixture. One manufacturer has made a kind of shotcrete that contains steel fibers. With steel fibers, the shotcrete will stick to rock more tightly and, thus, hold rocks together better.

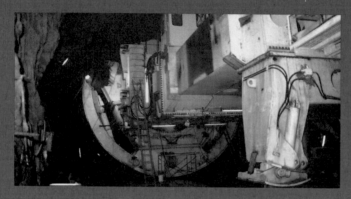

When a mixture is formed, each substance keeps its own physical properties. Therefore the parts of a mixture can be separated by physical means. For example, a mixture made up of red and green grapes can be separated by hand. Sand can be separated from water by a filter. Iron filings can be separated from a mixture of sulfur and iron filings. Notice in Figure 6-2 that the iron filings are attracted to a magnet but the sulfur is not.

Figure 6-2

A magnet can be used to separate iron and sulfur.

Teaching Tip Discuss with students the difficult task that sometimes faces chemists when they wish to separate mixtures into their components. Mixtures must be separated by physical processes to avoid altering the chemical properties of the compounds. Ask students to suggest some physical means for separating mixtures.

Thinking Skills

comparing
Students are asked to observe and compare the effect of a magnet on a mixture of sulfur and iron filings in Figure 6-2. They can conclude that the magnet is used to take advantage of the physical properties of the two kinds of matter in the mixture—one can be magnetized, but the other cannot.

PROCESS SKILLS
observing, recording data, comparing, predicting, inferring

Preparation   To minimize student handling of paper, precut the chromatography paper with pointed ends. By having the chromatography paper prepared before class, this avoids problems caused by hand oils, which are readily absorbed by the paper.

Teaching Tip   Have students wear lab aprons so ink does not get on their clothing.

Answers to Results and Conclusions
1. The number of colors will depend on the separation and on the kind of ink used. Carter's ink gives three colors; Sheaffer's ink gives four, one of which is the overlap of two other colors.
2. Each color represents a substance.
3. A blue-gray colored solution, it resembles a dilute solution of the original sample. You can make it more like the original by evaporating some of the water.
4. Students' models should include the observation that the water traveled up the paper. As water moved past the ink spot, it lifted different components of the ink at different rates. This caused the separate components to be carried to different levels. Accept any reasonable explanations by students.

Demonstration   Set up a simple distillation apparatus, and demonstrate the separation of black ink into its components. Relate this technique to the separation of the components of ink by paper chromatography in this section's activity.

Review and Skill Masters

CHALLENGE/CRITICAL THINKING, pages 39–40. See page 129c in this book for answers.

ACTIVITY   How Many Substances Are in Black Ink?

OBJECTIVE
Separate and compare the substances in ink.

MATERIALS
chromatography paper, forceps, ruler, capillary tube, black ink, 1 test tube, ring stand, clamp, cork stopper, thumbtack, graduate, distilled water, 3 small test tubes, test tube rack, dropper, stirring rod, lab apron

PROCEDURE
A. Place a small pencil mark about 3 cm from the pointed end of a strip of chromatography paper. Do not touch the paper with your fingers; use forceps.
B. Use a capillary tube to apply black ink to the chromatography paper. Place one end of the capillary tube in the ink, and let some ink rise in the tube. Put your finger on top of the tube, and transfer a small drop of ink to the pencil mark on the paper. Let the ink dry. Repeat the application once or twice.
C. Assemble the apparatus as shown in the figure. Fold the top of the paper strip over about 1 cm, and attach the strip to a cork stopper with a thumbtack. Place the strip in the test tube, and adjust the stopper so that the point of the strip is about 2 cm above the bottom of the test tube. Remove the stopper, and carefully pour 10 mL of distilled water into the test tube. Make sure that the walls of the test tube remain dry.
D. Place the stopper into the tube so that the point of the paper strip extends into the water. The ink mark should be about 1 cm above the water.
E. Allow the water column to rise to within 3 cm of the top of the strip. Remove the stopper, and hang the strip to dry.
F. Examine the dry strip, and record your observations.

G. Cut one color section from the strip. Cut the section into small pieces, and place them in a small test tube. Add 10 drops of water, and then mash the paper in the water with a stirring rod. Record your observations.
H. Repeat step G with each color section. Combine the liquids obtained. Compare them with the original ink.

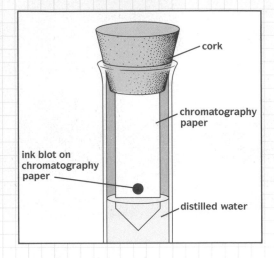

cork

chromatography paper

ink blot on chromatography paper

distilled water

RESULTS AND CONCLUSIONS
1. How many different colors did the separation procedure produce?
2. What might each color represent?
3. What resulted when you mixed the separate colors? How does the material produced in step H compare with the original ink? How could you make it more like the original ink?
4. Develop a model to explain how chromatography paper separated the parts of the ink. Base your model on your observations.

Scientists use many methods to separate mixtures. Some methods are used to identify the substances in a mixture. Other separation methods are used to purify a substance.

To separate mixtures of liquids, scientists use a method called *distillation* (dihs tuh LAY shuhn). In distillation, liquids are separated by differences in their boiling points. A mixture of methyl alcohol and water can be distilled. Methyl alcohol boils at 64.5°C. Water boils at 100°C. When the mixture is heated to 64.5°C, the alcohol will boil but the water will not. The alcohol can be collected as it boils out of the mixture. The water will be left behind.

Many plant oils used in perfumes, flavorings, and medicines are purified by distillation. Peppermint oil, which is used in toothpaste, is obtained in this way. The juices of the plant are distilled and the oil is collected.

In hospitals, modern instruments are used to separate mixtures such as blood. Blood is a mixture of water, cells, proteins, sugar, oxygen, carbon dioxide, and other substances. The substances in blood can be separated according to their densities. Tubes of blood are spun at very high speeds in a machine called a centrifuge. Figure 6-3 shows blood that has been spun in a centrifuge. The densest parts of the mixture are at the bottom of the tube. The least dense substances are at the top of the tube. Hospital technicians can then test the individual parts of the blood.

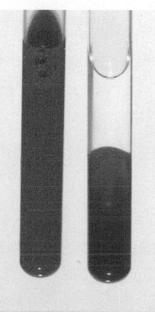

Figure 6-3

Which test tube of blood has been spun in a centrifuge?[1]

[1]The test tube of blood on the right has been spun.

REVIEW

1. Describe two ways in which mixtures are different from pure substances.
2. State whether each of the following mixtures is homogeneous or heterogeneous: muddy water, brewed coffee, orange juice, cough medicine, granite.

CHALLENGE Describe how you would separate each of the following mixtures: turpentine in water, gravel and sand, a colored liquid containing iron filings.

❸REVIEW/REINFORCEMENT

1. Mixtures are made up of two or more substances that can be separated by physical means. The physical properties of mixtures can vary from sample to sample; this is not true for pure substances.
2. Muddy water—heterogeneous; brewed coffee—homogeneous; orange juice—heterogeneous; cough medicine—homogeneous; granite—heterogeneous.

Challenge   Turpentine in water—pour off one layer; gravel and sand—use a sieve; colored liquid containing iron filings—use filter paper or a magnet.

6-2 MAKING SOLUTIONS

pages 136–140

1 MOTIVATION

Pour some tap water on a small block of wood to make a thin film of water. Place a small beaker containing 100 mL of ice water on top of the film of water on the block. Add 35 g of ammonium nitrate crystals to the ice water, and stir. Students will soon observe that the beaker is frozen to the wood block. Ask students how the beaker was frozen to the wood. (The dissolving ammonium nitrate absorbs energy from the film of water.) Ask students if they think that a dissolving solute always absorbs energy. (Students will learn later on that energy is sometimes given off by a dissolving solute.)

2 CONCEPT DEVELOPMENT

Teaching Tip   Tell students that the components of a solution may have been in different states before dissolving, but the final state of the solution is that of the solvent.

Thinking Skills

predicting
List the components and the physical state of several solutions, such as air, brass, carbonated water, syrup, silver amalgam, and camphor. Ask students to predict the physical state of the solute and solvent before they were mixed to form the solution.

6-2 MAKING SOLUTIONS

solvere (to dissolve)

Most of the materials that you come in contact with each day are mixtures. Many of these mixtures are solutions. The chemical reactions in your body take place in water solutions. The gasoline used in cars is a solution. Dental fillings are solid solutions of mercury in silver.

THE NATURE OF SOLUTIONS

A **solution** is a homogeneous mixture of two or more substances. Recall that a homogeneous mixture has the same makeup throughout. Solutions can be made by mixing substances in the solid, liquid, or gas states. For example, a soft drink contains a solution of carbon dioxide in water—a gas in a liquid.

The **solvent** in a solution is the substance that is present in the greater amount. The solvent usually determines the state of the solution. The substance present in the smaller amount in a solution is called the **solute**. In a soft drink, water is the solvent and carbon dioxide gas is the solute. The solution is in the liquid state, as is the solvent. Some solutions have more than one solute. Seawater is a solution in which many different substances are solutes dissolved in water.

In most solutions the solvent is a liquid and the solute is a solid, liquid, or gas. The solvent in most solutions is water. Solutions in which water is the solvent are called *aqueous solutions*. The solution shown in Figure 6-4 is an aqueous solution.

Figure 6-4

In an aqueous solution, water is the solvent.

solute

solvent

solution

When a solute enters a solution, the solute is said to *dissolve*. When you put sugar into water and then stir it, the sugar dissolves. The molecules of sugar spread out evenly among the molecules of water. When salt dissolves in water, each unit of sodium chloride separates into Na^+ and Cl^- ions. The ions spread out evenly among the molecules of water.

Solutions can contain dissolved molecules or ions or a combination of the two. Covalent compounds dissolve as molecules. Ionic compounds separate into ions when they dissolve. In a solution the solute particles are not visible. They will not settle to the bottom of the solution, no matter how long it is allowed to stand. The parts of a solution cannot be separated by filtering.

In solid solutions, both the solvent and the solute are solid. Many common metal objects are solid solutions. Such solutions are called *alloys*. For example, bronze, an alloy of copper and tin, is used to make statues like the one shown in Figure 6-5.

Some solutions conduct electricity. An electric current is carried in a solution by ions. Fluids in the human body contain ions such as sodium, Na^+, potassium, K^+, and calcium, Ca^{2+}. These ions allow body fluids to conduct electricity. In the human nervous system, information moves as electrical signals. The passage of these signals can be studied by machines like the one shown in Figure 6-6. A paste that is a solution containing ions carries the body's electrical signals to the wires that are attached to the machine.

Figure 6-5

This statue is made of bronze, a common alloy.

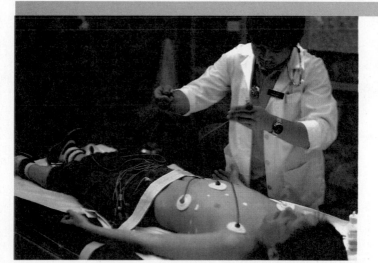

Figure 6-6

This machine is an electrocardiograph. It shows the electrical pattern produced by the heart.

Background Most alloys are solids. Solder, for example, is a heterogeneous mixture of lead in tin.

Background One kind of alloy is formed when the atoms of a metal form a lattice with the atoms of another substance arranged in the "holes" between the metal atoms. Tungsten carbide is an example of this kind of alloy. It is an extremely hard substance used in machine-operated cutting tools.

Review and Skill Masters

SKILL, page 38.
See page 129b in this book for answers.

Background   Water molecules are polar covalent and are associated through hydrogen bonding. Substances such as olive oil are nonpolar covalent and do not form hydrogen bonds. Thus nonpolar substances, such as oils, will not mix with water. Sugar molecules are covalent in nature. They contain many hydroxyl groups and can form hydrogen bonds, causing them to dissolve readily in water.

Background   In general, solutions form if the forces of attraction between solute and solvent particles are stronger than the forces between the solute particles and the forces between the solvent particles.

HOW SUBSTANCES DISSOLVE

Solutions form when particles of the solute spread out evenly in the solvent. Consider what happens when a cube of sugar dissolves in water, as shown in Figure 6-7. Recall that the sugar molecules in the cube are held together by attractive forces. For the sugar to dissolve, these forces must be overcome. Notice that when the sugar is placed in water, there is a strong attraction between sugar molecules and the water molecules. This attraction is greater than the attraction between sugar molecules alone. Thus the sugar molecules are pulled away from the cube and can mix with the water molecules. In general, a solution will form if the attraction between the solute particles and solvent particles is greater than the attraction between solute particles alone.

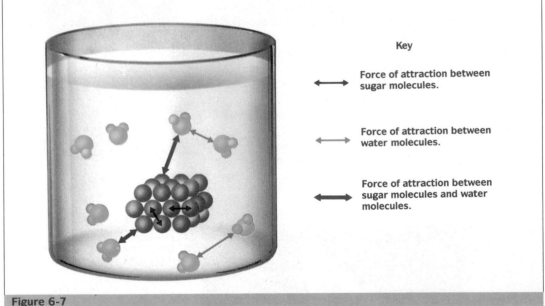

Key

Force of attraction between sugar molecules.

Force of attraction between water molecules.

Force of attraction between sugar molecules and water molecules.

Figure 6-7

As sugar dissolves, its molecules spread out through the water.

[1]Water molecules pull ions away from the crystal of sodium chloride.

Scientists say that in general, "like dissolves like." A polar solvent will dissolve a polar or ionic solute. In a polar molecule, one end is slightly negative and one end is slightly positive. Water molecules are polar. In a water molecule, the oxygen end is slightly negative. The hydrogen ends are slightly positive. Figure 6-8 shows sodium chloride, an ionic solute, dissolving in water. Notice that the positive ends of water molecules are attracted to the negatively charged chloride ions. How do these attractions cause salt to dissolve?[1]

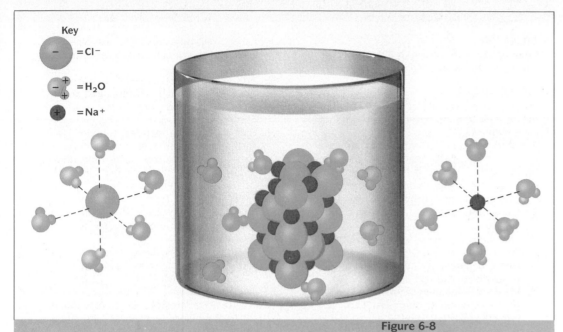

Key

$-$ = Cl^-

$+$ $+$ = H_2O

$+$ = Na^+

Figure 6-8

As sodium chloride dissolves, it separates into ions.

Nonpolar molecules do not have negative or positive ends. Hydrogen gas is a nonpolar molecule. A nonpolar solvent will dissolve a nonpolar solute. Fats and oils are nonpolar compounds that dissolve in gasoline, a nonpolar solvent.

In most cases, heat energy is either given off or absorbed when a solute dissolves. Dissolving some substances involves large amounts of energy. For example, when ammonium nitrate, NH_4NO_3, dissolves in water, the solution becomes very cold. Other substances, like calcium chloride, $CaCl_2$, or magnesium sulfate, Mg_2SO_4, produce heat when they dissolve. Their solutions are very hot. These properties are used in the instant cold or hot packs used to treat injuries.

RATE OF SOLUTION

How quickly a solute dissolves is called the rate of solution. The rate of solution depends on several factors. The smaller the solute particles are, the faster they dissolve. A spoonful of small crystals dissolves faster than a single large crystal. Breaking, crushing, or grinding a solid into smaller pieces increases the surface area of the solute. Solids dissolve only at the surface of the crystals. Thus, increasing the surface area of the solute increases the rate of solution.

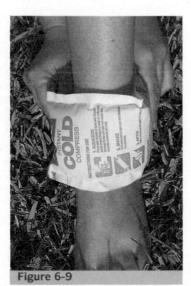

Figure 6-9

This instant cold pack absorbs heat as the substances in it dissolve.

ACTIVITY 30 minutes

PROCESS SKILLS
observing, recording data, comparing, predicting

Preparation   None required.

Safety Tip   Make certain that students wear safety goggles and a lab apron during this activity.

Answers to Results and Conclusions
1. The powder dissolved faster.
2. The smaller the solute particles, the faster they dissolve.

Extension   Students should predict that the crystals at 60°C begin to dissolve faster. Students' predictions should be verified by testing.

❸ REVIEW/REINFORCEMENT

1. The solute is the substance that is present in the smaller amount and the solvent is the substance that is present in the greater amount in a solution. In salt water, salt is the solute and water is the solvent. In a soft drink, carbon dioxide is the solute and flavored water is the solvent.

2. When sugar is placed in water, molecules of water begin to cluster around the surface of the sugar crystals. There is a strong attraction between water molecules and sugar molecules. As a result, the water molecules pull the sugar molecules away from the crystal and the sugar molecules mix with the water molecules.

3. Stirring or shaking brings more solvent molecules into contact with the solute, thus the rate of solution increases.

Challenge   To identify the appropriate solvent so that the stains can be dissolved and removed.

ACTIVITY   How Can the Rate of Solution Be Changed?

OBJECTIVE
Compare the rates at which different-sized particles dissolve in a solvent.

MATERIALS
safety goggles, spatula, copper (II) sulfate, balance, mortar and pestle, 2 test tubes, glass-marking pencil, 10-mL graduate, distilled water, 2 rubber stoppers, test-tube rack, lab apron

PROCEDURE
A. Wear safety goggles and a lab apron throughout this activity.
B. Obtain two large crystals of copper (II) sulfate.
C. Measure the mass of the smaller crystal. Record your result.
D. Grind the larger crystal to a fine powder, using the mortar and pestle.
E. Measure an amount of powdered copper (II) sulfate equal to the mass of the remaining whole crystal.
F. Label a test tube *crystal*, and another *powder*. Put the correct substance into each test tube.
G. Add 10 mL of distilled water to each test tube. Stopper each test tube, and shake strongly for 10 seconds. Record your observations.
H. Continue shaking each test tube for 10-second periods until all of the material in each tube is dissolved. Record the amount of time needed for the copper sulfate in each test tube to dissolve.

RESULTS AND CONCLUSIONS
1. In which form did the copper sulfate dissolve faster?
2. What can you conclude about the effect of particle size on the rate of solution?

EXTENSION
Test the relative rates of solution of a copper sulfate crystal placed in water at 10°C and a crystal placed in water at 60°C.

Stirring or shaking the mixture increases the rate of solution. When a solid dissolves, its particles slowly move away from the crystal. Stirring or shaking moves the solute particles away from the crystal faster. Thus, a fresh surface is exposed to the solvent. Stirring or shaking also moves the solvent over the solid more quickly.

Heating can increase the rate of solution by increasing the motion of particles. Solvent molecules pass more quickly over the surface of the solute. Heat also causes the solute particles to come off a solid more easily. Thus, the solid dissolves faster. Heating has the opposite effect on gases in solution. Gases dissolve faster in cold solutions than in warm ones.

REVIEW

1. How does a solute differ from a solvent? Give two examples of each.
2. Describe how sugar dissolves in water.
3. Explain how stirring or shaking affects the rate at which a solute dissolves.

CHALLENGE When you take clothing to the dry cleaner, it is important to identify any stains that are on the clothing. Why does the dry cleaner need this information?

6-3 PROPERTIES OF SOLUTIONS

Recall that the forces of attraction between particles play a major role in the solution process. For example, 100 g of water at 1°C will dissolve about 0.00009 g of silver chloride. The same amount of water at the same temperature will dissolve about 180 g of sucrose, a sugar. The bonds holding the silver chloride together are stronger than the bonds holding the sucrose together. Thus less silver chloride dissolves.

SOLUBILITY

The silver chloride can be said to have a low solubility (sahl yuh BIHL uh tee). **Solubility** is the amount of solute that will dissolve in a given amount of solvent at a given temperature. The solubility of sucrose at 1°C is 180 g per 100 g of water. Compared with that of silver chloride, the solubility of sucrose is high.

The effect of temperature on solubility is shown in Figure 6-10. The graph shows how much potassium nitrate, KNO_3, dissolves in 100 g of water over a range of temperatures. Such a graph is called a solubility curve. You can use the curve to find the solubility of potassium nitrate at any temperature. For example, at 0°C the solubility of this compound is about 12 g per 100 g of water. At 80°C it is about 160 g per 100 g of water. What is the solubility of potassium nitrate at 48°C?[1]

[1]80 g per 100 g of water.

Figure 6-10

The solubility of potassium nitrate varies with temperature.

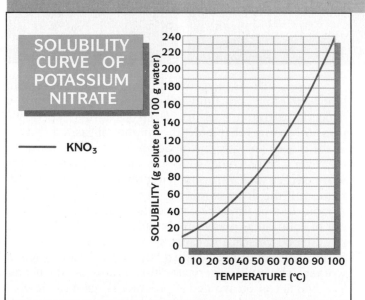

SOLUBILITY CURVE OF POTASSIUM NITRATE

—— KNO_3

After completing this section, you will be able to

- **discuss** the factors that affect solubility.
- **compare** saturated, unsaturated, and supersaturated solutions.
- **explain** how solute particles affect boiling point and freezing point.

The key terms in this section are
saturated solution
solubility
supersaturated solution
unsaturated solution

6-3 PROPERTIES OF SOLUTIONS
pages 141–146

OBJECTIVES
Refer to pupil page 141.

VOCABULARY
Key terms: saturated solution, solubility, supersaturated solution, unsaturated solution
Other terms: boiling point elevation, concentrated, dilute, freezing point depression

1 MOTIVATION

Add 100 mL of ice water to each of two 250-mL beakers. To one beaker add about 40 g of potassium nitrate; label the beaker potassium nitrate. To the other beaker add about 40 g of calcium acetate; label that beaker calcium acetate. The calcium acetate will dissolve completely, but the potassium nitrate will not. Place both beakers on a hot plate, and heat while stirring. As the temperature rises, the potassium nitrate will dissolve, but the calcium acetate will begin to settle out of solution. Ask students to describe and discuss their observations.

2 CONCEPT DEVELOPMENT

Thinking Skills

interpreting graphs
Students are asked to use the solubility curve in Figure 6-10 to determine the solubility of potassium nitrate at 48°C.

Demonstration   In a 100-mL graduate, measure exactly 50 mL of distilled water, and in another graduate, measure exactly 50 mL of isopropyl alcohol. Prior to mixing the contents of both graduates together, ask students to predict the total volume that they will have in a 100-mL graduate and to record their predictions. Mix the two liquids in a 100-mL graduate. Mixing these two liquids demonstrates that volumes of solutions are not additive. Elicit the number of correct predictions. Ask the other students to hypothesize why the result did not match their predictions. (The two liquids were completely miscible and the molecules of the solute fit in the spaces between the molecules of the solvent.)

Background   According to the kinetic theory, the amount of gas dissolved in a liquid is proportional to the pressure of the system. Increasing the concentration of gas when the pressure is raised hastens the dissolving process, and as a result, more gas dissolves.

Background   Solubility curves can be used to determine the solubility of a substance at different temperatures and to predict the amount of material that would settle out of solution if a solution of known composition was cooled to a certain temperature. These curves can also be used to determine the amount of additional material that will be used to reach saturation when the temperature is raised.

The solubility of a substance is a very important property. It can be used to distinguish one substance from another. For example, the solubility of sodium chloride at 25°C is 35.7 g per 100 g of water. At the same temperature the solubility of potassium bromide is 65 g per 100 g of water.

Unlike solids and liquids, the solubility of a gas decreases as temperature rises. When the temperature of a solution rises, the dissolved gas particles gain energy. They are then able to escape from the solution.

Pressure does not affect the solubility of solids and liquids. However, pressure does affect the solubility of gases. More gas dissolves in a liquid when pressure over the liquid increases. If the pressure over a liquid is less, less gas dissolves.

Figure 6-11

The diver must rise to the surface slowly, so that gases in solution will not form bubbles.

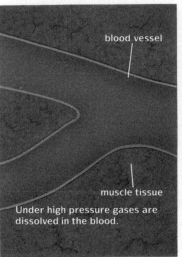

Under high pressure gases are dissolved in the blood.

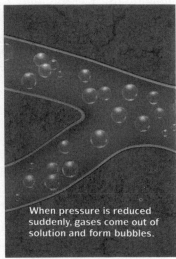

When pressure is reduced suddenly, gases come out of solution and form bubbles.

Gases, such as oxygen and nitrogen, are dissolved in blood and other body fluids. The amount of gas in solution depends partly on pressure. Deep-sea divers experience pressure changes that affect the amount of gases dissolved in the blood. The greater the depth, the more pressure on the diver's body. Under high pressure, the blood absorbs more oxygen and nitrogen. The pressure may be quickly reduced if the diver swims up quickly from the deep sea. A rapid loss of pressure causes the blood gases to come out of solution as many tiny bubbles. These bubbles clog small blood vessels and cause severe pain in muscles and joints. This condition is called "the bends." Construction workers who build underwater tunnels also risk the bends. The bends can be avoided if pressure is reduced slowly.

142

SATURATED AND UNSATURATED SOLUTIONS

Only a certain amount of solute will dissolve in a given amount of solvent. Look at Figure 6-12. At 20°C about 87 g of sodium nitrate, $NaNO_3$, will dissolve in 100 g of water. If you add more sodium nitrate, it will not dissolve, no matter how much you stir. The extra solid will settle to the bottom of the beaker. Such a solution is said to be saturated. A **saturated solution** is one in which all the solute that the solution can hold at a given temperature has been dissolved. Any solute added beyond this point will not dissolve.

Suppose you have a solution of 87 g of sodium nitrate in 100 g of water at 37°C. You can see from the graph that the solubility of sodium nitrate at this temperature is 100 g per 100 g of water. Therefore the solution can dissolve another 13 g of solid. A solution in which more solute can be dissolved is an **unsaturated solution**.

An unsaturated solution can be made with different amounts of solute in a given amount of solvent. If the amount of solute is small compared with the amount of solvent, the solution is *dilute*. If the amount of solute is large compared with the amount of solvent, the solution is *concentrated*. For example, if 10 g of sodium nitrate are dissolved in 100 g of water at 37°C, the solution is dilute. However, if the solution is made with 90 g of sodium nitrate, the solution is concentrated.

satur (full)

un- (not)

Figure 6-12

Solubility curves of sodium nitrate, potassium nitrate, ammonia, and sodium chloride.

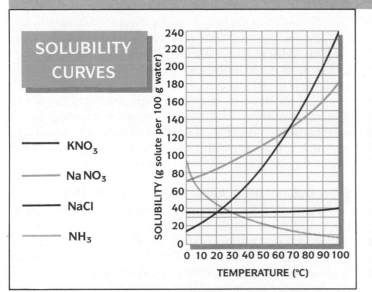

143

Teaching Tip Ask students to consider why a decrease in temperature aids in dissolving a gas in a liquid. Explain that the lower temperature decreases the number of gas molecules able to escape into the air.

Background A saturated solution has a fixed composition at a specific temperature. This composition, which is temperature dependent, is in grams of solute per 100 g of solvent. This composition is referred to as solubility. The dissolving process in a saturated solution is a dynamic process because when saturation is reached, solid solute is dissolving at the same rate as dissolved solute is crystallizing. This process represents a condition of equilibrium, when there is no longer any change in the system. Unsaturated and supersaturated solutions do not represent conditions of equilibrium. In an unsaturated solution the solute continues to dissolve until an equilibrium is reached. In a supersaturated solution an unstable condition exists because there is excess dissolved solute at the temperature.

Thinking Skills

inferring
Ask students to name the type of solution that results when excess crystals settle out of a supersaturated solution. Students have probably noticed that honey sometimes crystallizes on standing. Ask them what kind of solution honey is.

Puzzler The protein lowers the freezing point of their blood; therefore, their blood does not freeze in cold waters.

SUPERSATURATED SOLUTIONS

Some solutions can be made to contain more solute than is normal for a given temperature. This can be done by making a saturated solution at a high temperature and then letting it cool slowly. As the solution cools, all of the solute will stay in solution. **A supersaturated solution** is a solution that has more dissolved solute than is normal for a given temperature. Such solutions are not stable.

super- (to excess)

Figure 6-13

If a supersaturated solution is disturbed, the extra solute will crystallize.

[1]If the added solute dissolves, the solution was unsaturated. If the added solute does not dissolve, the solution was saturated. If crystals form when a small amount of solute is added, the solution was supersaturated.

Figure 6-13 shows a supersaturated solution before and after a single solute crystal was added. As you can see, the additional crystal causes the excess solute to crystallize. How could adding solute help you find out whether a solution is unsaturated, saturated, or supersaturated?[1]

Gas solutes can also form supersaturated solutions. The amount of gas that dissolves in water increases as the temperature is lowered. If a gas is dissolved in water at a very low temperature and the solution is then allowed to warm slowly, it may become supersaturated.

SCIENCE PUZZLER

Have you ever wondered how fish survive in freezing-cold water? Fish that live in the Arctic or the Antarctic have an unusually high concentration of protein in their bloodstream. How does this help them survive?

BOILING POINT AND FREEZING POINT

Have you ever seen an overheated car parked along the road? A car overheats because water from its cooling system has reached the boiling point. By adding antifreeze to the radiator, the car's cooling system can be kept from boiling over in the summer and from freezing in the winter. Antifreeze contains ethylene glycol, a solute that changes the boiling point and freezing point of water.

144

For a liquid to boil, the liquid particles must gain enough energy to leave the liquid and form a gas. In a pure solvent there is only one kind of particle. However, there are two kinds of particles in a solution—solute and solvent. The solute particles take up space at the surface of the liquid. This makes it harder for the solvent particles to break away from the liquid. More energy is needed for the solvent particles to break free.

Increasing the temperature of the solution increases the energy of solvent particles. Thus, the solution boils at a higher temperature than the pure solvent does. The increase in boiling point caused by adding solute is called *boiling point elevation.*

Boiling point elevation does not depend on the nature of the solute particles. It also does not depend on the mass or size of the particles. Boiling point elevation depends only on the number of solute particles.

ACTIVITY — How Does Temperature Affect Solubility?

OBJECTIVE
Determine the effect of temperature on the solubility of a solid in water.

MATERIALS
safety goggles, lab apron, 250-mL beaker, hot plate, thermometer, potassium nitrate, test tube, 10-mL graduate, distilled water, stirring rod

PROCEDURE
A. Wear safety goggles and a lab apron during this activity.
B. Draw a data table like the one shown.
C. Place a 250-mL beaker half full of tap water on a hot plate and heat to about 90°C.
D. Your teacher will assign you a specific amount of potassium nitrate. Place this amount of potassium nitrate in a test tube.
   1. How many grams of potassium nitrate did you use?
E. Add 5 mL of distilled water to the test tube.
F. Place the test tube in the beaker of hot water, and stir the contents of the test tube until all of the potassium nitrate dissolves.
G. Remove the test tube from the hot water. Place a thermometer in the solution, and watch the temperature as the solution cools. Note the temperature at which the

potassium nitrate begins to crystallize. If crystals do not form by the time the solution has reached room temperature, place the test tube in a beaker of cold water.
   2. What is this temperature?
   3. At the temperature of crystallization, is the solution unsaturated, saturated, or supersaturated?
H. Record class data in the data table. Prepare a graph of this data, showing grams of potassium nitrate on the y-axis, and temperature of crystallization on the x-axis.

Temperature (°C)	Amount of Potassium Nitrate (g per 5 ml of water)

RESULTS AND CONCLUSIONS
1. At what temperature did the most potassium nitrate dissolve?
2. At what temperature did the least potassium nitrate dissolve?
3. Predict how much potassium nitrate could dissolve in 5 mL of water at 100°C.
4. Predict how much potassium nitrate could dissolve in 5 mL of water at 30°C.

3 REVIEW/REINFORCEMENT

1. Nature of the solute and solvent; temperature.
2. An increase in temperature decreases the solubility of a gas in a liquid, whereas an increase in pressure increases the solubility of a gas.
3. A saturated solution is one in which the maximum amount of solute has been dissolved in a given amount of solvent at a given temperature; a supersaturated solution is one in which there is more solute dissolved than the solvent can hold at that temperature; an unsaturated solution contains less dissolved solute than it can hold at that specific temperature.
4. When a solute is added to water, more energy is needed for the solvent particles to leave the solution and form a gas because the solute particles take up space at the surface, making it harder for the solvent particles to break away.
5. When sugar is dissolved in water, the freezing point is lowered because the sugar molecules take up space at the surface, making it harder for water to form ice crystals at its normal freezing point.

Challenge These are air bubbles forming from the air that is dissolved in the water. The solubility of the gas (air) decreases as the temperature rises. As the air bubbles gain more energy, they escape.

Adding solute to a solvent also changes the freezing point of the liquid. For a liquid to freeze and for crystals to form, energy must be removed. Solute particles inhibit crystal formation, so more energy must be removed. Thus, a solution freezes at a lower temperature than a pure solvent does. For example, adding salt to icy roadways and sidewalks decreases the freezing point of the ice. The decrease in freezing point caused by adding solute is called freezing point depression.

Freezing point depression depends only on the number of solute particles. The more solute particles there are, the lower the temperature at which a solvent will freeze. Freezing point depression does not depend on the nature, mass, or size of the solute particles.

Figure 6-14

Roads and sidewalks are salted to lower the freezing point of water.

REVIEW

1. Name two factors that affect the solubility of a solid.
2. Compare the effects that temperature and pressure have on the solubility of a gas in a liquid.
3. How does a saturated solution differ from a supersaturated solution? What is an unsaturated solution?
4. Why is the boiling point of a water solution different from that of pure water?
5. How is the freezing point of a water solution affected when sugar is dissolved in it?

CHALLENGE When water is heated slowly, small bubbles form in the liquid. These bubbles do not contain water vapor. What is in the bubbles, and why do they form?

6-4 SUSPENSIONS AND COLLOIDS

If you shake a bottle of salad dressing, the different substances from which it is made seem to be evenly mixed. However, if the bottle is left standing, the mixture will separate as shown in Figure 6-15. Many particles will settle to the bottom of the bottle. Salad dressing is an example of a suspension. A **suspension** is a heterogeneous mixture in which particles of a substance are temporarily mixed in a liquid.

A suspension differs from a solution in many ways. For example, the particles in a suspension occur in large clusters. These clusters can be seen with either the unaided eye or a magnifier. They can be separated from the liquid by filtering. The dissolved particles in a solution are very small—the size of atoms, ions, and molecules. These particles cannot be seen, and they cannot be filtered out of the liquid.

Figure 6-15

Salad dressing is a suspension. If it is left standing, the oil and vinegar will gradually separate.

Heavy particles settle from a suspension faster than do lighter particles. When a river floods, it picks up many kinds of rock and soil particles. As the suspension of muddy water flows downstream it begins to lose some of the particles. Gravel and other large particles settle out first. The finest silt particles stay suspended longer, and are carried farther downstream.

The particles in a solution never settle out. Dissolved minerals in the flooding river will stay in solution. Another kind of mixture contains particles that are larger than the particles in solutions but smaller than the particles in suspensions. Such mixtures are called colloids (KAHL oidz).

After completing this section, you will be able to

- **list** some properties of suspensions and colloids.
- **distinguish** between solutions, suspensions, and colloids.
- **give** examples of suspensions and colloids.

The key terms in this section are
colloid
suspension

OBJECTIVES
Refer to pupil page 147.

VOCABULARY
Key terms: colloid, suspension
Other term: Tyndall effect

1 MOTIVATION

Begin this section by demonstrating the differences between the properties of solutions and colloids. In a 250-mL beaker, dissolve about 1 g of sodium thiosulfate in about 150 mL of water, and then add about 1 mL of concentrated HCl. In a second beaker, dissolve about 10 g of sugar in about 150 mL of water. Place the beakers next to each other, turn the room lights off, and shine a beam of light from a flashlight through the contents of each beaker. Ask students to describe the beam of light as it passes through each liquid. Ask them for reasons for what they see.

Background   Some properties of colloids are due to the large surface area available on the colloid particles. Absorption is one such property. Colloidal particles selectively absorb certain materials, allowing these materials to adhere to the surface of the colloid. Electrically-charged particles may be selectively absorbed on colloidal surfaces.

Background   Visible light ranges in wavelength from about 400 nanometers to 700 nanometers, which is within the range of colloidal particle size. Waves are scattered by objects that have about the same diameter as the length of the wave being affected. The red color of the setting sun is the result of red light being scattered by colloidal particles in the atmosphere on days when the air contains many pollutants.

Enrichment   Have students find out why fog lights are usually yellow.

Thinking Skills

interpreting charts
Students are asked to compare the properties of colloids with those of solutions and suspensions by using Table 6-1.

Teaching Tip   Have students prepare some solutions and colloids and then test the way that light travels through them, determining whether filtration separates the dispersed solutes. Ask students to classify the tested materials.
Some colloids: Add a few drops of milk to distilled water and stir; add 100 mL of boiling water to a mixture of 1 g of gelatin in 50 mL of water, and let cool.

A **colloid** is a mixture whose properties are in-between those of a solution and suspension. Smoke, fog, mayonnaise, and egg white are examples of colloids. Gelatin is also a colloid.

Table 6–1 *Properties of Solutions, Colloids, and Suspensions*

Property	Solution	Colloid	Suspension
Particle type	Atoms, ions, molecules	Large particles, clusters of small particles	Large clusters of particles
Particles visible with microscope	No	No	Yes
Particles settle on standing	No	No	Yes
Particles separate by filtering	No	No	Yes
Particles scatter light	No	Yes	Yes
Example	Seawater	Soot in air	Muddy water

Colloids are similar to solutions in many ways. Table 6-1 compares the properties of solutions, colloids, and suspensions. Notice that, like solutions, colloids do not separate upon standing. Colloids also cannot be separated by filtering.

Like suspensions, colloids scatter light. The scattering of light by colloid particles is known as the *Tyndall effect*. Because of the Tyndall effect, you can see light beams from car headlights in a fog.

Figure 6-16

Fog is a colloid.

REVIEW

1. What is a suspension? Give two properties of suspensions.
2. What is a colloid? Give two properties of colloids.
3. How do solutions, suspensions, and colloids differ?
4. Give one example of a suspension and one example of a colloid.

CHALLENGE Describe how you would determine whether an unknown liquid mixture is a solution or a colloid.

CHAPTER SUMMARY

The main ideas in this chapter are listed below. Read these statements before you answer the Chapter Review questions.

- Mixtures are made up of two or more substances that can be separated by physical means. Homogeneous mixtures are the same throughout. Heterogeneous mixtures vary from one point to another. (6-1)

- In a solution the solute dissolves in the solvent. (6-2)

- The rate at which a solution forms depends on the size of solute particles, shaking or stirring, and the temperature of the mixture. (6-2)

- Solubility is the amount of solute that will dissolve in a given amount of solvent at a given temperature. (6-3)

- The solubility of solids increases with increasing temperature. The solubility of gases increases with decreasing temperature or increasing pressure. (6-3)

- A saturated solution has the maximum amount of solute that will dissolve at a given temperature. An unsaturated solution can dissolve more solute. A supersaturated solution is one that contains more solute than is normal for a given temperature. (6-3)

- The addition of solute particles raises the boiling point of a solution. (6-3)

- The addition of solute particles lowers the freezing point of a solution. (6-3)

- A suspension is a heterogeneous mixture that has particles of a substance temporarily mixed in a liquid. The particles of a suspension will settle if the mixture is left standing. (6-4)

- A colloid has properties in-between those of a solution and a suspension. The particles of a colloid will not settle if the mixture is left standing. (6-4)

The key terms in this chapter are listed below. Use each term in a sentence that shows the meaning of the term.

colloid	saturated solution	solvent
heterogeneous mixture	solubility	supersaturated solution
homogeneous mixture	solute	suspension
mixture	solution	unsaturated solution

3 REVIEW/REINFORCEMENT

1. A suspension is a heterogeneous mixture in which particles of a substance are temporarily mixed in a liquid; particles of solute settle on standing and can be separated by filtering.

2. A colloid is a mixture whose properties are between those of a solution and those of a suspension; colloid particles do not separate upon standing and cannot be separated by filtering.

3. Solutions do not scatter light; colloids scatter light; the clusters of particles in suspensions are visible with the unaided eye or with a magnifier.

4. Suspensions—muddy water, clay particles in water, suspended sand in water, dust in air, salad dressing; colloids—shaving cream, whipped cream, mists, sprays, fog, clouds, mayonnaise, gels, soot in air, paint, clay, colored glass.

Challenge   If the mixture is cloudy, it is a colloid; if it is clear, it could be a solution or a colloid. Pass a beam of light through the solution: A colloid will scatter the light, a solution will not.

Review and Skill Masters

VOCABULARY REVIEW, page 35.
See page 129b in this book for answers.

VOCABULARY

1. unsaturated solution 2. mixture 3. solution
4. colloid 5. saturated solution 6. supersaturated solution 7. suspension 8. heterogeneous mixture 9. solubility

CONCEPTS

1. Mixtures vary from sample to sample; properties of pure substances are constant.
2. Heterogeneous mixtures differ from point to point; homogeneous mixtures are the same throughout.
3. A liquid with a lower boiling point is collected as it boils off, and a liquid with a higher boiling point is left behind.
4. A centrifuge separates substances in mixtures; when the centrifuge spins, the densest parts of the mixture settle out.
5. The substance in the smaller amount is the solute. The substance in the greater amount is the solvent. Answers will vary.
6. When salt dissolves in water, each unit of sodium chloride separates into Na^+ and Cl^- ions. When a sugar cube is placed in water, the water molecules causes the sugar molecules to be pulled away from the cube and to be dissolved.
7. Molecules in solution cannot be seen; solute particles do not settle out; the solution cannot be separated by filtering.
8. Concentration, temperature, etc.
9. Increases with pressure and decreases with an increase in temperature.
10. Solubility increases with temperature, but is not affected by pressure.
11. A saturated solution is one in which all the solute at a given temperature has been dissolved; an unsaturated solution is one in which more solute can be dissolved; a supersaturated solution has more dissolved solute than it can hold.

Review and Skill Masters

CHAPTER REVIEW, pages 36–37.
See page 129b in this book for answers.

Chapter Review

VOCABULARY

Use the key terms from this chapter to complete the following sentences correctly.

1. A solution that can dissolve more solute at a given temperature is a/an _____.
2. Two or more substances that can be separated by physical means are called a/an _____.
3. A/An _____ is a homogeneous mixture of two or more substances.
4. A mixture in which particles remain suspended and cannot be filtered out is called a/an _____.
5. A solution in which the maximum amount of solute has been dissolved in the solvent is called a/an _____.
6. A solution that contains more dissolved solute than it normally can hold at a given temperature is a/an _____.
7. A heterogeneous mixture that has solid particles temporarily mixed in a liquid is a/an _____.
8. A mixture whose makeup differs from point to point is called a/an _____.
9. _____ is the amount of solute that will dissolve in a given amount of solvent at a given temperature.

CONCEPTS

1. How are mixtures different from pure substances? (6-1)
2. How do heterogeneous mixtures differ from homogeneous mixtures? (6-1)
3. Explain how distillation can be used to separate mixtures of liquids. (6-1)
4. How can differences in density be used to separate mixtures? What tool is used for this procedure? (6-1)
5. What is the difference between a solute and a solvent? Give an example of each. (6-2)
6. Describe how sodium chloride dissolves in water. How does this differ from the way sugar dissolves in water? (6-2)
7. List three properties of solutions. (6-2)
8. What factors determine the rate of solution? (6-2)
9. How do temperature and pressure affect the solubility of a gas in a liquid? (6-3)
10. How is the solubility of a solid in a liquid affected by temperature and pressure? (6-3)
11. Distinguish between a saturated solution and an unsaturated solution. What is a supersaturated solution? (6-3)

12. How does a dilute solution differ from a concentrated solution? (6-3)

13. Why does a solution boil at a higher temperature than does a pure solvent? (6-3)

14. How does adding solute to a solvent affect the freezing point of the solvent? (6-3)

15. Give one use of boiling point elevation and one use of freezing point depression. (6-3)

16. Name two ways in which a suspension is different from a colloid. (6-4)

17. How is a colloid like a solution? (6-4)

18. Give two examples of suspensions and two examples of colloids. (6-4)

19. What is the Tyndall effect? (6-5)

APPLICATION/
CRITICAL
THINKING

1. What tests can be used to find out if a liquid is a pure solvent or a solution?

2. A solution contains 90 g of $NaNO_3$ in 50 g of H_2O at 100° C. How much solute will remain dissolved at 20°C? How much will settle out? (Use the solubility curves given in the chapter.)

3. Benzene, C_6H_6, is a nonpolar substance. Which of the following would you expect to dissolve in benzene: NaCl, H_2O, motor oil (nonpolar), fat (nonpolar), $CaBr_2$?

4. Explain why warm water has a stale taste.

5. If you dissolve the same number of formula units of NaCl and $CaCl_2$ in equal volumes of water, the $CaCl_2$ solution will have a higher boiling point. Explain why.

EXTENSION

1. An estuary is an area where fresh water from a river mixes with salt water from the sea. Prepare a report on the ways in which living things in an estuary are affected by the mixing of these two solutions.

2. Find out what an emulsifier is. Present to your class a report on the uses of emulsifiers.

3. Hemodialysis is a technique used to cleanse the blood. Do library research on hemodialysis. Write a report that explains how hemodialysis makes use of the properties of liquid mixtures.

READINGS

Dickinson, E. *Colloids in Food*. New York: Elsevier, 1982.

Holden, Alan, and Phylis Morrison. *Crystals and Crystal Growing*. Cambridge, MA. MIT Press, 1982.

Updegraffe, Imelda, and Robert Updegraffe, *Seas and Oceans*. New York: Penguin, 1983.

---

12. In a dilute solution the amount of solute is very small; a concentrated solution has a large amount of solute.

13. The solute particles take up space at the surface of the liquid, so the solvent particles need more energy to break away.

14. For a liquid to freeze and for crystals to form, energy must be removed; this makes a solution freeze at a lower temperature than does a pure solvent.

15. A car's cooling system can be kept from boiling over in summer and from freezing in winter by adding antifreeze.

16. Suspensions have particles in large clusters that can be seen with the unaided eye and can be separated by filtering.

17. Like those in a solution, the particles in a colloid never settle out.

18. Suspensions—salad dressing, muddy water; colloids—mayonnaise, egg white.

19. The scattering of light by colloid particles.

APPLICATION/CRITICAL THINKING

1. By distillation if only one fraction is collected and no solid is left in the distilling flask; by finding the boiling point or freezing point, because these will differ for a solution and a pure solvent.

2. At 20°C, 88 g of $NaNO_3$ dissolves in 100 g of H_2O; thus, 44 g of $NaNO_3$ will dissolve in 50 g of H_2O at this temperature, and 46 g of $NaNO_3$ will settle out.

3. Motor oil and fat are both nonpolar and will dissolve in benzene.

4. The solubility of oxygen decreases as the water gets warm; when dissolved oxygen leaves the water, the water tastes flat.

5. A formula unit of NaCl has two ions, and a formula unit of $CaCl_2$ has three ions. A greater amount of solute requires a higher boiling point.

Test Masters

CHAPTER TEST, pages 21–24.
See page 129d in this book for answers.

You may think of your neighborhood drugstore as the place to buy school supplies or magazines. But the most important function of a pharmacy, or drugstore, is selling medicine.

Pharmacists provide the medicine specified in a doctor's or dentist's prescription. Usually the medicine is measured and put into a labeled container. The label includes directions and cautions to the patient. The pharmacist must keep an accurate record of each prescription. Pharmacists working in drugstores also help customers select medicines that do not require a prescription.

In addition to working in drugstores, pharmacists may work in hospitals or clinics. Pharmacists earn a five- or six-year college degree in pharmacy. They must then pass a test to be licensed. If you are interested in this career, you should take courses in biology and chemistry in high school.■

Pharmacist

Although pottery is an ancient craft, an understanding of physical science is helpful to the potter. Knowing the physical properties of various clays and paints enables the potter to produce the desired effect.

There are several different techniques of pottery-making. Many potters use a potter's wheel, a large heavy disc that spins as the potter works. The potter throws the wet clay on the center of the rotating wheel. By firmly pressing his or her hands on this spinning mass of clay, the potter gradually shapes an object.

Potters often work alone as independent craftworkers. They may sell their wares at craft shows and shops. Potters go to art school or work as an apprentice. If you are interested in becoming a potter, you should take crafts and fine arts courses in high school.■

Potter

Dr. Stephen Hawking is a theoretical physicist. He is famous for having proposed the existence of black holes before they were found by astronomers.

Dr. Hawking had theorized that a black hole forms when a large star grows old and stops producing energy. Its gravity causes the star to shrink and compress. As it compresses, the gravitational pull increases. Finally, not even light can escape from the black hole.

Like other theoretical physicists, Dr. Hawking makes his

Dr. Stephen Hawking, Physicist

predictions by using his imagination and mathematical calculations. But in some ways Dr. Hawking is different from others. He is almost completely paralyzed by a progressive nerve disease. Dr. Hawking is unable to write and his speech is so weak that he needs an interpreter to translate what he says. Yet Dr. Hawking prefers not to concentrate on his physical limitations. Instead he sees his illness as something that forces him to focus on basic physics, freeing him from distractions.■

Issues and Technology

Whether a person takes a job in a factory, in an office, on a farm, or in a mine, he or she expects the employer to provide a certain level of safety in the workplace. Many employers do make sure that their employees have comfortable and safe places in which to work. However, every year thousands of other employees are sickened, injured, or even killed while doing their jobs.

Some people insist these problems are mostly the fault of uncaring employers who do not want to spend time or money for adequate safeguards. Others say that employers are often not aware of dangers. At other times, careless workers cause their own injuries. Should employers be held responsible for these injuries?

With the growth in the use of chemicals, more and more cases of work-related illnesses and injuries are being reported. One such case involves a Baltimore fire fighter who used a heat-resistant paint to repaint fire engines. The paint contained an ingredient that had been shown to cause birth defects in animals. However, there were no warnings on the paint can that the fire fighter used. His superiors who had purchased the paint for the job did not warn him about any possible danger.

The fire fighter's wife, who was also exposed to the paint, was pregnant at the time. The couple's twin girls were born three months premature and died. During the next two years, 12 children of fire fighters who were exposed to the paint were born dead or died in early infancy. Two other children of

the fire fighters were born with deformities. The fire fighters concluded that the chemical in the paint was probably at fault.

Many people got hurt, but who is responsible here? Is it the company that made the chemical and allowed it to be put into the paint? Is it the employers who allowed the fire fighters to use the paint with no warning? Is it the government, which allowed the paint to be sold? Or is it the employees themselves, who did not question the paint's safety?

As employers and employees argue about who is at fault, about 120,000 cases of serious illness develop in the workplace each year. Right now there are over 2 million people disabled and more than 10,000 people dying from slow poisonings, fires, and other accidents at their jobs.

Figure 1 shows the rate at which work-related illnesses and injuries occurred over the past few years. It also shows the number of workdays lost through these illnesses and injuries.

APPLYING CRITICAL THINKING SKILLS

1. Which year had the greatest number of illnesses and injuries? Which had the least?
2. Did the rate of occurrence of illnesses and injuries generally go up or down over the 10 years shown? What might be a reason?
3. Which year had the greatest number of lost workdays? The least?
4. Work-related illnesses and injuries are bad for the employee. Why are they bad for the employer?

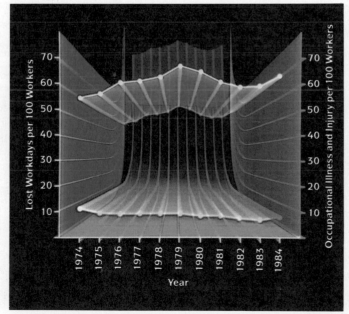

Figure 1

The following thinking skills will be applied in answering questions.
- *Interpreting* a graph.
- *Identifying* the effect of illnesses and injuries on an employer.
- *Hypothesizing* why the number of accidents and injuries has been going down.

Answers to questions

1. The most illnesses and injuries occurred in 1974. The fewest occurred in 1983.
2. Occupational illnesses and injuries generally went down over the 10 year period. This decline in the number of illnesses and injuries may be due to stricter safety rules and better safeguards in the workplace.
3. The greatest number of lost workdays occurred in 1979. The least occurred in 1974.
4. The employer may be liable for any work-related illnesses and injuries. In addition, any illness or injury that results in lost workdays will result in a lowered productivity and will therefore be bad for the employer.

The following thinking skills will be applied in answering questions.
- *Comparing* the information available on various chemicals.
- *Hypothesizing* reasons why more information is available on drugs than on other types of chemicals.
- *Drawing conclusions* about why some inadequately tested products are allowed to be available to the public.

Answers to questions

1. The most adequate information is available for drugs. This may be due to the fact that drugs can produce various harmful, and even potentially fatal, side effects.
2. Food additives contain the largest percent about which no information is available. Students will probably be surprised at this. However, they may also note that this is the group that involves the most chemicals.
3. Students may respond that there is a danger in using products that have not been adequately tested. Some of these chemicals may have been developed many years ago and used for many years without causing any problems. The government now requires more testing of new products.
4. Students may respond that the government should test new products to be sure that they are safe. A large increase in the number of tests performed would require the government to set up large testing laboratories. How would the cost of these laboratories be covered? The manufacturers may be in a better position to test their own products, with the government carefully monitoring the tests and their results.

Even though someone must take responsibility for the injuries and sicknesses of workers, it is often difficult to fix blame. Some work-related illnesses, like cancer, may not develop until 20 years after the exposure to an illness-causing substance. In these cases it is difficult to prove that something in the workplace 20 years earlier caused current illnesses. In cases like these, companies do not want to pay thousands, perhaps millions, of dollars for health problems that may not be their fault. In addition, employers say, there are many possible hazards in the workplace that are also present in the environment. Is it reasonable to expect employers to prevent every single hazard? How much would this cost? And is the public willing to pay that cost in higher prices for the companies' products?

On the other hand, some people say that employers often hide problems from their workers or the public. There have been cases in which companies knew about hazards and kept them secret.

There are many potential hazards. Many chemicals used to make everything from cars and computers to detergents and insect killers have been shown in tests to cause cancer and other illnesses.

With all these possibilities for worker illnesses, it is easy to see why employer negligence is not always to blame. Some say this responsibility should rest with the government.

In 1970 the government tried to solve some of these problems by creating two agencies to oversee worker safety. The Occupational Safety and Health Administration (OSHA) makes regulations to ensure that the workplace is safe. The National Institute of Occupational Safety and Health (NIOSH) does research to help establish health and safety standards for the workplace.

The government is not aware of the effects of many of the substances that are used by workers each day. In 1984 the National Academy of Science prepared a list of chemicals used in some products. This list also indicates how much is known about the effects of each of these chemicals. Figure 2 shows the results of this study.

APPLYING CRITICAL THINKING SKILLS

1. About which group of chemicals is there the most adequate information? Suggest a reason for this.
2. Which group of chemicals includes the largest percent about which no information is available? Does this surprise you? Why or why not?
3. Do you see any problem with allowing inadequately tested chemicals to come into contact with the public? Why, do you think, does the government allow the use of such chemicals?
4. If more chemicals are to be tested, who should carry out these tests?

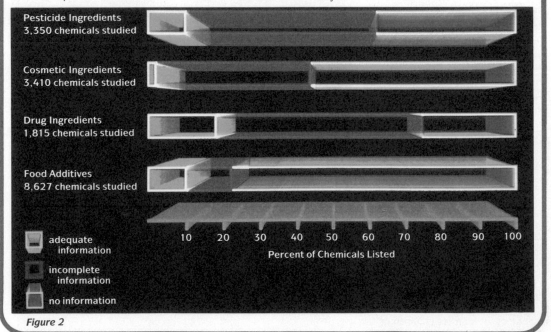

Figure 2

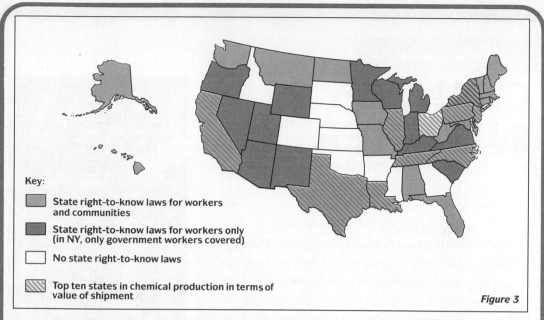

Key:

- State right-to-know laws for workers and communities
- State right-to-know laws for workers only (in NY, only government workers covered)
- No state right-to-know laws
- Top ten states in chemical production in terms of value of shipment

Figure 3

Are the companies the only party at fault if something goes wrong? Could companies argue that they cannot be expected to take responsibility if the government does not set guidelines? Should companies establish reliable safety standards? Since companies often invent substances, do they have a responsibility to test the substances?

Because of all the uncertainty, the "right to know" has become an important issue in worker safety. Right to know means that if hazardous substances are going to be in a workplace, workers have the right to know about them. Workers can then choose to work there or leave. Also, they can make sure they have protection. Federal, state, and local right-to-know laws have been passed. These laws compel employers to inform employees about hazardous substances they might come into contact with at work. Informing employees generally means labeling hazardous substances, listing their ingredients, giving infor-

mation on what levels of exposure are safe for workers, and citing possible health effects due to overexposure.

The federal right-to-know law, enacted in November 1983, requires that information on hazards be made available to some employees but not to the general public. This law covers only employees who work directly with the substances in manufacturing. People like secretaries, shipping clerks, security guards, and truck drivers who also work at places that use hazardous substances are often not covered by this law.

Many state and local right-to-know laws are more strict than the federal law. New Jersey's law, for instance, requires disclosure of hazards to all workers as well as to the communities in which facilities using the substances are located.

In general, the right-to-know laws will cost industries large amounts of money. It has been estimated that it will cost the chemical industry alone $160 million each year to com-

ply with the laws. Some companies have warned that the costs involved will cause them to lay off workers and to close factories. Thus some workers may have to choose between their health and their jobs.

Figure 3 shows where state and local right-to-know laws exist. It also shows where the greatest amount of chemical manufacturing is located.

APPLYING CRITICAL THINKING SKILLS

1. Which states have no state right-to-know laws?
2. Which ten states have the most chemical production in terms of value? Which of these states have their own right-to-know laws?
3. Do you think it is good for states to pass right-to-know laws, even though the federal law exists?
4. Do you think laws that allow residents in a community to get information on what a company is producing are a good idea? What problems might be involved with this?

The following thinking skills will be applied in answering questions.

- *Interpreting* data.
- *Identifying* the cause and effect of having companies give out more information to their surrounding communities.
- *Drawing conclusions* about the merits of having both federal and state right-to-know laws.

Answers to questions

1. Idaho, Colorado, South Dakota, Nebraska, Kansas, Oklahoma, Arkansas, Mississippi, Georgia, and Ohio have no state right-to-know laws. It may be helpful to provide a large map for students to use in identifying these states.
2. The ten states with the most chemical production are California, Texas, Louisiana, Illinois, Tennessee, North Carolina, Ohio, Pennsylvania, New York, and New Jersey. Of these states, only Ohio does not have its own state right-to-know laws.
3. Students may answer that states should pass their own right-to-know laws, since these laws are often stricter than federal laws.
4. Students will probably answer that laws that allow residents to find out what chemicals are produced in their community are a good idea. These laws could be expensive for the companies, which would need to take the time and resources to communicate with the public. Communicating with the public might increase the expenses of chemical companies. In addition, questions, opposition, and even lawsuits from community residents could hinder production in one company while competitors elsewhere produce similar products.

Unit 3

CHANGES IN MATTER

Unit Three

CHANGES IN MATTER

*H*ow matter changes from one form to another is important to physical scientists. Physical scientists want to know what chemical reactions can take place and what benefits the products of these reactions have. In this unit you will study various groups, or families, of elements. Different groups of elements react in different ways. You will compare metals, nonmetals, and metalloids. You will also study chemical reactions. ■

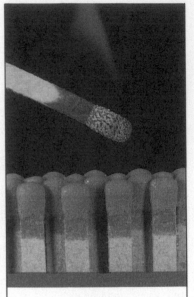

▲ Burning matches show a chemical change in matter.

▼ *Joseph Priestley's apparatus for experimenting on the composition of air. In 1775, Priestley demonstrated the presence of oxygen in the air.*

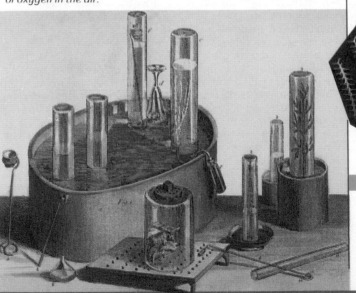

▲ Computer model of a poly-ethylene molecule. Chemicals like this are used in industry to make a variety of plastic objects.

Alchemy was perhaps the first study of chemistry. Some alchemists tried to change base metals into gold. Other alchemists, like those pictured here, tried to make medicines.

▲ *This flashlight fish lives over 30 m under the sea. It has phosphorescent chemicals, which glow in the dark.*

▼ *A hot spring at Yellowstone National Park. The hot water dissolves minerals in the soil, causing these colors.*

Sections appearing in red provide coverage of basic topics in this unit. See page T23.

CHEMICAL REACTIONS

ORGANIZER

Section	pages	Activity	pages	Reinforcement and Evaluation	pages	*Review and Skill Masters	pages	Other Components in Teacher Resource Package	pages
7–1 Chemical Equations	159–161			Review, Challenge	161			Study Guide	32
7–2 Balancing Chemical Equations	162–166			Puzzler Review, Challenge	164 166			Study Guide	33
7–3 Synthesis and Decomposition Reactions	167–169			Review, Challenge	169			Study Guide	34
7–4 Replacement Reactions	170–173	What Are the Types of Chemical Reactions?	173	Review, Challenge	173	Skill	44	Study Guide Lab Manual	35 37
7–5 Energy in Chemical Reactions	174–176	Does Temperature Change During a Reaction?	176	Review, Challenge	176			Study Guide	36
7–6 Changing the Rate of Reactions	177–181	What Factors Affect the Rate of a Reaction?	180	Review, Challenge	181	Challenge/Critical Thinking	45–46	Study Guide Lab Manual	37 39
CHAPTER SUMMARY	181					Vocabulary Review	41		
CHAPTER REVIEW	182–183			*Test Masters	25–28	Chapter Review	42–43		

*In the Teacher Resource Package. For answers, see pages 157b–157d in this book.

ACTIVITY MATERIALS   Quantities are based on a class of 30 students working in groups as indicated in parentheses.

What Are the Types of Chemical Reactions? p. 173 (groups of 2)	quantity	Does Temperature Change During a Reaction? p. 176 (groups of 2)	quantity	What Factors Affect the Rate of a Reaction? p. 180 (groups of 2)	quantity
lab apron	30	lab apron	30	safety goggles	30
safety goggles	30	safety goggles	30	lab apron	30
calcium hydroxide solution (limewater)	150 mL	graduate	15	magnesium ribbon	30 cm
graduate	15	distilled water		scissors	15
test tube	45	test tube	30	metric ruler	15
test-tube rack	15	test-tube rack	15	25-mL graduate	15
drinking straw	15	Celsius thermometer	15	hydrochloric acid	150 mL
copper (II) sulfate solution	150 mL	balance	15	50-mL Erlenmeyer flask	15
zinc strip	15	ammonium chloride	45 g	250-mL beaker	15
barium chloride solution	75 mL	rubber stopper	30	timer	1
potassium sulfate solution	75 mL	forceps	15		
		sodium hydroxide pellets	225		

REVIEW AND SKILL MASTERS

VOCABULARY REVIEW _____ Chapter 7

Find each word and then copy the letters below to unscramble the phrase.

1. c a t a l y s t
   <u>8</u>   <u>18</u>
2. c o e f f i c i e n t
            <u>14</u>
3. a c t i v a t i o n   e n e r g y
      <u>9</u> <u>7</u>
4. d e c o m p o s i t i o n   r e a c t i o n
         <u>4</u>
5. c h e m i c a l   e q u a t i o n
   <u>1</u>   <u>2</u>
      <u>15</u>
6. e n d o t h e r m i c   r e a c t i o n
   <u>5</u>   <u>3</u>
                              <u>6</u>
7. p r e c i p i t a t e
                  <u>10</u>
8. p r o d u c t s
      <u>13</u>   <u>17</u>
         <u>16</u>
9. e x o t h e r m i c   r e a c t i o n
                              <u>12</u>
   <u>11</u>

1. A substance that speeds up a chemical reaction

2. A whole number multiplier placed in front of a formula in a chemical equation

3. The amount of energy needed to start a reaction

4. A reaction in which a compound breaks down into two or more substances

5. A shorthand method used by scientists to show the changes that take place in a chemical reaction

6. A reaction that absorbs energy

7. An insoluble material that forms during a chemical reaction and that separates from a solution

8. The substances that are formed in a reaction

9. A reaction that gives off energy

The Law of C o n s e r v a t i o n   o f   M a s s
         1 2 3 4 5 6 7 8 9 10 11 12   13 14   15 16 17 18

41

CHAPTER REVIEW _____ Chapter 7

7-1 Chemical Equations

1. A ____chemical reaction____ is a process in which one or more substances are changed into one or more different substances.

2. Write the following equation using words.

   $Mg + Cl_2 \rightarrow MgCl_2$
   Magnesium plus chlorine yields magnesium chloride.

3. Identify the products and reactants in this question. The product is magnesium chloride and the reactants are magnesium and chlorine.

7-2 Balancing Chemical Equations

1. How does a balanced equation reflect the Law of Conservation of Mass? In a balanced equation, the total mass of the reactants equals the total mass of the products. In addition, the number of atoms on each side of the equation stays the same.

2. Balance the following equations:

   a. $H_2O \rightarrow H_2 + O_2$ $2 H_2O \rightarrow 2 H_2 + O_2$

   b. $Al + O_2 \rightarrow Al_2O_3$ $4 Al + 3 O_2 \rightarrow 2 Al_2O_3$

7-3 Synthesis and Decomposition Reactions

1. Compare synthesis reactions and decomposition reactions. In synthesis reactions, reactants combine to form a compound; in decomposition reactions, the reactants break down into two or more substances.

2. Balance the equation given below and identify it as as a synthesis reaction or a decomposition reaction. Potassium plus fluorine yields potassium fluoride.

   Synthesis reaction. $2 K + F_2 + 2 KF$

42

CHAPTER REVIEW (Continued) _____ Chapter 7

7-4 Replacement Reactions

1. Describe what takes place during a single replacement reaction and a double replacement reaction. In a single replacement reaction, one element replaces another in a compound, thus forming a new compound. In a double replacement reaction, the compounds in a reaction exchange ions.

2. What is a precipitate and what is its distinguishing property? A precipitate is a solid material that is formed in a chemical reaction and separates from the solution. A precipitate is not soluble.

3. Complete and balance the following reaction. What type of reaction is it?

   $AgNO_3 + NaCl \rightarrow$ AgCl + NaNO₃
   This is a double replacement reaction.

7-5 Energy in Chemical Reactions

1. Is activation energy necessary to a spontaneous reaction? Explain. Yes. A spontaneous reaction needs so little energy that it can absorb it from the surroundings.

2. What happens to energy during an exothermic reaction and during an endothermic reaction?
   Energy is given off during an exothermic reaction, and absorbed during an endothermic reaction.

7-6 Changing the Rate of Reactions

1. Identify the five factors that affect reaction rates. Temperature, surface area, concentration, catalysts, and nature of reactants are the five factors that affect reaction rates.

2. A ____catalyst____ is a substance that changes the rate of a chemical reaction.

43

SKILL/Classifying _____ Chapter 7

Identify the following types of chemical reactions. Write SR for single replacement, DR for double replacement, S for synthesis, and D for decomposition.

1. __SR__ $3 Zn (s) + 2 FeCl_3 (aq) \rightarrow 2 Fe (s) + 3 ZnCl_3 (aq)$

2. __S__ $N_2 (g) + 3 H_2 (g) \rightarrow 2 NH_3 (g)$

3. __DR__ $2 AgNO_3 (aq) + CaCl_2 (aq) \rightarrow 2 AgCl (s) + Ca(NO_3)_2 (aq)$

4. __SR__ $Cl_2 (g) + MgI_2 (aq) \rightarrow I_2 (g) + MgCl_2 (aq)$

5. __S__ $Na_2O (s) + SO_2 (g) \rightarrow Na_2SO_3 (aq)$

6. __DR__ $HCl (aq) + KOH (aq) \rightarrow KCl (aq) + H_2O (l)$

7. __D__ $2 KClO_3 (s) \rightarrow 2 KCl (s) + 3 O_2 (g)$

Balance the following equations.

8. $2 Mg (s) + O_2 (g) \rightarrow$ __2__ $MgO (s)$

9. $H_2SO_4 (aq) +$ __2__ $NaOH (aq) \rightarrow Na_2SO_4 (aq) + 2 H_2O (l)$

10. __2__ $NH_3 (g) + 3 CuO (s) \rightarrow$ __3__ $Cu (s) + 3 H_2O (l) + N_2 (g)$

11. $P_4O_{10} (s) +$ __6__ $H_2O (l) \rightarrow 4 H_3PO_4 (aq)$

Complete the following equations and identify the types of reactions as single replacement, double replacement, synthesis, or decomposition.

12. __SR__ $Fe (s) + CuSO_4 (aq) \rightarrow FeSO_4 (aq) +$ __Cu__ (s)

13. __DR__ $AgNO_3 (aq) + KCl (aq) \rightarrow KNO_3 (aq) +$ __AgCl__ (s)

14. __S__ $2 Na (s) + Cl_2 (g) \rightarrow 2$ __NaCl__ (s)

15. __D__ $2 NO_2 (g) \rightarrow$ __N₂__ $(g) + 2 O_2 (g)$

44

CHAPTER 7 PLANNING GUIDE

157b

Name_____ Date_____

CHALLENGE/CRITICAL THINKING _____ Chapter 7

For many people, having a car to use is almost as important as the air they breathe. Few people, however, stop and think about how closely cars and air are related. A car engine could not burn gasoline without air. After the gasoline is burned, the exhaust from the car can cause air pollution.

In 1975, a new program for controlling air pollution was begun in the automobile industry. This program required a device called a catalytic converter to be installed in some new cars. When a car engine burns gasoline, the gasoline is not completely burned. The catalytic converter converts the dangerous by-products of incompletely burned gasoline into harmless products.

These catalytic converters are made mainly of platinum (Pt) and palladium (Pd). The exhaust fumes from the engine pass over the metals, which act as catalysts. Catalytic converters turn unburned gasoline, carbon monoxide, and oxides of nitrogen into carbon dioxide, water vapor, oxygen, and nitrogen. Cars that have catalytic converters cannot use gasoline containing lead.

Cut-away View of Catalytic Converter

An Exhaust System

1. What is a catalyst?

   A catalyst is a substance that changes (usually speeds) the rate of a chemical

   reaction. It is not changed in the reaction.

2. Balance the following simplified equation that shows how gasoline is completely burned in a car engine.

   $2\ C_8H_{18} + 25\ O_2 \rightarrow \underline{\quad 16 \quad}\ CO_2 + \underline{\quad 18 \quad}\ H_2O$

3. Write the equation showing how carbon monoxide combines with oxygen to form carbon dioxide. Balance the equation. Is this equation single replacement, double replacement, a synthesis reaction, or a decomposition reaction?

   $2\ CO + O_2 \rightarrow 2\ CO_2$. It is a synthesis reaction.

45

Name_____ Date_____

CHALLENGE/CRITICAL THINKING (Continued) _____ Chapter 7

4. Where does the oxygen come from that combines with carbon monoxide in the catalytic converter?

   The oxygen comes from the air.

5. Carbon monoxide combines easily with oxygen on the surface of platinum or palladium. Why is this important?

   It is important because carbon monoxide, which is harmful, must combine with

   oxygen in order to make carbon dioxide, which is not harmful.

6. Oxides of nitrogen form when nitrogen and oxygen combine in the presence of high temperature. Where do the nitrogen and oxygen come from? What causes the high temperature?

   The nitrogen and oxygen are found in the air that is needed to burn gasoline in

   the car's engine. The high temperature occurs in the engine when the gasoline

   is burned.

7. Platinum or palladium catalysts can also convert sulfur (S), which is present in many gasolines, to sulfur trioxide (SO_3). This can be converted to sulfuric acid (H_2SO_4) in the presence of sunlight and moisture in the air. Sulfuric acid can corrode metal and stone. Why could this be a problem?

   Since sulfur trioxide can be produced in the presence of platinum or palladium,

   a catalytic converter could ultimately increase the amount of sulfuric acid in

   the air. This could significantly harm the environment.

8. Why do you think that cars with catalytic converters cannot use gasoline that contains lead?

   Answers will vary but should include that lead must somehow block, or

   destroy, the catalyst reaction.

46

TEST MASTERS

Quadrant 1 (Page 25)

Chapter 7

Chemical Reactions

PART 1

In the space below, write the term that each phrase defines.

Chapter Goal

1.	__inhibitors__	Substances that slow chemical reactions	6
2.	__synthesis reaction__	A chemical reaction in which two or more substances combine to form a compound	3
3.	__activation energy__	The name for the amount of energy needed to start a chemical reaction	5
4.	__chemical reaction__	A process in which one or more substances are changed into different substances	1
5.	__single replacement reaction__	A chemical reaction that takes place when one element replaces another element in a compound, forming a new compound	4
6.	__Law of Conservation of Mass__	A statement that, in a chemical reaction, the total mass of the reactants equals the total mass of the products	2
7.	__catalyst__	A substance that changes the rate of a chemical reaction	6
8.	__coefficient__	A whole number that shows the number of atoms or molecules involved in a chemical reaction	2
9.	__endothermic reaction__	A chemical reaction that absorbs energy	5
10.	__products__	Substances formed in a chemical reaction	1
11.	__decomposition reaction__	A chemical reaction in which compounds break down into two or more substances	3
12.	__double replacement reaction__	A chemical reaction in which the compounds in the reaction exchange ions	4

PART 2

Choose the term or phrase that best answers the question or completes the statement. Write the letter of that choice in the space at the left.

__b__ 1. Which of the following could be a product of a synthesis reaction?   3
   a. C   b. CO_2 c. Si   d. Br

__c__ 2. In a chemical equation, the expression $3CO_2$ stands for three: 2
   a. atoms of carbon.   c. molecules of carbon dioxide.
   b. atoms of carbon dioxide.   d. atoms of oxygen.

Silver, Burdett & Ginn Inc.

Quadrant 2 (Page 26)

PART 2

Choose the term or phrase that best answers the question or completes the statement. Write the letter of that choice in the space at the left.

Chapter Goal

__a__ 3. One of the characteristics of a chemical reaction that is always shown in equation is the: 1
   a. substances in the reaction.   c. rate of the reaction.
   b. energy of the reaction.   d. temperature of the reaction.

__c__ 4. Which of the following is a decomposition reaction?   3
   a. $2Na + 2H_2O \rightarrow 2NaOH + H_2$ c. $2NH_3 \rightarrow N_2 + 3H_2$
   b. $C_2H_4 + 5O_2 \rightarrow 3CO_2 + 4H_2O$ d. $H_2 + Cl_2 \rightarrow 2HCl$

__d__ 5. Which of the following chemical equations shows the formation of magnesium sulfide (MgS) from magnesium (Mg) and sulfur (S)?   1
   a. $S + MgS \rightarrow Mg$ c. $MgS \rightarrow Mg + S$
   b. $Mg + MgS \rightarrow S$ d. $Mg + S \rightarrow MgS$

__a__ 6. Which of the following chemical equations satisfies the Law of Conservation of Mass?   2
   a. $CH_4 + 2O_2 \rightarrow CO_2 + 2H_2O$ c. $CH_4 + O_2 \rightarrow CO_2 + 2H_2O$
   b. $CH_4 + 2O_2 \rightarrow CO_2 + H_2O$ d. $CH_4 + O_2 \rightarrow CO_2 + H_2O$

__b__ 7. In a double replacement reaction, HCl and $AgNO_3$ will form: 4
   a. either AgCl or HNO_3.   c. either HAg or $ClNO_3$.
   b. both AgCl and HNO_3.   d. both HAg and $ClNO_3$.

__c__ 8. Which of the following requires the greatest activation energy?   5
   a. an ice cube melting   c. a tree burning
   b. a battery working   d. a car rusting

__d__ 9. All methods of changing chemical reaction rates are based on the: 6
   a. amount of inhibitor.   c. energy of the products.
   b. concentration of reactants.   d. collisions of reactants.

__b__ 10. A precipitate forms in a chemical reaction when: 4
   a. one reactant does not combine with another.
   b. a product is not soluble in the solution.
   c. two compounds do not exchange ions.
   d. a chemical reaction has more than one product.

__c__ 11. Which of the following situations would result in the fastest reaction between the same two reactants?   6
   a. a solution of low concentration at a high temperature
   b. a solution of low concentration at a low temperature
   c. a solution of high concentration at a high temperature
   d. a solution of high concentration at a low temperature

__a__ 12. The burning of a log is an example of an: 5
   a. exothermic reaction with a high activation energy.
   b. endothermic reaction with a high activation energy.
   c. exothermic reaction that is also spontaneous.
   d. endothermic reaction that is also spontaneous.

© Silver, Burdett & Ginn Inc.

Quadrant 3 (Page 27)

PART 3

Look at the diagram. Then read the questions that follow. Choose the term or phrase that best answers the question or completes the statement. Write the letter of that choice in the space at the left.

Chapter Goal

__c__ 1. Which sentence describes what is happening in the first reaction?   2
   a. Aluminum chloride yields aluminum plus chloride.
   b. Aluminum chloride yields aluminum plus chlorine.
   c. Aluminum plus chlorine yields aluminum chloride.
   d. Aluminum plus chlorine yields aluminum plus chloride.

__b__ 2. What is the balanced equation for the first reaction?   2
   a. $3Al + 2Cl_2 \rightarrow 2AlCl_3$
   b. $2Al + 3Cl_2 \rightarrow 2AlCl_3$
   c. $3Al + 2Cl_2 \rightarrow 3AlCl_3$
   d. $2Al + 3Cl_2 \rightarrow 3AlCl_3$

__c__ 3. The atomic mass of aluminum is 27 g. The atomic mass of chlorine is 35 g. What is the total mass on each side of the balanced equation?   2
   a. 124 g   b. 159 g   c. 264 g   d. 396 g

__a__ 4. Which of the following is a reactant in the second reaction?   1
   a. Na_2S b. Fe_2S_3 c. NaBr   d. Fe_3Br

__d__ 5. The second reaction shown in the diagram is a: 4
   a. synthesis reaction.   c. single replacement reaction.
   b. decomposition reaction.   d. double replacement reaction.

© Silver, Burdett & Ginn Inc.

Quadrant 4 (Page 28)

PART 4

Read each question or direction and answer it using complete sentences.

Chapter Goal

1. List the steps involved in balancing an equation.   2

   1. Write a word equation to show the reaction.
   2. Substitute correct chemical formulas and symbols for the reactants and products.
   3. Adjust the coefficients so that the number of each kind of atom is the same on both sides of the equation.

2. Explain how an increase in the surface area of a substance in a reaction affects the rate of the reaction.   6

   As the surface area of a chemical in a reaction increases, the chance of contact among particles also increases. This causes an increase in the rate of the reaction.

3. What does the Law of Conservation of Mass say about chemical equations?   2

   The Law of Conservation of Mass says that the atoms can be rearranged, but the number of atoms of each element on each side of the equation must stay the same.

Silver, Burdett & Ginn Inc.

CHAPTER 7 PLANNING GUIDE

7

CHEMICAL REACTIONS

The questions in the CHAPTER TEST are based on these Chapter Goals.

1. Understand chemical reactions and how chemical equations describe them.
2. Balance simple chemical equations, and understand the Law of Conservation of Mass.
3. Describe characteristics and examples of synthesis reactions and decomposition reactions.
4. Describe characteristics of single replacement reactions and double replacement reactions.
5. Describe the role of energy in chemical reactions.
6. Identify factors that affect the rates of chemical reactions.

CHEMICAL REACTIONS

This photograph shows the formation of the compound sodium chloride from the elements sodium and chlorine. Sodium chloride is commonly known as table salt. This familiar compound can be formed as a result of several different kinds of chemical changes. In this case, as the new compound is formed, the chemical change gives off energy in the form of light. All chemical changes involve changes in energy.

- *What kinds of chemical changes are there?*
- *How do scientists describe these changes?*
- *What forms of energy are involved in chemical changes?*
- *What conditions affect the way chemical changes occur?*

7-1 CHEMICAL EQUATIONS

Iron and oxygen combine to form rust. Wood burns in air. These changes are examples of chemical reactions. A **chemical reaction** is a process in which one or more substances are changed into one or more different substances. Iron is a gray solid, and oxygen is a colorless gas. When these chemicals react, they form rust, a reddish-brown or orange solid. In a chemical reaction the original substances lose their identities and can no longer be recognized in the newly formed material or materials.

During a chemical reaction, the atoms in the substances that react are rearranged. Chemical bonds are broken, and new bonds are formed. When oxygen combines with iron, the bonds that hold oxygen atoms together are broken. New bonds form between the iron atoms and the oxygen atoms. Thus, a new molecule is formed.

When wood burns in air, the carbon in the wood reacts with oxygen in the air. This chemical reaction releases heat, a form of energy. All chemical reactions involve energy changes. However, some reactions take place slowly, so the energy change is hard to notice.

After completing this section, you will be able to

- **define** the term *chemical reaction.*
- **identify** the reactants and products in a chemical reaction.
- **write** a simple chemical equation, using either words or chemical formulas.

The key terms in this section are
chemical equation
chemical reaction
products
reactants

CHAPTER OPENING STRATEGY

Discuss the photograph with students. Explain that this chemical reaction involves the release of heat and light. Emphasize that most chemical reactions are not as violent as the one shown. Ask students for examples of chemical reactions that take place in their lives daily.

- What kinds of chemical changes are there? (Synthesis, decomposition, single replacement, and double replacement reactions.)
- How do scientists describe these changes? (Scientists describe chemical changes by using chemical equations.)
- What forms of energy are involved in chemical changes? (Heat and light.)
- What conditions affect the way chemical changes occur? (Temperature, surface area, concentration, catalysts, and the nature of the reactant.)

7-1 CHEMICAL EQUATIONS
pages 159–161

OBJECTIVES
Refer to pupil page 159.

VOCABULARY
Key terms: chemical equation, chemical reaction, products, reactants
Other terms: subscript

1 MOTIVATION

Have students create a bulletin board that shows chemical changes. Ask students to find pictures that depict examples of chemical changes, such as wood burning and iron rusting. Other examples of chemical changes may also be used. If possible, include some photographs or articles that pertain to industry and/or agriculture. This information will enable you to introduce the concept of chemical reactions. Ask students how the pictures demonstrate chemical changes.

2 CONCEPT DEVELOPMENT

Thinking Skills

classifying
Write on the chalkboard the equations that appear in the text, and ask students to classify the reactants and the products. Add several equations that do not appear in the text. Ask students to come to the chalkboard to label the reactants and the products.

Background   Many reactions are reversible. Hydrogen and oxygen combine to form water; water can be decomposed into hydrogen and oxygen.

Background   At times the removal of an element from a compound is the basis of an entire industry. Iron and oxygen that combined long ago formed iron oxide, or iron ore. To make steel the iron must be separated from the oxygen in iron ore. Knowledge of chemical changes and chemical reactions is important in the steel industry.

aequare (make equal)
-ion (process of)

Describing a reaction can take a great amount of space. A **chemical equation** is a shorthand method used by scientists to show the changes that take place in a chemical reaction. The reaction between carbon and oxygen can be shown by the following word equation.

CARBON PLUS OXYGEN YIELDS CARBON DIOXIDE

More often, symbols and chemical formulas are used in place of words when a chemical equation is written. Chemical formulas show the elements and the number of atoms present. Recall that the number of atoms is indicated by a *subscript*. A subscript of "1" is understood and is not written. Thus the word equation above can be written using chemical formulas.

$$C + O_2 \rightarrow CO_2$$

In this chemical equation, C stands for one atom of carbon, O_2 stands for one molecule of oxygen, and CO_2 stands for one molecule of carbon dioxide. The arrow in a chemical equation is read as *yields*.

The starting substances in a chemical reaction are called **reactants**. Reactants act together to form new substances. The new substances that are formed in a reaction are called **products**. In a chemical equation reactants are written to the left of the arrow and products are written to the right. In the equation above, carbon and oxygen are the reactants and carbon dioxide is the product.

Figure 7-1

When sulfur burns, it combines with oxygen gas.

Figure 7-1 shows sulfur reacting with oxygen to yield sulfur dioxide. The reactants are sulfur, a solid, and oxygen, a gas. The product is sulfur dioxide, a gas. The chemical equation for this reaction is as follows.

$$S + O_2 \rightarrow SO_2$$

When iron and sulfur are heated together, they react to form a new compound, iron sulfide. The equation for this reaction is shown below. How would you state this equation in words?[1]

$$Fe + S \rightarrow FeS$$

Identify the reactants and the products in this equation.[2] These substances are shown in Figure 7-2. What differences in their properties might you wish to investigate?[3]

[1]Iron plus sulfur yields iron sulfide.
[2]The reactants are iron and sulfur. The product is iron sulfide.
[3]Answers may include color, hardness, boiling point, and melting point.

Figure 7-2

Iron sulfide has formed in the center of the pile of iron filings.

REVIEW

1. What is a chemical reaction?
2. Identify the reactants and the products in this equation.

$$Pb + Cu(NO_3)_2 \rightarrow Cu + Pb(NO_3)_2$$

3. Write a word equation to describe each of the following reactions.
   a. $Fe + Cl_2 \rightarrow FeCl_2$
   b. $Mg + S \rightarrow MgS$
   c. $Zn + Cl_2 \rightarrow ZnCl_2$

CHALLENGE The reaction between hydrogen and chlorine is shown below. Why is there a 2 in front of the HCl?

$$H_2 + Cl_2 \rightarrow 2HCl$$

Enrichment   Sulfur dioxide is used as a food preservative because it destroys harmful organisms. Ask interested students to research this method of food preservation and to share the information with the class.

Teaching Tip   Ask students to replace symbols and formulas with their word equivalents. For example, have students translate the equation $Fe + S \rightarrow FeS$ into words. To reinforce this skill, reverse the process. Write an equation in words, and have students rewrite it with symbols.

❸ REVIEW/REINFORCEMENT

1. A chemical reaction is a process in which one or more substances are changed into one or more different substances by the breaking or forming of chemical bonds.
2. $Pb + Cu(NO_3)_2$—reactants; $Cu + Pb(NO_3)_2$—products.
3a. Iron plus chlorine yields iron (II) chloride.
 b. Magnesium plus sulfur yields magnesium sulfide.
 c. Zinc plus chlorine yields zinc chloride.

Challenge   Because there are two hydrogen atoms and two chlorine atoms on the left.

7-2 BALANCING CHEMICAL EQUATIONS

pages 162–166

1 MOTIVATION

Set up a Hoffman apparatus similar to the one shown in Figure 7-3. Ask students to estimate the ratio of hydrogen to oxygen. To verify the presence of hydrogen and oxygen, collect a test tube of each by water displacement. Test the oxygen with a glowing splint. The splint will reignite. Test the hydrogen with a burning splint. A loud "pop" will be heard. Point out that in the simple reactions now being studied, chemical reactants and their products are in ratios of small whole numbers.

2 CONCEPT DEVELOPMENT

Tie-in/Math   The term *coefficient* has the same meaning in science as it has in math. Ask students how and where coefficients are used in math. Use mathematical expressions like *2a* to show that the coefficient is 2. Point out the similarity of the coefficient 2 in the expression 2K, which represents 2 atoms of potassium.

7-2 BALANCING CHEMICAL EQUATIONS

After completing this section, you will be able to
- **balance** simple equations.
- **apply** the Law of Conservation of Mass to chemical reactions.

The key terms in this section are
coefficient
Law of Conservation of Mass

Water can be separated into hydrogen and oxygen. This reaction is shown by the following equation.

$$\text{WATER} \rightarrow \text{HYDROGEN} + \text{OXYGEN}$$

The reactants and the products can be identified from the equation. But this equation does not show the exact make-up of water, hydrogen, and oxygen. If symbols are used for the words, more information is given.

$$H_2O \rightarrow H_2 + O_2$$

This equation shows that a molecule of water is made of two atoms of hydrogen and one atom of oxygen. How many atoms of oxygen are there in one molecule of oxygen?[1] Notice that the number of oxygen atoms on each side of the equation is not the same. Since one oxgyen atom cannot form two oxygen atoms, the equation is not correct. The formulas for water, hydrogen, and oxygen are correct, however. These formulas cannot be changed to give the same number of oxygen atoms on each side of the equation.

To make the number of atoms on each side of the equation equal, coefficients must be used. A **coefficient** (koh uh FIHSH uhnt) is a whole number placed in front of a symbol or formula to show the number of atoms or molecules involved. Using coefficients makes it possible

[1]Two

Figure 7-3

This equipment breaks down water into hydrogen and oxygen.

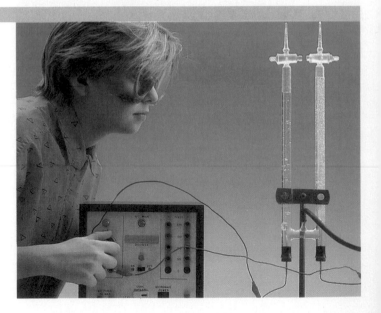

to change the equation so that the left side is equal to the right side. The coefficient "1" is not written but is understood. This changing of coefficients is called balancing the equation.

The number of oxygen atoms can be balanced by placing a 2 in front of the H_2O.

$$2H_2O \rightarrow H_2 + O_2$$

There are now two oxygen atoms on each side of the equation. However, there are now four hydrogen atoms on the left side of the equation and only two on the right side. Placing a 2 in front of the H_2 in the equation will balance the hydrogen atoms.

$$2H_2O \rightarrow 2H_2 + O_2$$

The equation is now balanced. There are four hydrogen atoms on each side of the equation. There are two oxygen atoms on each side of the equation. A balanced equation has the same number of atoms of each element on each side.

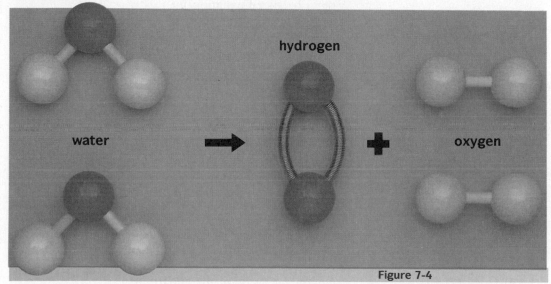

Figure 7-4

How many oxygen atoms are there on each side of the equation?[2]

Figure 7-4 shows two water molecules being separated into hydrogen and oxygen. Count the number of hydrogen and oxygen atoms represented on each side of the equation. Compare the number of atoms shown in the figure to the balanced equation for this reaction.[1] Notice that the left side of the equation in Figure 7-4 has the same number of hydrogen and oxygen atoms as the right side of the equation.

[1]They are the same.
[2]Two.

Teaching Tip   To reinforce Figure 7-4, show the decomposition of water by preparing two models of water molecules. Show only one model to students. Ask them how this molecule can separate to make H_2 and O_2. When students point out that another water molecule is needed, use the two models to show the following.

$$2H_2\,O \rightarrow 2H_2 + O_2$$

Write the equation on the chalkboard, and emphasize the need to balance an equation so that it represents the number of molecules involved.

Demonstration   To show conservation of mass, make solutions of any two materials that will form a precipitate. Put one solution in an unstoppered test tube and the other solution in an Erlenmeyer flask. Slide the test tube into the flask. Stopper the flask. Weigh the flask assembly, using a balance. Invert the flask. The two solutions will mix, forming a precipitate. Again weigh the flask assembly. The flask assembly should weigh the same as the previously established mass. Potassium dichromate and lead nitrate will produce a yellow precipitate.

Puzzler   Same. Weigh a flashbulb before and after the flash.

con- (with)
servare (to preserve)
-ion (process of)

The **Law of Conservation of Mass** says that in a chemical reaction the total mass of the reactants equals the total mass of the products. The law also says that the atoms can be rearranged, but the number of atoms on each side of the equation stays the same. A balanced equation satisfies the law of Conservation of Mass.

Writing a correctly balanced equation involves the following three steps.
1. Write a word equation to show the reaction. The word equation must actually represent the substances in the chemical reaction.
2. Substitute correct chemical formulas and symbols for the reactants and products.
3. Adjust the coefficients so that the number of each kind of atom is the same on both sides of the equation. Each time a coefficient is changed, check both sides of the equation to see if any other coefficients must be changed.

Sample Problem

Aluminum and oxygen react to form aluminum oxide. Write a balanced equation for this reaction.

1. Write the word equation.

$$\text{ALUMINUM} + \text{OXYGEN} \rightarrow \text{ALUMINUM OXIDE}$$

2. Write the formula equation.

$$Al + O_2 \rightarrow Al_2O_3$$

3. Adjust the coefficients to balance the equation. Begin by balancing the oxygen. Put a coefficient of 3 in front of the oxygen on the left side of the equation.

$$Al + 3O_2 \rightarrow Al_2O_3$$

This gives six oxygen atoms on the left side of the equation, and three oxygen atoms on the right side of the equation. Putting a coefficient of 2 in front of the aluminum oxide on the right side of the equation completes the balancing of the oxygen atoms. Notice that there are now six oxygen atoms on each side of the equation.

$$Al + 3O_2 \rightarrow 2Al_2O_3$$

The aluminum must now be balanced. There are four aluminum atoms on the right side of the equation, and only one on the left. Placing a coefficient of 4 in front of the aluminum on the left side of the equation will balance the aluminum atoms.

$$4Al + 3O_2 \rightarrow 2Al_2O_3$$

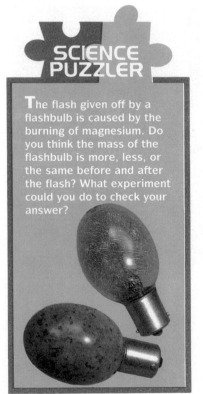

SCIENCE PUZZLER

The flash given off by a flashbulb is caused by the burning of magnesium. Do you think the mass of the flashbulb is more, less, or the same before and after the flash? What experiment could you do to check your answer?

Sample Problem

Zinc and hydrogen chloride react to form zinc chloride and hydrogen. Write a balanced equation for this reaction.

1. Write the word equation.

ZINC + HYDROGEN CHLORIDE →
ZINC CHLORIDE + HYDROGEN

2. Write the formula equation.

$$Zn + HCl \rightarrow ZnCl_2 + H_2$$

3. Adjust the coefficients to balance the equation.

$$Zn + 2HCl \rightarrow ZnCl_2 + H_2$$

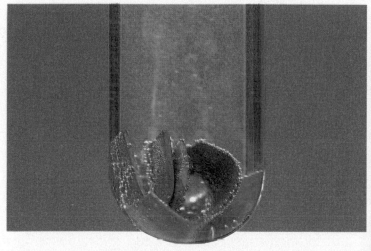

The balanced equation also can be used to show that the total mass of the reactants is equal to the total mass of the products. Look again at the equation above. The Periodic Table gives the atomic mass of each element. The atomic mass of zinc is 65. Hydrogen chloride, made of one hydrogen atom and one chlorine atom, has a mass of 36. Zinc chloride, made of one zinc atom and two chlorine atoms, has a mass of 135. A molecule of hydrogen, H_2, has a mass of 2. These values are substituted into the balanced equation for this reaction.

$$Zn + 2HCl \rightarrow ZnCl_2 + H_2$$
$$65 + 2(36) = 135 + 2$$
$$137 = 137$$

As you can see, the total mass on the left side of the equation is equal to the total mass on the right side of the equation.

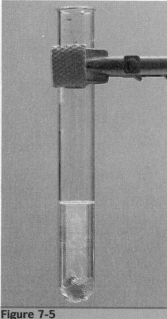

Figure 7-5

The bubbles being given off in this chemical reaction are made up of hydrogen gas.

Background   Seven elements exist in nature as diatomic molecules. These elements are hydrogen, nitrogen, oxygen, fluorine, chlorine, bromine, and iodine. When writing equations, the diatomic form of these elements should always be used: H_2, N_2, O_2, F_2, Cl_2, Br_2 and I_2, respectively.

Background   The classic, historical experiment to show conservation of mass was done by Lavoisier. In this experiment he oxidized a known amount of mercury and then decomposed the oxide. The same mass of mercury was produced upon decomposition of the mercuric oxide.

Background   Methane is the main constituent of natural gas. Methane is sometimes found in coal mines. When methane gas is found in a mine, it is a serious fire hazard for the miners.

Thinking Skills

predicting
Using Figure 7-6, ask students to predict what will happen when methane gas is burned. (It will form carbon dioxide and water.) Ask them how they know. (You can tell by the equation and by looking at the molecular models.) Ask students if they would have been able to make this prediction by knowing only the reactants. (Yes, perhaps.)

3 REVIEW/REINFORCEMENT

1.a. $2KClO_3 \rightarrow 2KCl + 3O_2$.
  b. $N_2 + 3H_2 \rightarrow 2NH_3$.
  c. $2Al + 6HCl \rightarrow 2AlCl_3 + 3H_2$.
  d. $4Sb + 3O_2 \rightarrow Sb_4O_6$.
  e. $Al_2O_3 + 3C + 3Cl_2 \rightarrow 2AlCl_3 + 3CO$.
2.a. 244.
  b. 108.
  c. 170.

Challenge   The mass of the hydrogen is 4 g.

When methane, CH_4, is burned, it combines with oxygen, producing carbon dioxide and water. As you can see in the calculations shown below, the total mass of reactants is 80 and the total mass of products is 80.

$$CH_4 + 2O_2 \rightarrow CO_2 + 2H_2O$$
$$16 + 2(32) = 44 + 2(18)$$
$$80 = 80$$

[1]Both show the same number and kinds of atoms in the reactants and products.

The reactants and the products of this reaction are represented by the models shown in Figure 7-6. How do the models and the equation satisfy the Law of Conservation of Mass?[1]

Figure 7-6

The reactants and the products both contain the same number of each kind of atom.

REVIEW

1. Balance the following equations.
   a. $KClO_3 \rightarrow KCl + O_2$
   b. $N_2 + H_2 \rightarrow NH_3$
   c. $Al + HCl \rightarrow AlCl_3 + H_2$
   d. $Sb + O_2 \rightarrow Sb_4O_6$
   e. $Al_2O_3 + C + Cl_2 \rightarrow AlCl_3 + CO$
2. Using the periodic table, calculate the sum of the atomic masses of all atoms on each side of the following equations.
   a. $KCl + AgNO_3 \rightarrow AgCl + KNO_3$
   b. $2MgO + Si \rightarrow 2Mg + SiO_2$
   c. $2NaNO_3 \rightarrow 2NaNO_2 + O_2$

CHALLENGE   Magnesium reacts with hydrogen chloride.

$$Mg + 2HCl \rightarrow MgCl_2 + H_2$$

If 48 g of magnesium and 146 g of hydrogen chloride yield 190 g of magnesium chloride, what is the mass of the hydrogen gas given off?

7-3 SYNTHESIS AND DECOMPOSITION REACTIONS

Chemical reactions can be grouped together based upon the type of chemical changes that occur. Two types of reactions that you will study in this lesson are synthesis reactions and decomposition reactions.

SYNTHESIS REACTIONS

A **synthesis reaction** is a reaction in which two or more substances combine to form a compound. This type of reaction can be shown by this general equation.

$$A + X \rightarrow AX$$

The new compound produced is shown as *AX*. An example of a synthesis reaction is the reaction between sodium and chlorine. The element sodium combines with the element chlorine to form the compound sodium chloride, which is common table salt. The balanced equation for this reaction is shown below.

$$2Na + Cl_2 \rightarrow 2NaCl$$

Another example of a synthesis reaction is the burning of magnesium in oxygen. When the element magnesium burns, it combines with the element oxygen from the air to form the compound magnesium oxide. The balanced equation for this reaction is as follows.

$$2Mg + O_2 \rightarrow 2MgO$$

Figure 7-7 shows the flare produced when magnesium reacts with oxygen. The bright flash of light is the energy released by the reaction when magnesium oxide is formed. This reaction causes the flash in fireworks and flashbulbs.

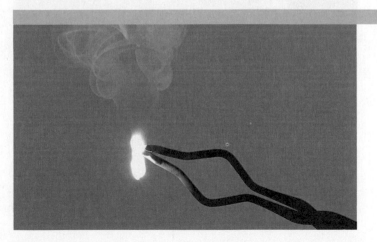

Figure 7-7

When magnesium burns, it combines with oxygen.

After completing this section, you will be able to

- **distinguish** between a synthesis reaction and a decomposition reaction.
- **identify** examples of synthesis reactions and decomposition reactions.

The key terms in this section are
decomposition reaction
synthesis reaction

OBJECTIVES
Refer to pupil page 167.

VOCABULARY
Key terms: decomposition reaction, synthesis reaction

1 MOTIVATION

Have students examine a small strip of magnesium ribbon. Ask students to list the metallic properties of the material. Point out that this substance is an element and that its symbol is Mg. Carefully ignite the ribbon in a burner flame. (Caution: Be careful of the heat and light given off. Hold the ribbon with tongs or forceps, and caution students not to look directly at the flame.) Compare this reaction with Figure 7-7. Ask students to examine the product of the reaction. A white, powdery magnesium oxide is the result of combining magnesium with oxygen from the air.

2 CONCEPT DEVELOPMENT

Teaching Tip Point out that it is easier to study general types of reactions than each specific reaction. In this section and the next, students will work with four different kinds of reactions. This simplification makes it possible to reach an understanding of many different reactions in a short time.

Teaching Tip Use a felt board to demonstrate synthesis and decomposition reactions. One color felt can represent metals, another color nonmetals. The students can visualize the combination of substances in a synthesis reaction and the separation in a decomposition reaction. Emphasize that the substances do not combine or separate without some energy involvement.

Tie-in/Language Arts Ask students to look up the term *synthesis* in a dictionary. Ask students how the prefix *de-* is used in the word *decomposition*. Explain that *de-* is a negative prefix; therefore, this word means *not* composing, or *not* putting together. The word means "to separate."

Demonstration Use this demonstration to illustrate a synthesis reaction: Half fill a crucible with iron filings. Weigh the crucible and filings. Heat the crucible and iron slowly for about 1 minute and then vigorously for 10–15 minutes. Again weigh the crucible. Elicit from students that the weight increase is due to the combination of iron with oxygen from the air.

Demonstration Use the following demonstration to illustrate a decomposition reaction: Place about 10 mL of 6 percent hydrogen peroxide in a test tube. Add two or three small crystals of potassium permanganate. The $KMnO_4$ is reduced to MnO_2, which catalyzes the reaction. Test for the emission of oxygen gas by using a glowing splint.

$$2H_2O_2 \rightarrow 2H_2O + O_2$$

Compounds also can combine directly in synthesis reactions. Ammonia and hydrogen chloride are both compounds. They combine to form ammonium chloride. This product is used to make fertilizers, dyes, and cough medicines. The equation for the reaction is shown below.

$$NH_3 + HCl \rightarrow NH_4Cl$$

When sulfur trioxide, SO_3, is mixed with water, sulfuric acid, H_2SO_4, is produced. Sulfuric acid is used in making dyes, explosives, and rayon. The balanced equation for the synthesis of sulfuric acid is shown below.

$$SO_3 + H_2O \rightarrow H_2SO_4$$

DECOMPOSITION REACTIONS

A **decomposition reaction** is a reaction in which a compound breaks down into two or more substances. Such a reaction can be shown by this general equation.

$$AX \rightarrow A + X$$

AX is the reactant, and A and X are the products. A soft drink contains carbonic acid, H_2CO_3. The carbonic acid can decompose, or break down, into water and carbon dioxide. If you leave a soft drink bottle open, the carbon dioxide gas can escape, leaving a "flat" soft drink. The equation for this reaction is as follows.

$$H_2CO_3 \rightarrow H_2O + CO_2$$

Figure 7-8

The bubbles given off contain carbon dioxide produced from the decomposition of carbonic acid.

Mercury (II) oxide is a red powder. This compound decomposes when it is heated. The products of the reaction are mercury, a shiny liquid metal, and oxygen, an invisible gas. This decomposition reaction can be shown by the following balanced equation.

$$2HgO \rightarrow 2Hg + O_2$$

Figure 7-9 shows several steps in the decomposition of mercury (II) oxide. Heating causes the bonds between the mercury and the oxygen to break. The shiny metal mercury condenses on the upper part of the test tube and runs back down into the tube. The oxygen atoms form molecules of oxygen gas that escape from the mouth of the test tube.

Figure 7-9

The decomposition of mercury (II) oxide.

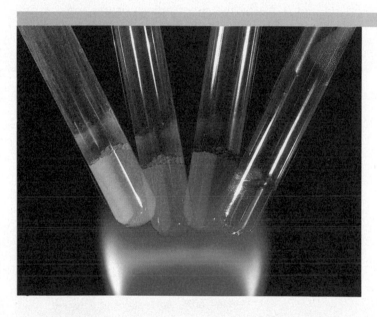

REVIEW

1. What is the difference between a synthesis reaction and a decomposition reaction?
2. Identify each of the following as a synthesis reaction or a decomposition reaction.
   a. $2MgO \rightarrow 2Mg + O_2$
   b. $2Hg + O_2 \rightarrow 2HgO$
   c. $2SO_2 + O_2 \rightarrow 2SO_3$
   d. $2KClO_3 \rightarrow 2KCl + 3O_2$

CHALLENGE Write a balanced equation to show the reaction between water and carbon dioxide. State whether this reaction is synthesis or decomposition.

Enrichment   Many substances are extremely harmful by themselves but not harmful in compounds. Sodium is an extremely active metal that reacts vigorously with water. Chlorine is a poisonous gas. When these two elements combine, they form sodium chloride, common table salt, a material vital for human survival. Ask interested students to research the product of this reaction and to report on the change of properties.

Background   Some metallic oxides, such as lead oxide, silver oxide, and mercuric oxide, will decompose when heated, forming the metal plus oxygen gas. Although mercuric oxide has been the classic example for decomposition reactions, its demonstration is not recommended unless a fume hood is used.

Thinking Skills

classifying
List on the chalkboard several synthesis and decomposition reactions not found in this chapter. Ask students to classify the equations as either synthesis reactions or decomposition reactions.

3 REVIEW/REINFORCEMENT

1. In a synthesis reaction substances are put together; in a decomposition reaction substances are taken apart.
2.a. Decomposition.
  b. Synthesis.
  c. Synthesis.
  d. Decomposition.

Challenge $H_2O + CO_2 \rightarrow H_2CO_3$; synthesis.

7-4 REPLACEMENT REACTIONS

pages 170–173

1 MOTIVATION

Drop a small piece of zinc or magnesium into a test tube half-filled with dilute hydrochloric acid. Bubbles of hydrogen gas will be liberated. Ask students to explain the origin of the gas. Point out that the zinc or magnesium took the place of the hydrogen in the acid. Ask the students to define the term *replacement*.

2 CONCEPT DEVELOPMENT

Teaching Tip   Replacement reactions are like school dances. In a single replacement reaction one substance (one person) takes the place of another substance (person). In a double replacement reaction, the substances (people) change partners. Pick some students to help show this concept. Have them note that boy replaces boy and girl replaces girl. A similar type of replacement occurs in chemical reactions: A metal will replace a metal, and a nonmetal will replace a nonmetal.

170

7-4 REPLACEMENT REACTIONS

After completing this section, you will be able to

- **distinguish** between single and double replacement reactions.
- **predict** the products of single replacement reactions and double replacement reactions.
- **identify** precipitates, using a reference table.

The key terms in this section are
double replacement reaction
precipitate
single replacement reaction

Recall that synthesis reactions and decomposition reactions are two kinds of chemical reactions. Two other kinds of reactions are single replacement reactions and double replacement reactions.

SINGLE REPLACEMENT REACTIONS

A **single replacement reaction** takes place when one element replaces another element in a compound, forming a new compound. This kind of reaction can be shown by the following general equation.

$$A + BX \rightarrow AX + B$$

A and *B* can be metals or other positive ions. *X* can be a nonmetal or other negative ion. In compounds that contain metals, metals are written first in the chemical formula. The replacing metal must be more active than the metal being replaced.

Chemists have done experiments to see which elements are more active than others. The results from this work can be put into a table, such as Table 7-1. In this table, potassium is the most active element. The least active element on the list is gold. Find aluminum and chromium in the table. Which of these elements is more active? Is copper more active than magnesium?[1]

Iron is more active than copper. If an iron nail is placed in a copper sulfate solution, the iron will replace the copper ion and combine with the sulfate ion to form iron sulfate. The copper will then be left uncombined. The balanced equation to show this reaction is as follows.

$$Fe + CuSO_4 \rightarrow FeSO_4 + Cu$$

[1]Aluminum. No.

Figure 7-10

In this reaction, iron is replacing copper ions.

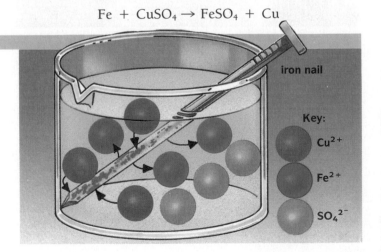

iron nail

Key:
Cu^{2+}
Fe^{2+}
$SO_4{}^{2-}$

What would happen if some lead metal were placed in a solution of iron chloride? Since the lead is less active than the iron, the lead could not replace the iron ion and no reaction would take place. Predict what would happen if a piece of aluminum were placed in a solution of silver nitrate![1]

DOUBLE REPLACEMENT REACTIONS

A **double replacement reaction** takes place when the compounds in a reaction exchange ions. This can be shown by the following equation.

$$AX + BY \rightarrow AY + BX$$

A and B are positive ions, and X and Y are negative ions. The reaction is shown in Figure 7-11. In this reaction, compound AX separates into positive and negative ions. Compound BY also separates into ions. Positive ion A then joins with negative ion Y. At the same time, positive ion B joins with negative ion X. Thus two new compounds, AY and BX, are formed. Notice that in each compound there is a positive ion attached to a negative ion. The positive ion is written first in a chemical formula.

Table 7-1 *Activity Series*

Symbol	Name	Activity
K	Potassium	High
Ca	Calcium	
Na	Sodium	
Mg	Magnesium	
Al	Aluminum	
Zn	Zinc	
Cr	Chromium	
Fe	Iron	
Ni	Nickel	
Sn	Tin	
Pb	Lead	
H	Hydrogen	
Cu	Copper	
Hg	Mercury	
Ag	Silver	
Au	Gold	Low

[1]Aluminum would replace silver ions.

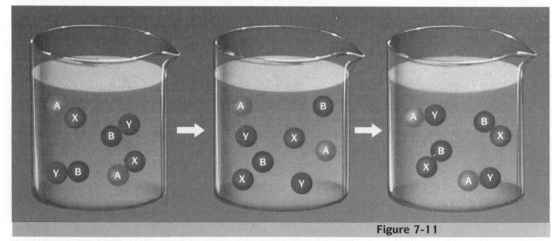

Figure 7-11

A double replacement reaction.

An example of a double replacement reaction is the formation of silver chloride and sodium nitrate from silver nitrate and sodium chloride. The reaction is shown by the following equation.

$$AgNO_3 + NaCl \rightarrow AgCl + NaNO_3$$

Sodium and silver are the positive ions. The nitrate ion and chloride ion are the negative ions.

Demonstration   To demonstrate double replacement, carefully mix 10 mL of 1.0 M HCl with 10 mL of 1.0 M NaOH in a small beaker or evaporating dish. Leave the mixture uncovered, and allow the water to evaporate. The crystals left are common table salt, sodium chloride.

$$NaOH + HCl \rightarrow HOH + NaCl$$

Enrichment   Precipitates of lead compounds are usually colored. The lead iodide produced when lead nitrate reacts with sodium iodide is bright yellow. Many years ago, lead compounds such as lead iodide were commonly used as pigments in the paint industry. Ask students why lead pigments are not used extensively today in paint manufacturing. (Lead-based paint chips could cause brain damage if accidently ingested by a child.)

Background   Replacement reactions occur because some metals are more active than others. At times these reactions cause the deterioration of metal structures. Metals in the earth or dissolved in water will react with pipelines, buried storage tanks, or hot-water heaters. To prevent this type of reaction from taking place in water heaters, expendable metal rods called anodes, often made of zinc or magnesium, are suspended in the heaters. The dissolved metal ions in the water react with the rods rather than with the steel of the heater tanks. Pipelines and storage tanks are similarly protected, but the anodes are outside the pipes or tanks rather than inside them.

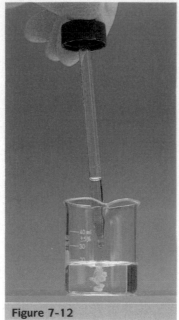

Figure 7-12
Lead iodide forms a yellow precipitate, and sodium nitrate remains dissolved.

[1]Iron and hydrogen are the positive ions. Sulfur and chlorine are the negative ions.

Another example of a double replacement reaction is the formation of hydrogen sulfide gas. Iron sulfide reacts with hydrochloric acid. The products of the reaction are iron chloride and hydrogen sulfide. Study the following balanced equation. Identify the positive and negative ions in this reaction.[1]

$$FeS + 2HCl \rightarrow FeCl_2 + H_2S$$

In some reactions one of the products is not soluble and is called a precipitate. A **precipitate** (prih SIHP uh tayt) is a solid material that is formed in a chemical reaction and that separates from the solution. Precipitates tend to sink to the bottom of the reaction container.

A table of solubilities is used to determine whether a precipitate will form in a chemical reaction. Look at Table 7-2, which gives the solubilities of different compounds in water. According to the table, aluminum chloride is soluble. Therefore it will not form a precipitate. Silver chloride, however, is not soluble. It will form a precipitate.

Figure 7-12 shows lead nitrate reacting with sodium iodide. The products are lead iodide and sodium nitrate. The reaction can be shown as follows.

$$Pb(NO_3)_2 + 2NaI \rightarrow PbI_2 + 2NaNO_3$$

The yellow precipitate formed is lead iodide.

Table 7-2 *Solubilities in Water*

S = Soluble P = Partially Soluble I = Insoluble	Bromide	Carbonate	Chloride	Hydroxide	Nitrate	Phosphate	Sulfate
Aluminum	S	—	S	I	S	I	S
Barium	S	P	S	S	S	I	I
Calcium	S	P	S	S	S	P	P
Copper II	S	—	S	I	S	I	S
Iron II	S	P	S	I	S	I	S
Iron III	S	—	S	I	S	P	P
Magnesium	S	P	S	I	S	P	S
Potassium	S	S	S	S	S	S	S
Silver	I	I	I	—	S	I	P
Sodium	S	S	S	S	S	S	S
Zinc	S	P	S	I	S	I	S

ACTIVITY What Are the Types of Chemical Reactions?

OBJECTIVE
Distinguish between different types of chemical reactions, using experimental data.

MATERIALS
safety goggles, lab apron, graduate, water, bromthymol blue, 3 test tubes, test-tube rack, drinking straw, copper (II) sulfate solution, zinc strip, barium chloride solution, potassium sulfate solution

PROCEDURE
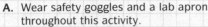
A. Wear safety goggles and a lab apron throughout this activity.
B. Draw a data table like the one shown.
C. Measure 10 mL of water into a test tube. Add 5 drops of bromthymol blue.
D. Using a clean drinking straw, gently blow into the solution. Record your observations in the data table.
E. Measure 10 mL of copper (II) sulfate ($CuSO_4$) solution, and pour the solution into a test tube. Rinse the graduate with water.
F. Place a zinc strip into the solution.
G. After 5 to 10 minutes, examine the zinc. Record your observations.
H. Measure 5 mL of barium chloride ($BaCl_2$) solution, and pour the solution into a test tube. Rinse the graduate with water.
I. Measure 5 mL of potassium sulfate (K_2SO_4) solution. Add this solution to the barium chloride solution in the test tube. Record your observations.

Reactants	Observations
H_2O, CO_2	
Zn, $CuSO_4$	
$BaCl_2$, K_2SO_4	

RESULTS AND CONCLUSIONS
1. What evidence is there that chemical reactions took place?
2. Write a balanced equation for each chemical reaction.
3. Which reaction(s) produced a precipitate?
4. Identify each type of reaction that occurred. Explain your answer.

REVIEW

1. Identify each of the following as a single replacement reaction or a double replacement reaction.
   a. $Mg + H_2SO_4 \rightarrow MgSO_4 + H_2$
   b. $KBr + AgNO_3 \rightarrow KNO_3 + AgBr$
   c. $HCl + NaOH \rightarrow H_2O + NaCl$
   d. $Al + FeCl_3 \rightarrow AlCl_3 + Fe$
2. Complete and balance each of the following equations.
   a. $K + AlCl_3 \rightarrow$
   b. $NaBr + AgNO_3 \rightarrow$
   c. $AlBr_3 + Ca(OH)_2 \rightarrow$
   d. $FeCl_2 + Na_3PO_4 \rightarrow$
3. Identify any precipitates in the equations given in questions 1 and 2.

CHALLENGE Predict which of the following reactions would occur. Write a balanced equation for each reaction that would occur.
   a. $Al + CuSO_4 \rightarrow$
   b. $Cu + AlCl_3 \rightarrow$
   c. $Zn + AgNO_3 \rightarrow$
   d. $Ag + ZnCl_2 \rightarrow$

ACTIVITY 30–40 minutes

PROCESS SKILLS
observing, measuring, classifying, comparing

Preparation Barium chloride and potassium sulfate can be prepared by dissolving 20–25 g of each compound per liter of water. Dissolve about 300 g of copper sulfate per liter of water.

Safety Tip Caution students not to suck in any of the chemicals.

Answers to Procedure

Reactants	Observations
H_2O, CO_2	Turned yellow
Zn, $CuSO_4$	Copper specks on zinc
$BaCl_2$, K_2SO_4	White precipitate

Answers to Results and Conclusions
1. There were color changes for each reaction.
2. $H_2O + CO_2 \rightarrow H_2CO_3$; $Zn + CuSO_4 \rightarrow ZnSO_4 + Cu$; $BaCl_2 + K_2SO_4 \rightarrow 2KCl + BaSO_4$.
3. Reaction 3 produced $BaSO_4$.
4.a. Synthesis; the two chemicals combined to form one product: **b.** Single replacement; the metal, iron, replaced the metal, copper: **c.** Double replacement; the compounds exchanged ions.

3 REVIEW/REINFORCEMENT

1. **a** and **d** single; **b** and **c** double
2.a. $3K + AlCl_3 \rightarrow 3KCl + Al$.
   b. $NaBr + AgNO_3 \rightarrow NaNO_3 + AgBr$.
   c. $2AlBr_3 + 3Ca(OH)_2 \rightarrow 3CaBr_2 + 2Al(OH)_3$.
   d. $3FeCl_2 + 2Na_3PO_4 \rightarrow Fe_3(PO_4)_2 + 6NaCl$.
3.1b. Silver bromide. 2c. Aluminum hydroxide. 2d. Iron (II) phosphate.

Challenge
a. Yes; $2Al + 3CuSO_4 \rightarrow Cu + Al_2(SO_4)_3$.
c. Yes; $Zn + 2AgNO_3 \rightarrow 2Ag + Zn(NO_3)_2$.
b. No.   d. No.

7-5 ENERGY IN CHEMICAL REACTIONS

pages 174–176

1 MOTIVATION

Both hot packs and cold packs are available in most drug stores. Bring one or both to class, and demonstrate the use of these first-aid devices. Introduce the terms *exothermic* (a chemical process in which energy is given off) and *endothermic* (a chemical process in which energy is absorbed) as students handle the packs. Point out that every chemical reaction involves a change in energy.

2 CONCEPT DEVELOPMENT

Demonstration   Use this demonstration to illustrate activation energy:
Show the class an unlit match. (For this purpose, a large fireplace or kitchen match works well.) Ask what might be done to make the match light. Strike the match, using some effort to show you are applying energy, and relate the energy expended to the concept of activation energy.

7-5 ENERGY IN CHEMICAL REACTIONS

After completing this section, you will be able to

- **define** the term *spontaneous reaction.*
- **define** the term *activation energy.*
- **distinguish** between exothermic reactions and endothermic reactions.

The key terms in this section are
**activation energy
endothermic reaction
exothermic reaction
spontaneous reaction**

When solutions of barium chloride and potassium sulfate are mixed, a precipitate forms. This is a spontaneous (spahn TAY nee uhs) chemical reaction. A **spontaneous reaction** takes place with so little energy added to start the reaction that it seems as if no energy is needed.

Many spontaneous reactions give off energy. Chemical reactions inside a battery release energy in the form of electricity. The chemical reaction in a battery is spontaneous. Figure 7-13 shows a variety of batteries and electrical cells. They all give off energy spontaneously. What are batteries used for? Why is a spontaneous reaction important for these uses?[1]

Some reactions need to receive a certain amount of energy before they can start. The amount of energy needed to start a chemical reaction is called the **activation energy**. All reactions require activation energy. Spontaneous reactions require little activation energy. This small amount of energy can be absorbed as heat from the surroundings.

Figure 7-13

In electrical cells and batteries, electrical energy is produced from chemical energy.

Paper burning is a chemical reaction. But to start the paper burning, energy, as in the form of a lit match, must be used. The match gives off the activation energy needed to start the paper burning. Once the paper is burning, the reaction will continue without adding more energy.

The amount of activation energy needed to start a reaction depends upon the nature of the reactants. The energy given off by a burning match will easily start paper burning. However, the same amount of energy from a match will not ignite wood in a campfire like the one shown in Figure 7-14. Why is a campfire or a fireplace fire usually started by first lighting some paper?[2]

[1] They provide the energy for flashlights, calculators, toys, and the starters of automobiles. Spontaneous reactions provide this energy quickly.
[2] The paper provides activation energy that starts the wood burning.

Figure 7-14

Burning is a chemical reaction that releases energy.

Some chemical reactions, such as burning, produce energy. A reaction that gives off energy is called an **exothermic** (ehk soh THER mihk) **reaction**. In the human body, digested food is broken down to release energy. The energy is used to carry out body functions, such as breathing and moving. Thus many reactions in the human body are exothermic.

exo- (outer)
-therm (heat)

The opposite of an exothermic reaction is an endothermic reaction. An **endothermic** (ehn doh THER mihk) **reaction** is a reaction that absorbs energy. Usually, in order to keep an endothermic reaction going, energy must be applied constantly. For example, in a process called photosynthesis, green plants use sunlight to make food. Photosynthesis is an endothermic reaction. Energy in the form of sunlight is used to keep the reaction going.

endo- (inner)

The manufacture of soap is an endothermic reaction. Fat or vegetable oil is mixed with lye in a large kettle, and the mixture is heated. The heat energy allows the atoms to rearrange to form soap and glycerine.

Demonstration   Use this demonstration to illustrate an exothermic reaction: Pour 10 mL of water into a test tube. Have a student hold the tube. Then take the test tube back and add 10 mL of concentrated sulfuric acid. Return the tube to the student. The student should immediately notice that the test tube is considerably warmer.

Demonstration   Use this demonstration to illustrate an endothermic reaction: Half fill a large Erlenmeyer flask with warm water. Have a student determine the temperature of the water with a thermometer. Add about 20 g of sodium acetate to the water. Stir and once again determine the temperature.

Background   Batteries, or electrochemical cells, react spontaneously because electrons of an active metal migrate to a material of lower activity. The outer shell of a dry cell (which is really moist inside) is made of zinc. There is a carbon rod in the center of the cell. The zinc shell and the carbon rod are electrodes. Separating the two electrodes is a paste of ammonium chloride, carbon, and manganese dioxide. Zinc, the more active metal, loses electrons, which are then gained by the carbon. The difference in charge between the two electrodes creates a voltage in the cell. A normal cell will provide 1.5 volts.

Thinking Skills

sequencing
Ask students to list the sequence of chemical events that took place to build the campfire in Figure 7-14. Ask students to list the sequence of chemical events for an endothermic reaction.

PROCESS SKILLS
observing, measuring, identifying cause and effect, inferring, interpreting data

Preparation Distilled water will give better results than tap water, but it is not essential. Make sure that the temperature of the water is at least 20°C–25°C (room temperature). The easiest way to accomplish this is to leave jugs of water out overnight. Endothermic reaction results are not as noticeable in colder water.

Safety Tip Sodium hydroxide is extremely corrosive. Read the label on the bottle, and follow the directions carefully.

Teaching Tip Ask students to feel each test tube to determine if it becomes warmer or colder. Encourage the use of the terms *exothermic* and *endothermic*.

Answers to Procedure
Data:

Reactant	Starting Temperature	Final Temperature
NH₄Cl	Variable	should decrease
NaOH	Variable	should increase

Answers to Results and Conclusions
1. Temperature changes.
2. Exothermic—temperature increases; endothermic—temperature decreases.
3. Heat from the water in the test tube.
4. Probably NaOH. There is a greater temperature change.

3 REVIEW/REINFORCEMENT

1. A spontaneous reaction is one that starts with no apparent supply of activation energy.
2. Activation energy starts a chemical reaction.
3. Exothermic reactions give off heat; endothermic reactions absorb heat.

Challenge The fire itself supplies the activation energy to keep other large pieces of wood burning.

176

ACTIVITY Does Temperature Change During a Reaction?

OBJECTIVE
Distinguish between endothermic and exothermic reactions.

MATERIALS
safety goggles, lab apron, graduate, distilled water, 2 test tubes, test-tube rack, thermometer, balance, ammonium chloride, 2 stoppers, forceps, sodium hydroxide pellets

PROCEDURE

A. Wear safety goggles and a lab apron throughout this activity.
B. Draw a data table like the one shown.
C. Using a graduate, measure 5 mL of distilled water with a graduate, and pour the water into a test tube.
D. Measure the temperature of the water. Record your result in the data table.
E. Measure 3 g of ammonium chloride and place it in the test tube.
F. Stopper the test tube and shake it for 1 minute. Record your observations.
G. Measure the temperature of the solution and record the result.
H. Using a graduate, measure 5 mL of distilled water, and pour the water into a test tube.
I. Measure the temperature of the solution. Record the result.
J. Using forceps, carefully add 15 sodium hydroxide pellets to the test tube, one pellet at a time. **Caution:** Do not touch the sodium hydroxide pellets.
K. Stopper the test tube and shake it for 1 minute. Record your observation.
L. Measure the temperature of the solution, and record the result.

RESULTS AND CONCLUSIONS

1. What evidence do you have that energy changes take place when chemicals react?
2. How can you determine which reaction is exothermic and which reaction is endothermic?
3. In the endothermic reaction you observed, what was the source of the energy for the reaction?
4. Which reaction had the greater energy change? Explain your answer.

Reactant	Observation	Starting Temperature	Final Temperature
Ammonium chloride			
Sodium hydroxide			

REVIEW

1. What is a spontaneous reaction?
2. What is the function of activation energy in a chemical reaction?
3. How do exothermic reactions and endothermic reactions differ?

CHALLENGE To start a fire, you must add activation energy to the substances you want to burn. A match provides enough activation energy to start paper burning, but not enough to start a large piece of wood burning. To start the wood burning, you need to use paper and small pieces of wood as kindling. Once you get the fire started, no more kindling is needed. Why don't you have to keep adding activation energy to this reaction?

7-6 CHANGING THE RATE OF REACTIONS

Plants grow well in a greenhouse. The rate of photosynthesis is increased by controlling such conditions as temperature, amount of light, and amount of reactants. The rates of other reactions can also be controlled.

To a scientist, reaction rate means how quickly or slowly a reaction takes place. To control the rate of a reaction, it is helpful to know what causes a reaction to speed up or slow down. Scientific studies have shown that there are five factors that affect reaction rates. They are temperature, concentration, surface area, the presence of a catalyst, and the nature of the reactants.

> *After completing this section, you will be able to*
> - **list** factors that affect the rate of a reaction.
> - **define** the term *catalyst*.
>
> *The key terms in this section are*
> catalyst   inhibitor

Figure 7-15
A greenhouse controls conditions, therefore the plants grow quickly.

TEMPERATURE

Temperature is the measure of the kinetic energy, or energy of motion, in the particles of a substance. As temperature increases, the particles move faster and come in contact more often. In order for two substances to react, the particles of those substances must collide with each other. The increased contact of particles causes a faster reaction rate. As the temperature decreases, the particles in the substances collide with each other less often. This causes a slower reaction. For example, foods cook more slowly at low temperatures than at high temperatures.

7-6 CHANGING THE RATE OF REACTIONS
pages 177–181

OBJECTIVES
Refer to pupil page 177.

VOCABULARY
Key terms: catalyst, inhibitor
Other terms: aqueous solution, enzymes

1 MOTIVATION

Half fill a 1000-mL Erlenmeyer flask with cold water. Half fill a second 1000-mL flask with hot water. Simultaneously drop an antacid tablet into each flask. Ask students which antacid tablet dissolves faster. (The one in hot water.) Ask students to supply reasons. (The water molecules move faster in hot water and cause reactions to proceed at a faster rate.)

2 CONCEPT DEVELOPMENT

Background   For chemical materials to react, the chemicals must come together, or collide. These collisions must bring the reactants into the proper orientation and spacing for old bonds to separate and new bonds to form. The rate at which these collisions occur affects the speed of reaction. Increasing the temperature of a system causes the materials to move faster and to collide more often, resulting in a faster reaction rate. Higher concentrations allow more particles to collide with each other. Increased surface area also provides more particles for collisions.

Demonstration The effect that surface area has on the rate of a reaction can be demonstrated by the following:

Weigh two identical amounts of copper (II) sulfate, using the largest crystals available. Pulverize one sample with a mortar and pestle. Put each sample into a separate 1000-mL flask that is half filled with water. Stopper both flasks. Ask two students to shake the flasks until the copper sulfate is dissolved. The finely crushed pieces will dissolve faster because of the increased surface area.

Demonstration Use the following demonstration to illustrate the effect of concentration on the rate of a reaction:

Half fill a test tube with *dilute* hydrochloric acid. Half fill a second test tube with *concentrated* hydrochloric acid. Cut two strips of magnesium ribbon, each 3 cm long. Drop a strip into each tube, and observe the reaction rates.

Thinking Skills

inferring
Temperature and surface area each affect the rate of a reaction. Students should infer that there is a cumulative effect. Ask students to list three or four ways to speed up (or slow down) a reaction.

Thinking Skills

interpreting diagrams
Have students look at Figure 7-16 and Figure 7-17. Then ask students to explain the impact of increasing surface area and concentration.

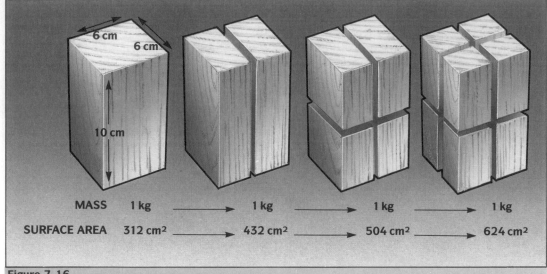

Figure 7-16

Cutting an object into smaller pieces increases the surface area on which reactions can take place.

[1]Beaker *B*.

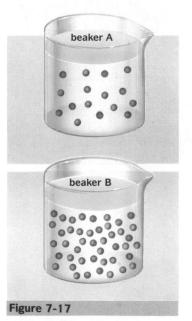

Figure 7-17

Which beaker contains the more concentrated solution?[1]

SURFACE AREA

To react, chemicals must come in contact with each other. Contact can only take place at the surfaces of the substances involved in the reaction. As surface area increases, the rate of a reaction increases because more particles can come together. Consider a 1-kg block of wood that has six sides. When the wood is burned, reaction with oxygen will occur on all surfaces. Suppose the block is cut in half. There is still 1 kg of wood, but now there are two more surfaces. Each time a piece of the wood is cut, more surface area is exposed, so more wood particles can react with oxygen. Thus the rate of reaction increases with increasing surface area.

Gasoline is vaporized in the carburetor of a car. This process increases the surface area of the gasoline. The gasoline can then burn faster because of the increased contact with oxygen in the air.

CONCENTRATION

Concentration tells how much solute there is in a solution. Figure 7-17 shows two beakers that contain reactants. Beaker *A* contains a less concentrated solution than does beaker *B*. Therefore, there are fewer solute particles in beaker *A* than in beaker *B*. As the concentration of a chemical increases, the chance of contact among particles also increases. This causes an increase in the rate of the reaction.

CATALYSTS

A **catalyst** (KAT uh lihst) is a substance that changes the rate of a chemical reaction. Most catalysts speed up reactions. Catalysts are not changed in a reaction. They are the same at the beginning and the end of a reaction.

Much of the fuel used in cars is made by using catalysts. With catalysts, large molecules found in crude oil break down into the simpler molecules in gasoline. Catalysts are also used to break down the waste products produced when gasoline burns. A catalytic converter in an automobile changes carbon monoxide and other pollutants into carbon dioxide and water.

Catalysts that slow down chemical reactions are called **inhibitors** (ihn HIHB uh tuhrz). Many inhibitors are used as preservatives in household products. A preservative slows down the rate of decay or spoilage. Without these chemicals, many foods would spoil faster.

inhibitus (to hold)

NATURE OF REACTANTS

You have seen that chemical equations show the substances that are involved in a reaction. Scientists sometimes need more information about the substances involved in a reaction. The nature of the reactants is usually given to make the equation clearer. To show the state of matter, the letter *s* stands for a solid, *l* stands for a liquid, and *g* stands for a gas. The letters *aq* stand for *aqueous* (AY kwee uhs) *solution*. This shows that a reactant is dissolved in water. These letters are placed in parentheses

SCIENCE & TECHNOLOGY

Until recently, the development of catalysts has been by trial and error. Scientists would test hundreds of chemicals to find one that worked for a specific reaction. With new technology, scientists can design catalysts.

The process of designing chemicals is called molecular engineering. Using new instruments, scientists are able to see how the shape of a catalyst is related to its function.

Molecular engineering has been used to produce

zeolites. Zeolites are an important group of catalysts that are found in some rocks and claylike materials. Scientists have been able to change the shape of zeolites to make them fit specific reactions. The photograph shows the shape of a zeolite. Part of the photograph has been computer enhanced to show a clearer pattern.

One such zeolite will be used to make gasoline from alcohol. With zeolites this can be done in only one step. In the past, this process took several steps.

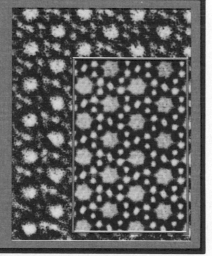

Demonstration　Use the following demonstration to illustrate the work of a catalyst: Rub some cigarette ashes into a sugar cube, and leave another cube untouched. Place each cube on a fireproof surface. Attempt to light each cube with a match. Some of the materials in the ash serve as catalysts, allowing the sugar to ignite.

Demonstration　The nature of reactants can be demonstrated by the following: Mix a gram or two each of barium chloride and potassium sulfate crystals in a watch glass on an overhead projector. No reaction takes place because the ions are not free to move and recombine. But mix solutions of the two materials, and a white precipitate is formed.

Tie-in/Social Studies　Plants grow in specific biomes, or geographical areas. Correlate how the topography of an area, the temperature, the soil type (nature of reactants), and rainfall (concentration of water), all affect the flora found in a locality.

Review and Skill Masters
CHALLENGE/CRITICAL THINKING, pages 45–46.
See page 157c in this book for answers.

PROCESS SKILLS

observing, measuring, comparing, identifying cause and effect, interpreting data, recording data

Preparation In advance, prepare enough 2.0 M hydrochloric acid for the students to use. Concentrated hydrochloric acid is 12.0 M. To prepare 2.0 M from 12.0 M, add 2 mL of 12.0 M HCl to 10 mL of water. Remember, always add acid to water.

Safety Tip Hydrochloric acid is extremely corrosive. Allow students to work only with small amounts. Require students to immediately wash with water any acid that might spill on them. Prepare a large jug of sodium bicarbonate (baking soda) solution. If students do spill acid on themselves, the sodium bicarbonate solution is an effective neutralizer.

Teaching Tip If the magnesium ribbon has become oxidized and looks dull instead of shiny, remove the oxide by pulling lengths of the ribbon through a folded piece of sandpaper. Many labs do not have hot tap water. In this case keep a liter flask of water warming on a hot plate. Flush any discarded acid with copious quantities of water. Floating strips or slivers of magnesium may account for irregularities in the data. A floating strip of magnesium has one surface that is not in contact with the acid.

Answers to Results and Conclusions

Data: Student times will vary, but there should be a decrease in time from the cold-water bath to the hot-water bath. There should also be a time decrease from rolled to slivered magnesium.

1. Answers will vary.
2. Control—quantities, surface area, and concentrations of reactants; variable—temperature.
3. Answers will vary.
4. Control—quantities, temperature, and concentrations of reactants; variable—surface areas.

ACTIVITY   What Factors Affect the Rate of a Reaction?

OBJECTIVE

Compare the rates of reaction under varying conditions.

MATERIALS

safety goggles, lab apron, magnesium ribbon, scissors, metric ruler, 25-mL graduate, hydrochloric acid, 50-mL Erlenmeyer flask, 250-mL beaker, timer

PROCEDURE

A. Wear safety goggles and lab apron throughout this activity.
B. Draw a data table like the one shown.
C. Cut a piece of magnesium ribbon 2 cm long.
D. Measure 10 mL of hydrochloric acid and pour it into an Erlenmeyer flask.
E. Place the flask in a 250-mL beaker half full of cold tap water. Chill the flask for 3 minutes, then take it out of the water. **Caution:** Hold the flask so that it does not tip over into the water.
F. Carefully slide the magnesium strip into the acid. **Caution:** Be careful not to splash the acid when adding the magnesium.
G. Record the time needed to dissolve the magnesium in the acid.
H. Empty and wash the flask according to your teacher's instructions.
I. Repeat steps **C** and **D**.
J. Warm the flask in a 250-mL beaker half full of very hot tap water for 3 minutes.
K. Carefully slide the magnesium into the acid.
L. Record the time needed to dissolve the magnesium in the acid.
M. Empty and wash the flask.
N. Measure 10 mL of hydrochloric acid and pour it into the flask.
O. Cut a piece of magnesium ribbon 2 cm long.
P. Roll the magnesium ribbon into a tight ball.
Q. Carefully slide the magnesium metal into the acid.
R. Record the time required to dissolve the magnesium in the acid.
S. Empty and wash the flask.
T. Measure 10 mL of hydrochloric acid and pour it into the flask.
U. Cut a piece of magnesium ribbon 2 cm long.
V. Cut the magnesium ribbon into fine slivers.
W. Add the magnesium to the acid in the flask.
X. Record the time required to dissolve the magnesium in the acid.
Y. Empty and wash the flask.

Reactants	Time
Magnesium, HCl (cold)	
Magnesium, HCl (hot)	
Magnesium (rolled), HCl	
Magnesium (slivered), HCl	

RESULTS AND CONCLUSIONS

1. How long did it take for the reaction to be completed in cold HCl? in hot HCl?
2. Identify the control and the variable in this part of the experiment.
3. How long did it take for the reaction to be completed using rolled magnesium? using slivered magnesium?
4. Identify the control and the variable in this part of the experiment.

---

[1]HCl is a liquid. Zn is a solid. ZnCl is in solution. H_2 is a gas.

[2]The ions from sodium bromide are able to move around and react only when they are in solution.

following the formula for each substance. What is the nature of each of the reactants in the following equation?[1]

$$2HCl(aq) + Zn(s) \rightarrow ZnCl_2(aq) + H_2(g)$$

It is important to know the state of matter of each substance in a reaction. Some reactions will take place only if the reactants are in certain states. For example, sodium bromide is a white solid that will react with chlorine only if both are dissolved in water.

$$Cl_2(g) + 2NaBr(s) \rightarrow \text{does not react}$$
$$Cl_2(aq) + 2NaBr(aq) \rightarrow Br_2(aq) + 2NaCl(aq)$$

Why does sodium bromide not react when it is solid?[2]

REVIEW

1. How is contact between particles related to reaction rate?
2. How does surface area affect the rate of a reaction?
3. How does a decrease in concentration of reactants affect the rate of a chemical reaction?
4. What is a catalyst?

CHALLENGE The following equation represents a spontaneous chemical reaction that proceeds slowly.

$$AB \rightarrow A + B$$

If you add substance X to the reaction, the rate of reaction increases. If you then add substance Y to the reaction, the rate of reaction returns to the original rate. Hypothesize about the role of substance Y in this reaction.

CHAPTER SUMMARY

The main ideas in this chapter are listed below. Read these statements before you answer the Chapter Review questions.

- In a chemical reaction, one or more types of substances are changed into one or more different types of substances. (7-1)

- The changes that take place in a chemical reaction can be written as a chemical equation. (7-1)

- In a chemical reaction the atoms can be rearranged, but the total number of atoms stays the same. (7-2)

- A reaction in which two or more substances combine to form a compound is called a synthesis reaction. (7-3)

- A reaction in which compounds break down into two or more substances is called a decomposition reaction. (7-3)

- In a single replacement reaction, one element replaces another element in a compound, forming a new compound. (7-4)

- A double replacement reaction takes place when the compounds in a reaction exchange ions. (7-4)

- Energy is transferred during chemical reactions. A reaction that gives off energy is called an exothermic reaction; a reaction that absorbs energy is called an endothermic reaction. (7-5)

- Five factors affect reaction rates. These factors are temperature, concentration, surface area, catalysts, and nature of reactants. (7-6)

The key terms in this chapter are listed below. Use each term in a sentence that shows the meaning of the term.

activation energy
catalyst
chemical equation
chemical reaction
coefficient
decomposition reaction
double replacement reaction
endothermic reaction
exothermic reaction

inhibitors
Law of Conservation of Mass
precipitate
products
reactants
single replacement reaction
spontaneous reaction
synthesis reaction

1. For two substances to react, they must come in contact with each other. The reaction rate increases as contact increases.
2. Increased surface area increases the rate of a reaction.
3. The rate slows down.
4. A catalyst is an added substance that changes the rate of a chemical reaction.

Challenge Substance Y reacted with the catalyst, substance X. The catalyst was thus removed from the reaction by substance Y.

Review and Skill Masters

VOCABULARY REVIEW, page 41.
See page 157b in this book for answers.

VOCABULARY

1. catalyst
2. activation energy
3. synthesis reaction
4. single replacement reaction
5. precipitate
6. chemical equation
7. exothermic reaction
8. inhibitor
9. reactants
10. products
11. endothermic reaction
12. coefficient

CONCEPTS

1. To show in shorthand form the changes that take place in a chemical reaction.
2. Reactants are the starting materials of a reaction, and products are the materials that are made.
3. A coefficient is a whole number placed in front of a symbol or formula to show the number of atoms or molecules involved.
4. To make the number of atoms of each element the same on both sides.
5.a. $FeS + 2HCl \rightarrow FeCl_2 + H_2S$.
   b. $H_2 + Cl_2 \rightarrow 2HCl$.
6.a. $2NaOH + H_2SO_4 \rightarrow Na_2SO_4 + 2H_2O$.
   b. $Ca + 2H_2O \rightarrow Ca(OH)_2 + H_2$.
7.a. 178.
   b. 76.
8. In synthesis reactions, materials combine to form new products. In decomposition reactions, materials separate to form new products.

Review and Skill Masters

CHAPTER REVIEW, pages 42–43.
See page 157b in this book for answers.

Chapter Review

VOCABULARY

Use the key terms from this chapter to complete the following sentences correctly.

1. A substance that speeds up a chemical reaction is called a/an _____ .
2. The energy needed to start a reaction is called _____ .
3. The reaction $2H_2O + O_2 \rightarrow 2H_2O_2$ is an example of a/an _____ .
4. In a/an _____ , an active metal replaces a less active metal.
5. An insoluble material that forms during a reaction is called a/an _____ .
6. A shorthand method for showing a chemical reaction is called a/an _____ .
7. A reaction that gives off heat is called a/an _____ .
8. A material that is added to food to slow the growth of bacteria is called a/an _____ .
9. The starting substances in a chemical reaction are the _____ .
10. The substances produced in a chemical reaction are called the _____ .
11. A/An _____ is a reaction that absorbs heat.
12. A whole number multiplier placed in front of a formula is called a/an _____ .

CONCEPTS

1. What is the purpose of a chemical equation? (7-1)
2. Distinguish between reactants and products in a chemical reaction. (7-1)
3. What is a coefficient? (7-2)
4. Why must chemical equations be balanced? (7-2)
5. Write and balance the equations for these reactions. (7-2)
   a. Iron sulfide plus hydrogen chloride yields iron chloride plus hydrogen sulfide.
   b. Hydrogen plus chlorine yields hydrogen chloride.
6. Balance the following equations. (7-2)
   a. $NaOH + H_2SO_4 \rightarrow Na_2SO_4 + H_2O$
   b. $Ca + H_2O \rightarrow Ca(OH)_2 + H_2$
7. Use the Periodic Table to calculate the sum of the atomic masses on each side of the equations given in question 6. (7-2)
8. Compare synthesis reactions and decomposition reactions. (7-3)

9. Complete and balance the following equations. State whether each reaction is a synthesis reaction or a decomposition reaction. (7-3)
   a. $Cu + O_2 \rightarrow$ **c.** $H_2O \rightarrow$ **e.** $Al + O_2 \rightarrow$
   b. $H_2CO_3 \rightarrow$ **d.** $Mg + Cl_2 \rightarrow$

10. How does a single replacement reaction differ from a double replacement reaction? (7-4)

11. Complete and balance the following equations. State whether each reaction is a single replacement reaction or a double replacement reaction. (7-4)
    a. $Al(NO_3)_3 + CaCl_2 \rightarrow$
    b. $Ca + FeBr_2 \rightarrow$
    c. $BaCl_2 + K_2SO_4 \rightarrow$
    d. $Al + Cu(NO_3)_2 \rightarrow$

12. How does a spontaneous reaction differ from a reaction that is not spontaneous? (7-5)

13. What is activation energy? (7-5)

14. Distinguish between exothermic reactions and endothermic reactions. (7-5)

15. Give two examples of an exothermic reaction. (7-5)

16. How does temperature affect the rate of a chemical reaction? (7-6)

17. Compare the effects of concentration and surface area on reaction rate. (7-6)

18. What is the purpose of a catalyst? (7-6)

APPLICATION/ CRITICAL THINKING

1. Many photographers keep unused film in the refrigerator. Explain why this makes the film last longer.

2. Explain why aluminum will react with iron chloride but not with magnesium chloride.

EXTENSION

1. Make a collection of food labels that show the use of preservatives.

2. Research the match. Why does a match light when struck? What kind of energy changes are involved? Present a report to the class.

READINGS

Angier, Natalie, "Hazards of a Toxic Wasteland." *Time,* December 17, 1984, p. 32.

Chishom, J., and M. Lynnington. *Chemistry,* Tulsa, Okla.: EDC Publishing, 1983.

9.a. $2Cu + O_2 \rightarrow 2CuO$; synthesis.
   b. $H_2CO_3 \rightarrow H_2O + CO_2$; decomposition.
   c. $2H_2O \rightarrow 2H_2 + O_2$; decomposition.
   d. $Mg + Cl_2 \rightarrow MgCl_2$; synthesis.
   e. $4Al + 3O_2 \rightarrow 2Al_2O_3$; synthesis.

10. In a single replacement reaction, one element replaces another element. During double replacement reactions, both metals and nonmetals change partners.

11.a. $2Al(NO_3)_3 + 3CaCl_2 \rightarrow 2AlCl_3 + 3Ca(NO_3)_2$; double replacement.
   b. $Ca + FeBr_2 \rightarrow CaBr_2 + Fe$; single replacement.
   c. $BaCl_2 + K_2SO_4 \rightarrow 2KCl + BaSO_4$; double replacement.
   d. $2Al + 3Cu(NO_3)_2 \rightarrow 2Al(NO_3)_3 + 3Cu$; single replacement.

12. A spontaneous reaction takes place with so little energy added to start the reaction that it seems as if no energy is needed. Other reactions require (activation) energy to get them started.

13. Activation energy is the energy needed to start a chemical reaction.

14. An exothermic reaction releases heat. An endothermic reaction absorbs heat.

15. Life processes and burning.

16. An increase in temperature speeds a chemical reaction. A temperature decrease slows a reaction.

17. An increase in concentration and surface area increases the reaction rate. A decrease of these factors slows the reaction rate.

18. A catalyst changes the speed of a reaction.

APPLICATION/CRITICAL THINKING

1. The reduced temperature found in a refrigerator slows the reaction rate of the chemicals found on photographic film.

2. Aluminum is more active than iron but less active than magnesium (Table 7-1).

Test Masters

CHAPTER TEST, pages 25–28.
See page 157d in this book for answers.

ACIDS, BASES, AND SALTS

ORGANIZER

Section	pages	Activity	pages	Reinforcement and Evaluation	pages	*Review and Skill Masters	pages	Other Components in Teacher Resource Package	pages
8–1 Properties of Acids	185–189	Which Acids Are Corrosive?	189	Review, Challenge	189			Study Guide	38
8–2 Properties of Bases	190–192			Review, Challenge	192			Study Guide	39
8–3 Indicators	193–196	How Can You Identify Acids and Bases?	196	Review, Challenge	196	Skill	50–51	Study Guide Lab Manual Transparency Poster	40 43
8–4 Reactions of Acids and Bases	197–201	What Happens in a Neutralization Reaction?	198	Puzzler Review, Challenge	200 201	Challenge/Critical Thinking	52	Study Guide Lab Manual	41 47
CHAPTER SUMMARY	201					Vocabulary Review	47		
CHAPTER REVIEW	202–203			*Test Masters	29–32	Chapter Review	48–49		

*In the Teacher Resource Package. For answers, see pages 183b–183d in this book.

ACTIVITY MATERIALS   Quantities are based on a class of 30 students working in groups as indicated in parentheses.

Which Acids Are Corrosive? p. 189 (groups of 2)	quantity	How Can You Identify Acids and Bases? p. 196 (groups of 2)	quantity	What Happens in a Neutralization Reaction? p. 198 (groups of 2)	quantity
safety goggles	30	safety goggles	30	safety goggles	
lab apron	30	lab apron	30	lab apron	30
150-mL beaker	75	glass-marking pencil	15	100-mL graduate	15
glass-marking pencil	15	50-mL beaker	120	hydrochloric acid	225 mL
100-mL graduate	15	100-mL graduate	15	pH paper	60 strips
hydrochloric acid	375 mL	sodium hydroxide solution	275 mL	bromthymol blue	30 mL
mossy zinc	15 g	red-cabbage indicator solution	60 mL	sodium hydroxide solution	100 mL
sulfuric acid	375 mL	dropper	15	distilled water	
acetic acid	375 mL	hydrochloric acid	275 mL	250-mL beaker	30
soda water	375 mL	distilled water		glass-stirring rod	15
lemon juice	375 mL	tea	275 mL	calcium oxide	150 g
		lemon juice	275 mL	filter paper	15 sheets
		ammonia water	275 mL	funnel	15
		white vinegar	275 mL	drinking straw	15
		liquid laundry detergent	275 mL		

REVIEW AND SKILL MASTERS

Name_____ Date_____

VOCABULARY REVIEW ——————————— Chapter 8

Use the clues to complete the puzzle.

Crossword answers:
- BASIC ANHYDRIDE
- BASE
- CONCENTRATION
- NEUTRALIZATION
- INDICATOR
- HYDROXIDE ION
- (down entries include: HYDROGEN ION, ACID ANHYDRIDE, DRY, SALT, PH SCALE, ACID, MONOXIDE, HYDRONIUM)

ACROSS

2. An oxide of a metal that forms a base when it is mixed with water (two words)

5. A substance that releases hydroxide ions when it dissolves in water

6. The amount of an ion present in a solution

7. The reaction between an acid and a base

9. A compound that changes color as the presence of H⁺ or OH⁻ ions changes

11. OH⁻ ions (two words)

DOWN

1. H_3O^+ ions (two words)

3. An oxide of a nonmetal that forms an acid when it is mixed with water (two words)

4. A compound formed from the positive metal ions of a base and the negative nonmetal ions of an acid

8. A measure of the H⁺ ion concentration of a solution (two words)

10. A substance that gives off hydrogen ions when it dissolves in water

© 1988 Silver, Burdett & Ginn Inc.

47

Name_____ Date_____

CHAPTER REVIEW ——————————— Chapter 8

8-1 Properties of Acids

1. What property makes a substance an acid? An acid is a substance that releases hydrogen ions when it dissociates. Acids are sour and conduct electricity.

2. What is the difference between a strong acid and a weak acid? A strong acid dissociates completely in water and releases many hydrogen ions in solution; a weak acid does not dissociate completely and releases few hydrogen ions in solution.

3. What is one way that hydrochloric acid is useful in industry? Hydrochloric acid is used to remove rust and corrosion from metals by a process called pickling

8-2 Properties of Bases

1. Describe bases, listing some of their properties. Bases are a group of compounds that give off hydroxide ions in solution. Bases usually contain a metal. They taste bitter, feel slippery, and conduct electricity.

2. Compare sodium hydroxide to aluminum hydroxide. Sodium hydroxide is a strong base because it dissociates completely into ions when dissolved in water. Aluminum hydroxide is a weak base because it dissociates to produce few ions when dissolved in water.

3. Name some household and industrial items that bases are used to produce. Bases are used in the manufacture of rayon, fertilizers, detergents, and household cleaners.

© 1988 Silver, Burdett & Ginn Inc.

48

Name_____ Date_____

CHAPTER REVIEW (Continued) ——————————— Chapter 8

8-3 Indicators

1. What is the pH scale? The pH scale is a scale from 0 to 14 that measures the H⁺ ion concentration of a solution.

2. Compare the concentrations of ions in a pH 3 solution and a pH 10 solution. A pH 3 solution would have more H⁺ ions than OH⁻ ions and be acidic. A pH 10 solution would have more OH⁻ ions than H⁺ ions and be basic.

3. What is an indicator? An indicator is a compound that changes color as the concentration of H⁺ or OH⁻ ions changes.

4. Name some natural indicators. Blueberries, beets, and red cabbage are natural indicators.

8-4 Reactions of Acids and Bases

1. Describe what happens and what results when an acid and a base react. What is this reaction called? When an acid and a base react, extra H⁺ ions from the acid combine with the extra OH⁻ ions from the base to produce water and a salt. This is a neutralization reaction.

2. What are salts? Salts are compounds formed from the positive metal ions of a base and the negative nonmetal ions of an acid.

3. What is an acid anhydride? An acid anhydride is an oxide that forms an acid when it is mixed with water.

4. What is a basic anhydride? A basic anhydride is a compound that forms a base when added to water.

5. Explain what determines if a metal will cause the release of hydrogen gas from an acid solution. Such a reaction depends on the type of acid and on the place of the metal in the activity series.

© 1988 Silver, Burdett & Ginn Inc.

49

Name_____ Date_____

SKILL/Interpreting a Scale ——————————— Chapter 8

The chemical formula for an acid contains hydrogen, H⁺. The chemical formula for a base contains hydroxide, OH⁻. Therefore, acids and bases can be identified by their formulas.

1. Look at the chemical formulas below. State whether each compound is an acid or a base.

a. HCl acid
b. KOH base
c. H_2SO_4 acid
d. NH_4OH base
e. HNO_3 acid
f. H_3PO_4 acid
g. $Mg(OH)_2$ base
h. $Ca(OH)_2$ base

2. Water can produce H⁺ ions and OH⁻ ions. Why does water not belong in the list above? Pure water molecules produce only one hydrogen ion and one hydroxide ion that cancel out each other. Pure water is neutral, and is neither an acid nor a base.

3. Use the pH scale below to determine the pH of the following substances.

a. stomach acid, pH 2.0
b. oranges, pH 3.5
c. milk, pH 6.5
d. sea water, pH 8.5
e. ammonia, pH 11.0

pH Scale

pH scale from 0 to 14 labeled: Stomach acid, Oranges, Tomatoes, Milk, Pure water, Human blood, Sea water, Household bleach, Ammonia

© 1988 Silver, Burdett & Ginn Inc.

50

Name_____ Date_____

SKILL/Interpreting a Scale (Continued) _____ Chapter 8

4. Write each substance in the proper place on the pH scale.
   a. tomatoes, pH 4.2   c. human blood, pH 7.4
   b. pure water, pH 7.0   d. household bleach, pH 9.0

5. Given the pH values above, tell whether each item is acidic or basic.
   Tomatoes are **acidic** with a pH value of under 7. Pure water is neutral with a

   pH value of 7.0. Human blood is only very slightly basic at pH 7.4. Household

   bleach is a base at pH 9.0.

6. Which substance on the scale would you say had the highest concentration of OH⁻ ions?
   Of H⁺ ions?
   Ammonia has the highest concentration of OH⁻ ions, since it has the highest

   pH value. Stomach acid has the highest concentration of H⁺ ions, since it has

   the lowest pH value.

7. Given the pH values on the scale, what color would each of the items in question 4 turn a
   piece of litmus paper? Why?
   Tomatoes are acidic and would turn litmus paper red. Human blood and

   household bleach are basic and would turn litmus paper blue. Pure water

   would not change the litmus paper at all since it is neither an acid nor a base.

Name_____ Date_____

CHALLENGE/CRITICAL THINKING _____ Chapter 8

Acid rain is formed when fossil fuels, such as coal and oil products, are burned. When these fuels are burned, they emit oxides of sulfur, carbon, and nitrogen into the air. These oxides combine with water in the air and fall to the earth as acid rain.

1. What type of compound is carbon dioxide? How does it form carbonic acid? Write the
   chemical equation for the formation of carbonic acid.
   Carbon dioxide (CO_2) is an acid anhydride. When it combines with water (H_2O),

   it forms carbonic acid (H_2CO_3). The chemical equation for the formation of

   carbonic acid is $CO_2 + H_2O \rightarrow H_2CO_3$.

2. Scientists sometimes use calcium oxide, or lime, to neutralize the acidity of lakes that have
   been polluted by acid rain. What kind of compound is lime? What does it form when added
   to water? Give the chemical equation that shows this.
   Lime is a basic anhydride. When mixed in solution with water, lime forms the

   base calcium hydroxide ($Ca(OH)_2$). The chemical equation for this is $CaO +$

   $H_2O \rightarrow Ca(OH)_2$. $Ca(OH)_2$ is a base because it contains hydroxide, or OH^-, ions.

3. Look at the chemical equation below. Describe what happens when a lime solution is used
   to treat lakes polluted by sulfuric acid in acid rain.

   $Ca(OH)_2 + H_2SO_4 \rightarrow CaSO_4 + 2H_2O$
   The basic lime solution ($Ca(OH)_2$) combines with sulfuric acid (H_2SO_4) to form a

   salt ($CaSO_4$) and water (H_2O). The positive metal ions of the base (Ca^+)

   combine with the negative nonmetal ions of the acid (SO_4^-) to form calcium

   sulfate ($CaSO_4$).

TEST MASTERS

PART 1 / Chapter 8

Name _____ Date _____ Score _____

Chapter 8

Acids, Bases, and Salts

PART 1

In the space below, write the term that each phrase defines.

Chapter Goal

1. **concentration** — The amount of any ion present in a solution, and the measurement that tells how much of a substance has dissolved in a solution — 3

2. **base** — A substance that releases hydroxide ions in solution — 2

3. **indicator** — A compound that changes color as the concentration of hydrogen or hydroxide ions changes — 3

4. **neutralization** — The reaction between an acid and a base that produces water — 4

5. **basic anhydride** — An oxide of a metal that forms a base when added to water — 5

6. **hydroxide ion** — An ion that is released by a base and that contains one oxygen atom and one hydrogen atom. — 2

7. **salt** — A compound formed from the positive metal ions of a base and the negative nonmetal ions of an acid — 4

8. **acid** — A substance that releases hydrogen ions when it dissociates — 1

9. **hydronium ions** — The H_3O^+ ions that form in an acid solution when a hydrogen ion and a water molecule combine — 1

10. **acid anhydride** — An oxide of a nonmetal that forms an acid when mixed with water — 5

PART 2

Choose the term or phrase that best answers the question or completes the statement. Write the letter of that choice in the space at the left.

_c_ 1. Acid anhydrides and basic anhydrides both contain: — 5
a. metals. b. salts. c. oxides. d. water.

_c_ 2. The pH of a solution produced by a complete neutralization reaction would be: — 4
a. 0. b. 5. c. 7. d. 14.

Chapter 8 Acids, Bases, and Salts — 29

© Silver, Burdett & Ginn Inc.

Name _____ Date _____ Score _____

PART 2

Choose the term or phrase that best answers the question or completes the statement. Write the letter of that choice in the space at the left.

Chapter Goal

_d_ 3. Which of the following would be most likely to react with HCl to form hydrogen gas? — 5
a. a basic anhydride c. hydrogen gas
b. hydroxide ions d. potassium metal

_c_ 4. Which of the compounds in the equation below is a salt? — 4
$NaOH_{(l)} + HCl_{(l)} \longrightarrow NaCl_{(aq)} + H_2O_{(l)}$
a. NaOH b. HCl c. NaCl d. H_2O

_d_ 5. A student determines that an unknown substance conducts electricity, tastes sour, and reacts with metals to produce hydrogen ions. The substance is most likely: — 1
a. a base. b. an indicator. c. a salt. d. an acid.

_c_ 6. Which of the following would dissociate to produce the most hydroxide ions? — 2
a. 1 mL of strong acid c. 1 mL of strong base
b. 1 mL of weak acid d. 1 mL of weak base

_a_ 7. A laboratory assistant would most likely place litmus paper in a solution to: — 3
a. test H^+ concentrations. c. release hydrogen gas.
b. form salt crystals. d. produce acid anhydrides.

_b_ 8. Which of the following would most likely be used to dissolve a grease stain on clothing? — 2
a. an acid c. a salt
b. a base d. an acid anhydride

_b_ 9. Which of the following would have the highest pH? — 3
a. an acid solution c. a salt solution
b. a basic solution d. a neutral solution

_a_ 10. Which of the following would most likely occur if a strong acid was mixed with a metal? — 1
a. The metal would be corroded.
b. A salt would be formed.
c. Hydroxide ions would be produced.
d. An acid anhydride would be formed.

Chapter 8 Acids, Bases, and Salts — 30

© Silver, Burdett & Ginn Inc.

Name _____ Date _____ Score _____

PART 3

Look at the chart. Then read the questions that follow. Choose the term or phrase that best answers the question or completes the statement. Write the letter of that choice in the space at the left.

Compound	pH	Characteristics
A	7.0	— liquid at room temperature — does not conduct electricity — dissociates to form H^+ and OH^- ions
B	1.0	— corrosive — conducts electricity — dissociates to form H^+ ions
C	7.0	— contains a metal and a nonmetal ion — forms crystals
D	12.0	— caustic — dissolves fats — dissociates to form OH^- ions
E	12.4	— contains a metal ion — used to neutralize acidic soil — contains no water molecules

Chapter Goal

_b_ 1. Compound D is most likely: — 2
a. an acid. b. a base. c. a salt. d. an indicator.

_a_ 2. Which of the following compounds would be most likely to react with calcium to release hydrogen gas and form a salt? — 5
a. B b. C c. D d. E

_d_ 3. If Compounds B and D were combined, they would react to form: — 4
a. an anhydride. b. an acid. c. a base. d. a salt.

_d_ 4. Which compound would cause litmus paper to turn blue? — 3
a. A b. B c. C d. D

_a_ 5. Compound B would most likely be used to: — 1
a. pickle steel. c. form crystals.
b. test pH. d. make soap.

Chapter 8 Acids, Bases, and Salts — 31

© Silver, Burdett & Ginn Inc.

Name _____ Date _____ Score _____

PART 4

Read each question or direction and answer it using complete sentences.

Chapter Goal

1. Describe three ways caustic bases are useful to humans. — 2

Caustic bases can dissolve certain substances, such as fats and oils. Sodium hydroxide, a caustic base found in lye, can be used to clean drains clogged with grease. This base is also used to make paper, rayon, detergents, and soap, and it is used in refining petroleum and vegetable oil.

2. Explain how the concentration of hydrogen and hydroxide ions in a solution determines its pH. — 3

The pH of a solution is determined by the concentration of hydrogen or hydroxide ions in it. If there are more hydroxide ions than hydrogen ions, the solution is basic. If there are more hydrogen ions than hydroxide ions, the solution is acidic. A solution has a neutral pH if the number of hydrogen ions is equal to the number of hydroxide ions.

3. What happens during a neutralization reaction? — 4

When an acid and a base are combined, they undergo a neutralization reaction. The acid dissociates to form H^+ ions, and the base dissociates to form OH^- ions. The H^+ and the OH^- ions combine to form water. The positive metal ions from the base and the negative nonmetal ions from the acid then combine to form a salt.

Chapter 8 Acids, Bases, and Salts — 32

© Silver, Burdett & Ginn Inc.

CHAPTER 8 PLANNING GUIDE

8

ACIDS, BASES, AND SALTS

1. Describe some properties and uses of acids.
2. Describe some properties and uses of bases.
3. Explain how indicators and the pH scale can be used to show ion concentration in acids and bases.
4. Describe characteristics of neutralization reactions and the properties of salts.
5. Explain how anhydrides form acids and bases, and identify metals that react with acids.

ACIDS, BASES, AND SALTS

Have you ever noticed how much darker brand-new jeans are
than old jeans? Denim cloth gets its blue color from a dye called
indigo. This dye will only dissolve in solutions that contain
chemicals called bases. It will not dissolve in solutions that
contain acids. Soap contains bases. When denim jeans are
washed in soapy water, some of the indigo dye in the cloth
dissolves. Thus, as they are washed, jeans lose some of their
color.

- *Do acids and bases affect the solubility of many chemicals?*
- *How is an acid different from a base?*
- *What happens when acids and bases are mixed?*

8-1 PROPERTIES OF ACIDS

Acids are an important group of compounds. They
are found in many familiar substances, such as fruit, soft
drinks, vinegar, and yogurt. Acids are also used widely in
the laboratory and in industry.

Acids can be identified by certain properties. They
taste sour, they react with some metals to produce hydrogen, and they conduct electricity. What substances can
you name that contain acids?[1]

Many compounds split into ions as they dissolve in
water. Such compounds are said to *dissociate* (dih SOH-
shee ayt) in water. An **acid** is a substance that releases
hydrogen ions when it dissociates. Hydrogen chloride,
HCl, dissociates in water as follows

$$HCl(g) \rightarrow H^+(aq) + Cl^-(aq)$$

The solution that forms is called hydrochloric acid. This
solution also contains water. The hydrogen ions produced
by an acid are attracted to water molecules. **Hydronium**
(hī DROH nee uhm) **ions** are H_3O+ ions. They are formed
in the following reaction.

$$H^+(aq) + H_2O(l) \rightarrow H_3O^+(aq)$$

After completing this section,
you will be able to

- **list** some properties of acids.
- **distinguish** between strong
  and weak acids.
- **describe** the uses of some
  common industrial and
  laboratory acids.

The key terms in this section are
acid   hydronium ions

---

acidus (sour)

---

[1]Students may list fruit
juices, milk, and vinegar.

Have students read the introductory paragraph. Explain to students that indigo dye
comes from plants. Explain to students that
indigo dye is colorless as a solution and turns
blue after it dries. Ask them to give a possible
reason for this. Ask students how they could
prevent their jeans from losing too much
color.

- Do acids and bases affect the solubility of
  many chemicals? (Yes.)
- How is an acid different from a base?
  (Acids and bases can be thought of as
  chemical opposites.)
- What happens when acids and bases are
  mixed? (They react to create a neutral
  substance.)

8-1 PROPERTIES OF ACIDS
pages 185–189

OBJECTIVES
Refer to pupil page 185.

VOCABULARY
Key terms: acid, hydronium ions
Other terms: corrosive acid, dissociate,
strong acid, weak acid

---

1 MOTIVATION

Have students bring in photographs of foods
that contain acid, such as fruit, fruit juices,
and vinegar. Make a collage of the photographs. Display the collage on the bulletin
board before beginning this lesson. Ask students what all these things have in common.
(They all have a sour taste.)

2 CONCEPT DEVELOPMENT

Background In 1787, Antoine Lavoisier defined an acid as a binary compound that always contains oxygen. In 1811, Sir Humphry Davy stated that oxygen was not necessarily part of an acid. In 1814, Joseph Gay-Lussac said that acids neutralized bases, and vice versa. In 1884, Svante Arrhenius proposed in his doctoral dissertation that acids, bases, and salts dissociate in water to form charged ions. His revolutionary theory was given a minimum passing grade.

Thinking Skills

interpreting charts
Have students look at Table 8-1. Ask them if all acids contain oxygen. Ask them if all acids contain carbon. Ask students what nonmetal each acid contains.

Background H_3O^+ ions are simply hydrated protons. It is these ions that are responsible for the acidic properties of a substance. It is convenient to simplify the dissociation equation for an acid by writing the H^+ ion instead of the H_3O^+ ion. Keep in mind, however, that it is H_3O^+ ions that are produced in aqueous solutions.

Teaching Tip Have students practice writing ionic equations for the dissociation of acids, such as HI, H_2CO_3, H_2SO_4, and HBr. The ionic equation for the dissociation of an acid, such as H_2SO_4 may be written in one stage or two.

$$H_2SO_4 \rightarrow 2H^+ + SO_4^{2-}$$

or

$$H_2SO_4 \rightarrow H^+ + HSO_4^-$$
$$HSO_4^- \rightarrow H^+ + SO_4^{2-}$$

Hydronium ions form in acid solutions. Acids are sometimes defined as substances that produce hydronium ions. However, it is the release of hydrogen ions that determines the behavior of acids. It is more convenient to discuss reactions of acids in terms of hydrogen ions.

Table 8-1 lists some common acids. Notice that all of these acids contain hydrogen. Acids also contain one or more nonmetals, such as chlorine. Acids usually do not contain metals.

When an acid dissolves in water, some of the units may not dissociate. Thus some acids produce more H^+ ions than do others. A *strong acid* is an acid that releases many hydrogen ions in water. Strong acids dissociate completely. Nitric acid, HNO_3, is a strong acid and dissociates as shown below.

$$HNO_3(aq) \rightarrow H^+(aq) + NO_3^-(aq)$$

Figure 8-1

What kind of acid is found in volcanic smoke (A), tomatoes (B), and rain (C)?[1]

Table 8-1 *Common Acids*

Name of Acid	Chemical Formula	Source
Acetic acid	CH_3COOH	Vinegar
Ascorbic acid (vitamin C)	$(CH_2COOH)_2COHCOOH$	Tomatoes, citrus fruits, vegetables
Carbonic acid	H_2CO_3	Rain water, soft drinks
Hydrochloric acid	HCl	Gastric juice in stomach
Sulfurous acid	H_2SO_3	Acid rain, volcanic smoke

[1]Sulfurous acid (A), ascorbic acid (B), and carbonic acid (C).

Figure 8-2

A corrosive acid will react with a metal.

One hundred HNO_3 units would produce 100 hydrogen ions and 100 nitrate ions, NO_3^-. There are very few strong acids. Hydrochloric acid and sulfuric acid are strong acids.

A *weak acid* produces few hydrogen ions in solution. Weak acids do not dissociate completely. Acetic acid, CH_3COOH, is a weak acid that dissociates as shown below.

$$CH_3COOH(aq) \rightarrow H^+(aq) + CH_3COO^-(aq)$$

One hundred of these molecules would produce about one hydrogen ion and one acetate ion, CH_3COO^-. The other 99 molecules would remain as CH_3COOH. Other common weak acids are carbonic acid and citric acid.

Some metals, such as zinc and iron, will react with acids and cause the release of hydrogen gas. This is a displacement reaction. The reaction between zinc and sulfuric acid is as follows.

$$Zn(s) + H_2SO_4(aq) \rightarrow ZnSO_4(aq) + H_2(g)$$

When metals react with an acid, they are corroded, or eaten away. A *corrosive* (kuh ROH sihv) *acid* is one that can eat away metals. Sulfuric acid, H_2SO_4, is an example of a corrosive acid. Its reaction with iron is shown in Figure 8-2. Citric acid is an example of an acid that is not corrosive. Would citric acid react with iron as shown in the figure?[1]

[1]No.

Background   The strongest acids are HCl, HNO_3, $HClO_4$, H_2SO_4, HBr, and HI. These acids may be considered 100 percent dissociated. Most other acids have varying degrees of dissociation, which is beyond the scope of this text. Strong acids are usually represented in their dissociation equations with one arrow, and weak acids use two arrows, as shown.
$$HCl \rightarrow H^+ + Cl^-$$
$$CH_3COOH \rightleftarrows H^+ + CH_3COO^-$$

Background   Because weak acids do not dissociate 100 percent, a certain amount of weak acid will produce fewer H^+ ions than will the same amount of strong acid.

Enrichment   Have students go to the library to find out how sulfuric acid is made commercially by the contact process and by the lead chamber process. Ask them to explain the differences in the acid produced by each method.

Tie-in/Social Studies   Sulfur-producing states in the United States are Texas and Louisiana. The sulfur is extracted from deep in the ground by a method called the Frasch process. Interested students may choose to further study this mining process and to build a model of the geologic structure from which the sulfur is extracted.

Figure 8-3

The etched glass has reacted with hydrofluoric acid.

Strong acids are very corrosive. Some weak acids also can be corrosive. For example, hydrofluoric acid, HF, is a weak but very corrosive acid. It will react with metals. This acid is so reactive that it will even react with glass. Hydrofluoric acid must be kept in plastic or wax-lined containers.

Acids are among the most useful chemicals known. Sulfuric acid is used more widely in industry than is any other chemical. Sulfuric acid is also called oil of vitriol (VIHT ree uhl) because it is a thick oily liquid. About 27 billion kilograms of sulfuric acid are produced in the United States each year. Sulfuric acid is used in the production of fertilizers, industrial chemicals, explosives, plastics, film, iron and steel.

Hydrochloric acid is another very important acid. It is prepared by combining hydrogen and chlorine gases to form hydrogen chloride gas.

$$H_2(g) + Cl_2(g) \rightarrow 2HCl(g)$$

The hydrogen chloride gas is then dissolved in water to make hydrochloric acid. Hydrochloric acid is used to remove rust and corrosion from metals by a process called pickling. The metal is placed in a large tank of hydrochloric acid. The acid attacks the corrosion and exposes the clean metal surface. Figure 8-4 shows steel being pickled. What do you think will happen if the metal is left in the acid too long?[1]

Figure 8-4

Pickling is an industrial process used to clean metals.

[1] The metal may be eaten away by the acid.

ACTIVITY   Which Acids Are Corrosive?

OBJECTIVE
Distinguish between corrosive and noncorrosive acids.

MATERIALS
safety goggles, lab apron, five 150-mL beakers, glass-marking pencil, 100-mL graduate, hydrochloric acid, mossy zinc, sulfuric acid, acetic acid, soda water, lemon juice.

PROCEDURE
A. Wear safety goggles and a lab apron during this activity.
B. Draw a data table like the one shown.
C. Label five beakers with the names of the acids to be used in this activity.
D. **Caution:** Acids can burn your eyes, skin, and clothing. If any acid spills on your skin or clothing, wash thoroughly with running water. Measure 25 mL of hydrochloric acid and pour it into the beaker labeled *hydrochloric acid*.
E. Carefully place one piece of mossy zinc into the beaker containing the hydrochloric acid. Record your observations.
F. Repeat steps **D** and **E** for the remaining four solutions.

G. Dispose of the chemicals according to your teacher's directions.

Name of Acid	Reaction Observed	Change in Metal

RESULTS AND CONCLUSIONS
1. Which acids reacted with the zinc?
2. Which acids did not react with the zinc?
3. Which acids are corrosive?
4. Write a balanced equation for each reaction that involved a corrosive acid.

EXTENSION
Place a rusty nail in a 150-mL beaker. Pour 25 mL of dilute hydrochloric acid over the nail. Explain what happens.

Ascorbic acid is vitamin C. This acid is found in tomatoes and citrus fruits. The human body needs vitamin C to maintain healthy bones and teeth and to aid healing. Without enough vitamin C, a disease called scurvy develops. This disease causes swollen bleeding gums, easy bruising, and slow healing. Many years ago, sailors who had been at sea for months would develop scurvy because they lacked fresh fruits and vegetables. This problem was solved by having citrus fruits available for the sailors.

REVIEW

1. What is an acid?
2. Name three properties of acids.
3. How are strong acids different from weak acids?
4. Name two acids, and give one use of each in industry.

CHALLENGE Sulfurous acid, H_2SO_3, is a weak acid that dissociates in two steps. Write equations to represent the first and second dissociation reactions of H_2SO_3.

---

3 REVIEW/REINFORCEMENT

1. An acid is a substance that releases hydrogen ions when it dissociates.
2. Traits include sour taste; corrosive; produce H^+ ions in water solution; may form H_2 when reacting with some metals; conduct electricity.
3. Strong acids dissociate completely; weak acids do not dissociate completely.
4. Sulfuric acid: uses include production of fertilizers, industrial chemicals, and explosives. Hydrochloric acid: used to remove rust and corrosion from metals.

Challenge
$H_2SO_3 \rightarrow H^+ + HSO_3^-$
$HSO_3^- \rightarrow H^+ + SO_3^{2-}$

8-2 PROPERTIES OF BASES

pages 190–192

OBJECTIVES
Refer to pupil page 190.

VOCABULARY
Key terms: base, hydroxide ion
Other terms: caustic, strong bases, weak bases

1 MOTIVATION

Ask a student to bring a sample of his or her hair to class the day before beginning this lesson. Place the hair in a beaker and pour lye over it. Label the beaker with the student's name. When the lesson begins, ask students what happened to the hair and what caused such a reaction. Ask them if they would wash their hair in this substance. Place a card in front of the beaker labeled *sodium hydroxide—a base—an ingredient in soap*. Ask students what is surprising about this label. Caution: NaOH is very caustic; handle it with care.

2 CONCEPT DEVELOPMENT

Teaching Tip   Students learned in Section 8-1 that acids usually do not contain metals. Since bases are often thought of as the chemical opposites of acids, students will not be surprised to discover that bases usually contain metals.

Background   There are a few compounds, such as aluminum and zinc hydroxides, that have both slightly acidic properties and slightly basic properties; these substances are called amphoteric.

After completing this section, you will be able to

- **list** some properties of bases.
- **distinguish** between strong bases and weak bases.
- **describe** the uses of some common bases.

The key terms in this section are
base   hydroxide ion

[1]Ammonium hydroxide.

Table 8-2 *Common Bases*

Name of Base	Chemical Formula
Ammonium hydroxide	NH_4OH
Calcium hydroxide	$Ca(OH)_2$
Potassium hydroxide	KOH
Sodium hydroxide	$NaOH$

Bases are another important group of compounds. Like acids, bases are widely used in the laboratory and in industry. They are used to make soap and other household cleaners. Bases are also used in making fertilizers, explosives, and petroleum products.

Bases are sometimes thought of as the chemical opposites of acids. Recall that acids release H^+ ions in solution. A **base** is a substance that releases hydroxide ions, OH^-, in solution. A **hydroxide** (hī DRAHK sīd) **ion** contains one oxygen atom and one hydrogen atom. Notice that there is a hydroxide group in the chemical formula for each base listed in Table 8-2. Bases usually have a metal in their chemical formulas. What base in Table 8-2 does not contain a metal?[1]

When bases dissociate, they produce positive ions and negative hydroxide ions. When sodium hydroxide dissolves in water, it dissociates as follows.

$$NaOH(s) \rightarrow Na^+(aq) + OH^-(aq)$$

Some bases produce more OH^- ions than others. Bases that dissociate to produce many OH^- ions are called *strong bases*. Metals in Groups 1 and 2 of the Periodic Table generally form strong bases. A Group 1 or 2 metal forms a strong base because the ionic bond between the metal and the OH^- ion is weaker than most ionic bonds. When the compound dissolves in water, the ionic bond is not strong enough to hold the metal ion and the OH^- ion together, so the compound dissociates. Sodium hydroxide, NaOH, and potassium hydroxide, KOH, are examples of strong bases. Figure 8-5 shows the dissociation of potassium hydroxide in water. Notice that all units of the base are dissociated.

Weak bases do not produce many hydroxide ions in water solution. Aluminum hydroxide, $Al(OH)_3$, is a weak base. It does not dissociate well, and produces very few OH^- ions.

$$Al(OH)_3(s) \rightarrow Al^{3+}(aq) + 3OH^-(aq)$$

For each aluminum ion produced there will be three hydroxide ions produced. Although each unit of aluminum hydroxide produces three OH^- ions, very few of the $Al(OH)_3$ units dissolve. Thus the total amount of OH^- ions is small. Other weak bases are magnesium hydroxide, $Mg(OH)_2$; zinc hydroxide, $Zn(OH)_2$; and ammonium hydroxide, NH_4OH.

Figure 8-5

A strong base produces many OH ions in solution.

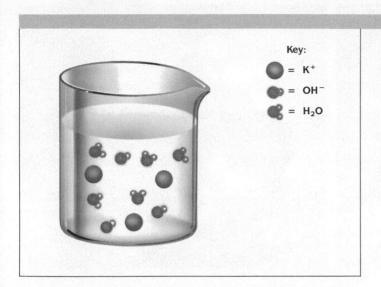

Key:

= K⁺

= OH⁻

= H₂O

Bases have certain properties by which they can be identified. They taste bitter, feel slippery, and conduct electricity. Bases also dissolve fats and oils. Lye, which is a solution of sodium hydroxide, is used to clean drains that are clogged with grease. The sodium hydroxide converts the grease clog into a substance that dissolves in water and washes down the drain.

Some bases are *caustic* (KAW stihk). They eat away certain substances and are irritating or damaging to the skin. Sodium hydroxide is a caustic base. Many products that contain sodium hydroxide have labels that warn about the caustic behavior of the base. Look at the label shown in Figure 8-6. What are the dangers of using this product?[1]

[1]It is harmful or fatal if swallowed. It causes severe burns.

Figure 8-6

Products that contain caustic substances must be used with care.

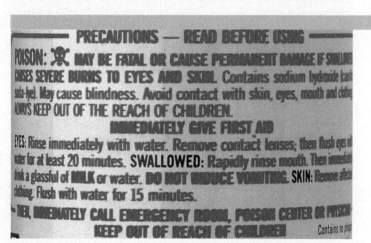

PRECAUTIONS — READ BEFORE USING

POISON: ☠ MAY BE FATAL OR CAUSE PERMANENT DAMAGE IF SWALLOWED. CAUSES SEVERE BURNS TO EYES AND SKIN. Contains sodium hydroxide (caustic soda-lye). May cause blindness. Avoid contact with skin, eyes, mouth and clothing. ALWAYS KEEP OUT OF THE REACH OF CHILDREN.

IMMEDIATELY GIVE FIRST AID

EYES: Rinse immediately with water. Remove contact lenses; then flush eyes with water for at least 20 minutes. SWALLOWED: Rapidly rinse mouth. Then immediately drink a glassful of MILK or water. DO NOT INDUCE VOMITING. SKIN: Remove affected clothing. Flush with water for 15 minutes.

THEN, IMMEDIATELY CALL EMERGENCY ROOM, POISON CENTER OR PHYSICIAN. KEEP OUT OF REACH OF CHILDREN   Contains no phosphates

Thinking Skills

predicting
Strong and weak bases differ in the extent to which they dissociate in solution. Have students compare the behavior of strong and weak bases and then predict what Figure 8-5 would look like if it showed a weak base.

Teaching Tip   Caution students that even though bases are described as tasting bitter and feeling slippery they should never be tested that way.

Thinking Skills

inferring
A compound has a bitter taste, dissolves grease, and dissociates slightly in water to produce Mg⁺ ions. Using the properties listed, students can infer whether the compound is acidic or basic and can identify the compound.

Teaching Tip   Remind students of the hair-dissolving demonstration at the beginning of the lesson. Explain that lye (sodium hydroxide, NaOH) is caustic and will dissolve tissues. It is harmful or fatal if swallowed. It can cause severe burns. Many products containing sodium hydroxide have warning labels. However, sodium hydroxide also dissolves grease. Therefore, small quantities of caustic soda (lye) are used with fat to make soap.

Background Rayon is a synthetic yarn that is made from cellulose. Cellulose is obtained from wood pulp or from cotton fibers. NaOH is used as a soaking solution for the cellulose to remove unwanted pulp material.

Tie-in/Social Studies The first person to see the possibility of making an artificial fiber by a process similar to the spinning of a silkworm was Robert Hooke, an English scientist. Have interested students research the history of synthetic fibers and share the information with the class.

Enrichment Have students research how soap is made and how soaps differ from one another. Students could bring in varieties of soaps and create a display.

3 REVIEW/REINFORCEMENT

1. A base is a substance that releases hydroxide ions, or OH⁻ ions, in solution.
2. Bases taste bitter, feel slippery, and conduct electricity. They also dissolve fats and oils; some are caustic.
3. A strong base produces many hydroxide ions; a weak base produces few.
4. Sodium hydroxide: production of rayon, paper, detergents, and soap. Ammonium hydroxide: production of rubber, fertilizers, and ink. Answers may vary.

Challenge Use a weak base. It would remove stains from clothing without damaging the cloth. Weak bases do not dissociate readily and, therefore, would not dissolve the grease. A stronger base—one that produces many hydroxide ions—is needed to clear a clogged drain.

Figure 8-7

Sodium hydroxide is used in the production of rayon, a synthetic fiber.

Like acids, bases have many uses. Sodium hydroxide is used to make the rayon shown in Figure 8-7. It is also used in the production of paper, detergents, and soap. Petroleum and vegetable oil refining involve the use of sodium hydroxide. The food industry uses sodium hydroxide to remove the peel from fruits and vegetables.

Ammonium hydroxide is a base that is used in the manufacture of many substances, including rubber, fertilizers, and ink. The cleaning product that is sold as ammonia is a solution of ammonium hydroxide in water.

Because bases are used in the making of soap, many household products contain bases. Read the labels on some of the cleaning products used in your home. Look for chemical names that include *hydroxide*. Which products contain bases?[1]

¹Students may list detergents, household cleaners, drain cleaners.

REVIEW

1. What is a base?
2. Name three properties of bases.
3. What is the difference between a strong base and a weak base?
4. Name two common bases used in industry, and describe their uses.

CHALLENGE Bases dissolve fats and oils. Would you use a weak base or a strong base to remove a grease stain from your clothes? Could you use this same solution to clear a clogged drain? Explain your answer.

8-3 INDICATORS

Recall that acids and bases dissociate as they dissolve in water. Water molecules also can dissociate into ions. The equation for this reaction is as follows.

$$H_2O(l) \rightarrow H^+(aq) + OH^-(aq)$$

This reaction takes place in pure water and in solutions. In pure water very few molecules dissociate. Notice that a water molecule can produce one hydrogen ion and one hydroxide ion. Thus water is neither an acid nor a base and is said to be a *neutral substance*.

If the numbers of H^+ and OH^- ions are not equal in a water solution, the solution is not neutral. If there are more H^+ ions than OH^- ions, the solution is acidic. If there are more OH^- ions than H^+ ions, the solution is basic. Look at Figure 8-8. Identify the acidic, basic, and neutral solutions.[1]

After completing this section, you will be able to

- **explain** how the acidity of a solution can be expressed using the pH scale.
- **interpret** pH values in terms of ion concentrations.
- **describe** how indicators measure the pH of a solution.

The key terms in this section are
concentration   pH scale
indicator

[1]A is neutral.   B is acidic.
C is basic.

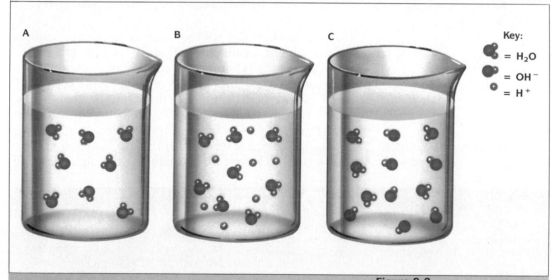

A   B   C   Key:
                                  = H_2O
                                  = OH^-
                                  = H^+

Figure 8-8

The relative amounts of H^+ and OH^- ions determine if a solution is acidic, basic, or neutral.

The amount of any ion present in a solution is called its **concentration** (kahn sehn TRAY shuhn). The concentration tells how much of a substance has dissolved in a solution. Do not confuse concentration with strength. Remember that strength refers to how much the compound dissociates. An acid can be concentrated and weak at the same time. For example, concentrated acetic acid contains many dissolved molecules of CH_3COOH, but very few of these molecules dissociate in water.

con (with)
centrum (center)

OBJECTIVES
Refer to pupil page 193.

VOCABULARY
Key terms: concentration, indicator, pH scale
Other terms: litmus, neutral substance

1 MOTIVATION

Place 25 mL of 0.1M HCl in a petri dish on an overhead projector. Exhibit bottles of the indicators phenolphthalein, bromothymol blue, and methyl red. Note the indicators' colors. Add two drops of each to the HCl. Drop by drop, stir in 0.1M NaOH. The indicators will change colors at different pH levels. Repeat using a piece of blue litmus. Litmus will turn red and then change to blue. Have students discuss the color changes.

2 CONCEPT DEVELOPMENT

Background   Water dissociates very slightly. Only one water molecule in every 500 million dissociates into a H^+ ion and an OH^- ion. Water can act as either an acid or a base, depending upon the circumstances.

Teaching Tip   Show students some reagent bottles with varying concentration labels. Explain that the smaller the number, the more dilute the solution. Solution concentrations can be expressed as a percentage, (moles per 1000 cm^3) molality, (moles per 1000 g) or normality (in terms of a fixed standard).

Transparency

The Teacher Resource Package includes a color transparency and a black-line master of Figure 8-8. You may wish to use these in your discussion of acids and bases.

Thinking Skills

interpreting diagrams
Students are asked to identify the nature of each substance shown in Figure 8-9. Have students identify the substances that are acidic and those that are basic.

Teaching Tip   Interpret Figure 8-8 for the class. A substance with a low pH has more H^+ ions than OH^- ions. A substance with a high pH has less H^+ ions and more OH^- ions.

Demonstration   Use a conductivity tester (available commercially) to show that distilled water is a nonconductor because it dissociates very little. Then slowly add a small amount of dilute $CaCl_2$ solution to illustrate how minerals cause water to become a conductor.

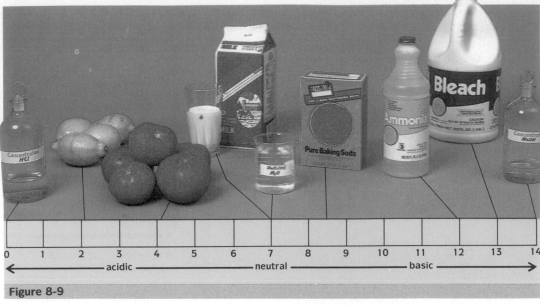

Figure 8-9

The pH scale.

The acidity of a solution can be expressed using a scale of numbers called the pH scale. The **pH scale** gives a measure of the H^+ ion concentration of a solution. This scale ranges from 0 to 14. An acid has a pH between 0 and 7, with 0 being the pH of the strongest acid. A base has a pH between 7 and 14, with 14 being the strongest base. Pure water, which is neither an acid nor a base, has a pH of 7. Figure 8-9 shows the pH scale. Which substance shown has the lowest pH? Which has the highest pH?[1]

[1]Hydrochloric acid; sodium hydroxide

DO YOU KNOW?

The sandbox tree grows in tropical regions of Central and South America. This tree is tall, sometimes reaching a height of 36 m. Its toothed leaves form a crown around the fruit at the top of the tree. The trunk is covered with short, stiff spines.

Inside the tree is a white caustic sap. This sap is basic and is harmful to the skin and eyes. The people who cut down these trees wear heavy gloves to protect their hands. They must also wear face shields, because the sap can cause blindness if it gets in someone's eyes.

In spite of its caustic nature, the sap has found an odd use. People mix sand with the sap, and throw it into lakes and streams. The mixture stuns fish, which are then caught. Surprisingly, fish caught in this manner do not seem to cause any problems for the people who eat them.

It is important for a scientist to know the pH of solutions. Some chemical reactions take place only in an acid solution. Other reactions take place only in a basic solution. Many reactions can be controlled by controlling the pH of the solutions in which they take place.

The pH of a solution can be measured accurately in the laboratory with a pH meter. What is the pH of the solution being tested in Figure 8-10? Is it an acid or a base? Does this solution contain more H^+ or OH^- ions?[1]

If a pH meter is not available, substances called indicators may be used to find the approximate pH of a solution. An **indicator** is a compound that changes color as the concentration of H^+ or OH^- ions changes. These compounds are sensitive to small changes in ion concentrations. *Litmus* (LIHT muhs) is an indicator that is blue in basic solutions and red in acidic solutions. Litmus paper may be placed in a solution in order to find the pH of that solution.

Other indicators are shown in Table 8-3. Notice that each indicator changes color at a different pH. How many color ranges does methyl red have? At what pH does phenol red change from orange to red?[2] Scientists often use more than one indicator to identify the pH of a solution.

Figure 8-10

A pH meter is an accurate laboratory tool.

indicare (to say)

[1] 10.5; base; OH^- ions.
[2] Three; approximately 8.0.

Background   The pH meter is an instrument that measures the difference in electrical potential between two electrodes— a reference electrode and an indicating electrode. The indicating electrode responds to changes in hydrogen ion concentrations.

Demonstration   Use a pH meter to determine the pH of dilute solutions of milk, tap water, baking soda, and apple juice.

Background   Litmus is an organic dye produced by lichen plants. The organic molecule contains a proton, which makes it an acid. The acid molecule is red. If the molecule loses its proton, it becomes a base and turns blue.

Table 8-3 *Indicators*

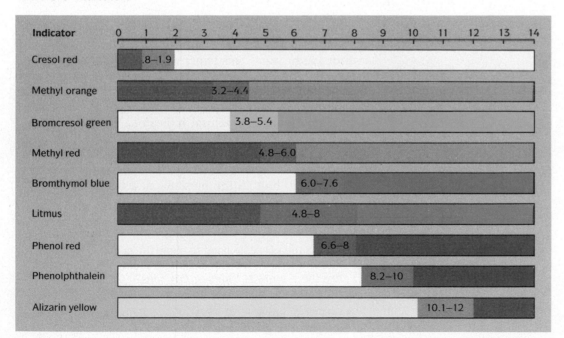

Review and Skill Masters

SKILL, pages 50–51. See page 183b–c in this book for answers.

Poster

The Teacher Resource Package includes a poster that shows pH indicators. You may wish to display this poster in your classroom.

ACTIVITY 30-40 minutes

PROCESS SKILLS
observing, classifying, inferring

Preparation   To prepare the red-cabbage indicator solution, shred a red cabbage. Stir the cabbage into 1 L of boiling distilled water, then cool. To prepare 0.1M HCl, add 9 mL of concentrated HCl to 100 mL of distilled water in a 1-L graduate. Add distilled water to reach the 1-L mark. To prepare 0.1M NaOH, weigh 4 g of NaOH pellets. Add to a 1-L graduate. Add distilled water to reach the 1-L mark, then mix until dissolved. To prepare 0.1M NH_4OH, place 100 mL of distilled water in a 1-L graduate. Add 7 mL of concentrated NH_4OH. Add distilled water to reach the 1-L mark.

Safety Tip   Wear safety goggles when preparing HCl, NH_4OH, and NaOH solutions. Do not touch NaOH pellets with your fingers.

Answers to Results and Conclusions
1. HCl, vinegar, lemon juice.
2. NaOH, tea, ammonia, laundry detergent.
3. Purple — it is purple in distilled water.
4. No. It doesn't have sharp color changes.

Extension   Litmus would be red in acids and blue in bases.
Answers for data table
NaOH—colorless, blue; HCl—colorless, pink; H_2O—colorless, purple; tea—yellow, blue-green; lemon—yellow, pink; ammonia—colorless, blue; vinegar—colorless, pink; detergent—white, blue (will vary)

3 REVIEW/REINFORCEMENT

1. The pH scale gives a measure of the H^+ ion concentration of a solution. An acid has a pH between 0 and 7.
2. Basic. More OH^- ions.
3. Change color as the concentration of H^+ or OH^- ions changes.

Challenge   Between 4.8 and 5.4.

ACTIVITY   How Can You Identify Acids and Bases?

OBJECTIVE
Determine whether a solution is an acid or a base.

MATERIALS
safety goggles, lab apron, glass-marking pencil, eight 50-mL beakers, 100-mL graduate, sodium hydroxide solution, red-cabbage indicator solution, dropper, hydrochloric acid, distilled water, tea, lemon juice, ammonia water, white vinegar, liquid laundry detergent

PROCEDURE
A. Wear safety goggles and a lab apron during this activity.
B. Draw a data table like the one shown.
C. Label eight beakers with the names of the chemicals to be tested in this activity.
D. **Caution:** If any chemicals spill on your skin or clothing, wash thoroughly with running water. Measure 25 mL of sodium hydroxide (NaOH), and pour the solution into the properly labeled beaker. Record in your data table the color of the solution.
E. Add 5 drops of red-cabbage indicator to the NaOH solution. NaOH is a strong base. Record the color change of the indicator.
F. Repeat steps **D** and **E**, using hydrochloric acid (HCl). HCl is a strong acid. Record the color change of the indicator.
G. Repeat steps **D** and **E** using the remaining six liquids.

Chemical	Color Before Indicator	Color After Indicator

RESULTS AND CONCLUSIONS
1. Which solutions are acids?
2. Which solutions are bases?
3. What color do you think the red-cabbage indicator would be in a neutral solution? Explain your answer.
4. Would red-cabbage indicator be good enough to use as an indicator in the laboratory?

EXTENSION
Repeat the activity, using litmus paper as the indicator.

Another way to find the pH of a solution is to use pH paper. Strips of paper are coated with mixtures of various indicators. This paper will give pH values that are accurate to 0.1 on the pH scale. Different pH ranges can be measured, depending upon the mixture of indicators in the paper.

Some foods are natural indicators. Juice from blueberries, beets, carrots, grapes, or red cabbage will change color depending on the pH of a solution. For example, red cabbage is a natural indicator. Red-cabbage juice turns from pink to blue in the presence of a base.

REVIEW

1. How is the pH scale used to show the acidity of a solution?
2. If a solution has a pH of 12, is the solution acidic or basic? Are there more H^+ ions or OH^- ions?
3. How do indicators show the pH of a solution?

CHALLENGE What is the pH of a solution in which Bromcresol green is green and methyl red is red-orange?

8-4 REACTIONS OF ACIDS AND BASES

An acid contains more H^+ ions than OH^- ions. A base contains more OH^- ions than H^+ ions. If an acid and a base are mixed, extra H^+ ions from the acid will combine with extra OH^- ions from the base. The equation for this reaction is as follows.

$$H^+(aq) + OH^-(aq) \rightarrow H_2O(l)$$

The product of this reaction is water, a neutral substance. The reaction between an acid and a base is called **neutralization** (noo truh luh ZAY shuhn). If the number of H^+ ions from the acid equals the number of OH^- ions from the base, neutralization will be complete. There will be no extra H^+ or OH^- ions.

If a base is added to an acid, a neutralization reaction will take place. If there are more H^+ ions from the acid than OH^- ions from the base, all the OH^- ions will be combined with H^+ ions. The solution will still contain some H^+ ions. Thus the solution will still be acidic.

Suppose a base is added to an acid and there are OH^- ions left in the solution after neutralization. Will the solution be acidic, basic, or neutral?[1]

Figure 8-11 shows the reaction that takes place when hydrochloric acid, HCl, and potassium hydroxide, KOH, are mixed. Notice that the H^+ and OH^- ions form a water molecule. What happens to the Cl^- ion from the acid and the K^+ ion from the base? If the water is evaporated, these ions will form potassium chloride, a salt. Neutralization reactions produce water and a salt.

> After completing this section, you will be able to
>
> - **identify** the products of a neutralization reaction.
> - **state** properties of salts.
> - **describe** how anhydrides form acids and bases.
> - **determine** which metals will release hydrogen from an acid solution.
>
> *The key terms in this section are*
> acid anhydride
> basic anhydride
> neutralization
> salt

[1]Basic.

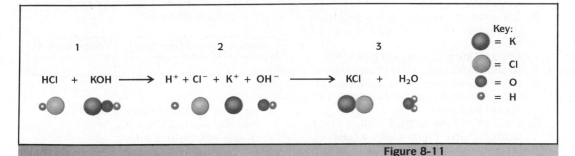

1	2	3	Key:
HCl + KOH $\longrightarrow$	$H^+ + Cl^- + K^+ + OH^- \longrightarrow$	KCl + H_2O	= K = Cl = O = H

Figure 8-11

The products of a neutralization reaction are water and a salt.

A **salt** is a compound formed from the positive metal ions of a base and the negative nonmetal ions of an acid. Most salts are ionic compounds. Recall that an ionic bond is formed when an atom gives its outer electrons to another atom. Ionic bonds are strong bonds. They hold the positive

OBJECTIVES
Refer to pupil page 197.

VOCABULARY
Key terms: acid anhydride, basic anhydride, neutralization, salt
Other terms: crystal

1 MOTIVATION

Set up a conductivity tester (available commercially). Place 150 mL of 0.1M $Ba(OH)_2$ in a 250-mL beaker. Add two drops of bromothymol blue indicator. Fill a 25-mL burette with 0.1M H_2SO_4. Place the electrodes of the tester in the $Ba(OH)_2$. Drop by drop, slowly add H_2SO_4. Students will observe the light changing from bright to dim to no light to dim to bright. The mixture will change in color from blue to green (no light) to yellow. Discuss with students what reaction is taking place and why the light intensity changes. Students should be able to conclude that varying amounts of free ions are being produced during the chemical reaction.

2 CONCEPT DEVELOPMENT

Background   One H^+ from an acid will neutralize one OH^- ion from a base. If the acid and base are both strong, a neutral salt solution will be formed. If one or both are weak, the resulting salt solution may be slightly acidic or slightly basic or neutral, depending upon the strengths of the starting acid and base.

Thinking Skills

interpreting diagrams

Ask students whether a salt is present if the water in Figure 8-11 did not evaporate. They should infer that the KCl is soluble in the water and that the K^+ and Cl^- ions are present and moving freely. The salt forms when these ions attract one another to create an ionic bond. Ask students if the solution will be acidic, basic, or neutral when a base is added to an acid and there are OH^- ions left after neutralization. (Basic.)

Background The Latin word for "salt" is *sal*. Salt was so valuable in ancient times that Roman soldiers used to be paid in salt. The word *salary* comes from the Latin word for "salt."

ACTIVITY two 30-minute periods

PROCESS SKILLS
observing, interpreting charts

Preparation Each student group will need one 100-mL graduate, one 100-mL beaker, 5 strips of pH paper, two 250-mL beakers, one glass stirring rod, one piece of filter paper, one funnel, and one straw. Prepare 0.1M HCl by adding 9 mL of concentrated HCl to 100 mL of distilled water in a 1-L graduate. Add distilled water to reach the 1-L mark, and mix thoroughly. Then pour the solution into a labeled reagent bottle. Prepare 0.1M NaOH by adding 4g of NaOH pellets to 100 mL of distilled water in a 1-L graduate. Add distilled water to reach the 1-L mark. Stir until all the NaOH is dissolved, and pour the solution into labeled dropper bottles. Place the labeled reagent bottles on the lab table.

Safety Tip Wear safety goggles when preparing HCl and NaOH solutions. When diluting the HCl, add the acid to the water; never add water to a concentrated acid. Handle the NaOH pellets with forceps.

---

and negative ions of a salt together in a *crystal*. Crystals have definite shapes, such as the shape of the sodium chloride crystals shown in Figure 8-12. The shapes of crystals aid in identifying substances.

Many salt crystals are soluble in water. They dissolve in water because the water molecules attract the ions that are present in the crystal. Salts dissociate as they dissolve in water.

$$NaCl(s) \rightarrow Na^+ \,(aq) + Cl^- \,(aq)$$

$$MgBr_2(s) \rightarrow Mg^{2+} \,(aq) + 2Br^- \,(aq)$$

ACTIVITY What Happens In a Neutralization Reaction?

OBJECTIVE
Demonstrate that mixing an acid and a base results in a neutral solution.

MATERIALS
safety goggles, lab apron, l00-mL graduate, hydrochloric acid, l00-mL beaker, pH paper, bromthymol blue, sodium hydroxide solution, distilled water, two 250-mL beakers, glass stirring rod, calcium oxide, filter paper, funnel, drinking straw

PROCEDURE
A. Wear safety goggles and a lab apron throughout this activity.
B. Draw a data table like the one shown.
C. Measure I5 mL of hydrochloric acid (HCl) into a l00-mL beaker.
D. Use a strip of pH paper to find the pH of the solution. Record the result in your data table.
E. Add 2 drops of bromthymol blue to the solution. Record the color of the solution.
F. Use a strip of pH paper to find the pH of the sodium hydroxide solution (NaOH). Record your result.
G. Carefully add the NaOH, 1 drop at a time, to the HCl until 1 drop causes a color change. Record the color of the solution. Use a strip of pH paper to find the pH of the solution. Record your result.
   1. Write the balanced equation for this chemical reaction.
H. Measure 100 mL of distilled water, and pour it into a 250-mL beaker.

I. While stirring, slowly add calcium oxide, CaO, until the powder stops dissolving.
   2. Write the balanced equation for this chemical reaction.
J. Fold a piece of filter paper as shown by your teacher. Place the paper in the funnel, and support the funnel in a ring stand. Place a 250-mL beaker below the funnel.
K. Pour the solution from step I through the filter paper. With a strip of pH paper, find the pH of the filtered solution. Record your result. Add 2 drops of bromthymol blue to the solution.
L. With a clean drinking straw, blow into the solution for 1 minute. Record your observations. Find the pH of the solution, and record your result.
   3. Write the balanced equation for this chemical reaction.

Solution	pH	Color Change	Observations

RESULTS AND CONCLUSIONS
1. Why was bromthymol blue selected as the indicator in step **E**? How did the color change with different pH's?
2. What kind of reaction occurred in step **G**?
3. What color was the pH paper in the CaO solution?
4. What type of substance is CaO?
5. What type of solution was formed in step **I**?
6. What two methods were used in this activity to prepare salts?

198

Ions from salts move freely in solution. These ions can conduct electricity. Tap water contains ions from dissolved salts. Therefore, tap water can conduct electricity. That is why electrical appliances often have labels to warn you not to get the appliance wet. If you placed the appliance in water while the electricity was on, you would get a serious shock. Distilled water does not conduct electricity. However, if distilled water is spilled, it may absorb ions from the surface on which it is spilled. The water would no longer be pure. It would conduct electricity.

You may have heard people talk about the effects of acid rain. In parts of North America, acid rain is said to be causing buildings, statues, and cars to corrode. Crop damage and the death of fish in some lakes and streams are also said to be caused by acid rain.

Fuels such as coal and petroleum often contain impurities such as sulfur. When these fuels are burned, sulfur oxide and nitrogen oxide are formed. When released into the air, these oxides combine with water in the air to form acids. Eventually these acids fall to the earth as rain.

Acid rain is formed from acid anhydrides. An **acid anhydride** (an HĪ drīd) is an oxide of a nonmetal that forms an acid when the oxide is mixed with water. *Anhydride* means "without water," so an acid anhydride may be thought of as an acid without water. For example, sulfur trioxide, which is produced by burning coal, is an acid anhydride. Sulfur trioxide combines with water to form sulfuric acid. The equation for this reaction is as follows.

$$SO_3(g) + H_2O(l) \rightarrow H_2SO_4(aq)$$

Figure 8-12

Sodium chloride, NaCl, is a common salt.

Figure 8-13

Acid rain probably caused some of this damage.

199

Tie-in/Language Arts Have students research the word parts of the word *anhydride*.

Teaching Tip Read about basic anhydrides in additional resources. Give examples of basic anhydrides, such as Na_2O, MgO, K_2O. Have students practice writing chemical equations between basic anhydrides and water. Discuss neutralization reactions between acid anhydrides and bases, and between basic anhydrides and acids. Use NaOH and SO_2, MgO and H_2SO_4, and KOH and SO_3.

Teaching Tip After students have read the section about acid rain, have them consider what chemical reaction might take place between acid rain and a car. ($2Fe + 3H_2SO_4 \rightarrow Fe_2(SO_4)_3 + 3H_2$) Continue with the reaction that might take place between a building and acid rain. ($CaCO_3 + H_2SO_4 \rightarrow CaSO_4 + H_2O + CO_2$)

Thinking Skills

predicting
Ask students to predict the formula of the salt formed when sodium oxide and sulfur dioxide react. (Na_2SO_3) Have them predict whether platinum will release hydrogen from dilute acid. (No; it is chemically similar to gold.) Refer students to Table 8-4 and ask which metals will not release hydrogen from dilute acid. (Cu, Hg, Ag, Au)

Puzzler Rain water usually contains dissolved CO_2, which makes the water acidic. When this water comes in contact with rock such as limestone, the $CaCO_3$ in the rock dissolves and forms $Ca(HCO_3)_2$, which is slightly basic. As the water evaporates, the pH goes toward neutral.

Review and Skill Masters

CHALLENGE/CRITICAL THINKING, page 52. See page 183c in this book for answers.

SCIENCE PUZZLER

A quarry is an area where stone is cut or mined. Sometimes rain water fills in the quarry after the stone has been removed. The pH of the water will become either acidic or basic, depending on the type of rock in the quarry. Why does the pH of the water change?

[1]The end products of both reactions are water and salt.

Table 8-4 *Activity Series*

Symbol	Name	Activity
K	Potassium	High
Ca	Calcium	
Na	Sodium	
Mg	Magnesium	
Al	Aluminum	
Zn	Zinc	
Cr	Chromium	
Fe	Iron	
Ni	Nickel	
Sn	Tin	
Pb	Lead	
H	Hydrogen	
Cu	Copper	
Hg	Mercury	
Ag	Silver	
Au	Gold	Low

Carbon dioxide is another example of an acid anhydride. Carbonic acid is formed when carbon dioxide in the air combines with water.

An oxide of a metal is a **basic anhydride**. Such a compound forms a base when added to water, so a basic anhydride may be thought of as a base without water. Calcium oxide, or lime, is a basic anhydride. Lime is an important chemical in industry. It is used in sewage treatment, food processing, and sugar refining.

As with acids and bases, neutralization reactions can take place between acid anhydrides and basic anhydrides. For example, lime is often used to neutralize soils that are too acidic. The neutralization between calcium oxide and carbonic acid in soil is shown below.

$$CaO(s) + H_2CO_3(aq) \rightarrow CaCO_3(aq) + H_2O(l)$$

How are the products of this reaction similar to the products of a neutralization between an acid and a base?[1]

One of the properties of acids is that they react with certain metals. Whether a reaction will take place depends on the type of acid and on the place of the metal in the activity series shown in Table 8-4. Metals that are higher in the table than hydrogen react with acids like HCl and dilute H_2SO_4 to form hydrogen gas and a salt. The reaction is a typical single replacement reaction.

$$Zn(s) + H_2SO_4(aq) \rightarrow ZnSO_4(aq) + H_2(g)$$

Under different conditions the reaction will yield other products. Zinc reacts with hot concentrated sulfuric acid to yield a salt, hydrogen sulfide gas, and water. This reaction is more complex than a single replacement reaction.

$$4Zn(s) + 5H_2SO_4(aq) \rightarrow 4ZnSO_4(aq) + H_2S(g) + 4H_2O(l)$$

Hot concentrated sulfuric acid will also react with metals below hydrogen in the activity table. The reaction between copper and hot concentrated sulfuric acid yields a salt, sulfur dioxide gas, and water.

$$Cu(s) + 2H_2SO_4(aq) \rightarrow CuSO_4(aq) + SO_2(g) + 2H_2O(l)$$

REVIEW

1. Name two compounds that are formed when an acid and a base react.
2. Name three properties of salts.
3. Explain how an acid is formed from an anhydride.
4. Which of the following metals will react with HCl to release hydrogen: copper, potassium, lead, or gold?

CHALLENGE   Write a balanced equation to show the reaction between magnesium oxide and hydrochloric acid. What type of reaction is this?

CHAPTER SUMMARY

The main ideas in this chapter are listed below. Read these statements before you answer the Chapter Review questions.

- An acid gives off hydrogen ions in water. (8-1)

- Acids taste sour, react with some metals to give off hydrogen, and conduct electricity in solution. (8-1)

- A base gives off hydroxide ions in water. (8-2)

- Bases taste bitter, feel slippery, conduct electricity in solution, and dissolve fats and oils. (8-2)

- Water molecules dissociate into equal numbers of H^+ ions and OH^- ions, so water is a neutral substance. (8-3)

- Solutions with more H^+ ions than OH^- ions are acidic. Solutions with more OH^- ions than H^+ ions are basic. (8-3)

- pH is a measure of the H^+ ion concentration in a solution. (8-3)

- An indicator is a compound that changes color as the concentration of H^+ or OH^- ions changes. (8-3)

- Neutralization is a reaction between an acid and a base, producing water and a salt. (8-4)

- A salt is formed from the positive metal ions of a base and from the negative nonmetal ions of an acid. (8-4)

- An anhydride is an oxide that forms an acid or a base when it reacts with water. (8-4)

- Acids react with metals that are more active than hydrogen to form hydrogen gas and a salt. (8-4)

The key terms in this chapter are listed below. Use each term in a sentence that shows the meaning of the term.

acid	basic anhydride	hydroxide ion	pH scale
acid anhydride	concentration	indicator	salt
base	hydronium ion	neutralization	

Background   Look at the chemical reactions on pages 200 and 201; these reactions use hot concentrated sulfuric acid. Explain that hot concentrated H_2SO_4 is a powerful oxidizing agent. It will cause the zinc and copper to lose electrons quickly, which will enable the S^{6+} to gain electrons quickly in forming compounds that contain S^{2-} or S^{4+} and H_2O.

3 REVIEW/REINFORCEMENT

1. A salt and water.
2. Traits include salty taste; ionic compound; soluble in water; conductor of electricity in water solution; crystalline in solid state.
3. A nonmetallic oxide reacts with water.
4. K, Pb.

Challenge $MgO + 2HCl \rightarrow MgCl_2 + H_2O$; neutralization.

Review and Skill Masters

VOCABULARY REVIEW, page 47.
See page 183b in this book for answers.

VOCABULARY

1. True
2. Neutralization
3. Acids
4. True
5. True
6. True
7. True
8. Hydronium ions
9. True
10. True

CONCEPTS

1. Taste sour, react with some metals to produce hydrogen, conduct electricity.
2. It produces H^+ ions and negative ions.
3. A corrosive acid reacts with a metal; a strong acid dissociates completely in water.
4. Production of fertilizers, industrial chemicals, explosives, plastics, film, iron and steel. Also, to remove rust and corrosion from metals.
5. A strong acid dissociates completely; a weak acid does not dissociate completely.
6. It may dissociate slightly but still react with metals. An example is hydrogen fluoride, HF.
7. They have a high pH and release OH^- ions in solution. Acids have a low pH and release H^+ ions in solution.
8. The ionic bond between the metal and the OH^- ion is weaker than most ionic bonds, so many OH^- ions are produced.
9. Taste bitter, feel slippery, conduct electricity, have a high pH, dissolve fats and oils; some are caustic.
10. A strong base dissociates completely; a weak base does not dissociate well and produces very few OH^- ions.
11. They dissolve fats and oils.
12. The higher the H^+ ion concentration, the lower the pH and the stronger the acid. The lower the H^+ ion concentration, the higher the OH^- ion concentration, the higher the pH, and the stronger the base.

Review and Skill Masters

CHAPTER REVIEW, pages 48–49.
See page 183b in this book for answers.

Chapter Review

VOCABULARY

Identify each statement as True or False. If a statement is false, replace the underlined term with a term that makes the statement true.

1. A hydroxide ion contains one oxygen atom and one hydrogen atom.
2. The reaction that takes place between an acid and a base is called concentration.
3. Bases are substances that give off hydrogen ions, H^+.
4. A compound that changes color as the concentration of H^+ or OH^- ions changes is called an indicator.
5. A salt is a compound formed from the positive metal ions of a base and the negative nonmetal ions of an acid.
6. Acids taste sour.
7. An acid anhydride is an oxide of a nonmetal that forms an acid when it is mixed with water.
8. Hydroxide ions have the chemical formula H_3O^+.
9. The acidity of a solution can be expressed using the pH scale.
10. The concentration of a substance is the amount of that substance present in a solution.

CONCEPTS

1. By what properties can acids be identified? (8-1)
2. Explain what happens when an acid dissociates. (8-1)
3. Distinguish between a corrosive acid and a strong acid. (8-1)
4. Name two uses of acids in industry. (8-1)
5. Distinguish between a strong acid and a weak acid. (8-1)
6. How is it possible for an acid to be both weak and corrosive? Give an example. (8-1)
7. Why are bases thought of as the chemical opposites of acids? (8-2)
8. Why do the metals in Groups 1 and 2 of the Periodic Table form strong bases? (8-2)
9. By what properties can bases be identified? (8-2)
10. Distinguish between a strong base and a weak base. (8-2)
11. Why are bases used in detergents? (8-2)
12. Discuss how pH is used to determine the strength of acids and bases. (8-3)
13. What is a neutral substance, and what is its pH? (8-3)

14. What is litmus paper, and how does it work? (8-3)

15. What products will be formed in the neutralization reaction between HCl and NH₄OH? (8-4)

16. Describe the type of chemical bonding found in salts. (8-4)

17. Explain why salt crystals dissolve in water. (8-4)

18. What is acid rain? (8-4)

19. What is a basic anhydride? Give an example of a basic anhydride, and describe its uses. (8-4)

20. Name two metals that will produce hydrogen from dilute HCl. (8-4)

APPLICATION/ CRITICAL THINKING

1. An unlabeled bottle half full of solution has been found near the acids and bases in your lab. How can you determine what kind of substance this unknown liquid is?

2. Explain why some salt solutions have acidic or basic pH's.

3. A solution with a pH of 4.5 is mixed with another solution. The resulting pH is 9.6. State whether each of these solutions is acidic or basic. Suppose the final pH was 7.0. What characteristics would you expect this solution to have?

4. Write the balanced equation for the reaction between barium hydroxide, Ba(OH)₂, and sulfuric acid, H₂SO₄.

5. In an unknown solution the indicator phenolphthalein is pink. In the same solution the indicator methyl orange is yellow, and bromthymol blue is blue. What is the approximate pH range of this solution? Is it an acid or a base?

EXTENSION

1. Research the disease scurvy, and explain why ascorbic acid is essential to the human body.

2. Write a report on the effects of acid rain on plant and animal life. Present your findings to your class.

3. Research the Bronsted-Lowry theory of acids and bases. How does this theory compare with the definitions of acids and bases given in this text?

4. In the human stomach, hydrochloric acid is produced. Find out why the body produces this strong acid, and why it does not damage stomach tissue.

READINGS

Cecil, George. *Salt*. New York:F. Watts, 1976.

La Bastille, Anne. "Acid Rain: How Great a Menace?" *National Geographic*, November 1981, p. 652.

Salisbury, David F. "Salt: An Untapped Source of Abundant Energy." *Science Digest*, December 1978, p. 45.

13. A neutral substance has an equal number of H^+ and OH^- ions in water solution. Its pH is 7.

14. Litmus paper is an indicator that is blue in basic solutions and red in acidic solutions. It changes color as the concentration of H^+ or OH^- ions changes.

15. NH_4Cl and H_2O.

16. Ionic bonds. Positive metallic ions of a base are bonded to the negative nonmetallic ions of an acid.

17. The water molecules attract the ions that are present in the crystal. Salts dissociate as they dissolve in water.

18. Acid rain is rain water that has absorbed sulfur oxide and nitrogen oxide from the burning of coal and petroleum. These acid anhydrides form acids when combined with water.

19. A basic anhydride is an oxide of a metal. Lime, CaO, is used in sewage treatment, food processing, and sugar refining.

20. Zinc, magnesium, or any metal above hydrogen in the activity series. (See Table 8-4.)

APPLICATION/CRITICAL THINKING

1. Test it with litmus paper to determine if it is acidic or basic.

2. They produce more H^+ or OH^- ions in solution, depending upon whether they have come from strong or weak acids or bases.

3. A pH of 4.5 is acidic; a pH of 9.6 is basic. The pH solution would be neutral and would have equal concentrations of H^+ and OH^- ions.

4. $Ba(OH)_2 + H_2SO_4 \rightarrow BaSO_4 + 2H_2O$.

5. Between 7.6 and 10; it is a base.

Test Masters

CHAPTER TEST, page 29.
See page 183d in this book for answers.

METALS

ORGANIZER

Section	pages	Activity	pages	Reinforcement and Evaluation	pages	*Review and Skill Masters	pages	Other Components in Teacher Resource Package	pages
9–1 Properties of Metals	205–208	How Do Metals Differ from Nonmetals?	208	Review, Challenge	208			*Study Guide*	42
9–2 The Alkali Metals	209–211	How Can Alkali Metals Be Identified?	210	Review, Challenge	211			*Study Guide* *Lab Manual*	43 51
9–3 The Alkaline Earth Metals	212–214			Puzzler Review, Challenge	214 214			*Study Guide*	44
9–4 The Transition Elements	215–220	Which Metal Is More Reactive, Copper or Zinc?	217	Review, Challenge	220	Challenge/Critical Thinking	58	*Study Guide*	45
9–5 The Inner Transition Elements	221–223			Review, Challenge	223	Skill	56–57	*Study Guide*	46
CHAPTER SUMMARY	223					Vocabulary Review	53		
CHAPTER REVIEW	224–225			*Test Masters	33–36	Chapter Review	54–55		

*In the Teacher Resource Package. For answers, see pages 203b–203d in this book.

ACTIVITY MATERIALS   Quantities are based on a class of 30 students working in groups as indicated in parentheses.

How Do Metals Differ from Nonmetals? p. 208 (groups of 2)	quantity	How Can Alkali Metals Be Identified? p. 210 (groups of 2)	quantity	Which Metal Is More Reactive, Copper or Zinc? p. 217 (groups of 2)	quantity
dry cell	15	graduate	15	safety goggles	30
insulated wire	9 m	safety goggles	30	lab apron	30
wire stripper	15	lab apron	30	10-mL graduate	15
light bulb and socket	15	Bunsen burner	15	test tube	30
samples of zinc, carbon, magnesium,		striker	15	zinc sulfate solution	150 mL
iron, sulfur, copper	15 each	test tube	120	copper wire	60 cm
watch glass	15	glass-marking pencil	15	scissors	15
		test-tube rack	15	copper (II) sulfate solution	150 mL
		lithium nitrate solution	30 mL	zinc metal	15 pieces
		platinum needle	15		
		hydrochloric acid	150 mL		
		100-mL beaker	15		
		sodium nitrate solution	30 mL		
		potassium nitrate solution	30 mL		
		cobalt glass plate	15		
		lithium chloride solution	30 mL		
		sodium chloride solution	30 mL		
		potassium chloride solution	30 mL		
		unknown solution containing one or more lithium, sodium, or potassium ions	30 mL		

REVIEW AND SKILL MASTERS

Name______________________ Date__________

VOCABULARY REVIEW ______ Chapter 9

Use the clues to complete the puzzle.

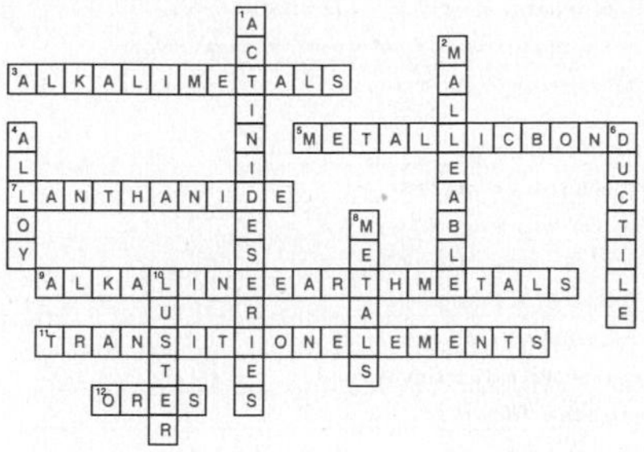

ACROSS

3. The elements in Group 1 of the Periodic Table (two words)
5. The force that holds metal ions together in a network (two words)
7. This series includes the 15 elements sometimes called the rare earth elements
9. The elements in Group 2 of the Periodic Table (three words)
11. The elements located between Groups 2 and 13 in the Periodic Table (two words)
12. The mixtures of compounds that contain metals and are found in the earth

DOWN

1. These are the radioactive inner transition elements (two words)
2. The characteristic of being able to be pounded into many different shapes
4. A mixture of metals, usually created by heating
6. The characteristic of being able to be drawn into a wire
8. Elements that are shiny, and are good conductors of heat and electricity
10. The characteristic of being shiny

Name______________________ Date__________

CHAPTER REVIEW ______ Chapter 9

9-1 Properties of Metals

1. What properties distinguish a metal from a nonmetal? No metal is a gas at room temperature, while many nonmetals are gases at room temperature. Metals are shiny, or have luster, while nonmetals do not have luster, and look dull. Metals are malleable and ductile, while nonmetals are brittle.

2. A metallic bond is the force of attraction that holds the network of metal ions together.

9-2 The Alkali Metals

1. Name two properties that make alkali metals easily identifiable. Alkali metals have luster and are very soft. When heated, they give off bright colors which can be used to identify the element.

2. Why are alkali metals the most chemically reactive elements? An atom of an alkali metal has one electron in its outer level. The atom can lose this electron and form an ion with a 1+ charge. This process takes place readily.

3. List three uses of an alkali metal compound. Answers may vary. Compounds of the alkali metals have many uses: table salt is used to flavor food, preserve food, and melt ice.

9-3 The Alkaline Earth Metals

1. Identify the properties common to both alkaline earth metals and alkali metals. Both metals are chemically reactive and, in nature, are found only in compounds. Both can form bases. Both groups of metals give off light when their atoms are heated.

Name______________________ Date__________

CHAPTER REVIEW (Continued) ______ Chapter 9

2. What kinds of compounds are produced when alkaline earth metals are combined with elements in groups 16 and 17? Ionic compounds.

3. Beryllium and magnesium are alkaline earth metals. Beryllium is used in X ray tubes. Magnesium is used in emergency flares.

9-4 The Transition Elements

1. The transition elements are located between Groups 2 and 13 in the Periodic Table.

2. Name two characteristics of transition elements. Each transition element has one or two electrons in its outer energy level. These elements can form more than one kind of ion.

3. What is an alloy? Give an example of an alloy. An alloy is a mixture of metals. Brass is an alloy.

9-5 The Inner Transition Elements

1. Identify the special properties of samarium, gadolinium, and promethium. Answers may vary. Samarium and gadolinium are magnetic; promethium is radioactive.

2. The inner transition elements are located in the sixth and seventh rows of the Periodic Table.

3. The two series that make up the inner transition elements are the lanthanide series and the actinide series.

4. List two uses for inner transition elements. Answers may vary. Uranium and plutonium are used in nuclear reactors to generate electricity. Curium is used as a fuel in nuclear batteries.

Name______________________ Date__________

SKILL/Comparing and Classifying ______ Chapter 9

Match the following characteristics with the appropriate group of elements. Write the letter of the characteristic on the line under the correct heading. When finished, use the letters under each heading to complete the example element for each group.

A - have two outer electrons
B - elements of Group 2
C - elements found between Groups 2 and 13
D - have malleability and ductility
E - Cr, W, and Hg are members of this group
G - have luster
I - Be, Mg, and Ca are members of this group
L - excellent conductors of heat and electricity
M - never found uncombined in nature
O - most chemically reactive metals
P - metals in this group are used in coins and jewelry
R - some can form more than one kind of ion
S - have one outer electron
U - elements of Group 1

ALL METALS	ALKALI METALS	ALKALINE EARTH METALS	TRANSITION ELEMENTS
D	M	A	C
G	O	B	E
L	S	I	P
	U		R
G O L D	S O D I U M	B A R I U M	C O P P E R

Different groups of elements have different properties. Compare and contrast the groups of elements discussed in the questions below.

1. Compare the luster of solid metals and solid nonmetals. Solid metals have luster. Solid nonmetals do not have luster, and thus look dull.

Name_____ Date_____

SKILL/Comparing and Classifying (Continued) ——————— Chapter 9

2. Compare the malleability of solid metals and solid nonmetals.

Solid metals are malleable. Solid nonmetals are not malleable, and thus are

brittle.

3. Compare the number of electrons in the outer energy level of the alkali metals and the alkaline metals.

The alkali metals have one electron in the outer energy level. The alkaline

metals have two electrons in the outer energy level.

4. Compare the hardness of the alkali metals with the hardness of the alkaline metals.

The alkali metals are not as hard as the alkaline metals (alkaline = harder than

alkali).

5. Compare the melting points of the alkali metals with the melting points of the alkaline metals.

The melting points of the alkali metals are lower than the melting points of the

alkaline metals (alkaline = higher melting point than alkali).

6. Number the following groups of elements according to their reactivity. 1 = least reactive, 3 = most reactive.

a. ___3___ alkali metals

b. ___2___ alkaline metals

c. ___1___ transition elements

7. Compare and contrast the number of ions formed by the alkali metals, alkaline metals, and transition elements.

Both the alkali metals and the alkaline metals form only one ion. Many

transition elements, however, can form more than one kind of ion.

Name_____ Date_____

CHALLENGE/CRITICAL THINKING ——————— Chapter 9

When oxygen forms compounds with metals, the oxygen ions usually have a charge of 2−. Similarly, when chlorine forms compounds with metals, the chloride ions have a charge of 1−. Many of the metals can form more than one kind of ion. For example, iron can form a 2+ ion (Fe^{2+}) or a 3+ ion (Fe^{3+}).

The formula for a compound is always balanced so that the overall charge is zero. Using 2− as the charge on an oxygen ion and 1− as the charge on a chloride ion, determine the charge on each metal ion in the following formulas. The first one is done for you as an example.

1. Fe_2O_3 — Iron (Fe) has a charge of 3+.

2. FeO — Iron (Fe) has a charge of 2+.

3. Cu_2O_3 — Copper (Cu) has a charge of 3+.

4. CuO — Copper (Cu) has a charge of 2+.

5. $SbCl_3$ — Antimony (Sb) has a charge of 3+.

6. Al_2O_3 — Aluminum (Al) has a charge of 3+.

7. Cr_2O_3 — Chromium (Cr) has a charge of 3+.

8. $MnCl_2$ — Manganese (Mn) has a charge of 2+.

9. $FeCl_3$ — Iron (Fe) has a charge of 3+.

10. $SnCl_2$ — Tin (Sn) has a charge of 2+.

11. $AlCl_3$ — Aluminum (Al) has a charge of 3+.

12. $FeCl_2$ — Iron (Fe) has a charge of 2+.

13. Hg_2O — Mercury (Hg) has a charge of 1+.

14. $HgCl_2$ — Mercury (Hg) has a charge of 2+.

15. MnO — Manganese (Mn) has a charge of 2+.

16. $CuCl_2$ — Copper (Cu) has a charge of 2+.

REVIEW AND SKILL MASTERS

TEST MASTERS

Page 33

Name _____ Date _____ Score _____

Chapter 9

Metals

PART 1 _____

In the space below, write the term that each phrase defines.

Chapter Goal

1. **alkali metals** — The elements in Group 1 in the Periodic Table — 2

2. **inner transition elements** — The elements that are located in the sixth and seventh rows of the Periodic Table, and that include the rare earth elements and the transuranium elements — 5

3. **ores** — Mixtures of compounds in the earth in which metals are found — 1

4. **alloys** — Mixtures of metals usually made by heating metals together — 4

5. **lanthanide series** — The group of elements, beginning with lanthanum, that are in the sixth row of the Periodic Table — 5

6. **transition elements** — The elements that are located between Groups 2 and 13 in the Periodic Table and that have one or two electrons in their outer energy levels — 4

7. **metallic bond** — The force of attraction that holds metal ions together in a network — 1

8. **alkaline earth metals** — The metals in Group 2 of the Periodic Table — 3

PART 2 _____

Choose the term or phrase that best answers the question or completes the statement. Write the letter of that choice in the space at the left.

__a__ 1. Alkaline earth metals are able to combine with elements in Groups 16 and 17 of the Periodic Table because the alkaline earth metals form: — 3
a. +2 ions. b. +3 ions. c. −1 ions. d. −2 ions.

__b__ 2. Uranium is similar to the transuranium elements because all of these metals are: — 5
a. synthetic. b. radioactive. c. corrosive. d. magnetic.

Chapter 9 Metals   33

Page 34

Name _____ Date _____ Score _____

PART 2 _____

Choose the term or phrase that best answers the question or completes the statement. Write the letter of that choice in the space at the left.

Chapter Goal

__a__ 3. A metal used to make thin plates to cover the wings of an airplane must be: — 1
a. malleable. b. luminous. c. radioactive. d. brittle.

__d__ 4. Like alkali metals, alkaline earth metals are able to combine with water to form: — 3
a. alloys. b. salts. c. ores. d. bases.

__d__ 5. Which of the following would most likely contain a network structure, made up of positively charged metal ions with electrons all around them? — 1
a. oxygen b. water c. carbon d. nickel

__b__ 6. How many electrons are found in the outer energy level of an alkali metal atom? — 2
a. 0 b. 1 c. 2 d. 3

__a__ 7. A substance has a low melting point, reacts violently with water, and gives off a colored light when heated. The substance will most likely be classified as: — 2
a. an alkali metal. c. a lanthanide.
b. a transition element. d. an actinide.

__c__ 8. Which of the following activities would most likely involve an alkali metal? — 2
a. taking a photograph c. fertilizing a garden
b. turning on a light bulb d. growing a zirconium crystal

__c__ 9. Pewter and steel are alloys made up mostly of: — 4
a. alkali metals. c. transition elements.
b. alkaline earth metals. d. inner transition elements.

__b__ 10. Which of the following most likely contains an alkaline earth metal? — 3
a. a copper penny c. a brass candlestick
b. a marble statue d. a salt block

__a__ 11. A geologist separates a metal from a deposit found in the earth. The metal is magnetic, and forms +3 ions. The geologist will most likely identify it as: — 5
a. a lanthanide. c. an actinide.
b. an alkali metal. d. a transuranium element.

__d__ 12. Mercury can produce two different products from the same reactants in a chemical reaction because mercury can: — 4
a. gain electrons during a reaction.
b. react with hydrogen chloride to release hydrogen gas.
c. form covalent bonds when part of alloys.
d. form more than one kind of ion.

Chapter 9 Metals   34

Page 35

Name _____ Date _____ Score _____

PART 3 _____

Look at the diagram. Then read the questions that follow. Choose the term or phrase that best answers the question or completes the statement. Write the letter of that choice in the space at the left.

Chapter Goal

__c__ 1. Which of the following are in Group 1 in the diagram? — 4
a. alkali metals c. transition elements
b. alkaline earth metals d. inner transition elements

__d__ 2. Which of the following groups in the diagram contain only elements that are radioactive? — 5
a. Group 1 c. Lanthanide Series
b. Group 18 d. Actinide Series

__b__ 3. Which group in the diagram contains the alkaline earth metals? — 3
a. Group 1 b. Group 2 c. Group 11 d. Group 12

__a__ 4. The elements in Group 1 form ions with a charge of: — 2
a. 1+. b. 2+. c. 2−. d. 3−.

__a__ 5. Which group in the diagram contains only elements that form metallic bonds? — 1
a. Group 2 b. Group 13 c. Group 14 d. Group 15

Chapter 9 Metals   35

Page 36

Name _____ Date _____ Score _____

PART 4 _____

Read each question or direction and answer it using complete sentences.

Chapter Goal

1. Why are alkali metals so reactive? — 2

The outer energy level of each alkali metal atom contains only one electron. The atom can lose this electron and form an ion with a +1 charge. This process occurs very readily, and it allows the alkali metals to react easily with other substances.

2. Explain how metallic bonds cause metals to be malleable and ductile. — 1

In a metallic bond, the outer electrons belong to the entire structure of a solid rather than to single atoms. This creates a sea of freely moving electrons around the metal ions. Because there are no individual bonds, the ions and electrons can be rearranged as the metal changes shape without cracking or breaking the solid.

3. Explain why the large atoms of the alkaline earth metal group are more reactive than the smaller ones. — 3

The outer electrons of the larger atoms are farther from the nucleus than they are in the smaller atoms. As a result, the larger atoms can lose electrons more easily than the smaller atoms. Alkaline earth metals lose two electrons to form +2 ions, which react readily with other substances.

Chapter 9 Metals   36

CHAPTER 9 · PLANNING GUIDE

203d

The questions in the CHAPTER TEST are based on these Chapter Goals.

1. Describe properties of metals and metallic bonds.
2. Describe properties and chemical behavior of alkali metals and the uses of alkali metal compounds.
3. Describe the properties, chemical behavior, and some uses of the alkaline earth metals.
4. Identify the transition elements and compare them with other metals.
5. Identify the inner transition elements and distinguish between the lanthanide series and the actinide series.

METALS

The bridge shown in the photograph is the Iron Bridge over the Severn River in England. Completed in 1781, it is the first bridge to have been built of metal. Before iron was used, wood or stone was used to build bridges. The use of iron made it possible to span the river with a single arch, leaving the river open for boats. Although the stonework at the sides of the bridge has been replaced, the metal arch of the bridge is the original iron.

- *What properties of metal make it a good material for making bridges and other structures?*
- *What other uses are there for metals?*

9-1 PROPERTIES OF METALS

Recall that the elements in the Periodic Table are arranged in columns called groups. Elements in a group have similar properties. In this chapter you will study the groups that have been classified as metals. Over three fourths of the elements in the Periodic Table are metals. Look at the Periodic Table in Appendix 1 at the back of this book. The elements located to the left of the heavy zigzag line are metals. The elements to the right of the line are called nonmetals.

Metals are elements that are shiny, that are good conductors of heat and electricity, and that can be pounded into various shapes. Copper, nickel, iron, gold, and most other metals are solids at room temperature. Mercury, however, is a liquid metal. No metal is a gas at room temperature. Many nonmetals are gases at room temperature, but others are solids or liquids.

Metals are shiny, and have **luster** (LUHS tuhr). Nonmetals do not have luster, and so they look dull. Metals are **malleable** (MAL ee uh buhl), which means that they can be pounded into many shapes, including thin sheets. Metals also are **ductile** (DUHK tuhl), which means that they can be drawn out into a wire. Wire made of metal can be bent without breaking. Solid nonmetals are brittle and

After completing this section, you will be able to

- **classify** elements as metals or nonmetals.
- **describe** some properties of metals.
- **describe** metallic bonds.

The key terms in this section are

ductile	metallic bond
luster	metals
malleable	ores

lustrare (to illuminate)

malleus (hammer)

Have students read the introductory paragraph. Point out that the Iron Bridge is over 200 years old. Ask students why the stonework of the bridge has been replaced but the metal of the bridge is still the original iron. Explain that the bridge has rusted over the years, but it was completely cleaned for the two-hundredth birthday of the bridge. Ask students how workers remove rust from metals. Ask them how rust can be prevented.

- What properties of metal make it a good material for making bridges and other structures? (Metal is strong, malleable, and ductile.)
- What other uses are there for metals? (Metals conduct electricity. They are used in many everyday products and appliances.)

9-1 PROPERTIES OF METALS
pages 205–208

OBJECTIVES
Refer to pupil page 205.

VOCABULARY
Key terms: ductile, luster, malleable, metallic bond, metals, ores
Other terms: reduction

1 MOTIVATION

Display samples of metals, such as copper, nickel, iron, zinc, sodium, calcium, and aluminum. Ask students to locate these metals in the Periodic Table and identify the groups they are in. Ask students to describe the appearance of these metals. Then ask what properties identify materials as metals.

2 CONCEPT DEVELOPMENT

Background   Metals have several distinctive characteristics. Chemically, they are all electropositive. Metals are opaque, and they reflect light. This gives them a bright luster. However, some metals tarnish rapidly when exposed to air, and as a result, their bright luster is not always obvious. To varying degrees, metals are good conductors of heat and electricity. They also have the ability to mix with each other to form alloys (or amalgams, when mercury is involved). Most solid metals are tough, ductile, and malleable, but there are exceptions. Some metals are very soft, and some are brittle. All metals but one, mercury, are solids at room temperature.

Teaching Tip   Point out to your students that mercury, the only liquid metal, is about 14 times heavier than water. Since mercury is an extremely toxic element, it should never be touched or be allowed to evaporate. If even a small amount is ingested, it can damage the nervous system and might result in death.

Teaching Tip   Review the concept of ionic bonding. Stress that the metallic and nonmetallic ions are held together by electrostatic attraction.

Thinking Skills

interpreting diagrams
Have students look at Figure 9-2. Ask students how many electrons the metal has in its outer energy level after it has lost the electron. (Eight.) Ask how many electrons the other atom has after it has gained the electron. (Eight.)

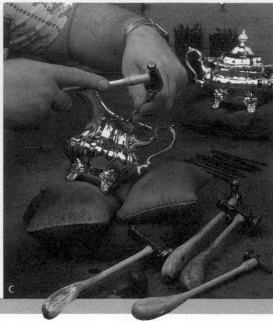

Figure 9-1

Tin being bent (*A*), copper wire (*B*), and silver being hammered (*C*).

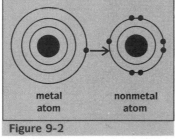

Figure 9-2

Metal atoms tend to lose electrons to nonmetal atoms.

[1]Metal is malleable (*A*). Metal is ductile (*B*). Metal is malleable and has luster (*C*). [2]Ionic bonds.

will break if you try to pound or bend them into different shapes. Look at Figure 9-1. What property of metals is shown by each photograph?[1]

Most metals have one, two, or three electrons in their outer energy level. During many chemical reactions, metal atoms lose their outer electrons to other atoms, usually nonmetals. The larger metal atoms lose their outer electrons the most easily, because these electrons are farther away from the pull of the positively charged nucleus. A metal atom becomes stable, or nonreactive, when it has lost its outer electrons. Notice in Figure 9-2 that another atom has gained the electron lost by the metal atom. What kind of chemical bond is being formed?[2]

The outer electrons in a metal atom are far from the nucleus. This causes them to be held in place loosely. In a metallic solid the atoms are so close together that their outer energy levels overlap. Because of these conditions, the outer electrons are able to move from one atom to another. Thus, in a metallic solid, the outer electrons are thought of as belonging to the whole structure. In other words, these electrons do not belong to any single atom. The metallic structure can be described as positively charged metal ions with electrons all around them. The force of attraction that holds the network of metal ions together is called a **metallic bond**.

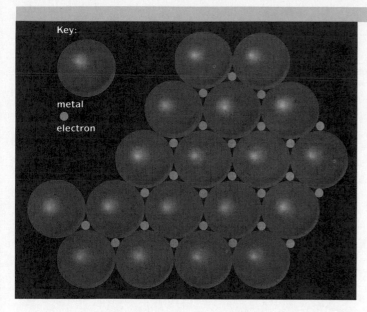

Figure 9-3
Metallic bonds hold metal atoms together in a network structure.

Key:

metal

electron

Look at Figure 9-3. This figure shows the structure of a metal. Scientists describe this arrangement as positive ions in a sea of electrons. This freely moving sea of electrons explains why metals conduct electricity. Electrons that enter one end of a wire flow through the wire and out the other end.

The metallic bond also explains why metals are malleable and ductile. Because there are no individual bonds, the ions and electrons can be moved into new positions without cracking or breaking the metal object. The sea of electrons and ions is rearranged each time a metal is forced into a new shape.

Most metals are found in the earth as a mixture of compounds called **ores**. Since most metals are not found alone, they must be removed from the other substances in the ores. For example, copper occurs in the ore chalcopyrite (kal kuh PĪ rīt) as copper (I) sulfide, Cu_2S. The copper can be removed from the Cu_2S by a process called *reduction*. The mineral is heated in the presence of air, and the following reaction takes place.

$$Cu_2S(s) + O_2(g) \rightarrow 2Cu(s) + SO_2(g)$$

The copper formed is called blister copper. It is not perfectly pure, because some of the Cu_2S is still present. It must be further refined to make the copper pure enough to be used for electrical wires.

Figure 9-4

Chalcopyrite ore contains copper, which is used to make wire.

Teaching Tip   Have students read the section about metallic bonds. Ask students to list all the elements in the Periodic Table that would exhibit metallic bonding.

Compare the ionic bond with the metallic bond. Discuss the properties of ionic solids. Compare these properties with the properties of metallic solids. Ask why solid ionic compounds aren't conductors of electricity but solid metals are. (In a solid ionic compound, ions are not moving freely; in a solid metal, they are moving freely.)

Teaching Tip   Have students look at Figure 9-3. Discuss how electrons move through a copper wire in an electric circuit. It is the outer electrons that move freely through the network and, thus, cause the metal to be an electrical and thermal conductor.

Background   Except for small amounts of copper, gold, silver, and some iron meteorites, metals usually do not occur free in nature. They are usually combined with other elements, in the mineral aggregates known as *ores*. The ore minerals are primarily oxides, carbonates, silicates, sulfides, arsenides, antimonides, and halides of various metals. Metals are extracted from ores by various complex processes.

Teaching Tip   Discuss ores. Ask students to name ores they may have heard about or read about. Discuss the minerals contained in each. Some examples include cinnabar, HgS; magnetite, Fe_3O_4; cassiterite, SnO_2; sphalerite, ZnS; and galena, PbS.

ACTIVITY 30–40 minutes

PROCESS SKILLS
observing, classifying, recording data, interpreting charts, inferring

Preparation Use 1.5-V dry cells. Each student will need two pieces of insulated wire about 20 cm long. You may use unoxidized iron nails and copper foil, aluminum foil, magnesium ribbon, and flowers of sulfur.

Safety Tip Caution students to be careful when stripping insulation off wire with wire strippers, or strip the wires yourself prior to setting up the experiment.

Teaching Tip Remind students that *luster* refers to the "shine" of a substance and that a substance which is not a conductor is an insulator.

Answers to Results and Conclusions
1. Yes.
2. Yes.
3. Zinc, magnesium, iron, copper.
4. Carbon, sulfur.

Background Carbon monoxide is a reducing agent of iron oxide. The iron that is formed by the reduction process is called pig iron. Its carbon content must be reduced to between 0.2 percent and 1.5 percent in steel. Minerals that occur as sulfides are changed to oxides by roasting or heating in air.

❸ REVIEW/REINFORCEMENT

1. To the left of the heavy zigzag line.
2. Properties include being lustrous, conductive, malleable, and ductile.
3. Attractions between positively charged ions and mobile outer electrons.
4. Mixtures of minerals found in the earth.

Challenge Gold, iron, and nickel.

ACTIVITY How Do Metals Differ from Nonmetals?

OBJECTIVE
Distinguish between metals and nonmetals.

MATERIALS
Dry cell; insulated wire; wire stripper; light bulb and socket; samples of zinc, carbon, sulfur, magnesium, iron, and copper; watch glass

PROCEDURE
A. Draw a data table like the one shown.
B. Set up the equipment as shown in the diagram. The ends of the wire should have 2 cm of the insulation removed. **Caution:** Do not touch the ends of the wires.

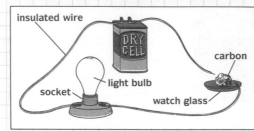

C. Obtain a small sample of one of the substances to be tested. Place the sample on a watch glass. Examine the sample to determine if it has luster. Record your observation.

D. Hold the insulated part of the wires, and touch the ends of the wires to the sample. Do not touch the ends of the wires to each other. If the light bulb lights, the element is a conductor. If the light bulb does not light, the element is not a conductor. Record your observation.
E. Repeat steps **C** and **D** for each of the other substances.

Element	Luster	Conductivity
Zinc		
Carbon		
Sulfur		
Magnesium		
Iron		
Copper		

RESULTS AND CONCLUSIONS
1. Do all of the materials that have luster show conductivity?
2. Do all of the materials that show conductivity have luster?
3. Which elements tested are metals?
4. Which elements tested are nonmetals?

Carbon or carbon monoxide may be used to reduce metals that are found as oxides. Iron occurs as Fe_2O_3 in an ore called hematite (HEHM uh tīt). The reaction between iron oxide and carbon monoxide is shown below.

$$Fe_2O_3(s) + 3CO(g) \rightarrow 2Fe(s) + 3CO_2(g)$$

The iron that is formed may contain some carbon. Much of this carbon is removed in electric furnaces during the manufacture of steel.

REVIEW

1. Where are the metals located in the Periodic Table?
2. Describe three properties of metals.
3. Describe metallic bonds.
4. What are ores?

CHALLENGE Which of the following solids show metallic bonding: gold, sulfur, carbon, iron, or nickel?

9-2 THE ALKALI METALS

The elements in Group 1 of the Periodic Table are the **alkali** (AL kuh lī) **metals**. Figure 9-5 shows the outer electron arrangement and relative sizes of the atoms of the alkali metals. Which of these metals has the largest atom? Which has the smallest atom?[1]

All of the alkali elements are metals with low melting points. For example, cesium melts at 29°C. Alkali metals have luster and are very soft. As you can see in Figure 9-5, sodium can be cut with a knife. Such softness makes alkali metals very malleable and ductile.

When alkali metal atoms are heated, they give off bright colors. The heat causes electrons in the atoms to move to higher energy levels. As the electrons return to their original levels, the atoms give off energy in the form of light. The color of the light given off by the metal can be used to identify the element.

All of the alkali metal atoms have similar electron arrangements. Although the total number of electrons is different in each element, the outer energy level is the same. An atom of any alkali metal has one electron in its outer level. The atom can lose this electron and form an ion with a 1+ charge. This process takes place readily. As a result the alkali metals are the most chemically reactive elements.

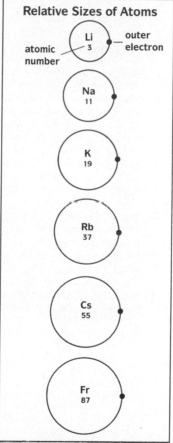

Relative Sizes of Atoms

atomic number — Li 3 — outer electron

Na 11

K 19

Rb 37

Cs 55

Fr 87

Figure 9-5

The alkali metals group (*right*) includes potassium (*A*), rubidium (*B*), cesium (*C*), and sodium (*D*).

9-2 THE ALKALI METALS
pages 209–211

OBJECTIVES
Refer to pupil page 209.

VOCABULARY
Key term: alkali metals

After completing this section, you will be able to

- **describe** the properties of the alkali metals.
- **explain** why the alkali metals are so chemically reactive.
- **list** uses of alkali metal compounds.

The key term in this section is **alkali metals**

1 MOTIVATION

Discuss with students the reactivity of the alkali metals with water. Have students look at Group 1 of the Periodic Table. Have them look at the atomic numbers of lithium and francium. Ask students how many electrons lithium and francium have. (Lithium—3, francium—87.) Ask which element has electrons farther from the nucleus. (Francium.) Have students theorize why the alkali metals increase in activity as you move down the group. (The elements are larger and the outer electrons are farther away from the nucleus.)

2 CONCEPT DEVELOPMENT

Background The alkali metals derive their name from the Arabic word *al-qili*, meaning "plant ashes." Plant ashes are rich in sodium and potassium carbonates.

Thinking Skills

interpreting diagrams
Have students examine the electron arrangements and relative sizes of the Group 1 elements shown in Figure 9-5. Ask students why these metals are very reactive. (Each alkali metal has one electron in its outer shell. Such an atom can readily lose its outer electron and thus form an ion with a 1+ charge.) Have students identify the largest alkali metal and explain why it is the largest. (Francium; it has the greatest number of electrons and the most energy levels.)

ACTIVITY 40–45 minutes

PROCESS SKILLS
observing, identifying cause and effect, inferring

Preparation To prepare dilute HCl, add 500 mL of concentrated HCl to 500 mL of distilled water. The other solutions may be prepared by adding about 2 g of each compound to 500 mL of distilled water. Stir until the substances are dissolved.

Safety Tip When diluting acids, add the acid to the water.

Teaching Tip Have students replace the HCl in the beaker after every two to three tests. Place the used HCl in a waste HCl bottle labeled and set aside for that purpose. All glassware should be thoroughly cleaned and dried before each test.

Answers to Results and Conclusions
1. Yes, crimson.
2. Yes, yellow-orange.
3. Yes, violet.
4. No.
5. Violet is seen when the cobalt glass is used. Blue glass will transmit blue or violet but not yellow or other colors.
6. Answers will vary.

Demonstration Heat a soft glass tube in a blue flame to show the presence of sodium by a flame test. You should see a yellow-orange color.

Background The flame tests for certain elements may be used to help identify the elements. The visible colors observed in the flames are part of the spectra—the "fingerprints"—of the elements. When light from excited atoms passes through a spectroscope, it reveals the electron configurations of the atoms.

ACTIVITY How Can Alkali Metals Be Identified?

OBJECTIVE
Distinguish between alkali metals.

MATERIALS
safety goggles; lab apron; Bunsen burner; striker; graduate; 8 test tubes; glass-marking pencil; test-tube rack; nichrome wire with handle; hydrochloric acid; 100-mL beaker; cobalt glass plate; solutions of: lithium nitrate, sodium nitrate, potassium nitrate, lithium chloride, sodium chloride, potassium chloride, unknown substance.

PROCEDURE
A. Wear safety goggles and a lab apron throughout this activity.
B. Draw a data table like the one shown. Label a test tube for each solution listed.
C. Place about 2 mL of lithium nitrate solution in a test tube. Light a Bunsen burner. Dip the looped end of a nichrome wire into the solution. Place the wire in the tip of the flame. Record your observation.
D. Measure 10 mL of dilute hydrochloric acid into a beaker. Clean the wire by dipping the needle into the acid and then placing it in the outer flame of the burner until no spurts of color are seen.
E. Repeat the flame test, using sodium nitrate solution. Clean the wire in the acid.
F. Repeat the flame test, using potassium nitrate solution. Clean the wire.
G. Repeat the flame test, using potassium nitrate solution, but observe the flame through a cobalt glass plate. Clean the wire.
H. Measure 1 mL of sodium nitrate solution and 1 mL of potassium nitrate solution into a test tube. Repeat the flame test.
I. Repeat the flame test, using the mixture from step H. Observe the flame through the cobalt glass plate. Clean the wire in the acid, as before.
J. Repeat the flame tests needed to complete the data table. Clean the wire after each test.

RESULTS AND CONCLUSIONS
1. Did both lithium solutions produce the same color? What color(s) did you see?
2. Did both sodium solutions produce the same color? What color(s) did you see?
3. Did both potassium solutions produce the same color? What color(s) did you see?
4. Is the flame test affected by a negative ion?
5. Compare the results of the potassium flame tests, with and without the cobalt glass plate. Why is the cobalt glass used?
6. What color was produced by your unknown? Identify the metal ion in the unknown.

Solution	Color of Flame (without cobalt glass)	Color of Flame (with cobalt glass)
Lithium nitrate		X
Sodium nitrate		X
Potassium nitrate		
Sodium nitrate/ potassium nitrate mixture		
Lithium chloride		X
Sodium chloride		X
Potassium chloride		
Unknown		

Because they are so reactive, the alkali metals are not found alone in nature. They are always combined with other elements, forming compounds. The alkali metals react violently with water to produce hydrogen gas and a base. Bases that contain alkali metals are strong bases.

$$2Na(s) + 2H_2O(l) \rightarrow 2NaOH(aq) + H_2(g)$$

If a piece of sodium is dropped into water, the hydrogen released can cause an explosion. Alkali metals also will

 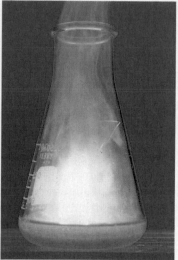 

Figure 9-6

This reaction between sodium and water (*left* and *middle*) can be avoided if the sodium is stored under an oil (*right*).

react strongly with water vapor in the air. To avoid the violent reaction shown in Figure 9-6, alkali metals are stored in oils such as kerosene. The metal will not react with the oil, which keeps water away from the metal.

The alkali metals will react with nonmetals, especially those in Groups 16 and 17. The products are ionic.

$$2K(s) + F_2(g) \rightarrow 2KF(s)$$
$$2Cs(s) + S(s) \rightarrow Cs_2S(s)$$
$$4Li(s) + O_2(g) \rightarrow 2Li_2O(s)$$

Because they are so reactive, alkali metals cannot be used in pure form. However, compounds of the alkali metals have many uses. Sodium chloride, NaCl, is used in foods as a flavoring and a preservative. Sodium chloride can be used to melt ice on sidewalks in the winter.

Fertilizers contain potassium compounds, especially potassium chloride, KCl, and potassium oxide, K_2O. The potassium ion is an important ion in plant and animal cells. Most of the potassium used in the United States is used to make fertilizers.

REVIEW

1. State two properties of alkali metals.
2. Describe how the electron arrangement of the alkali metals is related to their chemical activity.
3. List three uses of alkali metal compounds.

CHALLENGE Fluorine forms a 1− ion. Predict the formulas for sodium fluoride and cesium fluoride.

Background The alkali metals are found as chlorides, nitrates, and carbonates. Sodium chloride is the most abundant compound of sodium. Sodium may be obtained commercially, from sodium chloride, by a process called electrolysis.

Tie-in/Social Studies Ask students to find out which countries are the major producers of potassium.

3 REVIEW/REINFORCEMENT

1. Properties include being lustrous, conductive, very reactive, one electron in outer energy level, soft, low melting points, react with water.
2. The alkali metals have one electron in their outer energy level. They easily lose this electron, thus becoming 1+ ions. The larger the atom, the more reactive the element.
3. Answers will vary.

Challenge NaF and CsF.

9-3 THE ALKALINE EARTH METALS

pages 212–214

OBJECTIVES
Refer to pupil page 212.

VOCABULARY
Key term: alkaline earth metals

1 MOTIVATION

Drop some powdered magnesium into a test tube that is half filled with distilled water. Ask students if there is a reaction. Gently heat the water to boiling. Ask students if there is a reaction. Have students recall the discussion of the Group I elements and ask which is more reactive, sodium or magnesium. (Sodium.) Have students look at Figure 9-5 and Figure 9-7, and ask them why sodium is more reactive. (The sodium atom is larger. Also, magnesium must lose two electrons, which is more difficult.)

2 CONCEPT DEVELOPMENT

Background The alchemists called any substance that would not dissolve in water an "earth substance." CaO and MgO are "earth substances" that give alkaline reactions.

Thinking Skills

comparing
Ask students which is more reactive in water, calcium or magnesium. (Calcium.) Then ask why. (The calcium atom is larger.) Have students compare and arrange the elements in Figure 9-7 in order of increasing reactivity. (Be, Mg, Ca, Sr, Ba, Ra.)

After completing this section, you will be able to

- **compare** the alkaline earth metals with the alkali metals.
- **describe** the chemical behavior of the alkaline earth metals.
- **list** some uses of the alkaline earth metals.

The key term in this section is alkaline earth metals

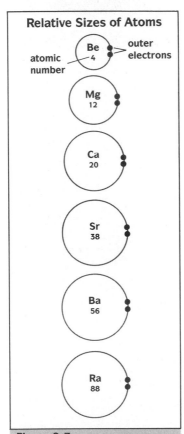

Relative Sizes of Atoms

Figure 9-7

The alkaline earth metals.

The elements in Group 2 of the Periodic Table are called the **alkaline** (AL kuh lin) **earth metals**. Alkaline earth metals are reactive, but not as reactive as the alkali metals. Most alkaline earth metals are found only in compounds in nature. The larger atoms of this group are more reactive than the smaller atoms. The outer electrons of the larger atoms are farther from the nucleus and thus are more easily lost than are electrons of the smaller atoms. Compare the sizes of the atoms of the alkaline earth metals in Figure 9-7. Predict which element is most reactive.[1]

The alkaline earth metals are harder than the Group 1 metals and have higher melting points. Radium, which has the lowest melting point of the Group 2 metals, melts at 700°C. This is higher than the melting point of any alkali metal.

An atom of an alkaline earth metal has two electrons in its outer energy level. These two electrons are lost during chemical reactions. Thus alkaline earth metals form ions with a 2+ charge. Because of this, they combine readily with negative ions such as carbonate, nitrate, or hydroxide.

The alkaline earth metals will react with water and release hydrogen gas. This reaction is not as violent as the reaction between alkali metals and water. Magnesium will react with water only if the water is hot.

$$Mg(s) + 2H_2O(l) \longrightarrow Mg(OH)_2(aq) + H_2(g)$$

Notice that this reaction also produces magnesium hydroxide, a base. The term *alkaline* is sometimes used to describe bases. The names *alkali metal* and *alkaline earth metal* refer to the fact that these metals can form bases. Bases that contain alkaline earth metals are weaker than bases that contain alkali metals.

Alkaline earth metals will combine with elements in Groups 16 and 17. These reactions produce ionic compounds.

$$Ba(s) + F_2(g) \longrightarrow BaF_2(s)$$
$$2Ca(s) + O_2(g) \longrightarrow 2CaO(s)$$

The alkaline earth metals are widely used. Beryllium (buh RIHL ee uhm), a rather rare element, has a very low density. Because of its lightness and strength, it is used in making space vehicles. Beryllium's small atomic size makes it useful in X-ray tubes. The X rays can pass through a beryllium X-ray tube easily.

[1]Radium is the largest atom, and beryllium is the smallest. Radium would be the most reactive.

Figure 9-8

The limestone being removed from this quarry contains calcium carbonate, CaCO₃.

Demonstration Burn a 3-cm piece of magnesium ribbon in the blue flame of a burner. (Caution students not to look directly at the flame.) Ask what substance is formed. (Magnesium oxide.)

Background Prior to the use of electric lights in footlights, burning calcium was used to light stages during performances. Calcium oxide, or *quicklime,* was formed. Thus the saying, "being in the limelight," originated.

Teaching Tip Soak a chicken bone in hydrochloric acid overnight to illustrate the importance of calcium in bone formation.

Magnesium metal burns with a bright white light and is used in photographic flash bulbs and emergency flares. In this reaction, magnesium oxide is formed.

$$2Mg(s) + O_2(g) \longrightarrow 2MgO(s)$$

You may be familiar with some magnesium compounds. Magnesium hydroxide, $Mg(OH)_2$, is commonly called milk of magnesia. Magnesium sulfate, $MgSO_4$, is sold as Epsom salts. Magnesium oxide is a good conductor of heat. Because of this behavior, it is used in electrical stoves.

Calcium is the most common of the Group 1 and 2 metals. Calcium compounds are found in rocks and minerals. Limestone, marble, chalk, and oyster shells all contain calcium carbonate, $CaCO_3$. The lime that is used on lawns contains calcium carbonate. Calcium is needed in the diet for the growth of strong bones and teeth. Calcium ions in the blood aid in clotting. Foods that are good sources of calcium include milk and cheese.

Pure barium is rather rare in nature but it is found as barium sulfate, $BaSO_4$. Barium sulfate is used in taking X rays of the digestive system. Notice the light area in the X ray shown in Figure 9-9. Barium atoms absorb most X rays, but soft tissues of the body absorb very few. The dark areas on the film show the areas where the X rays penetrated the tissues and reached the film. The light areas show where the barium blocked the path of the X rays.

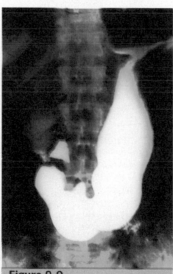

Figure 9-9

The light area in this X-ray photograph shows the patient's stomach. Barium in the stomach blocked the path of the X rays.

Tie-in/Language Arts Have students read the biography of Marie Curie. Then have them write papers which explain how radium was discovered and isolated.

Teaching Tip Review the concept of emitted light when alkali metal and alkaline earth metal atoms are heated. Explain that the absorption of energy causes electrons to jump to higher energy levels. Upon their return to the original energy levels, the electrons emit light.

Puzzler Strontium is chemically similar to calcium. But strontium is more active than calcium. It is above calcium on the activity series and can replace it.

3 REVIEW/REINFORCEMENT

1. Generally, alkali metals are more reactive than the alkaline earth metals.
2. Hydrogen and a base.
3. Answers will vary.

Challenge SrI_2, $CaSO_4$.

Figure 9-10

The bright colors in the fireworks are caused by the metals that are used.

SCIENCE PUZZLER

Bones contain large amounts of calcium. They also contain small amounts of strontium. If a person is exposed to large amounts of strontium, this metal will replace some of the calcium that is already in the bones. Why is strontium able to replace calcium?

Radium is a Group 2 metal that is radioactive. The nucleus of a radioactive atom gives off particles and energy. In this process the atom of one element becomes an atom of a different element. Radium goes through several changes, and becomes lead. The energy given off by a radioactive atom can be put to use. The energy given off by radium has been used to treat cancer.

Like the alkali metals, the alkaline earth metals give off light when their atoms are heated. Barium is used to provide a green color to fireworks. Calcium produces a red color. Strontium (STRON shee uhm) also produces red light. Which alkaline earth metal is used to produce a bright white flash?[1]

REVIEW

1. Compare the reactivity of alkaline earth metals with that of alkali metals.
2. What are the products of the reaction between an alkaline earth metal and water?
3. Name one use for each of the following: beryllium, magnesium, and calcium.

CHALLENGE Predict the chemical formulas for strontium iodide and calcium sulfate.

[1]Magnesium.

9-4 THE TRANSITION ELEMENTS

The **transition elements** are the elements located between Groups 2 and 13 in the Periodic Table. These elements are found only in the fourth through seventh rows of the Periodic Table. The ten transition groups once were thought to represent a gradual change, or transition, between groups at each end of the Periodic Table. Actually, the transition elements do not show definite patterns in their chemical properties. This is because of the varied ions that these elements form.

Notice in Figure 9-11 that each transition element has one or two electrons in its outer energy level. Although the number of outer electrons is the same for many transition elements, the total number of electrons is different for each element. Each element has one more proton and electron than does the element to its left in the Periodic Table. However, in these elements, the additional electrons may be in an inner energy level, instead of the outer level.

> *After completing this section, you will be able to*
>
> - **locate** the transition elements in the Periodic Table.
> - **compare** the chemical behavior of the transition elements with that of other metals.
> - **list** examples of alloys that contain transition elements.
>
> *The key terms in this section are*
> **alloys**
> **transition elements**

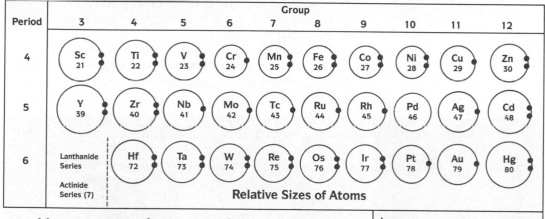

				Group					
Period	**3**	**4**	**5**	**6**	**7**	**8**	**9**	**10**	**11**	**12**
4	Sc 21	Ti 22	V 23	Cr 24	Mn 25	Fe 26	Co 27	Ni 28	Cu 29	Zn 30
5	Y 39	Zr 40	Nb 41	Mo 42	Tc 43	Ru 44	Rh 45	Pd 46	Ag 47	Cd 48
6	Lanthanide Series	Hf 72	Ta 73	W 74	Re 75	Os 76	Ir 77	Pt 78	Au 79	Hg 80
	Actinide Series (7)					**Relative Sizes of Atoms**				

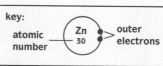

key:
atomic number — Zn 30 — outer electrons

Figure 9-11

The transition elements.

Many transition elements can form more than one kind of ion. Different kinds of ions form compounds with different chemical formulas. For example, copper can form a 1+ or a 2+ ion. Copper (I) chloride is $CuCl$. Copper (II) chloride is $CuCl_2$.

Iron can form a 2+ or a 3+ ion. Iron (II) oxide, FeO, is a black powder. Iron (III) oxide, Fe_2O_3, forms a dark red powder. These two compounds have different densities and melting points.

Mercury can form a 1+ or a 2+ ion. Mercury (I) nitrate is $Hg_2(NO_3)_2$. Mercury (II) nitrate is $Hg(NO_3)_2$. These two compounds have different densities, melting points, and crystal structures.

9-4 THE TRANSITION ELEMENTS
pages 215–220

OBJECTIVES
Refer to pupil page 215.

VOCABULARY
Key terms: alloys, transition elements

1 MOTIVATION

Display solutions of NaCl, KNO_3, $Ca(NO_3)_2$, $MgCl_2$, K_2CrO_4, $Ni(NO_3)_2$, and $CuSO_4$. Ask students to identify the major difference among them. (Some are colored; the rest are colorless.) Ask students to classify each compound according to the group of its metal. Ask what conclusion might be drawn regarding group versus color. (Transition elements form colored compounds.)

2 CONCEPT DEVELOPMENT

Teaching Tip Have students locate the transition elements in the Periodic Table. Ask what happens to the next-to-last energy level of the elements from left to right in the table. (Electrons are being added.)

Background Each of the transition elements has an incomplete inner shell. Atoms of these elements lose electrons from their outer and next-to-last energy levels.

predicting
Iron, cobalt, and nickel are chemically similar transition elements. Iron forms 2+ and 3+ ions. For instance, there are two nitrates of iron—iron (II) nitrate, $Fe(NO_3)_2$, and iron (III) nitrate, $Fe(NO_3)_3$. On the basis of this information, have students predict the formulas for the two nitrates of cobalt and of nickel. ($Co(NO_3)_2$ and $Co(NO_3)_3$; $Ni(NO_3)_2$ and $Ni(NO_3)_3$.)

Background   The mercury (I) ion exists as $(Hg_2)^{2+}$. Hot nitric acid is a powerful oxidizing agent. The $(Hg_2)^{2+}$ ion is oxidized to Hg^{2+}.

Teaching Tip   Review the activity series. Ask students what transition elements are above hydrogen. (Zn, Fe, Co, Ni, Cr, Mn.) Ask students what transition elements will not replace hydrogen from an acid. (Cu, Ag, Au, Pt, Hg.)

Demonstration   Show the variable activity of the transition elements by dropping a piece of nickel into dilute HCl. Test the liberated gas with a burning splint. Repeat, using a piece of copper. (Nickel will liberate hydrogen; copper will not.)

Thinking Skills ━━━

interpreting charts
Have students look at Figure 9-12. Ask why the silver deposits on the copper metal. (Copper is more active than silver and will replace silver in a solution of a silver compound.)

Transition metals are not as reactive as either alkali metals or alkaline earth metals. Some transition metals, such as zinc, will release hydrogen from acids.

$$Zn(s) + 2\ HCl(aq) \longrightarrow ZnCl_2(aq) + H_2(g)$$

Other transition metals, such as silver, will not react with hydrochloric acid. Recall that only metals above hydrogen in the activity series can displace hydrogen gas from an acid. All of the alkali metals and alkaline earth metals are above hydrogen. Only a few of the transition elements, such as zinc and nickel, are above hydrogen in the activity series.

Transition elements can take part in replacement reactions. For example, copper will replace silver in the following reaction.

$$Cu(s) + AgNO_3(aq) \longrightarrow CuNO_3(aq) + Ag(s)$$

Figure 9-12 shows the result of this replacement. Notice the deposits of silver on the copper. What other change can you see?[1] The silver has been replaced because copper is a more active metal than silver. If gold is used in place of the copper, no reaction would take place. Gold is a less active metal than silver.

The physical properties of transition metals also vary a great deal. Gold, platinum, and silver are very malleable, but titanium is not. Copper and tungsten are very ductile, but cadmium is not.

[1] The solution is changing color.

Figure 9-12

Copper can replace silver ions in the solution.

ACTIVITY Which Metal Is More Reactive, Copper or Zinc?

OBJECTIVE
Compare the chemical activity of two metals.

MATERIALS
safety goggles, lab apron, 10-mL graduate, 2 test tubes, zinc sulfate solution, copper wire, scissors, copper (II) sulfate solution, zinc metal

PROCEDURE

A. Wear safety goggles and a lab apron throughout this activity.
B. Measure 10 mL of zinc sulfate solution into a test tube.
  1. What color is zinc sulfate solution?
C. Cut a 4-cm piece of copper wire. Place the copper wire in the zinc sulfate solution.
  2. What color is the copper wire?
  3. What changes did you observe in the copper wire when it was placed in the solution?
4. What changes did you observe in the solution when the copper was added?
D. Measure 10 mL of copper (II) sulfate solution into a clean, dry test tube.
  5. What color is copper (II) sulfate solution?
E. Place a piece of zinc in the copper (II) sulfate solution.
  6. What color is the zinc metal?
  7. What changes did you observe in the zinc metal when it was placed in the solution?
  8. What changes did you observe in the solution when the zinc was added?

RESULTS AND CONCLUSIONS
1. In which test tube(s) did a reaction take place?
2. Which metal is more reactive, the copper or the zinc?

Metals often are combined in mixtures called **alloys**. Alloys are made when metals are heated together. An alloy has different properties than the metals from which it is made. For example, silver is a very soft metal. Adding copper to silver makes sterling silver, an alloy that is harder than pure silver.

Several other alloys are listed in Table 9-1. Notice that there are no chemical formulas given. An alloy is not a compound. It does not form as the result of a chemical reaction. Thus the makeup of an alloy can vary. The percents shown for each alloy stand for only one of the possible compositions.

Table 9-1 *Alloys*

Alloy	Composition	Use
Brass	70% Cu, 30% Zn	Hardware, plumbing
Bronze	90% Cu, 10% Sn	Artwork, domes of buildings
Gold alloy	70% Au, 17% Ag, 10% Cu, 1% Pt, 1% Zn, 1% Pd	Dentistry, jewelry
Pewter	85% Sn, 7% Cu, 6% Bi, 2% Sb	Cups, candlesticks
Solder	60% Pb, 40% Sn	Connecting metal pieces together
Stainless steel	74% Fe, 18% Cr, 8% Ni	Cutlery
Steel	99% Fe, 1% C	Bridges, buildings
Sterling silver	93% Ag, 7% Cu	Jewelry, tableware

PROCESS SKILLS
observing, comparing, inferring

Preparation   To prepare 0.1M $ZnSO_4$, add 8 g of $ZnSO_4$ to a 500-mL graduate. Add distilled water to reach to the 500-mL mark, and mix thoroughly. Repeat, using 8 g of $CuSO_4$ to make 0.1M $CuSO_4$.

Safety Tip   Caution students to be careful in handling the copper wire. It could puncture the skin.

Teaching Tip   Have students note and compare the physical properties of the copper and zinc.

Answers to Procedure
1. Colorless.
2. Orange-brown.
3. None.
4. None.
5. Blue.
6. Silver-gray.
7. The zinc metal becomes covered with copper.
8. It turned almost colorless.

Answers to Results and Conclusions
1. Zinc and copper (II) sulfate.
2. Zinc.

Teaching Tip   Review the definition of a mixture. State the properties of mixtures. Emphasize that alloys are mixtures. Refer students to Table 9-1.

Background   Gold foil used in the lettering on office doors or in the crowns of teeth is so thin that 300,000 sheets of it would make a pile 2.5 cm thick.

Demonstration   Make the alloy *Wood's metal*. Mix together in a crucible 4 g of bismuth, 2 g of lead, 2 g of tin, and 1 g of cadmium. Melt the mixture. Then pour it into a plaster of Paris mold of a spoon. Allow the mold to harden. Heat some water in a beaker while stirring with the spoon. The Wood's metal softens as it heats.

Steel can contain as little as 0.2 percent carbon, or as much as 1.5 percent carbon. Changing the amount of carbon in steel changes the properties of the alloy slightly. For example, as more carbon is added to steel, the hardness of the alloy increases. Figure 9-13 shows this increase. At what percent of carbon does the hardness of steel stop increasing?[1]

[1]0.60 percent.

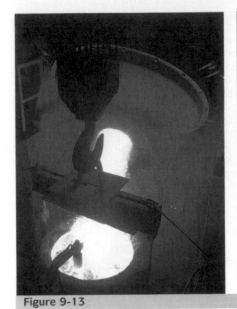

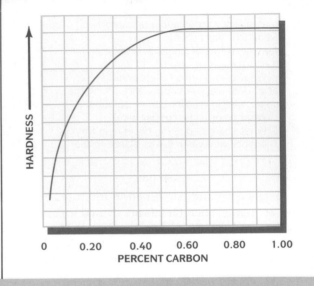

Figure 9-13

The hardness of the steel being produced depends on the percent of carbon in the mixture.

Sometimes, the metals in an alloy can be changed. Pewter can be used to make plates and other tableware. This alloy used to contain lead as part of the mixture. It was discovered that the lead, which is poisonous, was being absorbed by food. After this, pewter was made without the lead.

Why can alloys vary in their makeup but compounds cannot? Recall that compounds are held together by covalent or ionic bonds. Each atom can form only a certain number of such bonds. Metals are held together by metallic bonds. Mixing different metal ions into the sea of electrons in an alloy does not require exact ratios of elements, nor special arrangements of atoms.

Many transition elements are good conductors of electricity. Tungsten (TUHNG stuhn), a good conductor, is used to make filaments for light bulbs. As electricity flows through the tungsten filament, the temperature of the filament goes up. This makes the filament glow. The higher the temperature becomes, the more light the tungsten gives off. Tungsten has a melting point of about 3400°C, the highest melting point of any metal. Since its melting point is so high, it can become white hot without melting. At high temperatures, tungsten will react with oxygen.

$$2W(s) + 3O_2(g) \longrightarrow 2WO_3(s)$$

The oxide formed would reduce the amount of light that could be produced. To avoid this problem, light bulbs contain a mixture of nitrogen and argon instead of air. Tungsten metal does not react with these gases.

A burned-out light bulb looks black because some of the tungsten atoms are evaporating from the tungsten filament. The tungsten then deposits on the inside of the bulb. The loss of tungsten slowly weakens the filament, which eventually will break.

The transition elements have widespread use in industry and everyday life. Copper, silver, gold, and nickel are used in coins. Before 1960, dimes and quarters were made of silver. Notice in Figure 9-15 that newer coins have copper sandwiched between thin layers of silver.

Jewelry is made of gold, silver, platinum, and copper. Platinum is a very hard metal, and can be used in its pure form. Gold and silver are much softer, and alloys of these metals are used for jewelry. The gold content in jewelry is expressed in units called *carats*. Each carat stands for 1/24 of the mixture. Pure gold is 24 carat gold. Gold that is marked 18 carat is 18 parts gold and 6 parts other metals. What are the proportions of metals in 14 carat gold?[1]

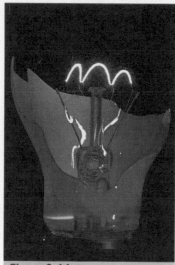

Figure 9-14

The tungsten filament in this broken light bulb is reacting with oxygen in the air.

[1]14 parts gold and 10 parts other metals.

Figure 9-15

Transition elements are used in making coins.

Students may have noticed that the letter symbols for copper, iron, gold, mercury, and silver do not resemble the English names of the metals. Ask students to look up the Latin names for these elements and then discuss the origin of the symbols. (*Cuprum, ferrum, aurum, hydrargyrum, argentum.*)

Background Alloys generally are solids composed of two or more metals, but they may contain nonmetals such as carbon, silicon, nitrogen, or phosphorus mixed with metals. The resulting mixtures are considered alloys only when their properties are metallic.

Enrichment Ask students to find out the names of some substances that Thomas Edison tested as filaments.

Thinking Skills

inferring
Have students read the paragraph about tungsten in the text and then look at Figure 9-14. Ask them how you can tell if a bulb is burned out by looking at it. (The filament will be broken and there will be blackened glass.)

Thinking Skills

inferring

Ask students to infer what happens to the dark areas of a photographic negative, such as that shown in Figure 9-16, when it is printed onto light-sensitive paper. (They are reversed and become light areas.)

Teaching Tip   If possible, bring in a burned-out light bulb for students to examine. Also have them examine a bulb that is slightly blackened but not yet burned out.

Demonstration   Show that a Canadian nickel contains more nickel than does a United States nickel. Bring a magnet near each. The Canadian nickel will be attracted; the United States nickel will not be attracted.

Background   Gold does not react with any one acid but will dissolve in aqua regia, a mixture of hydrochloric and nitric acids. Platinum can be used in dentistry—in bridges, braces, and inlays. Platinum is chemically similar to gold.

3 REVIEW/REINFORCEMENT

1. Groups 3 through 12.
2. Sodium reacts violently; magnesium, less violently; zinc reacts the least violently. All liberate hydrogen.
3. Solder and pewter.
4. Answers will vary.

Challenge Hg_2O and HgO.

Review and Skill Masters

CHALLENGE/CRITICAL THINKING, page 58.
See page 203c in this book for answers.

DO YOU KNOW?

Gold has been used to fix teeth since the time of ancient civilizations. The Etruscans were probably the first people to use gold for dental work. The Etruscans lived during the sixth century B.C., along what is now the western shore of Italy. They were experts at working with iron, bronze, and gold. A goldsmith's shop often would be visited by doctors and their patients. Here, false teeth were fitted to the patient.

The replacement tooth would be attached to the patient's own teeth by means of strips of gold. The gold strips were placed around the teeth on either side of the gap left by the missing tooth. A replacement tooth was placed into the gap and held in place by rivets. Sometimes the tooth that was lost would be put back in place. In other cases, an animal tooth would be used. Sometimes a replacement tooth was made completely of gold.

Gold is still used in dentistry today. Cheaper alloys from other metals have been developed, but no substitute has matched gold. The long history of gold in dentistry is likely to continue.

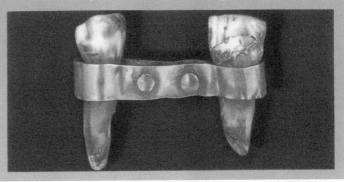

[1]The areas that look dark have been changed the most by light.

Figure 9-16

The areas that look dark in this negative will look light when the photograph is printed.

A zircon (ZER kahn) is a compound of zirconium (zer-KOH nee uhm) that is sometimes used as a substitute for a diamond. A cubic zirconia is a zirconium oxide crystal grown in a laboratory. These crystals are used in jewelry.

Photographic film uses silver compounds that are sensitive to light. The silver compounds are dissolved in a thin layer of gelatin. Light begins the reaction that changes the silver ions in silver bromide to pure silver.

$$Ag^+ + e^- \longrightarrow Ag$$

The electron shown in the reaction comes from the bromide ion in silver bromide. The silver that is produced leaves black deposits on the film. Look at the photographic negative shown in Figure 9-16. What parts of the negative have been changed the most by light?[1]

REVIEW

1. Where are the transition elements located in the Periodic Table?
2. Compare the chemical reactivity of zinc, magnesium, and sodium in acids.
3. Name two alloys that contain tin.
4. List three uses of transition metals.

CHALLENGE Recall that mercury can form two different ions. Predict the formulas for the two oxides of mercury.

9-5 THE INNER TRANSITION ELEMENTS

The **inner transition elements** are located in the sixth and seventh rows of the Periodic Table. These elements should follow barium and radium, but they are placed at the bottom of the Periodic Table. If the inner transition elements were shown in the sixth and seventh rows, the Periodic Table would be almost twice as wide.

The **lanthanide** (LAN thuh nīd) **series** includes the 15 elements beginning with lanthanum in the sixth row of the Periodic Table. These elements are sometimes called the rare earth elements, although some, like cerium (SIHR-ee uhm), are not rare. The lanthanide elements usually are found together in deposits in the earth. Their chemical properties are quite similar, so they are difficult to separate. Because they are so similar, the lanthanides that occur together are sometimes used in mixtures.

Some lanthanides have special properties. Samarium (suh MAHR ee uhm) and gadolinium (gad uh LIHN ee uhm) are magnetic. Promethium (proh MEE thee uhm) is radioactive. Promethium is not found in nature. It is recovered from the waste products of nuclear reactors. Because it gives off light, promethium is used in the paint for luminous watch dials.

The lanthanide elements are somewhat reactive, and they usually form a 3+ ion. Many of these elements will react with water, to release hydrogen gas. What other group of metals reacts with water to release hydrogen?[1]

Oxides of several lanthanides can absorb the harmful ultraviolet rays in sunlight. These compounds are used in making tinted glass, shown in Figure 9-17. Lanthanide compounds are also used in making lasers.

[1] Alkali metals.

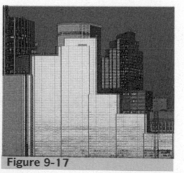

Figure 9-17

The tinted glass used in these buildings absorbs harmful rays in sunlight.

OBJECTIVES
Refer to pupil page 221.

VOCABULARY

Key terms:	actinide series, inner transition elements, lanthanide series
Other terms:	phosphorus, transuranium elements

1 MOTIVATION

Darken the classroom. Show students a watch dial that has been painted with luminous paint. Ask students what makes the dial glow in the dark. (Radioactivity.) Ask students if this watch is dangerous. (No. The radioactivity is very slight.)

2 CONCEPT DEVELOPMENT

Teaching Tip   Locate the lanthanide series in the Periodic Table. Have the class recite the names of these elements aloud to check for proper pronunciation. Look at the atomic structures of the inner transition elements. Point out the three incomplete outer energy levels.

Thinking Skills

predicting
Students are aware that the element uranium is the natural element with the greatest atomic mass. Have students predict how the synthetic elements, which have greater atomic masses than does uranium, were discovered and formed.

Background   Transuranium elements are all synthetic. They are made in nuclear accelerators by bombarding particles (atoms) with other particles (protons, neutrons, and alpha particles). These elements may have once been present in the universe as a result of nuclear reactions. However, their short half-lives resulted in their disintegrating into longer-lived elements, such as uranium.

Teaching Tip   Locate the actinide series in the Periodic Table. Have the class recite the names of these elements aloud to check for proper pronunciation.

Tie-in/Language Arts   Ask students to determine the origins of the names of the transuranium elements.

Europium oxide has several uses. It is one of the phosphors (FAHS fuhrz) used in color televisions. *Phosphors* are chemicals that give off light when they are exposed to radiation. Europium gives off red light. Europium oxide also is used in the glue on postage stamps. Laser beam scanners in sorting machines can identify first-class mail because of the phosphor in the glue.

Figure 9-18

Automatic sorting machines can identify first-class mail by the europium in the stamps.

The **actinide** (AK tuh nīd) **series** includes the elements beginning with actinium (ak TIHN ee uhm) in the seventh row of the Periodic Table. The actinide elements are radioactive and, with the exception of uranium, are not found in large amounts in nature.

Those elements which follow uranium in the Periodic Table are called *transuranium elements*. Uranium is one of the densest elements found naturally on earth. All of the transuranium elements are denser than uranium, but they are synthetic. Neptunium and plutonium were the first elements made in nuclear reactors. Uranium and plutonium are used in nuclear reactors to generate electricity.

Curium (KYUR ee uhm) is used as a fuel in nuclear batteries that power the radio transmitters left behind on the moon. Plutonium also can be used in nuclear batteries in the space program, in satellites and space probes. Some scientists believe that a plutonium battery may someday power heart pacemakers and artificial hearts.

REVIEW

1. Where are the inner transition elements located in the Periodic Table?
2. Name the major difference between the lanthanide elements and the actinide elements.
3. Give a use for two inner transition elements.

CHALLENGE If someday an artificial heart is made using an isotope of plutonium, what special precaution will have to be taken?

CHAPTER SUMMARY

The main ideas in this chapter are listed below. Read these statements before you answer the Chapter Review questions.

- Over three fourths of the elements in the Periodic Table are metals. (9-1)

- Metals have luster, are malleable, and are ductile. They are conductors of heat and electricity. (9-1)

- Most metals have one or two electrons in their outer energy level. Metal atoms usually lose their outer electrons during chemical reactions and form positive ions. (9-1)

- Metal atoms are held together in a solid by an attractive force called metallic bonds. (9-1)

- The Group 1 elements are called the alkali metals. Alkali metals are the most chemically reactive metal group. (9-2)

- Alkali metals have one electron in their outer energy level. An alkali metal will lose its one outer electron and become a 1+ ion. (9-2)

- The elements of Group 2 are called the alkaline earth metals. The alkaline earth metals are less chemically reactive than the alkali metals. (9-3)

- The alkaline earth metals have two outer electrons. An alkaline earth metal will lose its outer electrons and become a 2+ ion. (9-3)

- The transition elements are metals located in the fourth through seventh rows, after Group 2 in the Periodic Table. (9-4)

- The transition elements usually form more than one type of ion. (9-4)

- The inner transition elements are found within the transition elements in the sixth and seventh rows, after the Group 2 elements. The lanthanide series and actinide series make up the inner transition elements. (9-5)

- Elements in the lanthanide series are sometimes called rare earth elements. (9-5)

- All of the actinide elements are radioactive. (9-5)

The key terms in this chapter are listed below. Use each term in a sentence that shows the meaning of the term.

actinide series
alkali metals
alkaline earth metals
alloys
ductile
inner transition elements
lanthanide series
luster
malleable
metallic bond
metals
ores
transition elements

Tie-in/Math Have students calculate the number of neutrons in some actinide atoms such as uranium, plutonium, and einsteinium.

Enrichment Have students research the beneficial uses of radiation in the world today.

3 REVIEW/REINFORCEMENT

1. At the bottom of the Periodic Table.
2. Unlike lanthanide elements all the actinide elements are radioactive.
3. Uses of inner transition elements include oxides of certain lanthanide elements in making tinted glass; phosphors to invisibly label postage stamps and other objects; promethium for luminous watch dials; curium in nuclear batteries; and uranium to fuel nuclear power plants.

Challenge The artificial heart will have to contain shields to prevent the radioactive rays from escaping. Also, the artificial heart will have to be small and lightweight because the plutonium is extremely heavy.

Review and Skill Masters

VOCABULARY REVIEW, page 53.
See page 203b in this book for answers.

VOCABULARY

1. metallic bond
2. alloys
3. ductile
4. alkaline earth metals
5. transition elements
6. ores
7. malleable
8. alkali metals
9. inner transition elements
10. luster
11. metals

CONCEPTS

1. Luster, malleable, ductile, conductor.
2. One to three.
3. Because the outer electrons are far from the positive attraction of the nucleus, those electrons are not tightly linked to the atomic structure.
4. The positive metallic ions attract the negative electrons moving about the ions.
5. Its atoms are held together by metallic bonds. The electrons are freely moving.
6. They give off bright-colored light.
7. They each have one electron.
8. Francium; lithium.
9. Hydrogen and a base.

Review and Skill Masters

CHAPTER REVIEW, pages 54–55.
See page 203b in this book for answers.

Chapter Review

VOCABULARY

Use the key terms from this chapter to complete the following sentences correctly.

1. A/an _____ is the force of attraction that holds metal ions together.
2. Metals that are combined in mixtures are called _____ .
3. A metal that can be drawn into a thin wire is said to be _____ .
4. _____ are the elements that are found in Group 2 in the Periodic Table.
5. The _____ are located between Groups 2 and 13 in the Periodic Table.
6. Metals are found in the earth as a mixture of compounds called _____ .
7. Metals can be pounded into many shapes, including thin sheets. Because of this property, metals are described as _____ .
8. Elements in Group 1 of the Periodic Table are called _____ .
9. Elements located in the sixth and seventh rows after the Group 2 metals in the Periodic Table are called _____ .
10. _____ is the property of metals that gives them a shiny appearance.
11. _____ are elements that are shiny, that are good conductors of heat and electricity, and that can be pounded into various shapes.

CONCEPTS

1. Name three properties of metals. (9-1)
2. How many electrons do metals usually have in their outer energy level? (9-1)
3. Why do larger metal atoms lose their outer electrons easily? (9-1)
4. Describe the formation of the structure of a metallic solid. (9-1)
5. Why is copper a good conductor of electricity? (9-1)
6. What happens to alkali metals when they are heated? (9-2)
7. What is the electron arrangement of the outer energy levels of Group 1 elements? (9-2)
8. Which metal in Group 1 has the largest atoms? Which has the smallest atoms? (9-2)
9. What are the products of a reaction of an alkali metal and water? (9-2)

10. How many electrons do the Group 2 metals have in their outer energy levels? (9-3)

11. Compare the chemical behavior of the Group 1 metals in water with that of the Group 2 metals. (9-3)

12. Give two uses for each of the following Group 2 elements: barium, calcium, and magnesium. (9-3)

13. In which rows of the Periodic Table are the transition elements located? (9-4)

14. How does the reactivity of the transition elements compare with that of the alkaline earth metals? (9-4)

15. Name two alloys that contain transition elements. (9-4)

16. What two ions can copper form? (9-4)

17. Name some industrial uses of the transition elements. (9-4)

18. In which rows do the inner transition elements belong in the Periodic Table? (9-5)

19. Which elements are known as the rare earth elements? (9-5)

20. What is the unique characteristic of the actinide elements? (9-5)

APPLICATION/ CRITICAL THINKING

1. Write and balance the equation for the reaction between calcium and water.

2. Which metal would probably be more chemically reactive, magnesium or potassium? Why?

3. After repeated pounding, metals become brittle because the movement of electrons slows down. How could you make these metals malleable again?

EXTENSION

1. Write a report on the effects of sodium chloride on the human circulatory system.

2. Go to the library and obtain an earth science book. Research how limestone and marble are formed. Find out how these minerals are similar, and how they differ.

3. Talk to a professional photographer. Determine how film is developed.

READINGS

Siberner, J. "New Factor in Salt." *Science News,* December 16, 1983, p. 372.

"Sodium Bicarb Use Questioned." *Science News,* May 18, 1985, p. 311.

"A Tungsten Coat for Silicon." *Science News,* March 16, 1985, p. 173.

10. Two.
11. Group 1 metals are generally more re-active.
12. Barium salts are used in paint and X-ray photography. Calcium compounds are useful as chalk, marble, antacids, and drying agents. Magnesium compounds are used as laxatives and for electrical and thermal insulation.
13. The fourth through seventh rows.
14. Generally, the transition elements are less reactive.
15. Sterling silver and pewter.
16. 1^+ and 2^+.
17. Tungsten used to make filaments for light bulbs, and copper, silver, gold, and nickel used in coins.
18. The sixth and seventh rows.
19. Lanthanides.
20. They are radioactive.

APPLICATION/CRITICAL THINKING

1. $Ca + 2H_2O \rightarrow Ca(OH)_2 + H_2$.
2. K; it is larger; also, potassium is an alkali metal with only one electron to lose. The alkali metals are the most chemically re-active.
3. Heat them.

Test Masters

CHAPTER TEST, pages 33–36.
See page 203d in this book for answers.

NONMETALS AND METALLOIDS

ORGANIZER

Section	pages	Activity	pages	Reinforcement and Evaluation	pages	*Review and Skill Masters	pages	Other Components in Teacher Resource Package	pages
10–1 Comparing Nonmetals and Metalloids	227–228			Review, Challenge	228			Study Guide	47
10–2 The Boron and Carbon Groups	229–235	How Is a Nonmetal Used to Extract a Metal?	234	Puzzler Review, Challenge	232 235			Study Guide	48
10–3 The Nitrogen and Oxygen Groups	236–241	How Much Oxygen Is in the Air?	240	Review, Challenge	241	Challenge/Critical Thinking	63–64	Study Guide	49
10–4 The Halogens	242–244			Review, Challenge	244			Study Guide Lab Manual	50 53
10–5 The Noble Gases	245–246			Review, Challenge	246			Study Guide Lab Manual	51 57
10–6 Hydrogen	247–248	How Can Gases Be Prepared?	248	Review, Challenge	249	Skill	62	Study Guide	52
CHAPTER SUMMARY	249					Vocabulary Review	59		
CHAPTER REVIEW	250–251			*Test Masters	37–40	Chapter Review	60–61		

*In the Teacher Resource Package. For answers, see pages 225b–225d in this book.

ACTIVITY MATERIALS   Quantities are based on a class of 30 students working in groups as indicated in parentheses.

How Is a Nonmetal Used to Extract a Metal? p. 234 (groups of 2)	quantity	How Much Oxygen Is in the Air? p. 240 (groups of 2)	quantity	How Can Gases Be Prepared? p. 248 (groups of 3)	quantity
lab apron	30	metric ruler	15	safety goggles	30
safety goggles	30	test tube	15	lab apron	30
balance	15	balance	15	test-tube rack	10
copper (II) oxide	15 g	iron filings	60 g	test tube	40
test tube	15	400-mL beaker	15	glass-marking pencil	10
test-tube rack	15	ring stand	15	one-hole rubber stopper	10
powdered charcoal	30 g	burette clamp	15	glass tubing (40 cm long)	10 pieces
glass stirring rod	15			rubber tubing (50 cm long)	10 pieces
ring stand	15			masking tape	10 rolls
burette clamp	15			water bath or gas-collecting trough	10
Bunsen burner	15			50-mL graduated cylinder	10
striker	15			hydrochloric acid	50 mL
250-mL beaker	15			mossy zinc	25 g
spatula	15			wood splints	10
				wooden matches	10 boxes
				vinegar	100 mL
				baking soda	1 box
				hydrogen peroxide	200 mL
				manganese dioxide	50 g

REVIEW AND SKILL MASTERS

VOCABULARY REVIEW _____ Chapter 10

Use the clues to fill in the puzzle.

ACROSS

2. A substance that conducts electricity at some temperatures and not others
5. Process of adding hydrogen to a compound
8. The elements of group 17
9. Supercooled liquid so viscous that it appears to be a solid
10. Elements that lack luster, ductility, and malleability
11. Different structural forms of the same element

DOWN

1. A molecule made up of three atoms of a single element (two words)
3. A molecule made up of two atoms of a single element (two words)
4. Group of elements with properties of both metals and nonmetals
5. Process in which halogens combine with covalent compounds
6. Group of elements once known as inert gases (two words)
7. Process in which oxygen combines with any element or compound

© 1988 Silver, Burdett & Ginn Inc.

59

CHAPTER REVIEW _____ Chapter 10

10-1 Nonmetals and Metalloids

1. Explain why nonmetals cannot be hammered into a new shape without breaking.
   They are brittle because they lack the kind of bonds found in metals. Their electrons form individual bonds that do not allow free movement of electrons.

2. What type of bond is formed when a nonmetal atom combines with a metal atom?
   An ionic bond is formed.

3. What type of bond is formed when a nonmetal atom combines with a nonmetal atom?
   A covalent bond is formed.

4. What are metalloids? Metalloids are elements that have properties of both metals and nonmetals.

10-2 The Boron and Carbon Groups

1. Name the only metalloid in Group 13 and list its properties. Boron is Group 13's only metalloid. Its atom is small and holds its three outer electrons tightly; therefore, it does not form a positive ion by giving them up. Boron forms only covalent bonds with other atoms. Boron does not exist as a free element. It can be used as a semiconductor.

2. An element found in the Boron group is the most abundant metal in the earth's crust. Name both the metal and its ore. Aluminum is the most abundant metal in the earth's crust. Bauxite (aluminum oxide) is the ore source for commercially-used aluminum.

3. Define the term *allotrope*. Name the two allotropes of carbon. Allotropes are different structural forms of the same element. Graphite and diamond are the allotropes of carbon.

© 1988 Silver, Burdett & Ginn Inc.

60

CHAPTER REVIEW (Continued) _____ Chapter 10

10-3 The Nitrogen and Oxygen Groups

1. How do the atoms of elements in Group 15 differ from those of the elements in Group 16?
   Each of the atoms in Group 15 has five electrons in its outer energy level, while each of the atoms in Group 16 has six electrons in its outer energy level.

2. Describe one type of oxidation reaction. A combustion reaction, or burning, is an oxidation reaction that gives off heat and light.

10-4 The Halogens

1. What structural property of the halogens makes them so reactive? They have seven electrons in their outer energy levels, and thus need only one more electron to complete these levels.

2. List two uses of halogens. Answers will vary. Fluorides are added to toothpaste and chlorine is used as a disinfectant.

10-5 The Noble Gases

1. Explain the very low reactivity of the noble gases. Their low reactivity is due to their atomic structure. Each of these elements has a complete outer energy level and does not gain or lose electrons. Thus, they are very stable.

2. List two uses of noble gases. Answers will vary. Helium is used in blimps and neon is used in lights.

10-6 Hydrogen

1. When hydrogen gives up an electron and forms a positive ion, to what group of elements is hydrogen similar? The alkali metals.

2. When hydrogen gains an electron and forms a negative ion, to what group of elements is it similar? The halogens.

© 1988 Silver, Burdett & Ginn Inc.

61

SKILL/Interpreting Charts _____ Chapter 10

Elements of the same family in the Periodic Table have similar or related properties. Complete the following chart which compares elements from different families. Use statements from below to fill in the column entitled "Element Characteristics."

A - colorless, odorless gas that makes up 21 percent of earth's atmosphere
B - soft, dense metal that melts easily
C - when electric current is sent through this gas, it emits red light
D - a halogen that is a liquid at room temperature
E - compounds of this element are very poisonous
F - the most abundant metal in the earth's crust

Name of Element	Symbol	Period	Group	Number of Outer Electrons	Metal, Nonmetal, or Noble Gas	Physical State at Room Temperature	Element Characteristics
Oxygen	O	2	16	6	Nonmetal	Gas	A
Lead	Pb	6	14	4	Metal	Solid	B
Arsenic	As	4	15	5	Metalloid	Solid	E
Neon	Ne	2	18	8	Noble gas	Gas	C
Bromine	Br	4	17	7	Nonmetal	Liquid	D
Aluminum	Al	3	13	3	Metal	Solid	F

© 1988 Silver, Burdett & Ginn Inc.

62

CHAPTER 10 PLANNING GUIDE

225b

Name_____ Date_____

CHALLENGE/CRITICAL THINKING _____ Chapter 10

Approximately 21 percent of the earth's atmosphere is oxygen. The rest of the atmosphere is made up of nitrogen (78 percent) and other gases (1 percent). All living things on the earth depend on the atmosphere in order to live. They depend on the atmosphere for oxygen. They depend on the atmosphere to protect them from the harmful, high-energy, ultraviolet rays of the sun. They also depend on the atmosphere to help keep the earth warm.

The ozone layer is a layer of air that lies approximately 24 kilometers above the earth's surface. This layer contains a higher concentration of ozone than the rest of the air. The ozone layer helps to absorb heat from the sun and to protect plants and animals from ultraviolet rays. Ozone (O_3) is formed when oxygen (O_2) absorbs energy from ultraviolet rays. The third atom of oxygen is not bonded strongly to the other two. Because of this, direct contact with ozone can be harmful to living things.

In the 1970s, scientists worried that *fluorocarbons*, then found in aerosol spray cans, would damage the ozone layer. Fluorocarbons contain fluorine and carbon. These particular fluorocarbons also contained chlorine. After being released into the atmosphere, they rose to the ozone layer. Ultraviolet rays caused the fluorocarbons to break apart and release chlorine, which reacts with ozone.

1. Balance the simplified equation of the conversion of oxygen to ozone.

$$\underline{3}\ O_2 + energy \rightarrow \underline{2}\ O_3$$

2. Think about how ozone is formed. Why do you think there is a higher concentration of ozone in the upper part of the atmosphere than in the lower part of the atmosphere?

Ozone is formed from oxygen and energy. This energy comes in the form of

ultraviolet rays. There is more ozone in the upper part of the atmosphere

because there is a higher concentration of ultraviolet rays in the upper part of

the atmosphere. Thus, more oxygen is converted to ozone.

3. The same amount of gas molecules take up the same amount of room. O_3 is a molecule of ozone. O_2 is a molecule of oxygen. How dense do you think ozone is compared to oxygen? Explain your reasoning.

Ozone is 1.5 times as dense as oxygen. This is because ozone has three atoms

for every two atoms that oxygen has. Since each molecule takes up the same

amount of room, ozone has three atoms taking up the same amount of space

that only two atoms of oxygen take up. Therefore, ozone is 3 ÷ 2, or 1.5 times

as dense as oxygen.

© 1988 Silver, Burdett & Ginn Inc.

Name_____ Date_____

CHALLENGE/CRITICAL THINKING (Continued) _____ Chapter 10

4. Ozone is a very reactive gas compared to oxygen. Why do you think this is so?

Since the third atom of oxygen in ozone is not bonded strongly to the other

two, ozone can revert easily back to oxygen. This leaves the third atom of

oxygen free to react with other atoms or molecules.

5. Why do you think the use of fluorocarbons containing chlorine in aerosol spray cans is destructive to the ozone layer? What significance is this to the ecology?

Since ozone is a very reactive gas, the chlorine released by the fluorocarbons

reacts with the ozone. This destroys the ozone, and thus harms the ozone

layer. This is very important to the ecology because without the ozone layer

animals and plants cannot survive.

6. Ozone can be produced in the laboratory and used to purify drinking water that contains bacteria. Why does this work?

Since the third atom of oxygen is not bonded strongly to the other two, it can

harm living things if it comes in direct contact with them. Treating the water

with ozone will kill bacteria.

7. Some scientists think that automobiles add ozone to the atmosphere near the earth's surface. Is this good or bad? Explain your answer.

Raising the amount of ozone near the earth's surface is bad. This is because

direct contact with ozone can be harmful to living things.

© 1988 Silver, Burdett & Ginn Inc.

TEST MASTERS

Name _____ Date _____ Score _____

Chapter 10

Nonmetals and Metalloids

PART 1 _____

Chapter Goal

In the space below, write the term that each phrase defines.

1. diatomic molecule — A molecule that is made up of two atoms of a single element ... 3

2. metalloids — Elements that have properties of both metals and nonmetals ... 1

3. hydrogenation — The process by which hydrogen is added to a compound ... 6

4. noble gases — The elements in Group 18 of the Periodic Table, which have a complete outer energy level ... 5

5. glass — A supercooled liquid that is so viscous that it appears to be solid ... 2

6. oxidation — The reaction that occurs when oxygen combines with any element or compound ... 3

7. halogens — The elements in Group 17 of the Periodic Table, which join with metals to form salts ... 4

8. allotropes — Different structural forms of the same element ... 2

9. halogenation — The process by which halogens combine with covalent compounds ... 4

10. nonmetals — Elements that are hard and brittle, lack luster, and do not conduct electricity or heat ... 1

PART 2 _____

Choose the term or phrase that best answers the question or completes the statement. Write the letter of that choice in the space at the left.

Chapter Goal

__d__ 1. Nonmetallic solids differ from metallic solids in part because nonmetallic solids are: ... 1
   a. malleable.   b. ductile.   c. shiny.   d. brittle.

__c__ 2. Which of the following elements contains six electrons in its outer energy level? ... 3
   a. nitrogen   b. carbon   c. sulfur   d. boron

Chapter 10 Nonmetals and Metalloids   37

Name _____ Date _____ Score _____

PART 2

Choose the term or phrase that best answers the question or completes the statement. Write the letter of that choice in the space at the left.

Chapter Goal

__b__ 3. Which of the following is formed when a halogen combines with a metal? ... 4
   a. a tincture   b. a salt   c. an allotrope   d. a base

__d__ 4. The process by which hydrogen nuclei combine to form helium is called: ... 6
   a. electrolysis.   b. combustion.   c. oxidation.   d. fusion.

__c__ 5. In which of the following would neon and argon most likely be used? ... 5
   a. fireworks   b. detergents   c. lightbulbs   d. soft drinks

__d__ 6. Chlorine and iodine are both used commercially as: ... 4
   a. fuels.   c. semiconductors.
   b. lubricants.   d. disinfectants.

__d__ 7. Which of the following is formed when hydrogen is burned in the presence of oxygen? ... 6
   a. hydrogen sulfide   c. lithium hydride
   b. ammonia   d. water

__b__ 8. Nitrogen is collected as a gas by the process of: ... 3
   a. oxidation.   c. halogenation.
   b. distillation.   d. hydrogenation.

__a__ 9. In contrast with the halogen gases, the noble gases usually exist as: ... 5
   a. single atoms.   c. ionic compounds.
   b. diatomic molecules.   d. covalent compounds.

__b__ 10. Hydrogen differs from all other elements in the Periodic Table because it: ... 6
   a. occurs only in compounds.   c. reacts only with water.
   b. contains only one electron.   d. exists only as an inert gas.

__d__ 11. Graphite and diamond are similar because they both have: ... 2
   a. weak bonds.   c. metallic networks.
   b. hard textures.   d. crystal structures.

__b__ 12. When two nonmetals combine, they form: ... 1
   a. ionic bonds.   c. diatomic molecules.
   b. covalent bonds.   d. allotropes.

__c__ 13. Aluminum and boron are similar because they both are able to: ... 2
   a. exist as free elements.   c. conduct electricity.
   b. form positive ions.   d. lose their outer electrons.

__c__ 14. Helium is safer to use in blimps than hydrogen because helium: ... 5
   a. reacts readily with oxygen.
   b. forms halides with metals.
   c. has a complete outer energy level.
   d. loses electrons during hydrogenation.

Chapter 10 Nonmetals and Metalloids   38

Name _____ Date _____ Score _____

PART 3 _____

Look at the chart. Then read the questions that follow. Choose the term or phrase that best answers the question or completes the statement. Write the letter of that choice in the space at the left.

Element	Number of Electrons in Outer Level	Charge of Ion Formed	Number of Structural Forms	Formation of Diatomic Molecule	Conductor
A	1	(+) or (−)	1	yes	no
B	6	(−)	1	yes	no
C	5	(−)	1	yes	no
D	4	(+)	2	no	no
E	4	(+)	1	no	yes
F	8	does not form ions readily	1	no	no
G	7	(−)	1	yes	no

Chapter Goal

__b__ 1. Which of the elements on the chart has allotropes? ... 2
   a. C   b. D   c. E   d. G

__c__ 2. Element B would be identified as: ... 3
   a. silicon.   b. nitrogen.   c. oxygen.   d. krypton.

__d__ 3. Which of the following elements is likely to be the most stable? ... 5
   a. A   b. B   c. E   d. F

__c__ 4. Which of the elements on the chart is most likely a metalloid? ... 1
   a. B   b. C   c. E   d. G

__d__ 5. Element A on the chart is most likely: ... 6
   a. neon.   b. boron.   c. carbon.   d. hydrogen.

Chapter 10 Nonmetals and Metalloids   39

Name _____ Date _____ Score _____

PART 4 _____

Read each question or direction and answer it using complete sentences.

Chapter Goal

1. How does the arrangement of atoms affect the hardness of the two allotropes of carbon? ... 2

In graphite, each carbon atom is covalently bonded to three other carbon atoms, and the atoms are arranged in layers. The distance between the layers is too large for covalent bonds to form between them. As a result, the graphite layers are held together loosely and can be made to slide past each other. This structure makes graphite very soft. In a diamond, each carbon atom shares electrons with four other carbon atoms. These strong bonds cannot easily change shape, and so diamonds are very hard.

2. Explain why halogens are so reactive. ... 4

Halogens have seven electrons in their outer energy level. Thus, they need only one more electron to complete this level and become very stable. They will react quite readily to accept one electron and form a +1 ion. They will also form covalent bonds by sharing electrons.

3. Why is it difficult to classify hydrogen as a metal or a nonmetal? ... 6

It is difficult to classify hydrogen as a metal or a nonmetal because it has properties of both types of elements. Hydrogen is similar to an alkali metal in that it can give up an electron and form a +1 ion. It is like a nonmetal because it is a gas at room temperature, and because it forms covalent and ionic bonds instead of metallic bonds.

Chapter 10 Nonmetals and Metalloids   40

CHAPTER 10 PLANNING GUIDE

225d

10

NONMETALS AND METALLOIDS

The questions in the CHAPTER TEST are based on these Chapter Goals.

1. Distinguish between nonmetals and metalloids.
2. Describe the properties and uses of elements in Group 13 and Group 14.
3. Describe the properties and uses of elements in Group 15 and Group 16.
4. Describe the properties and uses of the halogens.
5. Describe the properties and uses of the noble gases.
6. Explain why hydrogen does not properly belong to any group of elements, and describe the properties and uses of hydrogen.

NONMETALS AND METALLOIDS

Most of the things that you see in this photograph are made up of nonmetals. The balloon is being prepared for a parade. It is made of rubber, and filled with helium gas. These substances are nonmetals. The nonmetals carbon, hydrogen, oxygen, and nitrogen are found in the bodies of the people who will hold the balloon. The pavement on which the people will walk contains nonmetals, too.

- *What are the properties of nonmetals?*
- *Why are some nonmetals in the gas state while others are solids or liquids?*
- *How do nonmetallic elements combine to form compounds?*

10-1 COMPARING NONMETALS AND METALLOIDS

Over three fourths of the elements in the Periodic Table are metals. The remaining elements are nonmetals and metalloids. Look at the Periodic Table in the back of this book. Except for hydrogen, nonmetals and metalloids are found on the right side of the table. Hydrogen and metals are found on the left side of the table.

Nonmetals are elements that lack luster, that generally do not conduct electricity or heat, and that are not ductile or malleable. Nonmetals cannot be drawn out into wire or hammered into sheets. Most nonmetals are solids or gases at room temperature. For example, carbon is a nonmetallic solid, and nitrogen is a nonmetallic gas. Bromine is the only liquid nonmetal.

Solid nonmetals tend to be hard and brittle. They are brittle because they lack the kind of bonds found in metals. Recall that in a metallic solid the positive ions are held together in a sea of electrons. This structure allows a metal to be hammered into a new shape without breaking. In a nonmetallic solid, individual bonds form between atoms. These bonds do not allow free movement of electrons. Look at Figure 10-1 on the next page. What would happen if you tried to hammer these nonmetals?[1]

After completing this section, you will be able to

- **distinguish** between nonmetals and metalloids.
- **describe** some properties of nonmetals.

The key terms in this section are
metalloids semiconductor
nonmetals

non- (not)

[1] They would shatter.

---

2 CONCEPT DEVELOPMENT

Thinking Skills

comparing
Show students a variety of elements that are metals and nonmetals. Ask students to compare the metals and nonmetals by using their physical properties only.

Background   A heavier atom in a period is smaller than a lighter atom in the same period. As the number of protons in the nucleus increases, the positive nuclear charge increases. A larger nuclear charge exerts a greater attraction on the negative electron cloud surrounding the nucleus, causing the cloud to shrink.

Background   Within a given group, the size of the atom increases as the atomic number increases. In going from one element to the next in a group, another energy level is added. The additional energy level extends the outer limit of the atom.

Teaching Tip   Discuss the fact that nonmetallic chemical behavior increases as the number of outer electrons increases and atomic size decreases.

3 REVIEW/REINFORCEMENT

1. Unlike nonmetals, metalloids may have luster and a high melting point; they may also be semiconductors.
2. Both are often found in compounds with metals.
3. Nonmetals are generally nonconductors, are not ductile or malleable, and lack luster.
4. Ionic or covalent bonds.

Challenge   Nonmetals gain electrons and become negative ions just like the hydroxide ions that are in all bases. Ions of a nonmetal would not form ionic bonds with hydroxide ions to form bases.

228

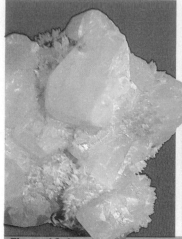

Figure 10-1

Sulfur (*left*), coal (*middle*), and diamond (*right*) all are examples of nonmetals.

-oid (like)

Figure 10-2

Notice how small a silicon chip is.

Nonmetal atoms form either ionic or covalent bonds. Some atoms tend to complete their outer energy levels by gaining electrons in reactions. If it gains electrons, a nonmetal atom becomes a negative ion. The bond formed is ionic. A nonmetal atom may complete its outer energy level by sharing electrons with another nonmetal. In this case the bond formed is covalent.

Some elements have properties of both metals and nonmetals. These elements, which are found along the heavy zigzag line in the Periodic Table, are called **metalloids**. Tellurium is an example of a metalloid. Like metals, tellurium has a high melting point. Like nonmetals, tellurium is often found in compounds with metals.

Some metalloids are semiconductors. A **semiconductor** is a substance that conducts electricity at some temperatures but not at other temperatures. Metalloids such as silicon are used as semiconductors in computer chips. Chips like the one shown in Figure 10-2 are used in electronic devices such as pocket calculators.

REVIEW

1. How do nonmetals differ from metalloids?
2. How are nonmetals and metalloids similar?
3. List three properties of nonmetals.
4. What kinds of bonds can nonmetals form?

CHALLENGE Metals often make up parts of compounds that are bases. Nonmetals often make up acids. Why don't nonmetals form bases?

10-2 THE BORON AND CARBON GROUPS

Group 13 of the Periodic Table is the boron group. Group 14 of the Periodic Table is the carbon group. The zigzag line that separates the metals and nonmetals runs through these groups. As a result, elements in these groups do not all share the same properties.

THE BORON GROUP

The elements in the boron group are shown in Figure 10-3. Notice that the atoms of these elements have three electrons in their outer energy level. Recall that metal atoms have one, two, or three electrons in their outer energy level. Except for boron, all the elements in this group are metals.

Boron borders the zigzag line in the Periodic Table, so it is classified as a metalloid. The boron atom is small, and it holds its three outer electrons tightly. Unlike metal atoms, the boron atom does not give up its outer electrons. Thus, it does not form a positive ion. Boron forms only covalent bonds with other atoms.

In nature, boron does not exist as a free element. It is found only in compounds. Two common compounds of boron are boric acid, H_3BO_3, and borax, $Na_2B_4O_7 \cdot 10H_2O$. Boric acid is used as a mild antiseptic, and borax is used as a preservative in some foods.

Because it is a metalloid, boron can be used as a semiconductor. It is a poor conductor of electricity at low temperatures, but it becomes a better conductor as its temperature increases.

> After completing this section, you will be able to
> - **describe** some properties of Group 13 and Group 14 elements.
> - **define** the term *allotrope*.
> - **list** some uses of the elements in Group 13 and Group 14.
>
> *The key terms in this section are*
> allotropes   glass

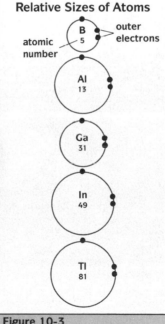

Relative Sizes of Atoms

atomic number — B 5 — outer electrons

Al 13

Ga 31

In 49

Tl 81

Figure 10-3

Boron *(left)* and gallium *(right)* are elements in the boron group.

10-2 THE BORON AND CARBON GROUPS
pages 229–235

OBJECTIVES
Refer to pupil page 229.

VOCABULARY
Key terms: allotropes, glass

1 MOTIVATION

Have students observe samples of elements from groups 13 and 14, such as aluminum, carbon (diamond and the graphite in a "lead" pencil), and lead. Ask students to compare aluminum with lead. (Both are metals; lead is heavier.) Ask which element makes up a diamond and the "lead" in a pencil. (Carbon.) Ask students for possible explanations for the differences in properties of diamond and graphite, which consist of atoms of the same element. (The atoms must be put together differently.) Tell students that this difference in structure will be further investigated in this section.

2 CONCEPT DEVELOPMENT

Teaching Tip   Discuss the increasing metallic chemical behavior of Group 13 elements, from the top to the bottom of the group, as atom size increases.

Background   The chemical behavior of boron differs from that of the other elements in Group 13, mainly due to boron's small size. Its chemical behavior resembles that of silicon and germanium more than it does that of aluminum.

Demonstration   Illustrate the metallic behavior of aluminum by dropping a small piece of aluminum metal into dilute hydrochloric acid. Ask students to compare the behavior of aluminum with that of the previously discussed metal, magnesium. (Aluminum is less reactive.)

Background   Aluminum oxide is a stable compound that is not easily decomposed into its elements. Bauxite, or aluminum ore, must be dissolved in Na_3AlF_6 and then electrolyzed to decompose.

Enrichment   Ask students to research why solid gallium is less dense than is liquid gallium.

Background   About 20 percent of aluminum comes from recycling. Aluminum cans are turned in by consumers at recycling centers to be made into aluminum products.

The next element in Group 13 is aluminum. Although aluminum is found along the zigzag line in the Periodic Table, it is a metal rather than a metalloid. It conducts electricity very well, and has other properties of metals. In a chemical reaction, aluminum loses its three outer electrons and forms a 3+ ion.

$$4Al(s) + 3O_2(g) \longrightarrow 2Al_2O_3(s)$$

Aluminum is the most abundant metal in the earth's crust. It occurs in nature, in ores such as bauxite (BAWK-sīt). Bauxite contains aluminum oxide, Al_2O_3. This ore is the source of almost all of the aluminum metal used commercially. Because it is light and cools quickly, aluminum is used to make cans for soft drinks. Lightweight alloys of aluminum are used in cooking utensils and aircraft parts. These alloys are also used to make lightweight racing bicycles, like those shown in Figure 10-4. Aluminum sulfate, $Al_2(SO_4)_3$, and other aluminum salts are used in sewage treatment, making paper, and dyeing cloth.

Figure 10-4

Aluminum ore is mined as bauxite. Aluminum is used to make lightweight bicycles (*inset*).

The remaining elements in Group 13 are gallium (GAL-ee uhm), indium (IHN dee uhm), and thallium (THAL ee-uhm). All three elements are grayish metals. Gallium is an unusual element in that solid gallium is less dense than liquid gallium. Most elements are denser in solid form than in liquid form.

THE CARBON GROUP

The Group 14 elements make up the carbon group. Notice in Figure 10-5 that each atom of the carbon group has four electrons in its outer energy level. These elements usually form covalent bonds in compounds. Sometimes the larger atoms in the group can lose electrons. For example, lead forms a 2+ ion. How many electrons have been lost by the lead atom?[1] Group 14 has more widely varying properties than any other group in the Periodic Table. Carbon is a nonmetal, silicon and germanium are metalloids, and tin and lead are metals.

More than 80 percent of all known compounds contain carbon. Most carbon compounds are organic compounds. Organic compounds include sugar, proteins, plastics, and gasoline. Only a few carbon compounds are not organic. These compounds include oxides and sulfides of carbon, as well as carbonic acid and its salts.

Free, or uncombined, carbon has two forms. Different structural forms of the same element are called **allotropes**. The two allotropes of carbon are graphite and diamond.

Graphite is a soft, black, crystalline solid. Notice in Figure 10-6 that the carbon atoms in graphite are arranged in layers. Within a layer, each carbon atom is covalently bonded to three other carbon atoms. You might think that each carbon atom forms a fourth bond with a carbon atom in another layer. Notice in the figure, however, that the distance between layers is greater than the distance between carbon atoms within a layer. The distance between

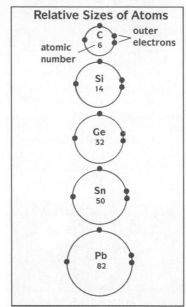

Relative Sizes of Atoms

Figure 10-5

The carbon group.

allos (another)
tropos (way)

[1] Two electrons.

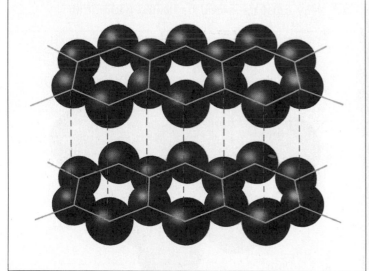

Figure 10-6

Graphite is an allotrope of carbon.

Thinking Skills

comparing
Students are asked to compare the electron configuration of the elements in the carbon group. Attention is drawn to the fact that each of the elements has four electrons in the outer energy level of its atom. Students should infer that this is the reason why these elements have similar properties.

Teaching Tip   Have students look at the atoms in Figure 10-5. Discuss why tin and lead are metals. Show the class samples of tin and lead and of alloys made from these metals, such as solder and pewter.

Background   Organic compounds always contain the atoms carbon and hydrogen and may also contain atoms of oxygen, nitrogen, phosphorus, and others.

Tie-in/Language Arts   Ask students to research the origin and the meaning of the word *graphite*.

Teaching Tip Ask students to look at Figure 10-6 and Figure 10-7. Have them count the number of bonds around each carbon atom and then compare graphite with diamond. Discuss bond strength. The diamond bonds are very strong, and the crystalline structure is rigid.

Enrichment Have interested students research how diamonds are formed in the earth. Students may ask a jeweler how diamonds are cut and weighed and ask about the importance of diamonds in industry. Have students report their findings to the class.

Thinking Skills

comparing
Students are asked to compare the structures of two allotropes of carbon—graphite and diamond. Students may infer that pressure is responsible for the strong bonds between the carbon atoms of diamond.

Demonstration Obtain a kerosene lamp. Show students the black deposit of soot that accumulates on the glass chimney when kerosene burns. Ask them to identify the element. (Carbon.)

Background When soft coal is heated in the absence of air, coke is formed.

Puzzler High pressure would be needed to force the carbon atoms closer together so that they would bond rigidly.

SCIENCE PUZZLER

The photograph shows synthetic diamonds that were made from graphite. Synthetic diamonds have the same molecular structure that naturally occurring diamonds have. What change in the structure of graphite would result in the diamond structure? How could such a change be accomplished?

[1]If air is present, CO_2 and CO will be produced instead of charcoal.

Figure 10-7

Diamond is an allotrope of carbon. This diamond has not been cut, or faceted, for jewelry.

layers is too great for covalent bonds to form. Thus the fourth outer electron of each carbon atom is free to move in the space around the atom. The moving electrons create a weak force that holds the graphite layers together.

Because they are held together weakly, the graphite layers can be made to slide past each other. When stress is applied, the weak force between the layers is overcome. This property makes graphite useful as a lubricant. Graphite is also used to make the "lead" in pencils. Graphite is so soft that it is mixed with clay. The hardness of pencil lead depends on the makeup of the mixture of graphite and clay.

The other allotrope of carbon is diamond. Diamond is a clear, colorless crystal. Look at the diamond structure shown in Figure 10-7. Notice that the atoms are closer together in diamond than they are in graphite. Diamonds form under great pressure in the earth. Each carbon atom shares electrons with four other carbon atoms. The three-dimensional pattern of bonds in a diamond makes it the hardest substance known. Diamonds are used in cutting tools and are highly valued as gemstones.

Natural gas, petroleum, and coal contain carbon compounds. These compounds are burned as fuels. When carbon burns in air, it combines with oxygen to form carbon monoxide, CO, and carbon dioxide, CO_2. Another product formed when carbon compounds burn is soot, a form of graphite. It is used as black pigment and is added to rubber tires to improve wear. Charcoal is another form of carbon. Charcoal is made from wood that has been heated without air. Why must the wood be heated without air?[1]

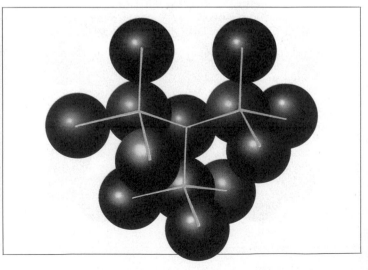

Silicon is the second most abundant element in the earth's crust. However, it does not occur naturally as a free element. It is found in many minerals—mainly silica, SiO_2, and silicates. Silicates are silicon-oxygen-metal compounds. The gemstone zircon, $ZrSiO_4$, is an example of a natural silicate. A common form of silica is quartz, which is found in most types of rocks. Sand, flint, and agate are other natural forms of silica.

Figure 10-8

Quartz (*left*), flint (*middle*), and agate (*right*) are forms of silica, SiO_2.

Silicon has a crystalline structure similar to that of carbon. Each silicon atom bonds covalently to four other silicon atoms to form a diamondlike crystal. Silicon also is able to form chains of atoms, but these are shorter than carbon chains.

Silicon and its compounds have many important uses. For example, when silica is melted, it loses its crystalline structure. As it cools, it forms a glass. A **glass** is a super-cooled liquid that is so viscous that it appears to be solid.

Silicates are used to make ordinary glass, such as window glass. Window glass is a mixture of sodium silicate and calcium silicate. The glass is made by melting together sodium carbonate, limestone, and silicon dioxide from sand. The equations for this reaction are as follows.

$$CaCO_3(s) + SiO_2(s) \longrightarrow CaSiO_3(1) + CO_2(g)$$
$$Na_2CO_3(1) + SiO_2(s) \longrightarrow Na_2SiO_3(1) + CO_2(g)$$

To make the heat-resistant glass used in baking dishes and laboratory glassware, some of the silicon dioxide is replaced by borax. This type of glass is able to stand rapid changes in temperature without breaking.

Background   Silicon does not form long chains by bonding with other silicon atoms as carbon does. Therefore, far fewer silicon compounds than carbon compounds are possible. Silicon usually forms silicon-oxygen bonds, while carbon usually forms carbon-carbon bonds.

Background   Supercooling occurs when a liquid does not crystallize at its freezing point. The liquid particles do not line up properly as cooling takes place. Thus the correct crystalline pattern does not form when the temperature falls below the freezing point.

Enrichment   Have interested students research the special type of glass called quartz or silica glass, which is used in optical instruments. Have students report their findings to the class.

PROCESS SKILLS
observing, classifying, predicting

Preparation If powdered charcoal is not available, pulverize the charcoal prior to the start of the lab period.

Teaching Tip Instruct students to measure the copper(II) oxide and charcoal on previously weighed pieces of paper.

Answers to Procecure
1. It is black and brittle.
2. It is black and powdery.
3. It is reddish orange in color and powdery.

Answers to Results and Conclusions
1. Carbon and copper(II) oxide.
2. Copper and carbon dioxide.
3. $2CuO + C \rightarrow 2Cu + CO_2$.
4. Iron and carbon dioxide.

Background   Very pure silicon is used in solar cells. When sunlight hits silicon, electrons are released by the silicon and an electrical current is produced by the moving electrons.

ACTIVITY   How Is a Nonmetal Used to Extract a Metal?

OBJECTIVE
Separate a metal from its metal oxide by using carbon.

MATERIALS
safety goggles, balance, spatula, copper (II) oxide, test tube, test-tube rack, powdered charcoal, glass stirring rod, ring stand, clamp, Bunsen burner, striker, 250-mL beaker

PROCEDURE
A. Wear safety goggles during this activity.
B. Measure 1 g of copper (II) oxide, and place it in a clean, dry test tube.
   1. Describe the color and appearance of this substance.
C. Measure 2 g of powdered charcoal.
   2. Describe the color and appearance of this substance.
D. Add the charcoal to the test tube, and mix with a stirring rod.
E. Assemble the apparatus as shown in the diagram.
F. Heat the test tube with a low flame for about 1 minute. Then turn up the flame, and heat strongly for about 10 minutes.
G. Allow the test tube to cool completely. Pour the contents of the test tube into a 250-mL beaker.
H. Place the beaker in the sink, and slowly run cold water into the beaker until all of the unreacted charcoal has floated away.
I. Pour out the water from the beaker, and examine the material left on the bottom.
   3. How does this material differ from the starting materials?

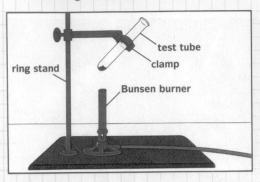

RESULTS AND CONCLUSIONS
1. Identify the reactants in this reaction.
2. Identify the products in this reaction.
3. Write a balanced chemical equation for this reaction.
4. To make steel, carbon and iron oxide are heated together in a blast furnace. Predict the products of this reaction.

One of the most important uses of silicon is in the electronics industry. Silicon's properties as a semiconductor allow it to be used in transistors. Transistors are small devices that control electric currents in televisions, radios, and computers. Semiconductors are also important in solar cells, which are used to convert sunlight to electricity.

Germanium is a metalloid found in some metal sulfide ores. Like silicon and carbon, germanium crystals have a diamondlike structure. Germanium is used mainly in semiconductors. It also has some special uses, such as in alloys sometimes used in dental work.

Tin and lead are the metals in Group 14. Tin is a soft metal that has three allotropes. At room temperature, tin is a silvery-white metal called white tin. At temperatures below 13°C, tin becomes less dense and has semiconductor properties. This kind of tin is called gray tin. At temperatures of 161°C and above, tin shatters easily and is called brittle tin.

Many semiconductors are made from the element silicon. However, a new compound called gallium arsenide may replace silicon as the most widely used semiconductor. Gallium arsenide conducts electricity faster than silicon does and can withstand higher temperatures.

However, there have been problems in manufacturing gallium arsenide crystals. Gravity prevents the liquids that form these crystals from mixing properly. The crystals do not form well, and they contain defects. Defective crystals do not conduct electricity very well.

Space may provide an answer to these problems. Away from the earth's gravity, there are no mixing problems, and defects are not likely to occur in the crystals. Some experts say that the chances of producing good crystals is ten times greater in space than on the earth.

Gallium arsenide semiconductors will be used in electronic circuits in complex devices. Companies in the United States and Japan are already producing supercomputers that use semiconductors made of gallium arsenide. As better gallium arsenide crystals are produced, these semiconductors will be used in communications and scientific instruments.

---

1. They all have three electrons in their outer energy level; all are metals except boron, which is a metalloid.
2. They all have four electrons in their outer energy level; they usually form covalent bonds.
3. An allotrope is one of the different structural forms that an element may have; carbon.
4. Answers will vary but may include boron, as a mild antiseptic; aluminum, for cans; carbon, for fuels; and silicon, for semiconductors.

Challenge Graphite has free electrons that are available for conductivity in its structure; diamond does not.

Tin is used in a variety of compounds. For example, tin (II) fluoride, SnF_2, is used as an anticavity ingredient in toothpaste. You may have heard this compound referred to as stannous fluoride.

Lead is a soft, dense metal that melts easily. When exposed to the air, lead forms a thin oxide layer that resists corrosion. A type of lead compound called red lead, Pb_3O_4, is used in special paint that prevents corrosion of steel in buildings and bridges. Another lead compound, lead chromate, $PbCrO_4$, is used as a pigment. In the past, lead was used in house paint, but because lead is toxic, it is being replaced by other compounds.

REVIEW

1. List two properties of Group 13 elements.
2. List two properties of Group 14 elements.
3. What is an allotrope? Name an element that forms allotropes.
4. Choose two elements from Group 13 and two from Group 14 and give one use of each.

CHALLENGE The bonds between graphite layers are weak and easily separated. The bonds within each graphite layer are strong and difficult to break. The diamond has no weak bonds in its structure. How does the structure of each of these two allotropes of carbon affect their ability to conduct electricity?

Figure 10-9

Paint that contains red lead is being used to protect this bridge.

10-3 THE NITROGEN AND OXYGEN GROUPS
pages 236–241

OBJECTIVES
Refer to pupil page 236.

OBJECTIVES
Refer to pupil page 236.

VOCABULARY
Key terms: diatomic molecule, oxidation, triatomic molecule
Other terms: combustion reactions, oxide, phosphate rock

---

1 MOTIVATION

Have students look at the Periodic Table and name all of the elements in groups 15 and 16. Ask which elements are metals, nonmetals, and metalloids. Have students explain why they classified the elements as they did.

2 CONCEPT DEVELOPMENT

Teaching Tip   Draw the N_2 molecule, showing a triple covalent bond. Discuss the extreme stability of the N_2 molecule. It is essentially inert except under highly energetic conditions.

Enrichment   Have students research the nitrogen cycle and report their findings to the class.

After completing this section, you will be able to

- **classify** the elements of Group 15 and Group 16 as metals, metalloids, or nonmetals.
- **compare** the properties of nitrogen and oxygen.
- **give** some uses of Group 15 and Group 16 elements.

The key terms in this section are
diatomic molecule
oxidation
triatomic molecule

[1]Gain electrons.

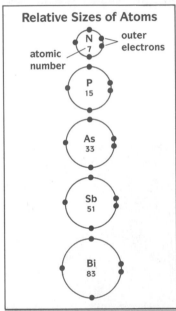

Relative Sizes of Atoms

atomic number — N 7 — outer electrons

P 15

As 33

Sb 51

Bi 83

Figure 10-10

Phosphorous *(inset)* and bismuth are elements in the nitrogen group.

Group 15 of the Periodic Table is the nitrogen group. Group 16 is the oxygen group. The elements in each group include nonmetals, metalloids, and metals. Thus, their properties vary.

THE NITROGEN GROUP

The elements in the nitrogen group are shown in Figure 10-10. Notice that each of these atoms has five electrons in its outer energy level. Would elements in this group gain or lose electrons in a chemical reaction?[1]

Nitrogen is the smallest atom in Group 15. Its properties are quite different from those of the other elements in this group. Nitrogen can gain up to three electrons or lose up to five electrons in a chemical reaction. It can also form compounds with three covalent bonds, as in ammonia, NH_3.

Uncombined, or free, nitrogen occurs as a diatomic molecule, N_2. A **diatomic molecule** is made up of two atoms of a single element. In free nitrogen, two atoms of nitrogen are covalently bonded together in one molecule. Free nitrogen is a colorless, odorless, nontoxic gas. It makes up about 78 percent of the earth's atmosphere. Small amounts of nitrogen are found in sodium nitrate, $NaNO_3$, and potassium nitrate, KNO_3, in the earth's crust.

Living things need nitrogen to form proteins and other complex molecules. Most living things get their nitrogen in a combined form. For example, plants take in nitrogen in the form of nitrates from the soil. But some living things are able to use nitrogen gas from the air.

Nitrogen for commercial use is obtained by the process of distillation. Air is liquified by cooling it to a very low temperature under high pressure. The liquid air is then allowed to warm slowly. Each of the gases that make up air boils off at a different temperature. Nitrogen boils at $-196°C$ and is collected as it boils out of the mixture.

Nitrogen is used to make ammonia and other important chemicals. Fertilizers contain nitrogen, mainly as ammonium nitrate (NH_4NO_3). Nitrogen (I) oxide, N_2O, an anesthetic used in dentistry, is made by heating ammonium nitrate at 170–260°C.

$$NH_4NO_3(s) \longrightarrow N_2O(g) + 2H_2O(g)$$

Liquid nitrogen is used to cool substances for reactions that take place at very low temperatures. Liquid nitrogen is also used to freeze foods quickly.

Figure 10-11

Liquid nitrogen freezes objects quickly.

Phosphorus is a nonmetal that has several allotropic forms. The two most common allotropes are white phosphorus and red phosphorus. White phosphorus is a soft, waxy, white solid that melts at 44°C. It is very reactive and burns spontaneously in air. Therefore, it must be stored underwater.

Red phosphorus forms when white phosphorus is heated to about 250°C without air. It also forms when white phosphorus is exposed to light. Red phosphorus is much less reactive than white phosphorus. Phosphorus is not found uncombined in nature. A mineral deposit called *phosphate rock* contains calcium phosphate, $Ca_3(PO_4)_2$. Phosphate rock is the source for most of the phosphorus used in fireworks and matches. What property of phosphorus makes it useful for these purposes?[1]

[1] It is very reactive and burns spontaneously.

Background   Nitrogen dilutes the oxygen in the air, reducing the combustibility of substances in air.

Background   Ammonia is prepared from nitrogen and hydrogen in the presence of an iron catalyst, using special conditions of temperature and pressure.

$$N_2 + 3H_2 \rightarrow 2NH_3$$

Enrichment   Ask students to find out how a match works. After they report on the subject, demonstrate to the class the result of their findings.

Enrichment Have students research how detergents differ from soaps. Ask students to report to the class and to demonstrate the cleansing powers of each.

Thinking Skills

inferring
Students are asked to notice the effect of phosphates in water on plant growth. Students should infer that the bacteria that break down dead plants use up the oxygen in the water, making it unfit for aerobic organisms to live there.

Teaching Tip Discuss reasons why arsenic and antimony are metalloids. One of their allotropes has properties of a metal. Another allotrope has properties of a nonmetal. Explain that bismuth is a metal because it behaves chemically as a metal. It usually appears in the Bi^{3+} form that allows it to act as a metal.

Teaching Tip Encourage students to predict the chemical behaviors of the elements in Group 15, based upon the electrons in their outer level and their atomic size.

Phosphates were once widely used in detergents. It was found, however, that phosphates in waste water contribute to water pollution. Water plants grow more rapidly in the presence of large amounts of phosphates. Look at the dense plant growth shown in Figure 10-12. When these plants die and then decay, the oxygen in the water will be used up. Eventually the other forms of life in the water may die from lack of oxygen. For this reason, the use of phosphates in detergents has been reduced.

Figure 10-12

Pollution from phosphates causes a rapid increase in the amount of algae and plants in the water.

Arsenic and antimony are Group 15 metalloids. Each element has two allotropic forms. One form is a gray, lustrous crystal. The other form is a nonmetallic, yellow solid. Yellow arsenic and arsenic compounds are very poisonous. Antimony is much less toxic.

Both arsenic and antimony are used to harden lead alloys. Such alloys are used in bullets and bearings. Antimony has been used in medicines. Antimony potassium tartrate, for example, is used in humans to treat infections caused by some parasites.

Bismuth is the only metal in Group 15. It is hard, brittle, and reddish-white. Although it is a metal, it does not conduct electricity or heat well. Bismuth is used in low-melting alloys for electrical fuses and automatic sprinkler systems.

THE OXYGEN GROUP

Elements in Group 16, the oxygen group, have six electrons in their outer energy level. They can gain electrons to complete the outer level and form ionic bonds. They also can form covalent bonds by sharing electrons.

Oxygen is the most abundant element in the earth's crust. It is a very active element and can combine with almost any other element. A compound of oxygen and another element is called *oxide*. The combination of oxygen with any element or compound is called **oxidation**. Some oxidation reactions give off heat and light. These reactions are called *combustion reactions*, or burning. The reaction between phosphorus and oxygen in the air is a combustion reaction.

$$P_4(s) + 5O_2(g) \longrightarrow P_4O_{10}(s)$$

Uncombined oxygen is found as a diatomic covalent molecule, O_2. Free oxygen is a colorless, odorless, tasteless gas. It makes up about 20 percent of the earth's atmosphere. Most living things need oxygen to survive. Oxygen also occurs as ozone, O_3. Ozone is a triatomic molecule. A **triatomic molecule** is made up of three atoms of a single element. Ozone is a highly reactive gas that is formed naturally from oxygen gas by lightning and ultraviolet radiation. A layer of ozone in the air protects living things from the harmful effects of ultraviolet radiation.

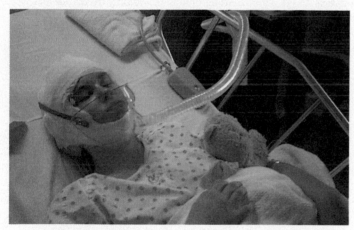

Oxygen can be produced by the electrolysis of water. This process separates water into hydrogen gas and oxygen gas. Oxygen is also prepared in large amounts by the distillation of liquid air. Oxygen is used in making steel and other metal products. It is also used to make compounds that contain oxygen.

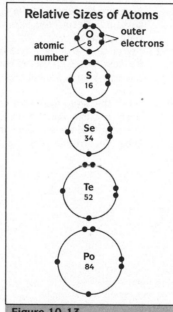

Relative Sizes of Atoms

atomic number

outer electrons

Figure 10-13

This patient is being given oxygen to help her breathe. Oxygen is the most abundant element in this group.

ACTIVITY 45 minutes

PROCESS SKILLS
observing, measuring, inferring, interpreting data, calculating

Preparation   Have large test tubes available for this activity.

Teaching Tip   Have students measure the iron filings on a previously weighed piece of paper.

Answers to Results and Conclusions
1. Test tube *A* has more water; the oxygen was removed from the air in the test tube by the rusting iron, and water took the place of the oxygen that was removed.
2. The iron filings oxidized and rusted.
3. $4Fe + 3O_2 \rightarrow 2Fe_2O_3$.
4. Answers will depend on the amount of iron oxidized, but should be close to 20 percent.

Teaching Tip   Have students practice writing equations for reactions involving sulfur and metals such as zinc, silver, and calcium. Sulfides of the metals are produced.

Background   In sulfur dioxide, SO_2, sulfur is 4^+. Oxygen has a greater ability to attract electrons than does sulfur, thus making sulfur positive in the molecule.

ACTIVITY   How Much Oxygen Is in the Air?

OBJECTIVE
Measure the percentage of oxygen in the air.

MATERIALS
balance, iron filings, 2 test tubes, 2 400-mL beakers, 2 ring stands, 2 clamps, ruler

PROCEDURE
A. Measure 2 g of iron filings.
B. Label two test tubes *A* and *B*. Rinse the inside of test tube *A* with water.
C. Add the iron filings to the test tube and shake it lightly so that a thin layer of filings covers the bottom three fourths of the tube.
D. Turn the test tube over, allowing any loose filings to fall out onto a piece of paper.
E. Fill a 400-mL beaker half full of water. Turn the test tube upside down, and set up the apparatus as shown in the diagram. Measure the length of the air space in the test tube. Record this information as your data for day 0.
F. Set up a control using test tube *B*. Rinse the test tube with water, but do not add any iron filings. Repeat step **E** with this test tube.
G. Allow the setup to remain for 3 days. On each day, examine the setup and measure the length of the air space in each test tube. Record this data.

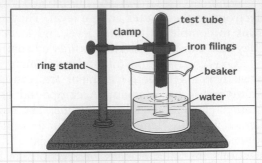

RESULTS AND CONCLUSIONS
1. Compare the changes in water levels in the two test tubes. Suggest a reason for any difference.
2. What happened to the iron filings in test tube *A*?
3. Write the balanced equation for this chemical reaction.
4. Using your data, calculate the percentage of oxygen in the air.
   a. Find the difference between the length of the air space in test tube *A* on day 0 and the length of the air space in the test tube on day 3.
   b. Divide your answer from question **4a** by the length of the air space in the test tube on day 0. Multiply by 100 to find the percentage.

Sulfur combines with some metals to form compounds known as sulfides, such as zinc sulfide, ZnS. Oxides of sulfur combine with some metals to form sulfates, such as magnesium sulfate, $MgSO_4$. Large deposits of free sulfur are found in Texas and Louisiana. These deposits are the source of most of the sulfur used commercially. The major use of sulfur is in the manufacture of sulfuric acid, an important industrial chemical.

Deposits of sulfur are also found on the slopes of volcanoes. Hydrogen sulfide, H_2S, is found in volcanic gases. When hydrogen sulfide is released, some of it reacts with oxygen in the air to form sulfur dioxide, SO_2. Some of the sulfur dioxide then reacts with more hydrogen sulfide. The free sulfur that is formed falls out onto the volcano slopes, as shown in Figure 10-14. The equation for the second reaction is shown below.

$$2H_2S(g) + SO_2(g) \longrightarrow 2H_2O(g) + 3S(s)$$

Figure 10-14

Sulfur is deposited on the surface of volcanoes. Sulfur crystals (*inset*) also form at the vents of volcanoes.

Sulfur or sulfur compounds are used in matches, fireworks, and gunpowder. Sulfur is also used to make dyes, medicines, and rubber.

Selenium and tellurium are among the rarest elements. They are usually found with sulfide ores of metals such as copper and lead. Selenium has several allotropes, including two crystalline forms. Tellurium has no allotropes. Both selenium and tellurium are semiconductors.

REVIEW

1. State whether arsenic, bismuth, sulfur, and tellurium are metals, metalloids, or nonmetals. Identify the groups to which these elements belong.
2. Give two ways in which nitrogen and oxygen are similar.
3. Name two uses of Group 15 elements. Give two examples of how elements in Group 16 are used.
4. What is an oxide?

CHALLENGE Plants cannot use nitrogen from the air. They get the nitrogen they need from compounds such as nitrates. Some kinds of bacteria can take in nitrogen from the air and produce nitrates. These bacteria are found in the roots of some plants, including clover. Why does planting clover enrich soil?

Background   Selenium's conductivity is increased 1000 times when it is exposed to light. It is therefore used in solar cells.

3 REVIEW/REINFORCEMENT

1. Arsenic—metalloid, Group 15; bismuth—metal, Group 15; sulfur—nonmetal, Group 16; tellurium—metalloid, Group 16.
2. They are both nonmetals and diatomic.
3. Answers will vary but may include nitrogen, to make ammonia; phosphorus, to make matches; oxygen, for respiration in most living things; and sulfur, to make sulfuric acid.
4. An oxide is a compound of oxygen and another element.

Challenge   The clover contains nitrogen-fixing bacteria in its roots. These bacteria remove nitrogen from the air and convert it to nitrates, which enrich the soil.

Review and Skill Masters

CHALLENGE/CRITICAL THINKING, pages 63–64. See page 225c in this book for answers.

10-4 THE HALOGENS

pages 242–244

10-4 THE HALOGENS

OBJECTIVES

Refer to pupil page 242.

VOCABULARY

Key terms: halogenation, halogens
Other terms: chlorination, tincture, trace amounts

1 MOTIVATION

List the names of the halogens on the chalkboard. Have the students look at labels on bottles and cans that list any of the halogens as ingredients. Have them make a bulletin board display of the labels under their respective elements.

2 CONCEPT DEVELOPMENT

Tie-in/Language Arts   Have students research the word *halogen* and give the meaning of the word.

Teaching Tip   After students have read page 242, discuss structures of ionic halides, such as NaCl and CaF_2, and covalent halides, such as CCl_4 and CH_3Cl.

Background   Halogenation reactions involve the introduction of halogen atoms into a molecule, either by substituting a halogen atom for another atom, such as hydrogen, or by adding a halogen atom by breaking a bond.

After completing this section, you will be able to

- **locate** the halogens in the Periodic Table.
- **describe** the chemical properties of the halogens.
- **list** some uses of halogens.

The key terms in this section are
halogenation   halogens

[1]They are very reactive and combine with other elements readily.

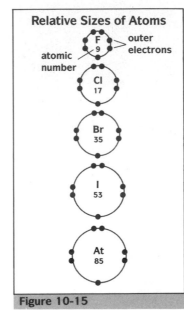

Relative Sizes of Atoms

atomic number
outer electrons

F 9
Cl 17
Br 35
I 53
At 85

Figure 10-15

Bromine (*left*) and iodine (*right*) are elements in the halogen group.

The elements in Group 17 are called **halogens**, from a Greek word meaning "salt former." These elements combine with metals to form salts. Group 17 contains only nonmetals.

Halogen atoms are very reactive. Notice in Figure 10-15 that halogens have seven electrons in their outer energy level. Thus, they need only one more electron to complete this level. Halogens can accept one electron and form $1-$ ions. They also form covalent bonds in compounds by sharing electrons. Uncombined halogens are found as diatomic covalent molecules. None of the halogens are found uncombined in nature. Why are halogens not found uncombined?[1]

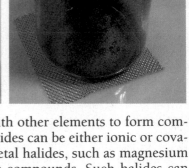

Halogens combine with other elements to form compounds called halides. Halides can be either ionic or covalent compounds. Many metal halides, such as magnesium chloride, $MgCl_2$, are ionic compounds. Such halides can be formed from the reaction between an acid and a base.

$$2HCl + Mg(OH)_2 \longrightarrow 2H_2O + MgCl_2$$

Halogens also combine with covalent compounds, in a process called **halogenation**. The reaction between methane and chlorine is an example of this process.

$$CH_4(g) + Cl_2(g) \longrightarrow CH_3Cl(g) + HCl(g)$$

Halogenation is an important process in the chemical industry. It is used to make compounds such as pesticides.

Halogen compounds are commonly found in salt deposits, oceans, and natural saltwater wells, also called brine wells. Table 10-1 gives the concentration of halogen ions in seawater. Notice that iodine is not listed in the table. Only 0.00006 g of iodine are found in 1 kg of water. Amounts this small are sometimes called *trace amounts*. Which halogen ion occurs in the greatest amount?[1]

[1]Chloride ion.

Table 10-1 *Halogens in Seawater*

Halogen Ion	Amount (g/kg)
Chloride	19.353
Bromide	0.067
Fluoride	0.001

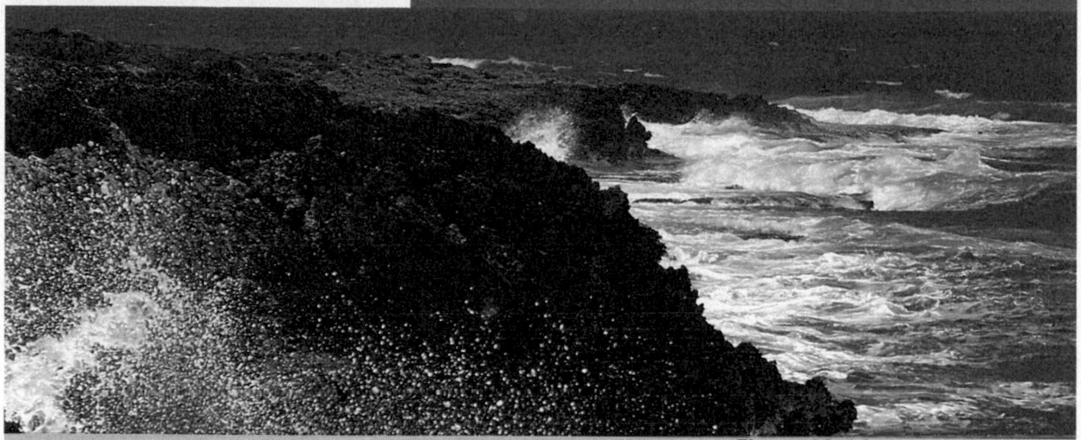

Figure 10-16

Seawater contains many halogen compounds.

Fluorine is the most reactive halogen. Free fluorine, F_2, is a corrosive, pale yellow gas. It is obtained by passing an electric current through a mixture of hot liquid fluorides. Fluorides, such as hydrogen fluoride, HF, are compounds that contain fluorine.

Probably the most familiar use of fluorine is in toothpaste and drinking water. Fluoride salts make teeth resistant to the acids that cause tooth decay.

Chlorine, Cl_2, is a poisonous, yellow-green gas. Because of its larger atomic size, it is not as reactive as fluorine. However, chlorine reacts with most elements and easily forms chloride ions, Cl^-.

Chlorine is used to treat sewage and to purify drinking water. Chlorine is used as a disinfectant in swimming pools. *Chlorination* is the process of adding chlorine to water. This process kills bacteria and other living things that cause disease. It also changes chemicals that cause

Thinking Skills

interpreting tables
Students name the halogen from Table 10-1 that is present in seawater in the largest amount. (Chlorine.) Students may also relate the size of the halogen to its reactivity. Fluorine, the smallest halogen, is the most reactive.

Teaching Tip Review the meaning of the word *corrosive*. Explain that fluorine gas reacts with metals, forming fluorides; these are F^- ions.

Enrichment Have students research the reactions that take place in chlorinated swimming pools. Let students explain the effect of chlorine on bacteria. (Chlorine oxidizes the bacteria, destroying them.)

Background   Many bleaches contain a chlorine compound, such as sodium hypochlorite, NaOCl. This chlorine compound releases oxygen in water. Bleaching is actually an oxidation reaction caused by the oxygen released by the chlorine compound.

Background   Iodine sublimes, or passes from a solid to a vapor at room temperature, because iodine crystals have a high vapor pressure. This enables the iodine solid to change into a vapor without melting first.

Demonstration   Place two or three iodine crystals on a watch glass at the beginning of the class period. Later in the period ask students to observe that the iodine crystals have vanished. Have students explain where the iodine went.

❸ REVIEW/REINFORCEMENT

1. In Group 17.
2. The halogens need to gain only one electron to complete their outer energy level.
3. Answers will vary but may include toothpaste, bleaches, and medicine.

Challenge   The chlorine in the pool bleached the swimsuit. The color change was slight because the chlorine solution was dilute.

[1] Chlorine-containing bleach was spilled on it.

bad odors and tastes in the water into odorless and tasteless substances. Chlorine is used to bleach fabrics and paper during the making of these products. It is also used to remove stains from clothing. What do you think happened to the fabric shown in Figure 10-17?[1]

Figure 10-17

The effect of chlorine on dyed fabric.

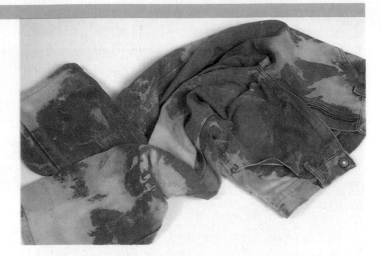

Bromine, Br_2, is the only nonmetal that is a liquid at room temperature. It is corrosive and causes burns on the skin. Bromine occurs in nature in compounds called bromides, which are found in the oceans and in brine wells. In agriculture bromine is used in chemicals that kill fungus infections in plants.

Iodine, I_2, is a poisonous solid. When exposed to the air, iodine changes to a gas without passing through a liquid state. Pure iodine is obtained mainly from seaweed. In medicine tincture of iodine is used as a disinfectant for wounds. A *tincture* is a solution in which the solvent is alcohol. Iodide ion is important in the human diet. Therefore, sodium iodide or potassium iodide is added to table salt, which is then sold as iodized salt.

REVIEW

1. Where are the halogens found in the Periodic Table?
2. Why are halogens very reactive?
3. Give three uses of halogens.

CHALLENGE Suppose you go swimming in a large pool nearly every day of the summer. At the end of the season, you notice that your swimsuit is lighter in color than it was at the beginning of the summer. Explain why.

10-5 THE NOBLE GASES

The elements in Group 18 of the Periodic Table are called the **noble gases**. Notice in Figure 10-18 that each of these elements has a complete outer energy level. Unlike other gases, these elements exist as single atoms.

At one time the Group 18 elements were referred to as the inert gases. No compounds of these elements had been found. Therefore, it was assumed that they were inert, or unreactive. Later, however, scientists were able to produce two compounds containing xenon (ZEE nahn) and fluorine: $XePtF_6$ and XeF_4. The reaction for the formation of $XePtF_6$ is shown below.

$$Xe(g) + PtF_6(g) \longrightarrow XePtF_6(s)$$

Now many stable synthetic xenon compounds are known. There are also some krypton (KRIHP tahn) compounds and at least one radon (RAY dahn) compound. So far, no compounds of helium, neon, or argon have been formed.

The very low reactivity of the noble gases is due to their atomic structure. Except for helium, all the noble gases have eight electrons in their outer energy level. Therefore, they do not need to gain or lose electrons to complete that level. Helium has an energy level that is completed by its two electrons.

Helium is the second lightest gas. It is much less dense than air, so it is used in blimps. Hydrogen is less dense than helium, but it burns explosively. Helium, which does not burn, is much safer. Why does helium not burn?[1]

After completing this section, you will be able to

- **locate** the noble gases in the Periodic Table.
- **describe** the chemical properties of the noble gases.
- **list** some uses of the noble gases.

The key term in this section is
noble gases

[1] It is unreactive and will not combine with oxygen.

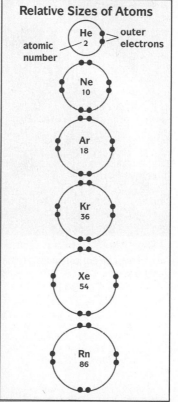

Relative Sizes of Atoms

Figure 10-18

The helium used in this blimp (*left*) is an element in the noble gas group (*right*).

10-5 THE NOBLE GASES

OBJECTIVES
Refer to pupil page 245.

VOCABULARY
Key term: noble gases
Other term: cryogenics

1 MOTIVATION

Obtain a helium-filled balloon, release it in class at the beginning of the class period. Ask students what gas might be in the balloon. Discuss why helium is used in the balloon. (It is less dense than air and is safe to use.)

2 CONCEPT DEVELOPMENT

Background   Noble gases do not form diatomic molecules because of their unreactive nature. Weak van der Waals forces between molecules allow for some attractions and thus account for these elements being gases.

Thinking Skills

inferring
Students are asked why helium does not burn. They should infer that it does not burn because its outer energy level is complete, causing it not to combine with oxygen.

Teaching Tip Call attention to the fact that helium has a boiling point of −269°C. Mention that argon has a boiling point of −186°C. Ask which element has the higher boiling point. (Argon.)

Demonstration Hold a fluorescent light tube while rubbing your feet on a carpet. Touch the ends of the tube, and it will light. The tube contains argon and mercury. Ask students to explain what happened. (Electrons jump from the carpet to the person holding the tube, to the tube and across the inside of the tube, thus completing the circuit across the terminals.)

Demonstration Obtain samples of helium, neon, and argon in gas tubes. Excite the gases in the tubes by connecting each tube to high voltage d.c. electricity. Have each student look through a diffraction grating and then identify each gas by matching the spectrum viewed to color charts of spectra.

3 REVIEW/REINFORCEMENT

1. In Group 18.
2. They have a stable outer energy level and do not need to gain or lose electrons to complete that level.
3. Answers will vary but may include in balloons, in light bulbs, and for high-speed flashes in photography.

Challenge Group 18; according to the Periodic Table, it would have to have the atomic number 118.

Helium boils at about −269°C, the lowest boiling point of any substance. Liquid helium is used to supercool metals. Supercooling increases the ability of some metals to conduct electricity. Liquid helium is also used for *cryogenics*, the study of matter at very low temperatures.

Neon is used in some electric lights. Look at the neon lights shown in Figure 10-19. In neon lights there is no metal filament. When an electric current is passed through the gas, the gas gives off a bright red glow. Argon and other gases can be added to neon lights to get a blue or green color instead of red. A mixture of argon and nitrogen is used in ordinary light bulbs. In these light bulbs the metal filament glows and the gases do not glow. The gases keep the metal from evaporating off the filament.

 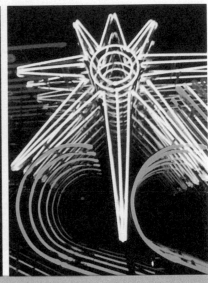

Figure 10-19

An electric current can make a noble gas glow.

Krypton and xenon are not widely used, because they are scarce. They are used mainly in long-life light bulbs, flashbulbs, and high-speed flashes for photography.

REVIEW

1. Where are the noble gases found in the Periodic Table?
2. Why are the noble gases so unreactive?
3. Describe two uses of noble gases.

CHALLENGE Look at the Periodic Table in the back of this book. If a new noble gas were discovered, to what group would it belong? Predict what the atomic number would be.

10-6 HYDROGEN

Unlike the other elements in the Periodic Table, the element hydrogen does not properly belong to any group. It is a nonmetal, but it is placed on the left side of the table, with the alkali metals in Group 1. Hydrogen is similar to the alkali metals in that it can give up an electron and form a 1+ ion. Hydrogen is also similar to the halogens in that it can gain an electron. Because it sometimes forms a 1− ion, hydrogen is sometimes placed with Group 17. Some forms of the Periodic Table may show hydrogen in both Group 1 and Group 17.

Hydrogen is the most abundant element in the universe. On the earth, hydrogen is found in more compounds than any other element. Water, petroleum, and biological substances such as proteins and fats all contain hydrogen. Hydrogen is important in acid-base chemistry. Recall that the acidic properties of a solution result from the presence of hydrogen ions.

Free hydrogen exists as a diatomic molecule, H_2. It is a colorless, odorless, tasteless gas. Some reactions with hydrogen are very slow or require a catalyst. However, hydrogen is very flammable. It combines with oxygen in an explosive reaction that yields water.

$$2H_2(g) + O_2(g) \longrightarrow 2H_2O(l)$$

As you can see in Figure 10-20, the hydrogen atom contains one electron. In most reactions, a hydrogen atom shares its electron with another atom and forms a covalent compound. Hydrogen sulfide, H_2S, and hydrogen peroxide, H_2O_2, are covalent hydrogen compounds. In some chemical reactions, however, hydrogen gains an electron and forms a 1− ion. For example, hydrogen combines with lithium, a reactive metal, and forms lithium hydride, an ionic compound.

$$2Li(l) + H_2(g) \longrightarrow 2LiH(s)$$

On the sun, hydrogen nuclei combine to form helium. The process is called *fusion*, and it yields great amounts of energy. Fusion on the sun provides the energy that is needed for life on the earth.

Hydrogen for industrial use can be obtained from water. Water can be decomposed to hydrogen and oxygen by passing an electric current through it. The major use of hydrogen is in the manufacture of ammonia, NH_3. Ammonia is made by combining nitrogen and hydrogen under high pressure.

After completing this section, you will be able to

- **explain** why hydrogen is difficult to classify as a metal or a nonmetal.
- **describe** the properties of hydrogen.
- **list** some uses of hydrogen.

The key term in this section is **hydrogenation**

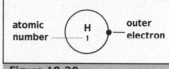

Figure 10-20

Hydrogen does not properly belong to any group.

10-6 HYDROGEN
pages 247–249

OBJECTIVES
Refer to pupil page 247.

VOCABULARY
Key term: hydrogenation
Other term: fusion

1 MOTIVATION

Ask students to name the most abundant element in the universe. (Hydrogen.) Mention that although hydrogen makes up 93 percent of the atoms in the universe, it makes up only 3 percent of the atoms on the earth. Ask why this is so. (The earth's gravity is not able to hold onto these very light atoms.) Ask why almost all the hydrogen on the earth is in a combined state. (Hydrogen combines easily with oxygen in the air.)

2 CONCEPT DEVELOPMENT

Teaching Tip   Discuss the danger of using hydrogen gas in blimps and rockets. (Highly flammable.)

Thinking Skills

inferring
Students will infer that when hydrogen burns, water is formed.

Enrichment   Ask students to determine how fusion reactions occur on stars.

ACTIVITY three 30-minute periods

PROCESS SKILLS
observing, inferring, predicting, interpreting diagrams

Preparation Place the glass tubes in the stoppers prior to the start of the lab.

Safety Tip Emphasize *immediately* in steps **E, J,** and **O.**

Teaching Tip Use only about ½ teaspoon of baking soda in step **O.**

Answers to Results and Conclusions
1. It went out in the test tube and relit as it was withdrawn; yes.
2. The splint burned brightly.
3. Carbon dioxide.
4. Step **E:** $Zn + 2HCl \rightarrow ZnCl_2 + H_2$
   Step **J:** $2H_2O_2 \rightarrow 2H_2O + O_2$

Background Hydrogenation of liquid fats and oils makes the molecules more saturated—that is, there are fewer double or triple bonds. Saturated molecules have been scientifically linked to high cholesterol levels. Cholesterol is thought to be responsible for clogged arteries.

Review and Skill Masters

SKILL, page 62.
See page 225b in this book for answers.

ACTIVITY How Can Gases Be Prepared?

OBJECTIVE
Prepare hydrogen, oxygen, and carbon dioxide gases by simple chemical reactions.

MATERIALS
safety goggles, lab apron, 3 Erlenmeyer flasks, test tube, glass-marking pencil, glass tubing inserted in a one-hole rubber stopper, rubber tubing, water bath, masking tape, 50-mL graduate, hydrochloric acid, mossy zinc, wood splints, matches, hydrogen peroxide, manganese dioxide, vinegar, baking soda

PROCEDURE
A. Wear safety goggles and a lab apron throughout this activity.
B. Label 3 Erlenmeyer flasks *A*, *B*, and *C*.
C. Assemble the apparatus as shown in the figure. The water bath should be about half full. Fill the test tube with water. Place your thumb over the mouth of this filled test tube and turn it upside down in the water bath. Tape the test tube in place. Be sure that the water stays in the test tube.
D. Place 5 ml of hydrochloric acid in flask *A*. **Caution:** Handle acids with care.
E. Add a piece of mossy zinc to flask *A*. Immediately stopper the flask.
F. Let the bubbling go on until all the water in the test tube is replaced by a gas.
G. Remove the test tube, but do not turn it over. Light a wood splint, and then thrust it into the test tube. A popping sound indicates the presence of hydrogen.
H. Set up the gas-collecting equipment again.
I. Place 20 mL of hydrogen peroxide in flask *B*.

J. Using the end of a wood splint, add a small amount of manganese dioxide. Immediately place the stopper in the flask.
K. Let the bubbling go on until all the water in the test tube is replaced by a gas.
L. Remove the test tube. Test it with a wood splint, as in step **G**. Note what happens.

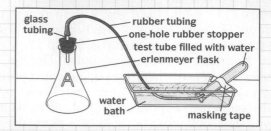

M. Set up the gas-collecting equipment again.
N. Place 10 mL of vinegar in flask *C*.
O. Using the end of a wood splint, add a very small amount of baking soda to the vinegar. Place the stopper in the flask immediately.
P. Let the bubbling go on until all the water in the test tube is replaced by a gas.
Q. Remove the test tube and turn it over. Light a wood splint, and thrust it into the unmarked test tube. Note what happens.

RESULTS AND CONCLUSIONS
1. What happened to the splint in step **G**? Was hydrogen present?
2. What happened to the splint in step **L**?
3. What gas was produced in step **Q**?
4. Write balanced equations for the reactions in steps **E** and **J**.

Hydrogen is used to convert liquid oils to solids. Liquid vegetable oils are treated with hydrogen to make margarine and other shortenings. This process is called hydrogenation. **Hydrogenation** is the addition of hydrogen to a compound. An important hydrogenation is the production of methyl alcohol from carbon monoxide.

$$CO(g) + 2H_2(g) \longrightarrow CH_3OH(g)$$

Hydrogen is used in the fuel mixture for rocket engines. Hydrogen may someday be used as a fuel in power plants, homes, and automobiles. What waste product is formed when hydrogen burns?[1]

[1]Water.

REVIEW

1. Why is hydrogen placed with the Group 1 metals? Why could it be placed with Group 17 elements?
2. Give three properties of hydrogen.
3. Describe two uses of hydrogen.

CHALLENGE What is the formula for the most common oxide of hydrogen?

CHAPTER SUMMARY

The main ideas in this chapter are listed below. Read these statements before you answer the Chapter Review questions.

- Nonmetals are elements that lack luster, generally do not conduct electricity, and are not ductile or malleable. (10-1)

- Nonmetals can form either ionic or covalent bonds. (10-1)

- Metalloids are elements that have properties of metals and nonmetals. (10-1)

- Group 13 of the Periodic Table is the boron group. Except for boron, which is a metalloid, all the Group 13 elements are metals. (10-2)

- Group 14 of the Periodic Table is the carbon group. Group 14 elements include metalloids, nonmetals, and metals. It has more varying properties than any other group. (10-2)

- Allotropes are different structural forms of the same element. (10-2)

- Group 15 of the Periodic Table is the nitrogen group. (10-3)

- Nitrogen is the smallest atom of Group 15. Living things need nitrogen to form proteins. (10-3)

- Group 16 of the Periodic Table is the oxygen group. (10-3)

- Oxygen is a very active element and can combine with almost any other element. (10-3)

- The elements in Group 17 are called halogens. The halogens all are nonmetals and are very reactive. (10-4)

- The halogens combine with metals to form salts. (10-4)

- The elements in Group 18 of the Periodic Table are the noble gases. (10-5)

- Noble gases are not very reactive, because of their atomic structure. (10-5)

- Hydrogen is a nonmetal that does not belong to any group. Hydrogen is placed on the left side of the Periodic Table. (10-6)

The key terms in this chapter are listed below. Use each term in a sentence that shows the meaning of the term.

allotropes	halogens	nonmetals
diatomic molecule	hydrogenation	oxidation
glass	metalloids	semiconductor
halogenation	noble gases	triatomic molecule

1. Hydrogen usually has a 1^+ oxidation number in its compounds; hydrogen sometimes has a 1^- oxidation number in hydride compounds.
2. Colorless, odorless, tasteless gas.
3. Answers will vary but may include in the manufacture of ammonia and in converting liquid oils and fats to solids.

Challenge H_2O.

Review and Skill Masters

VOCABULARY REVIEW, page 59.
See page 225b in this book for answers.

VOCABULARY

1. glass
2. noble gases
3. metalloids
4. hydrogenation
5. allotropes
6. diatomic molecule
7. nonmetals
8. halogenation
9. triatomic molecule
10. halogens
11. oxidation
12. semiconductor

CONCEPTS

1. Nonmetals lack luster, do not conduct electricity or heat, and are not malleable or ductile.
2. Like metals, some may have high melting points; like nonmetals, some are found in compounds with metals.
3. A semiconductor is a substance that conducts electricity at some temperatures but not at others. Semiconductors are used in computer chips and in electric devices.
4. Boron, aluminum, gallium, indium, thallium; all except boron form $3+$ ions; all have three electrons in the outer energy level; all except boron are metals.
5. Carbon is a nonmetal; silicon and germanium are metalloids; tin and lead are metals.
6. Graphite and diamond; graphite—conductor, black, soft, crystalline solid; diamond—nonconductor, transparent, colorless, crystalline, very hard.
7. Answers will vary but may include carbon dioxide, petroleum, and sugar.
8. In glass and semiconductors; silicon is a metalloid.
9. Red phosphorus and white phosphorus; white phosphorus is the more reactive.

Review and Skill Masters

CHAPTER REVIEW, pages 60–61.
See page 225b in this book for answers.

Chapter Review

VOCABULARY

Use the key terms from this chapter to complete the following sentences correctly.

1. A/An _____ is a supercooled, viscous liquid.
2. The elements in Group 18 that do not react easily are the _____ .
3. _____ have properties of both metals and nonmetals.
4. The addition of hydrogen to any compound is called _____ .
5. _____ are different structural forms of the same element.
6. A/An _____ is a molecule made up of two atoms of the same element.
7. Elements that lack luster and that are not ductile or malleable are called _____ .
8. A/An _____ reaction is the addition of a halogen to a compound.
9. Three atoms of the same element form a/an _____ .
10. Elements of Group 17 are known as _____ .
11. The reaction between oxygen and another element is called _____ .
12. A/An _____ is a substance that conducts electricity at some temperatures, but not others.

CONCEPTS

1. What are three properties of nonmetals? (10-1)
2. What properties of metalloids make them similar to metals and to nonmetals? (10-1)
3. What is a semiconductor? Where are semiconductors used? (10-1)
4. Name the elements found in Group 13 of the Periodic Table. List three properties of elements in this group. (10-2)
5. Classify each element in Group 14 as a metal, a metalloid, or a nonmetal. (10-2)
6. What are the two allotropic forms of carbon? Give the properties of each. (10-2)
7. List three examples of carbon compounds. (10-2)
8. Describe two uses of silicon. Is this element a nonmetal or a metalloid? (10-2)
9. Name two allotropic forms of phosphorus. Which allotrope is more reactive? (10-3)

10. Identify each element in Group 15 as a metal, metalloid, or nonmetal. (10-3)

11. How does nitrogen compare with oxygen in terms of chemical behavior? (10-3)

12. Choose two elements from Group 15 and two elements from Group 16, and describe their uses. (10-3)

13. What name is given to the elements in Group 17? Explain what is meant by the term *salt former*. (10-4)

14. Classify each element in Group 17 as a solid, a liquid, or a gas at its room temperature. (10-4)

15. Describe two uses of chlorine and one use of fluorine. (10-4)

16. Which group in the Periodic Table is made up of the noble gases? (10-5)

17. Why were the noble gases once called inert gases? (10-5)

18. How is the atomic structure of the noble gases related to their chemical properties? (10-5)

19. List three ways in which noble gases are used. (10-5)

20. What property of hydrogen makes it similar to the alkali metals in Group 1? In what other group could hydrogen be placed? (10-6)

21. What is the major industrial use of hydrogen? (10-6)

APPLICATION/ CRITICAL THINKING

1. Which metal group in the Periodic Table would the halogens react with the most?

2. Name a metal atom that could give an oxygen atom the two electrons it needs to complete its outer energy level.

3. Why are fluorine and chlorine so difficult to remove from their minerals?

EXTENSION

1. Do library research to prepare a report on the different types of semiconductors and their uses.

2. Research the use of cryogenics in the medical field. Present your findings to your class.

3. Investigate how to prepare the two crystalline allotropes of sulfur. Plan an experiment to be done as a class project.

READINGS

Bardeen, John. "To a Solid State." *Science 84*, October 1984, p. 143.

Morgan, Diana. "How Does Fluoride Fight Tooth Decay?" *Science 84*, December 1984, p. 27.

Richardson, Stephen H., and others. "Antique Diamonds." *Current Science*, October 1984, p. 6.

10. Nonmetals—nitrogen and phosphorus; metalloids—arsenic and antimony; metal—bismuth.

11. Nitrogen is less reactive than is oxygen.

12. Answers will vary but may include Group 15—arsenic and antimony are used to harden lead alloys, antimony is used to treat parasites—and Group 16—oxygen is used in making steel, sulfur is used in making matches and fireworks.

13. Halogens; they form salts when they combine with metals.

14. Fluorine and chlorine are gases; bromine is a liquid; iodine is a solid.

15. Answers will vary but may include chlorine used in treating sewage and purifying drinking water, and fluorine used in toothpaste.

16. Group 18.

17. Noble gases were not known to react chemically with other elements.

18. Noble gases have a stable outer energy level and therefore do not easily react.

19. Answers will vary but may include helium, used in blimps; and neon, argon, krypton, and xenon, used in light bulbs.

20. Hydrogen can form a 1^+ ion; in Group 17.

21. Manufacture of ammonia.

APPLICATION/CRITICAL THINKING

1. Group 1.
2. Magnesium, calcium, strontium, barium.
3. Their compounds are very stable and are difficult to decompose.

Test Masters

CHAPTER TEST, pages 37–40.
See page 225d in this book for answers.

CARBON COMPOUNDS

ORGANIZER

Section	pages	Activity	pages	Reinforcement and Evaluation	pages	*Review and Skill Masters	pages	Other Components in Teacher Resource Package	pages
11–1 Organic Compounds	253–255			Review, Challenge	255	Skill	68–69	Study Guide	53
11–2 Hydrocarbons	256–259	How Are Organic Molecules Represented?	259	Review, Challenge	259			Study Guide	54
11–3 Cyclic Hydrocarbons	260–261			Review, Challenge	261			Study Guide	55
11–4 Substituted Hydrocarbons	262–265	How Are Esters Made?	265	Puzzler Review, Challenge	264 265			Study Guide	56
11–5 Organic Polymers	266–267			Review, Challenge	267			Study Guide	57
11–6 The Chemistry of Living Things	268–271	How Is Soap Made?	270	Review, Challenge	271	Challenge/Critical Thinking	70	Study Guide Lab Manual	58 61
CHAPTER SUMMARY	271					Vocabulary Review	65		
CHAPTER REVIEW	272–273			*Test Masters	41–44	Chapter Review	66–67		

*In the Teacher Resource Package. For answers, see pages 251b–251d in this book.

ACTIVITY MATERIALS   Quantities are based on a class of 30 students working in groups as indicated in parentheses.

How Are Organic Molecules Represented? p. 259 (groups of 2)	quantity	How Are Esters Made? p. 265 (groups of 2)	quantity	How Is Soap Made? p. 270 (groups of 2)	quantity
student molecular model kit	15	safety goggles	30	safety goggles	30
		lab apron	30	lab apron	30
		250-mL beaker	15	graduate	15
		hot plate	15	evaporating dish	15
		test tube	45	olive oil	90 mL
		glass-marking pencil	15	sodium hydroxide solution	180 mL
		graduate	15	water	
		amyl alcohol	75 mL	ring stand	15
		acetic acid	30 mL	ring	15
		dropper	15	wire gauze	15
		sulfuric acid	37.5 mL	Bunsen burner	15
		test-tube rack	15	striker	15
		methyl alcohol	37.5 mL	stirring rod	15
		salicylic acid	30 mL	balance	15
		ethyl alcohol	75 mL	sodium chloride	45 g
		butyric acid	30 mL	paper towels	15 sheets
		test-tube clamp	15	250-mL flask	15
				rubber stopper	15

REVIEW AND SKILL MASTERS

Name_____ Date_____

VOCABULARY REVIEW _____ Chapter 11

Use the clues below to complete the puzzle and find the term in the boxes.

1. a l c o h o l
2. c a r b o h y d r a t e s
3. c a r b o x y l   g r o u p
4. a l k a n e s
5. a l k y n e s
6. v i t a m i n s
7. o r g a n i c   a c i d
8. n u c l e i c   a c i d s
9. p o l y m e r
10. i s o m e r s
11. l i p i d s
12. p r o t e i n s
13. s t r u c t u r a l   f o r m u l a
14. a l k e n e s
15. h y d r o c a r b o n s

1. A hydrocarbon in which a hydrogen atom is replaced by a hydroxyl group
2. Organic compounds that contain carbon, hydrogen, and oxygen
3. This is made of one carbon atom, two oxygen atoms, and one hydrogen atom (two words)
4. Hydrocarbons that have only single bonds between carbon atoms
5. Hydrocarbons that have a triple bond between carbon atoms
6. Complex organic compounds that control chemical reactions in the body
7. A hydrocarbon in which a hydrogen atom is replaced by a carboxyl group (two words)

8. Organic compounds that control the function of cells (two words)
9. A compound made of simple units that form a repeating structure
10. Compounds with the same chemical formula but different structural formulas
11. Organic compounds that store energy
12. Organic compounds made of carbon, oxygen, hydrogen, and nitrogen
13. The arrangement of atoms in a molecule (two words)
14. Hydrocarbons that have a double bond between carbon atoms
15. Compounds made of only carbon and hydrogen atoms

65

Name_____ Date_____

CHAPTER REVIEW _____ Chapter 11

11-1 Organic Compounds

1. Mark T for true or F for false.

a. __T__ Organic compounds contain carbon, while inorganic compounds generally do not contain carbon.

b. __T__ Carbon atoms can bond together in long chains or rings.

c. __F__ An isomer is a compound that has a different chemical formula but the same structural formula as another compound.

11-2 Hydrocarbons

1. What is a hydrocarbon? Give two examples of hydrocarbons. A hydrocarbon is a compound that contains only carbon and hydrogen atoms. Gasoline and turpentine are hydrocarbons.

2. What is the name and structural formula for C_2H_6? C_2H_4?

Ethane   Ethene

3. List two uses for hydrocarbons. Fuels, welding.

11-3 Cyclic Hydrocarbons

1. What is a cyclic hydrocarbon? Give two examples of cyclic hydrocarbons. A cyclic hydrocarbon is a hydrocarbon that has a ring structure. Cyclopropane and benzene are cyclic hydrocarbons.

2. Label the two structural formulas below as cyclohexane, C_6H_{12}, or benzene, C_6H_6.

Cyclohexane   Benzene

66

Name_____ Date_____

CHAPTER REVIEW (Continued) _____ Chapter 11

3. List two uses for some cyclic hydrocarbons. Paint remover, aspirin.

11-4 Substituted Hydrocarbons

1. In a(n) __substituted__ hydrocarbon, one or more hydrogen atoms is replaced by another atom or group of atoms. In a(n) __alcohol__ a hydrogen atom is replaced by a hydroxyl group. In a(n) __organic acid__ a hydrogen atom is replaced by a carboxyl group. A(n) __ester__ is the product of the reaction between an alcohol and an organic acid.

2. List two uses of substituted hydrocarbons. Solvents, perfumes.

11-5 Organic Polymers

1. What is a polymer? List two and their uses. A polymer is an organic molecule made up of a long chain of simple units in a repeating structure. Polyethylene is used to make plastic. Cellulose is used to make cloth.

2. Identify the polymer shown below.

Polyethylene

11-6 The Chemistry of Living Things

1. The four organic compounds found in living things are carbohydrates, lipids, proteins, and nucleic acids

2. Give one similarity and one difference between a carbohydrate and a lipid. A carbohydrate and a lipid both contain carbon, hydrogen, and oxygen atoms. Lipids contain many more hydrogen atoms than do carbohydrates.

3. Nucleic acids control the __building__ of proteins.

67

Name_____ Date_____

SKILL/Comparing _____ Chapter 11

Isomers are compounds that have the same chemical formula but different structural formulas. A bend does not result in a different structure. For example, the following all represent a straight-chain formula for butane:

However, this is the structural formula for the branched-chain isomer of butane:

Remember that the mirror images do NOT represent different isomers. For example,

is the same isomer as

1. The chemical formula for pentane is C_5H_{12} _____ Draw the structural formulas for the three isomers of pentane.

68

CHAPTER 11 PLANNING GUIDE

Name_____ Date_____

SKILL/Comparing (Continued) _____ Chapter 11

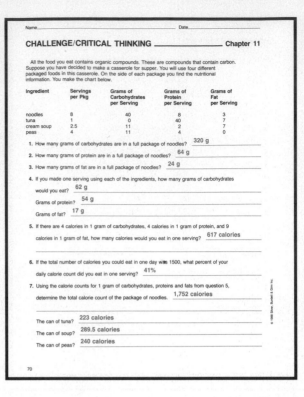

2. The chemical formula for hexane is C_6H_{14} _____ Draw the structural formulas for the five isomers of hexane.

© 1988 Silver, Burdett & Ginn Inc.

69

Name_____ Date_____

CHALLENGE/CRITICAL THINKING _____ Chapter 11

All the food you eat contains organic compounds. These are compounds that contain carbon. Suppose you have decided to make a casserole for supper. You will use four different packaged foods in this casserole. On the side of each package you find the nutritional information. You make the chart below.

Ingredient	Servings per Pkg	Grams of Carbohydrates per Serving	Grams of Protein per Serving	Grams of Fat per Serving
noodles	8	40	8	3
tuna	1	0	40	7
cream soup	2.5	11	2	7
peas	4	11	4	0

1. How many grams of carbohydrates are in a full package of noodles? 320 g

2. How many grams of protein are in a full package of noodles? 64 g

3. How many grams of fat are in a full package of noodles? 24 g

4. If you made one serving using each of the ingredients, how many grams of carbohydrates would you eat? 62 g

   Grams of protein? 54 g

   Grams of fat? 17 g

5. If there are 4 calories in 1 gram of carbohydrates, 4 calories in 1 gram of protein, and 9 calories in 1 gram of fat, how many calories would you eat in one serving? 617 calories

6. If the total number of calories you could eat in one day was 1500, what percent of your daily calorie count did you eat in one serving? 41%

7. Using the calorie counts for 1 gram of carbohydrates, proteins and fats from question 5, determine the total calorie count of the package of noodles. 1,752 calories

   The can of tuna? 223 calories

   The can of soup? 289.5 calories

   The can of peas? 240 calories

© 1988 Silver, Burdett & Ginn Inc.

70

REVIEW AND
SKILL MASTERS

TEST MASTERS

Carbon Compounds

PART 1

In the space below, write the term that each phrase defines.

			Chapter Goal
1.	**ester**	The compound produced in the reaction between an organic acid and an alcohol	4
2.	**aromatic hydrocarbons**	Molecules that have alternate single and double bonds in six-carbon ring structures	3
3.	**isomers**	Organic compounds that have the same chemical formula but different structural formulas	1
4.	**proteins**	Organic compounds that are made up of carbon, oxygen, hydrogen, and nitrogen	6
5.	**alkenes**	Hydrocarbons that contain one double bond between carbon atoms	2
6.	**cyclic hydrocarbon**	An organic compound that has a round, or ring-type, structure	3
7.	**saturated hydrocarbon**	A molecule in which all bonds between carbon atoms are single bonds	2
8.	**nucleic acids**	Organic compounds that control the functions of cells	6
9.	**structural formula**	A diagram that shows the arrangement of atoms in a molecule	1
10.	**alcohol**	A hydrocarbon in which a hydrogen atom is replaced by a hydroxyl group	4
11.	**polymer**	An organic molecule made up of simple units that form a repeating structure	5

PART 2

Choose the term or phrase that best answers the question or completes the statement. Write the letter of that choice in the space at the left.

d 1. Which of the following is a saturated hydrocarbon?   2
a. C_2H_2 b. C_6H_{12} c. $C_{10}H_{28}$ d. C_4H_{10}

a 2. Which of the following consists of molecules that are made up of many thousands of carbon atoms that form long chains in a repeating pattern?   5
a. rubber   b. alcohol   c. vinegar   d. gasoline

PART 2

Choose the term or phrase that best answers the question or completes the statement. Write the letter of that choice in the space at the left.

Chapter Goal

a 3. Carbohydrates, lipids, and proteins all contain: 6
a. oxygen.   b. sulfur.   c. nitrogen.   d. fluorine.

b 4. Which of the following is an organic compound?   1
a. H_2SO_4 b. C_2H_2 c. NaCl   d. CO_2

a 5. Which of the following is a substitution of benzene?   4
a. C_6H_5Cl b. $C_6H_{10}Cl_2$ c. $C_5H_{10}Cl_2$ d. $C_5H_{11}Cl$

b 6. In the chemical formula $(C_6H_{10}O_5)_n$, the "n" means that the structure of the compound is: 5
a. circular.   c. single-bonded.
b. repeating.   d. branched-chain.

b 7. How many hydrogen atoms are found in an alkene with 5 carbon atoms?   2
a. 5   b. 10   c. 12   d. 20

a 8. What is the name of the compound shown in the diagram?   3

a. cyclobutane   b. cyclobutene   c. cyclopentane   d. cyclopentene

b 9. Which of the following is the chemical formula for an organic acid?   4
a. $CH_3CH_2CHClCH_3$ c. $C_6H_5CH_2CH_2OH$
b. CH_3CH_2COOH d. $CH_3COOCH_2C_6H_5$

d 10. Fats, oils, and waxes are examples of: 6
a. amino acids.   b. nucleic acids.   c. proteins.   d. lipids.

a 11. Polypropylene would most likely be formed from which of the following compounds?   5
a. C_3H_6 b. C_3H_4 c. C_4H_8 d. C_4H_6

a 12. Isomers of the same compound have different: 1
a. physical properties.   c. chemical formulas.
b. molecular masses.   d. numbers of carbon atoms.

b 13. Which of the following diagrams shows an aromatic hydrocarbon?   3
a.   b.   c.   d.

PART 3

Look at the diagram. Then read the questions that follow. Choose the term or phrase that best answers the question or completes the statement. Write the letter of that choice in the space at the left.

A   **B**   **C**

Chapter Goal

b 1. Compounds A, B, and C are: 2
a. alcohols.   b. alkanes.   c. alkynes.   d. alkenes.

c 2. Which of the following would be a chemical formula for a cyclic hydrocarbon containing only single bonds that corresponds to Compound A?   3
a. C_6H_6 b. C_6H_{10} c. C_6H_{12} d. C_6H_{14}

b 3. Which of the following would be the chemical formula for compound B if it contained a triple bond in place of one of the single bonds between carbon atoms?   2
a. C_6H_6 b. C_6H_{10} c. C_6H_{12} d. C_6H_{14}

PART 4

Read each question or direction and answer it using complete sentences.

Chapter Goal

1. How is polyethylene formed?   5

As units of ethene connect, double bonds are changed to single bonds. These changes leave an unpaired electron at the end of each unit. More ethene units are able to connect at these points.

2. Explain the chemical difference between straight-chain structures and branched-chain structures.   1

In a straight-chain structure, each carbon atom is bonded to no more than two carbon atoms. In a branched-chain structure, one or more of the carbon atoms is bonded to three or four other carbon atoms.

3. List some polymers and their uses.   5

Polyethylene is a plastic used to make toys, bags, and bottles. Rubber is a natural polymer used to make tires, boots, and sports equipment. Cellulose is another natural polymer used to make cloth. Polyester is a polymer used to make a variety of fabrics. Other polymers are used to make records and tape. TFE is used to coat pots and pans to prevent food from sticking to them.

CHAPTER 11 PLANNING GUIDE

251d

11

CARBON COMPOUNDS

The questions in the CHAPTER TEST are based on these Chapter Goals.

1. Distinguish between organic and inorganic compounds and explain the variety of organic compounds.
2. Give examples of hydrocarbons; distinguish between alkanes, alkenes, and alkynes.
3. Give examples of cyclic hydrocarbons.
4. Recognize and distinguish between types of substituted hydrocarbons.
5. Describe the structure of polymers, and explain the uses of some polymers.
6. Identify some organic compounds that make up living things.

CARBON COMPOUNDS

The object that is burning is a piece of coal, which is made up mostly of carbon. Carbon is a part of more different compounds than any other element. Because of this, scientists study carbon compounds as a special group of compounds. Most of the compounds that we use as fuel contain carbon. Many of the compounds that make up your body also contain carbon. Carbon compounds are part of the clothing that you wear and the food that you eat.

- *What are the properties of carbon compounds?*
- *Why are there so many different carbon compounds?*
- *How are carbon compounds formed?*
- *What are some of the uses of carbon compounds?*

11-1 ORGANIC COMPOUNDS

There are over 3 million compounds that contain the element carbon. **Organic compounds** are compounds that contain carbon. The bodies of all living things contain organic compounds such as fats and proteins. The term *organic compound* was first used because scientists believed that these compounds come only from living things, or *organisms*. Now, however, scientists have found that many organic compounds can be made in the laboratory. Plastics, petroleum products, rubber, coal, and soap also are examples of organic compounds.

Compounds that do not contain carbon are called *inorganic compounds*. Table salt, water, sulfuric acid, and zinc sulfate all are inorganic compounds. A few simple compounds that contain carbon are classified as inorganic compounds. Carbon dioxide and calcium carbonate are examples of inorganic compounds that contain carbon.

Organic compounds are very varied. The carbon atoms in these compounds can bond together in a long chain, or in a ring shape. Carbon atoms can be joined by single bonds, double bonds, or triple bonds. Most bonds in organic compounds are covalent bonds.

After completing this section, you will be able to

- **distinguish** between organic and inorganic compounds.
- **give reasons** for the variety of organic compounds.
- **recognize** isomers of organic compounds.

The key terms in this section are
isomers
organic compounds
structural formula

Have students read the introductory paragraph. Explain that many chemical compounds in living things contain the element carbon. Ask students to name one substance in their body that does not contain carbon. Ask them to list some fuels that contain carbon. Ask students to suggest how these fuels came into existence.

- What are the properties of carbon compounds? (They usually form long chains. Carbon atoms can join as single, double, or triple bonds.)
- Why are there so many different carbon compounds? (Carbon has four electrons in its outer energy level. Carbon can therefore form many different kinds of compounds.)
- How are carbon compounds formed? (Carbon compounds are formed when carbon forms covalent bonds with other elements.)
- What are some uses of carbon compounds? (Carbon compounds are used for fuel, food, and clothing.)

11-1 ORGANIC COMPOUNDS
pages 253–255

OBJECTIVES
Refer to pupil page 253.

VOCABULARY
Key terms: isomers, organic compounds, structural formula
Other terms: branched-chain structure, inorganic compound, organisms, straight-chain structure

1 MOTIVATION

Ask students to bring in photographs of compounds that contain carbon. Use the photographs to make a collage as a class project. As work in this chapter progresses, have students add photographs of any additional compounds they learn about.

Background   Some differences between organic and inorganic compounds are the following.
- Most organic compounds melt at lower temperatures than do inorganic compounds.
- Most organic compounds are not soluble in water, but many inorganic compounds dissolve in water.
- Organic compounds are covalently bonded, but most inorganic compounds are ionically bonded.

Background   Organic reactions proceed more slowly than inorganic reactions. Because of the strength of the covalent bonds in organic molecules, large amounts of energy are needed to break the existing bonds and rearrange the atoms into new molecules.

Teaching Tip   Obtain some plastic foam balls of various sizes. Use latex or tempera paints to color each sphere to represent a different atom. (Do not use oil paints and/or lacquers, which might dissolve the foam.) Use short dowels to connect the spheres. Assemble a collection of various molecules to use as examples while teaching.

Background   As the number of carbon atoms in a molecule increases, the number of possible isomers also increases. Isomerism is not limited to hydrocarbons. For example, dimethyl ether (CH_3OCH_3) and ethyl alchohol (C_2H_5OH) are different structures for the molecular formula C_2H_6O. Propanol (CH_3CH_2CHO), an aldehyde, is an isomer of acetone (CH_3COCH_3), which is a ketone. Both compounds have the molecular formula C_3H_6O.

Review and Skill Masters

SKILL, pages 68–69. See pages 251b–c in this book for answers.

Figure 11-1

Methane is the simplest organic compound.

iso (equal)
meros (part)

The carbon atoms in an organic compound bond to atoms of other elements. Hydrogen atoms often are bonded to a carbon atom. Oxygen atoms, chlorine atoms, and nitrogen atoms also can bond to a carbon atom. At times many different kinds of atoms attach to a carbon chain. Each arrangement of atoms makes a different organic compound, with different properties and uses.

Why does carbon form so many bonding patterns? Recall that a carbon atom has four electrons in its outer energy level. To fill the outer level of the carbon atom, four more electrons must be added. Electrons from other carbon atoms or from atoms of other elements are shared to form covalent bonds. Each carbon atom can form four covalent bonds.

Methane (MEHTH ayn), CH_4, is the simplest organic compound. In a molecule of methane, the carbon and hydrogen atoms share electrons. As you can see in Figure 11-1, each hydrogen atom has only one electron and can form only one bond. Thus one carbon atom bonds to four hydrogen atoms.

A **structural formula** shows the arrangement of atoms in a molecule. As the number of carbon atoms in a chain increases, the number of possible structures also increases. Compounds that have the same chemical formula but different structural formulas are called **isomers** (Ī suh muhrz).

Table 11-1 *Isomers*

	Butane	Pentane
Formula	C_4H_{10}	C_5H_{12}
Straight chain structure	H–C–C–C–C–H (with H atoms)	H–C–C–C–C–C–H (with H atoms)
Branched chain structure	H–C–C–C–H branched with CH₃	H–C–C–C–C–H branched with CH₃
		H–C–C–C–H branched structure

As you can see in Table 11-1, butane C_4H_{10}, has two isomers and pentane, C_5H_{12}, has three isomers. There are 18 isomers of C_8H_{18}, 1858 isomers of $C_{14}H_{30}$, and 366,319 isomers of $C_{20}H_{42}$. Each isomer has different properties, and can be thought of as a different compound.

Chains of carbon atoms form molecules with either a straight-chain structure or a branched-chain structure. In a *straight-chain structure*, any carbon atom in the chain is bonded to no more than two carbon atoms. Notice in Figure 11-2A that this chain is a straight line. Count the carbon and hydrogen atoms in the chain. What is the chemical formula of this compound?[1]

[1]$C_{10}H_{22}$
[2]Yes.
[3]A straight chain has only two carbon atoms bonded to any carbon atom. A branched chain can have more than two carbon atoms bonded to any carbon atom.

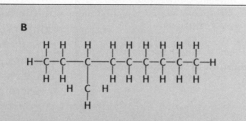

Figure 11-2

How does a straight-chain structure (A) differ from a branched-chain structure (B)?[3]

In a *branched-chain structure*, one or more of the carbon atoms in the chain is bonded to three or four other carbon atoms. This structure looks like a tree limb with branches. Figure 11-2B shows an example of a branched-chain structure. Note that the third carbon atom from the left has an extra carbon atom attached. Count the carbon and hydrogen atoms in this chain. Are the two molecules shown in the figure isomers?[2]

Branched-chain structures often are larger than the one shown in Figure 11-2. Vulcanized rubber is used to make many products, including the hockey puck shown in Figure 11-3. A single molecule of rubber contains thousands of carbon atoms in a branched-chain structure. This branched shape gives rubber its elastic property.

REVIEW

1. How are organic compounds different from inorganic compounds? Give one example of each.
2. Why are there many different organic compounds?
3. Draw the structural formula for propane, C_3H_8.
4. Define the term *isomers*. How many isomers of pentane are there?

CHALLENGE Draw a straight-chain structural diagram and a branched-chain structural diagram of hexane, C_6H_{14}.

Figure 11-3

The rubber used to make hockey pucks is made up of very large molecules.

predicting
Students can compare different carbon-chain structures in Figure 11-2A. Ask students to predict what the straight-chain molecule would look like if its formula were $C_{15}H_{32}$.

3 REVIEW/REINFORCEMENT

1. Organic compounds contain carbon. Inorganic compounds do not contain carbon. Plastic is organic. Table salt is inorganic.
2. There are many organic compounds because carbon has so many possible bonding patterns.
3.

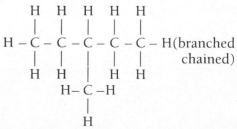

4. Compounds that have the same chemical formula but different structural formulas are called isomers. Pentane has three isomers.

Challenge Both drawings should contain 6 carbon atoms and 14 hydrogen atoms. All bonds are single bonds. The branched-chain molecule can have the branch on any non-end carbon. At least 1 carbon atom must have 3 other carbon atoms attached.

255

255

11-2 HYDROCARBONS

OBJECTIVES
Refer to pupil page 256.

VOCABULARY
  Key terms: alkanes, alkenes, alkynes, hydrocarbons, saturated hydrocarbon, unsaturated hydrocarbon

1 MOTIVATION

Show a movie about the oil-refining process. Point out that crude oil is a mixture of hydrocarbons. In the refining process, these hydrocarbons are separated into useful components. Obtain a flow chart that shows the products of an oil refinery. Many large oil companies or their advertising agencies have these available upon request.

2 CONCEPT DEVELOPMENT

Background The sharing of one pair of electrons by adjacent atoms is called a single bond. The sharing of two pairs of electrons by adjacent atoms is called a double bond. The sharing of three pairs of electrons by adjacent atoms constitutes a triple bond.

After completing this section, you will be able to

- **give examples** of hydrocarbons.
- **name** and **write** formulas for simple hydrocarbons.
- **list** uses of hydrocarbons.

The key terms in this section are
alkanes
alkenes
alkynes
hydrocarbons
saturated hydrocarbon
unsaturated hydrocarbon

Compounds made of only carbon and hydrogen are called **hydrocarbons** (HĪ droh kahr buhnz). This group of compounds includes natural gas and gasoline. Kerosene, used in some heaters, and turpentine, a paint thinner, also are hydrocarbons.

Crude oil is a complex mixture of hydrocarbons. These compounds are separated when the oil is processed in a refinery like the one shown in Figure 11-4. Each hydrocarbon has properties that differ from those of other hydrocarbons. In a refinery, these compounds are separated on the basis of their boiling points. Butane, used in some campers' stoves, is a four-carbon compound and is a gas at room temperature. Gasoline contains octane, an eight-carbon compound that is a liquid at room temperature. Waxes are much larger molecules and are solids at room temperature.

Figure 11-4

In a refinery the hydrocarbons in crude oil are separated to make many products.

Hydrocarbons can be grouped on the basis of the bonds found between the carbon atoms. **Alkanes** (AL kaynz) are hydrocarbons that have only single bonds between the carbon atoms. Table 11-2 shows the straight-chain structure of three alkanes. Notice that each carbon atom is bonded to the greatest possible number of hydrogen atoms. Because the molecule contains all the hydrogen atoms it can, an alkane is said to be saturated with hydrogen. A **saturated hydrocarbon** is a molecule in which all bonds between carbon atoms are single bonds. A saturated compound may contain other elements in addition to carbon and hydrogen, but all bonds between carbon atoms must be single bonds.

Table 11-2 *Structural Formulas of Alkanes*

Name	Formula	Structure
Hexane	C_6H_{14}	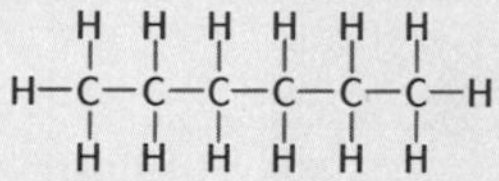
Nonane	C_9H_{20}	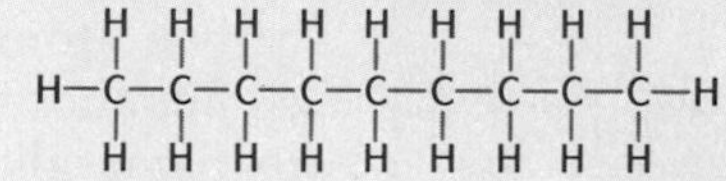
Decane	$C_{10}H_{22}$	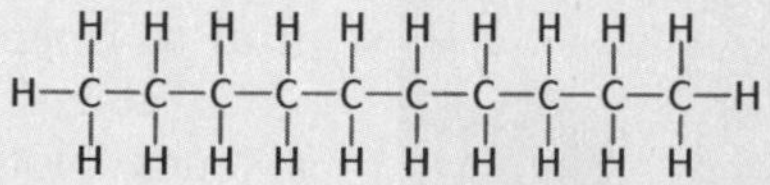

Scientists use a set of rules to name hydrocarbons. The first part, or prefix, of a hydrocarbon name tells the number of carbon atoms in the molecule. Table 11-3 shows the prefix used to stand for each number of carbon atoms, up to ten. The ending, or suffix, of the name of a hydrocarbon compound tells the bonding pattern. All alkanes, such as methane, ethane, and propane, have names that end in -*ane*.

Alkanes have single bonds between the carbon atoms. An ethane molecule contains two carbon atoms joined by a single bond. Each propane molecule contains three carbon atoms. How many carbon atoms are found in a molecule of nonane?[1]

Alkanes have a general formula of C_2H_{2n+2}, where n refers to the number of carbon atoms in the molecule. A molecule of methane has one carbon atom and four hydrogen atoms. This can be shown using the formula, with n equal to 1.

$$C_nH_{2n+2}$$
$$C(1)\ H[2(1)+2]$$
$$CH_4$$

A molecule of ethane contains two carbon atoms. To determine the number of hydrogen atoms, use the formula.

$$C_nH_{2n+2}$$
$$C(2)\ H[2(2)+2]$$
$$C_2H_6$$

Table 11-3 *Organic Prefixes*

Prefix	Number of Carbon Atoms
meth-	1
eth-	2
prop-	3
but-	4
pent-	5
hex-	6
hept-	7
oct-	8
non-	9
dec-	10

[1]Nine.

Background   Gasoline is a mixture of hydrocarbons. The octane rating of gasoline is determined by the mixture of hydrocarbons and their performance compared with isooctane.

Tie-in/Social Studies   Obtain a map that shows petroleum deposits, refineries, and pipelines. Ask students to locate refineries and oil deposits or ports where tankers arrive. Have students trace the pipelines that move the product to population centers.

Thinking Skills

predicting
Ask students to predict the formulas for alkanes with up to ten carbon atoms per molecule. Have students draw a structural diagram for the straight-chain isomer of each formula.

257

Background   Natural gas is about three-fourths methane. Most bottled gas is propane. Butane is sold as bottled gas in warmer climates because of its higher boiling point.

Teaching Tip   Use molecular models to show the differences between single, double, and triple bonds. Show that there is rotation on the axis of a single bond but not on the axis of a double or triple bond. A two-carbon molecule will be best suited for this demonstration.

Teaching Tip   The terms *single bonds* and *saturated hydrocarbons* both begin with the letter s. Have students keep this in mind to help remember the bonding pattern.

Teaching Tip   The names of the alkanes, alkenes, and alkynes vary in only one letter. If these hydrocarbons are arranged alphabetically, they also show order of bond number. This alphabetical arrangement also arranges the general formulas. Note that the number of hydrogens in each general formula decreases by two.

Name	Formula	Type of Bond
Alkane	C_nH_{2n+2}	single
Alkene	C_nH_{2n}	double
Alkyne	C_nH_{2n-2}	triple

Figure 11-5

This gas lamp burns methane.

[1]Furnaces, stoves, hot water heaters, Bunsen burners.

Many alkanes are used as fuels. They burn in air and release large amounts of heat energy. For example, methane, which makes up most of natural gas, combines with oxygen as it burns.

$$CH_4 + 2O_2 \rightarrow CO_2 + 2H_2O + energy$$

Figure 11-5 shows one use of methane gas. What other common uses can you name?[1]

Hydrocarbons that contain one double bond between carbon atoms are **alkenes** (AL keenz). The names of all compounds in this group end in *-ene*. The prefixes used to name alkanes are also used to name alkenes. Thus ethene, propene, and butene are examples of alkenes. Ethene, C_2H_4, is sometimes sprayed in orchards to cause the fruit to ripen more quickly.

Table 11-4 shows the structural formulas of some alkenes. Notice that each structure includes one double bond. A molecule that has double bonds between carbon atoms is said to be an **unsaturated hydrocarbon**. Alkenes are unsaturated. They contain fewer hydrogen atoms than do the alkanes.

Table 11-4 *Structural Formulas of Alkenes*

Name	Formula	Structure
Ethene	C_2H_4	
Propene	C_3H_6	
Butene	C_4H_8	

Hydrocarbons that have one triple bond between carbon atoms are called **alkynes** (AL kīnz). The prefix used to show the number of carbon atoms in an alkyne are the same as the prefixes used for alkanes and alkenes. The names of all alkynes end in *-yne*. Ethyne, C_2H_2, is the simplest alkyne. It also is known as acetylene (uh SEHT-uh leen), and is used for welding.

ACTIVITY How Are Organic Molecules Represented?

OBJECTIVES
Compare models of organic molecules.
Draw structural diagrams for each model.

MATERIALS
student molecular model kit

PROCEDURE

A. Assemble a model of methane, CH_4. Follow the assembly instructions given with a molecular model set to attach four hydrogen atoms to one carbon atom.

B. Draw a structural formula for methane. Also write the name and chemical formula. Take the model apart.

C. Construct a model of ethane, C_2H_6. Draw a structural diagram to match the model. Label the diagram with the name and formula. Save the model.

D. Change the model of ethane to a model of ethene, C_2H_4. Draw the structural diagram for the model. Label the diagram. Save the model.

E. Change the model of ethene to a model of ethyne, C_2H_2. Draw the structural diagram for the model. Label the diagram. Take the model apart.

F. Construct models and make diagrams of the following compounds: propane, butane (2 isomers), and pentane (3 isomers).

RESULTS AND CONCLUSIONS

1. Study the structural diagrams. How are molecules of ethane, ethene, and ethyne similar? How are they different?
2. What did you do to the model of ethane to change it to a model of ethene?
3. Write a balanced chemical equation to show how you changed a molecule of ethane to a molecule of ethene.
4. How are the isomers of pentane similar? How are they different?

Table 11-5 shows the structural formulas for ethyne and propyne. Look at the number of atoms in each molecule. How many bonds does each carbon atom have?[1]

[1]Four.

Table 11-5 *Structural Formulas of Alkynes*

Name	Formula	Structure
Ethyne	C_2H_2	H—C≡C—H
Propyne	C_3H_4	$\begin{array}{c} \text{H} \\ | \\ \text{H—C≡C—C—H} \\ | \\ \text{H} \end{array}$

REVIEW

1. List three examples of hydrocarbons and state a use for each.
2. Explain the meaning of the organic prefixes *meth-*, *eth-*, and *pent-*.
3. Write the structural formula for ethane.
4. What different types of bonds are there in alkanes, alkenes, and alkynes?

CHALLENGE Why are there no methene molecules or methyne molecules?

ACTIVITY 30–40 minutes

PROCESS SKILLS
sequencing, comparing, interpreting diagrams

Preparation Molecular model kits are available from most supply houses. Be sure all the necessary components are in the kits.

Answers to Results and Conclusions

1. They all have the same number of carbon atoms. They differ in the type of bonding and the number of hydrogen atoms per molecule.
2. Remove two hydrogen atoms, and change the bond between the carbon atoms from a single bond to a double bond.
3. $C_2H_6 \rightarrow C_2H_4 + H_2$.
4. They both have the same number of carbon atoms and hydrogen atoms in each isomer. They differ in the arrangement of the atoms or the shape of the molecule.

3 REVIEW/REINFORCEMENT

1. Answers may include: natural gas—heating, cooking, lighting; gasoline—automotive fuel; kerosene—heating fuel; turpentine—paint thinner.
2. Meth- —one carbon atom; Eth- —two carbon atoms; Pent- —five carbon atoms.
3.

$$\begin{array}{cc} \text{H} & \text{H} \\ | & | \\ \text{H — C — C — H} \\ | & | \\ \text{H} & \text{H} \end{array}$$

4. Alkanes—single bonds; Alkenes—double bonds; Alkynes—triple bonds.

Challenge Molecules ending with *-ene* or *-yne* have double bonds or triple bonds respectively. These types of bonding patterns require a minimum of two carbon atoms per molecule. A *meth-* molecule would have only one carbon atom; therefore, a double or triple bond between two carbon atoms is impossible.

11-3 CYCLIC HYDROCARBONS
pages 260–261

11-3 CYCLIC HYDROCARBONS

OBJECTIVES
Refer to pupil page 260.

VOCABULARY
Key terms: aromatic hydrocarbons, cyclic hydrocarbon

1 MOTIVATION

Display a model of a linear molecule five to six atoms long. Have students identify the molecule by giving its chemical formula. Now convert the linear model into a cyclic model. Ask students if this could happen. (Yes) Ask them if this new model is a cyclic hydrocarbon. (Yes) Then ask students if the properties of the new model will differ from those of the linear model originally shown. (No)

2 CONCEPT DEVELOPMENT

Teaching Tip Point out to students that although cyclic compounds ending in -ane all have single bonds, these compounds do not follow the general formula C_nH_{2n+2}.

Demonstration The use of molecular models will help to reinforce the concept of cyclic structures. Use a variety of techniques. Have some molecular models preassembled. Build some models in front of the class. Ask students to construct other molecular representations. Stress that the molecules themselves are three-dimensional, as shown by the models.

After completing this section, you will be able to

- **give** examples of cyclic hydrocarbons.
- **distinguish** betwen models of cyclohexane and benzene.
- **list** uses for some cyclic hydrocarbons.

The key terms in this section are
aromatic hydrocarbons
cyclic hydrocarbon

The word *cycle* describes round objects. For example, a bicycle has two round wheels. A **cyclic hydrocarbon** is a compound that has a round, or ring-type, structure.

Cyclopropane (sī kluh PROH payn) is a ring compound used as an anesthetic (an ehz THEHT ihk). The first part of the name, *cyclo-*, shows that the compound has a ring structure. The *-prop-* portion refers to a three-carbon structure. The ending, *-ane*, means that all of the bonds between the carbon atoms are single bonds.

The formula for cyclopropane is C_3H_6. Compare the straight-chain form of propane to the ring of carbon atoms in Figure 11-6. Other cyclic organic compounds have similar ring structures. Cyclohexane (sī kluh HEHK sayn) is a compound used in paint remover. Notice that the compounds shown in Figure 11-6 contain only single bonds.

Figure 11-6

Most straight-chain alkanes also have a ring structure.

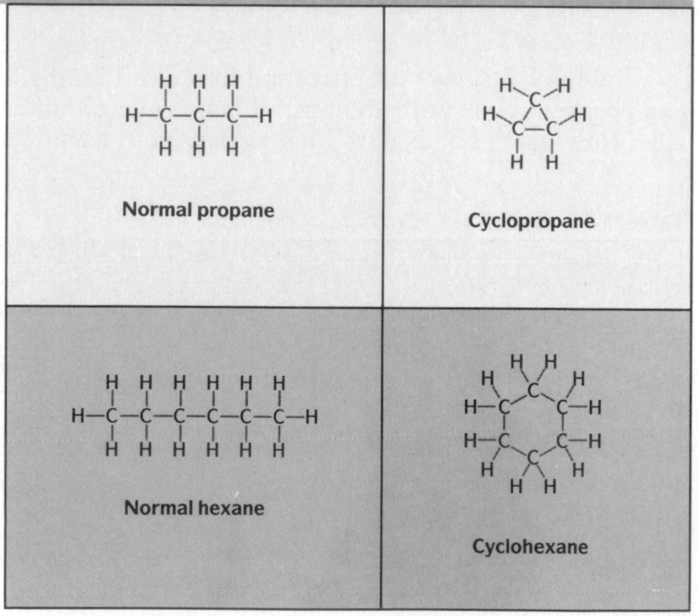

Normal propane

Cyclopropane

Normal hexane

Cyclohexane

Some cyclic molecules contain double bonds. **Aromatic hydrocarbons** are molecules that have alternate single and double bonds in six-carbon ring structures. The aromatic compounds were given this name because the first few of these compounds to be identified have strong aromas. However, many aromatic hydrocarbons do not have any odor, and many compounds that have a pleasant odor do not have the structure of the aromatic rings.

Benzene (BEHN zeen) is the most common aromatic compound. The formula for benzene is C_6H_6. The structure is shown in Figure 11-7. How many double bonds are there in the ring?[1] Notice that all around the ring there is an alternation between single bonds and double bonds between the carbon atoms. This bonding pattern is typical of benzene.

Benzene often is represented by the simplified form shown in Figure 11-7. Each point on the hexagon stands for a carbon atom, with its hydrogen atom. The circle inside the hexagon stands for the alternate single and double bonds in the ring.

Two or more benzene rings may be connected. The structure of one such compound is shown in Figure 11-8. This compound, anthracene (AN thruh seen), is used in many products, including dyes for fabrics.

Aromatic hydrocarbons have a variety of uses. These compounds are found in aspirin, moth balls, solvents, explosives, and plastic foam products.

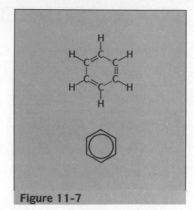

Figure 11-7

The hexagon with a circle is a simplified way to draw benzene rings.

[1] Three.

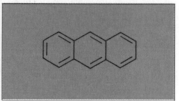

Figure 11-8

The white crystals are anthracene, $C_{14}H_{10}$. This compound is used to make dyes for fabrics like these.

REVIEW

1. Name three cyclic hydrocarbons, and state a use for each.
2. Draw a structural diagram for benzene.
3. State two ways in which cyclohexane and benzene are similar, and two ways in which they are different.

CHALLENGE Draw a structural formula of anthracene to show the position of all carbon and hydrogen atoms.

11-4 SUBSTITUTED HYDROCARBONS

pages 262–265

11-4 SUBSTITUTED HYDROCARBONS

OBJECTIVES
Refer to pupil page 262.

VOCABULARY
Key terms: alcohol, carboxyl group, ester, organic acid, substituted hydrocarbon

---

1 MOTIVATION

Organic substitution products have many uses. Bring in a bottle of perfume or after-shave lotion. Let students smell the contents. Identify the contents as alcohols and esters, which are hydrocarbon substitution compounds. Mention that organic acids, such as acetic acid found in vinegar, also belong to this general class of compounds. Stimulate a discussion to list some uses of the compounds.

---

2 CONCEPT DEVELOPMENT

Teaching Tip Use molecular models to show that methane, CH_4, has a tetrahedral structure. Replace a hydrogen atom with a chlorine atom to produce chloromethane, CH_3Cl. The process can be repeated to produce dichloromethane, CH_2Cl_2; trichloromethane, $CHCl_3$; and tetrachloromethane, CCl_4. CCl_4 is also known as carbon tetrachloride. It is a hazardous chemical that causes damage to the kidneys, liver, and lungs. CCl_4 was a common laboratory, cleaning, and fire-extinguishing agent many years ago. Any stock of this chemical should be handled with extreme caution and be properly disposed of.

After completing this section, you will be able to

- **recognize** substituted hydrocarbons.
- **distinguish** between alcohols, organic acids, and esters.
- **list** uses for several substituted hydrocarbons.

The key terms in this section are
  alcohol
  carboxyl group
  ester
  organic acid
  substituted hydrocarbon

[1]Three other substitutions are possible: CH_2Cl_2; $CHCl_3$; CCl_4.

Some organic compounds contain more than just carbon and hydrogen. A hydrocarbon in which one or more of the hydrogen atoms has been replaced by a different atom or group of atoms is called a **substituted hydrocarbon**. For example, one or more of the hydrogen atoms in a methane molecule, CH_4, can be replaced by a chlorine atom. Each change makes a new compound. Methane is changed to chloromethane by the following reaction.

$$CH_4 + Cl_2 \rightarrow CH_3Cl + HCl$$

Chloromethane is used as a solvent, and in making medicines. How many other chlorine substitutions can be made on a methane molecule?[1]

This kind of substitution makes it possible to form a great variety of compounds. There are over 50 different substitutions of methane. Many of these substituted hydrocarbons have practical uses. Freon (FREE ahn), CCl_2F_2, shown in Figure 11-9, is used in refrigerators and air conditioners. Freon also was used in aerosol (AIR uh sawl) cans until studies showed that this gas was harming the atmosphere.

Large hydrocarbons have more substitution compounds than do small ones because there are more hydrogen atoms that can be replaced. Changing the position of a substitution changes the compound that is formed.

Figure 11-9

Freon is a substituted methane molecule.

There are many possible substitutions of benzene. Figure 11-10 shows benzene and two substitutions of benzene. Toluene (TAHL yu een), $C_6H_5CH_3$, is used as a solvent for paint and glue. Other hydrogens on this ring also may be replaced. Chlorotoluene, $CH_3C_6H_4Cl$, is used in making dyes and perfumes.

If a hydroxyl, or -OH group, replaces a hydrogen on a benzene ring, the compound formed is called phenol, a type of alcohol. An **alcohol** is a hydrocarbon in which a hydrogen atom is replaced by a hydroxyl group. The general formula for an alcohol is R-OH. The R stands for the rest of the molecule. Table 11-6 shows the structure of some alcohols. As you can see, the atoms represented by the R vary, but the -OH group is always present. Methyl alcohol, CH_3OH, is the simplest alcohol. The prefix *meth-* shows that there is one carbon atom in the molecule. Methyl alcohol is used as a fuel and as a solvent for fats, waxes, and shellac. This alcohol is commonly known as wood alcohol. It is very poisonous and should be handled with care.

Ethyl alcohol, C_2H_5OH, is a common alcohol. The prefix *eth-* means that there are two carbon atoms in the molecule. Because ethyl alcohol can be made by fermenting sugar or grain, it is also known as grain alcohol. Millions of liters of ethyl alcohol are used each year in industry. This alcohol is used in making perfumes, flavorings, drugs, dyes, and rubber.

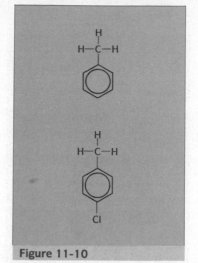

Figure 11-10

Toluene (*top*) and chlorotoluene (*bottom*) are substituted benzene molecules.

Thinking Skills

inferring
Students have an understanding of how hydrogen atoms in a methane molecule can be replaced by one or more chlorine atoms. Have students infer how this process might be repeated with methane and bromine or methane and fluorine.

Background Some alcohols contain two or three -OH groups. Ethylene glycol, permanent antifreeze, is a dihydroxyalcohol. Glycerine is a trihydroxyalcohol. There is never more than one -OH group attached to any one carbon atom in an alcohol molecule.

Table 11-6 *Alcohols*

Name	Formula	Structure
Methyl alcohol	CH_3OH	H | H—C—OH | H
Ethyl alcohol	CH_3CH_2OH	H H | | H—C—C—OH | | H H
Phenyl alcohol	C_6H_5OH	⬡—OH

263

Background   In most cases the aroma of a fruit is due to a blend of several esters. The list below shows the main ester present.
Apricot—amyl butyrate
Banana—amyl acetate
Orange—octyl acetate

Enrichment   Have students bring in candy and gum wrappers as well as labels from fruit flavorings and food products to show the abundance of esters. Often the listing will only indicate that artificial flavorings were used. If the actual name of an ester appears, the name will end in *-ate*. The first part of the name is derived from the alcohol, the second part from the acid. Ask students to be on the lookout for these products. Why?

Puzzler   A toluene molecule, as shown in Figure 11-10, with three NO_2 groups attached. If the benzene-ring carbon that contains the CH_3 group is counted as number 1, the NO_2 groups would be on carbon atoms numbered 2, 4, and 6.

SCIENCE PUZZLER

Many organic compounds can be used to make explosives. Trinitrotoluene, or TNT, is a powerful explosive. It is a substituted hydrocarbon that contains three nitrite groups. Its chemical formula is $CH_3C_6H_2(NO_2)_3$. Suggest a structural formula for this compound.

¹Water.

Figure 11-11

Pineapples contain this ester, made from an acid and an alcohol.

An organic acid is a compound formed when one hydrogen of a hydrocarbon molecule is replaced by a carboxyl (kahr BAHK suhl) group. A **carboxyl group** is made up of one carbon atom, two oxygen atoms, and one hydrogen atom. The formula for a carboxyl group is -COOH. The general formula for an organic acid is R-COOH. Again, R stands for the rest of the molecule.

Acetic acid, CH_3COOH, is an organic acid. Vinegar is a 5-percent acetic acid solution. Citric acid is found in lemons, oranges, and raspberries. Oxalic acid is found in rhubarb, grapes, and tomatoes.

An **ester** (EHS tuhr) is a product of the reaction between an organic acid and an alcohol. Esters have the group -COO- within the molecule. The general formula for an ester is R-COO-R′. The R stands for the part of the molecule on one side of the -COO- group, and R′ stands for the part of the molecule on the other side of the -COO- group.

Figure 11-11 shows how an ester is made from an acid and an alcohol. Locate the R-groups in the product. Notice that these two groups are on either side of a -COO- group. Notice also that some atoms are removed from the reactants in this reaction. A hydrogen atom is removed from the carboxyl group of the acid. A hydroxide group is removed from the alcohol. What product do these atoms form?¹ Esters are used in making perfumes. The flavor and odor of fruits are due to the presence of esters. Many foods contain esters as added flavorings. The ester produced in Figure 11-11 is one of the compounds found in pineapple flavoring.

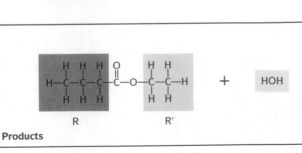

ACTIVITY   How Are Esters Made?

OBJECTIVES
Prepare esters from organic acids and alcohols.
Compare different esters.

MATERIALS
safety goggles, lab apron, 250-mL beaker, hot plate, 3 test tubes, glass-marking pencil, graduate, amyl alcohol, acetic acid, medicine dropper, sulfuric acid, test-tube rack, methyl alcohol, salicylic acid, ethyl alcohol, butyric acid, test-tube clamp

PROCEDURE

A. Wear safety goggles and a lab apron during this activity.
B. Half fill a 250-mL beaker with water. On a hot plate, heat the water to boiling. Adjust the setting of the hot plate so that the water continues to boil slowly.
C. Thoroughly clean and dry three test tubes. Label the test tubes *A*, *B*, and *C*.
D. Measure 5 mL of amyl alcohol into test tube *A*. Add 2 mL acetic acid and 5 drops of sulfuric acid. **Caution**: Be careful not to spill any acid on your skin or your clothing. Put the test tube in a test-tube rack.
E. Pour 5 mL of methyl alcohol into test tube *B*. Add 2 mL salicylic acid and 5 drops of sulfuric acid. Put the test tube in the test-tube rack.
F. Pour 5 mL of ethyl alcohol into test tube *C*. Add 2 mL butyric acid and 5 drops of sulfuric acid. Put the test tube in the test-tube rack.
G. Place all three test tubes in the boiling water. Allow the material to heat for about 1 minute.

H. Using the test-tube clamp, remove the test tubes from the hot water and place them in the test-tube rack. Turn off the hot plate.
I. Carefully waft the vapors from test tube *A* toward your nose, as shown in the drawing. **Caution**: Never directly inhale the fumes of any chemical. Record your observations.
J. Repeat step **I** with the other test tubes.
K. Empty and rinse the test tubes.

RESULTS AND CONCLUSIONS
1. Describe the odor of each ester formed.
2. Of what common substance does each ester remind you?
3. The name of an ester comes from the names of the compounds that make up the ester Names of esters end in *-ate*. For example, in test tube *A*, amyl alcohol combined with acetic acid to form amyl acetate. Name the esters formed in the other test tubes.
4. What chemicals would you combine to produce methyl butyrate?

REVIEW

1. Draw structural diagrams for methane and chloromethane.
2. Give the general formula for alcohols, organic acids, and esters.
3. Name four substituted hydrocarbons, and give a use for each.

CHALLENGE Methyl alcohol has one carbon atom in each molecule. Ethyl alcohol has two carbon atoms in each molecule. What clues about structure are given by the names methanoic acid and ethanoic acid?

265

ACTIVITY 45 minutes

PROCESS SKILLS
observing, measuring, comparing, predicting, identifying cause and effect

Preparation Salicylic acid is usually marketed as a powder. It will be necessary to dissolve the acid in methyl alcohol. A 20 percent to 30 percent solution is usually adequate. Be sure the sulfuric acid used for this reaction is concentrated.

Safety Tip Do not allow any open flames in the laboratory.
  Be sure to have adequate ventilation when performing this activity.
  Nitroglycerine is an ester. Be sure that no nitric acid and glycerine are available.

Teaching Tip A dry test tube is imperative.

Answers to Results and Conclusions
1. Test tube *A*—banana; fruit, candy, and so on. Test tube *B*—wintergreen; gum, candy, air freshener. Test tube *C*—pineapple; fruit, flavorings and so on.
2. Test tube *A*—fruit; test tube *B*—gum, candy, air freshener; test tube *C*—fruit.
3. Test tube *A*—amyl acetate; test tube *B*—methyl salicylate; test tube *C*—ethyl butyrate.
4. Methyl alcohol and butyric acid.

3 REVIEW/REINFORCEMENT

1. Methane. Chloromethane.

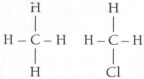

2. Alcohols—R-OH; organic acids—R-COOH; esters—R-COO-R′.
3. Freon—refrigerant; toluene—solvent for paint and glue; chlorotoluene—making dyes; methyl alcohol—solvent for fats.

Challenge Methanoic acid and ethanoic acid would contain one carbon atom and two carbon atoms respectively.

265

11-5 ORGANIC POLYMERS

pages 266–267

11-5 ORGANIC POLYMERS

OBJECTIVES
Refer to pupil page 266.

VOCABULARY
Key term: polymer

---

1 MOTIVATION

Obtain samples of some of the following materials: Nylon, plastic foam, a record, recording tape, a polyethylene plastic bag, a rubber ball. Point out that each substance is a polymer. Use the first two paragraphs of this section to explain the nature of polymers. Explain that the properties and appearances of each polymer are unique because the basic repeating units are different. Allow students to examine each substance and to note similarities and differences.

---

2 CONCEPT DEVELOPMENT

Background   The repeating unit of a polymer is called a monomer. Monomers can be linked together by either addition or condensation.

Thinking Skills

identifying cause and effect
As Figure 11-12 shows, a polymer is made up of identical basic units in a repeating structure. Figure 11-13 shows the basic unit of the polymer tetrafluoroethylene, TFE. Because atoms in the TFE molecules are strongly attracted to each other and not attracted to other atoms, this polymer is used to provide nonstick coatings for pots and pans. Ask students why other substances will not attach to tetrafluoroethylene or combine with it.

After completing this section, you will be able to

- **define** the term *polymer*.
- **recognize** a polymer structure.
- **name** several polymers and list their uses.

The key term in this section is polymer

poly- (many)
meros (part)

Many organic molecules have thousands of carbon atoms in long chains. These chains can be compared to the beads shown in Figure 11-12. You could break the chain of beads into many identical pieces. If you put these pieces together again, the chain of beads would be just like the original one. A long-chain organic compound such as the plastic that makes up the beads, is called a polymer (PAHL ih muhr).

A **polymer** is a molecule made up of simple units that form a repeating structure. Polyethylene (pah lee EHTH-uh leen), a common plastic, is a polymer. It is used to make plastic bags, toys, and bottles. Polyethylene is made up of units of ethene. As the polymer is formed, the double bond found in ethene is changed to a single bond. As you can see in Figure 11-12, this change leaves an unpaired electron at each end of the unit. More of the same units can combine to form a very large polymer. This process takes place about 2000 times to form polyethylene. The structural diagram uses the letter n to show that there are many repeating units.

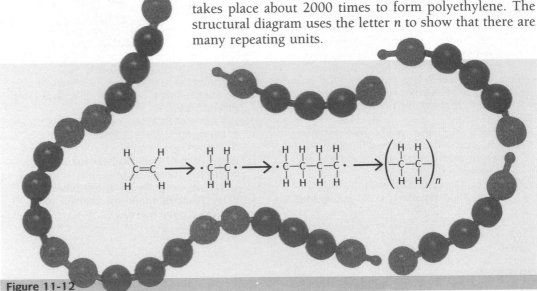

Figure 11-12

Like the beads, a polymer is made up of many small units.

Some of the first polymers that were known came from plants. Rubber is a natural polymer. So is cellulose, which makes up part of the cell walls of plants. Cellulose can be made into rayon, a polymer used to make cloth. Cellulose also can be made into celluloid. This polymer was first made over a century ago. It was used to make combs, movie film, and many other objects. Plastic is now used in place of celluloid.

266

266

SCIENCE & TECHNOLOGY

When cars are transported from factories to dealers, the car's surface may be damaged by dirt and weather. This is especially true for cars transported by ship from one continent to another. Salt-air and salt water can quickly corrode a car's finish.

To promise the buyer a clean, shiny paint job, many manufacturers apply a temporary coating to the car. This coating is made up of organic polymers that form a transparent film. After the cars reach the dealer, the film is washed off. The trouble with the coatings used now is that strong solvents are needed to wash them off. These solvents are dangerous to the environment. Disposing of the solvents can pollute water, threatening the plants and animals that live there. These solvents also are very flammable, making them dangerous to work with.

A new protective coating eliminates these problems. It is a water-based polymer. It can be washed off with mild solutions of alkaline compounds that do not harm the environment. In addition, the new coating is not flammable, so it is much safer to use.

The new coating may prove useful for more than cars. It may be used in a temporary paint. This paint could be used to mark roads for marathons and parades.

Polymers can be made from products of crude oil. Many common substances use these polymers. Polyester is used for making fabrics and carpets. Plastic foam is used for ice chests, cups, and packing material. Records, recording tape, and plastic pipe all are made from polymers.

Tetrafluoroethylene, TFE, is a polymer that has many uses. Figure 11-13 shows the basic unit of TFE. This compound is used to give pots and pans a non-stick surface. The atoms in the molecules of TFE are strongly attracted to each other. They are not attracted to other atoms. Thus, other substances cannot stick to this compound, or chemically combine with it.

REVIEW

1. Define the term *polymer*.
2. How are the structures of all polymers similar?
3. Name three polymers, and give a use for each one.

CHALLENGE Some raincoats are made of cloth that has been treated with a polymer that makes the cloth waterproof. Furniture and carpets are treated with a chemical that resists stains. Which polymer discussed in this section would you expect to be most like these compounds?

$$\left(\begin{array}{cc} \underset{\displaystyle F}{\overset{\displaystyle F}{|}} & \underset{\displaystyle F}{\overset{\displaystyle F}{|}} \\ -C- & -C- \\ \underset{\displaystyle F}{|} & \underset{\displaystyle F}{|} \end{array} \right)_{n}$$

Figure 11-13

TFE gives this pan a non-stick surface.

11-6 THE CHEMISTRY OF LIVING THINGS

pages 268–271

OBJECTIVES
Refer to pupil page 268.

VOCABULARY
Key terms: carbohydrates, lipids, nucleic acids, proteins, vitamins

Other terms: amino acids, photosynthesis

1 MOTIVATION

Display a chart, illustration, or overhead transparency that shows the four basic food groups. Ask students to keep a record of the foods they eat for a day or two. Have students determine how many of the food groups are in their daily diet. Point out that people need foods from each of the food groups to function properly. Ask students what could possibly happen if a person's diet eliminated some of these food groups.

2 CONCEPT DEVELOPMENT

Background   Glucose is a simple sugar. The chemical formula for glucose is $C_6H_{12}O_6$. Glucose is also known as blood sugar, grape sugar, or corn sugar. Glucose and fructose have the same chemical formula but different structures. Simple sugars, like glucose, are called monosaccharides. A more complex sugar called a disaccharide is formed from two simple sugars. Lactose ($C_{12}H_{22}O_{11}$), milk sugar, is a disaccharide. Sugars can polymerize to form starch, which is a polysaccharide.

Review and Skill masters

CHALLENGE/CRITICAL THINKING, page 70.
See page 251c in this book for answers.

After completing this section, you will be able to

- **identify** the major types of compounds that make up living things.
- **distinguish** between a carbohydrate, a fat, and a protein.
- **recognize** the function of nucleic acids.

The key terms in this section are

carbohydrates	proteins
lipids	vitamins
nucleic acids	

[1]Starches.

The human body is about two-thirds water. This means that a person with a mass of 51 kilograms would have 34 kilograms of water in his or her body. Water is a part of all the cells in the body. Water can be found in muscles, skin, teeth, heart, liver, and bones. Blood is mostly water. The remaining one-third of the human body is made up of many inorganic and organic compounds. The organic compounds include carbohydrates, lipids, proteins, and nucleic acids.

Carbohydrates (kahr boh HĪ drayts) are organic compounds that contain carbon, hydrogen, and oxygen, and that are the body's main source of energy. The hydrogen and oxygen atoms are in a 2:1 ratio, as they are in water. Starches and sugars are examples of carbohydrates. Sugars are made up of one or two ring-shaped structures. Starches are polymers made up of many sugar units. Figure 11-14 shows some foods that are rich in carbohydrates. Do these foods contain more starches or sugars?[1]

Figure 11-14

Carbohydrate foods provide energy for the body.

Organic compounds can be made from inorganic compounds. Plants use water and carbon dioxide to make sugars. This process uses light as a source of energy. The process by which a plant makes sugars is called *photosynthesis*. Plants use the sugar molecules as a source of energy for their cells. The sugar molecules also can be used to make starches, lipids, and proteins.

Figure 11-15

Foods that contain lipids (*A*) provide energy for the body to store. Foods that contain proteins (*B*) provide building materials for the body.

Lipids (LIHP ihdz) are organic compounds that contain carbon, hydrogen, and oxygen, and that are mostly used to store energy. Hydrogen and oxygen are not in a 2:1 ratio in a lipid molecule. There is much more hydrogen in a lipid molecule than in a carbohydrate molecule.

Fats, oils, and waxes all are lipids. Figure 11-15*A* shows some foods with a high lipid content. Lipids may be described as saturated or unsaturated. Recall that in a saturated molecule, the bonds between the carbon atoms are single bonds. Animal fats are saturated lipids. These lipids are solid at room temperature. Unsaturated lipids have double bonds between some carbon atoms. These lipids are liquid at room temperature, and they include plant oils like corn oil, peanut oil, and olive oil. It is believed that a good diet should contain more unsaturated oils than saturated fats.

Most of the organic part of muscles, skin, hair, and internal organs is made of proteins. **Proteins** (PROH teenz) are organic compounds that are made up of carbon, oxygen, hydrogen, and nitrogen. Some proteins also contain sulfur. Proteins are made up of small units called *amino acids* (uh MEE noh AS ihdz) like the one shown in Figure 11-16. Amino acids contain an amino group, -NH$_2$, and a carboxyl group, -COOH. Different *R* groups make about 20 different amino acids. Some proteins contain about 5000 amino-acid units. Because of the many combinations possible, there are more kinds of proteins than of carbohydrates or lipids.

Figure 11-15*B* shows some foods that contain proteins. When a person eats these foods, the proteins are broken down into amino acids. These amino acids are then used by the body to build new proteins.

lipos (fat)

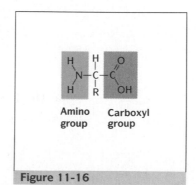

Figure 11-16

Amino acids contain an amino group and a carboxyl group.

Background   Lipids are usually insoluble in water. To dissolve a lipid, an organic solvent, such as alcohol, gasoline, or mineral spirits, is used. The difference between a fat and an oil is that a fat is a solid at room temperature but an oil is a liquid at the same temperature. Biologists refer to lipids as triglycerides.

Background   Proteins make up about 15 percent of the human body. The structure of a protein molecule can be either linear or helical. It is common for more than one protein structure to exist in a given protein. The hemoglobin of red blood cells is made of four protein structures.

Demonstration   Foods can easily be tested for protein. A hard-boiled egg white will turn yellow when treated with a few drops of dilute nitric acid. The yellow color will turn orange if a few drops of ammonium hydroxide are then added. These color changes indicate the presence of protein.

Thinking Skills

classifying
Figure 11-15*A* shows foods with high lipid content. Ask students to classify the lipids as saturated or unsaturated.

Enrichment   The sequence of amino acids in most proteins is not known. However, some protein chains have been isolated and studied. The structure of insulin is known to be two chains of amino acids connected by sulfur atoms. Hemoglobin contains over 500 amino acid units. Ask students to research these two proteins and to construct a model to represent each.

Background   DNA and RNA are named after the sugars deoxyribose and ribose. The sugars differ by one oxygen atom, with ribose being the more oxygen-rich. The term *deoxy-* means "without oxygen," or "oxygen-poor."

PROCESS SKILLS

observing, measuring, sequencing, comparing, identifying cause and effect, inferring, interpreting diagrams, recording data

Preparation   Use 6M sodium hydroxide. If your supply consists of solid NaOH, prepare the solution by dissolving 240 g of the solid in enough water (preferably distilled) to make 1 L of solution. Olive oil works well, but lard will also make good soap. Some vegetable oils will work.

Safety Tip   There may be splattering of the material if students apply heat too vigorously. This hot material could cause severe burns. Remind students to wear a lab apron and to heat the mixture slowly. Some students may have sensitive skin. Caution those students who have allergies to some soaps and/or have delicate skin to act as observers; they should not touch the soap.

Teaching Tip   The sodium chloride is added to aid in the precipitation of soap. The soap is a sodium stearate, and the sodium ion from the salt helps to shift any equilibrium toward the formation of additional soap by increasing the concentration of the sodium.

Answers to Results and Conclusions

1. The reactants slowly thickened.
2. Paste or thick butter or soap.
3. It feels slippery, or soapy.
4. Bubbles formed.
5. The soap feels slippery and makes bubbles.

Background   Prior to the 1950s, little was known about genetics and the structure of genes. James Watson and Francis Crick researched the chemistry and mechanics of gene action. Their discovery of the double helix structure of the DNA molecule is the basis for present-day genetics.

Background   Vitamins regulate the enzymatic functions in the body. Without vitamins, many of the body enzymes will not work.

ACTIVITY   How Is Soap Made?

OBJECTIVE
Prepare soap from a fat and a base.

MATERIALS
safety goggles, graduate, evaporating dish, olive oil, sodium hydroxide solution, ring stand, ring, wire gauze, Bunsen burner, striker, stirring rod, balance, sodium chloride, paper towel, 250-mL flask, rubber stopper, lab apron

PROCEDURE

A. Wear safety goggles and a lab apron during this activity. **Caution:** People with sensitive skin should be careful not to handle the chemicals used or the soap made.
B. Measure 6 mL of olive oil into an evaporating dish.
C. Add 12 mL of sodium hydroxide solution to the olive oil.
D. Set up the ring stand as shown in the diagram.
E. Slowly, with constant stirring, heat the mixture to boiling.
F. Cook the mixture, always stirring, until the material in the dish looks like lumpy oatmeal.
G. Turn off the burner. Allow the mixture to cool for 3 to 4 minutes.
H. Add 15 mL of water to the dish.
I. Stir 3 g of sodium chloride into the mixture.
J. Pour the excess fluid out of the dish.
K. Scrape the remaining solid from the dish onto a paper towel.
L. Shape the solid material into a "cake of soap."
M. Put the cake of soap into a 250-mL flask half filled with water. Stopper and then shake the flask.

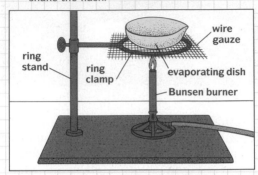

RESULTS AND CONCLUSIONS

1. Describe what happened to the reactants as heat was applied.
2. What does the newly formed soap look like?
3. Describe what the soap feels like.
4. What happened when the soap and water mixture was shaken?
5. What evidence is there that homemade soap is similar to commercial soap?

Nucleic acids (noo KLEE ihk AS ihdz) are organic compounds that control the functions of cells. One such function is the making of proteins. One nucleic acid, DNA, contains information about the arrangement of amino acids in a protein. Another nucleic acid, RNA, takes the information from the DNA and uses it to control the building of a protein. There is a different DNA pattern for each protein that the body can make.

vita- (life)

Vitamins are complex organic compounds used in small amounts to control chemical reactions in the body. Most vitamins are not made in the body. They are consumed in the foods you eat. Some vitamins, such as vitamin A, are fat-soluble vitamins. These vitamins usually are found in foods that contain lipids. Water-soluble vitamins, such as vitamin C, are not found in the lipid part of foods.

Most foods contain a mixture of organic compounds. For example, eggs and meats contain fats as well as proteins. Peanut butter contains proteins, carbohydrates, lipids, and some vitamins. Fresh fruits and vegetables are good sources of vitamins. They also contain carbohydrates and some proteins.

REVIEW

1. Name four types of compounds found in living things.
2. How is the makeup of a carbohydrate different from that of a lipid?
3. How are proteins different from carbohydrates and lipids?
4. What is the function of nucleic acids?

CHALLENGE Many fertilizers are partly made up of nitrogen compounds. Why is a source of nitrogen important to the growth of plants?

CHAPTER SUMMARY

The main ideas in this chapter are listed below. Read these statements before you answer the Chapter Review questions.

- Organic compounds all contain carbon. The carbon atoms in these compounds can form many different bonding patterns. (11-1)

- Hydrocarbons are organic compounds that contain only carbon and hydrogen. Many hydrocarbons are used as fuels. (11-2)

- Alkanes, alkenes, and aklynes are kinds of hydrocarbons. They differ in the kinds of bonds they contain. (11-2)

- Cyclic hydrocarbons have carbon atoms arranged in a ring structure. (11-3)

- Hydrogen atoms in a hydrocarbon molecule can be replaced by other atoms or groups of atoms. Such replacements form new compounds, including alcohols and acids. (11-4)

- A polymer is a molecule made up of a long chain of simple units in a repeating structure. (11-5)

- The organic compounds that make up living things are carbohydrates, fats, proteins, and nucleic acids. (11-6)

The key terms in this chapter are listed below. Use each term in a sentence that shows the meaning of the term.

alcohol	ester	proteins
alkanes	hydrocarbons	saturated hydrocarbon
aklenes	isomers	structural formula
aklynes	lipids	substituted hydrocarbon
aromatic hydrocarbons	nucleic acids	unsaturated hydrocarbon
carbohydrates	organic acid	vitamins
carboxyl group	organic compounds	
cyclic hydrocarbon	polymer	

3 REVIEW/REINFORCEMENT

1. Carbohydrates, lipids, proteins, nucleic acids.
2. A carbohydrate has hydrogen and oxygen atoms present in a ratio of 2:1. In a lipid there is much more hydrogen than there is in a carbohydrate.
3. Proteins contain nitrogen; lipids and carbohydrates do not.
4. Nucleic acids control the functions of the cells.

Challenge   The nitrogen compounds of fertilizer are essential to the building of plant proteins.

Review and Skill Masters

VOCABULARY REVIEW, page 65.
See page 251b in this book for answers.

VOCABULARY

1. True
2. False; saturated hydrocarbon
3. False; alkynes
4. False; alcohol
5. True
6. True
7. False; carbohydrates
8. True
9. False; vitamins
10. True
11. False; nucleic acids
12. False; aromatic hydrocarbons

CONCEPTS

1. Organic compounds contain carbon, and inorganic compounds do not. However, a few simple compounds that contain carbon are classified as inorganic.
2. The carbon atom has four outer-level electrons.
3. Both the composition and shape or structure of the molecule.
4. See Table 11-1.
5. In a straight chain a carbon atom is bonded to no more than two other carbon atoms. In a branched chain one or more of the carbon atoms is bonded to three or four carbon atoms.
6. Saturated hydrocarbons contain only single bonds between carbon atoms. Unsaturated hydrocarbons can contain double or triple bonds.
7. Ten.
8.

Ethane	Ethene	Ethyne

Ethane:
```
    H   H
    |   |
H – C – C – H
    |   |
    H   H
```

Ethene:
```
  H       H
  |       |
  C  =  C
  |       |
  H       H
```

Ethyne:

$$H - C \equiv C - H$$

Review and Skill Masters

CHAPTER REVIEW, pages 66–67.
See page 251b in this book for answers.

VOCABULARY

Identify each statement as True or False. If a statement is false, replace the underlined term with a term that makes the statement true.

1. <u>Isomers</u> are compounds that have the same chemical formulas but different structural formulas.
2. <u>Unsaturated hydrocarbons</u> are molecules in which all bonds between carbon atoms are single bonds.
3. Hydrocarbons that have one triple bond between carbon atoms are called <u>alkenes</u>.
4. An <u>ester</u> is a hydrocarbon in which a hydrogen atom is replaced by a hydroxide group.
5. Organic molecules made up of simple units that form a repeating structure are called <u>polymers</u>.
6. The smallest units that make up proteins are called <u>amino acids</u>.
7. <u>Lipids</u> are organic molecules that have hydrogen and oxygen in a 2:1 ratio.
8. Compounds that contain carbon are called <u>organic compounds</u>.
9. <u>Nucleic acids</u> are organic compounds used in small amounts to control chemical reactions in the body.
10. <u>Carboxyl groups</u> have the general formula -COOH.
11. <u>Proteins</u> are organic compounds that control the functions of cells.
12. <u>Substituted hydrocarbons</u> are molecules that have alternate single and double bonds in six-carbon ring structures.

CONCEPTS

1. What is the difference between an organic compound and an inorganic compound? (11-1)
2. Why is each carbon atom able to form four bonds? (11-1)
3. What do structural formulas show? (11-1)
4. Using structural diagrams, show two isomers of a hydrocarbon with five carbon atoms and twelve hydrogen atoms. (11-1)
5. What is the difference between a straight-chain hydrocarbon and a branched-chain hydrocarbon? (11-1)
6. What is the difference between a saturated hydrocarbon and an unsaturated hydrocarbon? (11-2)
7. How many carbon atoms are there in a molecule of decane? (11-2)
8. Draw structural diagrams for ethane, ethene, and ethyne. (11-2)

9. List two uses of hydrocarbons. (11-2)

10. Compare the bonds found in benzene and cyclohexane. (11-3)

11. List two uses of cyclic hydrocarbons. (11-3)

12. What is a substituted hydrocarbon? (11-4)

13. List two uses of esters. (11-4)

14. Identify each of the following as an ester, an alcohol, or an organic acid. (11-4)

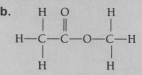

15. Describe the structure of polymers. (11-5)

16. Name a polymer used to make plastics. (11-5)

17. What groups of compounds are made by living things? (11-6)

18. Which groups of compounds found in living things contain only carbon, hydrogen, and oxygen? (11-6)

19. What is the function of DNA? (11-6)

20. What is the function of vitamins? (11-6)

APPLICATION/ CRITICAL THINKING

1. Predict the number of carbon atoms and the kind of bonds found in heptane, heptene, and heptyne.

2. Why is it impossible to have a molecule of cycloethane?

3. Name the hydrocarbon that has had chlorine atoms substituted for hydrogens to form $C_5H_9Cl_3$.

EXTENSION

1. Make a study of labels, magazine advertisements, or television commercials that deal with drugs, foods, or perfumes. Note how often organic compounds like polymers and benzene rings appear. Present a report to the class.

2. Vitamins, textiles, foods, and plastics all contain organic compounds. Research one of these groups of organic compounds. Make a bulletin-board display to share your knowledge with others.

3. Gasoline contains a mixture of several hydrocarbons. Find out what these compounds are, and how they are related to the octane rating system.

READINGS

Peterson, I., "Conducting a New Polymer into Batteries." *Science News,* November 23, 1984, p. 326.

"Polymer Power." *Scientific American,* November 1984, p. 72.

9. Fuel, orchard spray to ripen fruits.

10. Benzene has alternating single and double bonds between the carbon atoms. Cyclohexane has all single bonds between the carbon atoms.

11. Answers may include anesthetic, solvent, moth balls, explosives.

12. One in which one or more of the hydrogen atoms has been replaced by a different atom or group of atoms.

13. Making perfumes and flavorings.

14. a. Acid.
    b. Ester.
    c. Alcohol.

15. A polymer is a molecule made up of many repeating structures.

16. Polyethylene.

17. Carbohydrates, lipids, proteins, and nucleic acids.

18. Carbohydrates and lipids.

19. Control the building of protein.

20. Control chemical reactions in the body.

APPLICATION/CRITICAL THINKING

1. Heptane—seven carbon atoms, all single bonds; heptene—seven carbon atoms, one double bond between two adjacent carbon atoms; heptyne—seven carbon atoms, one triple bond between two adjacent carbon atoms.

2. At least three carbon atoms are needed to make a circle.

3. Pentane.

Test Masters

CHAPTER TEST, pages 41–44.
See page 251d in this book for answers.

Most things in your home are made from or coated with chemicals. Anything made of plastic, most types of carpeting, even parts of televisions and personal computers are made up of synthetic chemicals. Making and testing chemicals is the job of a chemical technician.

Chemical technicians prepare new mixtures of chemicals that will be used in various products. These technicians also test substances.

Chemical technicians may work for large corporations, such as oil or drug companies, or for small laboratories. Others work for the government, testing the safety of the products that the public uses.

Usually a four-year college degree in science is required for this job. On-the-job training is also provided. If you are interested in becoming a chemical technician, you should take courses in chemistry in high school.■

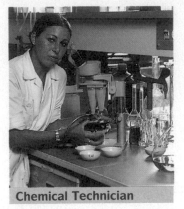

Chemical Technician

Have you ever looked at the hundreds of color chips in a paint or hardware store? Color chips are small samples of the various colors of paint that are available at the store.

Workers in the store prepare the colors that the customers choose. Directions for mixing each color of paint are provided by a paint analyst.

Paint analysts work for companies that manufacture paints. Their job is to mix basic colors together to produce new colors. These new colors must be easy to reproduce by the people who sell paint in the local stores.

Paint analysts receive on-the-job training. Some have college degrees, and most have artistic talent. If you are interested in this field, you will benefit from taking courses in art and chemistry in high school.■

Paint Analyst

People in Science

Dr. Shirley Ann Jackson, Physicist

Scientists are interested in learning how the structure of atoms or molecules in a material affects the properties of the material. Dr. Shirley Ann Jackson investigates atoms and molecules in solids.

Dr. Jackson is a physicist at Bell Laboratories. There are many different areas of research at Bell Laboratories. Some of the areas, like those of Dr. Jackson, deal with basic research. In other areas new kinds of communications are being developed.

Dr. Jackson wants to know why solids have certain properties. She studies how heat and pressure affect atoms in solids. She is asking a basic question: How does the arrangement of atoms in a solid affect the solid's properties?

Dr. Jackson believes that the answer to this question will allow scientists to produce useful new materials. Her findings may one day be incorporated into telephone systems, computers, or a number of other electronic devices.■

Issues and Technology

Each year, billions of kilograms of plastics are used in the United States. People drink from plastic cups and eat from plastic plates. People talk on plastic phones and listen to plastic radios. People drive in cars with plastic seats and bumpers and wear clothing made of plastic fibers. It is almost impossible to go through a day without using something made of plastic.

There are many different kinds of plastics, each with its own uses. Some plastics melt at just 100°C, but others can withstand temperatures over 500°C. Some plastics are fragile. Others are tough enough to stop a bullet. Some plastics are flexible enough to serve as food wraps. Still others are rigid and strong enough to use as support beams for buildings. In addition, plastics can be made in almost any shape and color.

Plastics are versatile and inexpensive, but they can be a source of problems. Plastic containers are complicating the problem of garbage disposal. Each American throws out an average of 600 kg of garbage per year. The amount of plastic in that garbage is increasing.

Years ago, one selling point of plastics was their disposability. Plastic plates and forks, for example, gave people convenience. Instead of washing dishes, people could use them once and throw them away. Today there are more and more disposable plastic items—from baking dishes to razors.

Times change. Now, convenience may not be the most important consideration when deciding on a material for a product. Landfills are closing, and communities are running out of space for garbage.

In some cases, plastics are also thought to be a potential health problem. Garbage is often burned in incinerators. Burning plastics can give off toxic fumes. Look at Figure 1 as you answer the following questions.

APPLYING CRITICAL THINKING SKILLS

1. What trend do you see in the production of plastic bottles between the years 1980 and 1985?
2. What do you think accounts for this change in the number of plastic bottles?
3. Suppose the number of plastic bottles drops drastically in the future. What do you think might cause such a drop? Do you think this might happen? Explain.
4. What factors do you consider most important in the regulation of plastic-container production?

The following thinking skills will be applied in answering questions.
- *Hypothesizing* why the production of plastic bottles has increased.
- *Identifying* possible factors that could cause the production of plastic bottles to drop.
- *Drawing conclusions* about which factors are the most important in the regulation of plastic-bottle production.

Answers to questions

1. The number of plastic bottles steadily increased between the years 1980 and 1985.
2. Plastic bottles are cheap to produce, light to carry, and widely accepted by the public.
3. Students' answers will vary. A drop in the production of plastic bottles could be the result of increased costs of producing plastic bottles. A change in the public's acceptance of plastic bottles could also cause a drop in their production.
4. Answers will vary. Important considerations include finding space for the disposal of plastics, using large amounts of raw materials to produce materials that are generally not recycled, and using materials for storage that may not always be safe.

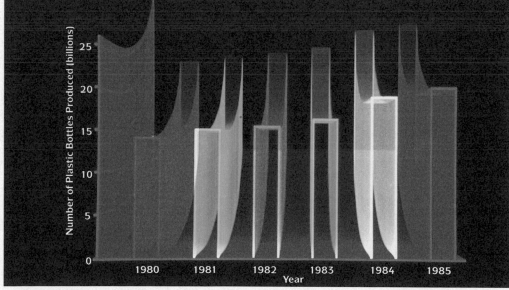

Figure 1

The following thinking skills will be applied in answering questions.
- *Interpreting* a graph.
- *Identifying* the effects of recycling laws.
- *Drawing conclusions* about the benefits of recycling plastics.

Answers to questions

1. The largest percentage of containers that were recycled were aluminum cans. The smallest percentage of containers recycled were plastic bottles.
2. Most students will probably answer that the growth of recycling is good. Recycling saves energy and raw materials.
3. Answers will vary. Increased use of plastics for packaging will produce more trash and cause more problems for wildlife.
4. Most students will respond that recycling laws are a good idea. Anything that fosters recycling is a good idea.

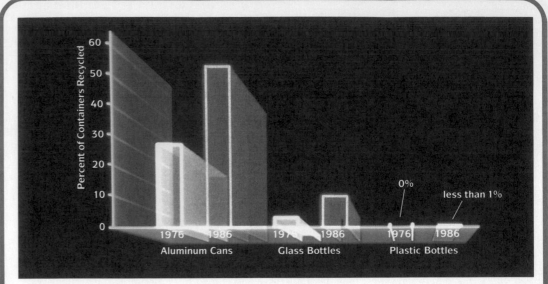

Figure 2

One of the biggest problems in using plastics is that they are not biodegradable (bī-oh dih GRAYD uh buhl): plastics do not break down in nature. Plastics that are thrown away remain unchanged for a long time. In contrast, other materials such as wood and paper decompose.

Every day over 630,000 plastic containers are deposited in the ocean. Thousands of kilograms of plastics, from fishing gear to detergent bottles, litter beaches and float in the ocean.

In some of the most remote parts of the world, plastic debris can be found floating on the water or washed up on what were once clean and isolated beaches. Plastic wastes have become a serious problem for wildlife. Sea birds, turtles, seals, and sea lions have been found entangled in plastic fishing line or strangled by the plastic rings that hold cans in six-packs.

Many other animals are found dead after accidentally swallowing plastic objects. The leatherback turtle, for instance, often mistakes plastic bags for its favorite food, the jellyfish. Once inside the turtle, the plastic blocks the turtle's digestive system. Birds can be similarly affected. A study by the United States Fish and Wildlife Service found that 90 percent of the albatross chicks on a Hawaiian island had some type of plastic inside their digestive system.

The solution might be to make people dispose of plastic more carefully. Another solution might be to make all plastic products biodegradable. Biodegradable plastic decomposes when it is exposed to ultraviolet radiation from the sun. Eight states now require that the plastic rings on six-packs be biodegradable. Twelve more states are considering this requirement. However, the plastic rings on six-packs represent a very small percentage of all plastic trash.

Many materials, such as aluminum, paper, and glass, can be recycled. The plastics that are replacing these materials currently cannot be recycled in large amounts. The effect of changing to plastic packaging will be an increase in the use of raw materials and an increase in trash.

However, some advances have been made in recycling plastics. PET (polyethylene terephthalate) bottles, which are used to hold soft drinks, can be collected and recycled. The recycled plastic is used for products such as floor tiles, auto parts, scouring pads, and pillow stuffing. However, PET bottles make up a very small percentage of the total amount of plastic containers. Figure 2 shows the percentage of recycling of three commonly used packaging materials.

APPLYING CRITICAL THINKING SKILLS

1. Which of these materials had the largest percentage recycled in 1986? Which had the smallest?
2. Recycling of all these materials has grown in the last few years. Do you think this growth is good? Explain.

3. The use of plastics as a packaging material is growing. Do you see this growth as a problem? Explain.
4. Most recycling occurs in the few states that have laws requiring deposits on cans and bottles. Do you think these laws are a good idea? Why or why not?

One of the fastest-growing uses of plastics is for food packaging. For example, cooking oils and catsup were once sold only in glass bottles. These bottles are among those being replaced by plastic bottles. Vegetables, both fresh and frozen, come wrapped in plastic. Everything from meat to bread can now be found in plastic packaging.

Many things about the new plastic packaging are good for both the public and the companies that use it. There are, however, some problems with plastic food containers. On occasion, plastics cause strange smells or tastes in food. An even more serious problem has been the leaching, or leaking

out, of chemicals from the plastics into the food. One type of plastic that has caused problems is polyvinyl chloride, or PVC. About one third of the PVC plastic produced contains a chemical additive called di(2-ethyl hexyl)phthalate, or DEHP. DEHP makes a normally rigid plastic more flexible. DEHP is not part of the plastic molecule. Therefore, DEHP can leach out of the plastic and into food. Since DEHP has been found to cause tumors in lab animals, DEHP leaching into food may be a serious problem.

Experts, however, point out that not many foods are packaged in PVC plastic. They also point out that the amount of DEHP that leaches out is very small. Research has shown that while DEHP harms some animals, it has never been shown to harm people.

Some people say that any amount of a chemical leaching into food is too much. And although the amount of leaching is small, no one knows the effect of these chemicals over

long periods of time. Look at Figure 3 to answer the following questions.

APPLYING CRITICAL THINKING SKILLS

1. What type of plastic is most commonly used for containers?
2. Are containers made of PVC used to hold any edible materials? If so, what? Do you believe leaching may be a problem?
3. What percentage of plastic containers are made of PVC? Only one third of the PVC containers have the additive DEHP. Since the percentage of containers with this additive is small, should the public worry about leaching? Why or why not?
4. DEHP has not been proven to be harmful to humans. Does this change your answer to question 3? Do you agree with the governmental policy of allowing a small amount of DEHP to leach from PVC containers? Explain your answers.

The following thinking skills will be applied in answering questions.
- *Interpreting* data.
- *Inferring* whether the materials used to make plastic containers are potentially dangerous.
- *Predicting* the effects of chemicals leaching from plastic containers.

Answers to questions

1. The most commonly used plastic for containers is high-density polyethylene.
2. Polyvinyl chloride is used to hold cooking oils and mouthwash. Leaching could be a problem in these products.
3. Polyvinyl chloride makes up only about 6 percent of plastic containers. Only about 2 percent have the additive DEHP. Answers will vary about whether there are grounds for concern about leaching in such a small percentage of containers. Even though the proportion of containers is small, it could affect many individuals. If leaching causes a health problem, it could be harmful to a number of people.
4. Answers will vary. The governmental policy of allowing a small amount of leaching may be harmless. It is possible that leaching of DEHP has no effect on humans and that eliminating all leaching would be costly and unnecessary. However, it is also possible that leaching is causing serious problems that will surface only later.

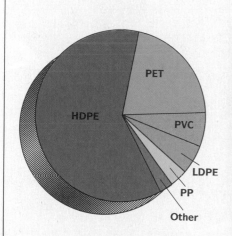

Type of Plastic	%	Used as Containers for
High-density polyethylene (HDPE)	66	Milk, liquid detergents, shampoos, juices, bottled water
Polyethylene terephthalate (PET)	18	Soft drinks, boil-in bag foods, meats, cosmetics
Polyvinyl chloride (PVC)	6	Cooking oils, mouthwashes, shampoos, floor polishes
Low-density polyethylene (LDPE)	5	Toiletries, cosmetics
Polypropylene (PP)	3	Materials placed in bottles hot, such as syrups
Other	2	Tablets, salves, ointments

Figure 3

FORCES AND ENERGY

Chapter 12 classifies kinds of forces and describes how they are measured. It also compares kinetic energy and potential energy.

Chapter 13 introduces the concepts of work and power, and surveys the major classes of machines.

Chapter 14 discusses Newton's three laws of motion, and explains how these laws are applied to circular motion.

Unit Four

FORCES AND ENERGY

The laws of motion are important to all human activities. Can you imagine the world without motion? What kinds of forces and energy cause motion? In this unit you will study the different varieties of forces and how they are measured. You will also learn how machines can change forces. You will study Newton's Laws of Motion and compare balanced and unbalanced forces. You will see how forces affect satellites in orbit in space. ■

▶ *This is a model of Galileo's pendulum clock from 1641.*

▼ Voyager, *an aerodynamic airplane, was flown around the world on one tank of gas.*

◀ *Multiple-image photographs like these are used in studies of forces and motion.*

▼ *Understanding forces and motion can help athletes perform better.*

Sections appearing in red provide coverage of basic topics in this unit. See page T23.

FORCE AND ENERGY

ORGANIZER

Section	pages	Activity	pages	Reinforcement and Evaluation	pages	*Review and Skill Masters	pages	Other Components in Teacher Resource Package	pages
12–1 Force	281–285			Review, Challenge	285			Study Guide	59
12–2 Measuring Force	286–289	What Is Center of Gravity?	287	Puzzler Review, Challenge	288 289			Study Guide Lab Manual	60 65
12–3 Forces in Fluids	290–294	What Is Archimedes' Principle?	291	Review, Challenge	294	Challenge/Critical Thinking	75–76	Study Guide Transparency	61
12–4 Kinetic and Potential Energy	295–299	How Can Forms of Energy Be Changed?	297	Review, Challenge	299	Skill	74	Study Guide	62
CHAPTER SUMMARY	299					Vocabulary Review	71		
CHAPTER REVIEW	300–301			*Test Masters	45–48	Chapter Review	72–73		

*In the Teacher Resource Package. For answers, see pages 279b–279d in this book.

ACTIVITY MATERIALS   Quantities are based on a class of 30 students working in groups as indicated in parentheses.

What Is Center of Gravity? p. 287 (groups of 2)	quantity	What Is Archimedes' Principle? p. 291 (groups of 2)	quantity	How Can Forms of Energy Be Changed? p. 297 (groups of 2)	quantity
string (30 cm long)	15 pieces	balance	15	ring stand	15
shoebox	15	250-mL beaker	15	ring clamp	15
lead sinker	15	overflow can	15	cork	15
dissecting needle	15	paraffin	15 blocks	thumbtack	15
metric ruler	15	string (30 cm long)	15 pieces	250-mL flask	15
		spring scale	15	one-hole rubber stopper	15
		metal object	15	string (40 cm long)	15 pieces
				glass bend	15
				hot plate	15

REVIEW AND SKILL MASTERS

VOCABULARY REVIEW _____ Chapter 12

Match each definition in Column A with the term in Column B.

Column A

K	1. The SI unit of force
J	2. A force caused by moving electric charges
I	3. The principle that energy cannot be created nor destroyed, but changed from one form to another
B	4. The point at which all of an object's mass appears to be located
G	5. An attraction between two objects that have mass
D	6. The ability to do work
F	7. A force that opposes motion
H	8. Energy of motion
O	9. Forces believed to cause the nuclei of atoms to break apart
E	10. A push or a pull that causes objects to move, change speed, or stop
L	11. An attractive force that holds the nucleus of an atom together
C	12. A force between two electric charges
N	13. Force acting on a unit area
A	14. An upward force applied to an object by a fluid in which the object is immersed
M	15. Stored energy
P	16. The amount of gravitational force between two objects

Column B

A. buoyant force
B. center of gravity
C. electrical force
D. energy
E. force
F. friction
G. gravitational force
H. kinetic energy
I. Law of Conservation of Energy
J. magnetic force
K. newton
L. nuclear force
M. potential energy
N. pressure
O. weak interactions
P. weight

© 1989 Silver, Burdett & Ginn Inc.

71

CHAPTER REVIEW _____ Chapter 12

12-1 Force

1. Briefly describe each of the following forces:

    a. gravitational force — an attraction between any two objects that have mass.

    b. nuclear force — an attraction that holds the nucleus of an atom together.

    c. electrical force — a force between electric charges.

    d. magnetic force — a force caused by moving electric charges.

    e. friction — a force that opposes motion.

    f. weak interactions — forces believed to break down an atom's nucleus.

2. What is the effect of unbalanced and balanced forces on an object at rest? Unbalanced forces acting on an object at rest cause it to move. Balanced forces acting on an object at rest do not cause motion.

12-2 Measuring Force

1. Explain the formula to find the weight of an object. $F = mg$ where F is the amount of force or weight of an object, m is the mass of the object, and g is the pull of gravity at sea level or 9.8 m/s^2.

2. What happens as an object moves away from the earth's center of gravity? The force of gravity, and therefore, the weight of an object, decreases as it moves away from the earth's center of gravity.

© 1989 Silver, Burdett & Ginn Inc.

72

CHAPTER REVIEW (Continued) _____ Chapter 12

12-3 Forces in Fluids

1. Define buoyant force and give an example of it working on an object. Buoyant force is an upward force applied to an object by a fluid. For example, a rock weighs 4.0 N in air, but only 3.0 N in water. Since the water displaced by the rock has a weight of 1.0 N, the buoyant force on the rock is 1.0 N.

2. How is pressure related to force? Pressure is force acting on a unit area. It depends on the size of a force and the area on which it acts. $P = F \div A$

3. State Pascal's law and give some examples of it. Pascal's law states the pressure exerted by a fluid in a closed container is the same at all points. It is used to operate lifts, dentist's chairs, and car brakes.

12-4 Kinetic and Potential Energy

1. Give an example of potential energy changing to kinetic energy. Students' answers will vary. The potential energy in the water at the top of Niagara Falls is released, changing to kinetic energy as the water falls.

2. Give an example of each of the following forms of energy:

    a. chemical energy — wood burning (other answers acceptable)

    b. electrical energy — lightning

    c. mechanical energy — a moving bicycle

3. What does the Law of Conservation of Energy state? The Law of Conservation of Energy states that energy can neither be created nor destroyed but can be changed from one form to another.

© 1989 Silver, Burdett & Ginn Inc.

73

SKILL/Interpreting a Diagram _____ Chapter 12

The scene below contains many examples of energy and forces. Study the drawing and underline the correct answers in the following paragraphs.

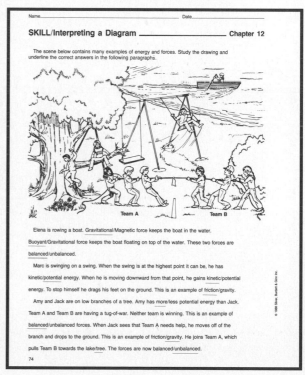

Team A   Team B

Elena is rowing a boat. Gravitational/Magnetic force keeps the boat in the water. Buoyant/Gravitational force keeps the boat floating on top of the water. These two forces are balanced/unbalanced.

Marc is swinging on a swing. When the swing is at the highest point it can be, he has kinetic/potential energy. When he is moving downward from that point, he gains kinetic/potential energy. To stop himself he drags his feet on the ground. This is an example of friction/gravity.

Amy and Jack are on low branches of a tree. Amy has more/less potential energy than Jack.

Team A and Team B are having a tug-of-war. Neither team is winning. This is an example of balanced/unbalanced forces. When Jack sees that Team A needs help, he moves off of the branch and drops to the ground. This is an example of friction/gravity. He joins Team A, which pulls Team B towards the lake/tree. The forces are now balanced/unbalanced.

© 1989 Silver, Burdett & Ginn Inc.

74

Name_____ Date_____

CHALLENGE/CRITICAL THINKING _____ Chapter 12

Aerodynamics is the study of air flow and its effect on objects in its path. It is very important in the design of airplanes. Air acts as a fluid, as do all other gasses. Fluid exerts pressure, and this pressure determines how an airplane will fly. An airplane flies because the pressure under the wings is greater than the pressure above the wings. This difference occurs because the air over the wings moves faster than the air under the wings. The top of the wing is longer than the bottom of the wing. Thus air must move a greater difference over the wing than under the wing, and so it moves faster. Bernoulli's principle states that pressure in a moving fluid decreases as the speed of the fluid increases.

Many different models of airplanes are tested to see which flies best in the air. One way of testing these models is in a wind tunnel. These tunnels can demonstrate air flow around airplane models. Think about the shape of the wings on an airplane. What shape is best suited for flight?

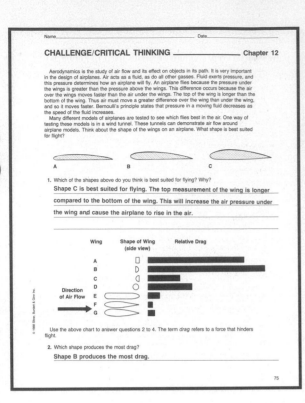

1. Which of the shapes above do you think is best suited for flying? Why?
   Shape C is best suited for flying. The top measurement of the wing is longer
   compared to the bottom of the wing. This will increase the air pressure under
   the wing and cause the airplane to rise in the air.

Use the above chart to answer questions 2 to 4. The term *drag* refers to a force that hinders flight.

2. Which shape produces the most drag?
   Shape B produces the most drag.

Name_____ Date_____

CHALLENGE/CRITICAL THINKING (Continued) _____ Chapter 12

3. Which shape produces the least drag?
   Shape F produces the least drag.

4. Is a rounded, flat, or elongated shape best suited for flying?
   An elongated shape is best suited for flying.

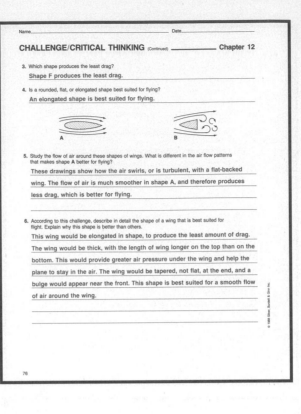

5. Study the flow of air around these shapes of wings. What is different in the air flow patterns that makes shape **A** better for flying?
   These drawings show how the air swirls, or is turbulent, with a flat-backed
   wing. The flow of air is much smoother in shape A, and therefore produces
   less drag, which is better for flying.

6. According to this challenge, describe in detail the shape of a wing that is best suited for flight. Explain why this shape is better than others.
   This wing would be elongated in shape, to produce the least amount of drag.
   The wing would be thick, with the length of wing longer on the top than on the
   bottom. This would provide greater air pressure under the wing and help the
   plane to stay in the air. The wing would be tapered, not flat, at the end, and a
   bulge would appear near the front. This shape is best suited for a smooth flow
   of air around the wing.

TEST MASTERS

Name _____ **Date** _____ **Score** _____

Chapter 12

Force and Energy

PART 1

In the space below, write the term that each phrase defines.

		Chapter Goal
1. potential energy	Energy that is stored	4
2. buoyant force	An upward force applied to an object by a fluid in which the object is immersed	3
3. force	A push or pull that causes an object to move, change speed, change direction, or stop moving	1
4. Law of Conservation of Energy	The principle that states that energy can neither be created nor destroyed but can be changed from one form to another	5
5. weight	The amount of gravitational force between two objects	2
6. newton	The SI unit of force	2
7. friction	A force that opposes motion and that occurs whenever two objects are in contact with each other	1
8. pressure	Force acting on a unit area	3
9. kinetic energy	The energy of motion	4

PART 2

Choose the term or phrase that best answers the question or completes the statement. Write the letter of that choice in the space at the left.

d 1. An object has a mass of 5.0 kg where the force of gravity is 9.8 m/s². What is the weight of the object? (F = mg) — Chapter Goal 2
a. 5.0 N   b. 1.96 N   c. 14.8 N   d. 49.0 N

b 2. A force of 1 N is applied to an object over an area of 1 m². What happens if that force is applied over a smaller area? — Chapter Goal 3
a. The pressure decreases.   c. The force increases.
b. The pressure increases.   d. The force decreases.

Chapter 12   Force and Energy   45

Name _____ **Date** _____ **Score** _____

PART 2

Choose the term or phrase that best answers the question or completes the statement. Write the letter of that choice in the space at the left.

Chapter Goal

b 3. A large building exerts a force on a nearby tree. This force is most likely: — 1
a. nuclear force.   c. magnetic force.
b. gravitational force.   d. electrical force.

d 4. The bright flash from the flashbulb of a camera is an example of: — 5
a. nuclear energy.   c. sound energy.
b. mechanical energy.   d. radiant energy.

d 5. Which of the following two forces oppose each other when a block of wood slides down a ramp? — 1
a. gravitational force and electrical force
b. electrical force and magnetic force
c. magnetic force and friction force
d. friction force and gravitational force

c 6. Which of the following has kinetic energy? — 4
a. a container of gasoline   c. a rolling ball
b. a rock on a mountain   d. a parked car

a 7. An object will float in a fluid if the object's: — 3
a. weight is less than the weight of the fluid it displaces.
b. weight is more than the weight of the fluid it displaces.
c. volume is less than the volume of the fluid it displaces.
d. mass is more then the mass of the fluid it displaces.

c 8. The pendulum of a clock has the greatest amount of kinetic energy when it is: — 4
a. gaining speed.   c. moving fastest.
b. losing speed.   d. not moving.

d 9. A generator is used to convert: — 5
a. electrical energy to chemical energy.
b. chemical energy to electrical energy.
c. electrical energy to mechanical energy.
d. mechanical energy to electrical energy.

d 10. A machine converts 300 J of mechanical energy to 200 J of sound energy and 100 J of heat energy. This is an example of: — 5
a. Pascal's law.
b. Bernoulli's principle.
c. Archimedes' principle.
d. the Law of Conservation of Energy.

c 11. As an airplane climbs into the sky, what happens to its weight and its mass? — 2
a. Both remain the same.
b. Both decrease.
c. Weight decreases, and mass remains the same.
d. Weight remains the same, and mass decreases.

Chapter 12   Force and Energy   46

Name _____ **Date** _____ **Score** _____

PART 3

Look at the diagram. Then read the questions that follow. Choose the term or phrase that best answers the question or completes the statement. Write the letter of that choice in the space at the left.

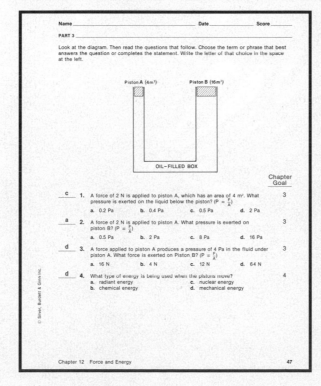

Piston A (4 m²)   Piston B (16 m²)

OIL–FILLED BOX

Chapter Goal

c 1. A force of 2 N is applied to piston A, which has an area of 4 m². What pressure is exerted on the liquid below the piston? (P = $\frac{F}{A}$) — 3
a. 0.2 Pa   b. 0.4 Pa   c. 0.5 Pa   d. 2 Pa

a 2. A force of 2 N is applied to piston A. What pressure is exerted on piston B? (P = $\frac{F}{A}$) — 3
a. 0.5 Pa   b. 2 Pa   c. 8 Pa   d. 16 Pa

d 3. A force applied to piston A produces a pressure of 4 Pa in the fluid under piston A. What force is exerted on Piston B? (P = $\frac{F}{A}$) — 3
a. 16 N   b. 4 N   c. 12 N   d. 64 N

d 4. What type of energy is being used when the pistons move? — 4
a. radiant energy   c. nuclear energy
b. chemical energy   d. mechanical energy

Chapter 12   Force and Energy   47

Name _____ **Date** _____ **Score** _____

PART 4

Read each question or direction and answer it using complete sentences.

Chapter Goal

1. Describe electrical force, and give an example of it. — 1

Electrical force is a force between electric charges. Objects with different charges attract, or pull toward, each other. For example, plastic wrap sticks to objects because it is attracted to objects that have opposite charges. Objects with the same charge repel, or push away from, each other.

2. What is meant by "center of gravity"? How does center of gravity determine whether an object will balance or fall? — 2

The center of gravity of an object is the point at which all of the object's mass appears to be located. An object will be balanced if its center of gravity is supported. If the center of gravity of an object is not supported, the object will fall.

3. Describe the energy conversions that take place in a coal-burning power plant. — 5

At the power plant, chemical energy is produced by burning coal. The chemical energy given off turns water to steam. The heat energy in the steam is changed to mechanical energy as the steam turns the turbines of the generator. The generator converts the mechanical energy to electrical energy.

Chapter 12   Force and Energy   48

CHAPTER **12** PLANNING GUIDE

12

FORCE AND ENERGY

The questions in the CHAPTER TEST are based on these Chapter Goals.

1. Identify different kinds of forces, and describe the effect of forces on an object.
2. Describe the relationship between gravity, mass, and weight, and describe conditions that can cause weight to vary.
3. Distinguish between force and pressure, and explain characteristics and uses of forces in fluids.
4. Distinguish between potential energy and kinetic energy.
5. Describe some forms of energy, and identify the Law of Conservation of Energy.

FORCE AND ENERGY

Have you ever been sailing? People have been using sailboats to travel and carry on trade for hundreds of years. Today sailing is a popular sport. The sailboat in the photograph can travel at an average speed of 18 km/h without using a motor. How is this possible? The wind exerts a force on the sail. When the wind pushes on the sail, the sailboat moves along in the water. The stronger the wind, the faster the boat can travel. The sailboat can use the wind to move in any direction.

- *What kinds of forces exist?*
- *How do forces affect matter?*
- *How are forces used in daily life?*

12-1 FORCE

A soccer player kicks a ball toward the goal. The goalie catches the ball and then throws it to a teammate. Each of these actions involves force. A **force** is a push or pull. Forces cause objects to move, change speed, or stop moving. The force of a kicker's foot causes the soccer ball to move, change speed, or change direction. The force of the goalie's hands causes the soccer ball to stop moving and then to move in another direction. What are some other examples of forces in daily life?[1]

Forces act when one object is in contact with another. If a force is used to slide a book across a desk, there is contact between the hand doing the pushing and the book being pushed. In a game of table tennis, force on the ball comes from contact with a paddle. Driving a nail into a piece of wood involves contact between the hammer and the nail.

Contact is not always needed for a force to act. Forces can act on objects that are far apart. For example, gravity acts on the sun and the earth. Gravitational force between the earth and the moon causes the tides to rise and fall. These forces are acting over long distances.

After completing this section, you will be able to

- **identify** the different kinds of forces.
- **describe** the effect of forces on an object.

The key terms in this section are
electrical force
force
friction
gravitational force
magnetic force
nuclear force
weak interactions

[1]Answers will vary but may include sports examples such as blocking in football or practical examples such as pushing a car.

The sailboat in the photograph uses the wind to move along in the water. This is a good example of how energy can be used to do work. Ask students what examples could be used to show how wind energy is converted to another form of energy. Explain that our ability to control energy has enabled us to perform many everyday activities. Ask students to name some forms of energy that they use to perform tasks.

- What kinds of forces exist? (The types of forces that exist are gravitational, nuclear, electrical, magnetic, frictional, and weak interaction.)
- How do forces affect matter? (Forces affect matter by causing matter to move or stop.)
- How are forces used in daily life? (Forces are used to perform all of our daily activities.)

12-1 FORCE
pages 281–285

OBJECTIVES
Refer to pupil page 281.

VOCABULARY
Key terms: electrical force, force, friction, gravitational force, magnetic force, nuclear force, weak interactions

1 MOTIVATION

Ask students to identify different forces that are familiar to them, such as pushing a lawn mower or pulling a sled. Give students a newspaper or magazine and ask them to find and share pictures that show various examples of forces. Have two or three students design a bulletin board showing a variety of forces.

Tie-in/Language Arts   The term *force* has several definitions in any dictionary. Ask students to compare these definitions with the scientific definition.

Background   Scientists agree that the types of forces known to exist are gravitational, electrical, magnetic, nuclear, frictional, and weak interaction. Some schools of thought place electrical forces and magnetic forces together as electromagnetic forces. Frictional force is often considered to be an electromagnetic force.

Thinking Skills

identifying cause and effect
Ask students to identify each force and its effect in Figure 12-1.

KINDS OF FORCES

Several kinds of forces are known to exist. They are gravitational force, electrical force, magnetic force, nuclear force, friction, and weak interactions.

gravis (heavy)

Gravitational force is an attraction between any two objects that have mass. As mass increases, the attraction increases. The sun and the planets have large masses; thus the attraction between them is very great. This gravitational force is strong enough to hold the planets in orbit around the sun. The gravitational force of the earth also causes objects to fall toward the earth.

Most masses are very small compared with those of the planets or the sun. Therefore the attractive force between small masses, such as two atoms or two people, is very weak. Gravitational force depends also on the distance between masses. As distance increases, gravitational force decreases.

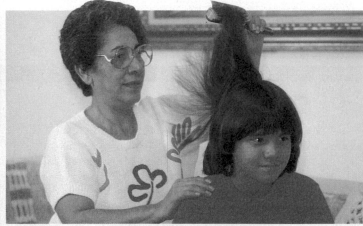

Figure 12-1

What kinds of forces are at work in each of these examples?[1]

[1]Gravitational force (diving). Electrical force (brushing hair). Friction (sliding).

Nuclear force is an attractive force that holds the nucleus of an atom together. Compared with other forces, the nuclear force is very strong. However, this force acts over very short distances. Gravity is a weaker force, but it acts over much longer distances.

Electrical force is a force between electric charges. Objects with different charges attract, or pull toward, each other. For example, plastic wrap sticks to objects because it is attracted to objects that have opposite charges. Objects with the same charge repel, or push away from, each other.

Magnetic force is a force caused by moving electric charges. Common magnets attract or repel each other because of magnetic force. Electric motors work because of magnetic forces caused by a flow of electrons.

Friction is a force that opposes motion. There is friction whenever two objects are in contact. When two objects rub together, the friction causes wear. Automobile tires become worn because of the friction between the tires and the road. But if there were no friction, the car would not move. The wheels would spin in one spot.

fricare (to rub)

Weak interactions are forces believed to cause the nuclei of some atoms to break apart. Because the nucleus of an atom is small, scientists have not learned much about weak interactions.

Background There are four fundamental forces at work in the universe. Gravitational force is the force acting between any two masses. It is the force that holds the universe together. Electromagnetic force has a similar function on the atomic level. This force holds together the atoms that make up molecules and binds the electrons of an atom to the nucleus.

The other two kinds of forces act only within a nucleus. Based on experiments, it seems that a strong nuclear force acts between any pair of particles in the nucleus—proton-proton, neutron-neutron, and proton-neutron. Neutrons serve as the nuclear "glue" that holds the nucleus together. The weak nuclear force, or weak interaction, has to do with beta particle decay in the nucleus, which occurs during radioactive decay.

Background This table shows that nuclear force is much greater than electromagnetic force. The table also puts the relative strengths of the other two forces in perspective.

Force	Relative strength
Strong nuclear	1
Electromagnetic	10^{-2}
Weak nuclear	10^{-13}
Gravitational	10^{-40}

DO YOU KNOW?

Many scientists believe that there are four basic forces in the universe. These four forces are gravity; electromagnetic force; the strong force, or nuclear force; and the weak force, or weak interactions. Other commonly recognized forces are examples of the four basic forces. For example, friction is thought to be a kind of electromagnetic force.

Now, scientists are searching for a fifth force. Some scientists think they have found one. This fifth force, called the hypercharge, is a very weak force. It opposes gravity and affects objects no farther apart than 200 m. This force is also believed to vary in strength from element to element, being strongest in iron.

The apparatus shown in the photograph can drop a feather and a ball at the same time. If the hypercharge exists, dropping an iron ball and a feather at the same time would cause the feather to hit bottom first. The iron ball's hypercharge would oppose gravity more than the feather's would. Thus, the ball would fall more slowly.

Apollo astronauts tried to test the hypercharge. They tried dropping a hammer and a feather on the moon. Both objects fell at the same rate and landed at the same time. Does this disprove the hypothesis about the fifth force? More experiments are needed. If the hypercharge exists, it may be so weak that the effect is too small to measure without extremely precise equipment.

Teaching Tip To help students remember the six forces—gravitational, nuclear, electrical, magnetic, frictional, and weak interaction—use the mnemonic aid *Give Nancy Eight More Fancy Wigs.* Or let students think of their own mnemonic device to help in recalling the forces.

COMBINED FORCES

A mass may be acted upon by more than one force at a time. Figure 12-2 shows two opposing forces. A magnetic force from the electromagnet is pulling the truck upward. At the same time, a gravitational force is pulling the truck down toward the earth. In which direction is the force on the truck greater?[1]

When the forces acting on a mass are not equal, these forces are said to be unbalanced. Unbalanced forces acting on a mass at rest cause the mass to move. Consider a train with many cars on a railroad track. For the train to move, the force applied by the engine must be greater than the forces holding the train in place. The forces that oppose motion are gravity and friction.

Combined forces can also act together, instead of against each other. Lifting a piano would be a very difficult task for one person. However, many people lifting together could move the piano easily.

When the forces acting on a mass are equal and opposite, these forces are said to be balanced. Balanced forces acting on a mass at rest do not cause motion. Imagine two teams having a tug of war. Suppose each team has the same number of people, and everyone is pulling equally hard. Neither team is able to move the other. Are the forces balanced or unbalanced?[2]

Figure 12-2

A crane equipped with an electromagnet can lift a heavy object, like this truck.

[1]The upward force is greater.
[2]The forces are balanced.

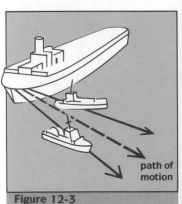
Figure 12-3

Two forces can combine to move an object.

284

284

Now suppose one of the teams adds an extra person. Are the forces balanced or unbalanced? What would you expect to happen in this game?[1]

In a tug of war, forces act in opposite directions. In many situations, forces act in directions that are at an angle. Look at Figure 12-3. The two tugboats are pulling in different directions. The front of the ship cannot move in both directions at the same time. Instead, it moves along a path that is between the two lines of force.

If you have ever tried to put up a tent, you know that forces acting in different directions are hard to balance. Very large tents can be used as public buildings. Look at the tent shown in Figure 12-4. Each support wire represents one of the forces that must be balanced to support the tent.

[1]The forces are now unbalanced. The team with the extra person exerts more force and would win.

Figure 12-4

This complex tent is the roof of an airport terminal.

REVIEW

1. Name six types of forces.
2. How are electrical and magnetic forces related?
3. Why would it be impossible to walk if there were no friction?

CHALLENGE Identify the forces acting on a sled being pulled across a snow-covered field. Draw a diagram to show the direction of the forces.

Teaching Tip Divide the class into teams. Ask each team to prepare three different diagrams, showing how two students can move a desk across the floor. Present each diagram to the class, and have students discuss the various forces that are interacting. Have them decide which forces are most effective in performing the task.

Teaching Tip Show pictures of the 20-mule-team wagons and a modern truck used to haul borax out of Death Valley. Have students compare the forces used and the forces overcome by both modes of transportation.

Enrichment After they have read pages 284 and 285, ask students to design an experiment to show the effect of combined forces.

3 REVIEW/REINFORCEMENT

1. Gravitational, nuclear, electrical, magnetic, frictional, and weak interaction.
2. Both are the result of electric charges.
3. If there were no friction, your feet would slide along the ground and you would not be able to pull yourself forward.

Challenge Gravity pulling downward, electrical force in the electrons being rubbed off the runners of the sled, friction between the snow and the runners of the sled, and combined forces if two or more people are pulling the sled.

12-2 MEASURING FORCE

pages 286–289

OBJECTIVES
Refer to pupil page 286.

VOCABULARY
Key terms: center of gravity, newton, weight

1 MOTIVATION

Ask students to stand and bend over and touch their fingers to their toes without bending their knees. Most of them will do it with relative ease because they will maintain their center of gravity over their feet as they move part of their body backward. Next ask students to repeat the exercise with their back and their heels against the wall. Students will fall forward because they cannot maintain their center of gravity over their feet. The center of gravity will shift ahead of the feet.

2 CONCEPT DEVELOPMENT

Teaching Tip   A newton is approximately equal to one-quarter pound. To familiarize students with this concept, compare a newton to the familiar quarter-pound hamburger. A newton is the metric measurement of the amount of force exerted on a particular mass.

Background   The gravitational attraction of the moon is approximately one-sixth that of the earth. For this reason the weight of an object on the moon is one-sixth the weight of the same object on the earth. The weight of the same object can also vary at different places on the earth. As an object moves further from the center of the earth, the object's weight decreases.

12-2 MEASURING FORCE

After completing this section, you will be able to

- **describe** the relationship between gravity, mass, and weight.
- **describe** conditions that can cause weight to vary.

The key terms in this section are
center of gravity
newton
weight

The amount of force acting on a mass can be measured. The SI unit of force is a **newton** (N). One force that can be measured is gravitational force. The amount of gravitational force between two objects is called **weight**. Weight is different from mass. Recall that mass is a measure of the amount of material that makes up an object. The mass of an object is constant, no matter how much force acts on it. Weight varies with the distance between the two objects.

For example, on the earth, an object's weight is a measure of the gravitational force between the object and the earth. On the moon, an object's weight is a measure of the gravitational force between the object and the moon. The force of gravity on the moon is less than the force of gravity on the earth. Therefore, an object will weigh less on the moon than on the earth. But the mass of the object is the same on the moon as it is on the earth.

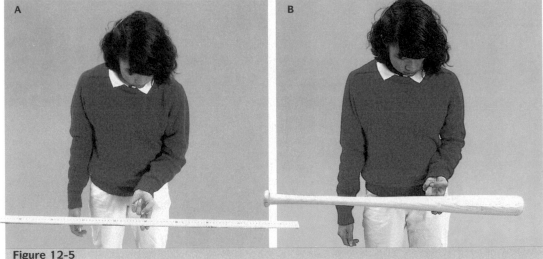

Figure 12-5

The center of gravity of an object affects how the object will balance.

Figure 12-5A shows a meterstick balanced at the 50-cm mark. The gravitational force acting on the whole stick seems to be focused at this one point. In other words, the weight of the meterstick seems to be concentrated in one place. This point is called the center of gravity. The **center of gravity** of an object is the point at which all of an object's mass appears to be located. An object is balanced if its center of gravity is supported. If the center of gravity of an object is not supported, the object falls.

A meterstick is uniform in size along its entire length. However, not all objects have a uniform shape. The baseball bat shown in Figure 12-5B has an uneven shape. The center of gravity is not at the exact center of the bat but toward the end with the larger diameter. Why is the center of gravity of the bat closer to its larger end?[1]

The earth is nearly a perfect sphere. Thus the earth's center of gravity is near the planet's center. When objects are weighed on the earth, the weight of the object depends on its distance from the earth's center of gravity.

The gravitational force, and thus, weight, decreases as an object moves away from the earth's center of gravity. An object weighed at the top of a high mountain would weigh less than it would at sea level. An object that weighs 10.00 N at sea level would weigh 9.99 N on Pikes Peak, which is 4301 m high.

[1]There is more mass at the larger end.

Background An understanding of the center of gravity is an advantage in athletics. For example, high-jumpers arch their body to lower their center of gravity. When flipping over the bar, the body rotates around the lower center of gravity, permitting the jumper to clear a higher bar.

ACTIVITY What Is Center of Gravity?

OBJECTIVE
Predict and **find** the center of gravity of an object.

MATERIALS
2 boxes, string, lead sinker, dissecting needle, metric ruler

PROCEDURE
A. Examine an unweighted box.
　1. Predict where the center of gravity is.
B. Attach a lead sinker to a 30-cm long piece of string. Tie the string to a dissecting needle. Stick the needle into the broad surface of the box at any point near the edge of the box. Mark this point.
C. Let the box and the weighted line hang freely from the needle, as shown in the figure. With a pencil, mark the position of the weighted line at the edge of the box.
D. Remove the dissecting needle. Use a ruler to draw a line between the two points that you marked.
E. Repeat this procedure for three more points on the surface of the box. Remember to mark each point near the edge of the box. The point at which the four lines cross shows the center of gravity of the box.
F. Examine a weighted box.
　2. Predict where the center of gravity is.

G. Repeat steps **B** through **E** with the weighted box.
H. Extend your index finger and try to balance each box on your finger.
I. Place each box, with the marked side up, on a flat surface. Spin each box.

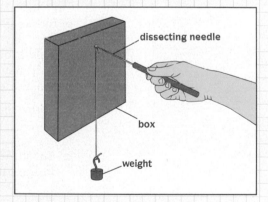

dissecting needle

box

weight

RESULTS AND CONCLUSIONS
1. How do your predictions compare with the actual location of the center of gravity of each box?
2. How is the center of gravity related to the way each box balances?
3. How is the center of gravity related to the way each box spins?

ACTIVITY 20–25 minutes

PROCESS SKILLS
predicting, observing, inferring

Preparation Weight half the boxes in advance. Secure the weights with glue. Blocks of wood or metal make excellent weights.

Teaching Tip Use a pair of boxes of the same size for each team of students. If different weights are secured in different places in the boxes, all the teams will find different centers of gravity.

Answers to Procedure
1–2. Answers will vary.

Answers to Results and Conclusions
1. Answers will vary.
2. The box balances at the center of gravity.
3. The box spins with the center of gravity as its axis.

Puzzler The center of gravity is directly in line with and below the pivot point. This establishes a stable system.

Tie-in/Math Have students transpose the equation F = mg to solve for m or g. Supply sample problems to reinforce their efforts.

Enrichment Have interested students investigate and report on the different kinds of tides and the forces which cause them.

SCIENCE PUZZLER

The object shown in the photograph is called a kinetic sculpture. When touched, it wobbles and moves around its pivot. However, it does not fall over easily. Why does this sculpture keep its balance so well?

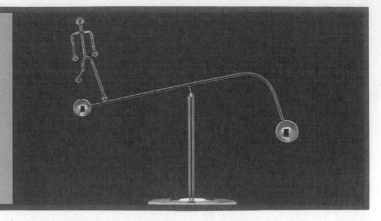

The following formula is used to find the weight of an object on the earth.

$$F = mg$$

In this equation, F is the amount of force and m is the mass of the object. The g is a constant, 9.8 m/s^2. This number equals the pull of gravity on objects at or very near sea level. At sea level, gravity causes falling objects to accelerate, or gain speed, at the rate of 9.8 m/s^2. If you know the mass of an object, you can find the gravitational force that the earth exerts on the object. This force is equal to the weight of the object.

Sample Problem
An astronaut has a mass of 75 kg. Find the weight of the astronaut on the earth.

1. Write the formula.

$$F = mg$$

2. Substitute the numbers in the problem for the symbols in the formula.

$$F = (75 \text{ kg}) (9.8 \text{ m/s}^2)$$

3. Determine the unit that will be part of the answer. In this case the unit is kilogram-meter per second squared (kg·m/s^2).

$$F = 75 \times 9.8 \text{ kg·m/s}^2$$

4. Complete the calculations that are required.

$$F = 735 \text{ kg·m/s}^2$$

The astronaut has a weight of 735 kg·m/s². One newton is equal to 1 kg·m/s². Thus the astronaut has a weight of 735 N. What is the weight of an object that has a mass of 45 kg?[1]

Table 12-1 shows what happens to the astronaut's weight as the distance from the earth's center of gravity increases. The loss of weight by an astronaut traveling into space is like the weight change of an object being weighed at different altitudes. Notice that the value for g decreases as altitude increases. What happens to the mass of the astronaut?[2]

[1]441 N.
[2]The mass does not change.

Figure 12-6

The gravitational force acting on this astronaut depends on the mass of the astronaut and the distance from the center of the earth.

Table 12-1 *Changes in Gravitational Force*

Mass (kg)	Distance from the center of the earth (km)	g (m/s²)	Weight (N)
75	6,376	9.8	735
75	12,752	2.4	184
75	19,128	1.1	82

REVIEW

1. How does gravity affect mass and weight?
2. How do mass and weight differ?
3. Why does an astronaut weigh less on the moon than on the earth?
4. Explain why a 1-kg object weighs less on Pikes Peak than it does at the seashore.

CHALLENGE To find the weight of an object on the moon or on another planet, you need to know the value for g at that place. This value on the moon is 1.6 m/s². What is the weight of a 75-kg astronaut on the moon?

interpreting charts
In Table 12-1, students interpret what happens to weight as the distance from the center of the earth increases.

Thinking Skills

predicting
After working through the sample problem on page 288, students should be able to predict the weights, in newtons, of various objects with different masses.

3 REVIEW/REINFORCEMENT

1. Gravity has no effect on mass. Since weight is a measure of gravitational attraction, weight varies with the distance between the two objects being measured.
2. Mass is a measure of the amount of material in an object; the mass of an object never changes, no matter where the object is. Weight is the amount of gravitational force between two objects; weight changes, depending on the distance between the objects.
3. The moon has less mass than the earth and therefore has less gravitational attraction.
4. Pikes Peak is further from the earth's center of gravity than is the seashore. The gravitational attraction is therefore less at the top of Pikes Peak.

Challenge   F = (75 kg)(1.6 m/s²)
F = 120 kg • m/s²
F = 120 N

12-3 FORCES IN FLUIDS

pages 290-294

12-3 FORCES IN FLUIDS

OBJECTIVES
Refer to pupil page 290.

VOCABULARY
Key terms: buoyant force, pressure
Other terms: Archimedes' principle, Bernoulli's principle, hydraulic, Pascal's law

1 MOTIVATION

Divide the class into groups. Give each group of students a rock. Tell them that they have 10 minutes to find the volume of the rock—the amount of space it takes up. Specify that they do not actually have to do anything as long as they can explain how the task should be done. This will give students a chance to review displacement of water. If the students perform the task they will see that the rock pushes aside the volume of water that equals the volume of the rock.

Transparency

The Teacher Resource Package includes a color transparency and a black-line master of Figure 12-7. You may wish to use these in your discussion of Archimedes' principle.

After completing this section, you will be able to

- **define** the term *buoyant force*.
- **distinguish** between force and pressure.
- **explain** and **give examples** of forces in fluids.

The key terms in this section are
buoyant force   pressure

Fluids are materials that flow. Liquids and gases are fluids. They do not have a definite shape, and they will take the shape of a container. Liquids have definite volumes, but gases do not. A gas will expand to fill a container. Because they are not rigid like solids, fluids can exert special kinds of forces.

ARCHIMEDES' PRINCIPLE

Suppose the rock in Figure 12-7A weighs 4.0 N in air. When the rock is put into water and weighed, the scale reads 3.0 N. The rock appears to have lost weight in the water. The force pulling the rock downward seems to have decreased, because the water exerts a force upward on the rock. Therefore, the upward force of the water makes the rock seem lighter. This force is called buoyant force.

A **buoyant force** is an upward force exerted on an object by a fluid in which the object is immersed. When an object is placed into a fluid, the object displaces some of the fluid. The volume of the fluid displaced is equal to the volume of the object. The amount of buoyant force is equal to the weight of the displaced fluid. The water displaced by the rock in Figure 12-7B has a volume of 0.1 L. The weight of this water is 1.0 N. Therefore the buoyant force on the rock is 1.0 N.

Figure 12-7

An object placed in water appears to lose weight.

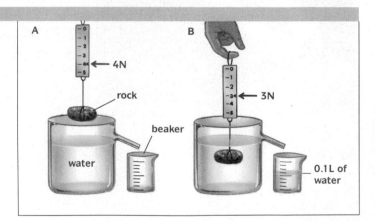

About 2000 years ago a Greek scientist named Archimedes observed the behavior of objects in water and other fluids. Archimedes concluded that an object in a fluid is acted on by a force equal to the weight of the fluid displaced by the object. This statement is known as *Archimedes' principle*.

ACTIVITY   What Is Archimedes' Principle?

OBJECTIVE
Measure the buoyant effect of water.

MATERIALS
balance, 250-mL beaker, overflow can, paraffin block, string, spring scale, metal object

PROCEDURE
A. Draw a data table like the one shown.
B. Use a balance to find the mass of an empty 250-mL beaker.
   1. What is the mass of the beaker?
C. Fill an overflow can with enough water to bring the level of water in the can to the spout. Place the beaker under the spout.
D. Tie a piece of string around a paraffin block. Attach the free end of the string to the hook on a spring scale.
E. Use the spring scale to find the weight of the paraffin block. Record your answer in the data table.
F. Lower the paraffin block into the overflow can. Make sure that the beaker catches all the water that comes out of the spout. Take care not to touch the bottom or the sides of the overflow can.
G. Record the weight of the paraffin block while it is suspended in water.
H. Find the mass of the beaker and the water.
   2. What is the mass of the beaker and the water?
   3. What is the mass (in kilograms) of the water displaced?
I. Calculate the weight (in newtons) of the water displaced. Record your answer.
J. Repeat steps C through I, using a metal object instead of the paraffin.

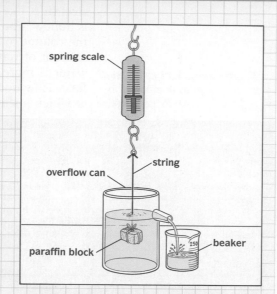

spring scale

overflow can — string

paraffin block — beaker

Measurement	Paraffin	Metal
Weight in air		
Weight in water		
Apparent loss of weight		
Weight of water displaced		

RESULTS AND CONCLUSIONS
1. How does the weight of each object in air compare with its weight in water?
2. How does the weight loss of each object compare with the weight of the water it displaced?

2 CONCEPT DEVELOPMENT

ACTIVITY 25–30 minutes

PROCESS SKILLS
measuring, recording data, comparing

Preparation   Have all the materials for this activity readily available. Cut the paraffin into blocks of usable size.

Teaching Tip   A nail or a weight with a hook work well as metallic objects. The activity can be extended by using materials other than paraffin and metal. Some students may wish to research Archimedes' classic experiment with the king's crown and follow Archimedes' procedure with some of their own jewelry.

Answers to Procedure
1–3. Answers will vary.

Answers to Results and Conclusions
1. The weight in air is greater than the weight in water.
2. The weight loss equals the weight of the displaced water.

Whether an object sinks or floats in a fluid or gas depends on Archimedes' principle. An object floats if its weight is equal to or less than the weight of the fluid it displaces. A block of wood that weighs 1.0 N floats because it displaces more than 1.0 N of water. The weight of the wood is less than the buoyant force of the fluid.

An object sinks if its weight is greater than the weight of the fluid it displaces. A piece of steel that weighs 1.0 N sinks because it displaces only 0.13 N of water. The weight of the piece of steel is greater than the buoyant force of the fluid.

Thinking Skills

hypothesizing
Students will hypothesize about the effect of cargo on the water level of a ship. Have them hypothesize about how the principles developed in this section apply to everyday situations that involve floating and sinking.

Background A submarine contains tanks that can be filled with water to adjust the buoyancy of the ship. Adding water to these tanks adds enough weight to cause the submarine and the water outside to have the same density. The sub can therefore "float" beneath the surface of the water.

Life preservers are made of material of low density. The large bulk of the life preserver provides adequate buoyancy to keep the wearer afloat.

Background Pascal's law can be used to explain the operation of hydraulic tools, like presses and jacks. Airbags used in rescue operations also work on the principle of Pascal's law.

[1] A large amount of cargo will cause a ship to float lower in the water.

A block of steel will not float in water. Why does a steel ship, like the one shown in Figure 12-8, float? A ship is hollow. The open spaces in the hull of the ship increase the volume of the ship. Thus, the ship will displace a large amount of water. As long as the weight of the displaced water is more than the weight of the ship, the ship will float. How does a large amount of cargo affect the height at which a ship floats?[1]

Figure 12-8

Because a ship displaces a large amount of water, the buoyant force on the ship is large.

PASCAL'S LAW

Buoyant force is one example of fluid force. Other fluid forces also exist. For example, a fluid in a container pushes against, or exerts a force on, the walls of the container. Force acting on a unit area is called **pressure**. The amount of pressure exerted on an object depends on the size of the force and the area on which it acts. Pressure is calculated by using the following formula.

$$P = \frac{F}{A}$$

In this equation, P stands for pressure, F stands for force, and A stands for area.

Sample Problem
What is the pressure exerted by a piston if a force of 10 N is applied over an area of 0.10 m^2?

1. Write the formula.

$$P = \frac{F}{A}$$

2. Substitute the numbers in the problem for the symbols in the formula.

$$P = \frac{10 \text{ N}}{0.10 \text{ m}^2}$$

3. Determine the unit that will be part of the answer. In this case the unit is N/m^2.

$$P = \frac{10}{0.10} \text{ N/m}^2$$

4. Complete the calculations that are required.

$$P = 100 \text{ N/m}^2$$

The pressure exerted is 100 N/m^2. One N/m^2 is also called a pascal. The pascal (Pa) is the SI unit of pressure and is equal to 1.0 N/m^2. What is the pressure exerted by a 10-N force acting on an area of 1.0 m^2?[1]

In a closed container the pressure exerted by a fluid is the same at all points. This property of fluids is called *Pascal's law*. Pascal's law is used in devices such as lifts, dentist chairs, and the brake systems in cars.

Figure 12-9 shows how a hydraulic lift works. The term *hydraulic* refers to systems that work on the principle of fluid pressure. Notice that there are two pistons supported by fluid. When a force of 1 N is applied to piston A, a pressure of 100 Pa is exerted on the fluid under this piston. According to Pascal's law, the fluid exerts the same pressure at all points. Thus the pressure exerted on piston B is 100 Pa. Notice that the area of piston B is 1.0 m^2. When the pressure of 100 Pa is applied over an area of 1.0 m^2, the upward force on the piston is 100 N. Thus a force of 1 N is used to lift a weight of 100 N.

[1]10 Pa.

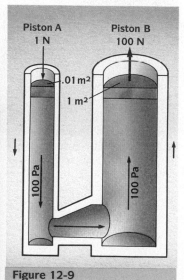

Piston A
1 N

Piston B
100 N

.01 m²

1 m²

100 Pa

100 Pa

Figure 12-9

Pascal's law explains how a hydraulic lift works.

Demonstration To demonstrate Pascal's law, use a pressure syringe (available commercially from Sargent-Welch). This shows that pressure in a fluid is transmitted equally in all directions.

Thinking Skills

interpreting diagrams
Have students study Figure 12-9. Ask them how pressure is shown. Have students trace the effect of pressure throughout the system.

interpreting diagrams
Ask students to study Figure 12-10. Have them determine that the air passing over the wing travels farther than does the air under the wing. Correlate this with Bernoulli's principle.

Teaching Tip   Ask students why water comes out of a hose with a nozzle at a greater speed than out of one without a nozzle. (The nozzle decreases the area, which increases the speed, as according to Bernoulli's principle.)

3 REVIEW/REINFORCEMENT

1. The upward force exerted on an object by a fluid in which the object is immersed.
2. Force is a push or a pull. Pressure is the force exerted on a unit area.
3. Pascal's law states that in a closed container the pressure exerted by a fluid is the same at all points. Answers will vary but might include that fluid pressure is used to operate lifts, dentist chairs, and brake systems in cars.
4. Bernoulli's principle states that the pressure in a moving fluid decreases as the speed of the fluid increases. Answers will vary but might include the concept of lift derived from the structure of an airplane wing.

Challenge   Zero newtons, since it displaced the amount of water that weighs as much as the block of material; the buoyant force equals its weight.

Review and Skill Masters

CHALLENGE/CRITICAL THINKING, pages 75-76. See page 279c in this book for answers.

BERNOULLI'S PRINCIPLE

Airplane flight depends on fluid pressure. Air, like other gases, is a fluid. For an airplane to fly, the air pressure under the wings must be greater than the air pressure above the wings. The difference in pressure occurs as the airplane moves forward, as shown in Figure 12-10. Notice that the air moving over the top of the wing must travel farther than the air moving under the wing. To travel the longer distance in the same amount of time, the air moving over the wing must move faster than the air moving under the wing. When the air moves faster, air pressure decreases. Thus the difference in air pressure holds the airplane up. This property of fluid is known as Bernoulli's principle. *Bernoulli's principle* states that pressure in a moving fluid decreases as the speed of the fluid increases.

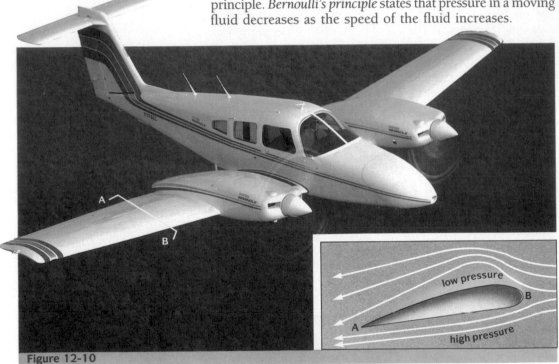

Figure 12-10

Bernoulli's principle explains how an airplane is able to fly.

REVIEW

1. What is buoyant force?
2. How do force and pressure differ?
3. What is Pascal's law? How is it used?
4. What is Bernoulli's principle? Give an example of its use.

CHALLENGE   A block of material weighs 4.0 N. This object floats in water. What will its apparent weight be when it is floating?

12-4 KINETIC AND POTENTIAL ENERGY

Energy is the ability to do work. The energy from the burning of gasoline moves a car along the highway. Stored chemical energy in a dry cell battery causes a flashlight to light. Heat energy cooks food and warms a home.

There are two types of energy—potential energy and kinetic energy. **Potential energy** is stored energy, or energy which a body has because of its position or structure. **Kinetic energy** is energy of motion.

A lump of coal has potential energy. The energy will be released as the coal burns. The water at the top of a waterfall has potential energy. The amount of potential energy in the water depends on the mass of the water and the height of the falls. As the water falls, its potential energy is changed to kinetic energy. The amount of kinetic energy in the water depends on the mass of the water and the speed at which it moves.

A moving object has kinetic energy. Look at the roller coaster shown in Figure 12-11. The car of a roller coaster has the most potential energy at the high points, and the least potential energy at the low points. The car has the most kinetic energy at the point where it moves the fastest. Where does the car move the fastest?[1]

·*After completing this section, you will be able to*

- **distinguish** between potential energy and kinetic energy.
- **describe** some forms of energy.
- **state** the Law of Conservation of Energy.

The key terms in this section are
energy
kinetic energy
Law of Conservation of Energy
potential energy

[1] At the low points.

Figure 12-11

As a roller coaster car moves downward, it converts potential energy into kinetic energy. As it moves upward it converts kinetic energy into potential energy.

12-4 KINETIC AND POTENTIAL ENERGY
pages 295–299

OBJECTIVES
Refer to pupil page 295.

VOCABULARY
Key terms: energy, kinetic energy, Law of Conservation of Energy, potential energy
Other terms: chemical energy, electrical energy, heat energy, mechanical energy, nuclear energy, radiant energy, sound energy

1 MOTIVATION

Demonstrate the different forms of energy by showing dramatic examples of each form. The following are some suggestions.
- Chemical—immersing zinc in dilute hydrochloric acid.
- Heat—using a hair dryer; burning a wood splint.
- Mechanical—spinning gyroscope; a moving toy train engine.
- Radiant—different light sources; different colors of light.
- Sound—any sound system; tuning fork.
After these demonstrations, have students discuss other examples of forms of energy.

2 CONCEPT DEVELOPMENT

Teaching Tip Many films, videotapes, and filmstrips about energy are available from film libraries or commercial suppliers; they range in scope from a general introduction of energy to specific areas of energy instruction. Use one or more of these audio-visual aids to accompany this section.

Teaching Tip   Find a Rube Goldberg cartoon or drawing. Make an overhead transparency to show to the class. Identify as many energy changes as possible.

Teaching Tip   Use the mnemonic aid *Can Ed Have More Natural Red Strawberries?* to help students remember the seven different forms of energy: chemical, electrical, heat, mechanical, nuclear, radiant, and sound. Have students make up other mnemonics for remembering the energy forms.

Enrichment   Ask students to sketch or describe an actual or invented machine or series of machines that convert energy from one form to another.

Demonstration   Set up a series of pieces of equipment that will show changes of energy from one state to another. A typical example might start with a solar cell hooked to a battery charger; the charger could then be hooked to a battery attached to a motor that has a grinding wheel attached. A nail could be sharpened on the wheel. In this example the energy changes would be from radiant to electrical to chemical to electrical to mechanical to heat.

Review and Skill Masters

SKILL, page 74.
See page 279b in this book for answers.

296

Although all energy can be classed as potential or kinetic, there are several different forms of energy. Chemical energy, electrical energy, heat energy, mechanical energy, nuclear energy, radiant energy, and sound energy are different forms of energy.

Chemical energy is given off during chemical changes. This energy comes from the chemical bonds that are broken during the change. For example, when fuels such as wood and oil burn, energy is given off. Chemical energy can be released quickly or slowly. Figure 12-12 shows two different chemical reactions that involve steel. Which reaction involves a rapid chemical reaction?[1]

Figure 12-12

Welding and rusting both cause chemical changes in steel.

[1]Welding.
[2]Answers will vary but may include cooking, heating, and cooling.

Electrical energy is produced by moving charges. Lightning is a natural form of electrical energy. Televisions, radios, and many appliances are powered by electrical energy. Computers also are powered by electrical energy. What other household uses of electrical energy can you name?[2]

When you rub your hands together, your skin gets warmer. The friction from rubbing causes the particles in your skin to move faster and to collide more often. The energy transferred by colliding particles is called *heat energy*. Heat energy is commonly produced from electrical energy or chemical energy.

Vibrating particles produce *sound energy*. The sound energy of thunder can make a house shake and the windows rattle. The speakers of a rock band can cause the whole room to vibrate.

296

The windmill shown in Figure 12-13 is turned by energy in the wind. Many farms have windmills like this one. The energy of the turning windmill is changed to energy to run a water pump. The water pump draws water out of the ground. The turning windmill and the running water have mechanical energy. For centuries people have used the windmills and water wheels to produce mechanical energy. *Mechanical energy* is the energy in moving objects. Other moving objects, such as a pounding hammer, a moving bicycle, and a falling tree, have mechanical energy.

The nucleus of an atom is the source of nuclear (NOO-klee uhr) energy. *Nuclear energy* is released when the forces that hold together the nucleus of an atom are overcome. Nuclear reactions on the sun produce the large amounts of heat and light needed for life on the earth. Nuclear energy has been produced on the earth for only a few decades. Many electric companies use nuclear energy to generate electricity. Some submarines also are powered by nuclear energy.

Figure 12-13

A turning windmill has mechanical energy.

ACTIVITY How Can Forms of Energy Be Changed?

OBJECTIVE
Demonstrate how electrical energy can be changed to other forms of energy.

MATERIALS
ring stand, ring clamp, string, cork, thumbtack, 250-mL flask, one-hole rubber stopper, glass bend, hot plate

PROCEDURE
A. Assemble a ring stand and ring clamp as shown in the figure. Tie one end of a piece of string to the ring clamp. Use a thumbtack to fasten the other end of the string to a cork.
B. Fill a 250-mL flask about half full with water.
C. Assemble the rest of the apparatus as shown in the figure. Make sure the cork hangs directly in front of the glass bend.
D. Heat the water to boiling. **Caution:** Steam can burn your skin. Do not touch the glass bend or the cork while the water is heating.
E. Record your observations of any changes that take place.

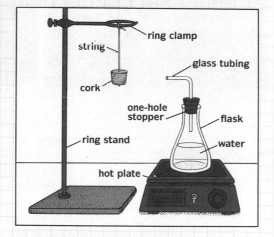

RESULTS AND CONCLUSIONS
1. List the changes in the forms of energy that took place in this activity. Provide evidence for each change.
2. Describe the motion of the cork.
3. How could the apparatus be changed to make different forms of energy?

Enrichment Students should understand energy conversions after studying this section. Ask some students to prepare a chart or bulletin board to show these changes. As the basis of this project, ask students to identify 10–12 appliances or machines found around the house, garage, and garden. Tell students to describe the energy changes that take place as the machines operate.

Tie-in/Social Studies Some countries have bountiful energy resources. Other countries are limited in the energy resources available to them. Ask students to prepare a graph to compare energy resources in various countries.

The energy produced on the sun reaches the earth in the form of radiant energy. *Radiant energy* is energy that travels in waves. Radiant energy travels at a speed of about 300,000,000 m/s. The radiant energy of a microwave oven heats and cooks food. Other examples of radiant energy are light, X rays, and radio and television waves. When radiant energy from the sun is collected and changed into other forms of energy it is often referred to as solar energy.

Figure 12-14

The chemical energy in fuel is changed into electrical energy (*A*). This energy is carried to many places (*B*). Electrical energy is changed to mechanical energy (*C*).

Energy can be changed from one form to another, as shown in Figure 12-14. At the power plant, chemical energy is produced by burning coal. The chemical energy given off turns water to steam. The heat energy in the steam is changed to mechanical energy as the steam turns the turbines of the generator. The generator converts the mechanical energy to electrical energy. The electrical energy is changed back to mechanical energy when you use an appliance such as a power saw or an electric can opener. Although energy can be changed from one form to another, it cannot be created or destroyed. This principle is known as the Law of Conservation of Energy. The **Law of Conservation of Energy** states that energy can neither be created nor destroyed but can be changed from one form to another.

REVIEW

1. What is the difference between potential energy and kinetic energy?
2. Describe chemical energy, nuclear energy, and sound energy.
3. What is the Law of Conservation of Energy?

CHALLENGE   Explain how water at the bottom of a waterfall can have both potential energy and kinetic energy.

CHAPTER SUMMARY

The main ideas in this chapter are listed below. Read these statements before you answer the Chapter Review questions.

- A force is a push or a pull. (12-1)
- Several kinds of forces exist. They are gravitational force, electrical force, magnetic force, nuclear force, friction, and weak interactions. (12-1)
- A mass may be acted upon by more than one force at a time. (12-1)
- The amount of force acting on a mass is measured in newtons. (12-2)
- Weight is the amount of gravitational force between two objects. (12-2)
- The center of gravity in an object is the point at which all of the object's mass appears to be located. (12-2)
- A buoyant force is an upward force exerted on an object by a fluid. The amount of force exerted on the object depends on the amount of water displaced by the object. (12-3)
- Pressure is force acting on a unit of surface area. (12-3)
- Energy is the ability to do work. (12-4)
- The two types of energy are potential energy and kinetic energy. (12-4)
- The Law of Conservation of Energy states that energy cannot be created or destroyed but can be changed from one form to another. (12-4)

The key terms in this chapter are listed below. Use each term in a sentence that shows the meaning of the term.

buoyant force	gravitational force	nuclear force
center of gravity	kinetic energy	potential energy
electrical force	Law of Conservation of Energy	pressure
energy	magnetic force	weak interactions
force	newton	weight
friction		

1. Potential energy is stored energy; kinetic energy is energy of motion.
2. Chemical energy is given off during chemical changes; nuclear energy is released when the forces that hold together the nucleus of an atom are overcome; sound energy is produced by vibrating particles.
3. Energy can neither be created nor destroyed, but it can be changed from one form to another.

Challenge   The water has the kinetic mechanical energy from the falling water. If not at sea level, the water has the kinetic energy of motion as it flows to the sea and the potential energy of position above sea level.

Review and Skill Masters

VOCABULARY REVIEW, page 71.
See page 279b in this book for answers.

VOCABULARY

1. False; kinetic energy.
2. False; nuclear force.
3. True.
4. False, center of gravity.
5. True.
6. False; force.
7. True.
8. True.
9. False; gravitational force.
10. True.
11. True.
12. False, pressure.

CONCEPTS

1. They both have large masses.
2. Gravitational, nuclear, electrical, magnetic, friction, weak interactions.
3. When objects have the same charge, they repel each other.
4. Treads on tires of a car; brakes on a car; treads on steps; treads on rubber soles.
5. Equal and opposite forces acting on a mass, resulting in no motion.
6. The measure of gravitational attraction between two objects.
7. On top of the mountain, the object is farther from the earth's center of gravity.
8. The point at which all of an object's mass appears to be located.
9. 833 N.
10. It would increase.

Review and Skill Masters

CHAPTER REVIEW, pages 72–73.
See page 279b in this book for answers.

Chapter Review

300

VOCABULARY

Identify each statement as True or False. If a statement is false, replace the underlined term with a term that makes the statement true.

1. <u>Potential energy</u> is energy of motion.
2. <u>Magnetic force</u> is the force that holds the nucleus of an atom together.
3. A force that opposes motion is <u>friction</u>.
4. In an object the point at which all the mass appears to be located is the object's <u>weight</u>.
5. <u>Weak interactions</u> are forces that sometimes cause atoms to break apart.
6. <u>Potential energy</u> is a push or a pull.
7. The upward force applied on an object by a liquid is called the <u>buoyant force</u>.
8. <u>The Law of Conservation of Energy</u> states that energy cannot be created or destroyed.
9. A <u>nuclear force</u> is the attraction between any two objects with mass.
10. <u>Electrical energy</u> is a force caused by moving electric charges.
11. The SI unit of force is the <u>newton</u>.
12. Force acting on a unit area is <u>energy</u>.

CONCEPTS

1. Why is the gravitational force between the earth and the sun large? (12-1)
2. List three kinds of forces. (12-1)
3. Under what conditions do electrical forces cause objects to repel each other? (12-1)
4. Give an example of useful friction. (12-1)
5. What are balanced forces? Give an example of balanced forces. (12-1)
6. What does weight measure? (12-2)
7. Why does an object weigh less at the top of a high mountain than it does at sea level? (12-2)
8. What is meant by the center of gravity? (12-2)
9. Find the weight on the earth of an object that has a mass of 85 kg. (12-2)
10. Jupiter has more mass than does the earth. What would happen to your weight if you traveled to Jupiter? (12-2)

11. What happens to the weight of an object when it is placed in water? Why? (12-3)
12. What two factors determine the amount of pressure exerted on an object? (12-3)
13. What is Pascal's law? (12-3)
14. How does an airplane remain up in the air during flight? (12-3)
15. How do moving particles transfer energy? (12-4)
16. Name three uses of radiant energy. (12-4)
17. What is mechanical energy? Give an example of an object that has mechanical energy. (12-4)
18. When is the chemical energy in a piece of wood considered to be potential energy? When is it considered to be kinetic energy? (12-4)
19. How is the Law of Conservation of Energy demonstrated when you turn on a flashlight? (12-4)

APPLICATION/
CRITICAL
THINKING

1. Why is oil put into the engine of a car?
2. Two objects fall the same distance. Both objects fall at the same rate. Why does the object with the larger mass have more kinetic energy than the object with the smaller mass?
3. Explain why electrical energy can be made from chemical energy, heat energy, or mechanical energy.
4. Explain why a force can sometimes be applied to an object without causing the object to move.

EXTENSION

1. Find out how Bernoulli's principle is used in the carburetor of a car.
2. Plot a graph to show what happens to the potential energy and kinetic energy of a ball as it rolls down a hill.
3. Prepare a bulletin-board display that shows the mass of an astronaut staying constant while weight changes. Have the astronaut appear on all nine planets.

READINGS

Galligan, Mary. "In Solar Village, Sunshine Is Put in Harness." *U.S. News and World Report*, February 11, 1985, p. 72.

Kakela, Peter. "Low Head Hydropower for Local Use." *Environment*, January/February 1985, p. 31.

Schefter, Jim. "Solar Power, Cheaper than Coal, Oil, Gas." *Popular Science*, February 1985, p. 77.

11. The weight appears to decrease because of the buoyant effect of the water.
12. The size of the force and the area the force is exerted on.
13. In a closed container the pressure exerted by a fluid is the same at all points.
14. According to Bernoulli's principle, air pressure under the wing is greater than air pressure on top of the wing, because the air moving over the top of the wing is going faster than the air moving under the wing.
15. As kinetic energy.
16. Microwave ovens, light, X rays, radio waves, and television waves.
17. Mechanical energy is the energy in moving objects; answers will vary.
18. Potential when the wood is a branch of the tree, kinetic when the tree is falling; potential before burning, kinetic during burning.
19. The chemical energy of the battery is turned to radiant energy of light and to some heat energy.

APPLICATION/CRITICAL THINKING

1. To reduce the friction between the moving parts.
2. Because the amount of kinetic energy in an object depends upon its mass and velocity. The object with greater mass would make a larger dent in something that it strikes, proving that it has more energy.
3. Because energy can be changed from one form to another.
4. To move an object, applied force must be greater than the frictional force.

Test Masters

CHAPTER TEST, pages 45–48.
See page 279d in this book for answers.

WORK AND MACHINES

ORGANIZER

Section	pages	Activity	pages	Reinforcement and Evaluation	pages	*Review and Skill Masters	pages	Other Components in Teacher Resource Package	pages
13–1 Work and Power	303–306	How Can Work Be Calculated?	305	Review, Challenge	306			Study Guide	63
13–2 Simple Machines	307–310			Review, Challenge	310			Study Guide	64
13–3 Inclined Planes	311–315	Mechanical Advantage of an Inclined Plane	314	Review, Challenge	315			Study Guide	65
13–4 Three Classes of Levers	316–319	How Do First-Class Levers Differ?	317	Puzzler Review, Challenge	318 319			Study Guide Lab Manual Transparency	66 71
13–5 Machines That Turn	320–322	Mechanical Advantage of a Pulley System	321	Review, Challenge	322	Skill	80–81	Study Guide Lab Manual	67 67
13–6 Compound Machines	323–324			Review, Challenge	324	Challenge/Critical Thinking	82	Study Guide Poster	68
CHAPTER SUMMARY	325					Vocabulary Review	77		
CHAPTER REVIEW	326–327			*Test Masters	49–52	Chapter Review	78–79		

*In the Teacher Resource Package. For answers, see pages 301b–301d in this book.

ACTIVITY MATERIALS
Quantities are based on a class of 30 students working in groups as indicated in parentheses.

How Can Work Be Calculated? p. 305 (groups of 2)	quantity	Mechanical Advantage of an Inclined Plane p. 314 (groups of 2)	quantity	How Do First-Class Levers Differ? p. 317 (groups of 2)	quantity	Mechanical Advantage of a Pulley System p. 321 (groups of 2)	quantity
wood	30 blocks	inclined-plane board	15	meterstick	15	ring stand	15
spring scale	15	spring scale	15	lever clamp	15	extension clamp	15
meterstick	15	meterstick	15	lever support	15	pulley with hook	45
string (50 cm long)	15 pieces	string (50 cm long)	15 pieces	string (50 cm long)	15 pieces	string (70 cm long)	15 pieces
		book (7 for each group, same thickness)	105	100-g masses	90	1-kg mass	15
						spring scale	15
						meterstick	15

REVIEW AND SKILL MASTERS

VOCABULARY REVIEW _____ Chapter 13

Use the correct words to complete the sentences below.

compound machine	inclined plane	resistance distance
efficiency	joules	resistance force
effort arm	lever	screw
effort distance	mechanical advantage	simple machine
effort force	moveable pulleys	watts
fixed pulleys	power	wedge
fulcrum	pulley	wheel and axle
gears	resistance arm	work

A scientist would call using force to move an object **work**

The force used to do the work is the **effort force** . The force that

opposes motion is the **resistance force** . Scientists measure work in

units called **joules** . The amount of work done in a period of

time is called **power** , which can be measured in

watts

A(n) **simple machine** can be used to change the direction or the

amount of effort force needed to do work. The number of times a machine multiplies this force

is its **mechanical advantage** . The ratio of the work output to the work input of

a machine is its **efficiency**

There are six classes of simple machines. They are the **inclined plane**

wedge **screw**

lever **pulley** , and the

wheel and axle Levers have three parts, known as the

fulcrum or fixed point, the

effort arm , and the **resistance arm**

There are two types of pulleys: **fixed pulleys** and

moveable pulleys **Gears** are

interlocking toothed wheels. They are used in a bicycle, which is an example of a(n)

compound machine

77

CHAPTER REVIEW _____ Chapter 13

13-1 Work and Power

1. How would a scientist define work? **A scientist would define work as using a force to move an object through a distance.**

2. Using the formula W = F × d, calculate the work done by a force of 50 N that moves an object 2 m. **W = F × d, W = 50 N × 2 m, W = (50 × 2) J, W = 100 J.**

3. What is the difference between effort force and resistance force? **An effort force is the force used to do work; the resistance force is the force that opposes motion.**

13-2 Simple Machines

1. What does a simple machine do? **A simple machine changes the size or direction of a force being used to do work.**

2. The six classes of simple machines are **the lever, the inclined plane, the wedge, the screw, the pulley, and the wheel and axle**

3. Using the formula MA = R/E, calculate the mechanical advantage of a machine that uses a force of 30 N to move an object weighing 150 N. **MA = R/E, MA = 150 N/30 N, MA = 5.**

13-3 Inclined Planes

1. A ramp is an example of a machine called a(n) **inclined plane**

   A(n) **wedge** is one modification of this machine, having one thick end and one thinner or sharper end. A(n) **screw** is another modification of this machine, in which the machine is wound around a cylinder.

2. What is efficiency? What common force decreases the efficiency of a machine? **Efficiency is the ratio of the work output to the work input of a machine. Friction decreases the efficiency of a machine.**

78

CHAPTER REVIEW (Continued) _____ Chapter 13

13-4 Three Classes of Levers

1. Name and describe the parts of a lever. **The fixed point of the lever is called a fulcrum. The distance from the effort force to the fulcrum is called the effort arm. The distance from the resistance force to the fulcrum is called the resistance arm.**

2. In **first** class levers the fulcrum is located between the effort force and the resistance force. In **second** class levers the resistance force is between the effort force and the fulcrum. In **third** class levers the effort force is between the resistance force and the fulcrum.

13-5 Machines that Turn

1. What is a pulley? **A pulley is a machine made up of a rope that turns around a wheel.**

2. A single fixed pulley has **one** supporting rope(s). A single moveable pulley has **two** supporting rope(s).

3. How is a wheel and axle like a lever? **In a wheel and axle, the radius of the wheel is like one arm of the lever. The radius of the axle is like the other arm of the lever.**

4. Define gears. **Gears are interlocking toothed wheels.**

13-6 Compound Machines

1. What is a compound machine? **A compound machine is a combination of two or more simple machines.**

2. Name the simple machines in a bicycle. **There are wheel and axle machines, levers, and gears in a bicycle.**

79

SKILL/Classifying _____ Chapter 13

Mechanical advantage is the number of times a machine multiplies the effort force acting on the machine. The force acting on the machine is called the effort force; the force the machine overcomes is called the resistance force.

Below are seven sketches of machines. Write the type of machine and the mechanical advantage in the chart below the sketches.

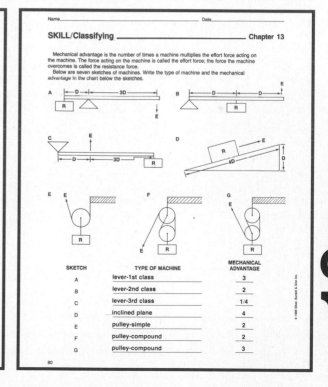

SKETCH	TYPE OF MACHINE	MECHANICAL ADVANTAGE
A	lever-1st class	3
B	lever-2nd class	2
C	lever-3rd class	1/4
D	inclined plane	4
E	pulley-simple	2
F	pulley-compound	2
G	pulley-compound	3

80

CHAPTER **13** PLANNING GUIDE

301b

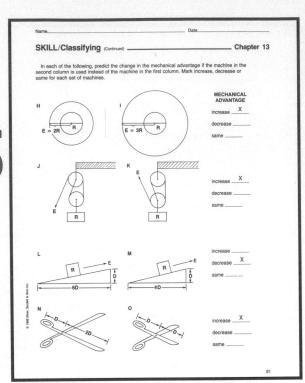

Name_____ Date_____

SKILL/Classifying (Continued) ———————— Chapter 13

In each of the following, predict the change in the mechanical advantage if the machine in the second column is used instead of the machine in the first column. Mark increase, decrease or same for each set of machines.

	MECHANICAL ADVANTAGE
H, I	increase __X__ decrease ____ same ____
J, K	increase __X__ decrease ____ same ____
L, M	increase ____ decrease __X__ same ____
N, O	increase __X__ decrease ____ same ____

© 1988 Silver, Burdett & Ginn Inc.

81

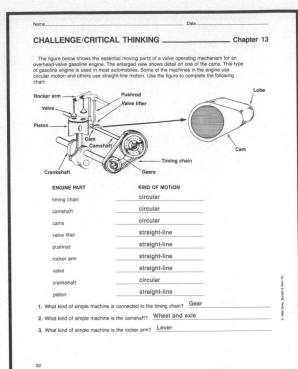

Name_____ Date_____

CHALLENGE/CRITICAL THINKING ———————— Chapter 13

The figure below shows the essential moving parts of a valve operating mechanism for an overhead-valve gasoline engine. The enlarged view shows detail on one of the cams. This type of gasoline engine is used in most automobiles. Some of the machines in the engine use circular motion and others use straight-line motion. Use the figure to complete the following chart.

ENGINE PART	KIND OF MOTION
timing chain	circular
camshaft	circular
cams	circular
valve lifter	straight-line
pushrod	straight-line
rocker arm	straight-line
valve	straight-line
crankshaft	circular
piston	straight-line

1. What kind of simple machine is connected to the timing chain? __Gear__

2. What kind of simple machine is the camshaft? __Wheel and axle__

3. What kind of simple machine is the rocker arm? __Lever__

© 1988 Silver, Burdett & Ginn Inc.

82

TEST MASTERS

PART 1 — Chapter 13

Name _____ Date _____ Score _____

Chapter 13

Work and Machines

PART 1

In the space below, write the term that each phrase defines.

		Chapter Goal
1. efficiency	The ratio of the work output to the work input of a machine	3
2. gears	A set of interlocking, toothed wheels in a machine	5
3. joule	A unit of work, equal to one newton-meter	1
4. simple machine	A device that changes the size or direction of a force being used to do work	2
5. inclined plane	A simple machine that has a sloping surface that is longer than its vertical side	3
6. wheel and axle	A machine that is made up of two wheels that turn around the same pivot	5
7. lever	A bar that turns, or pivots, around a fixed point	4
8. work	The process of using a force to move an object through a distance	1
9. pulley	A machine that is made up of a rope that turns around a wheel	5
10. mechanical advantage	The number of times a machine multiplies an effort force	2
11. compound machine	A machine that is a combination of two or more simple machines	6
12. effort arm	The distance from the effort force to the fulcrum of a lever	4

PART 2

Choose the term or phrase that best answers the question or completes the statement. Write the letter of that choice in the space at the left.

d 1. Which of the following is an example of a compound machine?　　6
　　a. wrench　　b. screwdriver　　c. gear　　d. lawn mower

c 2. Which of the following is an example of a simple machine?　　2
　　a. wheelbarrow　　b. bicycle　　c. ramp　　d. car

Chapter 13 Work and Machines　　49

Name _____ Date _____ Score _____

PART 2

Choose the term or phrase that best answers the question or completes the statement. Write the letter of that choice in the space at the left.

Chapter Goal

a 3. A construction worker uses a pulley system to lift a steel beam that weighs 1500 N. It takes a force of 100 N to lift the beam. What is the mechanical advantage of the pulley system? $(MA = \frac{R}{E})$　　2
　　a. 15　　b. 150　　c. 1500　　d. 150,000

a 4. A lever has an effort arm that is 6 m long and a resistance arm that is 1.5 m long. What is the mechanical advantage of the lever? $(MA = \frac{EA}{RA})$　　4
　　a. 4　　b. 4.5　　c. 7.5　　d. 9

d 5. A student uses a force of 60 N to pull a box a distance of 3 meters. How much work has the student done? $(W = Fd)$　　1
　　a. 20 W　　b. 60 N　　c. 63 m　　d. 180 J

d 6. The hand brake of a bicycle is a:　　6
　　a. gear.　　c. wheel and axle.
　　b. pulley.　　d. lever.

a 7. A teacher pushes a pile of papers across the top of a desk. Which of the following does the teacher use to do the work of moving the papers?　　1
　　a. effort force　　c. work output
　　b. resistance force　　d. mechanical advantage

b 8. When the effort force in a first class lever moves downward, the resistance force moves:　　4
　　a. downward.　　c. toward the fulcrum.
　　b. upward.　　d. away from the fulcrum.

b 9. The pedals of a bicycle make up which type of simple machine?　　6
　　a. inclined plane　　c. pulley
　　b. wheel and axle　　d. gear

c 10. Knives and axes are both examples of:　　3
　　a. screws.　　c. inclined planes.
　　b. levers.　　d. wheel and axles.

b 11. The efficiency of a machine will increase if the machine does:　　3
　　a. more work against the effort force.
　　b. less work against friction.
　　c. more work against the work input.
　　d. less work against the resistance force.

b 12. A wheel and axle and a pulley are both like a lever in part because all three of these machines always:　　5
　　a. contain a rope.
　　b. have a fulcrum.
　　c. stay still when they are used.
　　d. form gears when they are used.

Chapter 13 Work and Machines　　50

Name _____ Date _____ Score _____

PART 3

Look at the diagram. Then read the questions that follow. Choose the term, phrase, or figure that best answers the question or completes the statement. Write the letter of that choice in the space at the left.

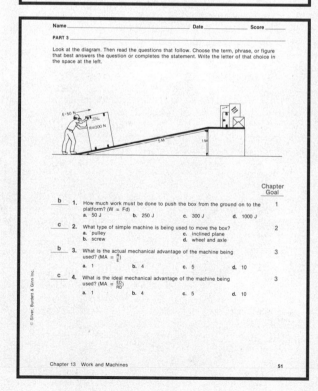

Chapter Goal

b 1. How much work must be done to push the box from the ground on to the platform? $(W = Fd)$　　1
　　a. 50 J　　b. 250 J　　c. 300 J　　d. 1000 J

c 2. What type of simple machine is being used to move the box?　　2
　　a. pulley　　c. inclined plane
　　b. screw　　d. wheel and axle

b 3. What is the actual mechanical advantage of the machine being used? $(MA = \frac{R}{E})$　　3
　　a. 1　　b. 4　　c. 5　　d. 10

c 4. What is the ideal mechanical advantage of the machine being used? $(MA = \frac{ED}{RD})$　　3
　　a. 1　　b. 4　　c. 5　　d. 10

Chapter 13 Work and Machines　　51

Name _____ Date _____ Score _____

PART 4

Read each question or direction and answer it using complete sentences.

Chapter Goal

1. How is a wheel and axle like a lever?　　5

In a wheel and axle, the radius of the wheel is like one arm of the lever. The radius of the axle is like the other arm of the lever. Both the wheel and axle pivot around the same fixed point. This point is like the fulcrum of a lever.

2. Describe the three classes of levers, and explain how the effort and resistance forces move in each type.　　4

In a first class lever, the effort force and the resistance force are on opposite sides of the fulcrum. These forces move in opposite directions as the lever moves. In a second class lever, the resistance force is between the effort arm and the fulcrum. The effort force and the resistance force move in the same direction as the lever moves. In a third class lever, the effort force is between the resistance force and the fulcrum. Both forces move in the same direction.

3. Describe how gears work on a bicycle.　　6

The pedals on a bicycle turn a gear that is connected by a chain to the gears on the rear wheel. Each of the gears on the rear wheel is a different size. Because each rear gear is smaller than each front gear, the bicycle wheel turns more times than the pedals. The ratio of the number of teeth on the front gear to the number of teeth on the rear gear determines how many times the wheel turns for one turn of the pedals. A bicycle that has many gears, such as a ten-speed bicycle, allows the rider to use different combinations of gears to increase or decrease the speed of the bicycle.

Chapter 13 Work and Machines　　52

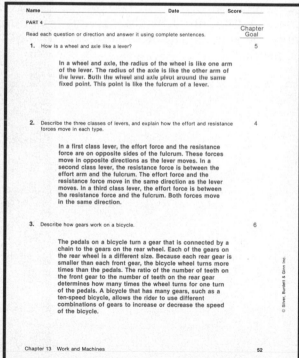

13

WORK AND MACHINES

The questions in the CHAPTER TEST are based on these Chapter Goals.

1. Define work, calculate work done, and compare effort and resistance forces.
2. Identify the six classes of simple machines, and calculate the mechanical advantage of a machine.
3. Identify types of inclined planes and modified inclined planes, and describe factors that affect the efficiency of a machine.
4. Identify three classes of levers, their characteristics, and their parts.
5. Distinguish between a fixed pulley and a movable pulley; explain how the wheel and axle is like a lever and how wheels are used in gears.
6. Recognize compound machines, and identify the simple machines that make up a bicycle.

WORK AND MACHINES

You see many machines every day. Each machine does a certain kind of work. The machine shown in the photograph is an escalator, or a moving staircase. It moves people from one floor to another. Because this escalator is curved, it is very complicated. Its parts must be put together carefully. Although the escalator is a complicated machine, its design is based on a simple machine.

- *What are the kinds of simple machines?*
- *How are simple machines used?*
- *How are complex machines made?*

13-1 WORK AND POWER

The word *work* has many meanings. You may think of work as a job to earn money or as a task that is difficult. To a scientist the word *work* has a very specific meaning. **Work** is defined as using a force to move an object through a distance. In order for any work to be done, the object must be moved by the force that is applied. Lifting a bag of groceries from the floor to the kitchen counter is work. Holding a bag of groceries in a steady position is not work.

FORCES AND WORK

Suppose you have to move a desk across a carpeted floor. If you try to push the desk, you are using force. The force that is applied to do work is called the **effort force**. If you cannot push against the desk with enough force, the desk will not move and no work will be done. The force of friction between the desk and the carpet is greater than your effort force. A force that opposes motion is called a **resistance force**. In this example, friction is the resistance force.

What determines if the desk will move? To move an object, you must apply an effort force that is greater than the resistance force. If you can provide an effort force that is greater than the force of friction between the desk and the carpet, the desk will move. Thus, work will be done.

After completing this section, you will be able to

- **define** the term *work*.
- **calculate** work done.
- **compare** effort and resistance forces.

The key terms in this section are
effort force
joule
power
resistance force
watt
work

Have students make observations about the photograph. Ask what simple machines are used to make this escalator. Have students list the complex machines that they use or see each day. Ask students to name the simple machines that make up these complex machines.

- What are the kinds of simple machines? (The kinds of simple machines are the lever, the pulley, the inclined plane, the wheel and axle, the screw, and the wedge.)
- How are simple machines used? (Simple machines are used to make work easier.)
- How are complex machines made? (Complex machines are made from combinations of simple machines.)

13-1 WORK AND POWER
pages 303–306

OBJECTIVES
Refer to pupil page 303.

VOCABULARY
Key terms: effort force, joule, power, resistance force, watt, work

1 MOTIVATION

Have students bring in photographs of work being done, such as a helicopter lifting a space capsule and a person pushing a loaded food cart. Ask students what the work in each picture has in common. (A force is moving an object through a distance.) Ask students which pictures show the greatest amount of work being done. Ask them which pictures show a small resistance force. Ask which show a large effort force.

2 CONCEPT DEVELOPMENT

Background When work is done on an object, energy is added to the object. Work is done in lifting a desk against the force of gravity. The desk acquires gravitational potential energy from the energy expended by lifting the desk. The higher the desk is raised, the more gravitational potential energy it has. The desk itself can do work if it falls from a higher position.

Teaching Tip Have students raise a book over their head to illustrate work being done. Then have them hold the book over their head to show no work. Have them determine the gravitational force overcome when they lifted the book. (The book weighs about 9.8 N per kilogram of mass, or 1 kg of mass weighs 9.8 N at sea level.)

Thinking Skills

interpreting diagrams
Students are asked to interpret the diagram in Figure 13-1B and to tell why carrying a desk is not considered to be work. The diagram helps to show that work is done only when the effort force overcomes a resistance force. Students should see that carrying does not overcome either gravity force or friction force.

Now suppose you lift the desk and carry it across the room. The only part of this task that is work is lifting the desk. Carrying the desk is not considered work. Why is this so? For work to be done, the effort force must overcome a resistance force. When you push the desk, your effort overcomes friction. When you lift the desk, your effort overcomes gravity. Figure 13-1B shows these forces. You can see that the effort and resistance forces act in opposite directions. Notice that there is no resistance to carrying the desk. The lift force is not applied in the direction in which the desk moves. The desk moves but no work is done by the lift force.

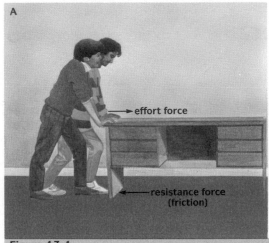 

Figure 13-1

To move an object you must apply an effort force that is greater than a resistance force.

Use the following formula to calculate work.

$$W = Fd$$

In this formula, W stands for the work done, F stands for the force, and d stands for the distance through which the force moves.

Sample Problem
A person uses a force of 20 N to move a box a distance of 5 m. How much work is done?

1. Write the formula.

$$W = Fd$$

2. Substitute the amounts given in the problem for the symbols in the formula.

$$W = 20 \text{ N} \times 5 \text{ m}$$

ACTIVITY How Can Work Be Calculated?

OBJECTIVE
Measure force and use this data to **calculate** work done.

MATERIALS
2 blocks of wood, string, spring scale, meterstick

Block	Weight (N)	Force Needed to Lift (N)	Force Needed to Slide (N)
A			
B			

PROCEDURE
A. Draw a data table like the one shown.
B. Obtain two wood blocks. Tie a piece of string around each block, so that you can pick up the block by the string.
C. Use a spring scale to weigh each block. Record the weights in the data table.
D. Using the spring scale and a steady pull, lift block A 0.5 meters high. Record in the data table the force needed to lift the block.
E. Using the spring scale and a steady pull, slide block A 0.5 meters along the floor. Be sure the spring scale is held parallel to the floor. Record in the data table the force needed to slide the block.
F. Repeat step **D**, using block B.
G. Repeat step **E**, using block B.

RESULTS AND CONCLUSIONS
1. Calculate the work done in lifting block A.
2. Calculate the work done in lifting block B.
3. Calculate the work done in sliding block A.
4. Calculate the work done in sliding block B.
5. Is there a difference between the amount of work done to slide and to lift the same block? Explain your answer.
6. Why is there a difference in the amount of work done lifting block A compared with lifting block B?

3. Determine the unit that will be part of the answer. In this case, the unit is a newton-meter (N·m).

$$W = 20 \times 5 \text{ N·m}$$

4. Complete the calculations that are required.

$$W = 100 \text{ N·m}$$

The amount of work done is 100 N·m. Work is also measured in units called joules (joolz). A **joule** (J) is a unit of work and is equal to one newton-meter. Thus, one joule of work is done when a force of one newton moves an object one meter. How many joules of work are done when a force of 50 N is used to lift a box of books to a height of 0.5 m?[1]

[1]25 J.

Like work, the term *power* has a specific meaning in science. **Power** is the amount of work done in a period of time. Thus power is the rate at which work is done. Power can be calculated by using the following formula.

$$P = \frac{W}{t}$$

In this formula, P stands for power, W stands for work, and t stands for time.

Teaching Tip Calculate the sample problem. Assign additional work problems as needed.

Demonstration Ask students to estimate how much power a student would generate in running up a flight of stairs at school. Measure the height of the stairs. Ask a student what his or her weight is in kilograms. Convert the weight to newtons. (9.8 N/kg.) Time the student. Calculate his or her power in joules per second. Compare it with the class estimate.

Background Automobile power is usually measured in horsepower. James Watt proposed the term *horsepower*. One good English horse was supposed to generate 550 foot-pounds of work per second. Since horses vary from place to place, one horsepower was redefined to equal 746 watts, or 746 J/sec.

ACTIVITY 45 minutes

PROCESS SKILLS
measuring, recording data, calculating, interpreting data, identifying cause and effect

Preparation None required.

Teaching Tip Be sure that students use steady vertical and horizontal pulls.

Answers to Results and Conclusions
1–4. Answers will vary.
5. Yes, because sliding overcomes the force of friction, and lifting overcomes the force of gravity.
6. The blocks do not have identical weights.

Tie-in/Social Studies   James Watt invented the first practical steam engine in the late 1700s. Although Watt's engine was not the first steam engine, he is given most of the credit because his version greatly improved on those of his predecessors. Watt's engine worked faster and more efficiently because of the double-action principle. This allowed the steam to be used first on one side of the piston and then on the other. Watt's engine greatly reduced the cost of operation.

Teaching Tip   Have students read pages 305–306 and calculate the sample problem on page 306. Assign additional power problems as needed. Convert watts to kilowatts by dividing watts by 1000.

3 REVIEW/REINFORCEMENT

1. Work is defined as using a force to move an object through a distance.
2. One newton-meter is equal to one joule.
3. **a.** $W = Fd = 50 \text{ N} \times 10 \text{ m} = 500$ N•m or 500 J
   b. $W = Fd = 20 \text{ N} \times 0.20 \text{ m} = 4.0$ N•m or 4.0 J
   c. $W = Fd = 6.0 \text{ N} \times 50 \text{ m} = 300$ N•m or 300 J
4. An effort force is the force applied to do work; a resistance force is the force that opposes the object's motion.

Challenge
$W = Fd = 8 \text{ N} \times 15 \text{ m} = 120 \text{ N•m}$
$W = Fd = 24 \text{ N} \times 0.8 \text{ m} = 19.2 \text{ N•m}$
Total work $= 120 \text{ N•m} + 19.2 \text{ N•m} = 139.2 \text{ N•m}$ or 139.2 J

Figure 13-2

The faster an elevator rises, the more power it uses.

¹600 W.
²1.2 kW.

Sample Problem
A person weighing 600 N gets on an elevator. The elevator lifts the person 6 m in 10 seconds. How much power was used to lift the person?

1. Write the formula.

$$P = \frac{W}{t}$$

2. Substitute the amounts given in the problem for the symbols in the formula. Recall that work is equal to force times distance.

$$P = \frac{600 \text{ N} \times 6 \text{ m}}{10 \text{ s}}$$

3. Determine the unit that will be part of the answer. In this example, the unit will be newton-meters per second, or joules per second (J/s).

$$P = \frac{600 \times 6}{10} \text{ J/s}$$

4. Complete the calculations that are required.

$$P = 360 \text{ J/s}$$

The elevator used 360 J/s of power to lift the person. The unit of power is also called a watt. A **watt** (W) is a unit of power and is equal to one joule per second. Thus, the elevator used 360 W of power. How much power would have been used to lift the person in 6 seconds?[1]

If you use a 60-W light bulb, it takes 60 W of power to make the bulb glow. A watt is a small unit of power. For large amounts of power, it is useful to use kilowatts (kW). One kilowatt is equal to 1000 W. How many kilowatts of power are used by a 1200-W hair dryer?[2]

REVIEW

1. What is the scientific meaning of the term *work*?
2. How is a newton-meter related to a joule?
3. Calculate the amount of work done in each of the following.
   a. You use a force of 50 N to push a chair 10 m.
   b. A box that weighs 20 N is lifted 0.20 m.
   c. A force of 6.0 N is used to pull a cart 50 m.
4. What is an effort force? What is a resistance force?

CHALLENGE It takes 8 N of force to push a box that weighs 24 N. If the box is pushed a distance of 15 m and then lifted to a table 0.8 m high, how much work is done?

13-2 SIMPLE MACHINES

If you were asked to name some machines, you might list a car, a bicycle, or a blender. These all are very complex machines. But did you know that many simple things you use also are machines? The handle of a faucet is a machine. So is a doorknob or a chisel. What do these simple machines have in common? They all do work by changing your effort force in some way.

A **simple machine** is a device that changes the size or direction of a force being used to do work. Remember that work is done whenever a force moves an object through a distance. There are six classes of simple machines. They are the lever, inclined plane, wedge, screw, pulley, and wheel and axle. Some examples are shown in Figure 13-3.

Many machines make work easier by reducing the amount of effort force needed. They are said to multiply your effort force. Other machines can multiply the distance through which your effort force moves. The device shown in Figure 13-3A is used to enlarge a pattern. Notice that the effort force traces a small pattern, but the machine makes a larger copy.

After completing this section, you will be able to

- **define** the term *simple machine.*
- **name** the six classes of simple machines.
- **calculate** the mechanical advantage of a machine.

The key terms in this section are
effort distance
mechanical advantage
resistance distance
simple machine

machina (a device)

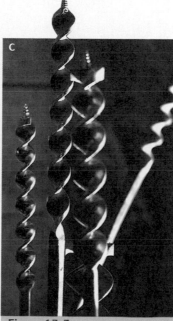

Figure 13-3

The pantograph (*A*) is a device that uses levers to multiply distance. The ramp (*B*) is an inclined plane. It multiplies an effort force. The drills (*C*) are screws that also multiply an effort force.

13-2 SIMPLE MACHINES
pages 307–310

OBJECTIVES
Refer to pupil page 307.

VOCABULARY
Key terms: effort distance, mechanical advantage, resistance distance, simple machine
Other terms: work input, work output

1 MOTIVATION

Ask students to list machines they use each day. Write the responses on the chalkboard. Ask students what their lives would be like without these machines. Tape pictures of the six simple machines on the chalkboard. Have students choose different machines listed on the chalkboard and identify which simple machines are used in their choices.

2 CONCEPT DEVELOPMENT

Thinking Skills

interpreting diagrams
Students are asked to compare the effort distance and the resistance distance in the enlarging machine shown in Figure 13-3A.

Teaching Tip   Have students work through the sample problems on page 308. Let students do additional problems involving mechanical advantage.

Tie-in/Math   Have students look at Figure 13-4 and calculate the effort force that would be needed to lift a 6000-N rock if the mechanical advantage is 10. (600 N.)

MECHANICAL ADVANTAGE

The number of times a machine multiplies an effort force is called the **mechanical advantage** of the machine. The mechanical advantage of a machine may be calculated using the following formula.

$$MA = \frac{R}{E}$$

In this formula, MA stands for mechanical advantage, R stands for resistance force, and E stands for effort force.

Sample Problem
A lever uses a force of 200 N to move a rock that weighs 2000 N. Find the mechanical advantage.

1. Write the formula.

$$MA = \frac{R}{E}$$

2. Substitute the amounts given in the problem for the symbols in the formula.

$$MA = \frac{2000 \text{ N}}{200 \text{ N}}$$

3. Determine the unit that will be part of the answer. Both effort and resistance are expressed in newtons. These units cancel. There is no unit for mechanical advantage.

$$MA = \frac{2000}{200}$$

4. Complete the calculations that are required.

$$MA = 10$$

Figure 13-4

With this simple machine, an effort force of 200 N can be used to move a resistance force of 2000 N.

resistance force
2000 N

effort force
200 N

The mechanical advantage of the lever is 10. This means the effort force is multiplied ten times.

Do you notice anything else about the rock and the lever? As the effort force pushes downward, the rock moves upward. The effort force and resistance forces are moving. The distance that the effort force moves is called the **effort distance**. The distance that the resistance force moves is called the **resistance distance**. In order to lift the rock upward 3 cm, the lever was pushed downward 30 cm. Another way to find the mechanical advantage of a machine is to compare the effort distance and the resistance distance, using the following formula.

$$MA = \frac{ED}{RD}$$

In this formula, ED stands for effort distance and RD stands for resistance distance.

Figure 13-5

The distance that the rock moves is the resistance distance. The distance that the opposite end of the lever moves is the effort distance.

Sample Problem
While using the lever shown in Figure 13-5, the student moves an effort force 30 cm to move a resistance force 3 cm. What is the mechanical advantage of the machine?

1. Write the formula.

$$MA = \frac{ED}{RD}$$

2. Substitute the amounts given in the problem for the symbols in the formula.

$$MA = \frac{30 \text{ cm}}{3 \text{ cm}}$$

Background   When the effort force is reduced, the distance the force must move is proportionately increased. In contrast, a larger resistance force moves a proportionately smaller distance.

Demonstration   Show students how difficult it is to open a wooden box when the lid is nailed shut. Have a student try to open the lid by using his or her hands only. Then have the student use a crowbar or screwdriver. Ask why it is easier with the crowbar. (A longer effort distance gives a greater mechanical advantage.)

Background   When mechanical advantage is calculated, friction is not taken into account, but calculations using forces do take friction into account. Therefore, the machine's mechanical advantage determined by using distances is larger than its mechanical advantage determined by using forces, because friction reduces the mechanical advantage.

Teaching Tip   Have students solve additional mechanical advantage problems involving effort and resistance distances. Ask students which mechanical advantage formula is unaffected by friction. (MA = ED/RD.)

Enrichment   Work input actually exceeds work output. Have students explain why this is true. (Friction causes an increase in effort force.)

Teaching Tip   Students look at Figure 13-6 and see that the mechanical advantage is 3. Ask if they can think of another way to find the mechanical advantage in the diagram. (They can count the number of supporting strands of rope.)

3 REVIEW/REINFORCEMENT

1. A simple machine is a device that changes the size or direction of a force being used to do work.
2. Lever, inclined plane, pulley, wedge, wheel and axle, screw.
3. Answers will vary but may include a knife, a broom, a pizza cutter, and a ramp.
4. $MA = \dfrac{R}{E} = \dfrac{500}{20} = 25$

Challenge   Three; lever, wheel and axle, screws.

[1]Yes.

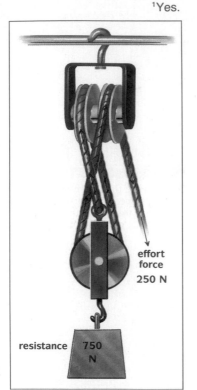

Figure 13-6

This kind of pulley system is called a block and tackle.

[2]The mechanical advantage is 3.

3. Determine the unit that will be part of the answer. As before, the units will cancel and there will be no unit for mechanical advantage.

$$MA = \frac{30}{3}$$

4. Complete the calculations that are required.

$$MA = 10$$

The mechanical advantage of the lever is 10. Does this agree with the previous calculation?[1]

WORK INPUT AND WORK OUTPUT

Although a simple machine can multiply an effort force, it cannot multiply work. When you use a machine, you do work. Your effort force moves through a distance. The work that you do in using a simple machine is called the *work input*.

The block and tackle shown in Figure 13-6 is a kind of pulley system. The effort force of 250 N pulls downward on the rope. If this force moves a distance of 3.0 m, the work input is 750 J.

$$W = Fd = 250 \text{ N} \times 3.0 \text{ m} = 750 \text{ N·m} = 750 \text{ J}$$

While the effort force pulls on the rope, the block and tackle does work in lifting the resistance. The work done by a simple machine is called the *work output*. The resistance has a weight of 750 N, and is lifted a distance of 1.0 m. The work output is 750 J.

$$W = Fd = 750 \text{ N} \times 1.0 \text{ m} = 750 \text{ N·m} = 750 \text{ J}$$

Notice that the work output is not larger than the work input. The machine did not multiply the work input. A machine cannot do more work than is put into it. However, the machine did multiply the effort force. What is the mechanical advantage of this machine?[2]

REVIEW

1. What is a simple machine?
2. List the six classes of simple machines.
3. List three examples of simple machines.
4. A machine can move a 500 N object with a force of 20 N. What is the mechanical advantage?

CHALLENGE How many simple machines are there in a wheelbarrow? Name them.

13-3 INCLINED PLANES

Have you ever tried to load something heavy, like a lawn mower, into the trunk of a car? A ramp can be used to make such a job easier. The ramp is an example of an inclined plane. An **inclined plane** is a simple machine that has a sloping surface that is longer than its vertical side.

MECHANICAL ADVANTAGE

An inclined plane has a large mechanical advantage. Notice in Figure 13-7 that the effort distance is the sloping side, or length. The resistance distance is the vertical side, or height. The resistance distance is shorter than the effort distance. The resistance force is the weight of the object being moved. The effort force is the amount of force needed to move the object along the inclined plane.

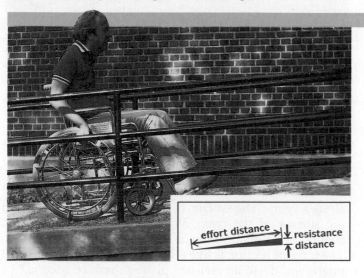

Figure 13-7

A ramp is an inclined plane.

To calculate the mechanical advantage of an inclined plane, compare the effort and resistance distances. The inclined plane shown in Figure 13-8 on the next page has an effort distance of 3 m and a resistance distance of 1 m. Recall the formula for finding mechanical advantage by comparing distances.

$$MA = \frac{ED}{RD} = \frac{3 \text{ m}}{1 \text{ m}}$$

The calculation of mechanical advantage of this inclined plane is 3. This inclined plane should multiply the effort force three times.

13-3 INCLINED PLANES
pages 311–315

OBJECTIVES
Refer to pupil page 311.

VOCABULARY
Key terms: efficiency, inclined plane, screw, wedge
Other terms: actual mechanical advantage, ideal mechanical advantage, pitch

1 MOTIVATION

Show students an inclined plane. Ask them to list uses for this simple machine. Have students make a bulletin-board display of machines that are inclined planes. Ask students what each machine has in common. (A sloping surface.)

2 CONCEPT DEVELOPMENT

Background   An inclined plane has a large mechanical advantage because the effort distance (the slope) is much longer than the resistance distance (the height). This enables the effort force to be small in comparison to the resistance force. As the resistance distance decreases, the mechanical advantage increases.

Enrichment   Have interested students find out how the work output of an inclined plane might be increased.

Background   Mountain roads are constructed to wind back and forth instead of going straight up a mountain. The safest grade, or percent of incline, is 10 percent.

Teaching Tip   Have students discuss the actual and ideal mechanical advantages of the ramp shown in Figure 13-8.

Tie-in/Math   Have students calculate the work input and work output of the ramp shown in Figure 13-8.

Thinking Skills

comparing
Students are asked to compare the ratio of the effort distance to the resistance distance of an inclined plane and the ratio of the effort force to the resistance force.

[1]Cover it, wax it, use conveyor belts, wheels or rollers, and so on.

Figure 13-8

An effort force of 800 N is being used to move an object that weighs 2000 N.

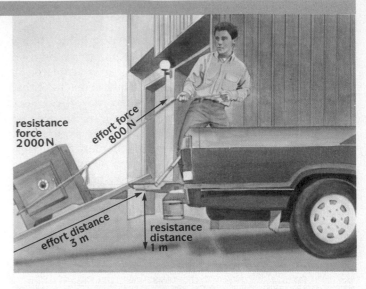

Look at the forces shown in Figure 13-8. Is the 800-N effort force multiplied three times? To find out, compare forces to find the mechanical advantage.

$$MA = \frac{R}{E} = \frac{2000 \text{ N}}{800 \text{ N}}$$

According to this calculation, the mechanical advantage is 2.5. The two calculations of mechanical advantage do not agree. How can you account for the difference?

Think about what happens as an object is pushed along a ramp. The surface of the object is in contact with the surface of the ramp. When surfaces touch, friction occurs. Recall that friction is a force that opposes motion. The force of friction is like a second resistance force. What might you do to an inclined plane to reduce friction?[1]

The calculation of mechanical advantage based on effort and resistance distances is called the *ideal mechanical advantage* because it ignores the problems caused by friction. The calculation of mechanical advantage based on effort and resistance forces is called the *actual mechanical advantage*. This method compares the forces that actually exist when the machine is used.

There is friction in many machines. The work done against the force of friction is the difference between the work input and work output of the machine. In Section 13-2 you saw a machine in which the work output and work input were equal. This does not always happen. Work input is usually greater than work output.

EFFICIENCY

Look at the simple machine in Figure 13-9. A force of 1200 N is needed to move the box up the ramp. The ramp is 4.0 m long. The work input is 4800 J.

$$W = Fd = 1200 \text{ N} \times 4.0 \text{ m} = 4800 \text{ J}$$

The ramp raises the 3200-N resistance to a height of 1.0 m. The work output is 3200 J.

$$W = Fd = 3200 \text{ N} \times 1.0 \text{ m} = 3200 \text{ J}$$

Notice that these two calculations differ by 1600 J. This difference is the work done against friction. Friction is a problem for many reasons. It causes machines to become worn. Friction produces heat, which can damage machines. This heat is wasted energy. Thus friction decreases the efficiency of a machine. **Efficiency** is the ratio of the work output to the work input of a machine. It is calculated by using the following formula.

$$\text{efficiency} = \frac{\text{WO}}{\text{WI}} \times 100\%$$

In this formula, WO stands for work output and WI stands for work input. In this example, the efficiency is less than 100 percent.

$$\text{efficiency} = \frac{3200 \text{ J}}{4800 \text{ J}} \times 100\% = 67\%$$

This machine is 67 percent efficient. Thus 67 percent of the work put into the machine moved the resistance. What happened to the other 33 percent of the work input?[1]

[1]It went into overcoming friction.

Figure 13-9

An effort force of 1200 N is being used to move an object that weighs 3200 N.

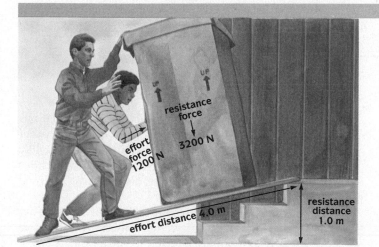

resistance force

3200 N

effort force 1200 N

effort distance 4.0 m

resistance distance 1.0 m

Background   The Law of Conservation of Energy states that energy cannot be created or destroyed. A machine cannot have a greater work output than its work input. Friction prevents the work output from equaling the work input.

Teaching Tip   When students calculate the efficiency of the inclined plane shown in Figure 13-9, point out that a 100 percent efficient machine would be frictionless, which is an impossibility.

Enrichment   Have interested students research the meaning and plausibility of a *perpetual motion machine*. Have them report their findings to the class.

Thinking Skills

inferring
Students are asked to infer what happened to cause the difference between the work input and the work output in Figure 13-9.

Tie-in/Social Studies   Have students research the use of inclined planes by ancient Egyptians in building the pyramids.

PROCESS SKILLS
measuring, recording data, interpreting data, calculating, comparing

Preparation   None required.

Answers to Results and Conclusions
1. The higher the inclined plane, the greater the effort force needed.
2. The actual mechanical advantage increases as the height decreases.
3. The ideal mechanical advantage increases as the height decreases.
4. Ideal mechanical advantage is greater than actual mechanical advantage, due to friction between the two surfaces.

Extension   The efficiency of the cart is greater than that of the book because the wheels of the cart reduce friction.

ACTIVITY   Mechanical Advantage of an Inclined Plane

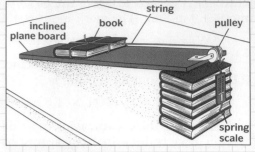

OBJECTIVE
Determine the effect of the height of an inclined plane on its mechanical advantage.

MATERIALS
inclined-plane board, 7 books (same thickness), string, spring scale, meterstick

PROCEDURE
A. Draw a data table like the one shown.
B. Support an inclined-plane board on a pile of six books, as shown in the figure.
C. Use a piece of string to attach a seventh book to a spring scale. Use the spring scale to find the weight of the book. Record the weight in the data table under resistance force, R, for trial 1.
D. Measure the height of the pile of books, in centimeters. This is the resistance distance. Record this measurement for trial 1.
E. Measure the length of the board in centimeters. This is the effort distance. Record the length in the data table.
F. Place the book near the bottom of the board. Using the spring scale, pull the book slowly up the board, to the top. Record the effort force for trial 1.
G. Remove three books from the pile. Measure the height of the pile of three books. Record the height for trial 2.
H. Repeat the experiment. Record all data.

RESULTS AND CONCLUSIONS
1. How does height affect the effort force of the inclined plane?
2. How does a decrease in height affect the actual mechanical advantage of the inclined plane?
3. How does a decrease in height affect the ideal mechanical advantage of the inclined plane?
4. How do the ideal mechanical advantages compare with the actual mechanical advantages? Account for any difference.

EXTENSION
Calculate the efficiency of this machine. Then repeat the experiment, using a small cart or roller skate in place of the book as the resistance force. Compare the efficiency of this setup with the original one.

Trial	Resistance Force R (N)	Length (cm)	Height (cm)	Effort Force E (N)	Actual MA = $\frac{R}{E}$	Ideal MA = $\frac{Length}{Height}$
1						
2						

MODIFIED INCLINED PLANES

A **wedge** is a type of modified inclined plane that has a thick end and a thinner or sharper end. Knives and other cutting tools are examples of wedges. Some wedges, like a knife, have one sloping surface. Others, like an ax, have two sloping surfaces. These wedges are like two inclined planes placed base-to-base.

An inclined plane usually stays still while objects are moved along its surface. But wedges often are moved as they are used. A wedge may be used to push objects apart.

If you use an ax to split wood, you push the fibers of the wood apart. A downward effort force is changed to a force that pushes sideways to split the wood.

A screw is another kind of modified inclined plane. A **screw** is an inclined plane wound around a cylinder. Look at the threads on the screw shown in Figure 13-10. The threads slowly move forward into the wood as the screw turns. When the screw makes one complete turn, the threads move into the wood one space. The distance between two threads is called the *pitch* of the screw.

Screws are used to raise and lower some kinds of car jacks. They also are used in leveling devices on appliances and stereos. The balance you use in science lab may have a metal mass on a screw thread. As you turn the mass, it moves along the threads, leveling the arm of the balance.

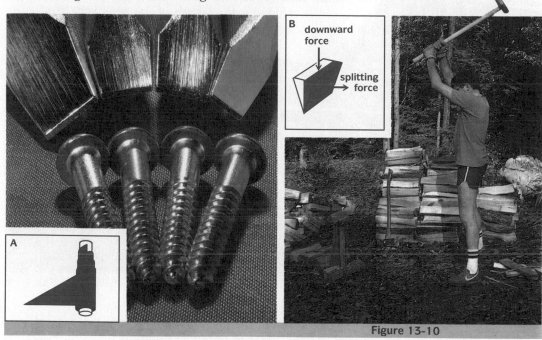

Figure 13-10

A screw is an inclined plane wrapped around a cylinder (*A*). An ax is an example of a wedge (*B*).

REVIEW

1. Give two examples of inclined planes.
2. How are the wedge and the screw related to the inclined plane?
3. What is the pitch of a screw?
4. Give two examples of wedges.

CHALLENGE When might friction on an inclined plane be useful?

1. Stairs, ramps.
2. The wedge is a modified inclined plane that has a thick end and a thinner or sharper end; a screw is an inclined plane wound around a cylinder.
3. The distance between two threads.
4. Ax, knife.

Challenge When you want an object to move slowly for safety reasons, and when you want to keep an object from sliding backward.

13-4 THREE CLASSES OF LEVERS

pages 316–319

OBJECTIVES
Refer to pupil page 316.

VOCABULARY

Key terms: effort arm, fulcrum, lever, resistance arm

Other terms: first-class lever, second-class lever, third-class lever

1 MOTIVATION

Prepare overhead transparencies of pictures of various machines: a spoon, a wedge, a person's arm, a ramp, a pliers, a broom, a screw, an ax, and a bottle opener. Ask students to select the machines that have a bar that pivots around a fixed point. (All except the wedge, the screw, and the ramp.) Point out that these machines are all levers.

2 CONCEPT DEVELOPMENT

Background   The law of levers states that the effort force times the effort arm equals the resistance force times the resistance arm. These two products are sometimes called moments or torques. In a lever the moments of all the efforts on one side of the fulcrum must equal the moments of all the efforts on the other side.

Teaching Tip   Have students look at Figures 13-11, 13-12, and 13-13. Discuss the positions of the effort force, the resistance force, and the fulcrum in each example. Have students locate the effort and the resistance arms in each. Have them determine the directions in which the two forces move.

13-4 THREE CLASSES OF LEVERS

After completing this section, you will be able to

- **name** the parts of a lever.
- **identify** and **give examples** of the three classes of levers.

The key terms in this section are
effort arm
fulcrum
lever
resistance arm

A **lever** (LEHV uhr) consists of a bar that turns, or pivots, around a fixed point. The fixed point of a lever is called a **fulcrum** (FUL kruhm). The distance from the effort force to the fulcrum of a lever is called the **effort arm**. The distance from the resistance force to the fulcrum of a lever is called the **resistance arm**. The mechanical advantage of a lever can be found by comparing the lengths of the arms of the lever. The mechanical advantage is calculated using the following formula.

$$MA = \frac{EA}{RA}$$

In this formula, EA stands for the length of the effort arm and RA stands for the length of the resistance arm.

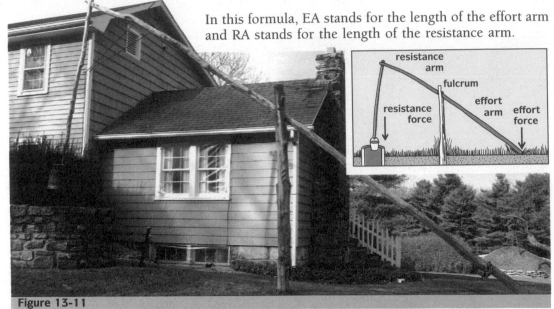

Figure 13-11

This lever is called a well sweep. It was used to lift a bucket of water from a well.

Sample Problem

What is the mechanical advantage of a lever that has a resistance arm 2 m long and an effort arm 8 m long?

1. Write the formula.

$$MA = \frac{EA}{RA}$$

2. Substitute the amounts given in the problem for the symbols in the formula.

$$MA = \frac{8 \text{ m}}{2 \text{ m}}$$

ACTIVITY   How Do First Class Levers Differ?

OBJECTIVE
Compare first class levers with different mechanical advantages.

MATERIALS
meterstick, lever clamp, lever support, string, six 100-g masses

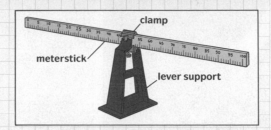

clamp
meterstick
lever support

PROCEDURE
A. Draw a data table like the one shown.
B. Assemble a lever, using a meterstick and a lever clamp. Adjust the position of the clamp until the meterstick balances in a lever support, as shown in the figure. The point at which the lever balances will be the fulcrum of the lever.
C. Use a piece of string to hang 200 g of mass from the meterstick. Convert this mass to newtons. Record this force as the resistance force for lever 1. Position the resistance 20 cm to the right of the fulcrum. Record this distance as the length of the resistance arm.
D. Use another piece of string to hang 200 g of mass to the left of the fulcrum. Convert this mass to newtons. Record this force as the effort force. Move this mass until the lever balances. The distance between the effort and the fulcrum is the length of the effort arm.
   1. How do the lengths of the arms compare?

E. Leave the resistance in place, and replace the effort with one 100-g mass. Balance the lever, and record all data for lever 2.
   2. How do the lengths of the arms compare?
F. Leave the resistance in place and replace the effort with four 100-g masses. Balance the lever, and record all data for lever 3.
   3. How do the lengths of the arms compare?
G. Calculate the mechanical advantage of each lever, comparing the forces. Record this information under R/E in the data table.
H. Calculate the mechanical advantage of each lever, comparing the lengths of the lever arms. Record this information under EA/RA.

RESULTS AND CONCLUSIONS
1. Is the mechanical advantage of a first class lever always greater than 1?
2. How would it be possible to balance two separate resistance forces on one side with only one effort force on the other side?

Lever	Resistance Force (N)	Resistance Arm (cm)	Effort Force (N)	Effort Arm (cm)	R/E	EA/RA
1						
2						
3						

3. Determine the unit that will be part of the answer. Both lengths are expressed in meters. These units cancel.

$$MA = \frac{8}{2}$$

4. Complete the calculations.

$$MA = 4$$

The mechanical advantage of this lever is 4. An effort force will be multiplied four times. How much resistance could be moved by a 5-N force applied to this lever?[1]   [1]20 N.

Background The word *lever* is derived from the Latin word *levare,* which means "to raise or lift." Levator muscles lift body parts.

Puzzler The downward force on the other side of the fulcrum is the weight of the lever. It is located at the center of gravity of the stick.

Figure 13-12

The oars (*left*) and the seesaws (*right*) are examples of first class levers.

¹Oar locks (*left*); bar on which seesaw rests (*right*).

A lever in which the fulcrum is located between the effort force and the resistance force is called a *first class lever.* In a first class lever, like the well sweep shown in Figure 13-11, the effort force and resistance force are on opposite sides of the fulcrum. The forces move in opposite directions. Figure 13-12 also shows some first class levers. Where is the fulcrum in each of these levers?[1]

In the two other classes of levers, the effort and resistance forces are on the same side of the fulcrum. In a *second class lever,* the resistance force is between the effort force and the fulcrum. The effort force and resistance force move in the same direction. Look at the second class lever in Figure 13-13A. Because the effort arm is always longer than the resistance arm, a second class lever always has a mechanical advantage greater than 1.

In a *third class lever,* the effort force is between the resistance force and the fulcrum. Notice in Figure 13-13B that the effort arm is shorter than the resistance arm. A third class lever has a mechanical advantage less than 1.

SCIENCE PUZZLER

The lever shown in the photograph is balanced on its fulcrum.
The weight of the apple is a downward force on one side of the fulcrum. What is the downward force on the other side of the fulcrum? Where is this force located?

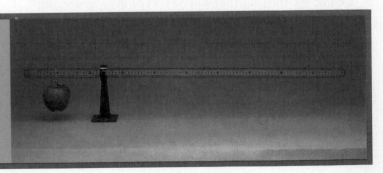

In a third class lever, a small resistance force requires a larger effort force. The effort force is much larger than is needed to move the resistance without the lever. Why use such a machine? A third class lever does not multiply force. Instead it multiplies speed and distance.

Your body contains third class levers. Figure 13-13C shows the bones and muscles of the arm. The fulcrum is the elbow and the effort is the muscle. The resistance is the weight of the forearm and is located at the center of gravity of the forearm. A large motion of the arm is produced by a small motion of the muscles. This arrangement makes it possible for you to wave, swim, or throw a ball.

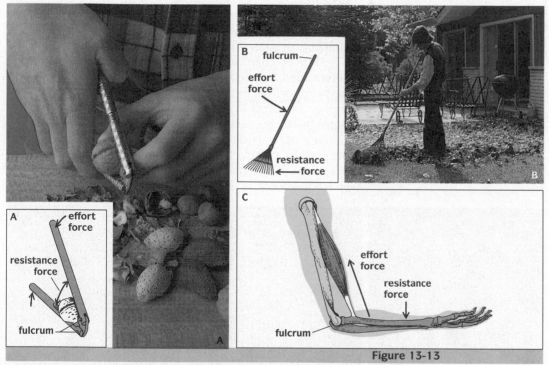

Figure 13-13

This nutcracker contains two second class levers (A). A rake is used as a third class lever (B). The human body contains third class levers (C).

REVIEW

1. What are the three parts of a lever?
2. Compare the positions of the three parts of each class of lever.
3. Name one example of each of the three classes of levers.

CHALLENGE If a third class lever has a mechanical advantage of 0.2, how much resistance force can be balanced by an effort force of 10 N? If the effort force moves up 5 cm, how high is the resistance lifted?

13-5 MACHINES THAT TURN

pages 320–322

OBJECTIVES
Refer to pupil page 320.

VOCABULARY
Key terms: fixed pulley, gears, movable pulley, pulley, wheel and axle

1 MOTIVATION

Take the class outside to the flagpole. Have a student raise and lower the flag. Ask students to identify the machine being used. Ask students where else pulleys are used. (In construction, for lifting materials or for loading trucks.)

2 CONCEPT DEVELOPMENT

Background   A supporting strand of a pulley bears all or part of the weight of the resistance force. A rope pulled downward over a pulley does not support the resistance and does not reduce the effort force needed. A rope pulled upward does support the resistance and reduces the effort force needed. Fixed pulleys are useful when someone wants to change the direction of the effort force. A movable pulley provides a better mechanical advantage.

Teaching Tip   Have students examine Figure 13-14. Have them count the number of strands of rope supporting the resistance force in each example shown. Ask students to discuss two ways of finding the mechanical advantage of fixed and movable pulleys. Ask students which mechanical advantage is ideal. (That which is found by counting the strands of rope.) Ask which mechanical advantage is affected by friction. (MA = R/E).

320

13-5 MACHINES THAT TURN

After completing this section, you will be able to

- **describe** the pulley as a simple machine.
- **distinguish** between a fixed pulley and a movable pulley.
- **compare** the wheel and axle with a lever.
- **describe** gears.

The key terms in this section are
fixed pulley
gears
movable pulley
pulley
wheel and axle

¹The center.

Many of the machines you have studied so far have a limited range of movement. A lever pivots up and down on its fulcrum, but it does not spin all the way around. Some simple machines spin on an axis as they do work. These machines are the pulley, the wheel and axle, and gears.

PULLEYS

A **pulley** is a machine that is made up of a rope that turns around a wheel. A pulley is like a first class lever. Instead of a bar, a pulley has a rope. What part of the pulley is the fulcrum?¹ The pulley shown in Figure 13-14B is a fixed pulley. A **fixed pulley** is a pulley that is attached to something that does not move.

The mechanical advantage of a fixed pulley may be determined by counting the number of strands of rope that support the resistance force. The mechanical advantage of a fixed pulley is 1 because there is one supporting rope. Because a single fixed pulley has a mechanical advantage of 1, it does not multiply an effort force. The purpose of a single fixed pulley is to change the direction of a force. Single fixed pulleys are used only when a small resistance force is to be lifted.

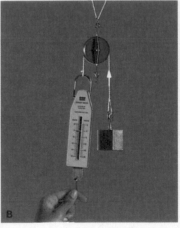

Figure 13-14

A combination of fixed and movable pulleys (*A*). A single fixed pulley (*B*). A single movable pulley (*C*).

Another type of pulley is shown in Figure 13-14C. Notice that this pulley is not fixed. This pulley is being pulled upward by an effort force. A pulley that moves with the resistance is called a **movable pulley**. Note that there are two strands of rope supporting the resistance. Thus, the mechanical advantage of a single movable pulley is 2.

320

ACTIVITY   Mechanical Advantage of a Pulley System

OBJECTIVE
Compare the mechanical advantages of several pulleys.

MATERIALS
ring stand, extension clamp, 1 single pulley, 1 double pulley, pulley cord, 1-kg mass, spring scale, meterstick

PROCEDURE
A. Attach a pulley to a clamp on a ring stand.

B. Run a piece of pulley cord over the pulley. Attach one end of the pulley cord to a 1-kg mass. Convert this mass to newtons, and record this force as the resistance force.

C. Attach the other end of the cord to a spring scale as shown in Figure 1.

D. Pull down on the spring scale until the weight is 20 cm from the table top. Use a meterstick to measure the correct height. Read and record the effort force shown on the spring scale.

E. Run the pulley cord under a pulley. Tie one end of the cord to the clamp on the ring stand. Attach the other end of the cord to a spring scale as shown in Figure 2.

F. Hang the 1-kg mass on the hook of the pulley, and support the pulley on the cord.

G. Pull up on the spring scale until the mass is 20 cm above the table. Read and record the effort force shown on the spring scale.

H. Set up three pulleys and the mass as shown in Figure 3. Attach a spring scale to the open end of the pulley cord.

I. Pull on the spring scale until the mass is 20 cm above the table. Read and record the effort force needed for this pulley system.

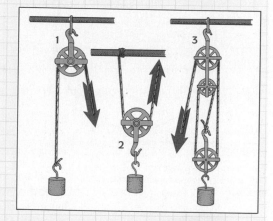

RESULTS AND CONCLUSIONS
1. Find the mechanical advantage of the single fixed pulley, the single movable pulley, and the combined pulleys by comparing resistance and effort forces.
2. How many supporting strands of cord are there for the single fixed pulley, the single movable pulley, and the combined pulleys?
3. How do the numbers of supporting strands of cord compare with the computed mechanical advantages?
4. How does the distance you had to pull the cord change in each system?

Fixed and movable pulleys may be used in combinations, as shown in Figure 13-14A. How many pulleys shown in the diagram are fixed? How many are movable? What is the mechanical advantage?[1]

WHEEL AND AXLE
A **wheel and axle** consists of two wheels that turn around the same pivot. The larger wheel is usually the effort wheel. The smaller wheel, or axle, is the resistance wheel. A small effort force applied to the large wheel will move a larger resistance on to the axle. The wheel and axle is like a lever. The radius of the wheel is like one arm of the lever, and the radius of the axle is like the other arm of the lever. The pivot around which they turn is like the fulcrum.

[1]Two pulleys are fixed; two are movable. The mechanical advantage is 4.

ACTIVITY   45 minutes

Demonstration Using an overhead projector, show how large a circle a wrench makes as it turns around a bolt. Ask students to compare this circle with the circle that the turning bolt makes. (The wrench makes a larger circle.)

Tie-in/Math Have students show with a drawing how the path of their hand when using a wrench is a circle. Have them point out the radius and the diameter of the circle they have drawn.

Thinking Skills

interpreting diagrams
Students are asked to notice in Figure 13-16 that each gear turns in the direction opposite that of the next gear. They can see from the diagram that motion and power are transferred from one part of the machine to another in this way.

③ REVIEW/REINFORCEMENT

1. A rope and a wheel.
2. The mechanical advantage of a fixed pulley is 1; that of a movable pulley is 2. In a fixed pulley the effort and the resistance move in opposite directions; in a movable pulley the effort and the resistance move in the same direction.
3. The larger wheel; the axle.
4. Gears are interlocking wheels with teeth.

Challenge A machine with many gears has more friction than does a machine with fewer gears.

Review and Skill Masters

SKILL, pages 80–81. See page 301b-c in this book for answers.

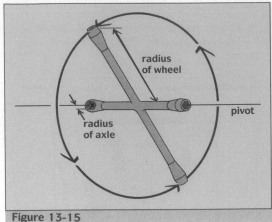

Figure 13-15

When you use a wrench to turn a nut or bolt, you are using a wheel and axle.

Figure 13-16

Gears are toothed wheels that interlock.

Have you ever tried to turn a bolt with your hand instead of with a wrench? The wrench increases the effort distance, thus allowing you to use a smaller effort force. The path of your hand on the wrench is a circle. This path is the wheel. The bolt is the axle. Notice that the radius of the axle is small. The mechanical advantage of a wheel and axle may be determined by comparing the radii.

GEARS

Look closely at Figure 13-16. The smaller wheels contain teeth that fit together with the teeth of the larger wheels. These interlocking toothed wheels are called **gears**. Notice that each gear turns in the direction opposite that of the next gear.

The transmission of a car has many gears. These gears change the speed or direction of the wheels. Most cars have neutral, reverse, and several forward gears. When the gears are in neutral, they are not touching. Since the gears are not interlocked, the wheels of the car do not turn. When the gears are in reverse, an extra gear causes the wheels to reverse their motion.

REVIEW

1. What are the parts of a pulley?
2. How do fixed and movable pulleys differ?
3. Which part of a wheel and axle is like the effort arm of a lever? Which part is like the resistance arm?
4. What are gears?

CHALLENGE Why would a machine with many gears have a low efficiency?

13-6 COMPOUND MACHINES

Many devices contain more than one simple machine. A machine that is a combination of two or more simple machines is called a **compound machine**.

A hand lawn mower contains several machines. The handle is a lever. The blade is a wedge. There are also wheels connected to an axle, and many screws and bolts. The mechanical advantage of a lawn mower would be difficult to find. You would have to know the mechanical advantage of each simple machine in it. The mechanical advantage of the lawn mower could then be found by multiplying all of the mechanical advantages together. The mechanical advantage of any compound machine is the product of the mechanical advantages of all its simple machines.

A bicycle is a compound machine. The wheels are wheel and axle machines. The pedals make up another wheel and axle system. Each pedal moves in a circle, like a wheel. The rod around which the pedals turn is an axle. A bicycle also contains several levers. Where are the levers in a bicycle?[1]

The gears in a bicycle make it possible for you to adjust the mechanical advantage of the bicycle. The pedals turn a gear that is connected by a chain to the gears on the rear wheel. Each of the gears on the rear wheel is a different size.

> *After completing this section, you will be able to*
> - **recognize** compound machines.
> - **name** the simple machines that make up a bicycle.
>
> *The key term in this section is* **compound machine**

[1]Gearshift levers; brake levers.

SCIENCE & TECHNOLOGY

Robots do many jobs that used to be done by humans. So it would seem that robots should be built to work like people.

Surprisingly, very few such robots are now used in assembly lines. Robots designed like humans have some of the same problems that the human body has. Humans are not very strong, and they are not good at doing tasks that must be repeated over and over. Yet assembly-line work requires strength and repeated actions.

New robots are simpler. They cannot do as many different jobs as humanlike robots. However, the new robots are able to work quickly and precisely.

The new robots are good at tasks like spot welding. Like humans, the early robots were not good at this task because the welding tool is heavy and awkward. The new robots can do precise welding very quickly.

In the future, robots will probably become specialized. Factories will use a team of robots, each doing one job.

13-6 COMPOUND MACHINES
pages 323–324

> **OBJECTIVES**
> Refer to pupil page 323.
>
> **VOCABULARY**
> Key term: compound machine

1 MOTIVATION

Have a student bring in a ten-speed bicycle. Ask students to count the gears at the pedal assembly and the rear wheel to determine why it is called a ten-speed bike. Ask students how the mechanical advantage of the bicycle could be changed. Ask them why the bicycle is a compound machine. Have students point out the simple machines that make up the bicycle.

2 CONCEPT DEVELOPMENT

Background   A compound machine makes work much easier than does a simple machine because it multiplies the mechanical advantages of each of the component simple machines. Many times a simple machine requires too much effort force for one person.

Teaching Tip   Ask students to name compound machines other than those mentioned in the text. Have students identify the simple machines in each compound machine.

Enrichment   Have interested students go to an automobile repair shop and ask to see a transmission with gears exposed or let students do research on the subject. Have them make a diagram of the gears. Allow students to report to the class on the drive, neutral, and reverse gears, explaining how they operate.

interpreting diagrams
Students look at Figure 13-17 and are asked to locate levers in a bicycle. Ask students how it is possible to determine the total mechanical advantage of the bicycle.

³ REVIEW/REINFORCEMENT

1. Answers will vary but may include a lawn mower, a pencil sharpener, and a can opener.
2. Levers, wheels and axles, screws, and gears.

Challenge   The mechanical advantage is 30.

A bicycle is a machine designed to multiply speed, not effort force. Because each rear gear is smaller than the front gear, the bicycle wheel turns more times than the pedals. The ratio of the number of teeth on the front gear to the number of teeth on the rear gear determines how many times the wheel turns for one turn of the pedals.

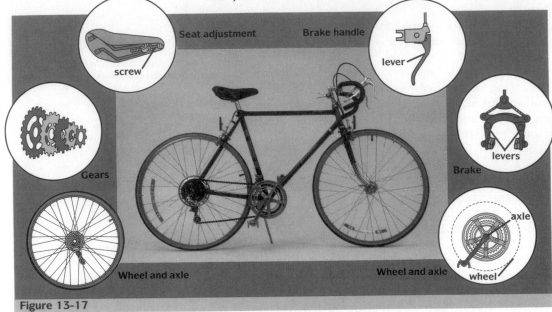

Figure 13-17

A bicycle contains many machines.

A ten-speed bicycle has two gears in front and five in the back. Thus, ten combinations of gears are possible. In the lowest gear the ratio of gear teeth is the lowest. In this gear it is easy to pedal the bicycle because a small effort force is needed. However, the bicycle moves slowly. One turn of the pedals causes only about 1.4 turns of the wheel.

In the highest gear the ratio of gear teeth is the highest. One turn of the pedals causes more than 3.5 turns of the wheel. The bicycle moves quickly, but a larger effort force is needed to turn the pedals.

REVIEW

1. Name three compound machines.
2. Name two simple machines present in a bicycle.

CHALLENGE The mechanical advantage of a lever is 6. The mechanical advantage of a pulley system is 5. What is the combined mechanical advantage of a compound machine made up of the lever and the pulley system?

CHAPTER SUMMARY

The main ideas in this chapter are listed below. Read these statements before you answer the Chapter Review questions.

- Work is done when an object is moved through a distance because of a force acting upon the object. (13-1)

- An effort force is the force that is applied to an object to do work. A resistance force is the force that opposes an effort force. (13-1)

- Power is the rate at which work is done. A watt is the unit of power. (13-1)

- A simple machine changes the size or the direction of a force that is being used to do work. The six classes of simple machines are the inclined plane, wedge, screw, lever, pulley, wheel and axle. (13-2)

- The mechanical advantage of a machine is the number of times an effort force is multiplied by the machine. (13-2)

- Effort distance is the distance the effort force moves. Resistance distance is the distance the resistance force moves. (13-2)

- An inclined plane is a machine that has a sloping surface that is longer than its vertical side. (13-3)

- A wedge is a modified inclined plane. It has a thin or sharp end and a thicker end. (13-3)

- A screw has spiral threads wound around a cylinder. The screw is a spiral inclined plane. (13-3)

- The efficiency of a machine is the ratio of work output to work input. Friction lowers the efficiency of machines. (13-3)

- A lever is a bar that pivots around a fixed point called a fulcrum. There are three classes of levers, based on the positions of the effort force, resistance force, and fulcrum. (13-4)

- A pulley is a machine that changes the direction of a force. A pulley is made up of a rope that turns around a wheel. (13-5)

- A fixed pulley is attached to something that does not move. A movable pulley moves with the resistance it supports. (13-5)

- A wheel and axle is a machine that has a large effort wheel and a small resistance wheel that turn around the same pivot. (13-5)

- Gears are interlocking toothed wheels. (13-5)

- Compound machines consist of two or more simple machines. The mechanical advantage of a compound machine is the product of the mechanical advantages of all of its simple machines. (13-6)

The key terms in this chapter are listed below. Use each term in a sentence that shows the meaning of the term.

compound machine	inclined plane	resistance distance
efficiency	joule	resistance force
effort arm	lever	screw
effort distance	mechanical advantage	simple machine
effort force	movable pulley	watt
fixed pulley	power	wedge
fulcrum	pulley	wheel and axle
gears	resistance arm	work

Review and Skill Masters

VOCABULARY REVIEW, page 77.
See page 301b in this book for answers.

VOCABULARY

1. g
2. h
3. e
4. i
5. b
6. o
7. a
8. l
9. p
10. f
11. j
12. d
13. m

CONCEPTS

1. An effort force is used to move an object; a resistance force opposes the motion.
2. Work is defined as using a force to move an object through a distance; W = Fd.
3. W = Fd = 40 N × 8 m = 320 N•m, or 320 J
4. A device that changes the size or direction of a force being used to do work; lever, pulley, inclined plane, wedge, screw, wheel and axle.
5. Divide the resistance force by the effort force or divide the effort distance by the resistance distance.
6. $MA = \dfrac{R}{E} = \dfrac{60\ N}{12\ N} = 5$
7. Work input is always larger than work output.

Review and Skill Masters

CHAPTER REVIEW, pages 78–79.
See page 301b in this book for answers.

Chapter Review

VOCABULARY

Write the letter of the term that best matches the definition. Not all the terms will be used.

1. A unit of work equal to one newton-meter
2. A bar that turns or pivots around a fixed point
3. Wheels with interlocking teeth
4. The number of times effort is multiplied by a machine
5. Distance from the effort to the fulcrum of a lever
6. A modified inclined plane that has a thick end and a thinner end
7. Combination of two or more simple machines
8. A force that opposes motion
9. Using a force to move an object a certain distance
10. A machine that has a long sloping surface
11. The amount of work done in a period of time
12. The fixed point around which a lever turns
13. An inclined plane wrapped around a cylinder

a. compound machine
b. effort arm
c. fixed pulley
d. fulcrum
e. gears
f. inclined plane
g. joule
h. lever
i. mechanical advantage
j. power
k. pulley
l. resistance force
m. screw
n. resistance distance
o. wedge
p. work
q. wheel and axle

CONCEPTS

1. How are an effort force and a resistance force related? (13-1)
2. What is work? How is it calculated? (13-1)
3. A person uses a force of 40 N to move a table a distance of 8 m. How much work is done? (13-1)
4. What is a simple machine? Name the classes of simple machines. (13-2)
5. Explain two methods for calculating mechanical advantage. (13-2)
6. Using a lever and a 12-N effort force, a person can move a 60-N resistance. What is the mechanical advantage of this lever? (13-2)
7. How are work input and work output different? (13-2)

8. Describe and give an example of an inclined plane. (13-3)
9. Name two examples of modified inclined planes. (13-3)
10. How is the actual mechanical advantage of an inclined plane found? (13-3)
11. What causes the efficiency of machines to be less than 100 percent? (13-3)
12. List the three parts of a lever. (13-4)
13. How do the three classes of levers differ? Give an example of each. (13-4)
14. Distinguish between a single fixed pulley and a single movable pulley. State the mechanical advantage of each. (13-5)
15. Explain why a pulley and a wheel and axle are like levers. (13-5)
16. Describe a wheel and axle. (13-5)
17. How is the mechanical advantage of a wheel and axle calculated? (13-5)
18. Describe a gear. (13-5)
19. What is a compound machine? (13-6)
20. Name two simple machines in a bicycle. Name two simple machines in a hand lawn mower. (13-6)

---

1. List the machines, simple or compound, that you use in a day.
2. Why is it easier to pull down on a rope over a pulley than to pull down on a rope thrown over a wood beam?
3. The pyramids of Egypt were built by workers who had to drag heavy stone blocks long distances. Name two machines that would have made their work easier. Explain your choices.

---

1. A perpetual motion machine has been an impossible dream for centuries. Do library research about these machines. Explain why there can never be a perpetual motion machine.
2. Find diagrams of water wheels and windmills. How do they use simple machines to turn grinding stones in a gristmill?
3. A belt-driven machine uses two wheels connected by a cord or belt. Compare belt-driven machines with gear-driven machines. What are the advantages and disadvantages of each?

Bargo, Michael. "All Gear Steering." *Popular Science*, July 1985, p. 60.
Brown, Stuart. "World's Most Advanced Bike." *Popular Science*, February 1985, p. 95.
"Up the Round Escalator." *Science News*, March 23, 1985, p. 187.

8. An inclined plane has a sloping surface that is longer than its vertical rise; stairs and ramp.
9. Wedge, screw.
10. By dividing the resistance force by the effort force.
11. Friction.
12. Effort arm, fulcrum, and resistance arm.
13. In a first-class lever, the effort force and the resistance force are on opposite sides of the fulcrum; seesaw. In a second-class lever, the resistance force is between the fulcrum and the effort force; nutcracker. In a third-class lever, the effort force is between the fulcrum and the resistance; broom.
14. A single fixed pulley does not move; its mechanical advantage is 1. A single movable pulley moves; its mechanical advantage is 2.
15. Both turn around a fixed point.
16. A wheel and axle consists of two wheels that turn around the same pivot.
17. By dividing the radius of the wheel by the radius of the axle.
18. A gear is one of a pair of interlocking toothed wheels.
19. A compound machine is one that is made up of two or more simple machines.
20. In a bicycle levers, wheels and axles, screws; in a lawn mower—screws, wheels and axles, lever.

APPLICATION/CRITICAL THINKING

1. Answers will vary but may include a knife, broom, pencil sharpener, and bicycle.
2. A pulley turns and reduces friction.
3. The pulley and the wheel and axle would have made the work easier because of the mechanical advantage they would have provided.

Test Masters

CHAPTER TEST, pages 49–52.
See page 301d in this book for answers.

MOTION

ORGANIZER

Section	pages	Activity	pages	Reinforcement and Evaluation	pages	*Review and Skill Masters	pages	Other Components in Teacher Resource Package	pages
14—1 The Nature of Motion	329–333			Review, Challenge	333	Challenge/Critical Thinking	87–88	*Study Guide*	69
14—2 Newton's First Law of Motion	334–338	What Is Newton's First Law of Motion?	337	Puzzler Review, Challenge	336 338			*Study Guide* *Lab Manual*	70 75
14—3 Newton's Second Law of Motion	339–341	What Is Newton's Second Law of Motion?	340	Review, Challenge	341			*Study Guide*	71
14—4 Newton's Third Law of Motion	342–344	What Is Newton's Third Law of Motion?	343	Review, Challenge	344	Skill	86	*Study Guide*	72
14—5 Circular Motion	345–348			Review, Challenge	348			*Study Guide*	73
CHAPTER SUMMARY	349					Vocabulary Review	83		
CHAPTER REVIEW	350–351			*Test Masters	53–56	Chapter Review	84–85		

*In the Teacher Resource Package. For answers, see pages 327b–327d in this book.

ACTIVITY MATERIALS   Quantities are based on a class of 30 students working in groups as indicated in parentheses.

What Is Newton's First Law of Motion? p. 337 (groups of 2)	quantity	What Is Newton's Second Law of Motion? p. 340 (groups of 2)	quantity	What Is Newton's Third Law of Motion? p. 343 (groups of 2)	quantity
scissors	15	inclined-plane board	15	fishing line	15 m
metric ruler	15	chalk	15	drinking straw	15
cardboard (20 cm x 5 cm long)	15 pieces	meterstick	15	balloon	15
ring stand	30	string (50 cm long)	15 pieces	masking tape	1 roll
masking tape	1 roll	small cart	15	table-tennis ball	15
small cart	15	mass holder	15		
100-g mass	15	5-g slotted mass	90		
		10-g slotted mass	90		
		stop watch	15		
		graph paper	15 sheets		

REVIEW AND SKILL MASTERS

VOCABULARY REVIEW _____ Chapter 14

Use the correct terms to complete the sentences below. Not all terms are used.

acceleration	Law of Conservation of	Newton's Second Law of
centripetal acceleration	Momentum	Motion
centripetal force	momentum	Newton's Third Law of
distance	motion	Motion
inertia	Newton's First Law of	speed
	Motion	velocity

Motion is the change in the position of an object compared with a reference point. There are many ways to describe how an object changes position in space. One way is **distance**, the length of the actual path traveled by an object. Another way is **speed**, the distance an object moves in a given amount of time. If you also know the direction in which the object moves, you can state its **velocity**

An object may change direction or speed over time. A change in velocity is an object's **acceleration**, which can be either positive or negative. If an object moves in a curved path, its change in velocity is called **centripetal acceleration**

The force that causes this change in velocity is **centripetal force**

An object's tendency to remain at rest or in motion is called **inertia**

Newton's First Law of Motion supports this by stating in part that an object at rest remains at rest until an unbalanced force acts on it. If an object is in motion, you can multiply the object's mass by its velocity. This calculation is the object's **momentum**. If an unbalanced force acts on an object, the object will accelerate in the direction of the force. This is stated by **Newton's Second Law of Motion**

Newton's Third Law of Motion states that for every action by a force, there is an equal and opposite reaction by another force.

© 1988 Silver, Burdett & Ginn Inc.

83

CHAPTER REVIEW _____ Chapter 14

14-1 The Nature of Motion

1. Speed is the **distance** an object moves in a given amount of time, whereas velocity is speed in a definite **direction**

2. A cat runs 6 meters in 4 seconds. What is its speed? **1.5 m/s**

3. Underline your answers. During constant velocity, velocity changes over time/remains the same. During acceleration, velocity changes over time/remains the same.

14-2 Newton's First Law of Motion

1. The inertia of an object depends on its **mass**

2. Newton's First Law of Motion states that **an object at rest remains at rest until an unbalanced force acts on it and an object moving at constant speed and in a straight line will continue to do so until an unbalanced force acts on it**

3. How are mass, velocity, and momentum related? **An object's mass multiplied by its velocity produces a quantity called its momentum.**

14-3 Newton's Second Law of Motion

1. Newton's Second Law of Motion states that **an unbalanced force on an object causes it to accelerate in the direction of the force**

2. Underline your answers. A greater force applied to an object will decrease/not change/increase its acceleration. A greater mass added to an object will decrease/not change/increase its acceleration.

3. An object of mass 50 kg has an acceleration of 2 m/s². What is the amount of force on this object? **F = 50 kg × 2 m/s², F = 100 kg-m/s² or 100 N**

14-4 Newton's Third Law of Motion

1. Newton's Third Law of Motion states that **for every action by a force, there is an equal and opposite reaction by another force**

© 1988 Silver, Burdett & Ginn Inc.

84

CHAPTER REVIEW (Continued) _____ Chapter 14

2. What is the action force and the reaction force of a book when it falls and hits the floor? **The action force is the force of the book hitting the floor. The reaction force is the force of the floor on the book.**

3. If you and a friend are pulling on opposite ends of a rope with equal strength, the forces at the center of the rope are **balanced**. The force of your feet upon the ground and the force of the ground upon your feet is an example of **action/reaction** forces.

14-5 Circular Motion

1. Explain the motion of a satellite using Newton's Laws of Motion. **Once a satellite is in motion, Newton's First Law explains that no force is needed to keep it moving at a constant speed. Newton's Second Law explains that the force of gravity causes the satellite to accelerate in the direction of the force (toward center of the earth) in a curved orbit.**

2. **Centripetal force** is the force that causes an object moving at constant speed to move in a curved path or circle. This force is towards the **center** of the circle.

3. Both a satellite and an object falling are in free fall. Why doesn't the satellite fall to earth? **The satellite does not fall to earth because it moves very fast in a direction parallel to the ground.**

4. Why does an astronaut seem weightless in a spacecraft? **An astronaut seems weightless in a spacecraft because both the astronaut and the spacecraft are experiencing free fall at the same time. The astronaut is falling as fast as the spacecraft is falling, and thus does not push against the spacecraft. This makes the astronaut seem weightless, even though the force of gravity is acting on the person.**

© 1988 Silver, Burdett & Ginn Inc.

85

SKILL/Classifying _____ Chapter 14

Sir Isaac Newton explained the motion of objects by three laws. Newton's three Laws of Motion hold that:

1. An object remains at rest or in motion in a straight line unless acted upon by an unbalanced force.
2. An unbalanced force on an object causes it to accelerate in the direction of the force.
3. For every action by a force, there is always an equal and opposite reaction by another force.

Write a 1, 2, or 3 in the blank before each occurrence listed below to indicate which of Newton's Laws of Motion applies best.

1 A. A book lies undisturbed on a desk.

2 B. A comet passing Jupiter is accelerated by Jupiter's great gravity.

3 C. A rocket soars skyward as its engine fires.

1 D. A baseball hits the catcher's mit when it is missed by the batter.

1 E. A car does not move until its engine is started and the car is put in gear.

3 F. A chair with wheels moves back when the secretary pushes on the desk.

2 G. A hit baseball accelerates past the pitcher who threw it.

2 H. A falling object accelerates as it falls.

2 I. An object thrown into the air eventually falls back to the ground.

3 J. An opened air-filled balloon flies around the room.

1 K. A dresser doesn't move when it is pushed.

2 L. A gust of wind blows an arrow in flight off target.

3 M. A bowling ball is deflected as it strikes the pins.

© 1988 Silver, Burdett & Ginn Inc.

86

CHAPTER **14** PLANNING GUIDE

CHAPTER 14 PLANNING GUIDE

Name_____ Date_____

CHALLENGE/CRITICAL THINKING ————— Chapter 14

Two people took a short ride in a car. As the driver started the car, the passenger recorded an initial odometer reading of 37450.9. One minute later the odometer read 37451.2. Odometer readings were taken nine more times at 1 minute intervals and recorded on the chart below.

Time (minutes)	Odometer (km)	Total Distance (km)
0	37450.9	0.0
1	37451.2	0.3
2	37451.9	1.0
3	37452.3	1.4
4	37453.1	2.2
5	37453.3	2.4
6	37454.2	3.3
7	37455.0	4.1
8	37455.9	5.0
9	37456.4	5.5
10	37457.0	6.1

1. Calculate the total distance traveled in the third column of the chart.

2. What was the average speed in kilometers per hour (km/h) during the first minute?
   18 km/h

3. What was the average speed during the first 5 minutes?
   28.8 km/h

4. What was the average speed during the second 5 minutes?
   44.4 km/h

5. What was the average speed for the full 10 minutes?
   36.6 km/h

6. Using the figures in the chart above, plot the motion of the car on the distance-time graph on the next page.

© 1988 Silver, Burdett & Ginn Inc.

87

Name_____ Date_____

CHALLENGE/CRITICAL THINKING (Continued) ————— Chapter 14

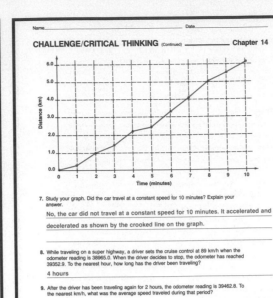

7. Study your graph. Did the car travel at a constant speed for 10 minutes? Explain your answer.
   No, the car did not travel at a constant speed for 10 minutes. It accelerated and decelerated as shown by the crooked line on the graph.

8. While traveling on a super highway, a driver sets the cruise control at 89 km/h when the odometer reading is 38965.0. When the driver decides to stop, the odometer has reached 39352.9. To the nearest hour, how long has the driver been traveling?
   4 hours

9. After the driver has been traveling again for 2 hours, the odometer reading is 39462.8. To the nearest km/h, what was the average speed traveled during that period?
   55 km/h

© 1988 Silver, Burdett & Ginn Inc.

88

TEST MASTERS

Sheet 1 (page 53)

Name _____ Date _____ Score _____

Chapter 14

Motion

PART 1

In the space below, write the term that each phrase defines.

Chapter Goal

1. **acceleration** — The change in the velocity of a moving object over time — 1
2. **inertia** — The tendency of an object to remain at rest or in motion — 2
3. **centripetal force** — The force that causes an object moving at constant speed in a curved path or circle — 5
4. **speed** — The distance an object moves in a given amount of time — 1
5. **Newton's Second Law of Motion** — The law that states that an unbalanced force on an object causes it to accelerate in the direction of the force — 3
6. **Newton's First Law of Motion** — The law that states that an object at rest remains at rest until an unbalanced force acts upon it, and that an object moving at constant speed and in a straight line will continue to do so until an unbalanced force acts on it — 2
7. **centripetal acceleration** — The acceleration of an object moving in a curved path at constant speed — 5
8. **Newton's Third Law of Motion** — The law that states that for every action by a force there is an equal and opposite reaction by another force — 4

PART 2

Choose the term or phrase that best answers the question or completes the statement. Write the letter of that choice in the space at the left.

a 1. A car at rest has more inertia than a bicycle at rest mainly because the car has greater: — 2
a. mass. b. velocity. c. deceleration. d. reaction force.

d 2. A student rolls a bowling ball with a mass of 5 kg and gives the ball an acceleration of 9 m/s². How much force did the student use to roll the ball? ($F = ma$) — 3
a. 5 N b. 9 N c. 14 N d. 45 N

e 3. A car moves 150 m in 5 s. What is the speed of the car? ($v = \frac{d}{t}$) — 1
a. 3 m/s b. 5 m/s c. 30 m/s d. 150 m/s

Chapter 14 Motion 53

Sheet 2 (page 54)

Name _____ Date _____ Score _____

PART 2

Choose the term or phrase that best answers the question or completes the statement. Write the letter of that choice in the space at the left.

Chapter Goal

b 4. A truck driver traveling at 80 km/h stops a fully loaded truck in 15 seconds. When the same truck is empty, the driver can stop in 10 seconds when traveling at 80 km/h. The full truck takes longer to stop in part because it has greater: — 2
a. acceleration. b. momentum. c. speed. d. velocity.

a 5. If a moving car changes direction, which of the following also changes? — 1
a. velocity b. mass c. speed d. momentum

a 6. A tractor pulls an empty wagon across a field. The wagon is then loaded, and the tractor pulls it back. The tractor accelerates more slowly when it pulls the loaded wagon than when it was pulling the empty wagon. This most likely occurs because the loaded wagon has more: — 3
a. mass. c. centripetal force.
b. momentum. d. centripetal acceleration.

d 7. According to Newton's Third Law of Motion, a force always: — 4
a. cancels another force. c. causes movement.
b. produces friction. d. has an opposite reaction force.

c 8. The acceleration of an object would most likely increase if there was an increase in the: — 3
a. inertia of the object. c. force on the object.
b. mass of the object. d. friction on the object.

d 9. Which of the following is being acted on by a balanced pair of forces? — 4
a. a rock thrown from a cliff c. a ball bouncing from the ground
b. a pencil rolling on a desk d. a rope pulled between two poles

b 10. A spacecraft is orbiting the earth. Newton's First Law of Motion explains that the spacecraft moves: — 5
a. in a curved path around the earth.
b. at a constant speed around the earth.
c. in free fall toward the earth.
d. toward the center of the earth.

b 11. A car is stopped at a stop light. Which of the following is an action force in this situation? — 4
a. the ground pushing upward on the car
b. the car pushing downward on the ground
c. friction between the car and the ground
d. the inertia of the car and the ground

a 12. Which of the following best explains why a person seems weightless in a spacecraft in orbit around the earth? — 5
a. Both the person and the spacecraft are affected equally by gravity.
b. Neither the person nor the spacecraft is affected by gravity.
c. Both the person and the spacecraft are slowed equally by friction.
d. Neither the person nor the spacecraft is slowed by friction.

Chapter 14 Motion 54

Sheet 3 (page 55)

Name _____ Date _____ Score _____

PART 3

Look at the graph. Then read the questions that follow. Choose the term or phrase that best answers the question or completes the statement. Write the letter of that choice in the space at the left.

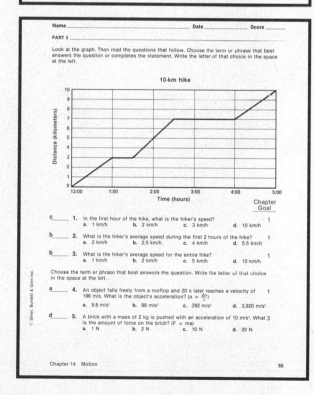

10-km hike

Chapter Goal

c 1. In the first hour of the hike, what is the hiker's speed? — 1
a. 1 km/h b. 2 km/h c. 3 km/h d. 10 km/h

b 2. What is the hiker's average speed during the first 2 hours of the hike? — 1
a. 2 km/h b. 2.5 km/h c. 4 km/h d. 5.5 km/h

b 3. What is the hiker's average speed for the entire hike? — 1
a. 1 km/h b. 2 km/h c. 5 km/h d. 10 km/h

Choose the term or phrase that best answers the question. Write the letter of that choice in the space at the left.

a 4. An object falls freely from a rooftop and 20 s later reaches a velocity of 196 m/s. What is the object's acceleration? ($a = \frac{\Delta v}{t}$) — 1
a. 9.8 m/s² b. 98 m/s² c. 392 m/s² d. 3,920 m/s²

d 5. A brick with a mass of 2 kg is pushed with an acceleration of 10 m/s². What is the amount of force on the brick? ($F = ma$) — 3
a. 1 N b. 2 N c. 10 N d. 20 N

Chapter 14 Motion 55

Sheet 4 (page 56)

Name _____ Date _____ Score _____

PART 4

Read each question or direction and answer it using complete sentences.

Chapter Goal

1. How are the mass, force, and acceleration of an object related according to Newton's Second Law of Motion? — 3

An unbalanced force applied to an object causes it to accelerate in the direction of the force. For a given object, the greater the force applied to it, the greater the acceleration. The greater the mass of an object, the smaller is its acceleration when a given force is applied to it.

2. Define inertia and momentum, and describe the factors that determine them. — 2

Inertia is the tendency of an object to stay at rest or to stay in motion. Momentum is an indication of the strength of an object's motion.

An object's inertia and momentum both depend on its mass. The greater an object's mass, the greater the force that is needed to cause it to begin moving if it is at rest, or to stop moving if it is in motion. The greater an object's mass, the greater is its strength of motion. Momentum depends on an object's velocity as well as its own mass. The greater an object's velocity, the greater its momentum.

3. How does Newton's Third Law of Motion explain the motion of a rocket? — 4

Newton's Third Law of Motion states that, for every action by a force, there is an equal and opposite reaction by another force. Forces always act in pairs. One force, the action force, is the opposite of the other force, the reaction force. The hot gases that shoot out from a rocket make up the action force. They produce a reaction force that causes the rocket to move in the opposite direction.

Chapter 14 Motion 56

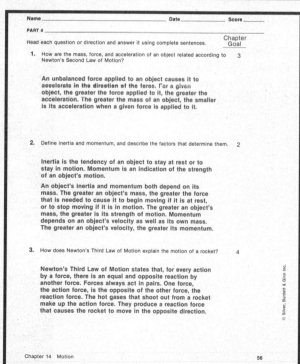

CHAPTER 14 PLANNING GUIDE

CHAPTER

14

MOTION

The questions in the CHAPTER TEST are based on these Chapter Goals.

1. Distinguish between speed and velocity and between constant velocity and acceleration; calculate the speed of a moving object.
2. Identify factors that determine inertia, identify Newton's First Law of Motion, and explain the relationship between mass, velocity, and momentum.
3. Identify Newton's Second Law of Motion, and explain the relationship between mass, force, and acceleration; calculate the force needed to produce a given acceleration on a given mass.
4. Identify Newton's Third Law of Motion, and distinguish between balanced forces and action and reaction forces.
5. Discuss how centripetal force, centripetal acceleration, and Newton's laws of motion can be used to explain the motion of a satellite or falling object; explain how a person can seem weightless in a spacecraft.

MOTION

Have you ever been on a ride at an amusement park? If so, you probably know what it is like to be pushed and pulled by forces. As you can see in the photograph, the people seem to stick to the wall when the carousel spins. They will remain stuck to the wall until the carousel slows down or stops. All objects on the earth are affected by forces.

- What holds the people against the wall?
- How are force and motion related?
- How does an object behave if no forces act on it?

14-1 THE NATURE OF MOTION

Cars and buses carry people from place to place. Baseballs and footballs are thrown and caught. What do these objects have in common? In each case the object is moving, or changing its position in space. You know that an object is in motion if you see a change in its position compared with the position of an object that is not moving. The object that is not moving is called a reference point. **Motion** is the change in the position of an object as compared with a reference point.

All motion is not the same. Think about the motion of a car or baseball. A car may travel in a straight line for a time or stop at a traffic light. It may make a turn or move up and down hills, all in the same trip. A baseball's motion is less varied. It may move up, down, in a straight line, or in a curved path. But it cannot stop and start again within the same trip.

There are many ways to describe and compare the motion of objects. One simple way is to measure how far each object travels. For example, you might say that a car has traveled 50 km from a starting point. You might say that a baseball was hit and then traveled 100 m from home plate. You might say that you travel 1.5 km from home to school. In each case the description of motion includes a distance. **Distance** is the length of the actual path traveled by an object.

After completing this section, you will be able to

- **distinguish** between speed and velocity.
- **calculate** the speed of a moving object.
- **distinguish** between constant velocity and acceleration.

The key terms in this section are
acceleration   speed
distance   velocity
motion

2 CONCEPT DEVELOPMENT

Background   In physics the study of classical mechanics is divided into two parts: dynamics and kinematics. Dynamics is the physical study of motion and force. Kinematics is the mathematical study of motion. Relationships like the following came from mathematics.

distance = speed × time

The laws of motion were developed by Isaac Newton and first published in his *Principia* in 1687. Newton's laws, described 300 years ago, are excellent examples of simple and reliable explanations of phenomena that take place at speeds lower than the speed of light. These laws have wide application. Even the scientists and engineers at NASA make use of Newton's laws when they launch space vehicles.

Figure 14-1

This runner is moving at a constant speed.

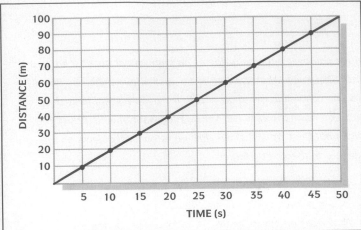

You could also measure the time it takes an object to travel a certain distance. **Speed** is the distance an object moves in a given amount of time. To calculate the speed of an object, use the following formula.

$$v = \frac{d}{t}$$

In this formula, v stands for speed, d stands for distance, and t stands for time.

Sample Problem

A runner travels 10 m in 5 s. What is the runner's speed?

1. Write the formula.

$$v = \frac{d}{t}$$

2. Substitute the amounts given in the problem for the symbols in the formula.

$$v = \frac{10 \text{ m}}{5 \text{ s}}$$

3. Determine the unit that will be part of the answer. The unit to express speed is meters per second (m/s).

$$v = \frac{10}{5} \text{ m/s}$$

4. Complete the calculations.

$$v = 2 \text{ m/s}$$

The speed of the runner is 2 m/s.

Motion can be plotted on a graph. Figure 14-1 shows a graph of the motion of the runner described in the sample problem. The straight line shows that the runner's speed is constant. How far could the runner travel in 40 s?[1]

Notice that speed is a ratio between two measurements—distance and time. If you state direction as well as speed, you are describing an object's velocity. **Velocity** (vuh LAHS uh tee) is speed in a definite direction. "Eighty kilometers per hour" is a statement of speed. "Eighty kilometers per hour north" is a statement of velocity.

The difference between speed and velocity can be shown by this example. Two cars traveling at 70 m/s, one north and the other south, are said to have the same speed, 70 m/s. However, their velocities would be different because they are traveling in different directions.

Few objects travel at a constant velocity or speed. Figure 14-2 shows the changes in speed as a family takes a car trip. If it starts out on city streets, the car stops and starts at traffic lights and moves slowly through crowded areas. On the highway the car travels at a greater speed but may slow down when traffic is heavy. The family may stop for lunch or for fuel.

Suppose that by the end of the trip, the family has covered 400 km in a total time of 5 hours. When the total distance is divided by the total time taken to travel this distance, the average speed is calculated. For this trip, the car's average speed is 400 km/5 h, or 80 km/h.

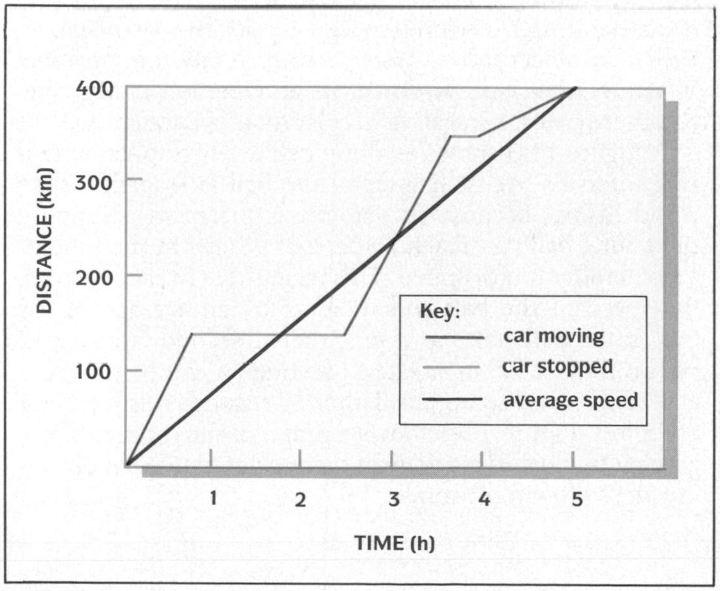

[1]80 m.

velocitas (swift)

Teaching Tip Explain to students that average speed is the distance traveled divided by the time taken to travel the distance. Someone traveling at a constant speed covers equal distances in equal periods of time, so a speedometer would have a constant reading.

Teaching Tip Tell students that, in physics, distance can be thought of as having a direction. The distance is called displacement.

Figure 14-2
How does a stop like this affect the average speed of a car?[2]

Review and Skill Masters

CHALLENGE/CRITICAL THINKING, pages 87–88. See page 327c in this book for answers.

[2]Making a stop during a trip decreases the average speed.

Demonstration   Drop a pencil to the floor from a height of 1 m. Ask students to state the pencil's initial velocity (0 m/s). The time needed for a pencil to fall through a distance of 1 m on the earth is about 0.1 seconds. Use that time value to compute the speed of the falling pencil (10 m/s). Next suppose that this speed is the final speed of the pencil before it hits the floor. Compute for students the acceleration of the pencil (10 m/s²).

Background   Aristotle taught that objects have a property called earthiness that causes them to fall toward the center of the earth. He said heavier objects fall faster than do lighter objects. Legend has it that Galileo called the latter statement into question and tested it by dropping objects from the Leaning Tower of Pisa. It is not known if Galileo really dropped objects from that tower. However, he is certainly given credit for calling into question Aristotle's ideas about falling bodies, stating that two objects would fall with the same speed from great heights. Galileo's statement is true if air resistance is not a factor, as has been shown in a vacuum and on the moon.

Teaching Tip   Mention to students that a gas pedal is called an accelerator. Then ask what part of a car could be called a decelerator. (The brake.)

Thinking Skills

interpreting graphs and diagrams
Students use the graph and the strobe photograph in Figure 14-3 to visualize the acceleration of a falling ball. They can see that the distance traveled by the ball increases during equal time intervals.

accelerare (quicken)

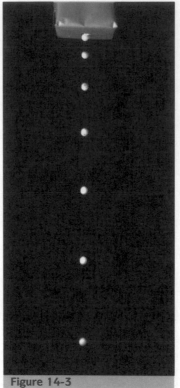

Figure 14-3

Objects accelerate as they fall; they do not fall at a constant speed.

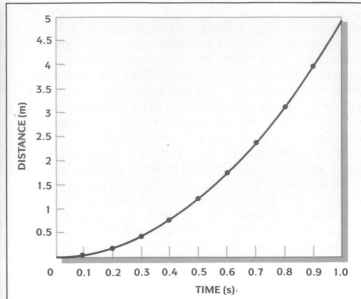

Think of a ball dropped from the top of a ten-story building. The ball travels in one direction—down. As it falls, it travels faster and faster. That is, velocity of the ball increases. The change in velocity over time is called **acceleration** (ak sehl uh RAY shuhn).

A ball thrown straight up into the air slows down as it moves upward. Because its velocity is changing, it also is accelerating. Acceleration can be positive or negative. When an object moves faster, its acceleration is positive. When an object slows down, its acceleration is negative. Another term for negative acceleration is *deceleration*.

Figure 14-3 shows a falling ball photographed at regular intervals. At each interval the ball falls farther than it did before, because its velocity is increasing. Suppose the falling ball can reach a speed of 98 m/s in the first 10 seconds after it is dropped. This means that in each second, the speed of the ball will increase by an average of 9.8 m/s. If the ball starts at 0 m/s, then 1 second later it will be traveling at 9.8 m/s. After 2 seconds it will be traveling at 19.6 m/s, and so on, until after 10 seconds it is traveling at 98 m/s. Figure 14-3 shows a graph of the motion of the accelerating ball. To calculate the acceleration of an object, use the following formula.

$$a = \frac{\Delta v}{t}$$

In the formula, a stands for acceleration. The symbol Δ, read "delta," means *the change in*. The Δv, read "delta vee," stands for the change in the object's speed. The change in an object's speed is equal to its final speed minus its initial speed. The t stands for the amount of time that it takes for the speed of the object to change.

Sample Problem

A sky diver falls freely for 5 seconds before opening the parachute. Just before the parachute opens, the speed is 49 m/s. Find the acceleration.

1. Write the formula

$$a = \frac{\Delta v}{t}$$

2. Substitute the numbers from the problem for the symbols in the formula. The initial speed is 0 m/s because the sky diver was not falling at the beginning of the 5-second period. The final speed is 49 m/s. This is the speed after 5 seconds.

$$a = \frac{(49 \text{ m/s} - 0 \text{ m/s})}{5 \text{ s}}$$

3. Determine the unit that will be part of the answer. The unit is equal to meters/second divided by second, or meters per second squared, m/s^2.

$$a = \frac{49 - 0}{5} \text{ m/s}^2$$

4. Complete the calculations.

$$a = 9.8 \text{ m/s}^2$$

The acceleration of the sky diver is 9.8 m/s^2. Recall from Chapter 12 that this is the value of g, acceleration caused by the force of gravity.

REVIEW

1. What is the difference between speed and velocity?
2. A train travels 85 km in 1.5 hours. What is the speed of the train?
3. What is the difference between constant velocity and acceleration?

CHALLENGE Assume that the moon travels at constant speed in a circular orbit around the earth. Is the moon's velocity also constant? Explain your answer.

Figure 14-4

A sky diver accelerates until the parachute opens.

Background Sky divers provide an example of air resistance in action. They assume a spread-eagle position, which increases the air resistance. This helps them prolong the time of the fall and guide the direction of the fall.

Background Air resistance retards the motion of falling objects. The magnitude of air resistance depends on the shape, size, and speed of the object. Heavy objects of similar size and shape that are dropped short distances accelerate and strike the ground at the same time. However, if objects of different mass are dropped from an airplane or other great height, air resistance may be greatly increased. The weight of the lighter object would be the first to be balanced by the force of the air resistance. Then the lighter object would no longer accelerate. It would begin to fall at a constant speed and would then have reached its terminal velocity. The heavier object would reach its terminal velocity at a later time, causing it to reach the ground first.

3 REVIEW/REINFORCEMENT

1. Speed is a measurement of the distance an object moves in a given unit of time; velocity is speed in a definite direction.
2. v = d/t = 85 km/1.5 h = 56.67 km/h.
3. Constant velocity implies a constant speed along a straight line, a constant direction; acceleration is a change in velocity over time and may involve a change in speed or a change in direction or both.

Challenge No, because the direction of motion is changing constantly.

14-2 NEWTON'S FIRST LAW OF MOTION

pages 334–338

1 MOTIVATION

Show a film that demonstrates the use of airbags to decrease injuries in car accidents. Tell students that the theory behind airbag protection is based on the information they will gain from this section. Ask students how airbags help to protect the driver and the passenger. Ask students if seat belts perform the same function.

2 CONCEPT DEVELOPMENT

Teaching Tip   Ask students to name some objects in the room that are at rest. Have the class discuss the forces acting on these objects. Point out that in each case the forces acting on the objects at rest are balanced.

14-2 NEWTON'S FIRST LAW OF MOTION

After completing this section, you will be able to

- **identify** the factors that determine inertia.
- **state** the First Law of Motion.
- **explain** the relationship between mass, velocity, and momentum.

The key terms in this section are
Newton's First Law of Motion
inertia
Law of Conservation of Momentum
momentum

Have you ever ridden in a car, bus, or train when it suddenly slowed down? Did you notice how you were thrown forward? And did you notice what happened when the vehicle made a sharp turn? Did you feel yourself being pushed to the side? What causes you to be pushed forward or to the side in a moving vehicle?

About 350 years ago, Sir Isaac Newton studied the way objects move. He explained that the motion of objects follows three laws. **Newton's First Law of Motion** states that an object at rest remains at rest until an unbalanced force acts on it. In addition, this law states that an object moving at constant speed and in a straight line will continue to do so until an unbalanced force acts on it.

Recall that balanced forces on an object are forces that are equal and opposite. For example, the forces on a ball that you hold are balanced forces. The force you apply to keep the ball from falling is equal and opposite to the force of gravity on the ball. However, if you release the ball, the force of gravity is no longer balanced by the force you apply. The force of gravity becomes an unbalanced force that pulls the ball to the floor. An unbalanced force is a force that is not opposed equally by another force on the same object.

force from student

force of gravity

force of gravity

Figure 14-5

Balanced forces on an object (*left*). Unbalanced forces on an object (*right*).

Newton's First Law of Motion can be illustrated by the following example. Suppose you want to move a book at rest on a desk. According to Newton's First Law of Motion, the book will remain at rest until an unbalanced force is applied to it. You can provide this force by pushing the book.

Friction from air is the main force that slows the speed of athletes in sports such as skiing, cycling, speed skating, and running. Air slows athletes by pushing against them as they move. This effect is called aerodynamic drag.

Recent developments in athletic clothing have reduced aerodynamic drag. For speed sports, clothing should be as smooth as possible, reducing the friction between the clothes and the air.

Studies on cyclists have shown that with helmets and clothes that reduce friction, drag can be decreased by as much as 10 percent. In a race, this could mean the difference between winning and losing.

Similar results were found in studies on runners. In tests, smooth, tight clothing was shown to reduce the amount of drag by 2 to 6 percent. In some races a change of just 2 percent can change the length of a runner's lead.

Newton's First Law of Motion also explains that once the book is moving, it should continue to move at constant speed and in the same direction until an unbalanced force acts on it. However, the book does not continue to move at constant speed. To keep the book moving, you must continue to apply a force.

The force needed to keep objects in motion is necessary only because of friction. Recall that friction is a force that tends to slow down a moving object. Also recall that friction can be caused by the rough surfaces between two objects. If the surfaces of objects were made smoother, there would be less friction between them. Less force would be needed to slide one object over another. If friction could be removed completely, how much force would be needed to keep objects moving once they were in motion?[1]

[1]None.

Figure 14-6

This skater moves freely because there is little friction between the ice and the skates.

Demonstration   If you have a hammer with a loose head, bring it to class to demonstrate how inertia can be used to tighten the hammer head. Strike the end of the hammer handle on the floor. The handle and the head will be in motion. When the end of the handle strikes the floor, the handle stops suddenly, but the hammer head continues in motion until stopped by the widened part of the handle. This tightens the hammer head. Have students explain what happened.

Background   Newton's First Law of Motion was revolutionary at the time it was formulated. The idea that an object in motion would continue in motion in a straight line contradicted what had been accepted by scientists from the time of Aristotle until the seventeenth century. Before Newton, most scientists would have stated that an object left to itself would move in a circular path, because the circle was considered to be the most perfect geometric figure. Newton's first law even held up when confronted with the obvious circular motion of the planets: The unbalanced force that keeps the planets from flying off into space in a straight line is the gravitational force of the sun.

Puzzler   When the passenger jumps up while the train is moving forward, the passenger will move forward and eventually stop. A person watching the train go by will see the passenger moving in a curved path. This happens because there is no horizontal force, only the pull of the earth's gravity.

Thinking Skills

hypothesizing
Students are asked to hypothesize about the effects of the First Law of Motion. Ask what would happen to an ice skater being pulled around in a circle on a frozen lake if he or she were to let go. Students should also hypothesize about what would occur if the skater came to the shore. Ask what would happen to the skater if friction played no role in the movement.

Teaching Tip   Remind students of the difference between mass and weight.

SCIENCE PUZZLER

The train in the photograph can travel at speeds up to 255 km/h. Suppose a passenger on the train jumps up while the train is moving forward. What would happen to the passenger? What would the passenger's motion look like to a person watching the train go by?

[1]The large car.
[2]Seat belts provide an unbalanced force that will stop the person's motion.

The tendency of an object to remain at rest or in motion is called **inertia** (ihn ER shuh). The inertia of an object depends on its mass. The greater the mass of an object, the greater the force needed to cause a change in its motion. For example, have you ever noticed that it is easier to push lightweight objects than heavyweight objects? Suppose you tried pushing a large car and then a smaller car across the street. You would notice that more force was needed to start the large car moving. Because the large car has more mass than the smaller car has, it also has more inertia. Thus more force is needed to start it moving. Suppose both cars were moving at the same speed. Which car would need more force to stop it?[1]

The First Law of Motion can be used to explain why you tend to keep moving forward in a moving vehicle when its brakes are applied. Suppose you are riding in a car. The car is moving at a constant speed in one direction. When you ride in a car moving at constant speed and in one direction, you move at the same speed and in the same direction as the car. When the brakes are applied suddenly, the car stops. But according to Newton's First Law of Motion, you tend to keep moving forward at the same speed as before. If the brakes are applied gently, the friction between you and the car seat will slow you down with the car. Look at Figure 14-7. How does a fastened seat belt protect the occupants of a car in a crash from the effects of Newton's first law?[2]

Figure 14-7

This crash test shows the importance of wearing a seatbelt.

ACTIVITY   What Is Newton's First Law of Motion?

OBJECTIVE
Observe how objects resist changes in motion.

MATERIALS
scissors, metric ruler, cardboard, 2 ring stands, small cart, 100-g mass, masking tape

PROCEDURE

A. Cut a piece of cardboard about 20 cm long and 5 cm wide. Tape the cardboard to two ring stands, as shown in the figure. Adjust the position of the cardboard so that the top of a small cart is at least 1 cm higher than the top edge of the cardboard.

B. Place the ring stands and cardboard on the floor.

C. Place a 100-g mass on the small cart. Place the cart on the floor about 1 m from the ring stands. *Gently* push the cart toward the cardboard so that the cart strikes it. Note the speed at which the cart moves. Observe what happens to the mass.

D. Repeat procedure C. This time, however, push the cart slightly harder, so that the speed of the cart is slightly greater. Observe what happens to the 100-g mass.

E. Using masking tape, attach the mass securely to the cart. Again push the cart toward the cardboard, so that it has the same speed as it did in procedure D. Observe what happens to the 100-g mass.

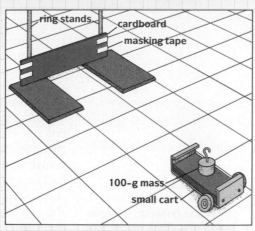

ring stands   cardboard
masking tape
100-g mass
small cart

RESULTS AND CONCLUSIONS

1. Describe what happened to the 100-g mass when the cart hit the cardboard in procedure C.

2. Describe what happened to the 100-g mass in procedure D when the speed of the cart was increased.

3. Compare the results of procedure C and D.

4. What happened to the momentum of the cart and mass when the cart hit the cardboard?

5. How do the results of procedure E explain why wearing seat belts can prevent injuries in a car crash?

Newton's First Law of Motion also can be used to explain why you seem to be forced against the side of a moving vehicle on sharp turns. According to this first law, you tend to keep moving in a straight line, even when the vehicle changes direction. Again, friction between you and the seat keeps you from hitting the side of the car.

It takes more force to stop a heavy object than to stop a light one. The force needed to stop a moving object depends on both its mass and its velocity. An object's mass multiplied by its velocity produces a quantity called its **momentum** (moh MEHN tuhm).

Momentum is an indication of the strength of an object's motion. For example, it usually takes more force to stop the motion of a car than that of a bicycle. A moving car has more momentum than a bicycle moving at the same speed because the car has more mass. The car or

momentum (moving power)

337

337

Background   When two or more objects collide or interact, the forces are arranged in pairs in such a way that when the momentum of one increases, the momentum of another decreases. Thus, in a system of objects, momentum is conserved.

3 REVIEW/REINFORCEMENT

1. Inertia is the tendency of an object to remain at rest or to remain in motion; answers will vary but may include the inertia of rest of a stalled car and the inertia of motion in a wagon rolling down a hill.
2. The mass of an object determines how much inertia it has.
3. Newton's First Law of Motion states that an object at rest remains at rest until an unbalanced force acts on it; this law also states that an object moving at a constant speed in a straight line will continue to do so until an unbalanced force acts on the object.
4. The greater the mass of an object, the greater the momentum; as the velocity of an object increases, the momentum also increases.

Challenge   Since friction is minimal on icy roads, the driver tries to slow down on a curve by braking; the car's momentum may cause it to slip sideways away from the center of curvature, or to skid.

[1]Zero.

[2]Friction between the balls and the surface of the pool table.

[3]The cue ball gets its momentum from the cue stick.

bicycle will gain momentum as its velocity increases. What is the momentum of a car or bicycle at rest?[1]

When moving objects collide, momentum can be transferred from one object to the other. The **Law of Conservation of Momentum** states that momentum can be transferred between objects but the total momentum is never lost.

Consider what happens when a cue ball strikes a pool ball on a pool table. Notice in Figure 14-8 that the light-colored cue ball stops but the red pool ball moves. As a result of the collision, the momentum of the cue ball is transferred to the pool ball. After the collision, the pool ball moves with the same speed that the cue ball had before the collision. If one of the moving balls hits the side of the pool table, it will bounce back with the same momentum. Eventually the moving pool balls will slow down and stop moving. What force interferes with the motion of the balls?[2]

Figure 14-8

Momentum can be transferred from one object to another. Where did the cue ball get its momentum?[3]

REVIEW

1. What is inertia? Give two examples of inertia.
2. What property of an object determines how much inertia the object has?
3. What is Newton's First Law of Motion?
4. How do mass and velocity affect momentum?

CHALLENGE   Explain why cars can skid on curves when the road is icy.

14-3 NEWTON'S SECOND LAW OF MOTION

Recall that Newton's first law of motion states that an unbalanced force on an object causes the object to change its motion. The effect of an unbalanced force on an object is explained in Newton's Second Law of Motion. **Newton's Second Law of Motion** states that an unbalanced force on an object causes it to accelerate in the direction of the force. Using his Second Law of Motion, Newton showed how force is related to mass and acceleration. According to his law, the greater the force applied to a given object, the greater its acceleration. For a given force, the greater the mass of an object, the smaller its acceleration.

Newton's Second Law of Motion can be illustrated by the following example. Suppose an empty truck has to pick up a load at a warehouse. The truck is driven to the warehouse and is fully loaded. As the truck leaves the warehouse, the driver notices that it takes longer to reach the same speed as before, when the truck was empty. According to Newton's Second Law of Motion, the fully loaded truck accelerates more slowly because it now has more mass. With the same force supplied by the engine, the truck's speed changes more slowly than when it had less mass. How does the Second Law of Motion explain why larger trucks usually have more powerful engines than do smaller trucks?[1]

> *After completing this section, you will be able to*
>
> - **state** the Second Law of Motion.
> - **relate** the acceleration of an object to the force applied to the object and the mass of the object.
> - **calculate** the force needed to produce a given acceleration on a given mass.
>
> *The key term in this section is*
> Newton's Second Law of Motion

[1]Larger trucks need more power to accelerate their mass than do smaller trucks.

Figure 14-9

To accelerate as quickly as possible, a drag-racing car has a very large engine.

14-3 NEWTON'S SECOND LAW OF MOTION

pages 339–341

OBJECTIVES
Refer to pupil page 339.

VOCABULARY
Key term: Newton's Second Law of Motion

1 MOTIVATION

Use a carpenter's level to show students the direction of acceleration by observing the motion of the bubble. Apply a force toward the left on a level that is at rest horizontally. Ask students which way the bubble will move. (Left.) The liquid moves to the right, forcing the bubble to move in the opposite direction. Students should see that it is the bubble, not the liquid, that indicates the direction of acceleration. Tell students that an accelerometer can be used to measure the direction of the force. It can also be used to indicate the magnitude of the force.

2 CONCEPT DEVELOPMENT

Background   For objects to experience constant velocities, the forces on them must be balanced. Objects accelerate only when unbalanced forces act upon them.

Teaching Tip Remind students that acceleration can be positive or negative and that it shows how velocity changes over time. Acceleration and deceleration are opposites, but both are caused by a force acting on an object. Deceleration is indicated by negative numbers, acceleration by positive numbers.

Background Acceleration expresses both magnitude and direction. It is therefore considered to be a vector quantity.

ACTIVITY 40 minutes

PROCESS SKILLS
observing, measuring, recording data, comparing, predicting, graphing data, interpreting graphs

Preparation None required.

Answers to Procedure
1. The cart will accelerate uniformly.
2. The cart accelerated uniformly.
3. The results verified the prediction.

Answers to Results and Conclusions
1. The acceleration of the cart varies directly with the force applied.
2. The graph should show a straight line.
3. Extended graphs will vary, depending on data.

ACTIVITY What is Newton's Second Law of Motion?

OBJECTIVE
Determine the relationship between the force applied to an object and the motion produced by the force.

MATERIALS
inclined-plane board, chalk, meterstick, string, small cart, mass holder, six 5-g slotted masses, six 10-g slotted masses, stopwatch, graph paper

PROCEDURE
A. Draw a data table like the one shown.
B. Place an inclined-plane board on a table so that the pulley on the board extends over the edge of the table. Make two chalk marks 50 cm apart on the board.
C. Tie one end of a 75-cm piece of string to a small cart. Tie the other end of the string to a mass holder.
D. Place the cart on the inclined-plane board, and place the string over the pulley. Place three 10-g masses on the cart.

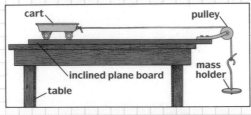

cart pulley mass holder inclined plane board table

E. Carefully add 5-g and 10-g masses to the mass holder until the cart will move along the board at a steady slow rate.
   1. Predict what will happen if you add an extra mass to the mass holder.
F. Move one 10-g mass from the cart to the mass holder.
G. Place the front wheels of the cart on the chalk mark farthest from the pulley, and release the cart. Use a stopwatch to measure the number of seconds it takes for the car to move from one chalk mark to the other. Repeat this procedure three times and record the average time in the data table.
   2. Describe what happened to the cart.
   3. How do these results compare with your prediction?
H. Repeat step **F** with a second and then a third 10-g mass moved from the cart to the mass holder.
I. The moved masses cause an accelerating force. Convert these values to newtons, and record the three accelerating forces in the data table.
J. Calculate the acceleration caused by each of the three forces, and record this information in the data table. The formula for calculating acceleration is given below. In the formula, *a* stands for acceleration, *d* stands for distance, and *t* stands for time. The distance in all trials is 0.5 m.

$$a = 2\frac{d}{t^2}$$

Added Mass (g)	Accelerating Force (N)	Time (s)	Acceleration (m/s²)
10g			
20g			
30g			

RESULTS AND CONCLUSIONS
1. What happens to the acceleration of the cart as the force applied to it increases?
2. Prepare a graph of the data. Show the accelerating force on the x-axis and the acceleration produced on the y-axis.
3. Extend the graph to predict the acceleration that would be caused by an accelerating force of 0.5 N.

Newton's Second Law can be written as a formula.

$$F = ma$$

The F stands for the force applied to an object, m stands for its mass, and a for its acceleration. The formula can be used to find any of the three quantities—force, mass, or acceleration—when two of the quantities are known.

Figure 14-10
A force applied to the bowling ball causes it to accelerate.

Sample Problem
An object with a mass of 6 kg is given an acceleration of 5 m/s^2. Calculate the amount of force on the mass.

1. Write the formula.

$$F = ma$$

2. Substitute the amounts given in the problem for the symbols in the formula.

$$F = (6 \text{ kg}) (5 \text{ m/s}^2)$$

3. Determine the unit that will be part of the answer.

$$F = (6) (5) \text{ kg·m/s}^2$$

4. Complete the calculations.

$$F = 30 \text{ kg·m/s}^2$$

Recall from Chapter 12 that 1 kg·m/s^2 is a newton (N). A newton is the force that gives a 1-kg mass an acceleration of 1 m/s^2. Thus the force in the problem is 30 N. What force would give the object an acceleration of 10 m/s^2?[1]

[1]60 N.

REVIEW

1. State Newton's Second Law of Motion.
2. How is the acceleration of an object affected by the force applied to it?
3. How much force is needed to give an object with a mass of 10 kg an acceleration of 8 m/s?

CHALLENGE   Using the formula a = F/m, explain why all objects in free fall, regardless of mass, have the same acceleration.

inferring
Students have learned that acceleration is directly proportional to the force and inversely proportional to the mass. After doing the sample problem on page 341, students are asked to use the concept of proportionality to infer what force would provide a certain acceleration. Their inference may help them solve some problems without performing calculations.

3 REVIEW/REINFORCEMENT

1. Newton's Second Law of Motion states that an unbalanced force on an object causes it to accelerate in the direction of the force.
2. The greater the unbalanced force applied to an object, the greater its acceleration.
3. F = ma = (10 kg) (8 m/s^2) = 80 kg m/s^2 = 80 N.

Challenge   The ratio of force (F) to mass (m) is the same for all objects in the same locality. Thus in free fall without air resistance, all objects have the same acceleration. The acceleration of a body depends on force and on mass. For example, a 10-kg object has twice as much mass as a 5-kg object; thus the 10-kg object has twice the inertia as the 5-kg object. However, twice the force acting to overcome twice the inertia produces the same acceleration as half the force acting to overcome half the inertia.

14-4 NEWTON'S THIRD LAW OF MOTION

pages 342–344

14-4 NEWTON'S THIRD LAW OF MOTION

OBJECTIVES
Refer to pupil page 342.

VOCABULARY
Key term: Newton's Third Law of Motion
Other terms: action force, reaction force

After completing this section, you will be able to

- **state** the Third Law of Motion.
- **identify** the action force and reaction force between two objects.
- **distinguish** between a pair of balanced forces and a pair of action and reaction forces.

The key term in this section is Newton's Third Law of Motion

1 MOTIVATION

Have several students stand facing a wall. Instruct them to stand up straight and push against the wall with the palms of their hands. Have another student describe what is happening in terms of forces. The student should deduce that pushing on the wall causes the wall to apply a reaction force (to push back). Then ask students to explain walking on a concrete surface in terms of pairs of forces. Ask why walking on ice is more difficult than walking on a sidewalk. Tell students that this section will deal with pairs of forces.

2 CONCEPT DEVELOPMENT

Thinking Skills

interpreting diagrams
Students are asked to find the unbalanced force in Figure 14-11.

Background   Newton's third law states that forces always come in pairs; the forces in a pair are equal in magnitude and opposite in direction. In the example provided in the *Motivation*, one force is that of the student pushing on the wall. The other is that of the wall pushing on the student.

The three main engines and two rocket boosters of the space shuttle provide the force to lift it off the ground. The force is needed to lift the approximately 68,000 kg-mass that makes up the shuttle.

Notice in Figure 14-11 the burning gases that escape from the engines and rocket boosters. The burning of fuel creates an unbalanced force when the gases escape from the engines and rockets. The unbalanced force is in a direction that is toward the ground. However, there must also be an unbalanced force that lifts the shuttle away from the ground. According to Newton's Second Law of Motion, an unbalanced force causes an object to accelerate in the same direction as the force. Where does the unbalanced force that lifts the shuttle come from? The cause of this second unbalanced force is explained by Newton's Third Law of Motion.

Figure 14-11
Rocket engines work on the principle of Newton's Third Law of Motion.

Newton's Third Law of Motion states that for every action by a force, there is an equal and opposite reaction by another force. If one object exerts a force on a second object, the second object always exerts on the first object an equal force in the opposite direction. For example, suppose a book is placed on a desk. Due to the pull of gravity, the book exerts a force on the desk. According to Newton's Third Law of Motion, the desk must also exert an equal and opposite force on the book.

Forces always act in pairs. One force is called the *action force* and the other is called the *reaction force*. In the case of a book resting on a desk, the action force is the force that the book exerts on the desk. The reaction force is the force that the desk exerts on the book.

You use action and reaction forces every day. For example, you use a pair of action and reaction forces when you walk. With your feet, you push against the ground. The ground then pushes forward on you. Which is the action force? Which is the reaction force?[1]

Newton's Third Law of Motion can be used to explain the motion of a rocket. The action force is the force of the hot gases escaping from the rocket. The force of the escaping gases causes a reaction force that moves the rocket in the opposite direction. Jet engines also work on the principle of Newton's Third Law of Motion. The action force is the movement of gases from the engine. The reaction force moves the jet forward.

[1]The action force is your push on the ground. The reaction force is the ground's push on you.

ACTIVITY — What is Newton's Third Law of Motion?

OBJECTIVE
Observe Newton's Third Law of Motion

MATERIALS
drinking straw, fishing line, balloon, tape, table-tennis ball, scissors, two chairs

PROCEDURE
A. Cut a drinking straw in half, and slide a fishing line through the two pieces. Tie each end of the line to the back of a chair. Pull the chairs apart so that the line is taut.
B. Slide the straws to one end of the fishing line.
C. Inflate a balloon and hold the end closed.
D. Have your partner tape the balloon to the first straw, as shown in the figure.
E. Release the balloon and note what happens.
F. Reinflate the balloon, hold it closed, and move it to the center of the fishing line.
G. Ask your partner to tape a table-tennis ball to the second straw. Move the second straw so that the ball is directly in front of the open end of the balloon.
H. Release the balloon and note what happens.

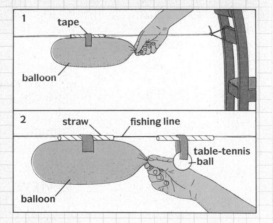

1 tape / balloon

2 straw / fishing line / table-tennis ball / balloon

RESULTS AND CONCLUSIONS
1. Compare the direction of the escaping air with the direction in which the balloon moved.
2. What effect did the air escaping from the balloon have on the table-tennis ball?
3. Identify the action force and the reaction force in this activity.

Thinking Skills

inferring
Students are asked to infer which is the action force and which is the reaction force when they walk or run. (They push back against the ground with their feet and the ground pushes forward on them.)

Teaching Tip Newton's third law can be confusing if it is not made clear that the action and reaction forces act upon different objects. Have students hit their desk tops with their hands. Have students identify the forces. Then ask if the forces were equal. (Yes.) Ask students what evidence they have to indicate that the forces were in opposite directions. (They felt the desks pushing up on their hands.)

Demonstration Attach a string to a toy car, and pull it across a tabletop or the floor. Then cut the string in half and insert a spring balance between the two cut ends to show that the car exerts a reaction force to your pull. Students can see the reaction force measured on the spring balance scale.

ACTIVITY — 25 minutes

PROCESS SKILLS
observing, comparing, identifying cause and effect

Preparation None required.

Answers to Results and Conclusions
1. The escaping air moves toward the open end of the balloon, causing the balloon to move in the opposite direction.
2. It caused the table-tennis ball to move in the direction opposite that of the motion of the balloon.
3. The escaping gas is the action force; the motion of the balloon is the reaction force.

Demonstration Stand on one roller skate and gently toss a basketball to a student. The effect of the reaction force to the toss will be seen in your backward motion. (Plan ahead and practice this so that it is done safely.)

Enrichment Have interested students research jet and rocket engines.

3 REVIEW/REINFORCEMENT

1. Newton's Third Law of Motion states that for every action by a force, there is an equal and opposite reaction by another force.
2. The action is the force of the hand pressed against the wall; the reaction is the force of the wall, which reacts automatically due to the action. The action and reaction forces are equal, in opposite directions, and on different objects.
3. The book exerts the force of its weight on the table—action; the table exerts an upward force on the book—reaction; these two forces are balanced. There is an unbalanced force—the force of gravity that pulls the book downward to the center of the earth; the book is resting on the table and cannot respond to this force.

Challenge The earth is pulled toward me, but it does not move. My mass and the mass of the earth cannot be compared. Newton's Second Law of Motion can be used to find the extent of the earth's motion in reaction to my force. The motion would be negligible.

Review and Skill Masters

SKILL, page 86. See page 327b in this book for answers.

You might expect equal and opposite forces to always cancel each other. Figure 14-12 shows two such forces on the center of the rope in a game of tug of war. If the force of pulling by each team is the same, the forces are balanced and they cancel. For one team to win, it must exert a larger force than the other team. Notice, though, that both teams are pulling on the same object—the rope. Equal and opposite forces cancel each other only when they act on the same object.

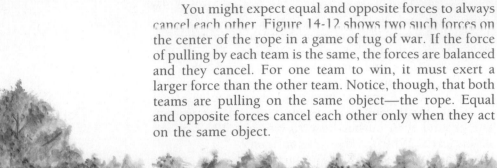

balanced forces

action-reaction forces

Figure 14-12

Many forces are involved in a tug of war.

Now look at the forces between the teams and the ground. The action force is exerted on the ground by each person's feet. The reaction force is exerted on the feet by the ground. These two forces are equal and opposite. However, they are exerted on different objects—the feet and ground. Action-reaction forces are always exerted on different objects and, therefore, do not cancel each other.

REVIEW

1. What does Newton's Third Law of Motion state?
2. What are the action and reaction forces when you press your hand against a wall?
3. Identify the balanced forces and action and reaction forces of a book resting on a table.

CHALLENGE Suppose you jump off a diving board into a swimming pool. You fall because the earth's gravity pulls you to its surface. According to Newton's third law, you pull upward on the earth with the same force that the earth pulls downward on you. Does this mean that the earth rises toward you? Explain your answer.

14-5 CIRCULAR MOTION

Did you ever wonder how hard you would have to throw or hit an object for it to leave the earth's surface permanently? In the seventeenth century, Newton explained how an object could be launched into orbit around the earth. He explained that an object could be launched into orbit if it could reach a high enough speed. For example, suppose a cannonball were fired in a horizontal direction from the top of a mountain. As you can see in Figure 14-13, if the speed of the cannonball were too slow, it would follow path 1, a curved path, and fall to the earth. At a higher speed the cannonball would follow path 2 and travel farther from the cannon. But the cannonball would still curve toward the surface of the earth and strike it.

At a still higher speed, the cannonball would follow path 3. The cannonball would be moving so fast that its path would extend past the earth, instead of hitting the earth's surface. Notice that the path of the cannonball would still curve toward the earth's surface. But because the earth is round, the surface curves the same amount as the path of the cannonball. Thus the cannonball would never reach the surface. It would travel around the earth and return to the top of the mountain.

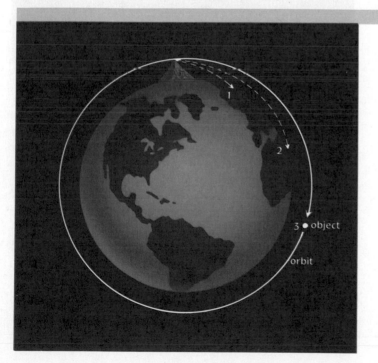

After completing this section, you will be able to

- **explain** the motion of a satellite, using Newton's laws.
- **describe** the effect of a centripetal force on a moving object.
- **explain** how a person can seem weightless in a spacecraft.

The key terms in this section are **centripetal acceleration centripetal force**

Figure 14-13
If an object moves fast enough, it can stay in orbit.

14-5 CIRCULAR MOTION
pages 345–348

OBJECTIVES
Refer to pupil page 345.

VOCABULARY
Key terms: centripetal acceleration, centripetal force
Other term: satellite

1 MOTIVATION

Tie an object to the end of a string 30 cm long, and rotate the object close to the floor. Ask students why the object moves in a circle. (The object moves in a circle because your hand exerts on the string a tension that keeps the object in motion.) Ask students to identify a reaction force. (The object that pulls on your hand by means of the string.) Rotate the object a little faster. Point out that the faster the object is rotated, the greater the amount of force that is needed.

2 CONCEPT DEVELOPMENT

Thinking Skills

comparing
Students study the diagram in Figure 14-13 and compare the paths of projectiles. Students can see that faster speeds at the optimum angle of projection cause a projectile to travel a longer curve.

Background   Rotational motion can be treated much like motion in a straight line. There is a kinematics and dynamics for rotational motion, just as for linear motion. A spherical object that is rotating about its axis, like the earth, does not require any force to maintain its rotation. However, for rotation Newton's first law does not apply to the earth orbiting the sun because in that case there is an unbalanced force, the gravitational force.

Thinking Skills

identifying cause and effect
Students use Figure 14-14 to find out how a satellite is pulled toward the center of the earth. They can also use the diagram to visualize the satellite as accelerating because it is always changing direction.

Actually, a cannonball cannot be launched into orbit with a cannon. This is because a cannon cannot accelerate the cannonball to a high enough speed. However, objects can be launched into orbit around the earth by using rockets. An object that moves in an orbit around the earth is called a *satellite* of the earth. For example, the moon is a satellite of the earth. Many artificial satellites have been placed in orbit around the earth. Some satellites provide weather information. Others are used for communication.

Figure 14-14

A satellite moves at a constant speed, but it is accelerating because it is always changing directions.

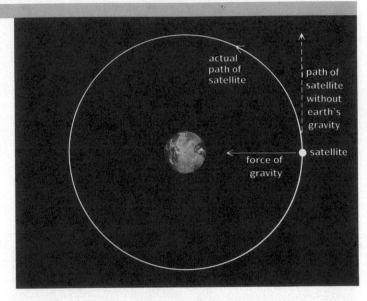

Newton's first and second laws of motion can be used to explain motion of satellites. Newton's First Law of Motion explains that once a satellite is in motion, no force is needed to keep it moving at a constant speed. Thus a satellite, such as the moon, needs no force to keep it moving at a constant speed.

Newton's Second Law of Motion describes the effect of the force of gravity on the satellite. The second law explains that the force of gravity causes the satellite to accelerate in the direction of the force. As you can see in Figure 14-14, the force of gravity is toward the center of the earth. Thus the acceleration of the satellite is also toward the center of the earth, which is also the center of the satellite's path. The acceleration of an object moving in a curved path or circle at constant speed is called a **centripetal** (sehn TRIHP uh tuhl) **acceleration**. The centripetal acceleration is toward the center of the circle in which an object is traveling.

centrum- (center)
-petere (seek)

The force that causes the centripetal acceleration is called the centripetal force. The **centripetal force** is the force that causes an object moving at constant speed to move in a curved path or circle. The centripetal force is toward the center of the circle in which an object is traveling. In the case of a satellite, gravity is the centripetal force that keeps it moving around the earth.

Suppose you tie an object to a cord and then swing it in a circle. As long as you keep applying a centripetal force on the ball, it will continue to move in a circle. If the cord breaks, you can no longer apply this force. The ball will no longer remain in the circle. It will fly off in a straight line. What would happen to the moon if the earth's gravity no longer acted on it?[1]

[1]The moon would fly off in a straight line.
[2]Gravity.

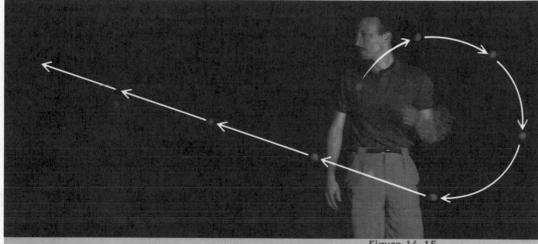

Figure 14-15

When the ball is released it flies off its circular path, and starts to move in a straight line. What force causes the ball to fall?[2]

The motion of a satellite in orbit can be compared with the motion of a falling object. When gravity is the unbalanced force acting on an object, the object is said to be in free fall. Since gravity is the only unbalanced force acting on a satellite, the satellite is also in free fall. However, a satellite moves fast enough in a direction along the ground that it does not hit the earth.

The speed needed to keep a satellite in a circular orbit around the earth depends on its distance from the earth. Satellites closer to the earth have to move faster than do those farther away. If a satellite does not have the right speed, it may escape from the earth, or fall back to the earth. In 1983 an orbiting space station called Skylab crashed into the earth when it lost speed. Skylab was slowed by friction with the earth's atmosphere.

Teaching Tip   Gravitational force does not always provide a centripetal force. Gravitational force is only centripetal when a lighter object is caused to move around a more massive object, as with the moon or an artificial satellite moving around the earth.

Teaching Tip   Students may ask about centrifugal force. They may use the term to describe the "force" felt by a passenger in a car that is traveling around a curve in the road. The "force" causes the passenger to feel pushed outward against the car door. Centrifugal force is a pseudo force. What the students may describe as centrifugal force is a result of inertia.

Enrichment   Have students find out about the invention of and uses of the centrifuge. Have groups make models to show how the centrifuge works. Display their models in class.

1. Newton's First Law of Motion describes how an object moving in a straight line will continue to move if no unbalanced forces act on it. Once a satellite is in motion, no force is needed to keep it moving at a constant speed in a straight line. Newton's Second Law of Motion explains what happens to an object moving in a straight line when an unbalanced force acts on it. The second law explains that the force of gravity causes the satellite to accelerate in the direction of the force. Curved motion occurs when an unbalanced force pulls an object toward the center of a circle, overcoming its tendency to travel in a straight line. The force of gravity is toward the center of the earth, accelerating a satellite toward the center of the earth.

2. An object moving at constant speed accelerates whenever it changes direction, as when it is moving in a curved path.

3. When gravity is the unbalanced force acting on an object, the object is said to be in free fall; because the force of gravity is the only unbalanced force acting on a satellite, the satellite is in free fall.

4. Objects in a spacecraft orbiting the earth are in free fall. With the force of gravity acting on the objects and the spacecraft, both are in free fall. As fast as the objects fall, the spacecraft falls equally fast. Therefore, the objects do not push on the floor of the spacecraft. If the objects were placed on a scale during this free fall they would show no weight, even though the force of gravity is acting on them.

Challenge   When the airplane dives downward; there is no push of the floor of the airplane against the astronauts' bodies. The astronauts feel weightless.

Because objects in orbit are in free fall, a person orbiting the earth in a spacecraft seems to be weightless. With gravity acting on the person and spacecraft, both are in free fall. Both fall at the same rate. Therefore, the person does not push on the floor of the spacecraft. Nor does the floor of the spacecraft push on the person. The person feels weightless, even though gravity is acting on him or her.

Imagine standing on a scale in an elevator and reading your weight. Suppose the cable holding the elevator snaps. As fast as you move toward the scale, the scale moves away from you. The reading on the scale drops to zero when you are in free fall.

Figure 14-16

Astronauts and all objects in a spacecraft are in free fall.

REVIEW

1. Use Newton's laws of motion to explain the motion of satellites.
2. How can an object moving at a constant speed have an acceleration?
3. How is the motion of a satellite similar to the motion of an object in free fall?
4. How can objects appear to be weightless even when they are pulled by gravity?

CHALLENGE   Astronauts train for weightlessness in an airplane that climbs very high and then dives downward. In which part of the flight do the astronauts feel weightless? Explain why.

CHAPTER SUMMARY

The main ideas in this chapter are listed below. Read these statements before you answer the Chapter Review questions.

- Motion is a change in the position of an object as compared with a reference point. Changes in the motion of an object are caused by unbalanced forces acting on the object. (14-1)

- The speed of an object is the distance the object travels in a given amount of time. Velocity is speed in a given direction. (14-1)

- Acceleration is a change in the velocity of an object over time. Acceleration can be either positive or negative. Negative acceleration is also called deceleration. (14-1)

- Inertia is the tendency of matter to resist any change in motion. Force must be applied to an object to overcome its inertia. (14-2)

- Newton's First Law of Motion states that an object at rest stays at rest and an object in motion stays in motion unless the object is acted on by an unbalanced force. (14-2)

- Momentum is equal to the mass of an object times it velocity. The Law of Conservation of Momentum states that momentum can be transferred from one object to another but the total momentum of the objects stays the same. (14-2)

- Newton's Second Law of Motion states that an unbalanced force causes an object to accelerate in the direction of the force. The amount of acceleration depends on the mass of the object and the force exerted on the object. (14-3)

- Forces act in pairs. One force is called the action force and the other is called the reaction force. Newton's Third Law of Motion states that for every action, there is an equal and opposite reaction. (14-4)

- Centripetal force causes a moving object to travel in a circular path. Gravity is an example of a centripetal force. A centripital force causes centripital acceleration. (14-5)

The key terms in this chapter are listed below. Use each term in a sentence that shows the meaning of the term.

acceleration
centripetal acceleration
centripetal force
distance
inertia
Law of Conservation of Momentum
momentum
motion
Newton's First Law of Motion
Newton's Second Law of Motion
Newton's Third Law of Motion
speed
velocity

Review and Skill Masters

VOCABULARY REVIEW, page 83.
See page 327b in this book for answers.

VOCABULARY

1. e 2. d 3. c 4. b 5.i.
6. l 7. j 8. h 9. a 10.g

CONCEPTS

1. An object is in motion if you see a change in its position as compared with a reference point.
2. The change of motion of an object is a result of an unbalanced force acting on the object; the unbalanced force overcomes the inertia of the object.
3. $v = d/t = 1500$ m/120 s $= 12.5$ m/s
4. Speed is the distance an object moves in a given amount of time; velocity is speed in a definite direction.
5. When an object accelerates, its speed or direction changes.
6. $a = \triangle v/t = (90$ m/s $- 10$ m/s$)/12$ s $= 80$ m/s $/ 12$ s $= 6.67$ m/s^2
7. Inertia.
8. Its mass; if it is moving, it tends to keep moving; if it is at rest, it tends to remain that way.
9. The 50-kg object has more inertia because of its larger mass.
10. Newton's First Law of Motion states that an object at rest stays at rest until an unbalanced force acts upon it; this law also states that an object in motion at a constant speed and in a straight line will stay in motion if no unbalanced force acts upon it.
11. Mass and velocity.
12. The momentum of the object decreases.
13. The Law of Conservation of Momentum states that momentum can be transferred from one object to another, but the total momentum of the objects stays the same.
14. Newton's Second Law of Motion states that an unbalanced force causes an object to accelerate in the direction of the force.
15. $F = ma = (20$ kg$) (3$ m/s$^2) = 60$ kg m/s$^2 = 60$ N

Review and Skill Masters

CHAPTER REVIEW, pages 84–85.
See page 327b in this book for answers.

Chapter Review

VOCABULARY

Write the letter of the term that best matches the definition. Not all the terms will be used.

1. Momentum can be transferred from one object to another
2. Property of matter that causes objects to resist changes in motion
3. The length of the actual path an object moves
4. The force that causes an object to move in a circular path
5. An unbalanced force causes an object to accelerate in the direction of the force
6. Speed in a given direction
7. For every action, there is an equal and opposite reaction
8. An object at rest stays at rest if no unbalanced force acts on it
9. A change in velocity over time
10. A change of position as compared with a reference point

a. acceleration
b. centripetal force
c. distance
d. inertia
e. Law of Conservation of Momentum
f. momentum
g. motion
h. Newton's First Law of Motion
i. Newton's Second Law of Motion
j. Newton's Third Law of Motion
k. speed
l. velocity

CONCEPTS

1. When is an object considered to be *in motion*? (14-1)
2. Explain the relationship between force and motion. (14-1)
3. What is the speed of a race horse that runs 1500 m in 2 minutes? (14-1)
4. Distinguish between speed and velocity. (14-1)
5. What happens when an object is accelerated? (14-1)
6. A car traveling at a rate of 10 m/s accelerates to 90 m/s in 12 seconds. Calculate its acceleration. (14-1)
7. What property of matter causes objects to resist changes in motion? (14-2)
8. What factors determine an object's inertia? (14-2)
9. Which has more inertia, a 50-kg object or a 20-kg object? Explain your answer. (14-2)
10. State Newton's First Law of Motion. (14-2)
11. What two factors determine an object's momentum? (14-2)

12. What happens to the momentum of an object moving at a speed of 15 m/s when its speed decreases to 10 m/s? (14-2)

13. State the Law of Conservation of Momentum. (14-2)

14. State Newton's Second Law of Motion. (14-3)

15. A 20-kg mass has an acceleration of 3 m/s². Calculate the force acting on the mass. (14-3)

16. Identify the action and reaction forces in a rocket takeoff. (14-4)

17. State Newton's Third Law of Motion. (14-4)

18. What force acts on an object moving in a circular path? (14-5)

19. Give two examples of centripetal force. (14-5)

20. Explain why a person in an orbiting spacecraft seems to be weightless. (14-5)

APPLICATION/CRITICAL THINKING

1. Describe the motion of a rising and falling ball in terms of its speed, velocity, and acceleration. Be sure to discuss how these variables change over time.

2. A horse is attempting to pull a cart. The force that the horse exerts on the cart is equal and opposite to the force that the cart exerts on the horse. Can the horse move the cart? Explain.

3. What factors affect the amount of the centripetal force needed to hold an object in a circular path?

4. Why must a spacecraft be "coasting," with engines off, for the astronauts to feel weightless?

5. Use Newton's laws to explain the motion of a car traveling along a curved road.

EXTENSION

1. Centrifugal force is sometimes called a fictitious force. Find out what centrifugal force is. Compare centrifugal force with centripetal force.

2. Do library research to determine under what conditions Newton's laws of motion are not valid.

3. Prepare a report explaining how astronauts train for long periods of weightlessness.

READINGS

Bendick, Jeanne. *Artificial Satellites*. New York: Franklin Watts, Inc., 1982.

Gardener, Robert, and David Webster. *Moving Right Along: A Book of Science Experiments and Puzzles About Motion*. New York: Doubleday and Co., 1978.

Smith, Howard E., Jr. *Balance It!* New York: Four Winds, 1982.

16. The action force is the force of the hot gases escaping from the rocket; the reaction force is the force that moves the rocket in the opposite direction.

17. Newton's Third Law of Motion states that for every action by a force, there is an equal and opposite reaction.

18. Centripetal force.

19. The force of gravity is the centripetal force that keeps a satellite moving around the earth. Also, the moon is held in orbit around the earth by the earth's gravity. The satellite and the moon move in a curved path because the gravitational force provides a centripetal force.

20. Both the spacecraft and the person in it are in free fall and therefore the person seems weightless.

APPLICATION/CRITICAL THINKING

1. As the ball rises, its speed decreases, its velocity decreases, and it has constant (negative) acceleration. At the top of the curve, it stops instantaneously; it then has zero speed and velocity, but its acceleration remains constant. As it falls, its speed increases and its velocity increases, but it still has a constant acceleration.

2. The cart's reaction force to the horse's action force will not stop the horse from moving the cart.

3. Mass, velocity, and the radius of the path.

4. For astronauts to feel weightless, the spacecraft must be in free fall.

5. According to the first law, a car will travel in a straight line at a constant speed unless it experiences an unbalanced force. Since the car is not traveling in a straight line, it must have some unbalanced force acting on it and causing its acceleration in the direction of the force (second law).

Test Masters

CHAPTER TEST, pages 53–56.
See page 327d in this book for answers.

Science in Careers

Have you ever noticed that the wings of an airplane are curved on the upper surface and flat on the bottom? This shape of the wing gives lift, or upward movement, to the airplane.

It is the job of an aeronautical engineer to design airplanes so that their shape serves their function. Aeronautical engineers may begin with a drawing and then use mathematical and engineering principles to refine their design. Based on the drawing, a small model is built.

Aeronautical engineers also use computers and computer graphics to design and study airplanes. Supercomputers are being used to show how airplanes will perform in flight.

Aeronautical engineers may work for private industry or for the government. They must have a college degree in engineering. To prepare for a career in engineering, you should take courses in physics and mathematics in high school.■

As you know, tools are objects used for work or for making things. But how are tools made?

Tools are made by tool and die makers. A die is a mold or other type of tool that can be used for shaping metal. A tool and die maker may use one type of die to form the threads of a screw. This type of die rotates around a blank screw, cutting out threads as it turns. Other dies may be molds into which molten metal is poured. Various other dies and tools may also be made.

Most tool and die makers are trained as apprentices; they receive several years of on-the-job training. If you are interested in a career as a tool and die maker, you should take courses in shop in high school.■

Aeronautical Engineer

Tool and Die Maker

People in Science

Dr. Franklin Chang-Diaz is both a physicist and an astronaut. When he was a small boy, he dreamed about traveling in space. Today he is one of the first Hispanic Americans to have flown on a space mission. Dr. Chang-Diaz also designs new types of rocket engines for future space exploration.

Dr. Chang-Diaz worked toward his goal by studying physics. This background has enabled him to design an ion engine. An ion engine may be used to travel the great dis-

Dr. Franklin Chang-Diaz, Astronaut

tances between the earth and the outer planets.

The chemical engines now in use require a great amount of fuel. To save fuel, rockets using chemical engines coast over long distances. In contrast, the ion engine would continue to propel the rocket throughout its course, reducing travel time. The heavy fuel tanks needed for chemical engines would be unnecessary in ion engine rockets. Dr. Chang-Diaz hopes to one day travel in rockets using the type of engine he designs.■

Issues and Technology

Robots were once thought of as a part of science fiction. Now robots are becoming more common. Robots can assemble cars and appliances. They can handle dangerous chemicals in laboratories. They can deliver mail in offices. They can even help guide airplanes through the sky.

Some people see the use of robots as a wonderful development. They say that work will get done more quickly and efficiently. They also believe that robots will take over many jobs that involve boring or dangerous work. Workers who had held these jobs would then be free to do better and more interesting jobs.

Other people see the use of robots as a problem. Sometimes robots replace workers who do not move on to better and more interesting jobs. These people move to lower-paying jobs or to the unemployment line.

Having machines take over the work of people is nothing new. It has happened all through history. For example, hundreds of years ago, books and documents were all written by hand. There were people called scribes whose job it was to simply copy things. They would spend a whole day copying only a few pages. In this way it could take years to copy just one book. The invention of the printing press meant that a book could be produced in a fraction of the time it would take a scribe to write it all by hand. This put many scribes out of work. But should the printing press have been outlawed to save the scribes' jobs?

Supporters of automation say that, like printing presses, robots and computers should be thought of as a part of normal progress. Figure 1 shows the effect of automation on one group of workers — long distance telephone operators. Study the graph and answer the following questions.

APPLYING CRITICAL THINKING SKILLS

1. Did the number of long-distance calls go up or down between 1950 and 1980?
2. How did the number of long-distance operators change between 1950 and 1980?
3. Do you think it is strange that your answers to questions 1 and 2 seem to contradict each other? How can you explain this seeming contradiction?
4. Do you think it is good that so many calls can be handled by so few operators? Why or why not?
5. Automation resulted in cheaper long-distance telephone calls. Does this information change your answer to question 4? Explain your answer.

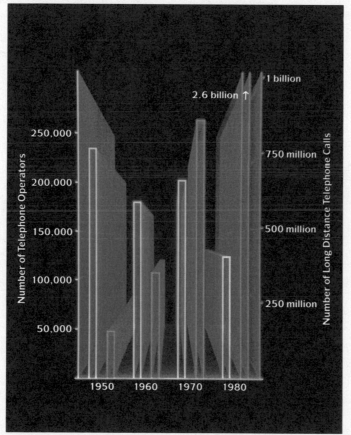

Figure 1

The following thinking skills will be applied in answering questions.
- *Interpreting* a graph.
- *Relating* the trends of the number of long-distance operators and long-distance telephone calls.
- *Comparing* the benefits of cost-cutting with the problems of job loss.

Answers to questions

1. The number of long-distance calls dramatically increased between the years 1950 and 1980.
2. The number of long-distance operators decreased during that period.
3. Answers will vary. Automation allowed the number of telephone operators to decrease while the number of telephone calls increased.
4. Some students may feel that it is better and more efficient that fewer people are needed to handle the extra workload. Others may be concerned that some operators have lost their jobs as a result of automation.
5. Some students might not have considered that automation has made it possible for them to make cheaper long-distance calls. This realization could change some minds.

The following thinking skills will be applied in answering questions.
- *Interpreting* a graph.
- *Identifying* trends in automobile production and the numbers of workers required.
- *Evaluating* the effects of automation of the automobile industry.

Answers to questions

1. The projection is that more cars will be produced each year between the years 1970 and 2000.
2. The number of people needed to produce these cars will be decreasing over the same period of time.
3. The two trends are opposite one another. As productivity increases, more cars are produced in the same amount of time as before and fewer workers are needed.
4. Answers will vary. The cost savings of having automation will provide cheaper transportation for the entire country. However, laying off large numbers of workers could affect the economy of the whole country. The layoffs could come full circle, hurting the companies that displaced the workers in the first place.

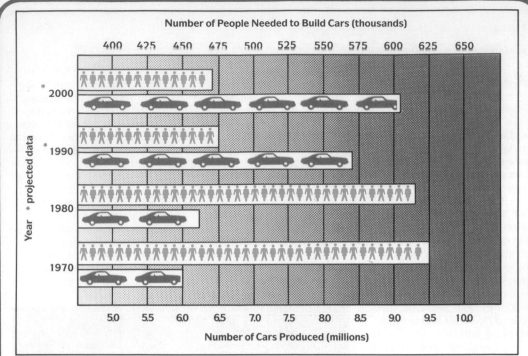

Figure 2

One of the industries that has used automation extensively is the automobile industry. In some plants most of the work is already done by robots that cut, weld, assemble, paint, and inspect car parts.

Some industry sources say that by the 1990s, up to 25,000 more robots will be replacing workers in the United States automobile industry. And that change will reduce the number of jobs in the industry by 20 percent.

Managers in the automobile industry say that they need automation in order to compete. Machines can make cars in a fraction of the time that it takes a person to do the job. This higher productivity, along with the savings in labor costs, means that cars should be cheaper to produce.

Robots are also moving into other industries. Using automated equipment, a manufac-

turing plant in Pennsylvania makes motor frames for locomotives. There a frame can be made in just 16 hours instead of the 16 days it used to take for mostly human workers to do the job. One totally automated operation in Texas can turn out a computer in less than 6 minutes. This is 75 percent more efficient than a traditional manufacturing system.

High productivity isn't the only advantage some companies see in using mechanical rather than human workers. Human workers get sick. They get involved in accidents and go on disability. These problems cost companies money in medical benefits, sick pay, and insurance. Robot workers don't require any of that. Human workers work an 8-hour day, 5 days out of 7. They take lunch hours and vacations and holidays. Robots can work around the clock, 7 days a week.

Look at Figure 2. It shows some of the projected effects of automation on the automobile industry.

APPLYING CRITICAL THINKING SKILLS

1. Describe the projected trend between the years 1970 and 2000 in the production of cars.
2. Describe the projected trend between 1970 and 2000 in the number of people needed to make these cars.
3. What is the relationship between the two trends?
4. Do you think automation of the automobile industry is a change for the better? Explain your answer.

The coming of robots will change the workplace. It will change not only the number of jobs but also the kinds of jobs that are available and the kinds of skills needed for these jobs.

In manufacturing, robots now perform such tasks as putting things together on assembly lines and carrying things from place to place. In years past, these types of factory jobs have usually been held by people without much education or training, and the jobs paid fairly good wages. With a number of these jobs disappearing, many people with little education and few skills will not be able to find jobs with good salaries.

The loss of such jobs will result in a lower standard of living for many people. There will be much less money to spend. And this drop in spending money could affect the whole economy. People with less money would buy fewer goods. Fewer goods would be produced, slowing down other industries and putting more jobs in jeopardy.

Although the lowest level of jobs has already been affected, higher levels will also be affected. With fewer workers, fewer supervisors and managers will be needed. As automation takes a firmer hold, some computers may even take over the job of directing workers.

One example of a fully automated system is something called computer integrated management (CIM). With CIM, one or two human computer operators can control an entire automated plant. Not only are assembly line workers cut, but the automatic flow of information through the factory eliminates the need for many middle managers and clerical workers as well. Does cutting all these workers mean real problems for the economy?

Figure 3 shows the projected growth in different areas of employment through the year 1995. This growth is mainly in the service sector of the economy. These are the jobs of people who perform services, such as serving food, in contrast to the jobs that produce goods. Much of this change in employment is due to automation and the shrinking number of manufacturing jobs.

APPLYING CRITICAL THINKING SKILLS

1. What five jobs will have the largest gains in employment between 1984 and 1995?
2. Half of these jobs have salaries well below the national average. Only two jobs pay much above the average. Do you see any problem with the fact that these jobs in growth industries have such low salaries?
3. Do you think many of the workers who are displaced from manufacturing jobs will be forced to take these jobs? Do you see this as a problem for them? Explain.
4. Will this change in the job market affect you as you start to look for a job? Why or why not?

The following thinking skills will be applied in answering questions.
- *Identifying* the jobs having the largest gains in employment.
- *Predicting* the effect of changing jobs on the individual and on the economy.
- *Evaluating* career plans in light of the information given.

Answers to questions
1. The job categories of cashier, registered nurse, janitor and cleaner, waiter and waitress, and truck driver will have the largest gains between 1984 and 1995.
2. In going from a higher paid factory job to a lower paid job in a service industry, an individual will be faced with paying for ongoing costs, such as a mortgage and car payments, with a shrinking paycheck. Students should also see the effect, on the whole economy, of less buying power for these workers.
3. Many of the displaced workers will need to take jobs in service areas. Any of the problems of going from a higher pay scale to a lower pay scale will affect them.
4. Answers will vary. The answers depend largely on what students see as their goals. Those who do not plan to go to college might see their opportunities as diminished, and they may reconsider the type of training they plan to get.

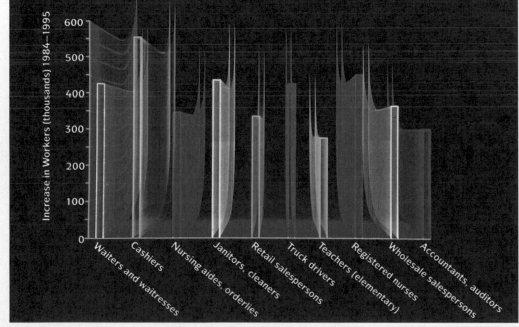

Figure 3

Unit 5

ENERGY AT WORK

UNIT OVERVIEW

Chapter 15 describes the effects of changes in heat content on matter, as well as the ways in which heat is transferred. It also discusses heat engines as practical uses of these principles.

Chapter 16 discusses the production and effects of static electricity. The production of current electricity and kinds of circuits are also included.

Chapter 17 describes the behavior of magnets, and examines the relationship between magnetism and electricity. It also surveys the development of modern electronic devices.

Chapter 18 introduces the properties and behavior of waves. It then applies this information to a discussion of the properties of sound.

Chapter 19 describes the nature and behavior of light, including reflection and refraction. It also compares wave and particle aspects of light.

Chapter 20 presents ways in which light can be used to produce images, and includes a discussion of mirrors, lenses, and holograms.

Unit Five

ENERGY AT WORK

*E*nergy can exist in a variety of forms. Forms of energy include heat, light, electricity, and sound. In this unit you will study heat and how it changes matter. You will also see how electricity and magnetism are related. You will learn about the nature of waves, light, and sound. Finally, you will learn how these concepts were applied in producing lasers, holograms, and optical fibers. ■

▲ *Section of a compact disc, showing patterns of light reflected from the surface.*

▼ *Lithograph of Benjamin Franklin's experiment proving that lightning is electricity.*

▲ *Michael Faraday used this apparatus to study the effects of electricity on matter.*

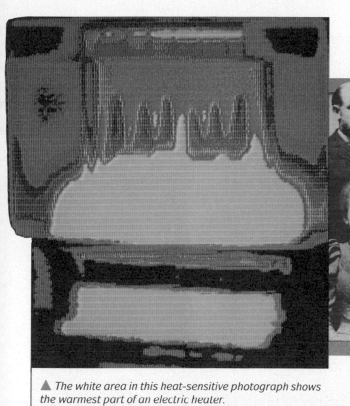

The white area in this heat-sensitive photograph shows the warmest part of an electric heater.

▼ This photograph, taken in December 1894, shows some of the people who worked for Thomas Edison.

▼ Lenses can bend light rays apart, or bring them together.

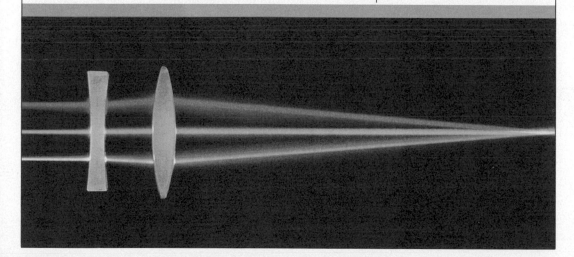

Sections appearing in red provide coverage of basic topics in this unit. See page T23.

HEAT

ORGANIZER

Section	pages	Activity	pages	Reinforcement and Evaluation	pages	*Review and Skill Masters	pages	Other Components in Teacher Resource Package	pages
15–1 Particles in Motion	359–360			Review, Challenge	360			*Study Guide*	74
15–2 Heat Energy	361–364	How Is Heat Exchanged?	363	Review, Challenge	364			*Study Guide*	75
15–3 Change of State	365–369	What Happens During a Change of State? What Is the Heat of Fusion of Water?	367 368	Review, Challenge	369	Skill	92	*Study Guide* *Lab Manual* *Transparency*	76 77
15–4 Expansion and Gases	370–372			Review, Challenge	372			*Study Guide*	77
15–5 Heat Transfer	373–376			Puzzler Review, Challenge	376	Challenge/Critical Thinking	93–94	*Study Guide*	78
15–6 Heat Engines	377–379			Review, Challenge	379			*Study Guide* *Transparency*	79
CHAPTER SUMMARY	379					Vocabulary Review	89		
CHAPTER REVIEW	380–381			*Test Masters	57–60	Chapter Review	90		

*In the Teacher Resource Package. For answers, see pages 357b–357d in this book.

ACTIVITY MATERIALS Quantities are based on a class of 30 students working in groups as indicated in parentheses.

How Is Heat Exchanged? p. 363 (groups of 2)	quantity	What Happens During a Change of State? p. 367 (groups of 2)	quantity	What Is the Heat of Fusion of Water? p. 368 (groups of 2)	quantity
100-mL graduate	15	safety goggles	30	plastic foam cup	30
plastic foam cup	30	250-mL beaker	15	balance	15
Celsius thermometer	30	hot plate	15	100-mL graduate	15
hot water		paradichlorobenzene (moth balls)	1 lb box	ice	
cold water		test tube	15	Celsius thermometer	15
		Celsius thermometer	15	stirring rod	15
		test-tube rack	15		
		clock or watch with second hand	15		

REVIEW AND SKILL MASTERS

Name_____ Date_____

VOCABULARY REVIEW _____ Chapter 15

Use the correct words to complete the sentences below.

Boyle's law   heat engine   pressure
Charles's law   heat of fusion   radiation
conduction   heat of vaporization   specific heat
convection   kinetic theory   temperature
heat

1. **Heat** _____ depends on the average kinetic energy and the number of particles in a sample of matter.

2. The amount of heat energy that will change a liquid at its boiling point to a gas at the same temperature is **heat of vaporization**

3. No particles are needed to transfer energy by **radiation**

4. **Boyle's law** _____ relates the volume of a gas to its pressure.

5. A measure of the average kinetic energy in a sample of matter is called **temperature**

6. **Specific heat** _____ is a measure of a substance's ability to absorb heat.

7. The _____ **kinetic theory** _____ says that all matter is composed of moving particles that have forces of attraction between them.

8. Heat transfer by direct contact between particles is called **conduction**

9. Force per unit area is called **pressure**

10. A device that changes heat energy from burning fuel into mechanical energy is a **heat engine**

11. Heat transfer in moving fluids is called **convection**

12. **Charles's law** _____ relates the volume of a gas to its pressure.

13. The amount of heat energy that will change a solid at its melting point to a liquid at the same temperature is **heat of fusion**

Name_____ Date_____

CHAPTER REVIEW _____ Chapter 15

15-1 Particles in Motion

1. State the kinetic theory. **The kinetic theory says that all matter is made up of moving particles that are held together by forces of attraction.**

2. What does kinetic energy have to do with temperature? **The higher the average kinetic energy, the higher the temperature. Temperature is a measure of average kinetic energy.**

15-2 Heat Energy

1. Does temperature alone indicate how much heat a substance has? Explain your answer. **No. The temperature of a substance is determined by its average kinetic energy. The heat of a substance is the total energy of all the particles in the substance.**

2. How much heat is needed to raise the temperature of 20 g of aluminum from 15 °C to 30 °C? **H = mCΔT = 20 g × 0.9 J/g°C × 15 °C = 20 × 0.9 × 15 = 270 J**

15-3 Change of State

1. How does adding heat energy to water cause it to change from ice to liquid water? **As heat is added to ice, the molecules gain enough energy to overcome the forces that hold them together as a solid. The molecules move farther apart and the ice melts into water.**

2. How much energy is needed to change 25 g of ice at 0 °C to water at 0 °C? **H = mL$_f$ = 25 g × 334 J/g = 25 × 334 J = 8,350 J**

3. How much heat energy is needed to change 5 g of water at 100 °C to steam at 100 °C? **H = mL$_v$ = 5 g × 2260 J/g = 5 × 2260 J = 11,300 J**

Name_____ Date_____

CHAPTER REVIEW (Continued) _____ Chapter 15

15-4 Expansion and Gases

1. Underline your answers. An increase in the space between the particles that make up an object is called contraction/expansion. A decrease in the space between the particles that make up an object is called contraction/expansion.

2. Which gas law uses temperature as a constant? State this law. **Boyle's law. The volume of a gas decreases as its pressure increases if the temperature stays the same.**

3. Which gas law uses pressure as a constant? State this law. **Charles's law. The volume of a gas increases as its temperature increases if the pressure stays the same.**

15-5 Heat Transfer

1. Imagine you are walking on a beach at the seashore. The sand is hot beneath your feet. The rays of the sun warm your shoulders, and there is a sea breeze. Name and describe the three types of heat transfer going on. **The sun's rays radiate heat to warm your shoulders and heat up the sand. The sand warms your feet by means of conduction, or direct contact. The sea breeze is a result of convection. This occurs when the air, warmed by the hot sand, rises and allows the cooler air over the ocean to move in and replace it.**

15-6 Heat Engines

1. What is a heat engine? **A heat engine is a device that converts heat energy from burning fuel into mechanical energy.**

2. Give three examples of an internal combustion engine. **Answers will vary. A gasoline engine, a diesel engine, and a jet engine.**

Name_____ Date_____

SKILL/Interpreting Data _____ Chapter 15

A 10 kg bag of ice accidentally was placed outside an ice freezer. The ice had a temperature of 0 °C. The air temperature was 25 °C. After two hours, half of the ice had melted and the water in the bag had a temperature of 0 °C.

1. What kind of energy caused the ice to melt? **Heat energy.**

2. Where did the energy come from? **The energy came from the air at 25 °C and also from the floor.**

3. Even though heat energy was added continuously for two hours, the temperature of the melted ice did not change. How can this be explained? **Energy is used to change 0 °C ice to 0 °C water. This is called the heat of fusion of water. All the energy added to the ice went into changing it into water.**

4. How much energy will be used to change 10 kg of solid ice at 0 °C to liquid water at 0 °C? It takes 3.3 × 10⁵ J to melt 1 kg of ice at 0 °C. **10 kg × 3.3 × 10⁵ J/kg = 3.3 × 10⁶ J**

5. It takes 4.2 × 10³ J to raise 1 kg of water 1 °C. How much energy will be needed to raise the temperature of 10 kg of water at 0 °C to 100 °C? **4.2 × 10³ J/kg°C × 10 kg × 100 °C = 4.2 × 10⁶ J**

6. If heat energy is added to 10 kg of water with a temperature of 100 °C, the water will turn to steam with temperature of 100 °C. How can this be explained? **Energy is used to change 100 °C water to 100 °C steam. This is called the heat of vaporization of water. The heat energy goes into changing the state of water, not its temperature.**

7. How much energy is needed to change 10 kg of 100 °C water to 100 °C steam? It takes 2.3 × 10⁶ J to change 1 kg of water at 100 °C to steam. **2.3 × 10⁶ J/kg × 10 kg = 2.3 × 10⁷ J**

Name_____ Date_____

CHALLENGE/CRITICAL THINKING _____ Chapter 15

A 90 g metal sphere with temperature of 74 °C is placed into a container containing 250 ml of water at 20 °C. Five minutes later the water temperature is 24 °C and the sphere's temperature is 24 °C. Study the drawings below and answer the questions.

74 °C (90 g)   **250 ml**   20 °C   24 °C

1. How many joules of heat were transmitted to the water?

   250 g × 4.18 J/g°C × 4 °C = 4180 J

2. How many joules of heat were lost by the metal sphere?   4180 J

3. What is the specific heat of the metal sphere?

   4180 J = 90 g × C × 50 °C, C = 4180 J ÷ 90 g × 50 °C, C = .93 J/g°C

A metal strip is made of a tin strip and an iron strip fused together. The strip bends as it temperature changes. The specific heat of tin is 0.52 J/g°C and the specific heat of iron is 0.107 J/g°C.

Tin   Iron

4. What would happen to the metal strip if it were heated?

   The metal strip would bend right toward the iron side.

5. Explain your above answer.

   The strip bends toward the iron side because tin expands more than iron. The

   specific heat of tin is lower than the specific heat of iron.

93

Name_____ Date_____

CHALLENGE/CRITICAL THINKING (Continued) _____ Chapter 15

You plan an experiment on heat energy using a metal ring and ball. At room temperature, the ball barely passes through the ring. When you heat the ball, it will not go through the ring. When you heat the ring, the ball goes through very easily. When you heat both the ball and ring, the ball doesn't go through the ring. Study the four drawings below and answer the following questions.

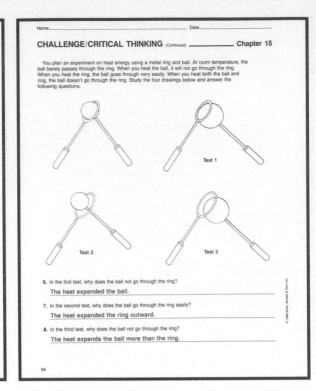

Test 1

Test 2

Test 3

6. In the first test, why does the ball not go through the ring?

   The heat expanded the ball.

7. In the second test, why does the ball go through the ring easily?

   The heat expanded the ring outward.

8. In the third test, why does the ball not go through the ring?

   The heat expands the ball more than the ring.

94

TEST MASTERS

Particles in Motion

PART 1 _____

In the space below, write the term that each phrase defines.

Chapter Goal

1. __conduction__ — The transfer of heat energy by direct contact between particles — 5

2. __heat__ — The total energy of all the particles in a sample of matter — 2

3. __convection__ — Heat transfer that occurs in moving fluids — 5

4. __specific heat__ — The amount of heat energy needed to raise the temperature of 1 g of a substance by 1°C — 2

5. __kinetic theory__ — The statement that all matter is made of particles that are in constant motion, and that there are forces of attraction between particles — 1

6. __Boyle's law__ — The statement that the volume of a gas decreases as its pressure increases if the temperature stays the same — 4

7. __heat engine__ — A device that changes the heat energy from burning fuel into mechanical energy — 6

8. __heat of vaporization__ — The amount of heat energy that will change a liquid at its boiling point to a gas at the same temperature — 3

9. __Charles's law__ — The statement that the volume of gas increases as its temperature increases if the pressure stays the same — 4

10. __temperature__ — The measure of the average kinetic energy in a sample of matter — 1

11. __heat of fusion__ — The amount of heat energy that will change a solid at its melting point to a liquid at the same temperature — 3

PART 2 _____

Choose the term or phrase that best answers the question or completes the statement. Write the letter of that choice in the space at the left.

__b__ 1. Which of the following types of engines has a piston but no spark plug? — 6
 a. four-stroke engine
 b. diesel engine
 c. jet engine
 d. rocket engine

__d__ 2. Molecules have no kinetic energy at a temperature of: — 1
 a. 273 K. b. −273 K. c. 273°C. d. −273°C.

Chapter 15 Particles in Motion — 57

Choose the term or phrase that best answers the question or completes the statement. Write the letter of that choice in the space at the left.

Chapter Goal

__b__ 3. As a substance is heated steadily, its temperature increases for a while. Then the temperature stops increasing. The temperature stops increasing because: — 3
 a. the molecules are losing kinetic energy.
 b. the substance is changing from a liquid to a gas.
 c. the substance is changing from a gas to a liquid.
 d. the molecules are moving closer together.

__c__ 4. The temperature of 100 g of water increases from 10°C to 12°C. How much heat has the water absorbed? The specific heat of water is 4.2 J/gc°. ($H = mc\Delta t$) — 2
 a. 200 J b. 420 J c. 840 J d. 8400 J

__d__ 5. How much energy is needed to change 100 g of solid benzene to liquid if the heat of fusion of benzene is 599 J/g? ($H = mLf$) — 3
 a. 5.99 J b. 599 J c. 5990 J d. 59,900 J

__c__ 6. In an internal combustion engine, each movement of a piston is called a: — 6
 a. cylinder. b. gear. c. stroke. d. valve.

__c__ 7. During which stroke of a four-stroke engine does burning take place? — 6
 a. intake b. compression c. power d. exhaust

__b__ 8. The total energy of a liquid depends in part on the liquid's: — 2
 a. specific heat.
 b. volume.
 c. heat of fusion.
 d. heat of vaporization.

__a__ 9. Mercury rises in the tube of a thermometer because mercury expands as its: — 1
 a. kinetic energy is increased.
 b. pressure is decreased.
 c. kinetic energy is decreased.
 d. pressure is increased.

__c__ 10. As the average kinetic energy of gas molecules is increased, the molecules: — 4
 a. contract more slowly.
 b. stay closer together.
 c. move faster.
 d. collide less often.

__c__ 11. Freon and other coolants are used to control air temperature by: — 5
 a. decreasing movement of the air.
 b. mixing with the air.
 c. absorbing heat from the air.
 d. giving off heat to the air.

__a__ 12. Charles's law can be used to explain: — 4
 a. why car tires are slightly larger after a long trip on a hot day.
 b. how a liquid-filled thermometer works.
 c. why a bottle of water cracks when it freezes.
 d. how large amounts of gas are stored in small containers.

__b__ 13. Which of the following is an example of convection? — 5
 a. The handle of a pot on a stove becomes hot.
 b. Warm air is found nearer to the ceiling than to the floor.
 c. A metal bar is warmed by heat from the sun.
 d. An egg is cooked in a frying pan.

58 — Chapter 15 Particles in Motion

Look at the graph. Then read the questions that follow. Choose the term or phrase that best answers the question or completes the statement. Write the letter of that choice in the space at the left.

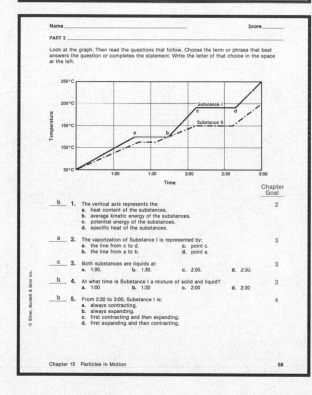

Chapter Goal

__b__ 1. The vertical axis represents the: — 2
 a. heat content of the substances.
 b. average kinetic energy of the substances.
 c. potential energy of the substances.
 d. specific heat of the substances.

__a__ 2. The vaporization of Substance I is represented by: — 3
 a. the line from c to d.
 b. the line from a to b.
 c. point c.
 d. point a.

__c__ 3. Both substances are liquids at: — 3
 a. 1:00. b. 1:30. c. 2:00. d. 2:30.

__b__ 4. At what time is Substance I a mixture of solid and liquid? — 3
 a. 1:00 b. 1:30 c. 2:00 d. 2:30

__b__ 5. From 2:30 to 3:00, Substance I is: — 4
 a. always contracting.
 b. always expanding.
 c. first contracting and then expanding.
 d. first expanding and then contracting.

Chapter 15 Particles in Motion — 59

Read each question or direction and answer it using complete sentences.

Chapter Goal

1. Describe the Kelvin scale and explain how it relates to the Celsius scale for measuring temperatures. — 1

 The SI temperature scale is the Kelvin scale. The units are Kelvins (K). One Kelvin is equal to one degree Celsius. On the Kelvin scale, the coldest possible temperature is absolute zero, written 0 K. Absolute zero on the Kelvin scale is equal to −273°C on the Celsius scale.

2. Describe the differences between solids, liquids, and gases in terms of particles of matter. — 3

 In the solid state, particles of matter are held together tightly. These particles cannot move around very much. In the liquid state, particles are held together loosely. Particles in a liquid move around more than do particles in a solid. Particles in a gas are not held together. Gas particles have more energy than do particles in solids or liquids.

3. How does a steam engine work? — 6

 In a steam engine, fuel is burned outside of the engine. A fuel such as coal is burned to boil water. Steam under high pressure pushes a piston. The energy of the moving piston is used to turn the wheels of a locomotive, to turn turbines, or to power machinery.

60 — Chapter 15 Particles in Motion

CHAPTER 15 PLANNING GUIDE

15

HEAT

The questions in the CHAPTER TEST are based on these Chapter Goals.

1. State the kinetic theory, and describe how the average kinetic energy of matter is measured.
2. Distinguish between heat and temperature, and calculate changes in heat energy.
3. Describe how adding or removing heat causes matter to change state, and calculate the amount of heat that will change a substance from one state to another.
4. Distinguish between expansion and contraction, and explain the relationship between the volume, temperature, and pressure of a gas.
5. Identify the ways in which heat is transferred, and describe how heat transfer is used to control air temperature.
6. Describe different types of heat engines and how they work.

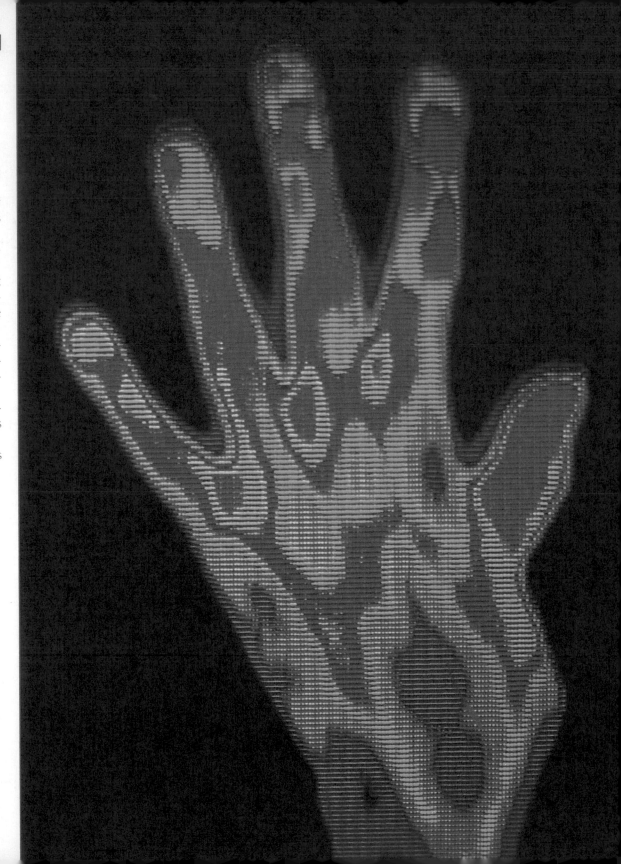

HEAT

This photograph is a thermogram of a hand. The thermogram was made with a heat-sensitive scanner that recorded the temperature of the hand. A thermogram uses color to show which areas are hot and which areas are cold. Red shows the warmest area, with orange, yellow, green, blue, and magenta showing decreasing temperature. Black shows the coldest area.

- *Would you say this hand is warm or cold?*
- *What other ways could thermograms be useful?*

15-1 PARTICLES IN MOTION

Have you ever passed a bakery on a breezy day and smelled bread or cake baking? Have you smelled the ocean while driving near a beach? Odors are caused by tiny moving particles. When these particles reach your nose, they stimulate your sense of smell.

All matter is made of atoms and molecules. These particles are in constant motion. The particles in a gas move around freely. The particles in liquids and solids have more limited movement. However, even the hardest substance, diamond, is made of particles in motion.

Observations about moving particles led scientists to develop the kinetic theory. The **kinetic theory** says that all matter is made of particles that are in constant motion. The kinetic theory also says that there are forces of attraction between particles. Without these forces, the particles in matter would just drift apart.

Scientists need to know how much energy there is in a sample of matter. The motion of the particles in matter is a form of energy called *kinetic energy*. The faster the particles move, the more kinetic energy they have. The measure of the average kinetic energy in a sample of matter is called **temperature**. Materials that have a high average kinetic energy have a high temperature. Materials with a low average kinetic energy have a low temperature. If you increase the kinetic energy of a sample of matter, its temperature will increase. If you decrease the kinetic energy, the temperature will decrease.

After completing this section, you will be able to

- **state** the kinetic theory.
- **describe** how the average kinetic energy of matter is measured.

The key terms in this section are
kinetic theory
temperature

---

kinetikos (to move)

Have students make observations about the photograph. Explain that thermograms have become a valuable tool for scientists and for medical personnel. Ask students how a thermogram could be used by space scientists. Ask students which part of the hand pictured is the warmest. Then ask which part of the hand is the coldest. The introductory questions are for discussion purposes.

- Would you say this hand is warm or cold? (Warm.)
- What other ways could thermograms be useful? (Thermograms can be used to detect areas of heat loss in a home. They can also be used in the medical field to detect tumors.)

15-1 PARTICLES IN MOTION
pages 359–360

OBJECTIVES
Refer to pupil page 359.

VOCABULARY
Key terms: kinetic theory, temperature
Other terms: absolute zero, kinetic energy

---

1 MOTIVATION

At the front of the classroom, set up a hot plate and a 250-mL beaker with 100 mL of water. Put one drop of blue ink in the water. Place the beaker carefully on the hot plate, and set the hot plate on high. Ask students to explain what happens to the ink as the water heats up. Point out that the movement of water molecules causes the ink to spread throughout the water. Use similar examples, such as the outward spread of heat from a fire or of the aromas from the cafeteria just before lunch, to introduce the kinetic theory of molecular motion. Ask students to provide other examples.

2 CONCEPT DEVELOPMENT

Background   Molecules are in constant motion. The constant collisions of molecules cause a wide range of molecular speeds. One collision may leave a particular molecule motionless until another collision starts it moving again. Another molecule may receive several collisions in a row, making it move at a very high speed. For this reason, the kinetic molecular theory takes into account the *average* kinetic energy of the sample—not the kinetic energy of each molecule in the sample.

Thinking Skills

comparing
Students are asked to compare the Celsius and Kelvin thermometers in Figure 15-1. Have students make a further comparison with a Fahrenheit thermometer.

3 REVIEW/REINFORCEMENT

1. All matter is made of particles that are in constant motion.
2. Answers will vary but might include movement of odors through air and color through liquids.
3. The measure of the average kinetic energy in a sample; with a thermometer.

Challenge   Methyl alcohol with a boiling point of 338 K.
K = °C + 273
K = 65°C + 273
K = 338

Temperature is measured with a thermometer. A thermometer is a long, sealed glass tube. The tube contains a liquid that expands or contracts with changes in temperature. In some thermometers the liquid is mercury. In other thermometers the liquid is alcohol. As temperature rises, the liquid expands and rises in the tube. As temperature falls, the liquid contracts and sinks in the tube.

Look at the thermometers shown in Figure 15-1. On the Celsius scale the freezing point of water is 0° and the boiling point is 100°. Thus, there are 100 degrees between the freezing point and boiling point of water on this scale.

The SI temperature scale is the Kelvin scale. The Kelvin scale does not use the degree symbol. The units are Kelvins (K), not degrees Kelvin. One Kelvin equals one degree on the Celsius scale. On this scale, the lowest possible temperature is *absolute zero,* written 0 K. At absolute zero, the average kinetic energy of particles is zero.

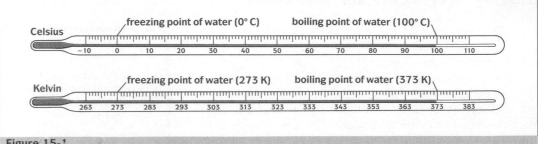

Figure 15-1

Notice that the units on a Celsius thermometer and on a Kelvin thermometer are the same size.

Absolute zero on the Kelvin scale is equal to −273°C on the Celsius scale. To change from the Kelvin scale to the Celsius scale, or to change from the Celsius scale to the Kelvin scale, use the following formula.

$$K = °C + 273$$

For example, the freezing point of water is 0°C + 273, or 273 K. What is the boiling point of water in Kelvin?[1]

¹373 K.

REVIEW

1. What is the kinetic theory?
2. Give two examples that support the idea that particles of matter are in motion.
3. What is temperature? How is it measured?

CHALLENGE Methane boils at 109 K. Methyl alcohol boils at 65°C. Which substance has a higher boiling point? Explain your answer.

15-2 HEAT ENERGY

Temperature and heat are different but related concepts. Recall that temperature is the average kinetic energy of the particles in a sample of matter. **Heat** is the total energy of all the particles in a sample of matter. Heat depends not only on the average kinetic energy of the particles, but also on how many particles there are in the sample.

To understand the difference between temperature and heat, look at Figure 15-2. The pailful of water shown has been taken from the lake. The temperature of the water in the pail is the same as the temperature of the water in the lake. The temperature of both water samples is the same because the molecules in both samples have the same average kinetic energy. However, there are more water molecules in the lake than in the pail. Because the lake has more moving particles, it has more total energy. Thus, the water in the lake has more heat than does the water in the pail.

Figure 15-2

The lake has more heat energy than does the pail of water removed from the lake.

It is difficult to calculate the total energy of a given object. Therefore, heat energy is measured in terms of the amount of energy that is added to or removed from an object. Thus, heat may be thought of as the amount of energy that is transferred between objects with different temperatures.

When heat is added to an object, its total energy increases. Its temperature may also increase. However, different substances need different amounts of heat to cause the same change in temperature.

15-2   HEAT ENERGY
pages 361–364

1 MOTIVATION

Using a ring-stand rod, clamp the rod horizontally to another ring stand. Place chips of paraffin or candle wax at intervals along the rod. With a Bunsen burner, heat the far end of the rod. Ask students what happens to the wax chips. Ask why the chips melt in an orderly pattern. Ask students how the heat moves down the rod. Ask them for additional examples of heat transfer.

2 CONCEPT DEVELOPMENT

Background   Temperature determines heat flow. Heat always flows from a material at a high temperature to a material at a lower temperature.

Demonstration   Pour 400 mL of water into a 500-mL beaker. Pour 100 mL of water into an identical beaker. Place a thermometer in each. Put both on hot plates set on high heat. Ask students to note that the temperature of the smaller quantity of water will rise more rapidly, even though both beakers are receiving the same amount of heat. Ask students to explain. (The same amount of heat is shared by fewer particles in 100 mL of water, so the average kinetic energy of the particles is greater.)

Thinking Skills

comparing

Students are asked to compare the specific heat of several substances in Table 15-1 to determine which materials have the highest specific heat. They should conclude that those substances with a higher specific heat need more heat to raise their temperatures.

Background   Many cooking vessels are made with copper bottoms because copper heats faster than do most other metals, enabling it to transfer heat to food faster. This property is due to the low specific heat of copper. Another comparison of specific heat can be made at the beach. Sand feels hotter to the feet than does the water because the water has a higher specific heat. Given the same amount of sunlight, the sand gets hotter.

Thinking Skills

interpreting graphs

Students are asked to notice the effect of the same amount of heat on two different substances in the graph in Figure 15-3. Students should notice that as heating continues, the temperature difference increases.

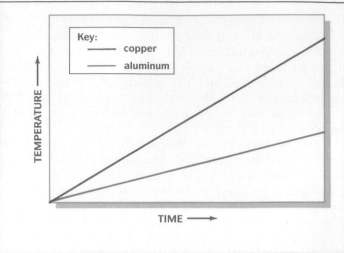

Figure 15-3

When objects like these pots are heated, their temperatures increase.

Table 15-1 *Specific Heats of Common Substances*

Substance	Specific Heat (J/g°C)
Aluminum	0.90
Copper	0.38
Gold	0.13
Ice	2.06
Iron	0.45
Lead	0.13
Steam	2.06
Water	4.18

For example, heating a copper pot would cause its temperature to increase. Suppose you heat an aluminum pot that has the same mass. Identical amounts of heat would not cause the same temperature change in both pots. Although both pots absorb the same amount of heat, the temperature of the copper pot would go up faster. As you can see in Figure 15-3, the longer the pots are heated, the greater the difference in their temperatures.

Each of the pots seems to have a different capacity for absorbing heat. The amount of heat energy needed to raise the temperature of 1 g of a substance by 1°C is called the specific heat capacity, or **specific heat**. Specific heat is a measure of the ability of a substance to absorb heat. Table 15-1 shows the specific heats of several substances. Which of the substances listed in the table has the largest specific heat?[1]

The higher the specific heat of a substance, the more heat it takes to raise the temperature of the substance. To find the amount of heat needed to raise the temperature of a sample of a substance, use the following formula.

$$H = mc\Delta t$$

In this formula, H stands for the amount of heat, m stands for the mass of the sample, and c stands for the specific heat. The symbol Δt, read "delta tee," stands for the change in temperature. The SI unit of heat energy is the *joule* (J). One joule is the amount of energy that is needed to raise the temperature of 0.24 g of water by 1°C.

[1]Water.

ACTIVITY — How is Heat Exchanged?

OBJECTIVE
Measure heat exchange between samples of hot and cold water.

MATERIALS
100-mL graduate, 2 plastic foam cups, 2 thermometers

PROCEDURE
A. Draw a data table like the one shown.
B. Add 50 mL of cold water to a cup. Add 50 mL of hot water to a second cup.
C. Measure and record the temperature of the two samples of water.
D. Immediately pour the cold water into the cup containing the hot water. As soon as the temperature remains steady, record this temperature in the data table.
E. The density of water is 1 g/mL. Therefore, 50 mL of water has a mass of 50 g. The specific heat of water is 4.18 J/g°C.
   1. Calculate the heat lost by the hot water.
   2. Calculate the heat gained by the cold water.
F. Repeat steps **B**, **C**, and **D**, but use 25 mL of cold water and 75 mL of hot water.
   3. Calculate the heat lost by the hot water.
   4. Calculate the heat gained by the cold water.
G. Repeat steps **B**, **C**, and **D**, but use 75 mL of cold water and 25 mL of hot water.
   5. Calculate the heat lost by the hot water.
   6. Calculate the heat gained by the cold water.

RESULTS AND CONCLUSIONS
1. How do the calculations of heat loss and heat gain from step **E** compare?
2. How do the calculations of heat loss and heat gain from step **F** compare?
3. How do the calculations of heat loss and heat gain from step **G** compare?
4. Does this experiment support the Law of Conservation of Energy? Explain.

Mass of Hot Water (g)	Temperature of Hot Water (°C)	Mass of Cold Water (g)	Temperature of Cold Water (°C)	Temperature of Mixture (°C)
50		50		
75		25		
25		75		

PROCESS SKILLS
observing, measuring, recording data, comparing, identifying cause and effect, inferring

Preparation Make sure the thermometers are calibrated in degrees Celsius. If hot tap water is not available, preheat enough water for the class.

Safety Tips Boiling water can cause severe skin burns. Heat the water only to between 50°C and 60°C. If a mercury thermometer breaks, the teacher, not students, should clean up the mercury with a small dropper.

Teaching Tip Styrofoam coffee cups work well for this activity. While not essential, a cover or lid will cut down on heat lost to the atmosphere. If heat lost does not equal heat gained, discuss the possible sources of experimental error.

Answers to Results and Conclusions
1–3. Answers should indicate that heat lost equals heat gained. There will probably be some experimental error.
4. Yes; energy (in this case, heat) is not created or destroyed.

Tie-in/Math Give additional examples of specific heat problems. Change the data given, and ask students to solve for temperature change or the mass of material.

Sample Problem
How much heat is needed to raise the temperature of 10 g of iron from 20°C to 30°C?

1. Write the formula.

$$H = mc\Delta t$$

2. Substitute the amounts given in the problem for the symbols in the formula. The specific heat of iron can be found in Table 15-1.

$$H = 10 \text{ g} \times 0.45 \text{ J/g°C} \times 10°C$$

3. Determine the units that will be part of the answer. The units g and °C will cancel, leaving J as the unit.

$$H = 10 \times 0.45 \times 10 \text{ J}$$

4. Complete the calculations.

$$H = 45 \text{ J}$$

Teaching Tip   Point out that according to the Law of Conservation of Energy, energy is conserved in a calorimeter because the heat given off by the sample is absorbed by the water.

3 REVIEW/REINFORCEMENT

1. The total energy of all particles in a sample of matter.
2. Temperature is the average kinetic energy in a sample; heat is the total amount of energy in a system. Heat depends not only on the average kinetic energy of the particles, but also on how many particles are in the sample.
3. 702.2 J must be taken away.

$$H = mC\triangle t$$
$$H = 24 \text{ g} \times 4.18 \text{ J/g°C} \times 7°C$$
$$H = 702.2 \text{ J}$$

Challenge   The temperature will go down 1.64 degrees Celsius.

$$H = mC\triangle t$$
$$\triangle t = \frac{H}{mC}$$
$$\triangle t = \frac{-845 \text{ J}}{250 \text{ g} \times 2.06 \text{ J/g°C}}$$
$$\triangle t = -1.64°C$$

It takes 45 J of heat energy to cause the temperature change in the sample problem. How much heat must be applied to 15 g of water to raise its temperature by 12°C?[1]

Changes in heat energy can be measured using a device called a *calorimeter* (kal uh RIHM uh tuhr). The calorimeter in Figure 15-4 is made of two chambers. The inner chamber is partly filled with water. The temperature of the water is recorded. The material being tested is then placed in the water. The heat given off by the sample is absorbed by the water. This transfer of heat causes the temperature of the water to rise. A thermometer in the water shows the change in temperature. The amount of heat gained by the water can then be calculated. If no heat is lost to the air, then the amount of heat gained by the water is equal to the amount of heat lost by the sample.

[1]752 J.

Figure 15-4

This kind of calorimeter can be used in the physical science laboratory.

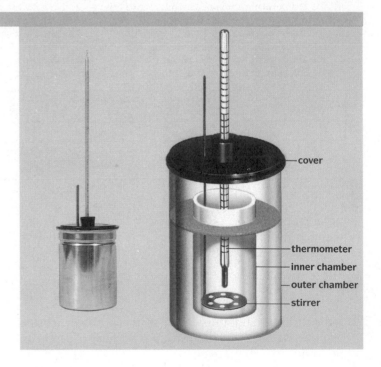

cover

thermometer

inner chamber

outer chamber

stirrer

REVIEW

1. What is heat?
2. How does heat differ from temperature?
3. How much heat energy must be taken away from 24 g of water to reduce its temperature by 7°C?

CHALLENGE How much will the temperature of 250 g of ice change if 845 J of energy is removed?

15-3 CHANGE OF STATE

Figure 15-5 shows snow on the ground on a warm day. Even though the air temperature rose above 0°C, much of the snow did not melt. Why does it take so long for the snow to melt? This question can be answered by studying what happens when matter changes from one state to another.

Recall that most matter on the earth exists in one of three states—solid, liquid, or gas. In the solid state, particles of matter are held together tightly. These particles cannot move around very much. In the liquid state, particles are held together loosely. Particles in a liquid move around more than do particles in a solid. Particles in a liquid have more energy than do particles in a solid.

Particles in a gas are not held together. These particles are free to spread out. Gas particles move more rapidly and have more energy than do particles in solids or liquids. Thus, the heat energy of a gas is greater than the heat energy of a solid or liquid made of the same material.

After completing this section, you will be able to

- **describe** how adding or removing heat causes matter to change state.
- **calculate** the amount of heat energy that will change a substance from one state to another.

The key terms in this section are
heat of fusion
heat of vaporization

Figure 15-5
The air temperature is above 0°C, but some snow remains on the ground.

When matter changes from one state to another, the amount of heat energy in the sample of matter also changes. For example, to change a solid to a liquid, heat must be added. To change a liquid to a gas, heat must also be added. To change a gas to a liquid, or a liquid to a solid, heat must be removed.

OBJECTIVES
Refer to pupil page 365.

VOCABULARY
Key terms: heat of fusion, heat of vaporization
Other terms: boiling point, melting point

1 MOTIVATION

Steam contains more heat than does an equivalent mass of boiling water. For this reason, steam is often used in commercial cooking. Have students check with the school cafeteria personnel to see steam cookers in operation. Ask students why steam cooks food faster. (The extra heat that goes into making the steam cooks the food faster.)

2 CONCEPT DEVELOPMENT

Teaching Tip   Have a feltboard and several circles of colored felt available to represent molecules. Start with the circles in an orderly, close arrangement to represent a solid. As more "energy" is added to the system, move the circles apart to represent a liquid and then a gas.

Background   The graph in Figure 15-6 is not unique to water. Any pure substance will produce a similarly shaped set of lines. The temperatures of the melting point and freezing point will be unique for each substance.

Background   The melting temperature is the same as the freezing temperature. The direction of change of state is determined by whether heat is added to or removed from the system.

Enrichment   Some materials, such as paraffin, are mixtures of substances. Ask students to predict and/or determine experimentally the shape of the melting-freezing portion of the change-of-state graph. (The graph at the melting-freezing point will consist of a series of steps; the number of steps will be dependent upon the number of substances in the mixture.)

Demonstration   Show that both a liquid state and a solid state of the same material can exist at the same temperature by putting ice into a beaker of water with a thermometer. At O°C both ice and water will be evident.

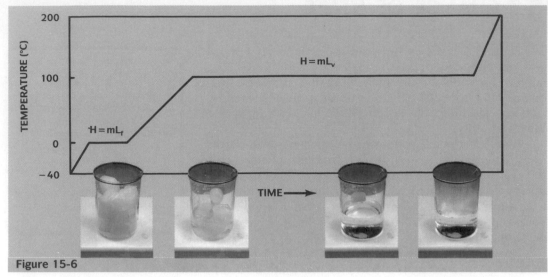

Figure 15-6

Heating a sample of matter causes a change in temperature or a change of state.

Figure 15-6 shows the changes in temperature that are measured as a sample of ice is heated. At the beginning the ice is at −40°C. As the ice is heated, the water molecules gain kinetic energy and move faster. The temperature of the ice rises to 0°C. Then it stops rising.

As more heat is added, the motion of the molecules in the ice does not increase. Instead the molecules overcome the forces that hold them together in the form of a solid. The molecules move farther apart and the ice melts. The temperature at which this occurs is called the *melting point*. Both solid and liquid exist at this temperature.

The amount of heat energy that will change a solid at its melting point to a liquid at the same temperature is called the **heat of fusion**. Each substance has a characteristic heat of fusion. The amount of energy needed to change a given amount of substance from a solid to a liquid can be calculated by using the following formula.

$$H = mL_f$$

Table 15-2 *Heat of Fusion and Heat of Vaporization*

Substance	Heat of Fusion (J/g)	Heat of Vaporization (J/g)
Aluminum	376	11,370
Gold	64	1,576
Iron	276	6,290
Lead	25	861
Mercury	12	293
Silver	88	2,332
Water	334	2,260

ACTIVITY What Happens During a Change of State?

OBJECTIVE
Measure the temperature of a substance as it changes from a liquid to a solid.

MATERIALS
safety goggles, 250-mL beaker, hot plate, paradichlorobenzene, test tube, thermometer, test-tube rack, clock or watch with second hand

PROCEDURE
A. Wear safety goggles during this activity.
B. Draw a data table to record time, temperature, and state of matter for at least 20 minutes.
C. Half fill a 250-mL beaker with water. On a hot plate, heat the water but do not boil it.
D. Place enough paradichlorobenzene in a test tube to fill it to a depth of about 2 cm. Place the test tube in the beaker of hot water.
E. After the substance has melted, put a thermometer in the test tube. When the temperature is above 65°C, remove the test tube from the beaker of hot water. Place the test tube in a test-tube rack.
F. Allow the material to cool. During this time, read the thermometer every 30 seconds. Record the time and the temperature in the data table. The first time reading should be 0 seconds. Also record with each reading the state of the material in the test tube. Continue until the temperature reaches 45°C.

RESULTS AND CONCLUSIONS
1. Make a graph of the results. Put the time on the x-axis and the temperature on the y-axis.
2. On the graph, mark the point at which crystals first formed. Label this point *A*. What was the temperature at this point?
3. On the graph, mark the point at which the last of the paradichlorobenzene solidified. Label this point *B*. What was this temperature?
4. What is the freezing point of paradichlorobenzene?

In this formula, H stands for heat, m stands for mass, and L_f stands for heat of fusion. Notice that there is no T in this formula. The temperature of a substance does not change as it melts.

Sample Problem
How much energy is needed to change 10 g of ice at 0°C to liquid water at 0°C?

1. Write the formula.

$$H = mL_f$$

2. Substitute the numbers from the problem for the symbols in the formula. The heat of fusion of water can be found in Table 15-2.

$$H = 10 \text{ g} \times 334 \text{ J/g}$$

3. Determine the units that will be part of the answer. The units for grams will cancel, leaving J as the unit.

$$H = 10 \times 334 \text{ J}$$

4. Complete the calculations.

$$H = 3340 \text{ J}$$

It takes 3340 J of energy to melt 10 g of ice.

ACTIVITY 30–35 minutes

PROCESS SKILLS
measuring, comparing, recording data, inferring

Preparation Make ice cubes at least a day in advance. Have hot water available.

Safety Tip If a mercury thermometer breaks, the teacher, not students, should clean up the mercury with a small dropper.

Teaching Tip Ice cubes from the refrigerator may be below 0°C. To prevent an error from this lower temperature, let the ice cubes stand at room temperature for a few minutes before using them.

Answers to Results and Conclusions
1–5. Answers will vary with differences in data. These differences will be due to the amount of heat lost to the atmosphere. There will also be differences in accuracy of measurement.

Demonstration   The boiling point depends on atmospheric pressure as well as on temperature. To show this, half fill a 250-mL beaker with water. Place a thermometer in the water. Put this assembly on the plate of a good vacuum pump, cover it with a bell jar, and start the pump. As the pressure decreases, bubbles will be seen forming on the walls and bottom of the beaker as well as on the thermometer. When the pressure is low enough, the water will boil. If your vacuum pump will not adequately reduce the pressure to make tap water boil, use slightly warmed water.

Review and Skill Masters
Skill, page 92.
See page 359b in this book for answers.

Think again about the unmelted snow on a warm winter day. The snow will melt as it absorbs heat energy from the warm air. How much energy is needed to melt 500 g of snow? What is the temperature of melting snow?[1]

[1]167,000 J; 0°C.

After the ice melts, the temperature of the water rises. As heat is added, the kinetic energy of the water molecules increases. The temperature of the water will increase until it reaches 100°C.

At 100°C, water begins to boil. Any heat added at this point will not increase the temperature of the water molecules. However, as energy is added, the molecules will overcome the forces that hold the molecules of the liquid together. The water will change from the liquid state to the gas state. Water in the gas state is called water vapor, or steam. During the change of state, both liquid water and water vapor will exist at the same temperature, called the *boiling point*.

The amount of heat energy that will change a liquid at its boiling point to a gas at the same temperature is called the **heat of vaporization**. Each substance has a char-

ACTIVITY   What Is the Heat of Fusion of Water?

OBJECTIVE
Measure the amount of heat absorbed as ice melts.

MATERIALS
2 plastic foam cups, balance, 100-mL graduate, ice, thermometer, stirring rod

PROCEDURE
A. Measure the mass of a plastic foam cup.
   1. What is the mass of the cup?
B. Add 100 mL of hot water to the cup. Measure the mass of the cup and the water.
   2. What is the mass of the cup and the water?
   3. What is the mass of the water?
C. Measure approximately 50 grams of ice into a second cup.
D. Measure the temperature of the hot water. Add the ice to the hot water, being careful not to add any water from ice that may have melted.
   4. What is the temperature of the hot water?

E. Stir the mixture until the last piece of ice has melted. Immediately measure and record the temperature of the water.
   5. What is the temperature of the water?
F. Measure the mass of the cup, the water, and the melted ice.
   6. What is this mass?
   7. How many grams of ice were melted?

RESULTS AND CONCLUSIONS
1. Calculate the amount of heat lost by the hot water as its temperature decreased.
2. Calculate the amount of heat gained by the melted ice as its temperature rose from 0°C to the final temperature.
3. To find the amount of heat absorbed by the ice as it melted, subtract the heat gained by the melted ice (question **2**) from the heat lost by the hot water (question **1**).
4. To find the heat of fusion, divide heat absorbed as the ice melted (question **3**) by the mass of ice used.
5. How does the experimental value for the heat of fusion compare with the value in Table 15-2? Suggest reasons for any differences.

acteristic heat of vaporization. The heat of vaporization of water is 2260 J/g. To change 1 g of water to steam requires 2260 J of energy. The heat energy needed to change a given amount of material from a liquid to a gas can be calculated by using the following formula.

$$H = mL_v$$

In this formula, H stands for heat, m stands for mass, and L_v stands for heat of vaporization.

Sample Problem

How much heat energy is needed to change 10 g of water at 100°C to water vapor at 100°C?

1. Write the formula.

$$H = mL_v$$

2. Substitute the numbers from the problem for the symbols in the formula. The heat of vaporization of water can be found in Table 15-2.

$$H = 10 \text{ g} \times 2260 \text{ J/g}$$

3. Determine the units that will be in the answer.

$$H = 10 \times 2260 \text{ J}$$

4. Complete the calculations.

$$H = 22,600 \text{ J}$$

As you can see, it takes much more energy to change a liquid to a gas than to change a solid to a liquid. To reverse these changes, heat energy must be removed from the sample of matter. For example, as water vapor changes to water in the liquid state, energy is released. If 10 g of water vapor are condensed, 22,600 J of energy are given off. What happens to the energy given off by the condensing steam in Figure 15-7?[1]

REVIEW

1. Explain how adding heat energy to a substance causes it to change from a solid to a liquid.
2. How does removing heat energy from a substance cause it to change from a gas to a liquid?
3. Calculate the amount of heat energy needed to change 15 g of silver from a solid to a liquid.

CHALLENGE How much heat energy must be applied to change 43 g of ice at −16°C to water vapor at 102°C?

Figure 15-7

Steam coming from the kettle is condensing on the metal nearby.

[1]The energy is absorbed by the surface on which the steam condenses.

3 REVIEW/REINFORCEMENT

1. Heat speeds up the molecules, so they move farther apart.
2. The molecules slow down and move closer together.
3. $H = mL_f$
   $H = 15 \text{ g} \times 88 \text{ J/g}$
   $H = 1320 \text{ J}$

Challenge

Step 1: Find the heat needed to change ice at -16°C to ice at 0°C.
$H = mC\triangle t$
$H = 43 \text{ g} \times 2.06 \text{ J/g°C} \times 16°C$
$H = 1417 \text{ J}$
Step 2: Find the heat needed to melt the ice.
$H = mL_f$
$H = 43 \text{ g} \times 334 \text{ J/g}$
$H = 14,362 \text{ J}$
Step 3: Find the heat needed to change water at 0°C to water at 100°C.
$H = mC\triangle T$
$H = 43 \text{ g} \times 4.18 \text{ J/g°C} \times 100°$
$H = 17,974 \text{ J}$
Step 4: Find the heat needed to change the water to steam.
$H = mL_v$
$H = 43 \text{ g} \times 2260 \text{ J/g}$
$H = 97,180 \text{ J}$
Step 5: Find the heat needed to change the steam to 102°C.
$H = mC\triangle t$
$H = 43 \text{ g} \times 2.06 \text{ J/g°C} \times 2°C$
$H = 177.16 \text{ J or } 177 \text{ J}$
Step 6: Add the answers from steps 1–5.
1417 J + 14,362 J + 17,974 J + 97,180 J + 177 J = 131,110 J

15-4 EXPANSION AND GASES

pages 370–372

pages 370–372

OBJECTIVES
Refer to pupil page 370.

VOCABULARY
Key terms: Boyle's law, Charles's law, pressure

Other terms: expansion, pascal

1 MOTIVATION

Ask a student to pull a deflated balloon over the top of an empty soft-drink bottle. Tell the student to place the bottle in a pan of hot water. Ask students what happens to the balloon. Have the class provide reasons for the change in the balloon. (The hot water caused the air in the bottle to warm up and expand, inflating the balloon.)

2 CONCEPT DEVELOPMENT

Demonstration   Use the classic ball-and-ring assembly to show how a solid expands when its temperature is increased. Pass the cool ball in and out of the ring. Heat the ball; then show that it will no longer fit through the ring.

Thinking Skills

hypothesizing
Students observe expansion and contraction in Figure 15-8. They are asked to consider what would happen to the bridge if there were no expansion joints.

Demonstration   Fill a flask with water to the brim. Heat the flask of water on a hot plate. The water will expand and overflow the flask. Colored water will make the demonstration more vivid.

370

15-4 EXPANSION AND GASES

15-4 EXPANSION AND GASES

After completing this section, you will be able to

- **distinguish** between expansion and contraction.
- **explain** the relationship between the volume, temperature, and pressure of a gas.

The key terms in this section are
Boyle's law   pressure
Charles's law

When the metal lid on a glass jar is stuck, the lid can usually be loosened by holding the jar under hot water. The hot water causes the metal lid to expand. It then twists off the jar easily.

Most substances expand when they are heated. *Expansion* is an increase in the space between the particles that make up an object. Recall that when an object is heated, its particles gain energy. As these particles move faster, they collide more often and with more force. The force of the collisions pushes the particles apart. Thus the object expands and its volume becomes larger.

When an object cools, its particles lose kinetic energy. As the motion of the particles decreases, the space between them also decreases. The object contracts and its volume becomes smaller.

Each substance expands and contracts at its own rate. A glass jar expands and contracts very little compared with its metal lid. This difference makes it possible to loosen the lid with hot water. The steel rods used to reinforce concrete expand at the same rate as the concrete. What would happen if they expanded at different rates?[1]

[1]The concrete would crack.

Figure 15-8

Expansion joints in a bridge (*left*), and reinforcing rods in concrete (*right*).

[2]It would probably buckle and break.

Many objects expand and contract depending on the weather. For example, a metal bridge expands on a hot day. Bridges are built with devices called expansion joints, as shown in Figure 15-8. As the bridge expands, the spaces in the joints are filled. What would happen to the bridge if there were no expansion joints?[2]

370

Liquids expand and contract in the same way as do solids. Suppose you filled a watering can early in the morning, when the air was still cool. As the temperature rose during the day, the water in the can would expand. By the end of the day, you might find that some of the water had spilled over.

When a gas is heated, its particles move faster and the gas expands. However, if the gas is heated in a closed container, the particles are confined by the walls of the container. As the gas particles move around, they strike the walls of the container. The force of the gas particles striking the inside of the container causes pressure. **Pressure** is force acting on a unit area. The SI unit of pressure is the *pascal* (Pa). A pascal is equal to 1.0 N/m².

pressura (to press)

Figure 15-9

These balloons have been filled with helium from the tank.

Two physical laws describe the relationship between the volume, pressure, and temperature of a gas. Boyle's law relates volume to pressure. According to **Boyle's law**, the volume of a gas decreases as its pressure increases if the temperature stays the same. If pressure on the gas increases, the particles are forced closer together. The gas takes up less space. If pressure on the gas decreases, the particles move farther apart. The gas takes up more space.

Helium gas is used to fill balloons. Because the gas is under pressure, a large amount of helium can be held in a small container. Look at Figure 15-9. The tank of helium was used to fill all of these balloons, and it still contains enough helium to fill many more. The total volume of the balloons is much greater than the volume of the tank. Where is the helium under the most pressure?[1]

[1] In the tank.

Background   Since warm air rises, students may think that the temperature at high elevations is higher than that at lower elevations. Of course, this is not true. Rising warm air expands, and as it does, the vibrating particles slow down, since there are fewer collisions. The expansion of a gas is a cooling process.

Demonstration   Place a dented table-tennis ball in a beaker of water. Heat the water. The gas in the ball will expand and push out the dent.

Teaching Tip   Computations involving Charles's law will work only if the temperatures are in terms of Kelvin degrees.

3 REVIEW/REINFORCEMENT

1. *Expansion* implies spreading out and growing larger; *contraction* implies becoming denser and smaller.
2. Its volume will decrease.
3. Its volume will decrease.

Challenge
$V_1 P_1 = V_2 P_2$
$1.0 \text{ L} \times 6000 \text{ Pa} = V_2 \times 0.5 \text{ L}$
$\dfrac{1.0 \text{ L} \times 6000 \text{ Pa}}{0.5 \text{ L}} = V_2$
$12{,}000 \text{ Pa} = V_2$

¹It will expand again.

²They turn off the burner. The cooling gas contracts, and the balloon sinks to the ground.

According to **Charles's law**, the volume of gas increases as its temperature increases if the pressure stays the same. If the temperature of a gas decreases while the pressure stays the same, the volume of the gas decreases. If you blow up a balloon indoors and then take it outside on a cold day, the balloon will get smaller. What would happen if you took the balloon indoors again?¹

A hot-air balloon rises because of Charles's law. A gas burner is used to heat the air in the balloon. The air expands and takes up more space. Although the volume of the balloon increases, the mass does not. The density of the balloon becomes less than the density of the air around it. The denser air exerts a buoyant force on the balloon, and so the balloon floats in the air just as a cork floats in water. How do you think the balloonists get back to the ground?²

Figure 15-10
Heating the air in a balloon causes the balloon to rise.

REVIEW

1. How is expansion different from contraction?
2. What will happen to the volume of a gas if its pressure increases while its temperature stays the same?
3. What will happen to the volume of a gas if its temperature decreases while its pressure stays the same?

CHALLENGE Suppose the initial pressure on 1.0 L of gas in a balloon is 6000 Pa. Use Boyle's law to predict the pressure on the gas if it is compressed to a volume of 0.5 L.

15-5 HEAT TRANSFER

Heat moves from an area of higher temperature to an area of lower temperature. This transfer of heat occurs by conduction, convection, or radiation.

Conduction is the transfer of heat energy by direct contact between particles. When particles with a large amount of kinetic energy strike particles with less kinetic energy, some energy is transferred to the lower-energy particles. This transfer will continue until all particles have the same kinetic energy and are at the same temperature. Most metals are good conductors. Wood, plastic, glass, and all gases are poor conductors. Why do some pots have wood or plastic handles?[1]

Convection is heat transfer that occurs in moving fluids. When a fluid is heated, it expands and becomes less dense. Less-dense materials rise above denser materials. Hot liquids and gases rise. Cold liquids and gases fall. This creates currents that carry heat energy.

Wind is caused by convection. On a sunny day, for example, the sun warms the earth and the earth heats the air above it. At a beach like the one shown in Figure 15-11, the sand warms quickly. The warm air over the sand rises, and cool air moves in to replace it. This movement of air causes a kind of wind called a sea breeze.

How does heat from the sun reach the earth through space? There is no matter to carry the energy. The sun's energy travels through space in the form of waves. The transfer of energy by waves is called **radiation**. No particles are needed to transfer energy by radiation.

After completing this section, you will be able to

- **identify** the ways in which heat is transferred.
- **describe** how heat transfer is used to control air temperature.

The key terms in this section are
conduction   radiation
convection

[1]These substances will not conduct heat to your hand.

radians (beam)

Figure 15-11

Transfer of heat can occur by conduction, convection, and radiation.

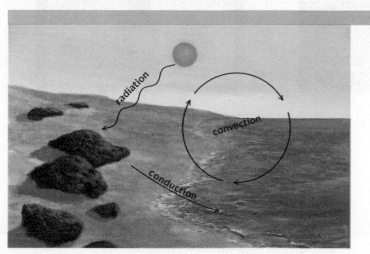

OBJECTIVES
Refer to pupil page 373.

VOCABULARY
Key terms: conduction, convection, radiation

1 MOTIVATION

To show that water is a poor conductor of heat and that only warm fluids rise, put several pieces of ice in a test tube. Hold the ice at the bottom of the test tube with some wire gauze or steel wool. Fill the test tube with water. Tip the test tube and heat the water near the top with a Bunsen burner. The water at the top will boil. Ask students why the water boiled at the top of the test tube while ice remained at the bottom. (The cold water at the bottom did not rise to mix with the warm water at the top.) Ask students what effect this has on large swimming pools, lakes, and the ocean.

2 CONCEPT DEVELOPMENT

Background   As the temperature increases in a blast furnace, waves of radiant-heat energy can often be seen as visible light. The approximate temperatures and colors of hot steel are dark red, 700°C; bright red, 900°C; yellow, 1200°C; and white, 1500°C.

Demonstration   To show that radiant energy will pass through a vacuum, pour some water into a flask. Put a thermometer in the water. Place the assembly on the plate of a vacuum pump, cover it with a bell jar, and turn on the pump. Outside the bell jar, direct a heat lamp toward the water, and watch the temperature rise.

Teaching Tip Have students use two empty soft-drink cans. Spray one with aluminum paint and the other with flat (not glossy) black paint or have students cover one can with aluminum foil and the other with black construction paper. Insert a thermometer into each can. Seal the hole with wax, putty, or clay. Place the two cans equidistant from a heat lamp, and record the temperature readings every 10 minutes for 30 minutes. The thermometer in the black can will give a higher reading than the thermometer in the shiny can. Ask students why this occurs.

[1] The rocks contain large amounts of heat energy, which can cause water to evaporate.

When waves of heat energy strike the earth, some are absorbed and some are reflected. Dark colors absorb more energy than do light colors. Dark rocks on a beach would absorb energy faster than the light sand would. If you touched the rocks and the sand on a sunny day, you would be able to feel the temperature difference. If there were a sudden shower, the rocks would dry quickly. Why?[1]

Heat transfer is used to control the air temperature in houses and other buildings. Heating systems transfer heat by conduction, convection, or radiation, or by a combination of these. Fireplaces heat mainly by radiation. Hot-water and steam heating systems use all three types of heat transfer. The hot water or steam transfers heat to the radiator by conduction. The air near the radiator is heated by radiation. Convection currents carry warm air through the room. Figure 15-12 shows these heating systems.

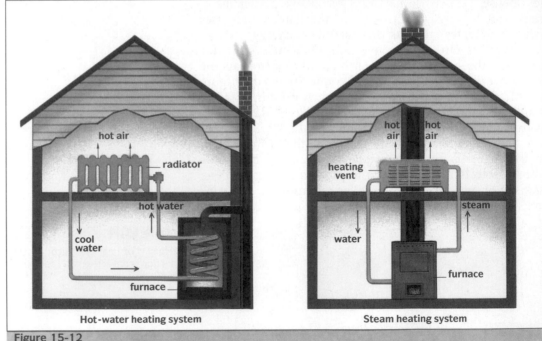

Figure 15-12

Hot-water heating system (*left*), and steam heating system (*right*).

In a steam heating system, heat from the furnace boils water. The steam produced rises into radiators. There the steam condenses, releasing heat to the room. The water flows back to the boiler where it is heated again. In a hot-water heating system, the water is heated, but not boiled. A pump circulates the hot water through radiators, and back to the furnace.

Review and Skill Masters

CHALLENGE/CRITICAL THINKING, page 93. See page 357c in this book for answers.

Heat transfer is also used in cooling systems. Cooling systems, such as refrigerators and air conditioners, use evaporation to absorb heat. Cooling systems have a liquid contained in metal tubing. As the liquid evaporates in the tubing, heat is absorbed from the food in the refrigerator or the air in the room. Freon is the liquid most commonly used in cooling systems. The heat of vaporization of Freon is 167 J/g. Thus each gram of Freon absorbs 167 J of energy as it evaporates in the tubing.

The Freon gas then flows to a compressor. The compressor increases the pressure of the gas and thus changes it back to a liquid. As the Freon gas condenses, heat is given off. The liquid Freon then flows back into the tubing to repeat the cycle. Why does the back of a refrigerator or the exhaust from an air conditioner feel warm?[1]

[1] The heat from the condensed Freon is released at the back of the refrigerator or the outside of the air conditioner.

Background Fiberglass is a type of insulation that slows the transfer of heat by the use of air spaces. Air and glass are poor conductors of heat. The air spaces in fiberglass are too small for convection to occur, so heat is not easily transferred.

SCIENCE & TECHNOLOGY

If people could see heat, then maybe they would be more interested in trying to save heat energy. This is the idea behind using thermograms, colored pictures that show heat loss from homes and buildings.

All objects give off infrared radiation, which can be detected by special cameras or scanners. The cameras change the pattern of radiation into pictures. The differences in temperatures are shown as colors. Usually the warmest temperatures show up as white, red, and yellow. The cooler temperatures show up as green, blue, and black.

One town in Michigan used thermograms to show where its residents were losing heat from their homes during the winter. From the thermograms, they found that windows and doors released most of the heat that was lost. Roofs that

were not well insulated also lost heat. On the thermograms many roofs, windows, and doors appeared white, red, and yellow. Windows with the shades drawn showed up as blue or green. This demonstrated the savings in energy from simply pulling down the shades at night. Many homeowners in the Michigan town responded to

the thermograms by insulating their attics, plugging leaks in doors and windows, and closing in porches.

Thermograms taken of entire cities show what kinds of buildings lose the most heat. By pinpointing heat losses, architects and engineers can know how to design buildings to conserve more energy.

Puzzler This action traps air, which is a good insulator, near the skin. Loss of body heat is therefore slowed down.

Teaching Tip Ask students why thermal underwear and blankets are effective insulators. Have an examination sample available to show the trapped, insulating air.

Teaching Tip Ask students why cold snow prevents the ground from freezing to great depths. Ask students why people stranded in a snowstorm should build a snow cave to keep warm. (The snow contains a great deal of air; the air is an insulator that slows down heat loss.)

Thinking Skills

comparing
Students learn that the air spaces in fluffy materials slow the rate of heat conduction. Ask students to compare the insulating qualities of a heavy coat with the insulating qualities of a down jacket.

3 REVIEW/REINFORCEMENT

1. Conduction is the transfer of heat energy by direct contact between particles; convection is the heat transfer that occurs in moving fluids.
2. Radiation is the transfer of energy by waves; examples—energy from the sun reaches the earth by radiation, air near a radiator is heated by radiation.
3. Heat from food is transferred to liquid Freon in the cooling coils of the refrigerator; as it evaporates, the Freon removes large quantities of heat from the food.

Challenge Heat of vaporization.

SCIENCE PUZZLER

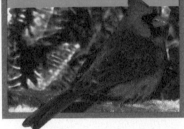

When mammals are cold, they fluff their fur. When birds are cold, they fluff their feathers. How do these actions help to keep the animals warm?

[1]The feathers have become packed together and have lost their air spaces.

The heating and cooling **systems** in a building have to work against natural heat transfer processes. Depending on the weather, heat must be added to, or removed from, a building to keep the inside temperature at a comfortable level. When the weather is cold and a building is being heated, the building is warmer than its surroundings. The building loses heat. When the weather is warm and a building is being cooled, the surroundings are warmer than the building. Then the building absorbs heat.

Most of this heat exchange takes place by conduction. Buildings are insulated to reduce the amount of heat transfer by conduction. Insulation does not stop heat transfer, but it slows the process. Materials that are poor conductors are good insulators. Recall that gases are poor conductors. Most insulation is made of fluffy materials. The air spaces in these materials slow the rate of heat conduction through the insulation. Down jackets and quilts work on the same principle. Down is made up of tiny, fluffy feathers. Sometimes an old jacket or quilt will seem to have lost its ability to provide insulation and hold in body heat. What might cause this change?[1]

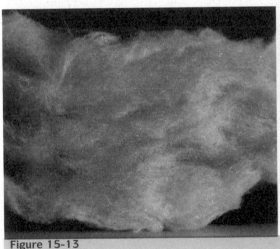
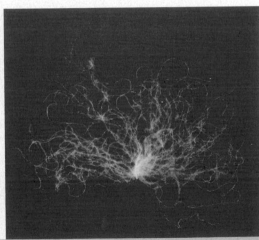

Figure 15-13

Fluffy materials like fiberglass (*left*) and down feathers (*right*) are good insulators.

REVIEW

1. Distinguish between conduction and convection.
2. What is radiation? Give an example of heat transfer by radiation.
3. How does a refrigerator lower the temperature of food?

CHALLENGE What is the name given to the amount of heat absorbed by Freon as it evaporates?

15-6 HEAT ENGINES

When a fuel such as gasoline burns, heat energy is given off. This heat energy can be changed into mechanical energy to do work. A **heat engine** is a device that changes the heat energy from burning fuel into mechanical energy.

A steam engine is a kind of heat engine called an external combustion engine. In an *external combustion engine,* fuel is burned outside the engine. Look at the locomotive shown in Figure 15-14. A fuel such as coal is burned to boil water. Steam under high pressure pushes a piston. The energy of the moving piston is transferred to the wheels of the locomotive.

Figure 15-14
The steam engine in this locomotive is an external combustion engine.

The gasoline engines and diesel engines in cars and trucks are internal combustion engines. In an *internal combustion engine,* fuel is burned inside the engine. This burning takes place in the cylinders.

The engines in most cars have four, six, or eight cylinders. Each cylinder is a container with two openings, controlled by valves. The intake valve lets a mixture of fuel and air into the cylinder. The exhaust valve lets the waste products of burning out of the cylinder. As the fuel burns, pistons move up and down in the cylinders. The motion of the pistons turns a rod called the crankshaft. The crankshaft transfers its power to the wheels by means of a series of gears.

After completing this section, you will be able to

- **describe** how a heat engine works.
- **give examples** of heat engines.

The key term in this section is **heat engine**

OBJECTIVES
Refer to pupil page 377.

VOCABULARY
Key term: heat engine
Other terms: compression stroke, exhaust stroke, external combustion engine, intake stroke, internal combustion engine, power stroke, stroke

1 MOTIVATION

Explain to students that mechanical energy is often used to do work, but much of the mechanical energy is wasted as it is being converted to heat energy. Ask students to list examples of mechanical energy that is used to do work. Ask them what would happen if many of the modern mechanical systems did not exist.

2 CONCEPT DEVELOPMENT

Thinking Skills

classifying
Students learn to classify engines as external or internal combustion types on the basis of where the fuel is burned.

Enrichment   Steam locomotives and steam-powered machines were once quite common. Ask students to research these engines and to draw a diagram that shows the operation of pistons in steam engines.

Background   Internal combustion engines produce large amounts of heat. The excess heat of an automobile engine is usually removed by a cooling system that uses a mixture of water and ethylene glycol (permanent antifreeze) as the heat transfer agent. The excess heat is then dissipated to the atmosphere through a radiator.

Background   Point out to students that diesel engines are more efficient than gasoline engines. However, because of the high compressions involved, the engine must be built considerably stronger, and therefore it must have more mass. Diesel engines are especially well suited for use in larger machines like tractor trailers and locomotives. In recent years, smaller diesel engines have been introduced into the automobile market.

Teaching Tip   Plastic replicas of automobile engines or single cylinders are available at hobby stores or from some scientific supply companies. Use one of these engines to demonstrate the operation of the four-cycle engine.

Thinking Skills

interpreting diagrams
Students are asked to interpret the diagram of the four-stroke engine in Figure 15-15 and to identify the intake, compression, power, and exhaust strokes.

Transparency

The Teacher Resource Package includes a color transparency and a black-line master of Figure 15-15. You may wish to use these in your discussion of heat engines.

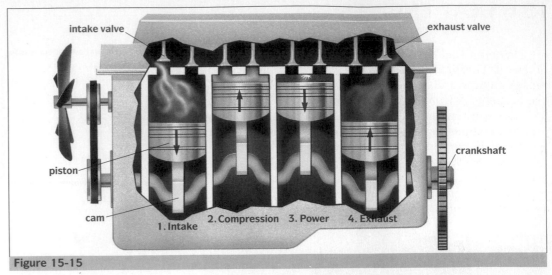

Figure 15-15

A four-stroke engine.

Figure 15-15 shows a four-stroke engine. Each upward or downward motion of a piston is called a *stroke*. Refer to the figure as you read about this process.

1. *Intake stroke* The piston moves downward. This causes a mixture of fuel and air to be drawn into the cylinder through the intake valve.
2. *Compression stroke* The intake valve closes and the piston moves upward. The fuel-air mixture is compressed into a smaller space.
3. *Power stroke* A spark plug creates a spark that ignites the gases in the cylinder. As the gases ignite and expand, they force the piston downward. This is the only stroke in which burning takes place.
4. *Exhaust stroke* The exhaust valve opens to let out the waste products of the burning reaction. This stroke is followed by the intake stroke of the next cycle.

A diesel engine works a little differently than a gasoline engine. There are no spark plugs in a diesel engine. A diesel engine compresses the fuel more than does a gasoline engine. As a result, the compressed gases become so hot that they burn spontaneously. The rest of the cycle is the same as for other four-stroke engines.

Jet engines are internal combustion engines that work on the principle of the Third Law of Motion. There are no pistons in a jet engine. Instead, hot gases produced by burning fuel are forced out of the engine. This is the action force. The reaction force to the escaping gases propels the jet forward. Rocket engines work in a similar way.

REVIEW

1. What is the purpose of a heat engine? Give two examples of heat engines.
2. Describe how a four-stroke engine works.
3. How is a jet engine different from a gasoline engine?

CHALLENGE Sometimes a piston in a car's engine will continue to ignite after the engine has been turned off and the spark plugs are no longer firing. This process is called dieseling. Why is this name appropriate?

CHAPTER SUMMARY

The main ideas in this chapter are listed below. Read these statements before you answer the Chapter Review questions.

- The kinetic theory states that particles of matter are always in motion. Forces of attraction prevent the particles from drifting apart. (15-1)

- Temperature is a measure of the average kinetic energy of a substance. (15-1)

- Heat is the total kinetic energy of moving particles in a sample of matter. Heat can be transferred from one substance to another. (15-2)

- Specific heat is the amount of heat energy needed to raise the temperature of 1 g of a substance 1°C. (15-2)

- Matter will change from one state to another if heat is added to, or removed from, a substance. (15-3)

- The heat energy needed to change a substance from a solid to a liquid is called the heat of fusion. (15-3)

- The heat energy needed to change a liquid to a gas is heat of vaporization. (15-3)

- Most substances expand when heated and contract when cooled. (15-4)

- Charles's law states that if pressure remains the same and the temperature increases, the volume of a gas will increase. (15-4)

- Boyle's law states that if the temperature stays the same and the pressure increases, the volume of a gas will decrease. (15-4)

- Conduction, convection, and radiation are the three different ways that heat energy is transferred from one substance to another. (15-5)

- Heat engines convert heat energy to mechanical energy by burning fuel. (15-6)

The key terms in this chapter are listed below. Use each term in a sentence that shows the meaning of the term.

Boyle's law	heat engine	pressure
Charles's law	heat of fusion	radiation
conduction	heat of vaporization	specific heat
convection	kinetic theory	temperature
heat		

1. A heat engine changes the heat energy of burning fuel into mechanical energy; examples—steam engine, gasoline engine, diesel engine, jet engine.
2. In this engine each upward or downward motion of a piston is called a stroke.
    a. Intake stroke—the piston moves downward, causing a mixture of fuel and air to enter the cylinder through the intake valve.
    b. Compression stroke—the intake valve closes and the piston moves upward, compressing the fuel-air mixture into a smaller space.
    c. Power stroke—a spark plug creates a spark that ignites the gases in the cylinder; as the gases expand they force the piston downward.
    d. Exhaust stroke—the exhaust valve opens to let out the waste products from the burning reaction; this stroke is followed by the intake stroke of the next cycle.
3. A gasoline engine has pistons; a jet engine has no pistons.

Challenge The fuel is being ignited by the heat of the engine and by compressional heat, not by spark plugs; this is the way a diesel engine works.

Review and Skill Masters

VOCABULARY REVIEW, page 89.
See page 357b in this book for answers.

VOCABULARY

1. convection	6. specific heat
2. kinetic theory	7. heat engine
3. pressure	8. conduction
4. temperature	9. heat of fusion
5. heat of vaporization	10. heat

CONCEPTS

1. Particles in a gas move around freely; particles in liquids and solids have more limited movement.
2. There are forces of attraction between particles.
3. a. 310 K (37 + 273).
   b. 283 K (10 + 273).
   c. 90°C (363 − 273).
   d. 0°C (273 − 273)
4. Lake; the mass of water is greater in a lake.
5. $H = mC\triangle t = 100\ g \times 0.45\ J/g°C \times 20°C = 900\ J$.
6. $H = mC\triangle t = 20\ g \times 4.18\ J/g°C \times 30°C = 2508\ J$.
7. $H = mC\triangle t = 20\ g \times 2.06\ J/g°C \times 10°C = 412\ J$.
8. The heat energy overcomes the forces that hold the liquid molecules close together.
9. $H = mL_v = 40\ g \times 2260\ J/g = 90,400\ J$
10. $H = mL_f = 300\ g \times 25\ J/g = 7500\ J$
11. The particles move farther apart.
12. Pressure is force acting on a unit area; in pascals, Pa.
13. The volume of a gas decreases as its pressure increases if the temperature remains constant.
14. The volume of a gas increases as its temperature increases if the pressure remains the same.

Review and Skill Masters

CHAPTER REVIEW, pages 90–91.
See page 357b in this book for answers.

Chapter Review

VOCABULARY

Use the key terms from this chapter to complete the following sentences correctly.

1. Heat is transferred in moving fluids by the process of _____ .
2. The _____ says that all matter is made of tiny particles in constant motion.
3. Force per unit area is called _____ .
4. _____ is the measure of the average kinetic energy of a sample of matter.
5. The amount of heat energy that will change a liquid to a gas is called the _____ .
6. The amount of heat energy needed to raise the temperature of 1 g of a substance by 1°C is called the _____ .
7. A/An _____ is a device that changes heat energy into mechanical energy.
8. The transfer of heat energy by direct contact between particles is called _____ .
9. _____ is the amount of heat energy that will change a solid to a liquid.
10. The total energy of the particles in a sample of matter is called _____ .

CONCEPTS

1. Compare the movement of particles in a gas, a liquid, or a solid. (15-1)
2. Why don't moving particles in a sample of matter keep moving apart? (15-1)
3. Convert the following temperatures to Kelvins or degrees Celsius. (15-1)
   a. 37°C =   K   c. 363 K =   °C
   b. 10°C =   K   d. 273 K =   °C
4. If a swimming pool and a lake are the same temperature, which has more heat? Why? (15-2)
5. How much heat is needed to raise the temperature of 100 g of iron by 20°C? (15-2)
6. How much heat is needed to raise the temperature of 20 g of water from 10°C to 40°C? (15-2)
7. How much heat is given off as 20 g of ice is cooled from −10°C to −20°C? (15-2)
8. Explain how adding heat energy to a substance causes it to change from a liquid to a gas. (15-3)

9. How much heat is needed to change 40 g of water at 100°C to steam at 100°C? (15-3)

10. How much heat is released as 300 g of lead changes from a liquid to a solid? (15-3)

11. What effect does increased temperature have on the movement of gas particles? (15-4)

12. What is pressure? In what unit is it measured? (15-4)

13. State Boyle's law. (15-4)

14. State Charles's law. (15-4)

15. List and explain the three ways heat can be transferred from one object to another. (15-5)

16. Describe how a refrigerator transfers heat from food to the air outside the refrigerator. (15-5)

17. Where do heat engines get their energy? What kind of energy do they produce? (15-6)

18. How is a diesel engine different from a gasoline engine? How are they similar? (15-6)

19. How does a steam engine differ from a gasoline engine? (15-6)

APPLICATION/CRITICAL THINKING

1. Explain why winter clothes are usually dark colored and summer clothes are usually light colored.

2. Why are radiators built to have a large surface area?

3. Water expands when heated and contracts when cooled. Why isn't water used to make thermometers?

4. Explain why the Great Lakes usually remain unfrozen in the winter while other lakes at the same latitude freeze.

EXTENSION

1. The diesel engine is sometimes used for automobiles. Do some research to find the good and bad features of the diesel engine.

2. The insulation used in buildings is rated for its R-value. Find out how these ratings are determined and what R-value is recommended for the area in which you live.

3. Research James Watt. Where were his steam engines first used?

READINGS

Bittman, M. "Keep Heat Inside with Outside Insulation." *Popular Science,* October 1984, p. 100.

Nelson, R. "A Look Inside The Super-engines." *Popular Mechanics,* February 1984, p. 80.

15. By conduction, which is the transfer of heat energy by direct contact between particles; by convection, which is heat transfer that occurs in moving fluids; by radiation, which is the transfer of energy by waves.

16. The heat of the food is transferred to Freon in the refrigeration tubing, changing the liquid Freon to a gas; the heat is carried by the Freon to the compressor of the refrigerator; pressure causes the Freon to condense, giving off heat that is transferred from the Freon to the air.

17. From burning fuel; mechanical energy.

18. A diesel engine has no spark plugs; both are internal combustion engines with pistons.

19. A steam engine is an external combustion engine; a gasoline engine is an internal combustion engine.

APPLICATION/CRITICAL THINKING

1. Dark colors absorb heat energy, making a person warmer; light colors reflect heat energy, keeping a person cooler.

2. The more surface in contact with the air, the more heat can be given off to the air.

3. Changes of state occur in water at temperatures normally encountered in the atmosphere; under these circumstances the water in the thermometer would freeze at 0°C and boil at 100°C, making it useless.

4. The large mass of water retains enough heat to keep the temperature above the freezing point.

Test Masters

CHAPTER TEST, pages 57–60.
See page 357d in this book for answers.

ELECTRICITY

ORGANIZER

Section	pages	Activity	pages	Reinforcement and Evaluation	pages	*Review and Skill Masters	pages	Other Components in Teacher Resource Package	pages
16–1 Static Electricity	383–385	How Is Static Electricity Produced?	385	Review, Challenge	385			Study Guide Lab Manual	80 81
16–2 Effects of Static Electricity	386–390	How Is an Electroscope Used to Detect Charge?	390	Review, Challenge	390			Study Guide	81
16–3 Current Electricity	391–396			Puzzler Review, Challenge	396			Study Guide Lab Manual	82 83
16–4 Electric Circuits	397–400	How Do Series and Parallel Circuits Differ?	399	Review, Challenge	400			Study Guide	83
16–5 Electric Power	401–404			Review, Challenge	404	Skill Challenge/Critical Thinking	98–99 100	Study Guide	84
CHAPTER SUMMARY	405					Vocabulary Review	95		
CHAPTER REVIEW	406–407			*Test Masters	61–64	Chapter Review	96–97		

*In the Teacher Resource Package. For answers, see pages 381b–381d in this book.

ACTIVITY MATERIALS Quantities are based on a class of 30 students working in groups as indicated in parentheses.

How Is Static Electricity Produced? p. 385 (groups of 2)	quantity	How Is an Electroscope Used to Detect Charge? p. 390 (groups of 2)	quantity	How Do Series and Parallel Circuits Differ? p. 399 (groups of 2)	quantity
rubber rod	15	electroscope	15	dry cell	15
glass rod	15	hard rubber rod	15	miniature light bulb	45
wool cloth	15 pieces	animal fur	15 pieces	miniature sockets	45
silk cloth	15 pieces	glass rod	15	switch	15
small strip of aluminum foil	15 strips	silk	15 pieces	wire (45 cm long)	45 pieces
pith ball with silk cord attached	15			screwdriver	15
ring stand	15				

REVIEW AND SKILL MASTERS

VOCABULARY REVIEW _____ Chapter 16

Unscramble and define the following terms about electricity.

1. croontdcu   conductor—a substance that allows electric charges to flow through easily

2. tawt   watt—a unit of power equal to one joule per second

3. rssaaceitne   resistance—the opposition to the flow of charges in a substance

4. lllpraea uicirtc   parallel circuit—a circuit in which there is more than one path for the current

5. nudoirngg   grounding—the process of removing the charge on a charged object by connecting it to the earth

6. wtltkioa-rohu   kilowatt-hour—the amount of electrical energy used when one kilowatt of power is used for one hour

7. yrd elcl   dry cell—an electric cell in which an electrolyte is a paste instead of a liquid solution

8. irnostula   insulator—a substance that does not allow electric charges to flow through easily

9. talgoev   voltage—a measure of the energy available to move charges in a circuit

10. iulontcdn   induction—the process of charging an object by the presence of a nearby charged object

11. tlececir rtcuner   electric current—the flow of electrons or charge

12. letercic llce   electric cell—a device that changes chemical energy into electrical energy

13. rseeis riticuc   series circuit—a circuit in which there is only one path for the current

© 1988 Silver, Burdett & Ginn Inc.

95

CHAPTER REVIEW _____ Chapter 16

16-1   Static Electricity

1. What are the two types of electric charges?   The two types of electric charges are positive and negative charges.

2. How do objects become electrically charged?   Objects become electrically charged by losing or gaining electrons.

3. Contrast conductors and insulators and give one example of each.   Conductors allow electric charges to flow easily, while insulators do not allow charges to flow easily. Copper is a conductor; rubber is an insulator.

16-2   Effects of Static Electricity

1. Describe two ways charged objects interact.   Objects with like charges repel and objects with unlike charges attract.

2. Describe how a positively charged object attracts an uncharged object.   When you place a positively charged object near an uncharged object, the negative charges within the uncharged object move toward the positively charged object.

3. How does an electroscope detect electric charges?   When the knob of the electroscope is touched with a charged object, the leaves spread apart. The leaves hang straight when there is no charge present.

16-3   Current Electricity

1. Define electric current and state its cause.   Electric current is the flow of electrons. It is caused by a difference in the number of electrons in two places.

2. What three factors affect a conductor's resistance?   Temperature, diameter, and length affect the resistance of a conductor.

© 1988 Silver, Burdett & Ginn Inc.

96

CHAPTER REVIEW (Continued) _____ Chapter 16

3. Use Ohm's law to calculate the resistance of a conductor if the current is 40 A and the voltage is 2400 V. $R = V \div I = 2400\ V \div 40\ A = 60\ \Omega$

16-4   Electric Circuits

1. List the three parts of a simple electric circuit.   The three parts of a simple electric circuit are a voltage source, a conductor, and a load.

2. Contrast a series circuit and a parallel circuit.   A series circuit has only one path for the current; a parallel circuit has more than one path for the current.

3. Name two safety devices in electric circuits and tell how they work.   A fuse contains a short piece of thin metal that melts when too much current flows in a circuit. A circuit breaker is a switch that opens when too much current flows through a circuit.

16-5   Electric Power

1. What is the relationship between the electric power of an electric device and the amount of energy it uses?   The amount of electrical energy a device uses each second is its electric power. The greater the power rating, the more energy it uses.

2. Calculate the energy used by a 100 W light bulb for 60 seconds. $E = Pt = 100\ W \times 60\ s = 6000\ W\text{-}s$

3. What is the cost to run an air conditioner with 2,000 watts for 5 hours at the cost of $.10 per kilowatt-hour? $2000\ W \times 5\ h = 10{,}000\ W\text{-}h = 10\ kW\text{-}h,$ $10\ kW\text{-}h \times \$0.10/kW\text{-}h = \$1.00$

© 1988 Silver, Burdett & Ginn Inc.

97

SKILL/Inferring _____ Chapter 16

Two circuits are illustrated below with a 6-volt dry cell battery and flashlight bulbs of equal value.

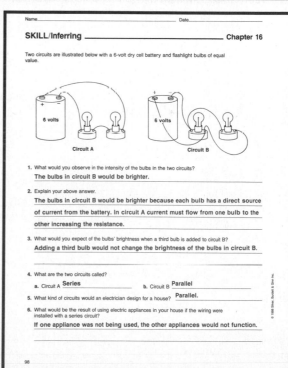

Circuit A   Circuit B

1. What would you observe in the intensity of the bulbs in the two circuits?
The bulbs in circuit B would be brighter.

2. Explain your above answer.
The bulbs in circuit B would be brighter because each bulb has a direct source of current from the battery. In circuit A current must flow from one bulb to the other increasing the resistance.

3. What would you expect of the bulbs' brightness when a third bulb is added to circuit B?
Adding a third bulb would not change the brightness of the bulbs in circuit B.

4. What are the two circuits called?
a. Circuit A   Series   b. Circuit B   Parallel

5. What kind of circuits would an electrician design for a house?   Parallel.

6. What would be the result of using electric appliances in your house if the wiring were installed with a series circuit?
If one appliance was not being used, the other appliances would not function.

© 1988 Silver, Burdett & Ginn Inc.

98

CHAPTER **16** PLANNING GUIDE

Name_____ Date_____

SKILL/Inferring (Continued) _____ Chapter 16

In the illustration below, the circuit contains a 12-volt storage battery, a high resistance wire, and a bulb.

12 volts

A — 5 ohms   B — 3 ohms
High resistance wire

7. When would the bulb be brightest—when the battery is connected at A or at B? **B**

When the light bulb is connected at point A, the resistance in the circuit is 5 ohms.

8. What is the current in the circuit? **2.4 amperes.**

9. What would be the voltage of the circuit if the current were 5 amps and the resistance were 10 ohms? **50 volts.**

10. Calculate the resistance in the circuit if the voltage was 30 volts and the current was 3 amps? **10 ohms.**

11. What would happen to the resistance in the circuit if the high resistance wire were replaced by a heavy copper wire?
The resistance would be reduced in the circuit.

12. Explain your above answer.
Since copper is a good electrical conductor, the resistance of the circuit would be greatly reduced.

13. What would happen to the resistance in the circuit if two more bulbs were added to the circuit in series?
The resistance of the circuit would increase because the electricity must flow through the additional resistance of the filament in the second and third bulbs.

99

Name_____ Date_____

CHALLENGE/CRITICAL THINKING _____ Chapter 16

Use the data from the two sample electric statements shown below to answer the questions that follow. Electrical rates are usualy rounded off to the nearest $0.001/kW-h. Use scientific notation for all joule calculations and round off to one place after the decimal.

ELECTRIC STATEMENT FOR NOVEMBER (meter reading in kW-h)

Present	Previous	Amount Due
37874	37018	$47.28

ELECTRIC STATEMENT FOR DECEMBER (meter reading in kW-h)

Present	Previous	Amount Due
39148	37874	$63.35

1. How many kilowatt-hours were used in November?
37874 kW-h − 37018 kW-h = 856 kW-h

2. What was the rate per kW-h in November?
$47.28 ÷ 856 kW-h = $0.0552336/kW-h, rounded to $0.055/kW-h

3. How many kilowatt-hours were used in December?
39148 kW-h − 37874 kW-h = 1274 kW-h

4. What was the rate per kW-h in December?
$63.35 ÷ 1274 kW-h = $0.0497252/kW-h, rounded to $0.050/kW-h

5. How many joules of energy are used to produce 1 kW-h of power?
1 kW = 1000 J/s, 1 kW-s = 1000 J, 1 kW-h = 3 00 × 1000 J,
1 kW-h = 3.6 × 10⁶ J

6. How many joules of energy were used in December?
1274 kW-h × 3.6 × 10⁶ J/kW-h = 4.5864 × 10⁹ J, rounded to 4.6 × 10⁹ J

7. What was the cost per joule in December?
$63.35 ÷ 4.6 × 10⁹ J = $1.4 × 10⁻⁸/J, rounded to $1.4 × 10⁻⁸/J

8. How long could you operate a 100-watt light bulb with one joule of energy?
1 W = 1 J/s: 1 J ÷ 100 J/s = 0.01 second

100

TEST MASTERS

Electricity

PART 1

In the space below, write the term that each phrase defines.

Chapter Goal

1. __electric circuit__   A system through which an electric current can travel   4

2. __grounding__   The process of removing the charge on a charged object by connecting it to the earth   2

3. __parallel circuit__   A circuit in which there is more than one path for the current   4

4. __resistance__   The opposition to the flow of charges in a substance   3

5. __static electricity__   The effects caused by electric charges at rest   1

6. __electric power__   The amount of electrical energy used each second by an electrical device   5

7. __insulator__   A substance that does not allow electric charges to flow through easily   1

8. __induction__   The process of charging a substance by the presence of a nearby charged substance   2

9. __kilowatt-hour__   The amount of electrical energy used when one kilowatt of power is used for one hour   5

10. __dry cell__   An electric cell in which the electrolyte is a paste instead of a liquid   3

PART 2

Choose the term or phrase that best answers the question or completes the statement. Write the letter of that choice in the space at the left.

__c__ 1. A piece of copper allows electrons to flow from one piece of wire to another. The copper is acting as: 1
   a. an insulator.   b. a battery.   c. a conductor.   d. a fuse.

__d__ 2. Which of the following units would most likely be used to measure the amount of electrical energy used in one second?   5
   a. amp   b. volt   c. ohm   d. watt

Chapter 16   Electricity   61

Choose the term or phrase that best answers the question or completes the statement. Write the letter of that choice in the space at the left.

Chapter Goal

__c__ 3. The amount of electric current that can flow in a conductor can be increased by increasing the conductor's: 3
   a. temperature.   b. length.   c. diameter.   d. resistance.

__d__ 4. What is the electrical power of a stereo that uses 2 A when plugged into a voltage of 120 V? ($P = VI$)   5
   a. 60 W   b. 118 W   c. 122 W   d. 240 W

__a__ 5. A battery produces a voltage of 9V and sends a current of 2A through a wire. What is the resistance in the wire? ($R = \frac{V}{I}$)   3
   a. 4.5 Ω   b. 7 Ω   c. 11 Ω   d. 18 Ω

__a__ 6. A glass rod becomes positively charged when rubbed on silk. The silk has most likely: 1
   a. gained electrons.   c. gained protons.
   b. lost electrons.   d. lost protons.

__b__ 7. A fuse that has melted performs the same function as: 4
   a. a load.   c. a voltage source.
   b. a switch.   d. an electrical conductor.

__a__ 8. When a metal rod is brought near the knob of a negatively charged electroscope, the leaves of the electroscope move farther apart. This is caused by electrons moving from the: 2
   a. knob to the leaves.   c. leaves to the rod.
   b. knob to the rod.   d. leaves to the knob.

__d__ 9. A series circuit contains three light bulbs. Which of the following will occur if one of the bulbs burns out?   4
   a. The other bulbs will stay lit.
   b. The voltage of each bulb will increase.
   c. A closed circuit will be formed.
   d. An open circuit will be created.

__c__ 10. A positively charged rod will have the strongest attraction for: 2
   a. an insulator that has more protons than electrons.
   b. a fuse that has more protons than electrons.
   c. a conductor that has more electrons than protons.
   d. a switch that has more protons than electrons.

Chapter 16   Electricity   62

Look at the diagram. Then read the questions that follow. Choose the term or phrase that best answers the question or completes the statement. Write the letter of that choice in the space at the left.

Chapter Goal

__a__ 1. With the switch in the open position, which light bulbs are lit?   4
   a. A and B   b. B and C   c. B and D   d. C and D

__d__ 2. The current that flows in the circuit in the diagram is 0.1 A. What is the resistance of the circuit? ($R = \frac{V}{I}$)   3
   a. 0.01 Ω   b. 1 Ω   c. 10 Ω   d. 100 Ω

__a__ 3. How much electrical energy does bulb A use in 60 seconds? ($E = Pt$)   5
   a. 12,000 W-s   b. 600 W-s   c. 400 W-s   d. 200 W-s

__b__ 4. How much does it cost to run these light bulbs for two hours at a cost of $.10 per kWh? (Cost = cost per kWh x power x time) (1 kW = 1000 W)   5
   a. $.05   b. $.10   c. $.20   d. $1.00

Chapter 16   Electricity   63

Read each question or direction and answer it using complete sentences.

Chapter Goal

1. How does a charged rod attract a piece of metal or paper? Explain why a charged rod attracts the metal better than it attracts the paper.   2

> A charged rod is able to attract a piece of metal or a piece of paper by causing electrons to move to one side of the foil or paper. The foil and paper become charged by the rod through the process of induction. The rod's attraction for paper is not as great as for metal because paper is an insulator, while metal is a conductor. Electrons do not move as easily in paper as they do in metal. Thus the charge that builds up in paper is less than the charge that builds up in the foil.

2. What is a wet cell? Explain the reactions that occur in wet cells to create voltage.   3

> A wet cell is an electric cell that contains a liquid electrolyte, such as an acid. A wet cell also contains electrodes that react with the electrolyte. One electrode, called the anode, reacts with the acid, causing electrons to accumulate. These electrons flow out of the cell, creating an electric current. Electrons return to the cell through another electrode, called the cathode. These electrons take part in a chemical reaction with the electrolyte. The reactions that occur between the electrodes and the electrolyte create an electrical pressure called voltage.

3. Describe circuit breakers, and explain why they are replacing fuses in modern homes.   4

> A circuit breaker is a safety switch in an electric circuit that opens the circuit when too much current flows through it. One advantage of a circuit breaker over a fuse is that it does not have to be replaced when it opens the circuit. A circuit breaker can be reset to close the circuit.

Chapter 16   Electricity   64

CHAPTER 16 PLANNING GUIDE

16

ELECTRICITY

The questions in the CHAPTER TEST are based on these Chapter Goals.

1. Describe two kinds of electric charges, explain how objects become electrically charged, and distinguish between a conductor and an insulator.

2. Describe the interactions between charged objects, and explain how charged objects can attract uncharged objects and how an electroscope can be used to detect an electric charge.

3. Explain the cause of electric current, describe the factors that affect resistance, and use Ohm's law to calculate voltage, current, and resistance.

4. Explain how the parts and safety devices in electric circuits work, and compare series circuits and parallel circuits.

5. Relate the electric power of an electric device to the amount of electrical energy it uses; calculate electric power, electrical energy, and the cost of electrical energy.

ELECTRICITY

Think of the number of times a day you switch on something that use electricity. How many times do you turn on a light, television set or radio, or pick up the telephone? Most of the electric devices we have come to depend on were invented in the last 50 years. And about 100 years ago, there were no electric power companies, transmission lines, or light bulbs.

- *How many forms of electricity are there?*
- *When is electricity dangerous?*
- *Why is electricity such a useful form of energy?*

16-1 STATIC ELECTRICITY

Have you ever walked across a carpet and received an electric shock when you touched a doorknob? Do you ever hear electricity crackling when you comb your hair? Electricity can form whenever objects rub against other objects. Electricity is a form of energy called electrical energy.

Recall that all substances are made up of tiny particles called *atoms*. The atoms contain electrically charged particles called protons and electrons. Protons have a positive charge. Electrons have a negative charge. Their charges are equal and opposite. Usually there are equal numbers of electrons and protons in atoms and in objects. Thus, atoms and objects are usually electrically neutral, or uncharged.

Uncharged objects, however, can become electrically charged. For example, two different uncharged objects can become charged when they are rubbed against each other. Electrons can be lost by one object and gained by the other. Each object no longer has equal numbers of protons and electrons. An electrically charged object has unequal numbers of protons and electrons. An object that has more electrons than protons is said to be negatively charged. An object that has fewer electrons than protons is said to be positively charged.

After completing this section, you will be able to

- **describe** two kinds of electric charges.
- **explain** how objects become electrically charged.
- **distinguish** between a conductor and an insulator.

The key terms in this section are
conductor
electricity
insulator
static electricity

2 CONCEPT DEVELOPMENT

Background   According to the hydrogen atom model proposed by the Danish physicist Neils Bohr in 1913, an atom has an extremely dense nucleus that is responsible for the positive charge in the atom and nearly all of its mass. Negatively charged electrons orbit the protons in the nucleus. A proton is almost 2000 times more massive than an electron, however the electric charge of a proton is equal but opposite to that of an electron.

Background   The atomic theory was accepted long before anyone had ever seen an atom. Now an electron microscope that magnifies more than 5 million times allows scientists to see images of atoms.

Thinking Skills

inferring
Students are reminded of an experience they may have had when they have walked across a carpet and then touched a doorknob or another person. Students are asked to infer what charge the carpet has. (Positive; it loses electrons to student's body.)

Teaching Tip   The relative conductivity of some materials can be expressed in magnitudes relative to each other. The following are some examples.

Materials	Magnitude
Conductors	
Silver, copper, aluminum	10^8
Iron, mercury	10^7
Nichrome, carbon	10^6
Semiconductors	
Germanium, silicon	10^3
Insulators	
Wood	10^{-10}
Glass	10^{-12}
Rubber	10^{-15}

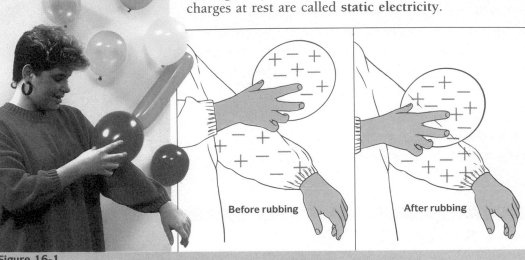

Figure 16-1

Objects become charged when electrons move from one object to another.

Notice in Figure 16-1 that the rubbing together of two objects does not make new electric charges. The rubbing causes the electrons that are already present to move from one object to the other. Once the rubbing has stopped and the two objects are separated, the electric charges stop moving. They remain at rest. The effects caused by electric charges at rest are called **static electricity**.

You are probably familiar with the static electricity produced when you walk across a carpet. The static electricity forms as your shoes rub against the carpet. Electrons are picked up by the shoes and are spread across your body. As a result, your body becomes negatively charged. What charge does the carpet have?[1]

The negative charge on your body does not remain there forever. If you touch a metal object, such as a doorknob, electrons will travel from your body through your fingers to the metal. You will probably feel a shock and hear a crackling sound. Sometimes you can see a spark. Even if you do not touch a metal object, the charge on your body will eventually be lost. The air contains water molecules, which attract negative charges. Electrons will slowly flow from your body to the air until your body loses its charge.

Unlike your body, some objects lose their electric charge almost as soon as they gain it. This is because electric charges can flow through these substances easily. The charges do not remain in place and build up. A substance that allows electric charges to flow through easily is called a **conductor**. Metals are conductors. Look at Table 16-1. Which metal shown is the best conductor?[2]

[1]Positive.
[2]Silver.

Table 16-1 *Conductors and Insulators*

Substance	Ability to Conduct Electricity
Silver	Best conductor
Copper	↑
Aluminum	
Carbon	
Water	
Human body	
Earth	
Plastic	
Glass	
Hard rubber	↓
Dry air	Best insulator

ACTIVITY How Is Static Electricity Produced?

OBJECTIVES
Explain how static electricity is produced.
Draw conclusions about how objects can become charged.

MATERIALS
rubber rod, small strip of aluminum foil, wool cloth, glass rod, silk cloth, pith ball with silk cord attached, ring stand

PROCEDURE
A. Bring a rubber rod near, but not touching, a small strip of aluminum foil.
  1. What do you observe? Explain your observation.
B. Rub the rubber rod with a wool cloth. Bring the rod near the aluminum foil.
  2. What do you observe? Explain your observation.
C. Bring a glass rod near, but not touching, the foil.
  3. What do you observe? Explain your observation.
D. Rub the glass rod with a silk cloth. Bring the rod near the foil again.
  4. What do you observe? Explain your observation.
E. Hang a pith ball from a ring stand. Rub the rubber rod with the wool. Bring the rod near, but not touching, the pith ball.
  5. What do you observe? Explain your observation.
F. Rub the glass rod with the silk. Bring the rod near, but not touching, the pith ball.
  6. What do you observe? Explain your observation.
G. Rub the rubber rod with wool. With the rod, touch the pith ball lightly.
  7. What do you observe? Explain your observation.
H. Rub the glass rod with the silk. With the rod, touch the pith ball lightly.
  8. What do you observe? Explain your observation.

RESULTS AND CONCLUSIONS
1. Describe how an object can become charged.
2. How can a charged object cause another object to become charged?
3. From your observations, can you determine if the charges on the rod and foil and on the rod and pith ball are alike or unlike? Explain your answer.

ACTIVITY 25 minutes

PROCESS SKILLS
observing, comparing, inferring

Preparation None required.

Answers to Procedure
1. Nothing happens; both uncharged.
2. The aluminum foil is attracted to the rod, which was charged by rubbing it with wool.
3. Nothing happens; both uncharged.
4. The same as in **2** except that the rod was charged by rubbing it with silk.
5. The pith ball reacts just as the foil did in **2**, for the same reasons.
6. The pith ball reacts just as the foil did in **4**, for the same reasons.
7–8. First they attract, then they repel; when the rod touches the pith, the rod transfers its charge to the pith.

Answers to Results and Conclusions
1. By rubbing two objects together, causing electrons to move from one object to the other.
2. It can make electrons move from one object to the other.
3. No; the activity showed that both rods are charged, but not what the charges are.

3 REVIEW/REINFORCEMENT

1. Positive and negative.
2. By rubbing, electrons are transferred from one object to another.
3. Conductors allow electric charges to flow easily; insulators do not.
   Conductor—silver; insulator—rubber.

Challenge Moisture makes the surface of objects conductive, so charges quickly leak off; this does not happen on dry days.

Some substances do not gain or lose an electric charge easily. This is because electric charges do not flow through these substances easily. Thus, the charges tend to remain in place. A substance that does not allow electric charges to flow through easily is called an **insulator** (IHN suh lay-tuhr). Insulators are very poor conductors of electricity. Rubber, plastic, and glass are examples of insulators. According to Table 16-1, which of these three substances is the best insulator?[1]

insula (island)

[1]Hard rubber.

REVIEW

1. What are two kinds of electric charges?
2. In what way can objects become electrically charged?
3. What is the difference between a conductor and an insulator? Give one example of each.

CHALLENGE Why would you be more likely to receive an electric shock when touching a doorknob on a dry day than on a humid day?

16-2 EFFECTS OF STATIC ELECTRICITY

pages 386–390

16-2 EFFECTS OF STATIC ELECTRICITY

OBJECTIVES
Refer to pupil page 386.

VOCABULARY
Key terms: electroscope, grounding, induction
Other term: leaves

1 MOTIVATION

Suspend two pith balls from silk threads, and charge them by touching each with a glass rod rubbed with silk. Bring the pith balls near each other, being careful not to let them touch. Have students give their observations of the pith balls. Then have a volunteer place a sheet of aluminum (or some other metal) between the pith balls. Have students describe what they see. (The balls should fall back to their normal positions as the charge diminishes; the electrical force will not pass through the metal.)

2 CONCEPT DEVELOPMENT

Background   In electrostatics, or charges at rest, like charges repel, and unlike charges attract. The amount of attraction or repulsion depends on the quantity of charge on two interacting bodies and the distance between them. An electroscope is just one type of instrument for measuring the amount of charge.

Background   Electric charge is involved in an interaction called electrical force, just as mass is involved in gravitational force. But electrical force is billions of times stronger than gravitational force.

After completing this section, you will be able to

- **describe** the interactions between charged objects.
- **explain** how charged objects can attract uncharged objects.
- **explain** how an electroscope can be used to detect electric charges.

The key terms in this section are
electroscope
grounding
induction

Have you ever noticed how a record taken out of its sleeve attracts dust? What force causes the clothes taken from a dryer to stick together? What causes objects to take on new properties when they become charged?

FORCES BETWEEN CHARGED OBJECTS

When objects become charged, they can exert forces on other objects. Recall that when two different objects are rubbed against each other, they can become oppositely charged. Figure 16-2A shows two pieces of clothing that rubbed against each other in the dryer. Notice that they attract each other. If two shirts rubbed against the same sweater, both shirts will have like charges. Figure 16-2B shows what happens when two shirts with like charges are brought together. Notice that they repel each other. These experiments show that objects with like charges repel and objects with unlike charges attract.

Figure 16-2
Objects that have unlike charges attract (A). Objects that have like charges repel (B).

A charged object can also attract an uncharged object close to it. For example, if you charge a comb by pulling it through your hair, the comb will pick up small pieces of paper. You can also make a balloon stick to a wall by first rubbing the balloon on your sleeve. These attractions take place because a charged object can cause the near end of a neutral object to become charged.

Figure 16-3A shows the effect of placing a positively charged rod just above a small piece of aluminum foil. Notice that negative charges in the foil move upward. This makes the top of the foil negatively charged. What charge does the bottom of the foil have?[1] Because substances with unlike charges attract, the rod attracts the top end of the foil. As a result the foil is pulled toward the rod.

[1]Positive.

Thinking Skills

identifying cause and effect
Students are asked to determine when static charges may be dangerous. Have students identify the possible cause of an explosion of a gasoline truck if the truck does not drag a chain at the rear.

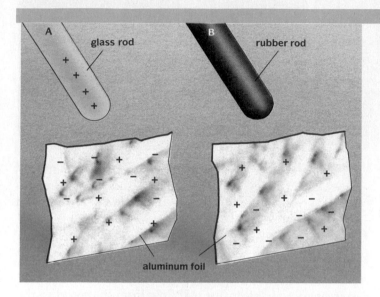

Figure 16-3

A piece of aluminum foil can be charged by the presence of a charged object.

Figure 16-3B shows what happens when a negatively charged rod is brought near the foil. Negative charges in the top end of the foil are repelled by the rod, and they move to the bottom end. The top end of the foil becomes positively charged. The negatively charged rod attracts the positively charged end of the foil. The rod also repels the negatively charged bottom end of the foil. However, this effect is weaker than the attraction at the top of the foil, because the bottom of the foil is farther from the rod.

A charged rod can also attract small pieces of paper. However, this attraction is not as great as that for metal. This is because paper is an insulator and metal is a conductor. Charges do not move as easily in paper as they do in metal. Thus the charge that builds up in paper is less than the charge that builds up in aluminum foil.

In both examples the charged rod causes electrons to move. The foil and paper become charged because of the charged rod near them. The process of charging an object by the presence of a nearby charged object is called **induction** (ihn DUHK shuhn).

in- (in)
-ducere (to lead)

Demonstration   Show the effect of a charged object on a thin stream of water. Rub a glass rod with silk to give it a positive charge, then hold the rod near a thin stream of water. The water will deflect toward the rod. Have students determine why this happens. Challenge them to test whether a negatively charged rod (produced by rubbing a rubber rod with fur) will also deflect a thin stream of water and to explain their observations.

Teaching Tip   Since water molecules are polar, they rearrange themselves with unlike ends toward a charged glass rod. The attraction between the unlike charges causes the deflection of a thin stream of water, regardless of whether the rod is positively charged or negatively charged.

Background   The earth's surface may be charged by induction during storms, but these charges are short-lived and localized.

Teaching Tip   Discuss with students the safety precautions to be taken during a thunderstorm. Information from the National Weather Service reveals that there is no place that is absolutely safe from lightning. Certainly an open field with no buildings is one of the worst places. Ask students why this may be. (A person in a field would be the tallest object around by which lightning could conduct its charge to the ground.)

Figure 16-4

Lightning occurs when electrons flow from clouds to the earth.

The earth's surface is sometimes charged by induction. During a storm, electric charges in a cloud can separate. As you can see in Figure 16-4, the top layer of the cloud becomes positively charged. The bottom layer of the cloud becomes negatively charged and repels negative charges in the ground. This causes the surface of ground to become positively charged.

When the build-up of charges in the cloud and ground is great enough, electrons will flow from the cloud to the ground. As the electrons flow, air along their path becomes heated. If the air is heated enough, a bright streak of light called lightning can be seen. The heating of the air also causes it to expand. When the flow of electrons is great enough, the air expands so rapidly that it produces a loud sound that is heard as thunder.

DETECTING STATIC ELECTRICITY

A device that can detect the presence of electric charges is the **electroscope** (ih LEHK truh skohp). The electroscope is made up of a container with a knob at the top. Hanging inside the container are two metal strips called *leaves*. The leaves hang straight down when there are no electric charges present.

When a negatively charged rod touches the knob, electrons flow into the electroscope. The electroscope becomes negatively charged. Electrons flow from the rod to the knob and then down to the leaves, which become negatively charged. Figure 16-5 shows the effect this has on the leaves.

Figure 16-5

When the electroscope is charged, the leaves repel each other.

When the knob is touched with a positively charged rod, electrons flow from the electroscope into the rod. The electroscope becomes positively charged. Electrons flow from the leaves to the knob and into the rod. The loss of electrons from the leaves makes them positively charged. Again, the leaves repel each other.

The leaves in an electroscope behave the same whether the charge on the electroscope is positive or negative. How, then, can the electroscope be used to determine the kind of charge on a charged object?

If the charge on an electroscope is known, it can be used to determine the kind of charge on a charged object. For example, suppose an electroscope is charged by touching it with a rod known to be negatively charged. Notice in Figure 16-6A that the leaves become negatively charged and they spread apart. When the rod is removed, the leaves remain spread apart. Now suppose a rod with an unknown charge is brought near the knob.

Figure 16-6

If a charged rod causes the leaves to move farther apart, the rod is shown to have a negative charge. Notice in Figure 16-6B that the negatively charged rod would cause electrons in the knob to be pushed down to the leaves. Adding negative charges to the negatively charged leaves would cause the leaves to spread apart more.

If a charged rod is brought near the knob and the leaves move closer together, the rod is shown to have a positive charge. Notice in Figure 16-6C that a positively charged rod would attract electrons from the leaves up to the knob. Removing electrons from the negatively charged leaves would cause the leaves to move together.

An electroscope can detect charges. Because only electrons can move in the electroscope, only negative charges are shown in the electroscope.

PROCESS SKILLS
observing, comparing, inferring

Preparation   None required.

Answers to Procedure
1. They spread apart.
2. The leaves spread apart more.
3. The leaves move closer together.
4. The leaves spread apart.
5. Touching the electroscope with the finger grounded it; when the finger was removed, the leaves spread apart again.

Answers to Results and Conclusions
1. Steps **A**, **D**, **E**.
2. Steps **B** and **C**, and the rod in step **E**.
3. The charge produced on the rubber rod was negative; on the glass rod, positive.

---

③ REVIEW/REINFORCEMENT

1. A charged object can attract or repel another charged object; a charged object can also attract an uncharged object close to it.
2. By induction.
3. By charging the electroscope with a rod that has a known charge. Bring the object with unknown charge near the knob: if the leaves move farther apart, the object has the same charge as the electroscope; if the leaves move closer together, the object has the opposite charge.

Challenge   The clothes rub against each other, building up electric charges.

ACTIVITY   How Is an Electroscope Used to Detect Charge?

OBJECTIVE
Explain how an electroscope is used to detect charge.

MATERIALS
hard rubber rod, fur, electroscope, glass rod, silk cloth

PROCEDURE
A. Rub a rubber rod with a piece of fur. Touch the rod to the knob of an electroscope.
   1. What happens to the leaves of the electroscope?
B. Rub the rubber rod with fur. Bring the rubber rod near, but not touching, the knob.
   2. What happens to the leaves?
C. Rub a glass rod with a silk cloth, and bring the rod near, but not touching, the knob.
   3. What happens to the leaves?
D. Touch the electroscope. Rub the rubber rod with fur. Touch the knob of the electroscope with the fur.
   4. What happens to the leaves?
E. Bring the rubber rod near the knob of the electroscope. Without removing the rod, touch the knob with your finger. Remove your finger from the knob first and then remove the rod.
   5. What happens to the leaves?

RESULTS AND CONCLUSIONS
1. In which steps was the electroscope charged by the flow of electrons into or out of the electroscope?
2. In which steps was the electroscope charged by induction?
3. Compare the charge produced on the rubber rod with the charge produced on the glass rod.

Figure 16-7

How has this electroscope been grounded?[2]

Bringing the charged rods near the electroscope does not add charges to or remove charges from the electroscope. It just causes the charges in the electroscope to move. Thus when the rods are removed, the electroscope still has the same amount of charge as it had when it was first charged.

You can remove the charge on a charged electroscope by touching the knob with your finger. If the electroscope had a negative charge, electrons would flow from the electroscope onto your finger and into the earth. If the electroscope had a positive charge, electrons would flow from the earth through your body and into the electroscope.

In both cases the electrons flow until the number of electrons and protons are equal in the electroscope. The process of removing the charge on a charged object by connecting it to the earth is called **grounding**. How would you describe the charge on a grounded object?[1]

REVIEW

1. What are two ways in which charged objects can interact?
2. How do charged objects attract uncharged objects?
3. How is an electroscope used to determine if an object has a positive or negative charge?

CHALLENGE   Explain how static electricity builds up in a clothes dryer.

[1]A grounded object has no charge; it is neutral.
[2]It has been touched.

16-3 CURRENT ELECTRICITY

Recall that charges at rest produce static electricity. Moving charges produce *current electricity*. The charges flow along a path called a *circuit*. Current electricity that flows in only one direction is called direct current. Current electricity that reverses its direction constantly is called alternating current, which will be discussed in Chapter 17.

MOVING CHARGES

Electrons can move easily through substances called conductors, such as metals. In the atoms of conductors electrons in the outermost level are held very loosely. The electrons are easily lost by the atoms. Once free, the electrons move randomly through the conductor.

The random movement of electrons can be changed to a steady flow. If electrons are added to one end of a conductor, they will flow from the place with more electrons to the place with fewer electrons. The flow of electrons, or flow of charge, is called **electric current**.

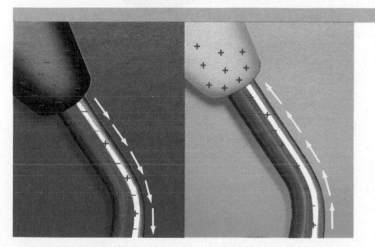

Figure 16-8

Electrons added to or removed from one end of a conductor will cause the flow of electrons.

ELECTRIC CELLS

To move electric charges in a circuit, energy must be supplied. This energy can be supplied by an electric cell. An **electric cell** is a device that changes chemical energy into electrical energy. Two or more electric cells combined make up a *battery*. An electric cell contains two different substances called *electrodes* (ih LEHK trohdz). The electrodes are placed in a conducting mixture called an *electrolyte*. Chemical reactions take place between the electrodes and substances in the electrolyte mixture.

1 MOTIVATION

Demonstrate a "lemon battery." Insert a zinc strip and a copper strip into a large, fresh lemon. Attach the strips to a voltmeter with wires and alligator clips. Ask students what item or items in the apparatus are the electrodes. Now replace the voltmeter with a light bulb. Ask students how to make the light bulb brighter. Attach two lemons in a series circuit, and observe the results. Ask students to predict what the voltage reading will be. Attach the voltmeter, and observe the results.

2 CONCEPT DEVELOPMENT

Background   Although it is convenient to talk about the "flow" of electricity, it can create some misunderstandings. Before a wire is connected to a voltage source, the electrons move randomly and chaotically in the wire at a speed of about 1000 km/s. There is no net flow of electrons one way or the other. When a voltage source is connected to the wire, there is a general charge movement along the wire toward the lower potential. This causes an electric field, not individual electrons, to travel through the circuit at a speed near the speed of light. Energy flows in the circuit, and this produces less motion in the electrons.

Background   A battery produces electrical pressure, or voltage, by chemical means. When the battery cables are attached to the positive and negative terminals, the circuit has potential. In a 12-V automobile battery, there is a difference of potential of 12 V. The positive terminal has a potential of $+12$ V and the negative terminal is grounded, or has a potential of zero volts.

Teaching Tip   Mention to students that heat moves to a place that is colder, and that water flows from a higher place to a lower place. Then tell them that electrical energy moves from a place where there is an oversupply of electrons to a place where electrons are needed. The analogy may be helpful in understanding the direction of energy flow.

¹Because they contain acid and lead.

An electric cell that contains an electrolyte in liquid solution is called a **wet cell**. Most automobile batteries, like the one shown in Figure 16-9, contain six wet cells. The electrolyte is sulfuric acid. The electrodes are made of lead and lead dioxide, PbO_2. Why is the automobile battery also called a lead-acid battery?[1]

Figure 16-9

An automobile battery contains wet cells.

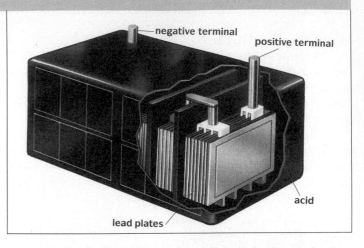

anodos (a way up)

cathodos (a way down)

When the lead electrode reacts with the acid, electrons accumulate in the electrode. These electrons flow out of the cell, creating an electric current. The electrode through which electrons leave the cell is called the **anode** (AN ohd). The anode is connected to the negative terminal of a battery.

Electrons return to the cell through the second electrode. The electrode through which electrons enter the cell is called the **cathode** (KATH ohd). The cathode is connected to the positive terminal of a battery. The electrons that enter the cell take part in chemical reactions between the lead dioxide of the cathode and the electrolyte.

The chemical reactions that take place in an electric cell occur in pairs. One reaction takes place at the anode, and a different reaction takes place at the cathode. Neither reaction can take place without the other. The reactions will not take place unless the cell is connected to a circuit that provides a path for the flow of electrons.

Which electrode will be the anode and which will be the cathode depends on the substances used in the electrodes. One substance will have a greater tendency to give up electrons than will the other. As electrons accumulate at one electrode a negative charge builds up there. As a result, an electrical pressure is created that causes electrons to flow. This electrical pressure is called *voltage* (VOHL tihj). Voltage is measured in volts (V). For example, the difference between lead and lead dioxide gives each cell of a lead-acid battery a voltage of 2 V. The six cells combined produce 12 V. How much voltage would be produced if all of the cells contained only lead electrodes?[1]

The cells that are used in toys, flashlights, and calculators are dry cells. A **dry cell** is an electric cell in which the electrolyte is a paste instead of a liquid. A dry cell is shown in Figure 16-10. The anode is the zinc container and the cathode is the carbon rod in the center. Unlike the lead-acid battery, the dry cell uses a base as an electrolyte. Thus, dry cells are sometimes called alkaline batteries. However, they are not really batteries—they are single cells.

Recall that the nature of the electrodes determines the voltage of a cell. Thus all of the carbon-zinc dry cells shown in Figure 16-10 have the same voltage, 1.5 V. How do these cells differ? Larger cells contain more reactants and produce electrons more rapidly than do smaller cells. However, all of these cells produce the same electrical pressure, or voltage.

[1]Zero voltage.

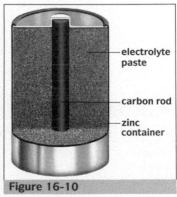

Figure 16-10

A dry cell contains a paste as its electrolyte.

electrolyte paste

carbon rod

zinc container

A cell will produce a current only if the chemical reactions that take place at the electrodes continue. When the reactants are used up, the cell will no longer produce a current. Some cells are rechargeable. If a cell is connected to an outside source of current, the flow of electrons can be reversed. This change reverses the chemical reactions in the cell, and regenerates the reactants.

inferring
Ask students how much voltage would be produced if all the cells in a lead-acid battery contained only lead electrodes. Students should infer that zero voltage would be produced, since no electrical pressure is created when both electrodes are the same.

Demonstration   Show students a dry cell that has been cut in half. Have them point out the parts mentioned in the text.

Enrichment   As a class project, students can find out which kind of dry cell batteries—regular, heavy-duty, or alkaline batteries—have the lowest cost of operation. Students will need two of each kind of battery of the same brand and three identical flashlights. Make sure everything, including the bulbs, is new. By turning on all three flashlights at the same time and checking to see how long the batteries work, students can compare the durability of the batteries. By dividing the operating time of each kind of battery by the cost in cents of two batteries, students can find out the minutes of operation per penny.

Background   Count Alessandro Volta, an Italian physics professor, was the inventor of the electric battery. Volta discovered that the chemical action of moisture and two metals such as iron and copper produced electricity. His voltaic piles of zinc and silver disks separated by moistened paper or cloth were the sources of the first steady electric current. The volt, a unit of electrical pressure, was named after him.

Background   Andre Marie Ampere, a French physicist, discovered that parallel electric currents attract each other if they move in the same direction but repel each other if they move in opposite directions. He also found that an electric current flowing through a coiled wire acts like a magnet; this led to the discovery of the galvanometer. He used the galvanometer to demonstrate that an electric current completes a circuit through the battery that produces a current. The ampere—the unit that measures the number of charges flowing past a point in one second—was named after him.

ELECTRICAL UNITS

Electric current is the flow of charges. Electric current is measured in units called *amperes* (AM pihrz), or amps (A). An ampere is a measure of the number of charges that flow past a point in one second. One ampere is equal to 6.25×10^{18} electrons per second.

As you have learned, chemical reactions in an electric cell cause electrons to accumulate at one electrode. Work was done to cause the build-up of electrons at this electrode. As a result, the electrons have gained potential energy. The electrode is described as being a region of high potential. Since the other electrode has not accumulated electrons, it is described as being a region of low potential. The difference in potential between the two electrodes is called voltage, or potential difference. **Voltage** is a measure of the energy available to move charges in a circuit. Voltage is measured in volts. It is voltage, sometimes called electrical pressure, that causes charges to flow in a circuit.

The number of electrons that can flow in a conductor depends on the voltage. The greater the voltage, the greater the number of electrons that can flow. The number of electrons that can flow in a conductor can be compared to the amount of water that can flow in a pipe. The voltage in the conductor can be compared to the water pressure in a pipe. The amount of water that can flow in a pipe depends on the water pressure. Similarly, the number of electrons that can flow in a conductor depends on the voltage.

Figure 16-11

Current can be compared to the amount of water that flows in this fountain. Voltage can be compared to the pressure that pushes the water through the fountain.

The number of electrons that can flow also depends on the extent to which the conductor opposes their flow. The opposition to the flow of charges in a substance is called **resistance** (rih ZIHS tuhns). Resistance is measured in units called ohms (Ω).

Several factors affect the resistance of a conductor. One factor is temperature. As the temperature of a conductor increases, its resistance also increases. Another factor is the diameter of the conductor. As the diameter of a conductor increases, its resistance decreases. Just as a large-diameter water pipe can allow water to flow more freely than can a smaller-diameter pipe, a large-diameter conductor allows electrons to flow more easily than does a smaller-diameter conductor. The length of a conductor also affects its resistance. The greater the length of the conductor, the greater its resistance. This greater resistance can be compared to water flowing through a long pipe. Water flows with greater difficulty through a long pipe than a short one.

Table 16-2 *Relative Resistance*

Material	Relative Resistance (at 0°C)
Silver	1.00
Copper	1.06
Aluminum	1.69
Tungsten	3.50
Iron	6.25
Platinum	6.88
Mercury	61.25
Carbon	2.19×10^3
Silicon	1.44×10^{11}
Glass	6.25×10^{20}
Hard rubber	6.25×10^{24}

Figure 16-12

Resistance depends on diameter, length, and nature of the conductor.

As you can see in Figure 16-12, conductors can be different lengths and diameters. They can be made of different substances. Recall that electrons flow more easily through conductors than through insulators. Table 16-2 compares the resistance of some conductors and insulators. Why is copper used for electrical wiring?[1]

[1] It has a low resistance.

OHM'S LAW

Not all conductors carry the same amount of electric current. For example, a wire connected to an electric stove carries more current than one connected to a light bulb. As you have seen, voltage and resistance affect the current in a circuit. In the early 1800s a German scientist named Georg S. Ohm studied the relationship of voltage, current, and resistance in electric circuits. The relationship of re-

Puzzler   Birds can perch on electric power lines without harm because every part of their body is at the same high potential as the wire.

3 REVIEW/REINFORCEMENT

1. At one of the electrodes, a reaction that produces electrons takes place; at the other electrode, a reaction that requires electrons takes place. The electrons produced at one electrode flow out of the cell along a wire and enter the cell at the other electrode; this flow of electrons creates an electric current.
2. Electric current is the flow of charges; voltage is the electrical pressure that causes electrons to flow.
3. High temperature, small diameter, and great length will all increase the resistance of a conductor.
4. $R = V/I = 24\,V \div 4\,A = 6\Omega$, or 6 ohms

Challenge   Four such cells must be combined to produce 6 V.

SCIENCE PUZZLER

The voltage on electric power lines can be as high as 400,000 V. Electrical repair people must be extremely careful when they work on the lines. If they accidently touched one of the lines, they would be killed instantly. However, birds can perch on the lines without any harm. Explain why.

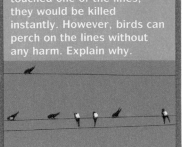

sistance, voltage, and current can be written as a formula, called **Ohm's law**.

$$R = \frac{V}{I}$$

In this formula, R stands for resistance, V stands for voltage, and I stands for current. Ohm's law can be used to calculate any of the three quantities—current, voltage, or resistance—in a wire when two of the quantities are known.

Sample Problem
The wire filament in a light bulb uses a current of 0.5 A when the voltage is 120 V. What is the resistance of the filament?

1. Write the formula.

$$R = \frac{V}{I}$$

2. Substitute the amounts given in the problem for the symbols in the formula.

$$R = \frac{120\,V}{0.5\,A}$$

3. Determine the unit that will be part of the answer. The unit of resistance is the ohm (Ω).

$$R = \frac{120}{0.5}\,\Omega$$

4. Complete the calculation that is required. Dividing 120 by 0.5 produces 240.

$$R = 240\,\Omega$$

The resistance in the filament is 240 Ω.

REVIEW

1. How does an electric cell produce an electric current?
2. What is the difference between electric current and voltage?
3. What factors affect the resistance of a conductor?
4. Calculate the resistance of a wire that carries a current of 4 A when the voltage is 24 V.

CHALLENGE The voltage of a dry cell is 1.5 volts. Explain how such dry cells can produce 6 volts.

16-4 ELECTRIC CIRCUITS

Electrical energy can result from the flow of charges. Recall that to move charges, such as electrons, a source of voltage, or electrical pressure, is required. But charges also need a path to flow along. For example, a battery has a voltage. But current does not flow between its terminals. However, if a conductor, such as a metal wire, is connected to the terminals, current will flow. The current will flow from the negative terminal through the wire to the positive terminal. The wire and battery form a system in which electrons flow. A system through which an electric current can travel is called an **electric circuit** (SER kiht).

An electric circuit in which the current flows in a complete path is called a *closed circuit*. If a connection is broken anywhere along the path of the current, the circuit is no longer complete. An electric circuit that is broken somewhere along the current's path is called an *open circuit*. Electric current will not flow in an open circuit.

After completing this section, you will be able to

- **describe** the parts of a simple electric circuit.
- **compare** a series circuit with a parallel circuit.
- **explain** how two kinds of safety devices in electric circuits work.

The key terms in this section are
electric circuit
parallel circuit
series circuit

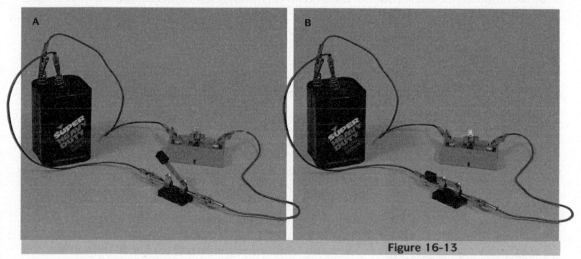

Figure 16-13

An open circuit (A) and a closed circuit (B).

A circuit can be opened or closed by using a device called a *switch*. Notice in Figure 16-13A that when a switch is open, the current's path is broken. Current cannot flow. When the switch is closed, as in Figure 16-13B, the path is complete and the current flows. Switches are used in almost all electric circuits. A common example of a switch is the light switch in a room. The light switch is connected to the same circuit as are the lights. Using the light switch, the lights can be turned on by closing the circuit or turned off by opening the circuit.

16-4 ELECTRIC CIRCUITS
page 397–400

OBJECTIVES
Refer to pupil page 397.

VOCABULARY
Key terms: electric circuit, parallel circuit, series circuit
Other terms: circuit breaker, closed circuit, fuse, load, open circuit, switch

1 MOTIVATION

If possible, obtain an old-fashioned set of Christmas lights (the kind that is wired in series), and replace one of the bulbs with a burned-out bulb. Give students a replacement bulb, and challenge them to find the burned-out bulb. They should find the procedure tedious and frustrating. This leads to a discussion of the problems with this type of circuitry. Later you will want to mention that series circuits can be useful in some situations.

2 CONCEPT DEVELOPMENT

Enrichment Have students research the life and work of one or more of the following people who worked with electricity: Charles Du Fay, Benjamin Franklin, Charles de Coulomb, Alessandro Volta, Andre Ampere, George S. Ohm, James Clerk Maxwell. Have students present their findings to the class.

Teaching Tip Discuss electrical accidents with students. People are killed every year by contact with common household circuits. Touching an appliance with a faulty wire when a person's skin is dry and feet are on dry ground does not usually cause injury because the body's resistance is great enough to keep the current low. Therefore the person receives only a mild shock. However, if the person's feet or hands are wet, the body's overall resistance is lowered, and a small current can be fatal. It happens all too frequently that someone in a shower is killed by turning on an electric appliance.

Tie-in/Language Arts Have students find a synonym for the verb form of the word *fuse,* and relate that synonym to how an electrical fuse works.

Background Electrical connections can be made in a single path (series circuit) or in alternate paths (parallel circuit). Current, resistance, and voltage are combined in different ways in each type of circuit. In a series circuit the current through any portion of the circuit is the same; the total resistance of the circuit is the sum of the individual resistances; and the total voltage applied to the circuit is divided among the resistances in the circuit. In a parallel circuit the total amount of current in the circuit is divided among the branches, and the amount of current in each branch is inversely proportional to the resistance along that branch; as parallel branches are added to the circuit, the overall resistance of the circuit decreases, and the voltage is the same across each resistance.

SCIENCE & TECHNOLOGY

Scientists have recently developed a battery that runs on everyday materials — aluminum, air, and salt water. Called the aluminum-air battery, the battery has an aluminum metal anode and an air cathode. Salt water is used as the electrolyte. The battery produces about 500 w of electric power as the aluminum anode dissolves in the salt water. The air cathode contains a special membrane that allows air to enter the electrolyte but does not allow gases or liquids to escape.

One advantage of an aluminum-air battery is its unusually long shelf life — 20 to 25 years. This makes it ideal for use during power failures. The batteries are packaged without salt water. To activate them, salt water is added. After use, the salt water is emptied and the battery is rinsed out with ordinary water. The battery can then be stored. Since the battery does not contain acid, it can be stored safely in the home almost indefinitely.

Electric cars powered by aluminum-air batteries are now being developed. The batteries can provide enough power to drive the cars for 400 km before water would have to be added to the batteries to refresh their electrolytes. At the end of every 2000 km, the batteries would need more aluminum.

Figure 16-14

Fuses can be many different shapes and sizes.

A simple electric circuit is made up of a voltage source, a conductor, and a load. In the circuit shown in Figure 16-13, the battery is the voltage source. It supplies the energy to move electrons. The wire is the conductor. It provides a path through which the electrons can flow. The light bulb is the load. The *load* is an electrical device that changes the energy of moving electrons to some other form of energy. In this circuit the load converts the energy of the moving electrons into light energy.

A special kind of switch called a fuse is sometimes used as a safety device in electric circuits. A *fuse* prevents a circuit from overheating when too much current flows in it. A fuse contains a short piece of thin metal. When too much current flows in a circuit, the metal melts and the circuit is opened. The current stops flowing before the circuit overheats and catches fire. The current does not flow until the fuse is replaced. Automobiles and many older houses have fuses in their electric circuits.

Another kind of safety device used in many electric circuits is a circuit breaker. A *circuit breaker* is a safety switch that opens the circuit when too much current flows through it. One advantage of a circuit breaker over a fuse is that a circuit breaker does not have to be replaced when it opens the circuit. It can be reset to close the circuit. Circuit breakers are used in the electric circuits in almost all modern homes.

There are two main types of electric circuits. One type is a series circuit. A **series circuit** is a circuit in which there is only one path for the current. The loads are connected one after the other. If any part of the path is broken, or opened, the current in all parts of the circuit stops. The current flowing through each load in a series circuit is the same.

serere (to join)

The other type of circuit is a parallel circuit. A **parallel circuit** is a circuit in which there is more than one path for the current. In this circuit there are separate paths, or branches, for the current. The voltage is the same in all branches of a parallel circuit. So different loads that operate at the same voltage can all be placed in a parallel

para- (side by side)

ACTIVITY   How Do Series and Parallel Circuits Differ?

OBJECTIVE
Compare series and parallel circuits.

MATERIALS
3 miniature light bulbs, 3 miniature sockets, screwdriver, wire, dry cell, switch

PROCEDURE
A. Place a light bulb into a socket.
B. Using a screwdriver and wire, connect this socket to a dry cell and to an open switch, as shown in Figure 1.
C. Close the switch. **Caution:** If any of the wires become warm, open the switch and notify your teacher.
D. Disconnect the dry cell, switch, and socket. Place two light bulbs into two sockets. Connect three sockets in series with the dry cell and to an open switch, as shown in Figure 2. Close the switch.
   1. Compare the brightness of each bulb with the brightness of the bulb in step **C**.
E. Remove any one of the bulbs in the circuit.
   2. What do you observe?
F. Disconnect the dry cell, switch, and the sockets. Connect the sockets parallel to the dry cell and to the open switch, as shown in Figure 3. Close the switch.
   3. Compare the brightness of the bulbs with that of the bulbs in steps **C** and **D**.
G. Remove any one of the light bulbs from its socket.
   4. What do you observe?

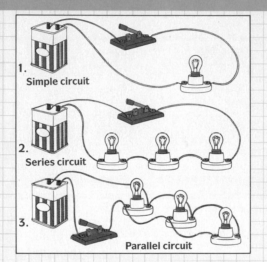

1. **Simple circuit**

2. **Series circuit**

3. **Parallel circuit**

RESULTS AND CONCLUSIONS
1. Compare the brightness of three bulbs connected in series with that of three bulbs connected in parallel.
2. Compare the result of removing one bulb from a series circuit with that of removing one bulb from a parallel circuit.
3. What can you conclude about the current flowing through each bulb in a series circuit and in a parallel circuit?
4. The brightness of each bulb is determined by its voltage. What do you conclude about the voltage of electric devices in series circuits and of those in parallel circuits?

Teaching Tip Discuss with students the fact that in the home, appliances are connected in parallel, in wall sockets. As more appliances are added to the circuit, the combined resistance of the circuit is lowered, and the current increases. Overload occurs when the circuit is carrying too much current. Ask students what may be the result of overload. (The wires can overheat and start a fire.) Ask them what prevents this from happening. (A fuse melts or a circuit breaker opens the circuit when an overload occurs.)

3 REVIEW/REINFORCEMENT

1. The parts of a simple electric circuit include a voltage source, a conductor, and a load. An electric circuit in which the current flows in a complete path is a closed circuit; if the circuit is broken somewhere along the current's path, it is called an open circuit.
2. A series circuit is a circuit in which there is only one path for the current; a parallel circuit is a circuit in which there is more than one path for the current.
3. They both open the circuit. A fuse contains a short, thin piece of metal that melts and thus opens the circuit when too much current flows in the circuit. A circuit breaker is a switch that opens the circuit when too much current flows through.

Challenge In series, to protect circuits from overloading.

circuit. The current flowing through each load will vary. If two loads in a parallel circuit have different resistances, they will use different amounts of current. If different loads in a parallel circuit use the same amount of current, what can you conclude about the resistances of the loads?[1]

[1]They are the same.

If one of the paths is broken, or opened, in a parallel circuit current can still flow through the other paths. The circuit is still closed. Strings of lights that are used for decoration are usually arranged in parallel circuits. If one bulb burns out, the remaining bulbs will still function. Figure 16-15 shows the effects of a bulb burning out in a parallel circuit and in a series circuit.

[2]The parallel circuit.

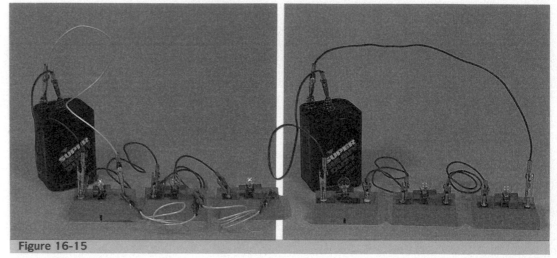

Figure 16-15
Only one light bulb has burned out in each circuit. Is it easier to find the burned-out bulb in the parallel circuit (*left*) or in the series circuit (*right*)?[2]

Wires in a circuit must be properly insulated. If uninsulated wires touch, current can pass from one wire to the other at the point where they touch. Because the current takes a shorter path than usual such a circuit is called a short circuit. A short circuit is dangerous because it can overheat or make sparks, causing a fire.

REVIEW

1. What are the parts of a simple electric circuit? How does an open circuit differ from a closed circuit?
2. How does a series circuit differ from a parallel circuit?
3. Compare how a fuse and a circuit breaker work in an electric circuit.

CHALLENGE Should a fuse or a circuit breaker be connected parallel to or in series with electric devices in a circuit? Explain your answer.

16-5 ELECTRIC POWER

The ability of electrical energy to be changed readily into other forms of energy makes it one of the most useful forms of energy. For example, electrical energy is changed into light energy by light bulbs, into heat energy by electric heaters, and into sound energy by stereos.

Not all electric devices use the same amount of electrical energy. Suppose you wanted to heat a room by using electrical energy. An electric heater would give off more heat than would a hair dryer. The electric heater would also use more current than would the hair dryer in the same amount of time. The more current an electric device uses, the more electrical energy it uses. The amount of electrical energy used each second is called **electric power**. The electric power of the electric heater is greater than the electric power of the hair dryer. This is because the electric heater uses more electrical energy each second than does the hair dryer.

Electric power is measured in watts (W). A **watt** is the SI unit of power. Recall from Chapter 13 that one watt is equal to one joule per second. The power rating of a light bulb is measured in watts and is printed on the bulb. The higher the number of watts, the brighter the light bulb will be, and the more energy it will use. For example, a light bulb may have a power rating of 60 watts, or 60 W. This means that it uses 60 joules of electrical energy every second. A larger unit of power than the watt is called the kilowatt (kW). A **kilowatt** is a unit of power equal to 1000 watts, or 1000 joules per second.

After completing this section, you will be able to

- **relate** the electric power of an electric device to the amount of electrical energy it uses.
- **calculate** electric power and electrical energy.
- **calculate** the cost of electrical energy.

The key terms in this section are
electric power
kilowatt
kilowatt-hour
watt

Figure 16-16

A lighthouse (*left*) uses more power than does a light bulb (*right*).

OBJECTIVES
Refer to pupil page 401.

VOCABULARY
Key terms: electric power, kilowatt, kilowatt-hour, watt

1 MOTIVATION

Discuss the cost of electricity in your area compared with that in other areas. Have students suggest reasons for the differences. (Different sources of power.) Discuss your local power source. If you have seasonal brownouts due to overdemand or occasional weather-related power failures, have students discuss why these occur.

2 CONCEPT DEVELOPMENT

Background   When an electric current flows, the electric charge moves from a higher potential to a lower potential. Every time this happens, work is done and energy is converted from one form to another. Electrical energy is transformed to heat energy in a toaster, to radiant energy in a light bulb, and to mechanical energy in a motor.

Teaching Tip   Talk with students about the kinds of appliances used at home and the amount of energy each uses in a day. Help students understand that even though an appliance has a high power rating, it may not use a great deal of energy if its typical usage time is short.

Teaching Tip   Make sure that students can distinguish between energy and energy used per unit time (power).

Thinking Skills

comparing
Students are asked to compare the relationship between the power ratings and the use of current for the appliances shown in Figure 16-17.

Teaching Tip   Remind students that not all the energy a light bulb uses is changed into radiant energy. About 90 percent goes into heat energy and only 10 percent is transformed into light.

The number of watts that an electric appliance uses, or its power rating, is usually printed on the appliance. Figure 16-17 shows the power ratings of some appliances. Devices that use large amounts of electric power also use large amounts of current. The relationship between electric power and current is shown by the following formula.

$$P = VI$$

In this formula, P stands for power, V stands for voltage, and I stands for current.

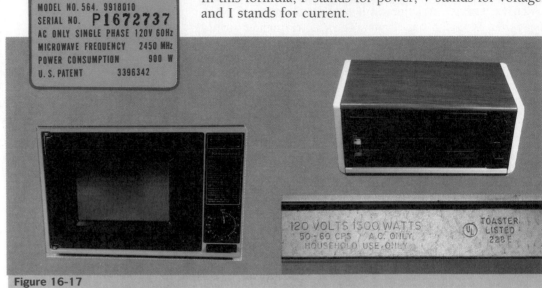

Figure 16-17

As you can see, the power ratings of appliances differ.

Sample Problem
How much electric power is used by a color television that uses 1.5 A when connected to a voltage of 120 V?

1. Write the formula.

$$P = VI$$

2. Substitute the amounts given in the problem for the symbols in the formula.

$$P = 120 \text{ V} \times 1.5 \text{ A}$$

3. Determine the unit that will be part of the answer. The unit of electrical power is the watt (W).

$$P = 120 \times 1.5 \text{ W}$$

4. Complete the calculations that are required.

$$P = 180 \text{ W}$$

The color television uses 180 W of power.

The amount of electrical energy used by an electric device depends on its power and the amount of time it is used. A color television with a power rating of 360 W would use twice as much energy every second as one with a power rating of 180 W. If a color television is turned on for 2 hours it will use twice as much energy as it would if it were turned on for 1 hour. Electrical energy can be calculated by using the following formula.

$$E = Pt$$

In the formula, E stands for electrical energy, P stands for power, and t stands for time.

Sample Problem

A hair dryer with a power rating of 1500 W is used for 120 seconds. How much electrical energy does it use?

1. Write the formula.

$$E = Pt$$

2. Substitute the amounts given in the problem for the symbols in the formula.

$$E = 1500 \text{ W} \times 120 \text{ s}$$

3. Determine the unit that will be part of the answer. This unit will be the watt-second (W-s).

$$E = 1500 \times 120 \text{ W-s}$$

4. Complete the calculations that are required.

$$E = 180,000 \text{ W-s}$$

The hair dryer used 180,000 W-s of electrical energy. A

Figure 16-18

How much power does this hair dryer use in 10 minutes?[1]

[1]900,000 W-s.

Background   Useful energy is lost as "joule heat" when electrical energy is converted to another form of energy. The heat-energy conversion results from electrons colliding with atoms or ions of a conductor. These collisions increase the internal heat energy of the conductor. In heating appliances, joule heating is promoted. The heating element of a hair dryer has a relatively low resistance, so there is a large current. A hair dryer with a power rating of 1500 W loses heat from the heating elements, but this heat is blown outward to dry hair.

Teaching Tip   Share a bill from the power company with students. Ask them to find the present meter reading and the previous one. Have them calculate the kilowatt-hours used in a month. Then have students find out how much a kilowatt-hour of electricity cost during the particular month.

Review and Skill Masters

CHALLENGE/CRITICAL THINKING, page 100.
See page 381c in this book for answers.

3 REVIEW/REINFORCEMENT

1. The amount of electrical energy used by an electric device depends on its power rating and the amount of time it is used.
2. $P = VI = 120$ V $\times$ 5 A $= 120$ V $\times$ 5 W $= 600$ W
3. $E = Pt = 500$ W $\times$ 50 s $= 25,000$ W-s
4. $E = Pt = \dfrac{2200 \text{ W} \times 0.5 \text{ h}}{1000 \text{ kW}} =$ 1.1 kW-h.

   1.1 kW-h $\times$ \$0.10 = \$0.11.

Challenge 100 W $\times$ .90 = 90 W = 90 J of heat.

Review and Skill Masters

SKILL, pages 98–99.
See pages 381b–c in this book for answers.

larger unit of electrical energy than the watt-second is the kilowatt-hour (kW-h). A **kilowatt-hour** is the amount of electrical energy used when one kilowatt of power is used for one hour. Electric meters in houses measure electrical energy in kilowatt-hours.

Electric companies bill their customers according to the number of kilowatt-hours of electrical energy they use. If you know the power rating of an appliance you can calculate its energy use, by using the formula on page 403. If you also know the cost per kilowatt-hour you can predict how much it will cost to use that appliance. For example, in 4 hours a 2000-W heater uses 8 kW-h of energy. At a cost of \$0.10 per kilowatt-hour, this energy would cost \$0.80.

$$8 \text{ kW-h} \times \$0.10/\text{kW-h} = \$0.80$$

Figure 16-19

Electric companies use meters to keep track of how much electricity is used.

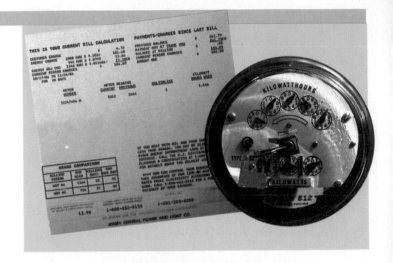

REVIEW

1. What does the amount of electrical energy that an electric device uses depend on?
2. Calculate the electric power rating of a vacuum cleaner that uses 5 A of current when connected to a voltage of 120 V.
3. An electric toaster with a power rating of 500 W is used for 50 s. How much electrical energy is used?
4. How much does it cost to run a 2200-W electric clothes dryer for half an hour at \$0.10 per kW-h?

CHALLENGE About 10 percent of the energy given off by a light bulb is in the form of visible light. The rest is given off as heat. How many joules of energy per second of heat would a 100-W light bulb give off?

CHAPTER SUMMARY

The main ideas in this chapter are listed below. Read these statements before you answer the Chapter Review questions.

- Substances can become electrically charged when two different uncharged substances are rubbed against each other. (16-1)

- Static electricity is a term used to describe electric charges that are not moving, or are at rest. (16-1)

- A conductor is a substance that allows an electric charge to flow through it easily. An insulator does not allow the easy flow of an electric charge through it. (16-1)

- Charged objects exert forces on other objects. Objects with opposite charges attract each other. Objects with the same charge repel each other. (16-2)

- Induction is a process by which a charged substance causes nearby, uncharged substances to become charged. (16-2)

- An electroscope is a device that detects electric charges. (16-2)

- An electric current is a flow of charges. (16-3)

- In electric cells chemical reactions produce a difference in potential that causes charges to flow. (16-3)

- Electric current, measured in amperes, is the rate of flow of charge. Voltage, given in volts, is a measure of the energy available to move charges in a circuit. Opposition to the flow of charges is called resistance, measured in ohms. (16-3)

- The amount of current flowing through a circuit is affected by the voltage and the resistance in the circuit. This flow is expressed as a formula called Ohm's law. (16-3)

- A series circuit is a circuit in which the current moves along only one path. A parallel circuit is a circuit in which there is more than one path for the current to flow. (16-4)

- Fuses and circuit breakers are devices for interrupting the flow of charges in a circuit. (16-4)

- Electric power is measured in watts. A watt is one joule per second. One thousand watts equal one kilowatt. (16-5)

- The amount of electrical energy used by an electric appliance depends on its power and how long it is used. (16-5)

The key terms in this chapter are listed below. Use each term in a sentence that shows the meaning of the term.

anode	electric current	insulator	series circuit
cathode	electric power	kilowatt	static electricity
conductor	electricity	kilowatt-hour	voltage
dry cell	electroscope	Ohm's law	watt
electric cell	grounding	parallel circuit	wet cell
electric circuit	induction	resistance	

Review and Skill Masters

VOCABULARY REVIEW, page 95.
See page 381b in this book for answers.

VOCABULARY

1. a 2. b 3. l 4. m 5. i 6. c 7. f 8. k
9. d 10. j

CONCEPTS

1. An uncharged object acquires a charge when it is rubbed by a different, uncharged object.
2. While walking across a carpet, a person acquires a negative charge as his or her shoes rub on the carpet; when the person touches a metal object, the acquired electrons are discharged from the body to the metal object.
3. A copper wire, a saltwater solution, aluminum.
4. Aluminum (least), copper, silver.
5. The charged comb causes the near end of the neutral papers to become charged.
6. The earth is sometimes charged by induction just before a storm. The bottom layer of a cloud becomes negatively charged and repels negative charges in the ground; this causes the ground to become positively charged.
7. Because like charges repel; because unlike charges attract.
8. They are oppositely charged; they have the same charge.
9. The flow of electrons, or flow of charges.
10. It contains two different substances called electrodes and a conducting mixture called an electrolyte; a chemical reaction takes place between the electrodes and the electrolyte. Electrons at one electrode flow to the other electrode through connecting wire.
11. Voltage is a measure of the energy available to move charges in a circuit. Resistance is a measure of how difficult it is to move charges through a conductor.
12. Temperature, diameter, and length of the conductor.

Review and Skill Masters

CHAPTER REVIEW, pages 96–97.
See page 381b in this book for answers.

Chapter Review

VOCABULARY

Write the letter of the term that best matches the definition. Not all the terms will be used.

1. A substance that allows charges to flow through easily
2. The flow of electrons or charges
3. A measure of the energy available to move charges in a circuit
4. A unit of power equal to one joule per second
5. The opposition to the flow of charges in a circuit
6. A device that detects electrical charges
7. Power equal to 1000 joules per second
8. The effects of charges at rest
9. Process of charging an object by the presence of a nearby charged object
10. A circuit that allows current to move in only one path

a. conductor
b. electric current
c. electroscope
d. induction
e. insulator
f. kilowatt
g. Ohm's law
h. parallel circuit
i. resistance
j. series circuit
k. static electricity
l. voltage
m. watt

CONCEPTS

1. How does an uncharged object acquire a charge? (16-1)
2. Explain why a person gets a shock by touching a metal object after walking across a carpet. (16-1)
3. Give three examples of conductors. (16-1)
4. List the following metals in order of increasing ability to conduct electricity: copper, silver, aluminum (16-1)
5. How does a charged comb pick up bits of paper? (16-2)
6. Explain how the earth's surface can become charged. (16-2)
7. Why do the leaves of a positively charged electroscope move farther apart when a positively charged object is brought near the knob? Why do the leaves move together when a negatively charged object is brought near? (16-2)
8. A charged object is brought near another charged object. What can be determined about the charge on each object if they attract? If they repel? (16-2)
9. What is an electric current? (16-3)
10. Describe the parts of an electric cell. How does the cell produce current? (16-3)
11. Distinguish between voltage and resistance. (16-3)
12. What factors affect the resistance of a conductor? (16-3)

13. What is Ohm's law? (16-3)

14. The current in a circuit is 5 A and the voltage is 20 V. What is the resistance of the circuit? (16-3)

15. Distinguish between a closed circuit and an open circuit. (16-4)

16. What is the difference between a series circuit and a parallel circuit? (16-4)

17. What is the purpose of a fuse or circuit breaker in an electric circuit? (16-4)

18. What does the amount of electrical energy used by an electric appliance depend on? (16-5)

19. A light bulb uses 4000 J of energy in 40 seconds. What is the power rating of the light bulb? (16-5)

20. A refrigerator uses 6 A and is connected to a 120-V source. How much does it cost to run the refrigerator for a day if the electric company charges $0.10 per kW-h? (16-5)

APPLICATION/CRITICAL THINKING

1. Lightning rods are often attached to houses to keep lightning from hitting the houses. Explain how a lightning rod would protect a house.

2. Explain why it is safe to be inside a car during a lightning storm.

3. Some kinds of clear food wraps stick to metal containers. How do they do this?

4. To save on the cost of a return wire, electric power companies use the earth as a return path for electric current. Explain how this is possible.

EXTENSION

1. Find out how to connect dry cells in series and in parallel. Using flashlight batteries, wire, and a flashlight bulb, compare the brightness of the flashlight bulb when it is connected to the batteries in series and in parallel.

2. Find out the electric power ratings of the electric appliances you use at home. Estimate the amount of time each appliance is used per month. Then calculate in kilowatt-hours the amount of energy each appliance uses per month. Which appliance costs the most to run? The least?

READINGS

Cooper, Alan. *Visual Science Electricity*. Morristown, N.J.: Silver Burdett Co., 1983.

Leon, George. *The Electricity Story: 2500 Years of Discoveries and Experiments*. New York: Arco Publishing, 1983.

Math, Irwin. *Wires and Watts: Understanding and Using Electricity*. New York: Scribner's, 1981.

13. Ohm's law states that the resistance of a wire is equal to the voltage across the wire divided by the current in the wire, or R = V/I.

14. $R = V \div I = 20 \text{ V} \div 5 \text{ A} = 4\Omega$.

15. An electric circuit in which the current flows in a complete path is called a closed circuit; an electric circuit that is broken somewhere along the current's path is called an open circuit.

16. A series circuit is a circuit in which there is only one path for the current; a parallel circuit is a circuit in which there is more than one path for the current.

17. A fuse and a circuit breaker are safety devices that prevent a circuit from overheating.

18. It depends on the power and the amount of time it is used.

19. $P = E \div t = 4000 \text{ J} \div 40 \text{ s} = 100 \text{ J/s} = 100 \text{ W}$.

20. $P = VI = 120 \text{ V} \times 6 \text{ A} = 720 \text{ W}$, or .72 kW
$E = P \times t = .72 \text{ kW} \times 24$ (hours in a day) $= 17.3$ kW-h
17.3 kW-h $\times \$0.10/\text{kW-h} = \$1.73$.

APPLICATION/CRITICAL THINKING

1. Lightning rods are grounded by a wire running from the rod to the ground; any charge given to the rod will be discharged into the ground. Lightning is more likely to strike the lightning rod because it is taller than the house.

2. If the car were struck by lightning, the electrons would travel over the outer metal surface of the car because they repel each other, and the electrons would arc to the ground from a low edge of the car.

3. By friction, and by rearrangement of charges.

4. The earth is a huge source of electrons.

Test Masters

CHAPTER TEST, pages 61–64.
See page 381d in this book for answers.

MAGNETISM

ORGANIZER

Section	pages	Activity	pages	Reinforcement and Evaluation	pages	*Review and Skill Masters	pages	Other Components in Teacher Resource Package	pages
17–1 Magnets and Magnetism	409–413	How Is a Magnetic Field Mapped?	412	Review, Challenge	413			*Study Guide* *Lab Manual*	85 89
17–2 Changing Electricity into Magnetism	414–418	How Is the Field of a Current Mapped?	416	Puzzler Review, Challenge	417 418	Challenge/Critical Thinking Skill	106 104–105	*Study Guide*	86
17–3 Changing Magnetism into Electricity	419–422	How Is a Current Created?	420	Review, Challenge	422			*Study Guide* *Lab Manual*	87 85
17–4 Electronics	423–429			Review, Challenge	429			*Study Guide*	88
CHAPTER SUMMARY	429					Vocabulary Review	101		
CHAPTER REVIEW	430–431			*Test Masters	65–68	Chapter Review	102–103		

*In the Teacher Resource Package. For answers, see pages 407b–407d in this book.

ACTIVITY MATERIALS   Quantities are based on a class of 30 students working in groups as indicated in parentheses.

How Is a Magnetic Field Mapped? p. 412 (groups of 2)	quantity	How Is the Field of a Current Mapped? p. 416 (groups of 2)	quantity	How Is a Current Created? p. 420 (groups of 2)	quantity
bar magnet	30	insulated copper wire (50 cm long)	15 pieces	bar magnet	15
magnet holder	15	dry cell (1.5 volts)	15	wire coil	1 roll
paper	135 sheets	small compass	15	galvanometer	15
iron filings	50 g	masking tape	1 roll		
metric ruler	15	heavy cardboard (21.5 cm x 28 cm)	15 pieces		

REVIEW AND SKILL MASTERS

VOCABULARY REVIEW _____ Chapter 17

Use the correct words to complete the sentences below. Not all words are used.

alternating current	electromagnetic induction	magnetic domain
amplifiers	electronics	magnetic field
computers	generators	magnetic force
direct current	integrated circuits	transistors
electric motors	magnet	vacuum tubes
electromagnet		

A(n) **magnet** is any substance that can attract iron or other

magnetic materials. It produces an area called a(n) **magnetic field**

around it, within which its force acts upon objects. A coil of wire wound around an iron core

becomes a(n) **electromagnet**. These devices have many uses.

When a wire is moved perpendicularly to a magnetic field, the current is produced through

electromagnetic induction. Mechanical energy is changed into

electrical energy by devices called **generators**. In power stations,

these devices produce a type of current that is a(n) **alternating current**.

With a commutator and two brushes, however, the current can be changed to make it a(n)

direct current.

Electronics is the study of the behavior of electrons in electric circuits. A

major advance in this field was the invention of **vacuum tubes** in

1906. However, these burned out quickly, and were replaced in 1948 by

transistors. These components allowed devices such as

computers, which process information, to be made smaller. In the

late 1950s, **integrated circuits** engraved on chips made circuits even

smaller. Tasks of circuits can now be carried out more quickly and with less power.

101

CHAPTER REVIEW _____ Chapter 17

17-1 Magnets and Magnetism

1. The north pole of a magnet will attract the _____**south**_____ pole of another magnet.

2. Why do magnets have poles and magnetic fields? **Magnets have poles and magnetic fields because many atoms of the magnetic material line up so their magnetic fields combine.**

3. Underline your answer. In a permanent/temporary magnet, the magnetic domains return to their original positions.

4. List two ways to push the domain of a permanent magnet out of line and thus cause the magnet to lose its magnetism. **Some ways to cause a permanent magnet to lose its magnetism are heat, hammering, and a stronger magnetic field.**

17-2 Changing Electricity into Magnetism

1. Which magnetic field looks more like that of a bar magnet—a straight wire or a coil of wire? **The magnetic field of a coil of wire looks like that of a bar magnet.**

2. How does decreasing the number of coils of wire affect an electromagnet? **Decreasing the number of coils of wire will weaken the electromagnet.**

3. What causes the coil of wire in an electric motor to turn? **When current flows through the coil of wire, the magnetic field of the permanent magnet exerts a magnetic force on the coil of wire. This causes the coil to turn.**

102

CHAPTER REVIEW (Continued) _____ Chapter 17

17-3 Changing Magnetism into Electricity

1. What does motion between a wire and a magnetic field produce? **Motion between a wire and a magnetic field produces a current.**

2. Underline your answer. A generator/motor works on the principle that when many loops or coils of wire are turned in a magnetic field, a greater current will be produced.

3. A(n) **alternating current generator** produces current that changes direction as a coil of wire turns in a magnetic field. A(n) **direct current generator** corrects this change with a commutator and two brushes.

17-4 Electronics

1. In a vacuum tube electrons are attracted to a positively-charged plate in a vacuum. Why must this happen in a vacuum? **In a vacuum, there are no air molecules to stop the electrons.**

2. Underline your answers. Electric current in a vacuum tube flows through a solid/vacuum. Electric current in a transistor flows though a solid/vacuum.

3. How did the invention of the integrated circuit affect computers? **The integrated circuit enabled computers to be made smaller. This invention also allowed computers to work more quickly and to have more computing power.**

103

SKILL/Comparing _____ Chapter 17

Figure **A** and Figure **B** represent two metal bars and their magnetic domains.

A

B

1. Which illustration, Figure **A** or Figure **B**, represents a magnet? **Figure B represents a magnet.**

2. Explain your above answer. **In a magnet the poles of magnetic domains have arranged themselves so all north or south poles point in one direction.**

3. How can a permanent magnet become demagnetized? **Heating or pounding disrupts the order of magnetic domains.**

104

Name_____ Date_____

SKILL/Comparing (Continued) _____ Chapter 17

The electromagnet shown below has five loops of copper wire wound around a large nail. It will pick up five paper clips.

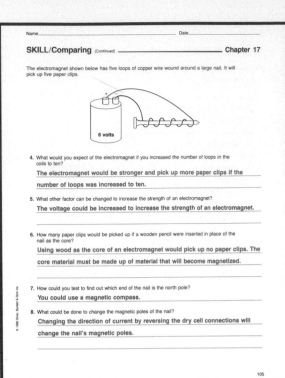

6 volts

4. What would you expect of the electromagnet if you increased the number of loops in the coils to ten?

The electromagnet would be stronger and pick up more paper clips if the number of loops was increased to ten.

5. What other factor can be changed to increase the strength of an electromagnet?

The voltage could be increased to increase the strength of an electromagnet.

6. How many paper clips would be picked up if a wooden pencil were inserted in place of the nail as the core?

Using wood as the core of an electromagnet would pick up no paper clips. The core material must be made up of material that will become magnetized.

7. How could you test to find out which end of the nail is the north pole?

You could use a magnetic compass.

8. What could be done to change the magnetic poles of the nail?

Changing the direction of current by reversing the dry cell connections will change the nail's magnetic poles.

© 1989 Silver, Burdett & Ginn Inc.

105

Name_____ Date_____

CHALLENGE/CRITICAL THINKING _____ Chapter 17

You are on a vacation at the northern tip of Ellesmere Island, Canada. You decide to go on a ride, so you take your compass and a map with you. When you look on the map, you notice that the magnetic north pole is not in the same place as the geographic north pole.

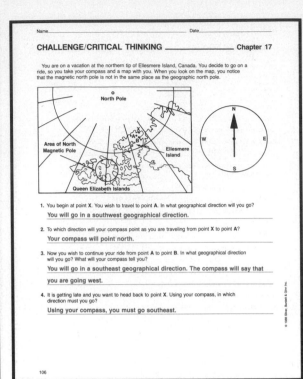

1. You begin at point **X**. You wish to travel to point **A**. In what geographical direction will you go?

You will go in a southwest geographical direction.

2. To which direction will your compass point as you are traveling from point **X** to point **A**?

Your compass will point north.

3. Now you wish to continue your ride from point **A** to point **B**. In what geographical direction will you go? What will your compass tell you?

You will go in a southeast geographical direction. The compass will say that you are going west.

4. It is getting late and you want to head back to point **X**. Using your compass, in which direction must you go?

Using your compass, you must go southeast.

© 1989 Silver, Burdett & Ginn Inc.

106

TEST MASTERS

Electromagnetism

PART 1 _____

In the space below, write the term that each phrase defines.

		Chapter Goal
1. magnetic field	The area around a magnet where the magnetic force acts	1
2. amplifier	A device used to increase the strength of a current	5
3. magnet	Any substance that has the ability to attract iron or other magnetic materials	1
4. electromagnet	A coil of wire wound around an iron core	3
5. induced current	The current produced when a wire is moved perpendicular to a magnetic field	4
6. magnetic domain	A region in a material in which the atoms are arranged so that their magnetic fields line up to form a larger magnetic field	2
7. electric motor	A device that changes electrical energy to mechanical energy	3
8. computer	A device that does calculations quickly and accurately according to a set of instructions	5
9. direct current	Electric current that travels in one direction in a circuit	4
10. magnetism	The attraction that magnets have for magnetic materials	2

PART 2 _____

Choose the term or phrase that best answers the question or completes the statement. Write the letter of that choice in the space at the left.

__b__ 1. The anode of a CRT is most like which part of a transistor?   5
a. grid   b. plate   c. filament   d. cathode

__c__ 2. The north pole of a magnet will have the greatest attraction for the: 1
a. north pole of a strong magnet.   c. south pole of a strong magnet.
b. north pole of a weak magnet.   d. south pole of a weak magnet.

PART 2 _____

Choose the term or phrase that best answers the question or completes the statement. Write the letter of that choice in the space at the left.

		Chapter Goal

__a__ 3. The magnetic force of any magnet comes from the magnetic force of: 2
a. its atoms.   c. other magnets.
b. the earth.   d. electric current.

__c__ 4. When a wire is coiled around an iron bar, and an electric current is passed through the wire, the iron bar becomes a: 3
a. magnetic domain.   c. temporary magnet.
b. magnetic field.   d. permanent magnet.

__d__ 5. In the weakest parts of a magnetic field, the magnetic field lines are: 1
a. thinner.   c. thicker.
b. closer together.   d. farther apart.

__d__ 6. Which of the following devices uses an electromagnet to measure electric current?   3
a. compass   c. electric motor
b. generator   d. galvanometer

__b__ 7. Which of the following could be increased in an ac generator to produce a greater current without changing the rate at which the current's direction changes?   4
a. speed of rotation of the coil
b. number of turns of wire in the coil
c. number of commutators
d. number of brushes

__d__ 8. The greatest amount of current will flow in a vacuum tube when the: 5
a. plate and grid are both negative.
b. plate is negative and the grid is positive.
c. plate is positive and the grid is negative.
d. plate and grid are both positive.

__d__ 9. Which of the following takes place in a dc generator?   4
a. The current leaving the generator changes once each revolution.
b. The current leaving the generator changes twice each revolution.
c. The current in the coil changes once each revolution.
d. The current in the coil changes twice each revolution.

__c__ 10. A substance in which magnetic domains are arranged randomly is a: 2
a. substance that is permanently magnetized.
b. temporary magnet that is magnetized.
c. magnetic substance that has no magnetism.
d. substance that cannot be magnetized.

PART 3 _____

Look at the diagram. Then read the questions that follow. Choose the term or phrase that best answers the question or completes the statement. Write the letter of that choice in the space at the left.

Chapter Goal

__a__ 1. A current could be made to flow in this device by holding the coil motionless and moving the: 4
a. magnet.   b. brushes.   c. commutators.   d. circuit wire.

__c__ 2. If a dry cell is connected to the circuit at A, the device will function as: 3
a. an ac generator.   c. an electric motor.
b. a dc generator.   d. an electromagnet.

__c__ 3. If current is flowing from B to C as in the diagram, after the coil completes a half revolution, the current will flow from: 4
a. B to C and from D to E.   c. C to B and from D to E.
b. B to C and from E to D.   d. C to B and from E to D.

__a__ 4. If the domains of the magnet were reversed, which of the following would occur?   2
a. Current in the coil would change direction.
b. Current would be carried by positively charged particles.
c. The amount of current flowing in the coil would increase.
d. The speed of the rotating coil would increase.

__b__ 5. The purpose of the parts labeled F and G is to control the: 4
a. direction of the magnetic field.
b. direction of current.
c. strength of the magnetic field.
d. strength of the current.

PART 4 _____

Read each question or direction and answer it using complete sentences.

Chapter Goal

1. How does the arrangement of domains determine the magnetic properties of a material?   2

Magnetic domains can be thought of as tiny bar magnets with tiny magnetic fields. These magnets can line up so that their north poles face in the same direction, creating a larger magnetic field. When domains in a magnetic material line up so that their magnetic fields combine, the material becomes a magnet.

2. Describe electric meters and how they work.   3

An electric meter measures electric current in an electric circuit. An electric meter contains a coil of wire set between the poles of a U-shaped permanent magnet. The current to be measured flows through the coil of wire. The magnetic field of the magnet exerts a force on the coil, causing it to turn. The turning of the coil moves a pointer across a scale. The amount of current can be measured from the distance the pointer moves across the scale.

3. Describe electromagnetic induction.   4

The current that is produced when a wire is moved at a right angle through a magnetic field is called an induced current. The process of producing the current is called electromagnetic induction. A current can also be induced by moving the magnet and holding the wire in a fixed position. As long as there is motion between a wire and a magnetic field, a current can be produced.

CHAPTER 17 PLANNING GUIDE

17

MAGNETISM

The questions in the CHAPTER TEST are based on these Chapter Goals.

1. Describe the effect between like and unlike magnetic poles.
2. Explain the cause of magnetism, and distinguish between temporary magnets and permanent magnets.
3. Compare the magnetic field produced by a coil of wire with that produced by a straight wire, describe the factors that affect the strength of an electromagnet, and explain how an electric motor works.
4. Describe how an electric current can be produced by a magnetic field, explain how a generator works, and compare an a.c. generator with a d.c. generator.
5. Explain how vacuum tubes work, compare a vacuum tube with a transistor, and relate the invention of the integrated circuit to the development of modern electronics.

MAGNETISM

Particle accelerators are the largest machines on the earth. Often shaped like donuts, they can be more than 6 km in circumference. The photograph shows the four electromagnets inside an accelerator. The electromagnets guide streams of charged particles, moving at nearly the speed of light, before the particles are smashed against each other. By smashing particles together in accelerators, scientists hope to find the building blocks from which all things are made.

- *How is magnetism related to electricity?*
- *What causes magnetism?*
- *How has magnetism made electric motors possible?*

17-1 MAGNETS AND MAGNETISM

People in ancient civilizations observed that some rocks could attract pieces of iron. These rocks were called magnetic because they were first found in Magnesia, a section of Asia. If these stones were hung by threads, the stones would point north. Sailors began to use them to guide their ships. Thus these stones were called leading stones or loadstones. These pieces of magnetic stone, or loadstones, were the first magnets.

THE NATURE OF MAGNETS

A **magnet** is any substance that can attract iron or other magnetic materials. Examples of magnetic materials are cobalt, nickel, iron, and alloys of these metals. Magnetic materials can be attracted by a magnet.

Magnets may be made in many shapes. No matter what shape a magnet has, its ability to attract magnetic materials is strongest at its ends. These ends are called *poles*. Suppose a magnet is hung by a thread so that it can turn freely. The magnet will turn so that one end of it points north. The end of the magnet that points north is called its north pole. The opposite end of the magnet is called its south pole. The ends are labeled *N* for north and *S* for south.

After completing this section, you will be able to

- **describe** the effect between like and unlike magnetic poles.
- **explain** the cause of magnetism.
- **distinguish** between temporary magnets and permanent magnets.
- **explain** why a permanent magnet loses its magnetism.

The key terms in this section are
magnet
magnetic domain
magnetic field
magnetism

Have students read the introductory paragraph. Ask them if they can name some common devices that use electromagnets. (Bells, buzzers.) Point out that charged particles are affected by magnetic fields. This property makes it possible to use electromagnets to accelerate and direct charged particles.

- How is magnetism related to electricity? (Magnetism can be used to produce electricity, and electricity can produce a magnetic field.)
- What causes magnetism? (Magnetism is caused by atoms in a magnetic material lining up so that their magnetic fields combine.)
- How has magnetism made electric motors possible? (The repelling force between two magnetic fields in the motor produce mechanical motion by turning a shaft.)

17-1 MAGNETS AND MAGNETISM
pages 409–413

OBJECTIVES
Refer to pupil page 409.

VOCABULARY
Key terms: magnet, magnetic domain, magnetic field, magnetism
Other terms: permanent magnet, poles, temporary magnet

1 MOTIVATION

Suspend an iron bar that is not a magnet from a support so that the bar is free to rotate. Bring a second unmagnetized bar near the suspended bar. Ask students if there is an interaction between the bars. Next bring a magnet near the suspended bar. Have students give their observations. Replace the suspended iron bar with a bar magnet, and repeat the previous steps.

2 CONCEPT DEVELOPMENT

Background   Thales of Miletus in 600 B.C. was probably the first person to note the peculiar property of magnetite, a magnetic oxide of iron, that causes it to attract bits of iron. Petrus Peregrinus summarized the known properties of loadstones in 1269.

Teaching Tip   The end of a magnet that points northward is called the north-seeking pole or north pole; the end of a magnet that points southward is called the south-seeking pole or south pole.

Teaching Tip   Stress the analogy of magnetism with electricity. There are positive and negative charges in electricity and north and south poles in magnetism. Like charges or poles repel, and unlike charges or poles attract.

Figure 17-1 shows what happens when two magnetic poles are brought near each other. When the north pole of one magnet is brought near the north pole of a suspended magnet, the poles repel each other. The magnet attached to the string moves away from the one being brought near it. However, when the south pole is brought near the north pole of the suspended magnet, the north pole moves closer. Thus you can see that there is an attraction between north and south poles. Much like electric charges, unlike magnetic poles attract each other and like magnetic poles repel each other.

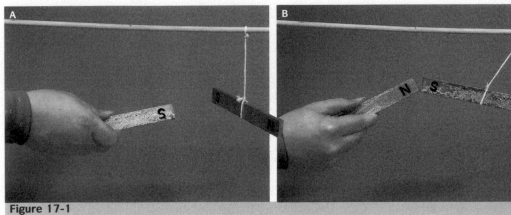

Figure 17-1

Like poles repel (*A*). Unlike poles attract (*B*).

The attraction that magnets have for magnetic materials, and the attraction and repulsion between magnetic poles, is called **magnetism** (MAG nuh tihz uhm). Magnetism is also called magnetic force. The area around the magnet where the magnetic force acts is called the **magnetic field**. The magnetic field of a bar magnet is shown in Figure 17-2*A*. Each line is called a magnetic field line. These lines show the strength of the magnetic force. The closer the lines, the stronger the magnetic force in that area.

The magnetic field around a magnet can be shown by sprinkling iron filings evenly around a magnet. The magnetic field causes the iron filings to line up along the magnetic field lines. The pattern formed by iron filings around a bar magnet is shown in Figure 17-2*B*. Where is the magnetic force strongest on the bar magnet?[1]

[1]The magnetic force is strongest at the ends of the magnet.

The strength of the magnetic force becomes less as you move away from the poles. Recall that a magnet can be attracted by the earth's North Pole, which may be far away. This shows that a magnetic force can act on a magnetic material even at very large distances.

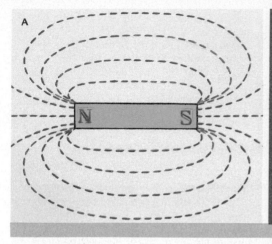
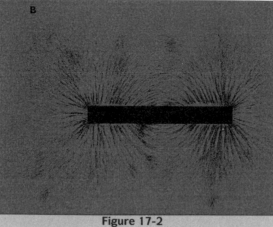

Figure 17-2

Magnetic field lines around a bar magnet.

What causes a magnet to have poles and a magnetic field? Recall that all matter is made up of atoms. Most atoms do not have magnetic fields. But in iron and other magnetic materials, the atoms have small magnetic fields. The atoms can be thought of as being tiny bar magnets with tiny magnetic fields. These "magnets" can line up so that their north poles face in the same direction, making a larger magnetic field. When atoms in a magnetic material line up so their magnetic fields combine, the material becomes a magnet. There is a north pole at one end and a south pole at the other.

Studies show that the atoms in magnetic substances act not alone but in groups called magnetic domains. A **magnetic domain** is a region in which the atoms are arranged so that their magnetic fields line up to form a larger magnetic field. In most magnetic materials the domains face in many directions. Their magnetic fields cancel. Thus these objects have no magnetism. In magnets the domains face in the same direction. This produces an overall magnetic field around the magnets.

In the magnetized piece of iron shown in Figure 17-3A, the domains are arranged so that their north poles face left. Which end of the piece of iron becomes a north pole?[1] Which end becomes the south pole?[2] In the unmagnetized piece of iron shown in Figure 17-3B, the domains face in different directions. If these domains can be made to line up, the piece of iron becomes a magnet. One way of doing this is by carefully sliding a magnet over the iron. This rearranges the domains in the iron so that they line up, creating a new magnet.

[1]The left end becomes the north pole.
[2]The right end becomes the south pole.

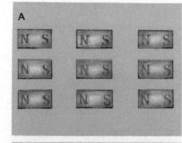

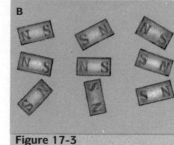

Figure 17-3

In a magnetized piece of iron, the domains are lined up in the same direction (A). In an unmagnetized piece of iron, the domains are not lined up (B).

Background   A magnetic field is the result of the motion of an electrical charge. A spinning electron is an electric charge in motion that creates a magnetic field. Most substances are not magnets because they have equal numbers of electrons spinning in opposite directions, thus canceling the fields. However, an iron atom has four electrons that do not spin in opposite directions; thus each iron atom is a tiny magnet. Atoms of nickel and cobalt behave in a similar way.

Teaching Tip   Ask students to describe what would happen to the poles of a magnet if the magnet was cut in half. (Each of the two pieces would be a magnet with two poles.) Ask students to imagine an almost infinite number of cuttings, down to the size of an atom. Explain to students that they would never find a single magnetic pole.

Thinking Skills

comparing
In Figures 17-3A and 17-3B, students compare the domains in a magnetized piece of iron and in an unmagnetized piece of iron to understand what happens when iron is magnetized.

PROCESS SKILLS
observing, comparing, identifying cause and effect

Preparation None required.

Answers to Results and Conclusions
1. At the poles; there are more iron filings there.
2. The sketch shows the attraction between the unlike poles.
3. The sketch shows the repulsion between the like poles.

Thinking Skills

inferring
Students observing Figure 17-4 may infer that each paper clip has become a temporary magnet.

Demonstration Show the lines of force around the poles of a horseshoe magnet by placing the magnet on the stage of an overhead projector. Place a piece of firm clear plastic over the magnet, and sprinkle iron filings evenly on the plastic. Turn on the projector, and tap the plastic gently to cause the filings to align with the magnetic field.

ACTIVITY How Is a Magnetic Field Mapped?

OBJECTIVE
Draw a diagram of a magnetic field.

MATERIALS
2 bar magnets, magnet holder, 4 sheets of paper, iron filings, metric ruler

PROCEDURE
A. Place one magnet in a magnet holder.
B. Place a sheet of paper over the magnet and holder so that the magnet is at the center of the paper.
C. Lightly sprinkle iron filings on the paper. Tap the paper gently. On another sheet of paper, sketch the pattern of the filings.
D. Return the iron filings to their container.
E. Place two magnets 2 cm apart in the holder so that two unlike poles face each other.
F. Place a sheet of paper over the magnets so that the center of the paper is over the two facing ends of the magnets.
G. Lightly sprinkle iron filings on the paper. Tap the paper gently. On another sheet of paper, sketch the pattern of the filings.
H. Return the iron filings to their container.
I. Place two magnets 2 cm apart in the holder so that two like poles face each other. Repeat steps **F** through **H**.

RESULTS AND CONCLUSIONS
1. Where is the strength of the magnetic field greatest? How can you tell?
2. What does the sketch you made in step **G** show about the magnetic field between two unlike poles?
3. What does the sketch you made in step **I** show about the magnetic field between two like poles?

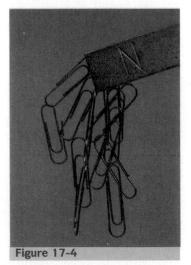

Figure 17-4
Nonmagnets, such as paper clips, can become temporary magnets.

Another way the domains in an unmagnetized piece of iron can be made to line up is by bringing a magnet near the iron. This causes the domains in the iron bar to line up with the magnetic field lines of the magnet. As a result, the iron bar becomes a magnet. When the magnet is removed, normal motion of atoms may cause the domains to return to their original positions. An object in which the domains return to their original positions when a magnetic field is removed is called a *temporary magnet*. The paper clips shown in Figure 17-4 are acting as temporary magnets.

Some objects stay magnetized even after a magnetic field has been removed. These materials are called *permanent magnets*. In permanent magnets the domains stay lined up because of the strong attraction between their poles. However, permanent magnets can lose their magnetism if their domains are pushed out of line. This can happen if the permanent magnet is heated or hit with a hammer. Heating or hammering the magnet increases the motion of the atoms. This tends to destroy the arrangement of domains by pushing the atoms out of line.

Also, a strong magnetic field can destroy the magnetism of a permanent magnet. This can happen if the magnet is placed in a magnetic field in a position where the domains are not lined up with this magnetic field. Just as a magnetic field can cause domains to line up, it can also cause them to be pushed out of line. Therefore, it is important to keep magnets away from other magnets.

THE EARTH'S MAGNETIC FIELD

A compass allows you to find direction because the earth is like a giant magnet. The fact that the north pole of a magnet points toward the geographic North Pole of the earth shows that this part of the earth acts like the south pole of a magnet. The earth's geographic and magnetic poles are shown in Figure 17-5. Notice that the earth's magnetic poles are not in the same place as its geographic poles. A compass points to the earth's magnetic north pole, not to the geographic North Pole. How does this fact affect finding direction using a compass?[1]

[1]For traveling over short distances, using a compass would be accurate. For traveling over long distances, the compass readings would have to be corrected.

Figure 17-5

The magnetic field of the earth is similar to the magnetic field of a bar magnet.

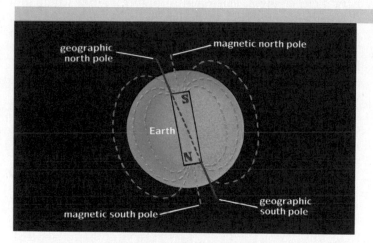

The earth's magnetic field is believed to be caused by molten, or melted, rock flowing far below the earth's surface. The molten rock contains metals. As the molten rock flows, the metals in it produce an electric current, which can produce a magnetic field. Throughout the earth's history, the movement of molten rock has changed. This is believed to have caused changes in the positions of the magnetic poles. The last time such a change took place was about 20,000 years ago.

REVIEW

1. What happens when like magnetic poles are brought together? What happens when the poles are unlike?
2. What causes the magnetism in a magnet?
3. What is the difference between temporary magnets and permanent magnets?
4. How does a permanent magnet lose its magnetism?

CHALLENGE Explain why iron fences can become magnetized over time.

Background   Scientists speculate that there may be a flow of charge in the earth's liquid outer core that gives rise to a magnetic field. This may be related to the speed of rotation of the earth. Saturn's magnetic field is about 1000 times stronger than that of the earth, and Jupiter's is about 10 times stronger than that of the earth. Both Saturn and Jupiter are gaseous and rotate very quickly, in 10 to 11 hours. In contrast, Venus and Mercury have weak magnetic fields and rotate very slowly.

Thinking Skills

comparing
In Figure 17-5, students compare the location of the magnetic poles with that of the geographic poles.

3 REVIEW/REINFORCEMENT

1. They repel each other; they attract each other.
2. When atoms in a magnetic material line up so that their magnetic fields combine, a magnet is formed.
3. Temporary magnets are materials in which the domains return to their original positions when a magnetic field is removed; permanent magnets remain magnetized after an external magnetic field is removed.
4. A permanent magnet loses it magnetism when it is heated, hit sharply, or placed in an external magnetic field, each of which can cause its domains to lose alignment.

Challenge   This may happen because of the force of the earth's magnetism.

17-2 CHANGING ELECTRICITY INTO MAGNETISM

pages 414–418

17-2 CHANGING ELECTRICITY INTO MAGNETISM

OBJECTIVES
Refer to pupil page 414.

VOCABULARY
Key terms: electric motor, electromagnet
Other terms: ammeter, electromagnetism, galvanometer, voltmeter

1 MOTIVATION

You can do the following as a demonstration or have students work in pairs: Prepare an electromagnet by wrapping a coil of wire around a soft iron core. Connect the wire in series with a switch and a 6-V dry cell. Tell students to pick up paper clips when the core is a magnet. Have them try again when the switch is open. Ask students to explain what happened.

After completing this section, you will be able to

- **compare** the magnetic field produced by a coil of wire with that produced by a straight wire.
- **describe** the factors that affect the strength of an electromagnet.
- **explain** how an electric motor works.

The key terms in this section are
electric motor
electromagnet

[1] The shape of the field is similar to the shape of the field around a bar magnet.

Recall that a magnet produces a magnetic field. In 1820 a Danish physicist named Hans Oersted found that an electric current could also produce a magnetic field. He observed that an electric current flowing through a wire could cause a compass needle to change direction. He also noted that the position of the compass needle changes if the current is reversed. The magnetic field lines are circles around the wire.

If the wire is made into a coil, the shape of the magnetic field changes, as shown in Figure 17-6A. Compare the shape of this field to the shape of the field of a bar magnet.[1] The ends of the coil become magnetic poles. If a bar of iron is placed within the coil of wire, as shown in Figure 17-6B, the magnetic field of the coil causes the domains in the iron bar to line up, creating a magnet. The strength of the magnetic field increases as the current through the coil and the number of turns of wire in the coil increase. Because electricity and magnetism are closely related, the term *electromagnetism* (ih lehk troh MAG nuh-tihz uhm) is used to describe this relationship.

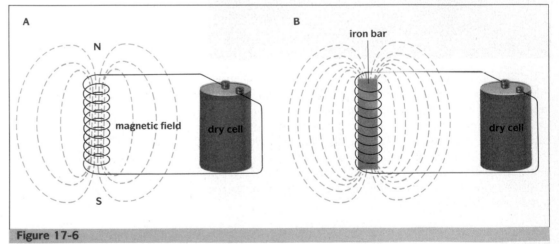

Figure 17-6

Magnetic field produced by a coil of wire (A). An electromagnet (B).

A coil of wire wound around an iron core is called an **electromagnet**. The magnetic field of the coil and the magnetic field of the iron core combine to produce a stronger magnetic field. When the dry cell is disconnected, the coil and core lose their magnetism. Thus the magnetism of an electromagnet can be turned on or off at will. The strength of an electromagnet can be increased by increasing the current or the number of turns in the coil of wire.

Electromagnets have many uses. They are used in doorbells and telephone bells. Electromagnets are also used in the earpieces of telephones and in loudspeakers.

A magnetic field can exert a force on a wire carrying an electric current. Michael Faraday, a scientist, observed that a magnetic field could push a current-carrying wire. This effect is shown in Figure 17-7A. A wire is connected to an open switch and to a dry cell. The wire is then placed between the poles of a magnet. When the switch is closed, current flows through the wire. Notice that the wire moves up. Then the switch is opened so that no current flows. The wire returns to its original position.

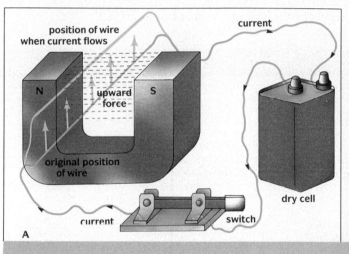

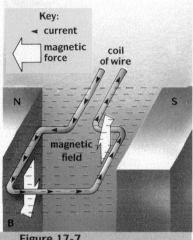

Figure 17-7

A magnetic field can exert a force on a current-carrying wire (A). The magnetic force on a current-carrying wire is greater if the wire is made into a loop (B).

Suppose the connections of the wire to the battery are reversed. When the switch is closed, the direction of the current also reverses and the wire moves down. This experiment shows that a magnetic force can be exerted on a current-carrying wire by a magnetic field. It also shows that the direction of a magnetic force on a current-carrying wire depends on the direction in which the current moves.

Figure 17-7B shows what happens if a wire is made into a loop and placed in a magnetic field. When current flows through the loop, a magnetic force will be exerted on two sides of the loop. But notice that the current in each side of the loop flows in opposite directions. This causes the magnetic force on each side of the loop to act in opposite directions. The magnetic force pushes one side of the loop upward while it pushes the other side downward. This pair of opposite forces causes the loop to turn.

2 CONCEPT DEVELOPMENT

Teaching Tip The core of an electromagnet is a magnet only when electricity flows through the wire. A magnetic field is caused by the electricity in the wire. The magnetic field is not present when electricity does not flow through the wire.

Background The nineteenth-century physicist James Clerk Maxwell explained the relationship between electric and magnetic fields and electromagnetic radiation with four mathematical equations. The first of Maxwell's equations is Coulomb's law, which states that the source of the electric field is an electric charge. The second of Maxwell's equations states that there are no magnetic monopoles; the basic structure of a magnet is a dipole—having both a north pole and a south pole. The third of Maxwell's equations is Faraday's law, which states that a changing magnetic field produces an electric field. Magnetic flux is an important concept in physics; flux is the product of magnetic field and area. It is really a changing flux that produces an electric current. The fourth of Maxwell's equations is called Ampere's law. Ampere's law states that an electric current produces a magnetic field. A straight-line current thus has magnetic-field lines circling it.

Teaching Tip Tell students that the direction of the magnetic field circling a wire is given by the left-hand rule. If the thumb of your left hand points in the direction of the current, the magnetic field coils around the wire as do your partially clenched fingers.

ACTIVITY 30 minutes

PROCESS SKILLS
observing, comparing

Preparation   None required.

Answers to Procedure
1. It always pointed in one direction, north.
2. It changed with the field direction, following the circle.
3. The magnetic field is reversed, so the needle points in a direction opposite that in each case in step **E**.

Answers to Results and Conclusions
1. When current flowed in the wire, it created a magnetic field that changed the direction of the needle, indicating the presence of a magnetic field other than that of the earth.
2. Current flowed in the opposite direction, changing the direction of the magnetic field.
3. The magnetic field is described by concentric circles about the wire.

Demonstration   Show how a voltmeter and an ammeter work. Have students explain how these meters operate.

Teaching Tip   In a voltmeter or an ammeter, a wire loop is mounted so that it can rotate in a magnetic field. As a current flows, the wire is forced to rotate, and an attached needle deflects proportionally.

The magnetic force on the loop of wire can be increased by increasing the strength of the magnetic field and the amount of current flowing in the wire. The magnetic force can also be increased by increasing the length of the wire in the magnetic field. This can be done by increasing the number of loops of wire or by using a coil. When an electric current flows through a coil, a magnetic force is exerted on each loop of wire. The magnetic forces on each loop combine to turn the coil.

A magnetic force turns a coil of wire in devices called electric meters. One type of meter, called a *galvanometer* (gal vuh NAHM uh tuhr), is used to measure tiny amounts of current. A meter that measures large amounts of current is an *ammeter* (AM eet uhr). A *voltmeter* (VOHLT mee tuhr) measures the voltage in an electric circuit.

ACTIVITY   How Is the Field of a Current Mapped?

OBJECTIVE
Map the magnetic field of an electric current.

MATERIALS
heavy cardboard, 50-cm length of insulated copper wire, 1.5 V dry cell, masking tape, small compass

PROCEDURE
A. Using the tip of a pen or pencil, carefully punch a small hole through the center of a piece of cardboard.
B. Push one end of a wire through the hole. Then attach the end of the wire to the positive terminal of a dry cell. Do not attach the other end of the wire to the negative terminal.
C. Adjust the wire so that it passes straight up and down through the cardboard. Tape one end of the cardboard to the edge of a table. Make sure the cardboard extends horizontally from the edge of the table.
D. Place a small compass on the cardboard about 3 cm from the wire. Move the compass in a circle around the wire.
   1. As you move the compass, what happens to the direction of the needle?
E. Close the circuit by attaching the free end of the wire to the negative terminal of the battery. Slowly move the compass in a circle around the wire.

2. As you move the compass, what happens to the direction of the needle?
F. Reverse the connections of the ends of the wire to the terminals. Slowly move the compass in a circle around the wire. Observe the direction of the needle.
   3. How does the direction of the needle now compare with the direction of the needle in step **E**?

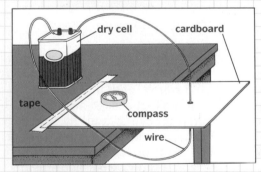

RESULTS AND CONCLUSIONS
1. Explain the effect that closing the circuit had on the direction of the compass needle.
2. Explain the effect that reversing the connections to the terminals of the dry cell had on the direction of the compass needle.
3. Describe the shape of the magnetic field around a wire carrying a current.

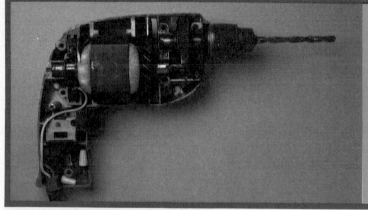

In the motor of an electric drill, the magnetic field is provided by an electromagnet rather than by a permanent magnet. Thus there are two electromagnets in this type of motor: one that takes the place of a stationary permanent magnet, and one that turns in the magnetic field. In what ways does this improve the compactness of a drill?

Puzzler Electromagnets can be smaller, lighter, and more powerful than permanent magnets.

Thinking Skills

interpreting diagrams
Students use Figure 17-8A to help them understand how an electric meter works.

Thinking Skills

comparing
Students are asked to compare the way an electric motor works in Figure 17-9 with the way an electric meter works in Figure 17-8.

These meters measure electric current in an electric circuit. As shown in Figure 17-8, an electric meter contains a coil of wire set between the poles of a U-shaped permanent magnet. The current to be measured flows through the coil of wire. The magnetic field of the magnet exerts a force on the coil, causing it to turn. The turning of the coil moves a pointer across a scale. Attached to the coil are two springs that resist the turning of the coil. The greater the current passing through the coil, the greater the magnetic force on the coil and the more the coil turns. The amount of current can be measured from the amount the pointer moves across the scale.

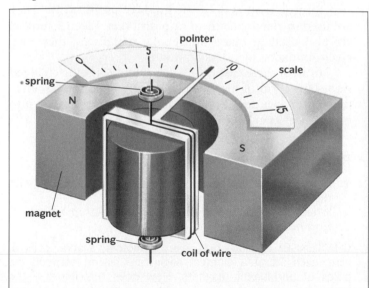

Figure 17-8

A magnetic force moves the needle in an electric meter like this voltmeter.

Review and Skill Masters

CHALLENGE/CRITICAL THINKING, page 106.
See page 407c in this book for answers.

Background In an electric motor, an electrical conductor called the armature rotates between the north and south poles of a stationary magnet. The armature becomes an electromagnet when a current passes through it. It is connected to a drive shaft so that it can move the parts of the motor and do work.

③ REVIEW/REINFORCEMENT

1. The magnetic field of a coil of wire closely resembles the field of a bar magnet; the magnetic field of a straight wire circles the wire.
2. The strength of an electromagnet can be increased by increasing the current in a wire coil or the number of turns in the coil.
3. An electric motor converts electrical energy into mechanical energy. When current flows through the coil, the magnetic field of the permanent magnet exerts a magnetic force on the coil; then the coil spins, causing a shaft to spin. The rotary motion is used to do work on objects.

Challenge It increases the current between the poles of permanent magnets, which increases the force on the coils; this enables the motor to turn faster or to use less energy if it turns at a slower rate.

Review and Skill Masters

SKILL, pages 104–105.
See page 407b–c in this book for answers.

As in an electric meter, in an electric motor a magnetic force turns a coil of wire. Notice in Figure 17-9 that an electric motor contains a coil of wire set between the poles of a permanent magnet. When current flows through the coil, the magnetic field of the permanent magnet exerts a magnetic force on the coil of wire. As in an electric meter, this causes the coil to turn. In the motor the coil is free to turn all the way around. This turning continues as long as there is current flowing in the wire coil. The turning coil is attached to a shaft that is also free to turn.

Figure 17-9

An electric motor consists of a coil of wire placed in a magnetic field. When the coil turns it turns gears, which make the model car move.

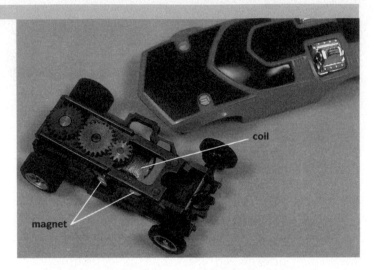

Electric motors do many kinds of useful work. They are used in electric drills to turn drill bits. Electric motors are also used in many household appliances; they turn electric mixers, blenders, and fans.

In all of these cases, electrical energy is being changed into some form of mechanical energy. Therefore an **electric motor** is a device that changes electrical energy into mechanical energy.

motus (moved)

REVIEW

1. How does the magnetic field of a coil of wire compare with the magnetic field of a straight wire?
2. What factors affect the strength of an electromagnet?
3. How does an electric motor work?

CHALLENGE In heavy-duty electric motors, several coils of wire, each set at a different angle, are placed between the poles of permanent magnets. How does this improve the motors?

17-3 CHANGING MAGNETISM INTO ELECTRICITY

You have learned that an electric current can produce magnetism. Can magnetism produce electricity? To answer this question, look at Figure 17-10. The wire is connected to a galvanometer. When the wire is moved downward between the poles of the magnet, the galvanometer needle moves. This shows that a current flows in the wire. What happens to the needle when the wire is moved upward through the magnetic field?[1] This shows that the current flows in the opposite direction. If the wire is not moved or if it is moved from pole to pole, no current flows in the wire. Thus, current can be produced in a wire when the wire is moved through a magnetic field and at right angles to that field.

The current that is produced when a wire is moved at a right angle through a magnetic field is called an *induced current*. The act of producing the current is called **electromagnetic induction**. A current can also be induced by moving the magnet and holding the wire in a fixed position. As long as there is motion that causes a wire to cut across the lines of a magnetic field, an electric current can be produced.

After completing this section, you will be able to

- **describe** how electric current can be produced by a magnetic field.
- **explain** how a generator works.
- **compare** an ac generator with a dc generator.

The key terms in this section are
alternating current
direct current
electromagnetic induction
generator

[1]The needle moves in the opposite direction.

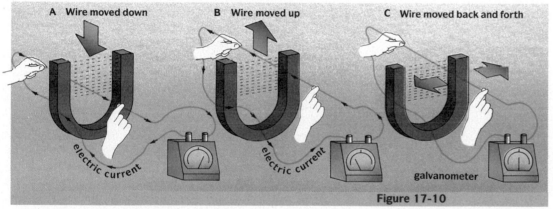

A Wire moved down electric current

B Wire moved up electric current

C Wire moved back and forth galvanometer

Figure 17-10

A current is induced when a wire is moved perpendicular to magnetic field lines (*A, B*). A current is not induced when a wire is moved parallel to magnetic field lines (*C*).

If the wire is made into a loop and rotated in a magnetic field, a greater current can be produced. This is how a generator (jehn uh RAY tuhr) works. A **generator** is a device that changes mechanical energy into electrical energy. In a generator, many loops of wire, or a coil of wire, are turned in a magnetic field to produce a current. Increasing the number of loops of wire increases the amount of current produced. Also, increasing the speed at which a coil rotates increases the amount of current produced.

17-3 CHANGING MAGNETISM INTO ELECTRICITY

pages 419–422

OBJECTIVES
Refer to pupil page 419.

VOCABULARY
Key terms: alternating current, direct current, electromagnetic induction, generator

Other terms: alternating current generator, brushes, commutator, direct current generator, induced current

1 MOTIVATION

Set up a circuit consisting of a wire and a galvanometer. Move the wire downward between the poles of a horseshoe magnet. Note the deflection of the galvanometer. Move the wire upward between the poles of the horseshoe magnet. Note the opposite deflection. Ask students to predict what the effect would be if a stronger magnet was used. If a stronger magnet is available, test their predictions. Ask students what effect moving the wire more rapidly would have. Test their predictions.

2 CONCEPT DEVELOPMENT

Thinking Skills

identifying cause and effect
Students identify cause and effect by observing the effects of certain kinds of movements of a wire between the poles of a magnet. Students then relate each effect to its cause.

Demonstration Using the materials and setup outlined in the *Motivation* section, coil the wire and drop it over one of the poles to produce a greater current.

Teaching Tip   Ask students to make an analogy between Faraday's law and Ampere's law: Just as an electric current produces a magnetic field, a changing magnetic field produces an electric current.

Background   Power is transmitted over great distances at high voltages and low currents. The voltage is stepped up or stepped down along the way by electromagnetic induction in various transformers.

ACTIVITY   How Is a Current Created?

OBJECTIVE
Demonstrate the factors that affect an induced current.

MATERIALS
bar magnet, wire coil, galvanometer

PROCEDURE
A. Using a bar magnet, wire coil, and galvanometer, set up a circuit as shown in the figure.
B. Insert the north pole of the magnet into the coil. Observe the galvanometer needle.

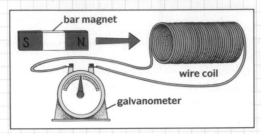

C. Insert the south pole of the magnet into the coil. Observe the galvanometer needle.
D. Repeat steps **B** and **C**, varying the speed in which the magnet is inserted. Record your observations.
E. Insert the magnet by moving the coil of wire instead of moving the magnet. Record your observations.

RESULTS AND CONCLUSIONS
1. Compare your observations of the galvanometer needle in steps **B** and **C**. What can you conclude about the direction of the current in the wire?
2. How did the speed at which the magnet was inserted into the coil in step **D** affect the needle? What can you conclude about the amount of current in the wire?
3. Compare the result of inserting the magnet by moving the coil to the result of inserting the magnet by moving the magnet.
4. What factors affect the direction and amount of an induced current?

In a generator, mechanical energy is used to rotate the coil. This energy can come from the falling water in a waterfall. The mechanical energy can also come from heat energy produced by the burning of coal or oil. The heat is used to boil water and create steam. The force of the moving steam turns the coil in the generator.

Almost all the electricity that you use at home or school is produced by huge generators in power plants. Also, gasoline engines, such as those in cars, use generators. These engines use generators to produce electricity for the engines' spark plugs. Hospitals have emergency generators that can operate in case of a power failure.

The current produced by generators in power plants is a type of current called alternating current. **Alternating current** (ac) is a type of electric current that changes direction at regular intervals in a circuit. For example, the alternating current in household circuits in North America moves back and forth 60 times each second.

Alternating current differs from the type of current produced by an electric cell or battery. Recall that the electric current produced by an electric cell or battery travels in only one direction. Electric current that travels in one direction in a circuit is called **direct current** (dc).

Figure 17-11

Generators in a power plant convert mechanical energy into electrical energy.

To see how a generator produces alternating current, look at Figure 17-12A. Notice the position of part **a** of the coil. As the coil turns through the magnetic field, part **a** moves upward through the field. One-half turn later, as shown in Figure 17-12B, part **a** of the coil moves downward through the field. Each time the coil makes a half turn, part **a** moves in the opposite direction in the field. Notice that this is also true for part **b** of the coil. Each time the coil makes a half turn, part **b** moves in the opposite direction. This change in the direction of the coil as it moves through the magnetic field causes the current in the coil to also change direction. As the coil turns, an alternating current is produced in the wire. A generator that produces an alternating current is called an *alternating current generator*. An ac generator is also called an *alternator*.

Background   The discovery that magnetism could be produced when electricity flows through a wire led to the exploration of a related question: Could electricity be produced by magnetism? Michael Faraday, a Scottish scientist, and Joseph Henry, an American physicist and a founding executive of the Smithsonian Institution, independently discovered in 1831 that a voltage was induced when a magnet was moved through a coil of wire. This phenomenon is called electromagnetic induction. It is dependent only on the relative motion of the conductor and the magnetic field.

Background   Each time the alternating current makes two changes of direction, a cycle is completed. The number of cycles completed per second is called the frequency of the alternating current. The frequency is measured in hertz (Hz). In the United States and Canada, the cycles in an alternating current occur with a frequency of 60 Hz.

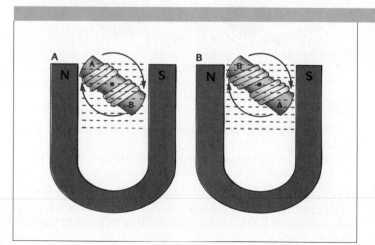

Figure 17-12

Each time a coil of wire is turned one-half turn in a magnetic field, the induced current reverses direction, producing alternating current.

Teaching Tip   Tell students that the major advantage of alternating current over direct current is that it can be easily transmitted. Current loses less energy when it travels at high voltages. However, high voltages are not safe to use in homes. Alternating current is useful because it can be stepped up or down by means of transformers. Have students discuss the location of transformers that are used in the area where they live.

Thinking Skills

sequencing
As students observe Figure 17-13, they are able to follow the sequence of steps during which direct current electricity is generated. Ask students to compare the generation of direct current in this diagram with the generation of alternating current in Figures 17-12A and 17-12B.

Enrichment   Students can gain a sense of some of the history of science by making a time line that shows some of the events described in this chapter. Have students also plot major historical events on their time line to put the history of science in perspective.

3 REVIEW/REINFORCEMENT

1. Motion in a wire can cut through a field and produce current.
2. Many loops of wire are turned in a magnetic field to produce a current.
3. A d.c. generator produces alternating current in a coil of wire just as an a.c. generator does; however, as it leaves the coil, the current is changed into direct current by means of a commutator and two brushes.

Challenge   Household current produces an alternating magnetic field at 60 cycles per second; this changing magnetic field occurs too quickly to cause visible effects on a compass needle.

Generators can also be made to produce direct current. This kind of generator is called a *direct current generator*. As in the ac generator, in a dc generator an alternating current is produced in a coil of wire. However, as it leaves the coil, the current is changed into direct current by a *commutator* and two *brushes*.

As you can see in Figure 17-13, a commutator is made up of two half rings. Each half is connected to one end of the coil. Touching the rings are metal or carbon strips called brushes. The two half rings turn with the coil, but the brushes do not move. During one half of a turn, each brush is in contact with one of the half rings. During the next half of a turn, each brush is in contact with the other half ring. Every half turn of the coil, the commutator and brushes reverse the direction of the current. This action changes alternating current to direct current.

Almost all power plants in the United States use ac generators. Power companies find that they can send electric power with less energy loss by using alternating current instead of direct current.

Figure 17-13

A dc generator uses two brushes and a commutator to produce direct current.

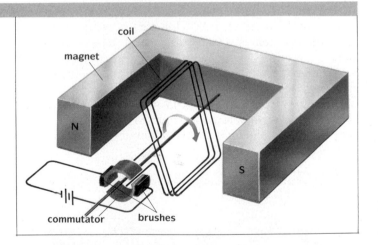

REVIEW

1. How can magnetism be used to produce electric current in a wire?
2. How does a generator produce electric current?
3. In what ways is a dc generator different from an ac generator?

CHALLENGE A compass needle does not change direction when brought near a wire that carries household current. Explain why.

17-4 ELECTRONICS

Many useful devices have been developed in the field of electronics (ih lehk TRAHN ihks). **Electronics** is the study of the behavior of electrons in electric circuits. A major advance in electronics took place with the invention of the vacuum tube in 1906. The vacuum tube made early radios and television sets possible. **Vacuum tubes** are electronic components that change alternating current to direct current and amplify, or increase, the current.

Thomas Edison discovered that when enough current flows through a thin wire called a filament, the wire gives off electrons. As shown in Figure 17-14, these electrons can then be attracted to a positively charged plate. This action must take place in a vacuum so that the electrons can move to the plate without being stopped by molecules in the air. This is the idea behind the vacuum tube.

In a vacuum tube the positive terminal of a battery is connected to the plate while the negative terminal is connected to the filament. The filament acts as the negative electrode while the plate acts as the positive electrode. Because this tube contains two electrodes, it is called a diode. When enough current flows through the filament, the filament glows and emits electrons. The electrons from the filament are attracted to the plate. If the connections to the terminals of the battery are reversed, making the plate negative and the filament positive, no current will flow. Thus the vacuum diode allows current to flow only in one direction.

After completing this section, you will be able to

- **explain** how vacuum tubes work.
- **compare** a vacuum tube and a transistor.
- **relate** the invention of the integrated circuit to the development of modern electronics.

The key terms in this section are
amplifier
cathode-ray tube
computer
electronics
integrated circuit
transistor
vacuum tubes

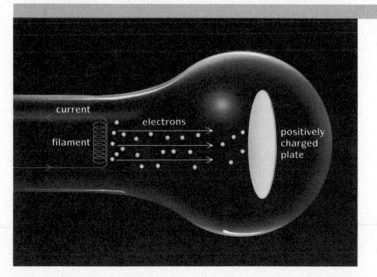

Figure 17-14

When enough current flows through a wire, electrons are emitted from a wire and can be attracted to a positive plate.

current
filament
electrons
positively charged plate

OBJECTIVES
Refer to pupil page 423.

VOCABULARY
Key terms: amplifier, cathode-ray tube, computer, electronics, integrated circuit, transistor, vacuum tubes
Other terms: chip, program

1 MOTIVATION

Have students discuss various electronic devices—radio, television, calculators, computers—with their parents and grandparents to establish a sense of the relative newness of these devices. Have students share their findings with the class. Discuss with students the possibility that the twentieth century may well be remembered as the Age of Electronics.

2 CONCEPT DEVELOPMENT

Background   In the early 1880s, Thomas Edison sealed an extra electrode into one of his electric lights. He noticed that when the light was on, the current flowed from the filament to the extra electrode. The current flowed in a plate circuit when the positive terminal of the battery was connected to the plate. When the negative terminal of the battery was connected to the plate, no current flowed. Edison recorded this so-called Edison effect; he even patented it. But he could not explain it. Actually, electrons were "boiled off" the hot filament and were attracted to the positive plate. When the connections were reversed, the electrons were repelled by the negatively charged plate; no current could then flow.

Thinking Skills

interpreting diagrams
Students use the diagram in Figure 17-15 to trace how electrons can be controlled and moved at will in a vacuum tube.

Background   The vacuum tube was greatly improved by the addition of a grid. This was the work of the American scientist Lee De Forest in 1907. He also developed a vacuum tube, which he called the audion, to amplify radio signals. This made radio possible.

Tie-in/Math   A 1-V change in the grid voltage produces a 1-milliamp (0.001-A) change in the plate current. A change in the plate current will therefore produce a change in the voltage across the resistance. If the resistance is 25,000 ohms, a 0.001-A current change would be $V = IR = (0.001\ A)(25,000\ \Omega) = 25\ V$. Students will see that a 1-V change in the grid voltage produces a 25-V change across the resistance. This is a substantial voltage amplification.

If a third electrode, called a grid, is placed between the filament and the plate in a vacuum tube, the tube is then called a triode. The grid acts like a valve, controlling the amount of current flowing in the tube. A change in the charge of the grid can produce a change in the current in the tube. If it has a negative charge, less current flows. If the grid is given a large negative charge, the current can be shut off completely. If the grid has a positive charge, the current increases. What would be the effect on the current if the grid is given a larger positive charge?[1] When the current in the tube is increased, it is said to be amplified. An **amplifier** is a device used to increase the strength of a current. A triode can be used as an amplifier.

[1]The current increases by a greater amount.

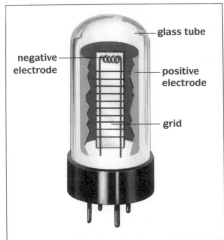

glass tube

negative electrode

positive electrode

grid

Figure 17-15

A vacuum tube called a triode contains three electrodes (*left*). Vacuum tubes glow when current passes through them (*right*).

A type of vacuum tube that is still in use today is the cathode-ray tube, or CRT. A **cathode-ray tube** is a tube in which an electron beam is directed to a small area on a screen to form a picture. These tubes are used in black-and-white television picture tubes and in screens on the monitors of computers. Figure 17-16 is a simple diagram of a CRT. The filament heats up and emits electrons. The electrons are attracted by the positive plate, or anode. Some of the electrons pass through the anode. They are focused by electric plates onto a screen. The screen is coated with chemicals called phosphors, which light up when electrons strike them. The electron beam is directed across the screen, making the screen glow.

Cathode-ray tubes require high voltages. They should be handled only by qualified technicians. The voltage is more than enough to kill a person.

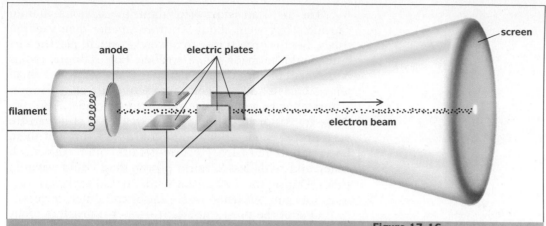

interpreting diagrams
Students use the diagram in Figure 17-16 to trace the route followed by the electron beam. They can observe how the electron beam controls the flow of electrons.

Figure 17-16

An electron beam is directed onto a screen in a cathode-ray tube.

In the 1940s, scientists were looking for an electronic device to replace the vacuum tube. One problem with early vacuum tubes was their large size. Vacuum tubes also used a large amount of electric power and produced a large amount of heat. They burned out easily and, therefore, were not reliable.

In 1948 the transistor was invented. A **transistor** is a solid electronic component that amplifies and controls the flow of electric current in a circuit. In a transistor the electric current flows through a solid rather than through a vacuum. As shown in Figure 17-17, a transistor contains three wires. Two wires act like the diode in a vacuum tube. Electrons are given off by one wire in the transistor and are received by the other wire. The third wire in the transistor acts like the grid in a vacuum tube. This section can increase or decrease the flow of electrons through the transistors.

trans (across)

Background   Transistors are made of semiconducting materials, such as silicon and germanium. Semiconductors have conductivities between those of conductors and those of insulators. When a voltage is applied across a semiconductor, just a small current flows because semiconductors have high resistance. However, adding certain chemical impurities to semiconductors lowers their resistance dramatically. The impurities enhance current flow in semiconducting materials.

Teaching Tip   Have students work together to make a list of modern devices that depend on diodes and transistors. Then have students make a second list of the kinds of technology that require computers.

Figure 17-17

A transistor contains three electrodes that control the flow of electrons in a circuit.

inferring

By looking at the early computer, ENIAC, in Figure 17-18, students can infer that bigger is not better. They learn that the 18,000 vacuum tubes in ENIAC were subject to burning out. The larger computers also took much longer to process information than do present-day computers.

Teaching Tip   Tell students that the word *transistor* is a combination of "trans" from *transfer* and "istor" from *resistance*. The gains in a transistor come from a transfer of resistance. This causes the output voltage to be much higher than the input voltage.

Background   Vacuum tubes require a heating element, or filament, that is not necessary in diodes and transistors. As a result, diodes and transistors use milliwatts of power in comparison with the watts of power used by a vacuum tube. This is a thousandfold savings.

The first transistors were about the size of a vitamin capsule. They were about 50 times smaller than vacuum tubes. Because the transistors were so small, electric circuits could be made much smaller. For example, radios with vacuum tubes were about the size of some small television sets today. Replacing vacuum tubes with transistors allowed pocket-size radios to be made. Also, because transistors are solid and are smaller in size than are vacuum tubes, electric current could flow through them faster and more easily. Thus transistors could work much faster and with less electric power than could vacuum tubes. During the 1950s, transistors began replacing vacuum tubes in television sets, radios, and other devices.

One of the most important uses of transistors today is their use in computers. A **computer** is a device that follows a set of instructions to process information. A set of instructions that a computer follows is called a *program*. A computer can do calculations quickly and accurately. It can also store and sort huge amounts of information.

The first computers came into use in the late 1940s, before transistors were invented. They were designed to do long, complicated calculations. One of these computers is shown in Figure 17-18. It contained over 18,000 vacuum tubes. A vacuum tube would burn out often, about every half hour. Every time a vacuum tube burned out, the computer had to be shut down. Replacing vacuum tubes with transistors made the computer more reliable.

Figure 17-18

ENIAC was the first large computer.

SCIENCE & TECHNOLOGY

Organs in the human body have magnetic fields, just as the earth or a horseshoe magnet has a magnetic field. The most common source of magnetism in the body is electric currents generated naturally by muscles and nerves. The heart and brain produce the most current.

New technology has provided better detectors for the tiny magnetic fields produced by organs. One of the newest and most sensitive detectors is known as SQUID. This name stands for ''superconducting quantum interference device.''

Much of the research done with SQUID on human magnetism is centered on the brain. Electric currents in the brain produce magnetic fields. When these fields are sensed by SQUID, they produce charts called

magnetoencephalograms, or MEG's. The MEG's sense small sources of activity in the brain. Thus, MEG's can define individual sources of electrical activity clearly. This can give doctors information to help diagnose brain disorders.

Epilepsy is one illness that is being better diagnosed with the help of MEG's. A person with epilepsy has disrupted electrical rhythms in the brain. MEG's help locate where in the brain the cause of the epilepsy is.

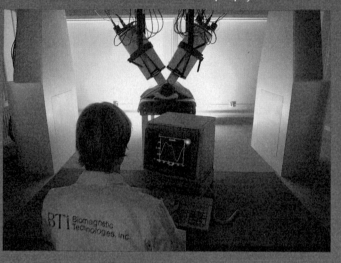

The transistor also allowed computers to be made smaller. However, some computers were still too large. They required many complicated circuits. Each circuit in a computer might contain 100 transistors. The large number of transistors made computers work slowly.

By the end of the 1950s, a way of making circuits smaller was invented. This invention was the integrated circuit. An **integrated circuit** is a circuit in which transistors and other electronic components have been engraved on a chip. A *chip* is a thin slice of material, usually silicon. It is about one-fourth the size of a postage stamp or smaller.

In ordinary circuits there are separate, individual components connected by wires. In integrated circuits there are no wires or separate components to connect. Different areas on a chip are coated with different chemicals. The chemicals give the different areas new electrical properties. For example, a certain chemical can determine which part of the chip acts as a transistor or as another component. The components are then connected by tiny metal channels instead of by wires.

Thinking Skills

inferring

Students learn that computer chips do not have separate, individual components connected by wires. Instead, different areas are coated with different chemicals. Students can infer that the chemicals are important in building the circuit.

Background   The components on a silicon wafer are connected by means of a photosensitive technique. The wafer is covered with a thin layer of photosensitive plastic. A photographic negative with the desired circuit pattern for the chips is placed on the wafer. It is then exposed to ultraviolet light. Wherever the light strikes the plastic coating, it hardens and remains in place when the unexposed part is washed away. A thin layer of metal is then added to the wafer. The hardened plastic is dissolved, and the metal in the same regions is removed with it. The metal pattern that is left behind connects the components.

Thinking Skills

comparing
Students compare the first integrated circuit, which contained fewer than 100 transistors on a chip, with a present-day chip, which is one-tenth the size of a postage stamp and contains 7000 transistors. Discuss with students the fact that present-day chips have the ability to perform 100,000 tasks in one second, using less than 1 W of electric power.

Background   The first fully electronic digital computer, ENIAC, was built in 1946 by engineers at the University of Pennsylvania. The invention of the transistor in 1947 by three workers at Bell Laboratories—John Bardeen, William Shockley, and Walter Brattain—won for these workers the Nobel Prize in physics. The transistor resulted in the production of faster and more reliable electronic computers. The development of the integrated circuit led to the design of minicomputers and high-speed mainframe computers that carry out instructions in billionths of a second. In the 1970s the microprocessor was developed, opening up the use of computers to the general public.

The first integrated circuits contained less than 100 transistors on a chip. Today, chips containing 1000 transistors are common. Scientists have been able to fit over 150,000 transistors on one silicon chip.

Because of the small size of integrated circuits, the electric current has to flow only very short distances. Thus the tasks of the circuits can be carried out more quickly and with less power. A chip one-tenth the size of a postage stamp can contain 7000 transistors and perform 100,000 tasks in one second. It can perform these tasks using less than one watt of electric power.

Figure 17-19

Because silicon chips are so tiny, complex electronic devices can be made very small.

Being able to fit more and more transistors on a single chip has allowed modern electronic devices to be made much smaller than was ever imagined. Computers once the size of rooms can now be made to fit on desk tops. Chips are put into automatic cameras to calculate the right exposure. Calculators and radios can be made the size of credit cards.

The small size of integrated circuits has allowed more computing power to be built into computers. The big computers of the 1950s needed dozens of people to run a single program. Today the simplest models of computers can run a variety of programs. A single desktop computer can run programs written for schools, doctors, hotels, lawyers, and accountants.

REVIEW

1. How does a vacuum tube change the current in an electric circuit?
2. In what ways are vacuum tubes and transistors similar? In what ways are they different?
3. How is the development of modern electronics related to the invention of the integrated circuit?

CHALLENGE If a computer can perform one billion functions per second, how long would it take that computer to perform an operation that has 100 steps?

CHAPTER SUMMARY

The main ideas in this chapter are listed below. Read these statements before you answer the Chapter Review questions.

- The magnetic properties of materials are caused by the arrangement of the atoms within the materials. (17-1)

- Certain materials, called magnetic materials, become magnets when placed in magnetic fields. (17-1)

- A circular magnetic field is produced around a wire that is carrying a current. If the wire is made into a coil, the ends of the coil become magnetic poles. (17-2)

- When a wire that is carrying a current is placed in a magnetic field, a magnetic force will be exerted on the wire. (17-2)

- When a wire is moved perpendicularly through a magnetic field or when a magnetic field is moved perpendicularly to a wire, a current is produced in the wire. (17-3)

- When a coil of wire is rotated in a magnetic field, an alternating current is induced in the coil. (17-3)

- Vacuum tubes and transistors are electronic components that amplify and control the flow of current in an electric circuit. (17-4)

- The integrated circuit allows electronic devices to work faster and to be made much smaller in size. (17-4)

The key terms in this chapter are listed below. Use each term in a sentence that shows the meaning of the term.

alternating current	electromagnet	magnetic domain
amplifier	electromagnetic induction	magnetic field
cathode-ray tube	electronics	magnetism
computer	generator	transistor
direct current	integrated circuit	vacuum tubes
electric motor	magnet	

3 REVIEW/REINFORCEMENT

1. Vacuum tubes contain electrodes that control current flow in one direction; this current flow may be increased or decreased by the addition of a grid. If the grid has a negative charge, less current flows or current can be shut off completely; if the grid has a positive charge, the current increases.
2. Vacuum tubes and transistors are similar in that they both can increase or decrease the flow of electrons between the two ends; they are different in that vacuum tubes use metal conductors as electrodes but transistors use semiconducting material. Also, transistors are a lot smaller and faster, and they consume less power.
3. The integrated circuit is composed of many components in a very small region; this allows for the creation of small, complex electronic circuits, which can be used in making electronic devices that were not possible before the integrated circuit.

Challenge $\dfrac{10^2}{10^9}$ s $= \dfrac{1}{10^7}$ s $= 10^{-7}$, or one 10-millionth, of a second to perform 100 steps.

Review and Skill Masters

VOCABULARY REVIEW, page 101.
See page 407b in this book for answers.

VOCABULARY

1. d 2. a 3. l 4. g 5. e 6. i
7. f 8. k 9. j 10. h 11. b 12. c

CONCEPTS

1. The north pole of a magnet points toward the earth's geographic north, indicating that this part of the earth acts like the south pole of a magnet.
2. As the domains are pushed out of line by heating or by being hammered, magnetism disappears.
3. A temporary magnet can be made by stroking a piece of soft iron in one direction with a magnet, by bringing a magnet near a piece of soft iron, or by wrapping a wire around a piece of soft iron and connecting the wire to a battery.
4. A permanent magnet can lose its magnetism if it is heated, hit with a hammer, or placed in another strong magnetic field.
5. It is shaped like the magnetic field of a bar magnet, and it has an *N* pole at one end and a *S* pole at the other end.
6. By increasing the current, by placing an iron bar within the coil, and by increasing the number of coils.
7. In an electric motor, electricity travels through a coil positioned within the magnetic field of a stationary magnet; as current flows, a magnetic field around the coil is produced, and the interaction between the two magnetic fields creates motion.
8. The current varies from zero to the maximum amount when a coil is rotated through a magnetic field; the current is maximum when wire is moved perpendicularly through a magnetic field; it is zero when the coil is parallel to the field.

Review and Skill Masters

CHAPTER REVIEW, pages 102–103.
See page 407b in this book for answers.

Chapter Review

VOCABULARY

Write the letter of the term that best matches the definition. Not all the terms will be used.

1. A device that follows a program
2. Electric current that reverses its direction
3. A solid device that amplifies and controls the flow of current
4. A device that changes mechanical energy into electrical energy
5. Electric current that flows in only one direction
6. A substance that attracts magnetic materials
7. A device that changes electrical energy into mechanical energy
8. The area where magnetic force acts
9. The area where magnetic fields of atoms are lined up
10. A group of electronic components engraved on a chip
11. A device used to increase the strength of a current
12. A tube in which an electron beam is focused on a screen to form a picture.

a. alternating current
b. amplifier
c. cathode-ray tube
d. computer
e. direct current
f. electric motor
g. generator
h. integrated circuit
i. magnet
j. magnetic domain
k. magnetic field
l. transistor
m. vacuum tubes

CONCEPTS

1. How can you tell that the magnetic pole near the earth's geographic North Pole is a magnetic south pole? (17-1)
2. How does the presence of domains in magnetic substances explain how they can gain or lose their magnetism? (17-1)
3. Describe how a temporary magnet can be made. (17-1)
4. Describe ways in which a permanent magnet can lose its magnetism. (17-1)
5. In what ways is the magnetic field of a coil of wire similar to the magnetic field of a bar magnet? (17-2)
6. Describe three ways that the magnetic field produced by a coil of wire can be increased. (17-2)
7. How is electricity converted into motion by an electric motor? (17-2)

8. Compare the amounts of electric current produced by turning a coil of wire in a magnetic field and by moving a wire perpendicularly through a magnetic field. (17-3)
9. Compare the effect of moving a wire through a magnetic field with that of moving a magnetic field around a wire. (17-3)
10. Compare how a generator works with how a motor works. (17-3)
11. How is an ac generator changed to a dc generator? (17-3)
12. What are some ways in which the electric current produced by a generator can be increased? (17-3)
13. How does a grid in a vacuum tube increase or decrease the flow of electrons in an electric circuit? (17-4)
14. Why was the transistor an improvement over the vacuum tube in electronic devices? (17-4)
15. How are the parts of a transistor similar to the parts of a vacuum tube? (17-4)
16. In what ways is an integrated circuit better than an ordinary circuit? (17-4)

1. If a magnet is divided into pieces, each piece is found to be a complete magnet having a north pole and a south pole. How is this explained by the presence of domains?
2. In some motors the magnetic poles are produced by electromagnets instead of by permanent magnets. Explain why.
3. The alternator in a car has rotating electromagnets inside fixed coils of wire. Explain how electric current is produced by an alternator.
4. Why are the magnetic poles in motors and generators curved?
5. Explain why there is a limit to how much a piece of iron or steel can be magnetized.

1. Do library research to find out how huge electromagnets are being used to contain high-temperature reactions in nuclear fusion reactors.
2. Do research to find out how electromagnets produce sound in loudspeakers or in earpieces of telephones.
3. Using a small compass, map the magnetic fields of different shapes of magnets.

Adler, David. *Amazing Magnets*. Mahwah, N.J.: Troll, 1983.
Stansell, John. *Discovering Communications*. London: Sceptre Books Ltd., 1983.

9. They are the same.
10. A motor changes electromagnetic energy into motion by passing a current through wires in a magnetic field; a generator creates electromagnetic energy from motion by rotating a coil of wire through a magnetic field.
11. A commutator and two brushes are used to change a.c. to d.c.
12. By turning the coil faster, by increasing the strength of the magnet, and by increasing the number of loops of wire turned through the magnetic field.
13. If the grid has a negative charge, less or no current flows; if the grid has a positive charge, the current increases.
14. Answers may vary.
15. A triode contains three electrodes—positive, negative, and the grid—to control the current; a transistor contains three segments to control the current.
16. An integrated circuit is better because it has no wires or separate components; it is smaller and more reliable, generates less heat, uses less power, and can carry out tasks more quickly.

APPLICATION/CRITICAL THINKING

1. Domains are not affected by cutting a magnet because each domain has its own north pole and south pole.
2. The electromagnets can be lighter and stronger than permanent magnets.
3. As the magnets turn, the coils of wire experience different magnetic forces; this change of magnetism creates a current in the wire.
4. The curvature of the poles allows the field to conform to the shape of the coils and to increase their effect on them.
5. There are only a certain number of domains that can be aligned in any piece of iron or steel.

Test Masters

CHAPTER TEST, pages 65–68.
See page 407d in this book for answers.

WAVES AND SOUND

ORGANIZER

Section	pages	Activity	pages	Reinforcement and Evaluation	pages	*Review and Skill Masters	pages	Other Components in Teacher Resource Package	pages
18–1 Properties of Waves	433–438			Review, Challenge	438			Study Guide Lab Manual Transparency	89 93
18–2 Wave Behavior	439–442	How Can the Behavior of a Wave Be Changed?	441	Review, Challenge	442			Study Guide	90
18–3 Sound	443–449	How Do Vibrations Make Sound?	448	Review, Challenge	449	Challenge/Critical Thinking	111–112	Study Guide	91
18–4 Musical Sounds	450–454	What Causes Pitch Changes?	454	Review, Challenge	454			Study Guide	92
18–5 Acoustics and Noise Pollution	455–457			Puzzler Review, Challenge	456 457	Skill	110	Study Guide	93
CHAPTER SUMMARY	457					Vocabulary Review	107		
CHAPTER REVIEW	458–459			*Test Masters	69–72	Chapter Review	108–109		

*In the Teacher Resource Package. For answers, see pages 431b–431d in this book.

ACTIVITY MATERIALS   Quantities are based on a class of 30 students working in groups as indicated in parentheses.

How Can the Behavior of a Wave Be Changed? p. 441 (groups of 2)	quantity	How Do Vibrations Make Sound? p. 448 (groups of 2)	quantity	What Causes Pitch Changes? p. 454 (groups of 2)	quantity
long spring	15	ring stand	15	250-mL plastic laboratory bottle	15
meterstick	15	ring	15	500-mL plastic laboratory bottle	15
clear tape	15 rolls	thread (20 cm long)	15 pieces	graduate	15
		thumbtack	15	water	
		small cork	15		
		different tuning forks	45		
		rubber mallet	15		

REVIEW AND SKILL MASTERS

VOCABULARY REVIEW _____ Chapter 18

Use the correct words to complete the sentences below. Not all words are used.

acoustics
amplitude
compression
compressional waves
decibel
diffraction
Doppler effect

frequency
harmony
intensity
interference
pitch
quality
rarefaction

reflection
refraction
resonance
reverberation
transverse waves
wave
wavelength

Music has three properties that can be distinguished by the human ear— **pitch**, loudness, and **quality**. When music is played, the sound waves may bounce off walls. This bouncing is called **reflection**. The waves also spread out past the edges of objects in their way. This spreading out is called **diffraction**.

Music is different from noise. Tones in music have a regular wave pattern. When two or more different tones are played at the same time and sound pleasing, **harmony** occurs. Noise is not a pleasing sound. Music played in a room that produces a mixture of repeating echoes, or **reverberation**, sounds like noise.

The study of sound is called **acoustics**. Sound waves are examples of mechanical waves. There are two types of mechanical waves: **transverse waves**, where matter vibrates at right angles to the wave direction, and **compressional waves**, where matter vibrates parallel to the wave direction. When two waves meet they cause **interference**.

Three characteristics of sound waves make each note special. The first is the distance, or **wavelength**, between the crests of two consecutive waves. The second is the height of the sound wave from its nodal line to a crest or trough, called the **amplitude**. The third is the number of waves that pass a point in a given period of time, called the **frequency**.

107

CHAPTER REVIEW _____ Chapter 18

18-1 Properties of Waves

1. A(n) **mechanical** wave transfers its energy through matter. A(n) **electromagnetic** wave carries its energy without using matter.

2. Underline your answers. In a transverse wave, matter moves at right angles/parallel to the direction in which the wave travels. In a compressional wave, matter moves at right angles/parallel to the direction in which the wave travels.

3. The distance from crest to crest in a wave is called the **wavelength**. The distance from crest to nodal line in a wave is called the **amplitude**.

4. Calculate the speed of a wave that is 0.5 m long with a frequency of 2.0 Hz.
$v = f\lambda$, $v = 2.0$ Hz $\times 0.5$ m, $v = 2.0 \times 0.5$ m/s, $v = 1$ m/s.

18-2 Wave Behavior

1. Define the term *reflection*. **Reflection is the bouncing back of waves that strike a surface.**

2. The spreading out of waves past the edge of a barrier is called **diffraction**. The change in direction of a wave as it passes from one medium to another is called **refraction**.

3. State the difference between constructive interference and destructive interference. **In constructive interference the waves reinforce each other. In destructive interference the waves cancel each other.**

18-3 Sound

1. Explain these two parts of a sound wave: rarefaction and compression. **Rarefaction is the part of the wave where the air molecules are spread apart (expand). Compression is the part of the wave where the air molecules are pushed close together (contract).**

108

CHAPTER REVIEW (Continued) _____ Chapter 18

2. How can the speed of sound be used to estimate distances? **The speed of sound can be used to estimate distances by timing an echo and estimating the distance from the reflection time.**

3. The **pitch** of a sound depends on the frequency of its sound wave. The **intensity** of a sound depends on amplitude of its sound wave.

4. Briefly define the Doppler effect. **The Doppler effect is the change in pitch that occurs when a source of sound and a listener are moving in relation to each other.**

18-4 Musical Sounds

1. Underline your answers. Music is sound that has a(n) irregular/regular wave pattern. Noise is sound that has a(n) irregular/regular wave pattern.

2. The lowest frequency that a musical tone can have is called the **fundamental frequency**. Whole-number multiples of this are called **overtones**.

3. Guitars and cellos are examples of **string** instruments. Clarinets and trumpets are examples of **wind** instruments. A drum is a(n) **percussion** instrument; however, a synthesizer that sounds like a drum is a(n) **electronic** instrument.

18-5 Acoustics and Noise

1. What is reverberation and how can it be controlled? **Reverberation is a mixture of repeating echoes. It can be controlled by sound-absorbing materials and room design.**

2. Give two examples of the effects of noise pollution. **Answers will vary but may include stress, hearing loss, high blood pressure, headaches, or fatigue**

109

SKILL/Inferring _____ Chapter 18

The source of any sound wave is vibration of matter. These vibrations may vary in size and frequency. A short, high-frequency vibration produces a high-pitched sound. A large amplitude in a wave indicates a loud sound. Study the diagram of sound waves below and answer the following questions.

1. Which vibration represents the following sounds?
   a. **A** A very loud sound
   b. **E** Music
   c. **C** The highest pitch
   d. **B** Noise
   e. **D** A very soft sound

2. When a person is playing a wind instrument, such as a flute, what is vibrating to produce the sound? **The air in the flute is vibrating to produce the sound.**

3. You can use an empty bottle to produce a musical tone by gently blowing across the opening. If you add water to the bottle, how will it affect the sound? Explain. **The pitch will be higher. There is less air in the bottle. Therefore, the frequency is greater and the pitch increases.**

4. Describe the way in which string instruments produce sound. **Vibrating strings cause the vibration of air, which produces sound.**

5. Describe two ways to raise the pitch of the sound made by a vibrating string. **Make the string shorter or tighter.**

110

431b

Name_____ Date_____

CHALLENGE/CRITICAL THINKING _____ Chapter 18

Sound is composed of longitudinal waves that travel at a speed of 334 m/s at 20 °C. The speed of sound increases at the rate of 0.6 m/s with every degree Celsius the air temperature rises.

You and a friend have taken a trip to a state park to camp. The sun is shining and the temperature is 20 °C. You decide to pitch your tent near a stream. After the tent is up, you watch your friend walk to the stream, pick up a stone, and throw it into the stream. After 0.10 second, you hear it splash in the stream.

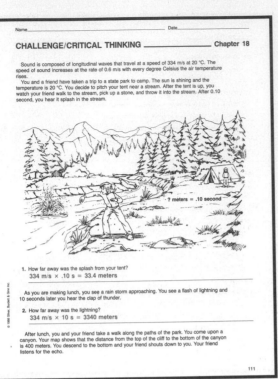

? meters = .10 second

1. How far away was the splash from your tent?

334 m/s × .10 s = 33.4 meters

As you are making lunch, you see a rain storm approaching. You see a flash of lightning and 10 seconds later you hear the clap of thunder.

2. How far away was the lightning?

334 m/s × 10 s = 3340 meters

After lunch, you and your friend take a walk along the paths of the park. You come upon a canyon. Your map shows that the distance from the top of the cliff to the bottom of the canyon is 400 meters. You descend to the bottom and your friend shouts down to you. Your friend listens for the echo.

111

© 1989 Silver, Burdett & Ginn Inc.

Name_____ Date_____

CHALLENGE/CRITICAL THINKING (Continued) _____ Chapter 18

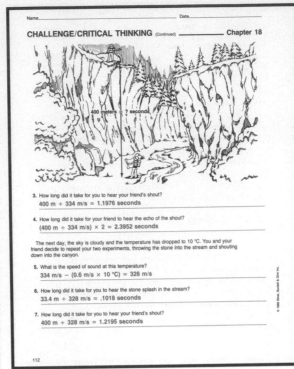

400 meters = ? seconds

3. How long did it take for you to hear your friend's shout?

400 m ÷ 334 m/s = 1.1976 seconds

4. How long did it take for your friend to hear the echo of the shout?

(400 m ÷ 334 m/s) × 2 = 2.3952 seconds

The next day, the sky is cloudy and the temperature has dropped to 10 °C. You and your friend decide to repeat your two experiments, throwing the stone into the stream and shouting down into the canyon.

5. What is the speed of sound at this temperature?

334 m/s − (0.6 m/s × 10 °C) = 328 m/s

6. How long did it take for you to hear the stone splash in the stream?

33.4 m ÷ 328 m/s = .1018 seconds

7. How long did it take for you to hear your friend's shout?

400 m ÷ 328 m/s = 1.2195 seconds

112

© 1989 Silver, Burdett & Ginn Inc.

TEST MASTERS

Name _____ **Date** _____ **Score** _____

Chapter 18

Waves and Sound

PART 1 _____

In the space below, write the term that each phrase defines.

			Chapter Goal
1.	reflection	The bouncing back of waves that strike a surface	2
2.	pitch	How high or low a sound is, depending on its frequency	3
3.	reverberation	A mixture of repeating echoes	5
4.	Doppler effect	The change in pitch that occurs when a source of sound and a listener are moving in relation to each other	3
5.	wave	A disturbance that travels through space or matter in a regular pattern	1
6.	harmony	A pleasing sound that results when two or more different tones are played at the same time	4
7.	interference	The effect caused by two or more waves passing through a medium at the same time	2
8.	acoustics	The study of sound	5
9.	quality	The distinct sound of a tone	4
10.	frequency	The number of waves that pass a point in a given period of time	1

PART 2 _____

Choose the term or phrase that best answers the question or completes the statement. Write the letter of that choice in the space at the left.

a 1. A sound has an overtone of 1,000 Hz. Which of the following could be the fundamental frequency of the sound?   4
   a. 250 Hz   b. 600 Hz   c. 900 Hz   d. 2,000 Hz

c 2. Sound waves travel fastest in: 3
   a. cold water.   b. cold air.   c. warm water.   d. warm air.

Chapter 18 Waves and Sound   69

Name _____ **Date** _____ **Score** _____

PART 2 _____

Choose the term or phrase that best answers the question or completes the statement. Write the letter of that choice in the space at the left.

Chapter Goal

c 3. Which of the following is the greatest cause of reverberations?   5
   a. refraction   c. reflection
   b. destructive interference   d. diffraction

d 4. Which of the following occurs when a point of greatest compression of one wave meets a point of greatest rarefaction of another wave?   2
   a. reflection   c. constructive interference
   b. refraction   d. destructive interference

c 5. A sound produces a pattern on an oscilloscope screen. A scientist is most likely to report the amplitude or intensity of the sound in: 3
   a. waves per second.   c. decibels.
   b. meters per second.   d. hertz.

d 6. If you shake a piece of rope so that a wave travels along the rope, the wave produced is: 1
   a. a reflected wave.   c. an electromagnetic wave.
   b. a compressional wave.   d. a transverse wave.

a 7. Which of the following guitar strings would produce the note having the highest pitch?   4
   a. a short, thin string   c. a long, thin string
   b. a short, thick string   d. a long, thick string

a 8. Which of the following is an example of diffraction?   2
   a. Sound waves spread out after they pass the edge of a building.
   b. Water waves reverse their direction when they strike a wall.
   c. Light waves bend when they pass from air into glass.
   d. Water waves increase in amplitude when they meet other waves.

b 9. The wavelength of a compressional wave is the distance between: 1
   a. the origin and destination of the wave.
   b. two points of greatest rarefaction.
   c. a crest and a trough.
   d. a point of greatest compression and a point of greatest rarefaction.

a 10. Which of the following types of sounds is most likely to break a glass window?   5
   a. high amplitude, high frequency
   b. high amplitude, low frequency
   c. low amplitude, high frequency
   d. low amplitude, low frequency

Chapter 18 Waves and Sound   70

Name _____ **Date** _____ **Score** _____

PART 3 _____

Look at the table. Then read the questions that follow. Choose the term or phrase that best answers the question or completes the statement. Write the letter of that choice in the space at the left.

Characteristics of Five Sounds			
Sound	Wavelength (m)	Intensity (dB)	Frequency (Hz)
A	100	10	50
B	50	20	100
C	25	15	200
D	200	100	25
E	10	75	500

Chapter Goal

d 1. Which of the following is an overtone of Sound B?   4
   a. 25 Hz   b. 75 Hz   c. 150 Hz   d. 200 Hz

c 2. All five sounds travel at the same speed. What is the speed?   1
   a. 100 m/s   b. 500 m/s   c. 5,000 m/s   d. 10,000 m/s

b 3. The distance between a crest and the next trough in the waves producing Sound A is: 1
   a. 10 m.   b. 50 m.   c. 100 m.   d. 200 m.

c 4. A person is most likely to be uncomfortable listening to Sound: 3
   a. A.   b. B.   c. D.   d. E.

d 5. In which of the following situations will a person hear the sound with the highest pitch?   3
   a. traveling away from the source of Sound D
   b. traveling towards the source of Sound D
   c. traveling away from the source of Sound E
   d. traveling towards the source of Sound E

Chapter 18 Waves and Sound   71

Name _____ **Date** _____ **Score** _____

PART 4 _____

Read each question or direction and answer it using complete sentences.

Chapter Goal

1. Contrast constructive interference and destructive interference.   2

   In constructive interference, crests meet and produce a higher crest. Where two troughs meet they produce a lower trough. The waves reinforce each other. When the crest of one wave meets the trough of another, the waves cancel each other.

2. How does a plane traveling faster than the speed of sound produce a sonic boom?   3

   When a plane flies faster than the speed of sound, it is moving faster than the compressional waves it makes. These compressions do not move ahead of the plane. Instead, the plane pushes against the compressions, forcing them closer together. The large compression that results is heard on the ground as a sonic boom.

3. Describe methods of controlling noise pollution.   5

   New jet engines are designed to produce less noise, and jets are not allowed to fly over land at supersonic speeds. When highways must be built near homes, high walls are put up to keep road noise from reaching the homes. Indoor noise is controlled by sound-absorbing materials like special ceiling tiles and wall coverings.

Chapter 18 Waves and Sound   72

CHAPTER 18 PLANNING GUIDE

431d

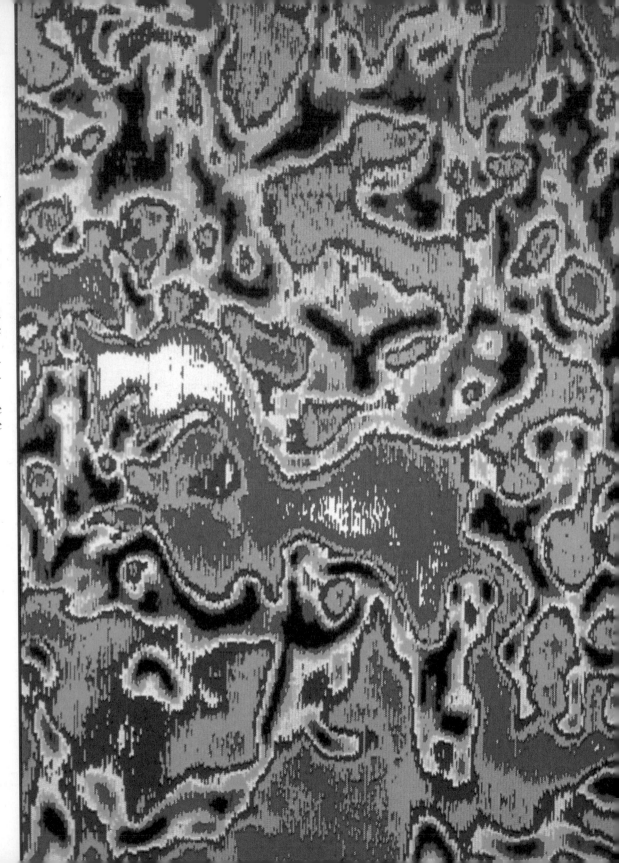

WAVES AND SOUND

The questions in the CHAPTER TEST are based on these Chapter Goals.

1. Distinguish between different kinds of waves, identify the parts of a wave, and calculate the speed of a wave.
2. Describe reflection, refraction, and diffraction, and distinguish between constructive interference and destructive interference.
3. Describe the parts, characteristics, and uses of sound waves, and describe the Doppler effect.
4. Identify the properties of music and musical tones, and classify musical intruments.
5. Describe reverberation and how it can be controlled, and identify the effects of noise pollution.

WAVES AND SOUND

This photograph was made using a Scanning Laser Acoustic Microscope, or SLAM. This device uses sound to make an image of an object. The object shown is a sample of sandstone. Sound passes through the stone and strikes a thin gold mirror. The sound makes the mirror move. A laser scans the mirror and produces an image of the movement. A computer displays the image and adds color to the image so that separate areas can be identified.

- *How are sounds made?*
- *How do sounds travel through matter?*
- *How are sounds used?*

18-1 PROPERTIES OF WAVES

If you drop a pebble into a still pond, a wave ripples out in all directions across the water. The surface of the water rises and falls in a regular pattern as the wave moves outward from the point where the pebble struck. What causes this wave to form?

ENERGY AND WAVES

The falling pebble has kinetic energy. When the pebble hits the water, this kinetic energy is transferred to water molecules. These molecules transfer energy to the molecules near them. Thus the energy moves through the water in the form of a wave. A **wave** is a disturbance that travels through space or matter in a regular pattern.

The energy carried by the wave causes water molecules to be displaced, or moved away, from their original position. In a water wave the molecules are displaced in an up-and-down pattern. If a piece of wood were floating in the water, it would bob up and down as the wave passes. However, the wood would not move along with the wave. After the wave passes, the wood would still be in its original position. The water molecules do not move with the wave, either. The water molecules move up and down. Only the wave of energy moves outward.

After completing this section, you will be able to

- **distinguish** between a mechanical wave and an electromagnetic wave.
- **distinguish** between a transverse wave and a compressional wave.
- **identify** the parts of a wave.
- **calculate** the speed of a wave.

The key terms in this section are
amplitude
compression
compressional wave
frequency
rarefaction
transverse wave
wave
wavelength

2 CONCEPT DEVELOPMENT

Background   It is possible to see strings on musical instruments vibrate. The wave motion of the strings is transverse.

Teaching Tip   Discuss transverse and compressional waves, and review Figure 18-1 and Figure 18-2 with students. Mention that they will have an opportunity to generate these different waves when they perform the *Activity* on page 441.

Demonstration   Secure one end of a long piece of rope or rubber tubing to a door handle. (If tubing is used, fill the tubing with water, and clamp both ends. The water in the tube will cause the wave to travel more slowly.) Hang a small bell near the secured end. Holding the free end, flick your wrist and send a wave down the rope or tubing. The bell will ring after the energy of the wave travels the entire length.

Enrichment   Seismic waves transmit the energy of an earthquake. Ask students to research earthquakes and to determine the types of waves made. Some students may want to report on seismographs and the Richter scale.

The wave in the pond is caused by a single disturbance, the pebble. Waves also can be caused by repeated disturbances. If you drop one pebble into the pool each second, you will cause one wave each second. The waves will move outward in a series of rings, one for each pebble you drop. Vibrating objects also produce repeated waves. The strings of a guitar can be plucked and made to vibrate. The strings cause the air near them to vibrate. These vibrations in the air make a sound wave.

TYPES OF WAVES

Sound waves and water waves are mechanical waves. *Mechanical waves* are waves that transfer energy through matter. Sound waves carry energy through gases, like air, and through some liquids and solids. Water waves carry energy through water. If there is no matter, there can be no mechanical waves. The matter through which mechanical waves travel is called the *medium*. Some waves, such as radio waves, X rays, and light, do not need matter to transfer energy. Waves that can carry energy without using matter are called *electromagnetic waves*. Electromagnetic waves are waves made up of electric and magnetic fields. They will be discussed in Chapter 19.

There are two kinds of mechanical waves—transverse waves and compressional waves. In a **transverse wave**, matter vibrates up and down at right angles to the direction in which the wave travels. Water waves are transverse waves. Figure 18-1 shows a transverse wave on a spring. The original disturbance is caused when one end of the spring is moved up and down. This displacement travels

transversus (to turn across)

Figure 18-1

In a transverse wave, matter vibrates at right angles to the direction in which the wave travels.

the length of the spring. After the wave has passed through the spring, the spring returns to its original position. Did energy move from one end of the spring to the other? Did matter move from one end of the spring to the other?[1]

Sound waves are compressional waves. A **compressional wave** is a wave that displaces particles of matter back and forth parallel to the direction of the wave. Compressional waves are also called longitudinal waves. Figure 18-2 shows a compressional wave on a spring. Notice that there is no up-and-down motion of the spring. The disturbance that starts this wave is a movement that pushes parts of the spring closer together and then returns the spring to its original position. The section of the spring that is pushed together is said to be compressed. As one section of the spring is compressed, it pushes on the section of the spring in front of it. Thus the compression moves along the spring. A **compression** is the part where particles of matter are pushed close together in a compressional wave. Notice that behind the compression is an area in which the spring is stretched instead of compressed. The part where particles of matter are spread apart in a compressional wave is called a **rarefaction** (rair uh-FAK shuhn).

[1]Energy moves from one end of the spring to the other, but matter does not.

compressare (to press together)

Figure 18-2

In a compressional wave, matter vibrates parallel to the direction of the wave.

A compressional wave is made up of one compression and one rarefaction. If you graph the amount of compression in a series of compressional waves, you would get a graph that looks like a series of transverse waves. Figure 18-3 on the next page shows such a graph. The line along the middle of the curve represents the condition of the spring when no waves move along it.

Background   Although they may look like transverse waves, water waves are a combination of transverse and compressional motions. The water particles move in more or less circular paths. The diameter of the circular paths decreases rapidly with depth. As a wave approaches the shallow water near shore, the water particles cannot complete their circular paths. The water is forced higher and steeper. When the water becomes more shallow, the particles are prevented from moving through the bottom part of their paths, and a wave breaks.

Thinking Skills

interpreting diagrams
Students are asked to interpret Figure 18-1 and Figure 18-2 to distinguish between transverse and compressional waves. Students are asked to infer from the diagram the different ways the pulses of energy move along the springs. Students also determine if matter and/or energy moves from one end of the spring to the other.

CHARACTERISTICS OF WAVES

Figure 18-3 shows several characteristics of waves. Points *A*, *C*, and *E* are crests. A *crest* shows the top of a transverse wave. It can also show the point of greatest compression in a compressional wave. Points *B*, *D*, and *F* are troughs (trawfs). A *trough* is the bottom of a transverse wave. It can also show the point of greatest rarefaction. The points marked *X* are called nodes. A *node* is a point halfway between the crest and the trough. The line that connects the nodes is the *nodal line*. The nodal line shows the original position of the matter carrying the wave.

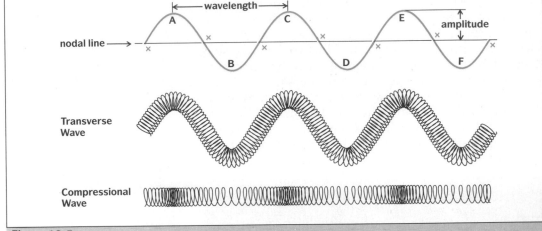

Figure 18-3

A graph can be used to show wave patterns.

The distance from point *A* to point *C*, or from crest to crest, is the wavelength. The **wavelength** is the distance from any point on a wave to the corresponding point on the next wave. Thus the distance from point *B* to point *D* is also one wavelength. Why is the wavelength not measured from one node to the next?[1]

Another characteristic of waves is amplitude (AM pluh-tood). The **amplitude** of a wave is a measure of the greatest displacement of matter from its normal resting position. Amplitude can be measured from the crest to the nodal line or from the trough to the nodal line. The greater the amplitude of a wave, the more energy the wave has.

It is possible for two waves to have the same wavelength but different amplitudes, as shown in Figure 18-4. Wave *A* has a greater amplitude than wave *B* has. Therefore wave *A* carries more energy. Because wave *A* carries more energy, it can displace matter farther. Thus, wave *A* can do more work than wave *B* can.

[1]That distance represents only one half of a wave.

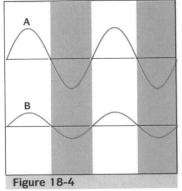

Figure 18-4

These waves have different amplitudes.

Wavelength and amplitude show the size of a wave. Waves also can be described in terms of frequency. **Frequency** is the number of waves that pass a given point each second. The frequency of a wave depends on the source of the wave. For example, suppose you are floating on a raft in a lake and a motorboat goes by. Waves caused by the boat reach the raft, causing it to bob up and down. The number of waves that pass the raft in 1 second is the frequency.

Figure 18-5

The boat disturbs the water, making waves.

Frequency can be written as waves per second or cycles per second. If the water waves lift the raft three times in 1 second, the frequency is 3 waves per second, or 3/s. The SI unit for frequency is the *hertz* (Hz). One hertz is equal to 1 wave per second. How would you write the frequency of these water waves in the SI unit?[1]

[1] 3 Hz.

SPEED OF WAVES

Frequency and wavelength can be used to calculate the speed at which a wave travels. You can count the number of water waves that pass a point in 1 second. You can measure the wavelength from one crest to the next. To find the speed of a wave, use the formula shown below.

$$v = f \lambda$$

In the formula, v stands for the speed of the wave, f stands for the frequency, and the Greek letter λ (lambda) stands for the wavelength.

Background   Pure transverse waves occur only in solids. Liquids and gases cannot support the kind of disturbance caused by a transverse wave because they do not have the restoring abilities of a solid.

Background   The SI unit for frequency, the hertz, is named in honor of Heinrich Rudolf Hertz. Hertz was a German physicist whose pioneering work with waves led to the development of modern radio, television, and radar.

Background   Explain to students the scientific meaning of "tuning in" a certain radio station. Actually, it means to adjust the circuit in a radio so that the circuit resonates electrically at the broadcasting frequency of the radio station.

Teaching Tip   Prepare a practice sheet that contains several different problems dealing with the frequency and wavelength of waves.

Thinking Skills

predicting
To emphasize the mathematical relationship between velocity, frequency, and wavelength, students are asked to predict the effect on the wavelength when the frequency of a wave decreases.

3 REVIEW/REINFORCEMENT

1. Mechanical waves are waves that transfer energy through matter; electromagnetic waves transfer energy without using matter.
2. In a transverse wave, matter vibrates up and down at right angles to the direction in which the wave travels; a compressional wave displaces particles of matter back and forth parallel to the direction in which the wave travels.
3. Crest, trough, and node for a transverse wave; compression and rarefaction for a compressional wave.
4. $v = f\lambda$
   $v = 15.0 \text{ Hz} \times 1.4 \text{ mm}$
   $v = 21 \text{ mm/s}$

Challenge

$f = \dfrac{v}{\lambda}$

$f = \dfrac{5 \text{ m/s}}{2 \text{ m}}$

$f = 2.5 \text{ wave/s}$

$f = 2.5 \text{ Hz}$

Sample Problem
Calculate the speed of a water wave 1.2 m long that has a frequency of 1.5 Hz.

1. Write the formula.
$$v = f\lambda$$

2. Substitute the amounts given in the problem for the symbols in the formula.
$$v = 1.5 \text{ Hz} \times 1.2 \text{ m}$$

3. Determine the units that will be part of the answer. Recall that 1 Hz equals 1 wave per second. Therefore, meters times hertz equals meters per second (m/s).
$$v = 1.5/s \times 1.2 \text{ m} = 1.5 \times 1.2 \text{ m/s}$$

4. Complete the calculations.
$$v = 1.8 \text{ m/s}$$

The wave moves through the water at a speed of 1.8 m/s. Any other waves in this system would move through the water at the same speed. The speed of a wave depends mostly on the nature of the substance through which it travels. A high-frequency wave will not travel faster than a low-frequency wave in the same medium. A wave with a frequency of 3.0 Hz would travel at the same speed as the wave in the sample problem. However, this wave would have a shorter wavelength.

$$1.8 \text{ m/s} = 3.0 \text{ Hz} \times \lambda$$
$$1.8 \text{ m/s} = 3.0 \text{ Hz} \times 0.6 \text{ m}$$

As you can see, if the speed of a wave is constant, increasing its frequency will decrease its wavelength. What happens to the wavelength if the frequency decreases?[1]

[1]Wavelength would be increased.

REVIEW

1. What is a mechanical wave? How does it differ from an electromagnetic wave?
2. How do transverse and compressional waves differ?
3. What are the parts of a wave?
4. What is the speed of a wave that has a wavelength of 1.4 mm and a frequency of 15 Hz?

CHALLENGE Suppose a wave is traveling at a speed of 5 m/s through a spring. If the wavelength is 2 m, what is the frequency of the wave?

18-2 WAVE BEHAVIOR

Recall that the speed of a wave depends on the nature of the medium through which it moves. The path of the wave also depends on the medium. When the medium through which the wave moves changes, the behavior of the wave may be changed.

REFLECTION

Have you ever been in a large empty room where sound echoed? An echo is caused by the reflection of sound waves. **Reflection** is the bouncing back of waves that strike a surface. The wave that strikes the surface is called an *incident wave*. The wave that bounces off is called a *reflected wave*.

Water waves can be studied in a device called a ripple tank. A ripple tank is a shallow container with a glass bottom. A light shines on the water in the tank. When waves are made in the water, their pattern can be seen in the water and below the tank. Figure 18-6 shows an incident wave and a reflected wave in a ripple tank. The arrows show the direction in which each wave is moving. As long as the medium in which the wave moves is constant, the path of the wave does not change. When the wave reaches the side of the tank, some of its energy is absorbed by the tank. But most of the wave's energy is reflected back into the water.

After completing this section, you will be able to

- **describe** how waves are reflected.
- **distinguish** between refraction and diffraction.
- **distinguish** between constructive interference and destructive interference.

The key terms in this section are
diffraction   reflection
interference   refraction

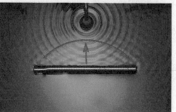

Figure 18-6

A ripple tank (left). Reflection is the bouncing back of waves that strike a surface (right).

18-2 WAVE BEHAVIOR
pages 439–442

OBJECTIVES
Refer to pupil page 439.

VOCABULARY
Key terms: diffraction, interference, reflection, refraction
Other terms: constructive interference, destructive interference, incident wave, reflected wave

1 MOTIVATION

Place a ripple tank on an overhead projector. Use a wave generator to generate different waves, such as straight waves and circular waves. Ask students how the ripple tank shows reflection and diffraction. Have students move the barriers of the ripple tank to different locations to see the effects on the waves.

2 CONCEPT DEVELOPMENT

Background   Even though water waves are diffracted at the edge of a barrier, there is often a region behind the barrier devoid of wave energy. The size of this region depends upon the size of the barrier and the wavelength. Waves bend, or diffract, around small barriers more easily than around large barriers. A wave with a long wavelength will fill in behind a barrier with more ease than a wave with a short wavelength.

Background The diffraction of sound waves is a common experience. You cannot see a person around the corner, but you can hear that person speaking. Sound waves can be bent by diffraction to go around the corner because the wavelength of sound waves is large. Light waves do not bend around the corner because the wavelength of light waves is small. The ability of waves to bend around objects depends on the wavelength and the size of the diffracting objects or openings.

Tie-in/Language Arts Christian Huygens was a Dutch physicist who studied waves. Have students do research on Huygens's theory of wave motion and how it applies to diffraction and refraction.

Figure 18-7

Diffraction is the spreading out of waves past the edge of a barrier.

DIFFRACTION

Waves are reflected when they strike a barrier. What happens when a barrier does not completely block the path of waves? Waves that strike the barrier are reflected. Waves that miss the barrier continue on their path.

Waves that hit the edge of the barrier show an unusual behavior. They seem to move around the corner. When a wave hits the edge of a barrier, a new wave spreads out from that point. The spreading out of waves past the edge of a barrier is **diffraction** (dih FRAK shuhn).

Diffraction also occurs at a hole or slit in a barrier. Figure 18-7 shows this situation. When waves reach a hole in a barrier, they start a new wave. This wave spreads out in all directions. The pattern produced by diffracted waves depends on the barrier that produces them. The pattern of the new waves does not depend on the pattern of the original waves.

Diffraction makes it possible for sound waves to be heard around corners. If someone around the side of a building calls your name, you can hear the sound even though you cannot see its source. The sound waves spread out from the end of the building.

REFRACTION

Recall that a wave is caused by a disturbance. The frequency of the wave depends on the frequency of the disturbance. A wave may pass from one medium to another. When this happens, the frequency of the wave does not change. However, the speed of the wave and the wavelength do change.

Figure 18-8

The speed of a wave changes as it passes from one medium to another. This change causes refraction.

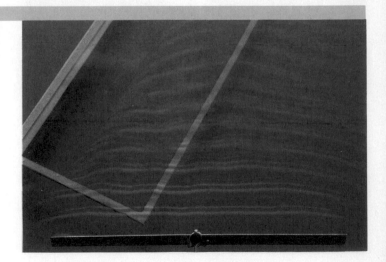

Suppose the speed of a wave decreases as the wave crosses the boundary from one medium to another. If the speed of the wave decreases, its wavelength decreases. Thus, crests will be closer together. If the path of the waves is perpendicular to the boundary the waves continue in the same direction.

Figure 18-8 shows waves that do not reach the boundary on a perpendicular path. Notice that these waves change direction as they cross the boundary. The change in direction of a wave as it passes from one medium to another is called **refraction** (rih FRAK shuhn).

Refraction is an important behavior of waves. Light waves can be refracted by prisms and lenses. Scientists know how to control the bending of light rays with the lenses in telescopes and microscopes.

re- (back)
-frangere (to break)

ACTIVITY How Can the Behavior of a Wave Be Changed?

OBJECTIVE
Demonstrate the characteristics and behavior of mechanical waves.

MATERIALS
long spring, meterstick, tape

PROCEDURE
A. With a partner, stretch a spring along the floor for a distance of 3 m. Place a small piece of tape on the spring, about 1 m away from you.
B. While your partner holds one end of the spring steady, push forward on the spring to produce a compression. Have your partner adjust the tension of the spring by gathering some of the coils until you can produce a compressional wave that is easy to see.
C. With a forward and backward motion, produce a single compression in the spring.
   1. Describe what happens to the spring.
   2. Describe the motion of the tape.
D. Now use a greater force to produce a single compression in the spring.
   3. How does this wave compare with the wave produced in step **C**?
E. While your partner holds one end of the spring, use a flick of the wrist to produce a transverse wave, or pulse, in the spring.
   4. Describe the motion of the tape.

F. Now produce a stronger transverse pulse.
   5. How does this wave compare with the wave produced in step **E**?
G. Have your partner gather about one fourth of the coils of the spring and hold them. The spring will be under more tension but should cover the same distance as before.
H. Produce a pulse to start a transverse wave.
   6. How does this wave compare with the waves produced in steps **E** and **F**?
I. Release the extra coils and return the spring to its original tension. Have your partner start a pulse to his or her right as you start one to your right.
   7. Do the waves move at the same speed?
   8. Describe what happens to the waves as they meet.
   9. What is the name for this effect?
   10. Describe what happens to the waves after they meet.

RESULTS AND CONCLUSIONS
1. Compare the motion of the tape in steps **C** and **E**.
2. Does the force of the wave affect its speed? What evidence do you have for your answer?
3. Does the tension of the spring affect the speed of the wave? What evidence do you have for your answer?

ACTIVITY 30 minutes

PROCESS SKILLS
observing, experimenting, comparing, identifying cause and effect

Preparation The day before this activity, advise students that they will be working on the floor and should come appropriately dressed.

Teaching Tip This activity can be extended into a graphing exercise. If your classroom floor is made of square tiles, use the tiles as a grid. Ask students to transfer their observations onto graph paper. Have students label the trough and crest of a transverse wave and the compression and rarefaction of a compressional wave. The amplitude and wavelength should be labeled on each graph.

Answers to Procedure
1. A pulse or wave moves down the spring.
2. The tape moves but returns to its original position.
3. The wave is larger.
4. The tape moves but returns to its original position.
5. The wave is larger.
6. The wave moves faster.
7. Yes.
8. They cancel each other.
9. Destructive interference.
10. After the waves meet, they pass each other, and continue to move along the spring.

Answers to Results and Conclusions
1. The tape moved but returned to its original position in both step **C** and step **E**.
2. No; the wave seemed to move at the same speed. It could be observed that the change in force changed the size but not the speed of the wave.
3. Yes; the wave moved faster.

Background Interference of two identical waves moving in opposite directions can produce a standing wave. A standing wave can be demonstrated by holding one end of a rope stationary and shaking the other end up and down. Reflected waves interfere with incoming waves, and the wave produced appears to be stationary.

Thinking Skills

interpreting graphs
As students analyze the graphs in Figure 18-9, they see that in constructive interference the combined wave has a greater amplitude than either of the other two waves, and in destructive interference the amplitude of the combined wave is less than either of the other two waves.

Background Alternation of destructive interference and constructive interference of sound waves results in a phenomenon known as beats. The human ear detects these beats as regular pulsing sounds. The difference in frequencies of the waves is equal to the number of beats produced each second. Musicians can often tune their instruments based upon the number of beats heard.

3 REVIEW/REINFORCEMENT

1. The waves bounce off the surface, or are reflected.
2. Refraction is the change in direction of a wave as it passes from one medium to another; diffraction is the spreading out of waves past the edge of a barrier.
3. In constructive interference the crest of two waves meet, and they reinforce each other. In destructive interference the crest of one wave meets the trough of another wave, and the waves cancel each other.

Challenge The waves will interfere with each other, either constructively or destructively.

442

INTERFERENCE

Two or more waves can pass through the same medium at the same time. When two such waves meet, they have an effect on each other's properties. The effects caused by two or more waves passing through a medium at the same time are called **interference**.

inter- (between)
-ferire (strike)

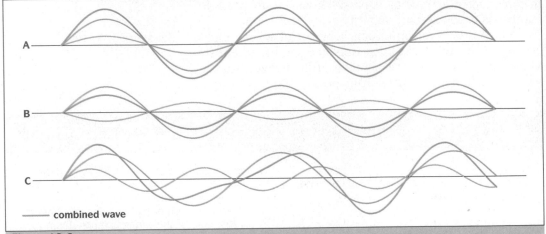

— combined wave

Figure 18-9

Constructive interference occurs when two crests, or two troughs meet (A). Destructive interference occurs when a crest meets a trough (B). When waves of different wavelengths meet, the interference is irregular (C).

Look at Figure 18-9. Where two crests meet, they produce a higher crest. Where two troughs meet, they produce a lower trough. These waves are said to reinforce each other. The amplitude of the combined wave is greater than that of either wave alone. This kind of interference is *constructive interference*. When the crest of one wave meets the trough of another, these waves cancel each other. This kind of interference is *destructive interference*.

If the two waves that meet have different wavelengths, the interference pattern is very irregular. Notice in Figure 18-9C that in some places one crest reinforces another. In other places a crest cancels a trough.

REVIEW

1. Describe what happens when a wave strikes a surface.
2. How is refraction different from diffraction?
3. How does constructive interference differ from destructive interference?

CHALLENGE If a barrier has two slits in it, diffraction will take place at each slit. What will happen to these two new sets of waves?

442

18-3 SOUND

Sound is produced by vibrating objects. Hard solids, such as a bell or a tuning fork, vibrate when struck. Flexible solids, such as rubber bands, vibrate when plucked. Gases, such as air, can be made to vibrate. When you blow a whistle, the sound is produced by a vibrating air column.

HOW SOUND WAVES TRAVEL

If you strike a bell with a hammer, the bell vibrates and produces sound waves. You hear the sound as the waves travel through the air from the bell to your ears. Suppose you place the bell in a jar attached to a vacuum pump. The pump draws all the air out of the jar. Will you still hear a sound when the hammer strikes the bell? The bell will vibrate. But without air or some other material to carry the wave, no sound can be heard.

Figure 18-10 shows a sound wave produced by a bell. As the bell vibrates, it expands and contracts. As the bell expands, air molecules are pushed close together. Thus, a compression is formed. When the bell contracts, air molecules are spread apart, and a rarefaction is formed. Each sound wave is made up of one compression and one rarefaction.

Figure 18-10

Sound waves are compressional waves that can travel through air (A). Sound waves cannot travel through a vacuum (B).

Sound waves can be passed between objects. A vibrating tuning fork makes the air around it vibrate. If you hold the base of the vibrating tuning fork against a table, the table will vibrate, too. The energy of the tuning fork makes the table vibrate. The transfer of wave energy by contact is sometimes called *forced vibration*.

After completing this section, you will be able to

- **identify** the parts of a sound wave.
- **describe** how the speed of sound can be used to measure distances.
- **distinguish** between pitch and intensity.
- **describe** the Doppler effect.

The key terms in this section are
decibel   pitch
Doppler effect   resonance
intensity

18-3   SOUND

pages 443–449

OBJECTIVES
Refer to pupil page 443.

VOCABULARY
Key terms: decibel, Doppler effect, intensity, pitch, resonance
Other terms: forced vibration, oscilloscope, sonar, sonic boom, sympathetic vibration, ultrasonic sounds

1 MOTIVATION

Set up the demonstration of a bell in a vacuum, as shown in Figure 18-10. With the bell ringing, pump the air out of the bell jar, and then allow the air to fill the system again. Ask students why the sound of the bell gets fainter and fainter until no sound can be heard. (Less and less air to transmit the sound.) Also ask why, when air reenters the bell jar, the sound can be heard again. (Air can transmit the sound again.)

2 CONCEPT DEVELOPMENT

Teaching Tip   Hearing aids often cause bones in the head to vibrate. Point out the necessity of hearing aids for the hearing impaired. Invite a hearing specialist or the school nurse to visit the class to talk about hearing problems and their remedies.

Background A violin string vibrating on a violin sounds different from the same violin string vibrating fastened to two steel posts. The string on the violin transmits its energy through the bridge of the violin to the entire body of the instrument, which vibrates to produce the characteristic sound.

Background Pianos have pedals that can be used to release dampers on the strings attached to the soundboard. With these dampers released, several strings will vibrate sympathetically when a note is struck.

Demonstration Sympathetic tuning forks mounted on resonance boxes are available from most scientific supply houses. Strike one fork with a rubber mallet, and then silence the fork. The other fork will be vibrating and can be heard.

Tie-in/Social Studies Traditionally, soldiers break step when crossing a bridge. In the 1800s a group of soldiers crossing a bridge in step set up a vibrational pattern that caused the collapse of the bridge. Ask students to research this incidental bit of history under the topic of bridges or vibrations, and have them report to the class.

If you hold the vibrating tuning fork near the table, the table will not vibrate. Yet if you hold the vibrating tuning fork near a glass of the right size, the glass will vibrate. Why does one object seem to pick up vibrations but another does not?

Any object that can be made to vibrate has a natural frequency. This frequency depends on the shape and nature of the object. If two objects with the same natural frequency are vibrating at the same time, their sound waves will match. When only one of these objects is caused to vibrate, the other will begin to vibrate. The sound waves produced will reinforce each other. The response that an object makes to vibrations that match its natural frequency is called **resonance** (REHZ uh nuhns). Vibrations that are produced by resonance are sometimes called *sympathetic vibrations*.

The vibrations caused by resonance can have a large amount of energy. Resonance caused vibrations in the glass shown in Figure 18-11A. The glass vibrated with so much force that it broke. A singer can break a glass in this way if he or she can make a loud sound at the natural frequency of the glass. The bridge shown in Figure 18-11B collapsed because it vibrated in the wind. Resonance between the wind and the bridge broke the bridge apart. Resonance will not take place between objects with different natural frequencies. Direct contact or very strong vibrations are needed to transfer wave energy between two objects that do not have the same natural frequency.

Figure 18-11

The effects of resonance.

SPEED OF SOUND

The speed of a sound wave depends on the medium through which it travels. Table 18-1 shows the speed of sound in different medium. Sound generally moves faster in solids and liquids than in gases. In air at 20°C, sound waves move at a rate of 334 m/s. In steel, sound moves at 5000 m/s. How fast does sound move in silver?[1]

Temperature has been shown to affect the speed of a sound wave. The speed of sound in air will increase by 0.60 m/s for each degree Celsius that the air temperature rises. At 0°C the speed of sound in air is 331.29 m/s. At 1°C the speed of sound is 331.89 m/s.

The speed of sound can be used to estimate distances. You probably have noticed that you usually see a flash of lightning before you hear the thunder it causes. The farther away the lightning, the greater the time difference between the lightning and the thunder. This time difference occurs because light waves travel faster than do sound waves. Light moves so quickly that it reaches you in a time interval too small for you to measure. Sound travels at 334 m/s. During every second that you count between the lightning and the thunder, the sound travels 334 m. If the time difference is 2 seconds, the lightning is 668 m away. How far away is the lightning if you hear the thunder 5 seconds after you see the flash?[2]

Table 18-1 *Speed of Sound*

Medium	Speed (m/s) at 20°C
Air	334
Aluminum	5104
Glass	5000
Lead	1227
Nickel	4973
Seawater	1490
Silver	2610
Steel	5000
Water	1461

[1]2610 m/s.
[2]1670 m.

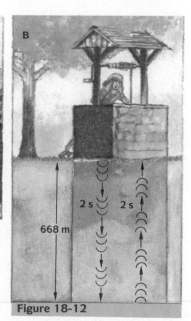

Another way that sound is used to measure distances uses echoes. An echo is a sound wave that reflects off a surface. Look at Figure 18-12B. If you direct a loud sound at a hard surface, the sound will bounce back to you. If a well is 668 m deep, you will hear your echo in 4 seconds. It takes 2 seconds for your sound to reach the bottom of the well and 2 seconds more for the sound to return to you.

Figure 18-12

The speed of sound can be used to estimate distances.

Thinking Skills

interpreting data

Students use Table 18-1 to find out the speed of sound through silver. Students can see that sound travels at different rates through different substances. Ask students to compare the speed of sound in several substances, such as in glass and lead.

Background   Sounds of different frequencies in the same medium are all transmitted at the same speed. If this were not true, listening to speech or music would be impossible. Tell students to try to imagine listening to a musical group if all the different frequencies generated traveled to the listener at different speeds.

Demonstration Have on hand two tuning forks of different pitches. Attach a microphone to an oscilloscope so their frequency and amplitude can be seen on the screen. Strike each tuning fork, and note the pattern on the screen. Students can hear the difference in the pitch and loudness of each fork and see the difference in wave patterns on the screen.

Background Sonic booms are continuous. They are not generated only at the moment a moving aircraft exceeds the speed of sound. The piled-up waves move continuously behind the aircraft. If an SST breaks the sound barrier on one side of the Atlantic Ocean, the sonic boom will follow the aircraft until it slows to a speed below that of sound, on the other side of the Atlantic.

The reflection of sound waves is used in a technology called sonar. *Sonar* stands for *sound navigation and ranging*. Sonar is used to find fish and other objects below the surface of the water. Figure 18-13 shows a fishing boat using sonar. The sound waves sent out are reflected by fish. These reflections appear as signals on a sonar screen. The signals are used to determine the size of a school of fish, as well as its distance and direction from the boat.

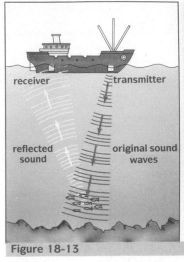

Figure 18-13

Sonar can locate objects in the water (*left*). Sonar was used to locate the *Titanic* (*right*).

Sonar also has been used to map the ocean floor. Small differences in the time it takes for sound waves to return to a ship are analyzed. These data can be used to make a map of the surface of the sea floor. Sonar can locate sunken ships. In September 1985, sonar was used to locate the *Titanic* 4000 m below the surface of the water.

INTENSITY AND PITCH

Recall that amplitude is the measure of the amount of energy a wave has. In a compressional wave the greater the compression, the greater the amplitude of the wave. The amplitude of a sound wave determines the **intensity** of the sound. A person hears the intensity of a sound as loudness.

A *sonic boom* is a loud sound produced as a plane flies at the speed of sound. When a plane flies, it pushes against the air in front of it. Thus the plane makes compressional waves in air. When a plane flies at less than the speed of sound, the compressional waves it makes move faster than the plane moves. The compressions move ahead of the plane.

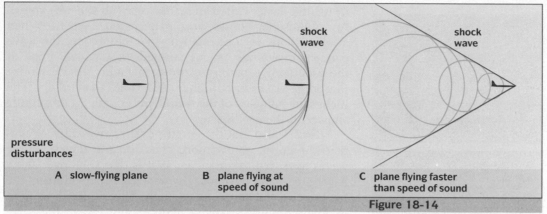

A   slow-flying plane

B   plane flying at
    speed of sound

shock
wave

shock
wave

C   plane flying faster
    than speed of sound

pressure
disturbances

Figure 18-14

As a plane gains speed, compressional waves in front of the plane are pushed together. This forms a sonic boom (C).

When a plane flies faster than the speed of sound, it is moving faster than the compressional waves it makes. These compressions do not move ahead of the plane. Instead, the plane pushes against the compressions, forcing them closer together. The large compression is heard on the ground as a sonic boom.

The unit used to measure sound intensity is the **decibel** (dB). A loud sound has a higher intensity than a quiet sound. Thus, thunder has a high decibel level, and a whisper has a low decibel level. Table 18-2 gives the intensity of some sounds. Sounds over 100 dB can cause hearing loss. Therefore, people who work around loud noise must wear earplugs or some other protective device.

Table 18-2 *Intensity of Sounds*

Intensity (dB)	Examples
10	Rustle of leaves, soft whisper
20	Quiet room
30	Quiet office, soft music
40	Quiet talking, average home
50	Common talking voice
60	Loud talking
70	Loud radio music, heavy traffic noise
80	Moving subway, very loud radio music
90	Air hammer
100	Riveter, full symphony orchestra
110	Loud thunder

ACTIVITY 20 minutes

PROCESS SKILLS

Preparation None required.

Teaching Tip Do not strike a tuning fork against a hard object; a nick in the fork can change the frequency. Use a rubber mallet. One is easily constructed by inserting a dowel into the hole in a rubber stopper.

Teaching Tip Allow students to demonstrate resonance by touching the vibrating tuning fork to a tabletop. Inserting the vibrating tuning fork into a beaker of water will show vibration.

Teaching Tip Point out the difference in tones with the variance in tuning-fork sizes.

Answers to Results and Conclusions

1. The fork vibrated, and a sound was produced.
2. The cork "bounced" around.
3. A sound was heard.
4. Each time the cork moved.

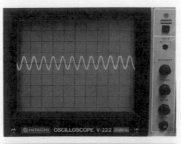

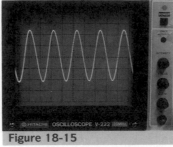

Figure 18-15

These wave patterns represent sound waves.

The intensity of different sounds can be compared by using a device called an *oscilloscope* (uh SIHL uh skohp). An oscilloscope shows wave patterns on a screen. When a microphone is connected to an oscilloscope, the wave patterns of sounds can be studied on a screen. Look at the oscilloscope patterns shown in Figure 18-15. Notice that some waves have higher amplitudes than others. The higher the intensity of the sound, the greater the amplitude shown on the oscilloscope.

Notice also that the lengths of the waves vary. Waves that are shorter show more crests on the screen. These waves have high frequencies. Waves that are longer show fewer crests and have low frequencies. A person hears the frequencies of a sound as its pitch. The **pitch** is how high or low a sound is. High-pitched sounds have high frequencies. Low-pitched sounds have low frequencies.

The range of human hearing is between 20 Hz and 20,000 Hz. Most humans cannot hear frequencies outside this range. Sounds with frequencies above 20,000 Hz are called *ultrasonic* (uhl truh SAHN ihk) *sounds*.

Some animals can hear ultrasonic sounds. For example, dogs can be trained to respond to ultrasonic whistles. Bats produce ultrasonic sounds. As bats fly, they use the echoes of these sounds to find their food in the dark. Ultrasonic sound, or ultrasound, is used in medicine. High-frequency sound waves are reflected off specific body tissues or organs. The echoes are used to study structure and movement in organs such as the heart.

ACTIVITY How Do Vibrations Make Sound?

OBJECTIVE
Demonstrate that sounds come from a vibrating object.

MATERIALS
ring stand, ring, 20 cm of thread, thumbtack, small cork, 3 different tuning forks, rubber mallet

PROCEDURE
A. Attach one end of a piece of thread to a ring on a ring stand. Using a thumbtack, fasten the other end to a cork.
B. Strike the smallest tuning fork with a mallet, and touch the cork with the tuning fork.
C. Repeat step **B** two times.
D. Repeat steps **B** and **C**, using the middle-size tuning fork.
E. Repeat steps **B** and **C**, using the largest tuning fork.

RESULTS AND CONCLUSIONS
1. What happened when a tuning fork was hit with a mallet?
2. What happened to the cork when it was touched with the tuning fork?
3. What evidence was there that each tuning fork made a sound?
4. What evidence was there that each tuning fork was vibrating?

THE DOPPLER EFFECT

If a listener or the source of a sound is moving, the listener may hear a pitch that is different from the frequency of the source. Suppose you are standing on a street corner and a car driving by blows its horn. As the car approaches, the pitch you hear is higher than the actual pitch of the horn. As the car passes, the pitch of the sound decreases. Figure 18-16 shows why this happens.

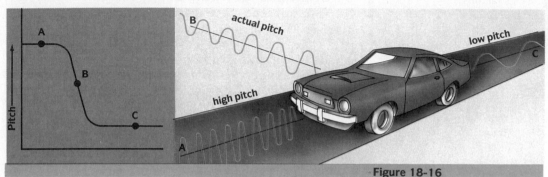

Figure 18-16
The Doppler effect.

A car's horn sends out sound waves in all directions. If the car is not moving, these sound waves all have the same frequency. But when the car moves forward, the sound waves in front of the car are closer together. The frequency of the wave is increased, and someone at point A will hear a higher pitch than the horn really produces. At the same time the sound waves behind the car are farther apart. The frequency is decreased. Someone at point B will hear a lower pitch than the horn really produces.

The pitch of the sound would also change if the car stayed in one place, and you moved instead. The change in pitch that occurs when a source of sound and a listener are moving in relation to each other is called the **Doppler effect**. The Doppler effect only happens when the listener is almost directly in front of or behind the source of the sound. Someone next to the car or off to one side of its path would hear the true pitch of the horn.

REVIEW

1. Name the parts of a sound wave.
2. How can an echo be used to measure a distance?
3. How does pitch differ from intensity?
4. What is the Doppler effect?

CHALLENGE Use the kinetic theory to explain why sound travels faster in warm air than in cold air.

OBJECTIVES
Refer to pupil page 450.

VOCABULARY
Key terms: harmony, quality
Other terms: fundamental frequency, over-
               tone

1 MOTIVATION

Take the class to the music room of your school. Demonstrate or ask a music teacher to demonstrate various instruments and the tones they produce. Ask students to compare the different sounds produced by the instruments, in terms of pitch and tone. Have students close their eyes and try to identify different instruments as they are played. Ask students how they can identify instruments without seeing them.

2 CONCEPT DEVELOPMENT

Demonstration   To demonstrate an overtone, choose any of the lower keys of a piano. Count up eight keys (an octave) from the key chosen. Push (do not strike) this second key without playing it. Now strike the first key with some degree of force, and release it. The note (pitch) of the second key can be heard.

Thinking Skills

inferring
Students are asked to infer from a wave pattern in Figure 18-17 that the tuning fork does not produce overtones, but the musical instruments shown do produce overtones.

18-4 MUSICAL SOUNDS

After completing this section, you will be able to

- **distinguish** between music and noise.
- **identify** the properties of musical tones.
- **classify** musical instruments.

The key terms in this section are
quality   harmony

What do rock-and-roll, a symphony, and an opera have in common? They are all forms of music. Musical sounds, or tones, are produced by regular vibrations. Sounds with an irregular wave pattern are called noise.

PROPERTIES OF MUSIC

Musical tones have three properties that can be distinguished by the human ear—pitch, loudness, and quality. The pitch depends on the frequency of the wave. Loudness depends on the amplitude of the wave, or how much energy it carries. The **quality** of a tone is its distinct sound. Quality enables you to tell a note played on a piano from the same note played on a flute.

Musical tones are most often produced by vibrating a string or a column of air. By changing the length of the string or the air column, you can change the pitch of the sound. The lowest frequency that a musical tone can have is called the *fundamental frequency*. Many higher tones can be produced. An *overtone* is a whole-number multiple of the fundamental frequency. For example, if the fundamental frequency of a string is 220 Hz, the overtones would be 440 Hz, 660 Hz, 880 Hz, and so on.

Most musical instruments produce a fundamental frequency and some of its overtones at the same time. The number and strength of the overtones will be different for different instruments. Interference between the fundamental sound waves and the sound waves of the overtones produces a different wave from each instrument.

Figure 18-17

Wave patterns of musical tones.

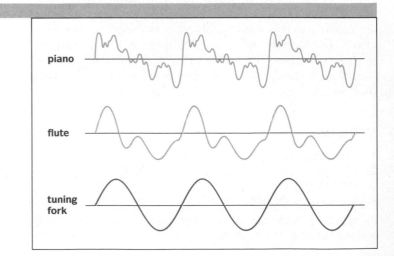

piano

flute

tuning
fork

Compare the wave patterns shown in Figure 18-17. Notice that all three patterns have the same frequency and amplitude. Only the shapes differ. The differences in the shapes of these waves are heard as the quality of each tone. Notice the shape of the wave produced by the tuning fork. How does this wave demonstate that a tuning fork does not produce overtones?[1]

Harmony (HAHR muh nee) is a pleasing sound that results when two or more different tones are played at the same time. Some combinations of frequencies produce a pleasant sound. Others do not. Musicians know from study and experience which tones will blend well.

MUSICAL INSTRUMENTS

There are four classes of musical instruments—string, wind, percussion, and electronic. They all produce vibrations in a regular pattern. Electronic instruments get the energy to produce sound from electricity. The other kinds of instruments get the energy to produce sound from the people who play them. Musical instruments contain a vibrator, which makes the sound, and a resonator, which increases the intensity of the sound.

[1]The wave pattern is a smooth curve, with no interference between overtones.

harmonia (agreement)

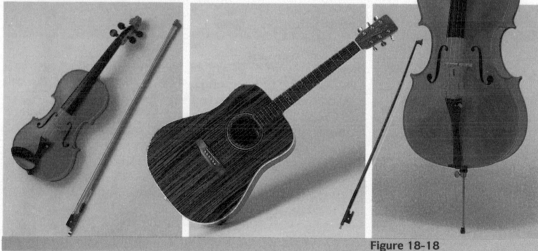

Figure 18-18

String instruments include the violin (*left*), the guitar (*middle*), and the cello (*right*).

String instruments include the violin, viola, cello, and guitar. Musical tones are produced when the strings of these instruments are made to vibrate. Air inside the wooden body of a string instrument resonates when the strings vibrate. The shape of the body gives the instrument many natural frequencies. Thus, it can produce resonance for different musical tones.

Background The combination of sounds that is unpleasant to the ear is referred to as dissonance.

Background Wind instruments are separated into two categories: woodwinds and brass. Woodwind instruments include the flute, piccolo, clarinet, oboe, and bassoon. Brass instruments include the trumpet, French horn, and trombone.

Background A viola is one-fifth larger and five notes lower in pitch than a violin.

Teaching Tip Students can build sample musical instruments and demonstrate their operation. A string instrument is easily made by stretching wires or rubber bands over a cigar box with an attached handle.

Teaching Tip   Have students identify the effect on pitch or frequency as the length, thickness, and tension of strings is changed. Ask students why the violin produces the highest-pitched tones of the string family and why the cello and the bass violin produce much lower pitched tones. (The violin has shorter strings than do the other two instruments.)

Teaching Tip   Play a recording of "Stars and Stripes Forever," by John Philip Sousa, and point out the distinctive piccolo section. Mention that the piccolo is the highest-pitched orchestral instrument. Bring in recordings of other musical compositions, play them, and ask students to identify the instruments.

Demonstration   To show that the pitch of a string instrument's sound depends upon the length, thickness, and tension of the strings, tighten and play a string of a guitar. Then loosen and play the string of the guitar. Point out that tight, thin strings produce the highest pitch, and loose, thick strings produce the lowest pitch. If you or a student plays the guitar, demonstrate how the fingers shorten the string and raise the pitch.

DO YOU KNOW?

In the seventeenth century in the small Italian village of Cremona, a handful of artists created the most beautiful-sounding violins ever made. When these masters—the Amati family, Guarneri del Gesu, and Antonio Stradivari—died, so did the secret of their art. No one has been able to make a violin with the same richness and evenness of tone.

Since the seventeenth century, many researchers have tried to find a scientific explanation for the unique sound of the old violins. Some say it's the wood. Others say it's how the wood was varnished. Still others claim that the construction of the violins is the secret.

One scientist, Dr. Joseph Nagyvary, of Texas A&M University, believes that the chemistry of the wood used to make violins is the key to producing a beautiful sound.

He studied how wood was treated in seventeenth-century Italy and found that the wood had been treated with mineral solutions. He also discovered that much of the wood had been stored in saltwater bays for as long as 5 years. This procedure changed the structure of the wood, giving it better tone-generating qualities.

Dr. Nagyvary also found that the Italian artisans used a different type of varnish than is used today. He believes that the old type of varnish improves the resonating properties of the violin.

Dr. Nagyvary has been making violins in a way that he believes is close to the methods of the great Italian masters. Some musicians who have played his violins say that his violins sound better than any others now made. But they still are not as good as a Stradivarius.

The pitch, or frequency, of the sound produced by a vibrating string depends on the length, thickness, and tension of the string. You may have noticed that a violin or a guitar has strings of different thicknesses. The lowest notes are produced by the thickest string. The highest notes are produced by the thinnest string.

Tightening a string causes it to produce higher sounds. Loosening a string causes it to produce lower sounds. To tune a guitar or other string instrument, the player adjusts the tension on the strings until they produce the right combination of frequencies.

To change the length of a string, the guitar player holds down the string so that only a portion of it vibrates. The shorter the string, the higher the sound produced. The lowest sound a string can produce is made when the full length of the string vibrates.

Wind instruments produce sound by using a column of air. Some of these instruments, like the clarinet, saxophone, and oboe, have a reed for a vibrator. When the clarinet player in Figure 18-19A blows into the instrument,

452

the reed vibrates, causing the air in the clarinet to vibrate. The frequencies of the musical tones depend on the length of the resonating air column. The longer the air column, the lower the sound. The shorter the air column, the higher the sound. Keys open and close holes, allowing the musician to control the length of the air column.

Lionel Hampton

Figure 18-19

In a clarinet, different pitches are produced by controlling the length of the air column (A). In the xylophone, different pitches are produced by striking bars of different lengths (B).

Other wind instruments, such as trumpets and trombones, depend on the vibrating lips of the musician to start the air in motion. A trumpet player changes the pitch of the sound by changing the vibrations of his or her lips. Also, the length of the air column is controlled by valves.

The sounds of percussion instruments are made by striking membranes, bells, or metal plates with a hammer or stick. The sounds of some percussion instruments do not last very long. A drum, for example, needs to be struck repeatedly or the sound fades quickly. The tone produced by a percussion instrument is determined by the shape of the instrument. These instruments do not have keys or valves that change the pitch of the sound produced. To get more than one tone from a percussion instrument, more than one shape must be used. Look at the xylophone shown in Figure 18-19B. Each bar is a different size and produces a different tone. Which bars would you expect to make the highest notes?[1]

[1]The shortest bars produce the highest notes.

PROCESS SKILLS
observing, comparing, measuring, inferring, identifying cause and effect

Preparation   None required.

Safety Tip   Any vessel can be used in place of bottles. Make sure the bottles are clean and germfree before students put them to their lips.

Answers to Procedure
1. The pitch gets higher.
2. The pitch gets higher.

Answers to Results and Conclusions
1. The air vibrating in the bottle.
2. It shortened the air column.
3. The shorter the air column, the higher the pitch.
4. The large bottle produced a lower-pitched sound.

Teaching Tip   Students should be able to classify musical instruments into one of the following categories: string, wind, percussion, and electronic. Show students a picture of a symphony orchestra. Point out various instruments, and ask students to classify each of them.

3 REVIEW/REINFORCEMENT

1. Musical sounds are produced by regular vibrations; sounds with irregular wave patterns are called noise.
2. Pitch, loudness, and quality.
3. Violin—string; bells—percussion; trumpet—wind; drum—percussion; keyboard synthesizer—electronic.

Challenge   When you tap the bottle, the water vibrates, and a large amount makes a low-pitched sound. When you blow across the top of the bottle, the air column vibrates, and a short air column makes a high-pitched sound.

ACTIVITY   What Causes Pitch Changes?

OBJECTIVE
Demonstrate that pitch is determined by the length of a vibrating air column.

MATERIALS
250-mL and 500-mL plastic laboratory bottles, graduate, water

PROCEDURE
A. Hold an empty 250-mL bottle up to your lips. With a steady breath, blow across the top of the bottle.
B. Pour 50 mL of water into the bottle. Hold the bottle up to your lips and blow across the top.
C. Add another 50 mL of water to the bottle. Blow across the top of the bottle.
D. Add another 50 mL of water to the bottle, and blow across the top again.
   1. What happens to the pitch of the sound each time more water is added to the bottle?
E. Hold an empty 500-mL bottle to your lips and blow across the top of the bottle.
F. Pour 100 mL of water into the bottle. Hold the bottle up to your lips and blow across the top.
G. Add another 100 mL of water to the bottle. Blow across the top of the bottle.
H. Add another 100 mL of water to the bottle, and blow across the top.
   2. What happens to the pitch of the sound each time more water is added to the bottle?

RESULTS AND CONCLUSIONS
1. What produced the sounds you heard?
2. What did the addition of water do to the length of the air column above the water?
3. How is the change in sound related to the change in the air column?
4. Compare the pitch of the sound produced with the empty large bottle with that of the empty small bottle.

Figure 18-20

A synthesizer produces the sounds of many different musical instruments electronically.

Electronic instruments are the newest kinds of instruments. These instruments were invented in the twentieth century. The most common kind of electronic instrument is the keyboard synthesizer. You have probably heard music made on a synthesizer. The synthesizer changes electrical signals into sound waves. The signals can be added together in different combinations to make different musical tones.

The synthesizer is able to duplicate the sounds of many instruments. By changing the mixture of overtones, it can copy the sound quality of instruments such as a piano, flute, or clarinet. The synthesizer copies the interference patterns of the instruments it imitates.

REVIEW

1. How is music different from noise?
2. What properties of musical tones can be heard by the human ear?
3. To which groups do the following instruments belong: violin, bells, trumpet, drum, keyboard synthesizer.

CHALLENGE   A bottle nearly full of water will make a low-pitched sound when you tap it. But when you blow across the top of the bottle, a high-pitched sound is made. Explain why.

18-5 ACOUSTICS AND NOISE POLLUTION

Have you ever heard a concert in an auditorium where the sound echoed? The music made by the performers may have bounced around the room. If the walls of the auditorium reflected sound strongly, then the echoes may have bounced around several times before fading away. These multiple echoes are called reverberations (rih ver-buh RAY shuhn). A **reverberation** is a mixture of repeating echoes. When sound *reverberates,* it seems to come from different places at different times. When the waves of the repeating sounds combine, they produce irregular wave patterns that sound like noise.

Rooms and buildings can be designed to control echoes and other unwanted noise. For example, hard surfaces like wood, stone, and plaster reflect sound waves. Soft materials like draperies and carpet absorb sound waves. Specially designed tiles also absorb sound waves. Therefore, the walls, floors, and ceilings of many rooms are covered with sound-absorbing materials. Look at Figure 18-21. Which office will be quieter?[1]

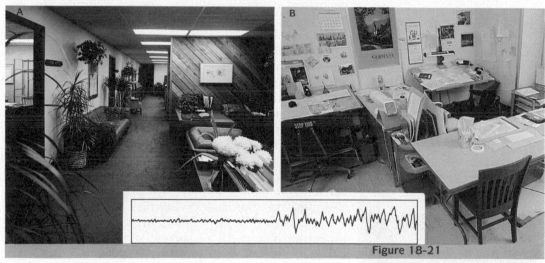

Figure 18-21

[1]The office with sound-absorbing materials.

Irregular wave patterns sound like noise (*inset*). Soft materials reduce noise levels.

akoustikos (related to hearing)

The office in Figure 18-21A was designed using the principles of acoustics (uh KOOS tihks). **Acoustics** is the study of sound. Scientists and acoustic engineers study sound to reduce noise and to improve the environment. Some concert halls, for example, have sloped ceilings and uneven walls. This kind of design uses the reflection of sound waves to improve the sound of the music. The design also reduces the amount of reverberation.

18-5 ACOUSTICS AND NOISE POLLUTION

pages 455–457

After completing this section, you will be able to

- **describe** reverberation and how it can be controlled.
- **give examples** of the effects of noise pollution.

The key terms in this section are
acoustics   reverberation

OBJECTIVES
Refer to pupil page 455.

VOCABULARY
Key terms: acoustics, reverberation
Other terms: noise pollution, reverberates

1 MOTIVATION

Take your class to the school auditorium. Ask students to point out the acoustic features of the room. Students should observe sloped ceilings, absorbent materials, and reflective materials. Ask one or more students to stand on the stage and talk at normal volume. Scatter the remaining students throughout the auditorium to determine if they can hear the sounds equally well. Ask students to explain "dead spots" by using the term *interference.*

2 CONCEPT DEVELOPMENT

Background   Materials that are good sound absorbers are also generally good heat absorbers or good insulators.

Background   The science of acoustics has many branches. Architectural acoustics deals with the listening conditions in rooms and buildings. Environmental acoustics deals with noise control in outdoor areas. Musical acoustics deals with musical sounds and their generation and transmission.

Review and Skill Masters

SKILL, page 110.
See page 431b in this book for answers.

Enrichment Ask students to research the acoustical problems encountered in installing public address systems in domed stadiums and to find out how the problems are remedied. Have students report back to the class.

Thinking Skills

inferring
In Figure 18-22, students infer whether a person at point A will hear a person at point B.

Puzzler All the sounds are absorbed; none are reflected.

Enrichment Ask students to observe acoustic deficiencies and sources of noise pollution in your school. Discuss the findings with the class. As a class project, have students suggest possible methods of correction.

Demonstration Demonstrate loud noises that contribute to noise pollution by using a sound-level meter that is calibrated in decibels. If a portable meter is available, measure the sound levels in different areas of your school.

Demonstration To demonstrate noise pollution, use a siren wheel. Direct a stream of air at the regularly spaced holes, pointing out the pleasant or musical sound. Then direct a stream of air at the irregularly spaced holes. Students should find this sound unpleasant and irritating.

Teaching Tip Government regulations now help to protect workers from excessive noise while they work. Contact your local office of OSHA (Occupational Safety and Health Administration), and ask them for specific information or for a guest speaker.

Background A sonic boom is a form of noise pollution.

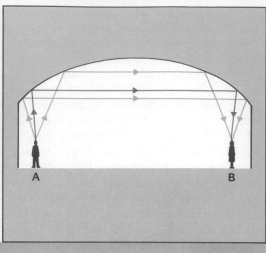

Figure 18-22
Statuary Hall in the United States Capitol is a "whispering gallery."

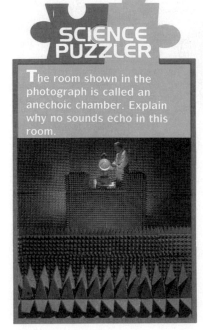

SCIENCE PUZZLER

The room shown in the photograph is called an anechoic chamber. Explain why no sounds echo in this room.

Noise has been found to affect health and to cause other problems. *Noise pollution* is the term used to describe unwanted noise and its effects. Stress and hearing loss can be caused by noise pollution. Noise pollution has also been found to cause high blood pressure, headaches, and fatigue.

Noise can damage buildings and other objects. High-frequency sounds can shatter glass. The sonic boom from a jet can damage windows and weaken plaster walls. Loud trucks driving past a house that is close to the road can have a similar effect.

Noise pollution can be controlled. New jet engines are designed to produce less noise, and jets are not allowed to fly over land at supersonic speeds. When highways are built near homes, walls are put up to keep road noise from reaching the homes. Indoor noise is controlled by sound-absorbing materials like ceiling tiles and wall coverings.

Sometimes the shape of a room gives it unusual acoustic properties. Figure 18-22 shows the "whispering gallery" in the United States Capitol in Washington, D.C. This room has a curved shape. If you stand at point A, a person at point B can hear you speak, even if you whisper. However, anyone standing between points A and B cannot hear your whispers. If a sound is made at point A, its waves spread out and hit the ceiling. The waves are reflected across the room, where they hit the ceiling again. From there the sound waves are reflected and become concentrated at point B. Will a person at point A hear the whispers of a person at point B?[1]

[1]Yes.

REVIEW

1. What is reverberation?
2. What kinds of materials reflect sound waves? What kinds absorb sound waves?
3. Describe two effects of noise pollution.

CHALLENGE Why does a concert rehearsal in an empty auditorium sound different from a performance in an auditorium full of people?

CHAPTER SUMMARY

The main ideas in this chapter are listed below. Read these statements before you answer the Chapter Review questions.

- A wave is a disturbance that travels through space and matter. Transverse waves vibrate at right angles to the direction in which the wave travels. Compressional waves displace particles back and forth parallel to the direction in which the wave travels. (18-1)

- Wavelength is the measure of distance from any point on a wave to the corresponding point on the next wave. Frequency is the number of waves that pass a point in a given time. (18-1)

- Reflection is the bouncing of a wave off a surface. Refraction is the change in direction of a wave as it passes from one medium to another. (18-2)

- Interference occurs when two or more waves pass through a medium at the same time. (18-2)

- Sound waves are compressional waves. One sound wave is made up of a compression and a rarefaction. (18-3)

- Resonance occurs when an object vibrates in response to vibrations that match its natural frequency. (18-3)

- Intensity is the loudness of a sound. Intensity is measured in decibels. (18-3)

- The pitch of a sound is determined by the frequency of the wave. The greater the frequency, the higher the pitch. The Doppler effect is a change in the pitch heard when the listener or the source of the sound is moving. (18-3)

- Sounds that produce regular patterns are called music. Sounds that produce irregular patterns are called noise. (18-4)

- The quality of a tone gives it a distinctive sound. Harmony occurs when two or more different tones played together result in a pleasing sound. (18-4)

- Acoustics is the study of sound. The principles of acoustics can be used to reduce noise pollution. (18-5)

The key terms in this chapter are listed below. Use each term in a sentence that shows the meaning of the term.

acoustics	Doppler effect	pitch	resonance
amplitude	frequency	quality	reverberation
compression	harmony	rarefaction	transverse wave
compressional wave	intensity	reflection	wave
decibel	interference	refraction	wavelength
diffraction			

1. Reverberation is a mixture of repeating echoes.
2. Hard materials, like wood, stone, and plaster, reflect sound waves; soft materials, like draperies and carpets, absorb sound waves.
3. Noise can damage buildings by shattering windows and weakening plaster walls; noise pollution has also been found to cause hearing loss, high blood pressure, headache, and fatigue.

Challenge The audience absorbs some of the sound waves.

Review and Skill Masters

VOCABULARY REVIEW, page 107.
See page 431b in this book for answers.

VOCABULARY

1. n	7. i
2. m	8. e
3. o	9. j
4. h	10. g
5. a	11. f
6. l	

CONCEPTS

1. Mechanical waves travel through matter; electromagnetic waves carry energy without using matter.
2. See Figure 18-3.
3. 12 m/s.
4. The amplitude is a measure of the greatest displacement of matter from its normal resting position.
5. Speed is the product of the frequency times the wavelength.
6. The wave bounces off a surface it strikes.
7. The speed of the wave and the wavelength change.
8. Waves that hit the edge of a barrier seem to move around the corner of a barrier as a series of new waves.
9. Interference is the effect of two waves meeting when they both pass through a medium at the same time: one wave reinforcing another wave is known as constructive interference; one wave canceling another is known as destructive interference.

Review and Skill Masters

CHAPTER REVIEW, pages 108–109.
See page 431b in this book for answers.

458

Chapter Review

VOCABULARY

Write the letter of the term that best matches the definition. Not all the terms will be used.

1. A disturbance that travels through space or matter in a regular pattern
2. A wave that vibrates up and down at right angles to its direction of travel
3. The distance from one point on a wave to the corresponding point on the next wave
4. How high or low a sound is
5. The study of sound
6. A mixture of repeating echoes
7. The part of a compressional wave where the particles of matter are spread apart
8. The spreading of waves around the edge of a barrier
9. The change in direction of a wave as it passes from one medium to another
10. The effect caused by two or more waves passing through a medium at the same time
11. The number of waves that pass a point in a given amount of time

a. acoustics
b. amplitude
c. compressional wave
d. decibel
e. diffraction
f. frequency
g. interference
h. pitch
i. rarefaction
j. refraction
k. resonance
l. reverberation
m. transverse wave
n. wave
o. wavelength

CONCEPTS

1. How do mechanical and electromagnetic waves differ? (18-1)
2. Make a sketch of a transverse wave. Label its parts. (18-1)
3. What is the speed of a wave with a frequency of 2 Hz and a wavelength of 6 m? (18-1)
4. What does the amplitude of a wave show? (18-1)
5. What determines the speed of a wave? (18-1)
6. What causes a wave to be reflected? (18-2)
7. What happens to waves when they move from one substance into another? (18-2)
8. What causes a wave to be diffracted? (18-2)
9. What is interference? Describe the two kinds of interference. (18-2)

458

10. Compare the frequencies of a high-pitched tone and a low-pitched tone. (18-3)

11. How are sympathetic vibrations different from forced vibrations? (18-3)

12. Compare the speed of sound in solids, liquids, and gases. (18-3)

13. Describe two uses of sonar. (18-3)

14. What characteristic of sound is determined by its amplitude? What characteristic of sound is determined by its frequency? (18-3)

15. What is a sonic boom? (18-3)

16. Why do you hear a change in pitch when a source of sound moves toward you? (18-3)

17. Compare the sound waves produced by music with those produced by noise. (18-4)

18. Why does a violin sound different than a trumpet? (18-4)

19. What are the three properties of music? (18-4)

20. How are wind instruments different from string instruments? (18-5)

21. Why do some rooms seem loud, and others, quiet? (18-5)

22. What is noise pollution? (18-5)

---

1. Why does sound travel faster in steel than in air?

2. How could the Doppler effect be used to measure the speed of an approaching car?

3. An astronaut claimed to hear an explosion while on the surface of the moon. Since the moon has no air to carry the sound, how could this be true?

4. At what position does a slide trombone make the lowest note? Why does a piccolo produce higher tones than does a flute?

APPLICATION/ CRITICAL THINKING

---

1. Research the term *sound barrier*. Find out who was the first person to break this barrier and what importance it had. Report back to the class on your findings.

2. Ask a hospital or a doctor for information about sonograms. Prepare a report for the class.

3. If you play a musical instrument, demonstrate to the class how it makes and varies sound.

EXTENSION

Knight, David C. *Silent Sound: The World of Ultrasonics.* New York: Morrow, Williams, and Co., Inc., 1980.

Ruby, D.J. "Visible Wind (Doppler Acoustic Sounder)." *Popular Science,* November 1983, p. 103.

READINGS

---

10. High-pitched sounds have high frequencies; low-pitched sounds have low frequencies.

11. Forced vibrations transfer wave energy by contact; sympathetic vibrations are produced by resonance.

12. Sound moves faster in solids and in liquids than in gases.

13. To locate fish, and to find their distance from the boat; to map the ocean floor.

14. Loudness; pitch.

15. A loud sound produced as a plane flies at or above the speed of sound.

16. Sound waves are moved closer together, increasing the frequency of the sound.

17. Musical sounds are produced by regular vibrations; noise waves show an irregular pattern.

18. There is a difference in quality and overtones.

19. Pitch, loudness, and quality.

20. String instruments make sounds by vibrating strings; wind instruments, by vibrating columns of air.

21. The construction of the room and the utilization of sound-absorbing and reflecting materials make the difference.

22. *Noise pollution* is a term used to describe unwanted noise and its effects.

APPLICATION/CRITICAL THINKING

1. Because the molecules in steel are closer together than they are in air.

2. The change of frequency of a signal reflected from an approaching car would indicate the speed of the approaching car.

3. The sound could travel through the surface of the moon.

4. At the fullest extension of the slide. The piccolo has a shorter air column.

Test Masters

CHAPTER TEST, pages 69–72.
See page 431d in this book for answers.

LIGHT

ORGANIZER

Section	pages	Activity	pages	Reinforcement and Evaluation	pages	*Review and Skill Masters	pages	Other Components in Teacher Resource Package	pages
19—1 The Electro-magnetic Spectrum	*461–462*			Review, Challenge	*462*			*Study Guide* *Poster*	*94*
19—2 How Light Travels	*463–467*	What Is the Path of a Light Wave?	*464*	Review, Challenge	*467*			*Study Guide* *Lab Manual*	*95* *99*
19—3 Reflection and Refraction	*468–472*	What Is the Law of Reflection?	*469*	Puzzler Review, Challenge	*471* *472*	Skill	*116*	*Study Guide* *Lab Manual*	*96* *95*
19—4 Color	*473–477*	How Are Colors Printed?	*476*	Review, Challenge	*477*	Challenge/Critical Thinking	*117–118*	*Study Guide*	*97*
19—5 The Wave Nature of Light	*478–481*			Review, Challenge	*481*			*Study Guide*	*98*
19—6 The Particle Nature of Light	*482–485*			Review, Challenge	*485*			*Study Guide*	*99*
CHAPTER SUMMARY	*485*					Vocabulary Review	*113*		
CHAPTER REVIEW	*486–487*			*Test Masters	*73–76*	Chapter Review	*114–115*		

*In the Teacher Resource Package. For answers, see pages 459b–459d in this book.

ACTIVITY MATERIALS
Quantities are based on a class of 30 students working in groups as indicated in parentheses.

What Is the Path of a Light Wave? p. 464 (groups of 2)	quantity	What Is the Law of Reflection? p. 469 (groups of 2)	quantity	How Are Colors Printed? p. 476 (groups of 2)	quantity
index cards	60	white paper (21 cm x 28 cm)	15 sheets	newspaper color comics	15 sheets
metric ruler	15	metric ruler	15	illuminated pocket microscope (30x)	15
hole punch	15	protractor	15		
slit rubber stopper	60	cardboard (30 cm x 30 cm)	15 pieces		
white paper	15 sheets	straight pins	30		
small flashlight	15	small mirror	15		
		slit rubber stopper	15		

REVIEW AND SKILL MASTERS

VOCABULARY REVIEW _____ Chapter 19

Match the definition in Column A with the term in Column B. Not all terms are used.

Column A

N	1. A type of energy that is transferred by electromagnetic waves
B	2. The different forms of electromagnetic waves
R	3. Allowing almost all light to pass through
Q	4. Allowing only some light to pass through
I	5. Allowing no light to pass through
F	6. The brightness of light
D	7. The light ray that strikes the surface of an object
P	8. The light ray that is reflected from the surface of an object
H	9. A statement that the angle of reflection is equal to the angle of incidence
O	10. The change in direction of a light ray at the point where it passes from one substance to another
E	11. A measure of the refraction of light in a substance as it enters from air or a vacuum
C	12. A substance that allows only certain colors of light to pass through it
S	13. The idea that light is made up of light waves
G	14. The result when two light waves meet and add or cancel each other
A	15. The spreading out of a light wave as it passes through a small opening or around a small object
M	16. The process of producing light with electromagnetic vibrations in one direction
L	17. The release of electrons from a metal when light strikes it
K	18. A tiny particle of energy that makes up light
J	19. An electric cell that changes light energy into electrical energy

Column B

A. diffraction
B. electromagnetic spectrum
C. filter
D. incident ray
E. index of refraction
F. intensity
G. interference
H. law of reflection
I. opaque
J. photocell
K. photon
L. photoelectric effect
M. polarization
N. radiant energy
O. refraction
P. reflected ray
Q. translucent
R. transparent
S. wave model of light

113

CHAPTER REVIEW _____ Chapter 19

19-1 The Electromagnetic Spectrum

1. List the parts of the electromagnetic spectrum. Radio waves, infrared rays, ultraviolet rays, visible light, X rays, gamma rays.

2. Name the six forms of radiant energy and give one characteristic of each form.
   a. radio waves—used in communication and broadcasting
   b. infrared rays—invisible heat radiation
   c. visible light—only form that people can see
   d. ultraviolet rays—causes skin to tan or sunburn
   e. X rays—used to photograph the inside of the body
   f. gamma rays—given off by radioactive substances

19-2 How Light Travels

1. Compare glass, wax paper, and wood. Which is transparent, translucent, or opaque? Glass is transparent; wax paper is translucent; wood is opaque.

2. Give one example that shows light travels in a straight line. Answers may vary. The light from a movie projector travels in a straight line.

3. How is the intensity of light related to the distance from the light source? The intensity of light decreases as light moves away from its source.

4. Name two methods used to measure the speed of light. Observing the eclipses of Jupiter's four moons; reflecting light from one side of a rotating eight-sided mirror.

19-3 Reflection and Refraction

1. Underline your answers. A mirror reflects parallel/scattered light rays off a smooth surface and forms an image. A wall reflects parallel/scattered light rays off a rough surface and does not form an image.

114

CHAPTER REVIEW (Continued) _____ Chapter 19

2. What happens to light as it enters a diamond? When light enters a diamond, it bends, or refracts, at an angle.

3. Explain the formation of a rainbow. Drops of water in the air disperse sunlight into colors to form a rainbow.

19-4 Color

1. Color is caused by visible light reflecting from objects

2. Contrast producing color by subtraction and by addition. A color may be produced by using filters or pigments to subtract colors of light. Combining separate light sources of different colors adds colors of light together.

19-5 The Wave Nature of Light

1. Give two examples of wave properties of light. Answers may vary. Reflection and refraction are wave properties of light.

2. What causes the diffraction and interference of light? Diffraction is caused by light waves spreading out. Interference is caused by two light waves adding or canceling each other.

3. Polarized light vibrates in ___one___ direction(s); ordinary light vibrates in ___many___ direction(s).

19-6 The Particle Nature of Light

1. What is the photoelectric effect? The photoelectric effect is the release of electrons from metals when light strikes.

2. How does the intensity and frequency of light affect the photoelectric effect? Increasing the intensity increases the number of photons. Increasing the frequency increases the energy of the photons.

3. Why is light said to have a dual nature? Light has both wave properties and particle properties.

115

SKILL/Interpreting a Diagram _____ Chapter 19

Two people are scuba diving in Florida looking for ship wrecks. They spot a wreck with their search light, but the light appears to bend, or refract, in the water. Study the diagram below about light refraction and answer the following questions.

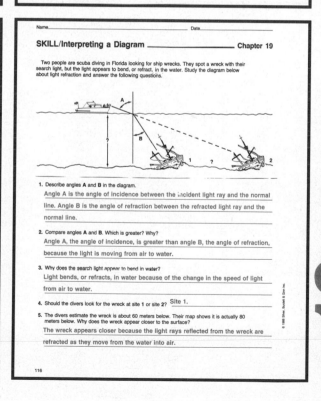

1. Describe angles A and B in the diagram.
   Angle A is the angle of incidence between the incident light ray and the normal line. Angle B is the angle of refraction between the refracted light ray and the normal line.

2. Compare angles A and B. Which is greater? Why?
   Angle A, the angle of incidence, is greater than angle B, the angle of refraction, because the light is moving from air to water.

3. Why does the search light appear to bend in water?
   Light bends, or refracts, in water because of the change in the speed of light from air to water.

4. Should the divers look for the wreck at site 1 or site 2? Site 1.

5. The divers estimate the wreck is about 60 meters below. Their map shows it is actually 80 meters below. Why does the wreck appear closer to the surface?
   The wreck appears closer because the light rays reflected from the wreck are refracted as they move from the water into air.

116

Name_____ Date_____

CHALLENGE/CRITICAL THINKING _____ Chapter 19

A classmate of yours went to a concert and told the class how much she enjoyed it. She especially enjoyed the colorful lighting used as part of the show. Your teacher heard this discussion and decided to give each student his or her own "lighting" assignment. Your assignment is as follows:

> You are the lighting expert for a band. This band wants a colorful show to help it look exciting. You have only four kinds of lights available for you to use: blue, green, red, and white. The colored lights you will use are actually white light bulbs covered with one of three filters: blue, green, or red. Design a light show for five songs. Write a report about your show.

1. Begin your report by defining filters and explaining how they are used to create blue, green, and red light from white light.

   Filters are transparent or translucent substances that allow only certain colors of light to pass through. All colors of light enter the filter from the white light bulb. The blue filter will allow only blue light to pass through. The green filter will allow only green light to pass through. The red filter will allow only red light to pass though.

2. You continue your report by discussing how you will make different colors of light. When you use more than one color of light at a time, is the resulting light a product of addition or of subtraction?

   When you use more than one color of light at a time, the resulting light is a product of addition.

3. You decide to finish your introduction on lighting by discussing how we see an object as a certain color. Explain why a blue flag appears blue in white light.

   A blue flag appears blue in white light because the flag absorbs all wavelengths of light except that of blue. The blue light is reflected, and that is why we see a blue flag.

4. For the first song you wish to create a quiet mood. You decide to bathe the stage in blue. Which lights will you use to do this?

   In order to bathe the stage in blue, you will use only the blue lights.

Name_____ Date_____

CHALLENGE/CRITICAL THINKING (Continued) _____ Chapter 19

5. You decide to use magenta light for the start of the second song. Which two lights will you use?

   You will use the blue lights and the red lights to make magenta light.

6. Halfway through the second song, you decide to change the lighting to red. How will you do this?

   To turn magenta to red, you need to turn off the blue lights, leaving the red lights on.

7. You want to use only the green lights for the entire third song. Every member of the band is wearing a green shirt. What color will the shirts appear during this song?

   A green shirt seen only in green light will appear green.

8. One member of the band has a red guitar. What color will the guitar appear during the third song? Why?

   The guitar will appear black during the third song. This is because the green light is absorbed and there is no red light present to be reflected.

9. You want to bathe the stage in white light for the fourth song. Describe two ways to do this.

   You could either use only the white lights or you could use a combination of the blue, green, and red lights.

10. The final song will be the most exciting. You will begin using only the red lights. Then you will add the green lights, followed in a few seconds by the blue lights. Then you will turn off the red lights, followed in a few seconds by the green lights. With what colors will you have bathed the stage?

    First the stage will be bathed in red. As the green lights are turned on, it will be bathed in yellow. As the blue lights are turned on, it will be bathed in white. As the red lights are turned off, it will be bathed in cyan. After the green lights are turned off, the stage will be bathed in blue.

Name_____ Date_____ Score_____

Light   Chapter 19

PART 1

In the space below, write the term that each phrase defines.

Chapter Goal

1. __radiant energy__ — A type of energy that is transferred by electromagnetic waves — 1

2. __photoelectric effect__ — The release of electrons from a metal when light strikes it — 6

3. __incident ray__ — A light ray that strikes a surface — 3

4. __opaque__ — A word used to describe a material that does not allow light to pass through — 2

5. __index of refraction__ — A measure of the refraction of light in a substance — 3

6. __electromagnetic spectrum__ — The different forms of electromagnetic waves — 1

7. __polarization__ — The process of producing light with electromagnetic vibrations in one direction — 5

8. __photocell__ — An electric cell that changes light energy into electric energy — 6

9. __filter__ — A substance that allows only certain colors of light to pass through — 4

10. __wave model of light__ — The idea that light is made up of waves — 5

11. __intensity__ — The brightness of light — 2

PART 2

Choose the term or phrase that best answers the question or completes the statement. Write the letter of that choice in the space at the left.

__d__ 1. A red light shining on a photocell is not producing a photoelectric effect. Which of the following changes to the light is most likely to produce the effect? — 6
a. an increase in the intensity   c. an increase in the wavelength
b. a decrease in the frequency   d. an increase in the frequency

__d__ 2. A sun lamp gives off a kind of radiant energy that causes skin to tan. In order to cause tanning, the lamp must give off: — 1
a. visible light.   c. gamma rays.
b. infrared rays.   d. ultraviolet rays.

Chapter 19 Light   73

Name_____ Date_____ Score_____

PART 2

Choose the term or phrase that best answers the question or completes the statement. Write the letter of that choice in the space at the left.

Chapter Goal

__c__ 3. Which of the following can produce a pattern of dark and light lines? — 5
a. reflection   b. refraction   c. interference   d. polarization

__c__ 4. Sunlight passes through a red filter and then falls upon a green leaf. The leaf will appear: — 4
a. green.   b. red.   c. black.   d. white.

__b__ 5. A person reaches into a pool of water in order to retrieve a watch that fell into the pool. Each time that he or she reaches in, the watch is not where it appears to be. This is most likely due to: — 3
a. reflection.   b. refraction.   c. dispersion.   d. polarization.

__c__ 6. Red and green beams of light are mixed to fall on a piece of white paper. The paper will appear to be: — 4
a. white.   b. black.   c. yellow.   d. blue.

__a__ 7. Which of the following is an example of a transparent object? — 2
a. window   c. frosted light bulb
b. mirror   d. wall

__c__ 8. According to the particle model of light, compared with blue light, red light has: — 6
a. waves with higher frequencies.   c. particles with less energy.
b. fewer particles.   d. longer wavelengths.

__b__ 9. All waves of light that pass through a particular polarizing filter must: — 5
a. move at the same speed.   c. vibrate with the same frequency.
b. vibrate in the same direction.   d. come from the same source.

__a__ 10. Which source uses radiant energy with the longest wavelength and lowest frequency? — 1
a. radio   b. light bulb   c. flashlight   d. X-ray machine

__b__ 11. In green light, a shirt that is white with blue stripes will appear: — 4
a. white with black stripes.   c. white with green stripes.
b. green with black stripes.   d. green with white stripes.

__b__ 12. Roemer's measurement of the speed of light was based on the: — 2
a. size of Jupiter's moons.
b. distance across the earth's orbit.
c. distance across Jupiter's orbit.
d. distance from Jupiter to the earth.

__d__ 13. In a prism, light separates into different colors because each different frequency of light: — 3
a. strikes the prism at a different angle.
b. strikes the prism at a different speed.
c. reflects at a different angle.
d. bends at a different angle.

Chapter 19 Light   74

Name_____ Date_____ Score_____

PART 3

Look at the table. Then read the questions that follow. Choose the term or phrase that best answers the question or completes the statement. Write the letter of that choice in the space at the left.

Characteristics of Energy from Five Light Sources			
Source	Wavelength (m)	Polarized	Speed (m/s)
A	1×10^{-5}	Yes	1.97×10^8
B	4×10^{-7}	No	2.25×10^8
C	6×10^{-7}	Yes	2.25×10^8
D	7×10^{-7}	No	2.25×10^8
E	1×10^{-11}	No	3.0×10^8

Chapter Goal

__d__ 1. Energy from which of the following sources would be most likely to produce the photoelectric effect? — 6
a. A   b. B   c. D   d. E

__a__ 2. Energy from which source is passing through the material with the highest index of refraction? — 3
a. A   b. B   c. C   d. D

__b__ 3. Energy from Source B falls on a diffraction grating 2 m away. In order to best observe diffraction, how large should the openings in the grating be? — 5
a. 2×10^7 m   b. 4×10^{-7} m   c. 6×10^7 m   d. 8×10^{-7} m

__d__ 4. Light from Source C covers an area of 1 m² at a distance of 1 m from the source. At 2 m from the source, an area of 4 m² is lit up. At 4 m from the source, what area will the light from Source C light up? — 2
a. 2 m²   b. 4 m²   c. 8 m²   d. 16 m²

Chapter 19 Light   75

Name_____ Date_____ Score_____

PART 4

Read each question or direction and answer it using complete sentences.

Chapter Goal

1. Describe ultraviolet rays and their effects. — 1

Ultraviolet rays are invisible radiation with frequencies just higher than that of visible light. Ultraviolet rays are the form of radiant energy from the sun that causes skin to tan. Too much ultraviolet radiation can cause a sunburn and can lead to skin cancer.

2. How is color produced in color television sets? — 4

The screens in color television sets contain red, green, and blue dots. To produce different colors, three electron beams are used to light up mixtures of the dots. For example, to produce white in a certain area on the screen, all the dots in that area are lit up equally. To produce yellow, red and green dots are lit up equally. By changing the intensity of the electron beams, various shades of colors can be produced.

3. Explain the transfer of energy that takes place in the photoelectric effect. — 6

When a photon strikes an electron in a metal, the energy of the photon can be transferred to the electron. When the electron gains this energy, it escapes from the metal. However, the photon must have a certain minimum amount of energy before the energy can be transferred to the electron. If the photon does not have this amount, its energy cannot be transferred to the electron. The electron remains on the metal.

Chapter 19 Light   76

19

LIGHT

The questions in the CHAPTER TEST are based on these Chapter Goals.

1. Identify the parts of the electromagnetic spectrum, and distinguish between different types of radiant energy.

2. Compare objects that are transparent, translucent, and opaque; give evidence for light traveling in a straight-line path, relate the intensity of light to the distance from a light source, and describe three methods used to measure the speed of light.

3. Compare how light reflects from a smooth surface and from a rough surface, predict the path of a light ray as it enters a substance from air, and explain how a rainbow forms.

4. Explain what causes color, and compare producing color by subtraction with producing color by addition.

5. Give examples of the wave behavior of light, explain the cause of diffraction and interference of light, and distinguish between polarized light and ordinary light.

6. Describe the photoelectric effect, compare the effects of intensity and frequency of light on the photoelectric effect, and expain the dual nature of light.

LIGHT

The colors of the rainbow come from light. A prism can be used to separate white light from the sun or from a light bulb into colors. Notice in the photograph that this process causes light rays to bend. To understand how this happens, the properties of light must be investigated.

- *Why does light from the sun appear colorless?*
- *Under what conditions does light produce colors?*
- *What causes the path of a light ray to change?*

19-1 THE ELECTROMAGNETIC SPECTRUM

Visible light is a form of radiant energy. **Radiant energy** is energy that is transferred by electromagnetic waves. These waves are made up of electric and magnetic fields. They do not need matter to carry them. They can travel through a vacuum. Other forms of radiant energy are *radio waves, infrared rays, ultraviolet rays, X rays,* and *gamma rays.* The different forms of electromagnetic waves make up the **electromagnetic spectrum.**

Electromagnetic waves are transverse waves. Recall that a transverse wave vibrates at right angles to the direction in which the wave travels. The wavelength is the distance from one point on a wave to a corresponding point on the next wave. The frequency is the number of waves that pass a given point each second.

As you can see in Figure 19-1 on the next page, each form of radiant energy has a different frequency and wavelength. Radio waves have the lowest frequency and longest wavelength. Radio waves are used in communications and broadcasting. Television waves are included in the part of the spectrum called radio waves.

Infrared rays are invisible heat radiation. They are shorter in wavelength and higher in frequency than are radio waves. Sunlight feels warm because of the infrared rays given off by the sun. Heat lamps used to warm rooms also give off infrared rays.

After completing this section, you will be able to

- **identify** the parts of the electromagnetic spectrum.
- **distinguish** between the different forms of radiant energy.

The key terms in this section are
electromagnetic spectrum
radiant energy

---

2 CONCEPT DEVELOPMENT

Background   All forms of radiant energy travel at a speed of about 300 million meters per second.

Teaching Tip   Use Figure 19-1 to point out the different frequencies and wavelengths that characterize the different forms of radiant energy.

Thinking Skills

interpreting charts
Have students observe Figure 19-1. Then have students identify the form of electromagnetic radiation when given a specified wavelength.

Demonstration   To show that infrared radiation is invisible heat radiation, hold a thermometer in the path of the rays of an infrared heat lamp. For a spectacular effect, focus the rays with a curved mirror, and cook a marshmallow.

3 REVIEW/REINFORCEMENT

1. Radio waves, microwaves, infrared rays, visible light, ultraviolet rays, gamma rays.
2. There are differences in frequencies and wavelengths.
3. Radio waves—used in communication and broadcasting; infrared rays—invisible heat radiation; visible light—can be seen, is made up of colors; ultraviolet rays—cause skin to tan; X rays—used to photograph the inside of the human body; gamma rays—given off by radioactive substances.

Challenge   Ultraviolet rays can penetrate the cloud cover.

Poster

The Teacher Resource Package includes a poster that shows the electromagnetic spectrum. You may wish to display this poster in your classroom.

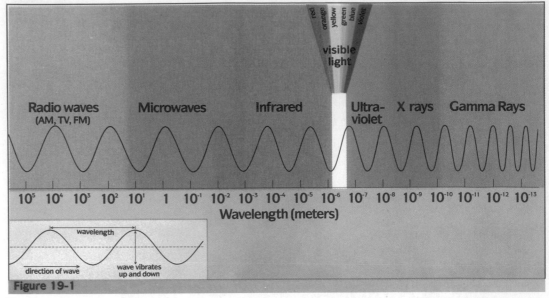

Figure 19-1

The electromagnetic spectrum.

As shown in Figure 19-1, visible light makes up only a small part of the electromagnetic spectrum. This light is the only form of radiant energy that people can see. Much of what people learn comes from light reaching their eyes. In addition, plants need light to grow.

Ultraviolet rays are a type of invisible radiation with a frequency just higher than that of visible light. Ultraviolet rays are the form of radiant energy that comes from the sun and causes skin to tan. Too much ultraviolet radiation can cause sunburn and can lead to skin cancer.

Higher in frequency than the ultraviolet rays are X rays and gamma rays. X rays and gamma rays are a form of radiant energy that can pass through most substances. X rays are often used by doctors and dentists to photograph the inside parts of the human body. Gamma rays are more penetrating than X rays. Gamma rays are given off by radioactive substances.

REVIEW

1. What are the parts of the electromagnetic spectrum?
2. How do the parts of the electromagnetic spectrum differ?
3. What are some characteristics of each form of radiant energy in the electromagnetic spectrum?

CHALLENGE Explain why it is possible to get a tan or sunburn on a cloudy day.

19-2 HOW LIGHT TRAVELS

People can see an object only when light coming from it enters their eyes. Objects that are seen either give off their own light or reflect light. An object that produces its own light is called a *luminous object*. Examples of luminous objects are the sun, stars, and electric lights.

An object that reflects light is called an *illuminated object*. An illuminated object can be seen only when light from a light source falls upon it. Some of this light is reflected from its surface. It is this light that is seen. Most of the things you see are illuminated objects. For example, this book reflects light from the lights in the room or from light that comes through the windows. Other examples of illuminated objects are the moon and the planets. What light source illuminates them?[1]

TRANSMISSION OF LIGHT

In order for light to reach your eyes, it passes through, or is transmitted by, the air. Only a very small part of the light is absorbed. Therefore, an object can be seen clearly through the air. A material that allows almost all light to pass through is described as **transparent** (trans PAIR uhnt). Air, glass, and still water are examples of transparent materials.

Some objects transmit only some light. A material that allows only some light to pass through is described as **translucent** (trans LOO suhnt). An object seen through a translucent object may appear distorted. Examples of translucent objects are wax paper, the frosted glass of a light bulb, and some plastics.

Most objects do not transmit light. A material that does not allow light to pass through is described as **opaque** (oh PAYK). When light falls on an opaque object, usually some of the light is reflected and some is absorbed. Bricks, wood, and metal are opaque.

Have you ever seen the beam of light coming from the movie projector in a darkened movie theater? Or have you seen the powerful beam of light coming from a searchlight? If so, you have observed one of the properties of light—that it travels in a straight line.

If an opaque object is placed in front of a light source, the space behind the object becomes dark. The dark space behind the object is called a shadow. A shadow forms because light travels in a straight line and does not bend around the corners of opaque objects. Thus you can see an object only if it is in your direct line of sight.

After completing this section, you will be able to

- **compare** objects that are transparent, translucent, and opaque.
- **give evidence** that light travels in a straight-line path.
- **relate** the intensity of light to the distance from the light source.
- **describe** two methods used to measure the speed of light.

The key terms in this section are

| intensity | translucent |
| opaque | transparent |

[1]The sun.

Figure 19-2

Most of the glass in the window is transparent. The colored glass is translucent. The other objects are opaque.

19-2 HOW LIGHT TRAVELS
pages 463–467

OBJECTIVES
Refer to pupil page 463.

VOCABULARY
Key terms: intensity, opaque, translucent, transparent
Other terms: illuminated object, light-year, luminous object

1 MOTIVATION

Obtain from a local window-glass dealer several examples of translucent glass. Bring in other translucent materials, such as wax paper and a plastic bottle. Also have available some examples of transparent materials, such as clear glass, a beaker of water, clear plastic, and a flask full of air. Randomly show the examples to students, and have them classify the examples into two groups. Develop the concept that transparent materials allow almost all light to pass through, but translucent materials allow only some light to pass through.

2 CONCEPT DEVELOPMENT

Demonstration   Use an illuminated Trippensee planetarium to demonstrate how the earth or the moon blocks part of the sun's light to produce an eclipse.

ACTIVITY 20 minutes

PROCESS SKILLS
observing, interpreting data

Preparation Slit the rubber stoppers in advance. Any small one-hole rubber stoppers will do nicely. If stoppers are not available, spring clothespins will make suitable supports for the index cards.

Teaching Tip The hole reference marks are ideal for the illuminated pocket microscope used in the *Activity* on page 476. If an alternate light source is used, the location of the punched holes may have to be changed. Align the index cards perpendicular to the reference line on the paper.

Answers to Procedure
1. A circle of light; the circle of light is larger than the hole in the preceding index card but smaller than the preceding circle of light.
2. A circle of light is seen on the first two index cards only.

Answers to Results and Conclusions
1. When the holes are in line, the light moves through the holes in the index cards.
2. The light did not change its direction when the index cards were moved out of line.
3. No; the holes must be aligned to allow light to pass through all three holes. Light travels in a straight line.

Extension Students may inquire why the circle of light on the 12-cm index card is larger than the circle on the 6-cm index card. Point out that this is an example of diffraction, which will be studied in Section 19-5.

ACTIVITY   What Is the Path of a Light Wave?

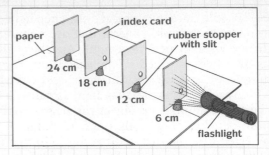

OBJECTIVE
Demonstrate that light travels in a straight line.

MATERIALS
4 index cards, metric ruler, hole punch, 4 slit rubber stoppers, sheet of white paper, small flashlight

PROCEDURE
A. Position an index card lengthwise in front of you. Mark a point 3.2 cm from the bottom and 2 cm from the right side. Hold this and two other cards together and, at the point, punch a hole through the cards.
B. Slide each card into a stopper so it stands upright on a lab table. The holes should be in the lower right corner.
C. Draw a line lengthwise down the middle of a sheet of white paper.
D. Starting from the bottom, mark the line at 6 cm, 12 cm, 18 cm, and 24 cm.
E. On each point at 6 cm, 12 cm, and 18 cm, place a card with a hole. The holes should line up. At the 24-cm mark, put the card with no hole. At the edge of the paper, put a flashlight so the light and holes are lined up as in the figure.

F. Darken the room. Turn on the flashlight. Observe the path of the light.
   1. What is seen on each card?
G. Block the light path by sliding the card at the 12-cm mark along the cross line.
   2. What is seen on each card?

RESULTS AND CONCLUSIONS
1. What evidence is there that light travels in a straight line?
2. How does this activity show that light does not travel around corners?
3. Is there any different way the cards could be arranged so the light beam could pass through the three holes? Explain your answer.

A spectacular example of a shadow is the shadow caused by a solar eclipse. A solar eclipse like the one shown in Figure 19-3 occurs when the moon is in-between the earth and the sun. Then, the moon casts a shadow on the earth. People in areas of the shadow find that light from the sun is either partly or totally blocked by the moon.

Figure 19-3

A shadow forms when an opaque object blocks the path of light (*right*). In a solar eclipse the moon blocks light from the sun, (left).

INTENSITY OF LIGHT

The straight-line path of light can explain how the brightness of a light decreases with distance. The brightness of light is called **intensity**. You probably have observed that a light source seems brighter if it is closer. If you are farther from the source, the light seems dimmer. The sun seems much brighter than other stars because the sun is much closer to the earth than are other stars.

Figure 19-4 shows what happens to light as it spreads out from its source. At a distance of 1 m from the source, an area of 1 m² is lit up. At 2 m from the source, the same amount of light spreads out over an area of 4 m². The light at 2 m covers four times the area as at the 1 m distance. Thus the intensity of the light is one fourth of what it was at 1 m. If the distance from the light source to the surface is increased to 3 m, the same light spreads out over an area of 9 m². Compare the intensity of light at 3 m with what it was at 1 m.[1]

[1]At 3 m the light intensity is one-ninth what it was at 1 m.

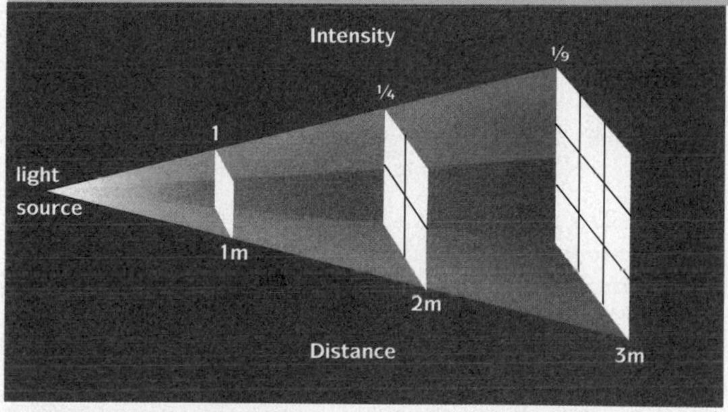

Figure 19-4

The intensity of light decreases as the distance from the light source increases.

SPEED OF LIGHT

Light from the sun travels 150 billion meters to the earth in about 8 minutes. In one second light could travel seven times the distance around the earth. Because light travels so fast, its speed is difficult to measure.

The first evidence that light had a travel time was found by Ole Roemer, a Danish astronomer, in 1676. Roemer had been observing the four large moons of the planet Jupiter. He observed the eclipses that occurred as the moons moved behind Jupiter. He found that the time between eclipses of a particular moon changed with the earth's orbit around the sun. When the earth was farthest from Jupiter, this time was about 1000 seconds longer than when the earth was at its closest point to Jupiter. Roemer concluded

Background   The brightness of light is inversely proportional to the square of the distance from the light source. This inverse square relationship is expressed mathematically as $I = 1/d^2$.

Teaching Tip   To show that the intensity of light decreases as the distance from the light source increases, use a light meter and a slide projector. Move the meter farther from the projector, and note that the reading on the meter decreases.

interpreting diagrams

To understand how the speed of light was measured by Roemer and Michelson, students will have to interpret the diagrams in Figure 19-5A and Figure 19-5B. Ask students to trace the path of light and the motions of the planets in Figure 19-5A. Then ask students to trace the path of light in Figure 19-5B. Point out that the light traveled a measured distance in a measured amount of time. From these measurements the speed of light was calculated.

Background Recent measurements of the speed of light have been made by using the laser as a measuring tool. The most recent calculations show that the speed of light in a vacuum is 2.9979×10^8 m/s.

that the light from this moon was taking longer to reach the earth because the light had farther to travel. Look at Figure 19-5A. The light had to travel 1000 seconds longer to cover the distance of 3×10^{11} m across the earth's orbit. From this information, Roemer calculated the speed of light to be 3×10^8 m/s.

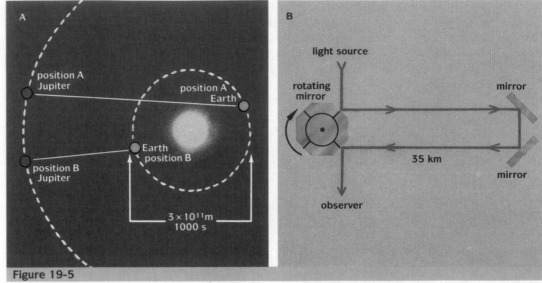

Figure 19-5

Attempts to measure the speed of light were made by Roemer (*A*) and by Michelson (*B*).

In 1926 an American scientist, Albert Michelson, made an accurate measurement of the speed of light on the earth. A diagram of his experiment is shown in Figure 19-5B. A beam of light was reflected from one side of a rotating eight-sided mirror. The beam of light then traveled to another mirror 35 km away. There the beam was reflected again, back to the eight-sided mirror. When the mirror was rotated at just the right speed, it made one eighth of a turn by the time the light returned.

The speed of light is calculated by dividing the distance the light travels by the traveling time. The total distance the light traveled was 70 km. Since the speed of the mirror was known, the time for the light to travel 70 km could be calculated. When the distance of 70 km was divided by the time, the speed of light in air was found to be 2.99×10^8 m/s.

Light travels more slowly in transparent mediums than in a vacuum. Notice in Table 19-1 that light travels more slowly in water than in a vacuum. Light travels more slowly in diamond than in water. What is the speed of light in water and in diamond?[1]

Table 19-1 *Speed of Light*

Medium	Speed of Light (m/s)
Vacuum	3×10^8
Air	2.99×10^8
Ice	2.29×10^8
Water	2.25×10^8
Glass	1.97×10^8
Diamond	1.24×10^8

[1]The speed of light is 2.25×10^8 m/s in water and 1.24×10^8 m/s in diamond.

Because it travels so quickly through space, light takes about 1.3 seconds to travel the distance between the earth and the moon. Light from the sun takes about 8 minutes to reach the earth. From the nearest star other than the sun, light takes a little over 4 years to reach the earth. Light from Polaris, the North Star, travels about 680 years before it reaches the earth.

Because of the great distances between stars in the universe, these distances are usually measured in light-years. A *light-year* is the distance that light travels in one year. Table 19-2 shows the distance in light-years of some stars from the earth. Which star is closer to the earth, Betelgeuse or Polaris?[1]

[1]Betelgeuse.

Table 19-2 *Distance to Some Stars*

Star's Name	Distance in Light-years
Proxima Centauri	4.3
Sirius	8.6
Vega	26.5
Betelgeuse	520.0
Polaris	680.0
Rigel	900.0

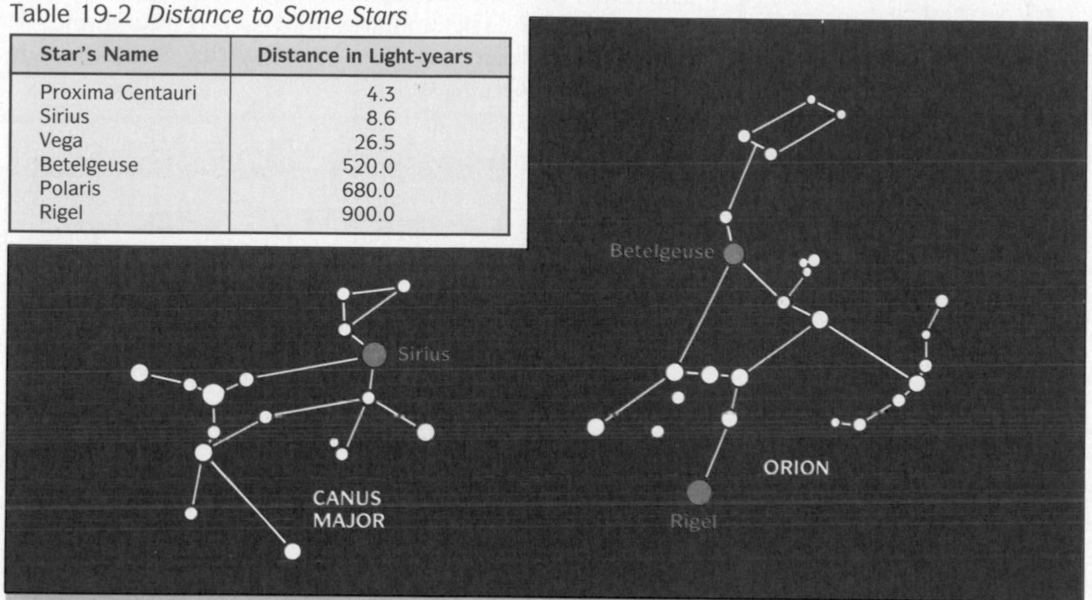

Figure 19-6

Distances to stars vary greatly. Proxima Centauri is the star that is closest to the earth.

REVIEW

1. What are the differences between transparent, translucent, and opaque objects?
2. What evidence shows that light travels in a straight path?
3. What happens to the intensity of light as the distance from the light source increases?
4. Describe two ways to calculate the speed of light?

CHALLENGE It takes 5 years for light from a certain star to reach the earth. In kilometers, how far away is this star from the earth?

Teaching Tip To help students comprehend the speed of light, ask them to calculate the time it takes for light to travel around the equator of the earth or between the earth and another planet.

Background A light-year is equal to approximately 5.9×10^{12} miles, or 9.5×10^{12} km.

REVIEW/REINFORCEMENT

1. Transparent—almost all light passes through; translucent—some light passes through; opaque—no light passes through.
2. Shadows have the same shape as the objects blocking the light.
3. The intensity of light decreases as the distance from the light source increases.
4. Roemer based his computation on the time needed for light to travel from a moon of Jupiter to the earth; two measurements were made, from opposite sides of the earth's orbit. Michelson reflected light from an eight-sided mirror; the computation of the speed of light was based on the speed of rotation of the mirror and the distance the light traveled.

Challenge 4.75×10^{13} km.

19-3 REFLECTION AND REFRACTION
pages 468–472

Refer to pupil page 468.

OBJECTIVES
Refer to pupil page 468.

VOCABULARY
Key terms: incident ray, index of refraction, law of reflection, reflected ray, reflection, refraction

Other terms: angle of incidence, angle of reflection, angle of refraction, dispersion, normal line

---

1 MOTIVATION

There are many good filmstrips that deal with reflection and refraction of light. Use one of these filmstrips to introduce this section. Ask students to note the key terms used in the filmstrip and in this chapter.

2 CONCEPT DEVELOPMENT

Teaching Tip   Point out that most things we see are visible to us because of reflected light. For example, the page of a textbook is visible because light is reflected from the page to the eye.

Demonstration   Show reflection by building a periscope using a long cardboard tube and two mirrors. Cut openings at opposite ends of the tube. Mount a plane mirror at an angle of 45° with respect to each opening; the light entering one hole will be reflected by the mirrors and shine out the other hole. Students can view objects around corners with this instrument. Ask the class if a periscope bends light around corners. (No; the light is reflected from the image to a mirror to a second mirror to the eye.)

19-3 REFLECTION AND REFRACTION

After completing this section, you will be able to

- **compare** how light reflects from a smooth surface and from a rough surface.
- **predict** the path of a light ray as it moves between mediums.
- **explain** how a rainbow forms.

The key terms in this section are
incident ray
index of refraction
law of reflection
reflected ray
reflection
refraction

Recall from Chapter 18 that when waves reach a surface, their path may be changed. Like sound waves or water waves, light waves can be reflected or refracted.

REFLECTION

Both a wall and a mirror can reflect light. **Reflection** is the bouncing back of light rays from a surface. In addition, a mirror can reflect an image of an object facing it. But a wall cannot reflect an image of an object. How is the reflection from a mirror different from the reflection from a wall?

Imagine the beam of light to be made up of single, individual rays of light. To see how a ray is reflected, look at Figure 19-7. The light ray that strikes the surface is called the **incident ray**. The light ray that is reflected is called the **reflected ray**.

Figure 19-7

When a light ray strikes a surface, the angle of incidence equals the angle of reflection.

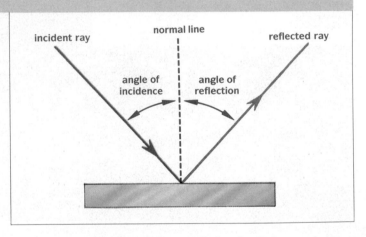

To measure the angles made by the light rays, a line is drawn perpendicular to the surface where the reflection takes place. This line is called the *normal line*. The angle between the incident ray and the normal line is called the *angle of incidence*. The angle between the reflected ray and the normal line is called the *angle of reflection*.

When a light ray strikes a smooth surface, the reflected ray leaves the surface at the same angle at which the incident ray hits the surface. The reflected ray follows the law of reflection. The **law of reflection** states that when a ray of light is reflected from a smooth surface, the angle of reflection is equal to the angle of incidence.

re- (back)
flectere (to bend)

ACTIVITY   What Is the Law of Reflection?

OBJECTIVE
Demonstrate the behavior of a reflected light ray.

MATERIALS
sheet of white paper (21 cm × 28 cm), metric ruler, protractor, cardboard (30 cm × 30 cm), 2 straight pins, small mirror, slit rubber stopper

PROCEDURE

A. Draw a line across the middle of a sheet of paper. Mark the midpoint as point *O*.

B. Place the vertex of a protractor on point *O*. Mark point *A* at 90°. Draw line segment *AO* by connecting point *A* and point *O*. Extend the line segment 15 cm from point *O*.

C. Using the protractor, mark point *B* at 30° to the right of line segment *AO*, as shown. Draw a line segment *BO*. Extend line segment *BO* 15 cm from point *O*. This line will represent an incident light ray.
   1. What does angle *BOA* represent?

D. Place the paper on a piece of cardboard. Insert a straight pin on line *BO*, about 10 cm from point *O*.

E. Slide a mirror into the slit of a rubber stopper. Stand the mirror so that the back of the mirror is lined up with the line across the paper. Position the center of the mirror on line *AO*.

F. Stand to the left of line *AO* and locate the image of the pin in the mirror. Adjust your position until the image of the pin and the image of line *BO* are lined up in front of you. Place a second pin directly in front of these images about 10 cm from point *O*. Mark this as point *C*.

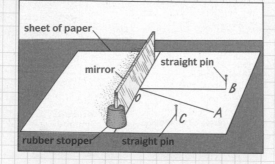

sheet of paper
mirror
straight pin
rubber stopper
straight pin

G. Remove both pins and the mirror. Draw line segment *CO*.
   2. What does angle *COA* represent?

H. Using the protractor, measure angle *COA*.

RESULTS AND CONCLUSIONS
1. How do angles *COA* and *BOA* compare?
2. Compare the angle of incidence of a light ray to its angle of reflection.

ACTIVITY 25 minutes

PROCESS SKILLS
observing, measuring, recording data

Preparation Slit the rubber stoppers before class. A #5 or larger one-hole rubber stopper will work well. If rubber stoppers are not available, modeling clay or spring clothespins can be used to support the mirror.

Teaching Tip Large dissecting pins work better than do smaller sewing pins. Students sometimes have difficulty lining up the pins; it may be necessary for these students to try the exercise one more time.

Answers to Procedure
1. The angle of incidence.
2. The angle of reflection.

Answers to Results and Conclusions
1. The angles should be equal.
2. They should be the same.

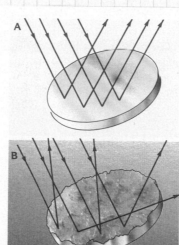

Figure 19-8

Reflection by a smooth surface (*A*) and by a rough surface (*B*).

In Figure 19-8*A* a beam of light is being reflected from a smooth surface, such as a mirror. The incident light rays are parallel. Notice that the light rays follow the law of reflection. Each ray of light is reflected so that its angle of reflection is equal to its angle of incidence. Thus the rays remain parallel after they are reflected. The reflected rays form a pattern, and an image can be seen.

In Figure 19-8*B* a beam of light is being reflected from a rough surface, such as a wall. While a ceiling or wall may feel smooth to the touch, its surface actually is rough. The surface of this page, for example, is rough. It is made up of millions of tiny surfaces facing in different directions. The incident light rays are parallel. When these light rays strike a rough surface, each one follows the law of reflection. Because of the many different surfaces, the light rays are reflected in many different directions. The reflected rays do not form a pattern so no image is seen.

Background　At sunset the bottom of the sun often appears to be flattened. This happens because the rays from the bottom of the sun pass through a thicker portion of the atmosphere than do the rays from the upper part of the sun. The two different thicknesses of atmosphere result in refraction, which produces the flattened-bottom appearance.

REFRACTION

Figure 19-9A shows a light ray passing through a piece of glass. Notice that the light ray changes direction. The change in direction of a light ray as it passes from one medium to another is called **refraction**. The *angle of incidence* is the angle between the incident light ray and the normal line. The *angle of refraction* is the angle between the refracted light ray and the normal line. Notice that the angle of incidence is greater than the angle of refraction. Notice also that refraction occurs again as the light ray leaves the glass. In this case the angle of incidence is less than the angle of refraction.

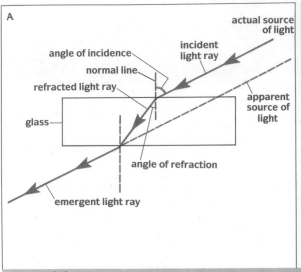

Figure 19-9

A light ray is refracted when it passes from one medium to another (*A*). Refraction of light causes these pencils to appear bent (*B*).

The light ray that leaves the glass is not on its original path. Instead, it is on a path that is parallel to the original path. When you see the light ray that leaves the glass, you cannot tell what the original path of light was. Thus you may "see" an object as distorted or in the wrong place.

Refraction of light can be seen when a pencil is placed at an angle in water. When seen from above, the pencil appears bent. This is because the light coming from the pencil bends as it passes from the water to the air. But light from the part of the pencil above water does not bend. Above the water, the light passes through only one medium, the air.

Refraction of light is caused by a change in the speed of light. Recall that the speed of light varies in different mediums. Thus the amount of refraction of light is dif-

Review and Skill Masters

SKILL, page 116. See page 459c in this book for answers.

SCIENCE PUZZLER

In the middle of the day, when the sun is high in the sky, the sun appears almost white. Later in the day, as the sun moves lower it turns yellow, then orange. Just before the sun drops below the horizon, the sun looks red. What causes the change in the color?

ferent in each medium. A measure of the refraction of light in a medium as the light enters from air or a vacuum is called the **index of refraction.**

The indexes of refraction for different mediums are shown in Table 19-3. When entering from air, light bends more in mediums with large indexes of refraction than in those with smaller indexes of refraction. For example, light bends more when it passes from air into glass than when it passes from air into water. In which medium shown in Table 19-3 would light bend the most as it entered from air?[1]

Refraction also varies with the color of the light. As light enters a medium, each color of light bends a different amount. In 1666, Isaac Newton proved this by showing that sunlight is made up of different colors of light. He passed a beam of sunlight through a prism. The prism

Table 19-3 *Index of Refraction*

Medium	Index of Refraction
Vacuum	1.00
Air	1.00029
Ice	1.31
Water	1.333
Glass	1.52
Diamond	2.42

[1]Diamond.

Figure 19-10

Refraction occurs as light enters and leaves a prism.

Thinking Skills

comparing
Have students study Table 19-3. Ask which substance has the greatest index of refraction and which has the least. Ask students to compare the indexes of refraction of ice and diamond.

Enrichment   Have students use the information in Table 19-3 to make diagrams that show the bending of light as it passes from one medium to another.

Puzzler   The apparent color of the sun depends upon the amount of atmosphere through which the light must pass. Morning and night the light passes through thick layers of atmosphere, but at noon the light passes through a thinner layer of atmosphere. Red light, which has a long wavelength, is scattered least as it passes through thick layers of atmosphere. The colors with shorter wavelengths are scattered through the air. Therefore the sun appears red in the morning and evening. At noon the least amount of scattering occurs, so the sun appears white.

Demonstration To demonstrate the dispersion of light, shine a beam of light from a slide projector through a prism. Project the colors onto a screen. Point out that the colors are—in order—red, orange, yellow, green, blue, and violet. Violet light has the highest frequency and is bent the most. Red light has the lowest frequency and is bent the least. Align a second prism with the light of the first and show students that the colors are put back together to form white light.

Enrichment The beauty of a diamond is the result of reflection, refraction, and dispersion. Ask students to research the different cuts of diamonds and to determine the effect that cutting these gems has on reflection and refraction.

Background In order for a rainbow to be visible, water droplets in the air must be in front of the observer and the sun must be behind the observer. A water droplet will act as a prism if the angle between the eye of the observer, the water droplet, and the sun is approximately 42°. The combined dispersion effect of many water prisms is a rainbow.

3 REVIEW/REINFORCEMENT

1. The rays of light reflected from a mirror remain parallel after reflection, so an image is formed; the rays of light reflected from a white sheet of paper are scattered in many different directions, so no image is formed.
2. If light enters glass or water from air, the light is bent, or refracted.
3. Water droplets in the sky act as prisms to separate sunlight into the colors of the rainbow.

Challenge The higher index of refraction of diamond.

caused the light to separate into the different colors of the spectrum. Newton then passed these colors through a second prism. The second prism put the colors back together to form white light.

As you can see in Figure 19-11, the colors produced by a prism are red, orange, yellow, green, blue, and violet. The process of separating white light into colors is called *dispersion*. Violet light is bent the most. Red light is bent the least.

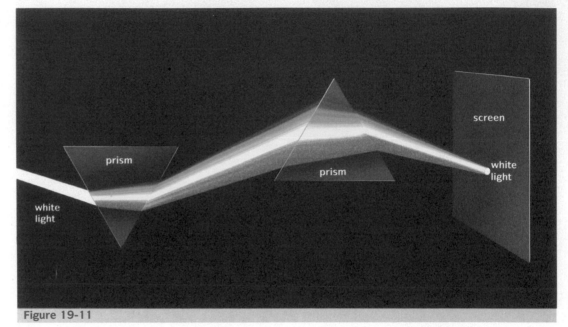

Figure 19-11

Newton's experiment proved that sunlight is made up of different colors of light.

In addition to glass, other materials can also cause dispersion. For example, water drops in the air can disperse sunlight into colors that form a rainbow. As in glass, in water the different colors in sunlight bend different amounts. The colors of the rainbow are the same as the colors produced by a prism.

REVIEW

1. How does the reflection of light from a mirror compare to the reflection of light from a white sheet of paper?
2. What happens to the path of light as it enters glass or water?
3. How does a rainbow form?

CHALLENGE What causes sparkling colors in diamond but not in glass?

19-4 COLOR

Objects can be seen because of the light they transmit or reflect. But what causes them to have color? What causes leaves to look green or roses to look red?

The color of objects comes from the colors in light. Light from the sun appears white in color. But this light is made up of many colors. Three of these colors, green, red, and blue, are the *primary colors* of light. These colors can be separated from each other through the use of filters. A **filter** is a transparent or translucent substance that allows only certain colors of light to pass through it.

A colored piece of glass is an example of a filter. Suppose a beam of white light enters a piece of green glass. Notice in Figure 19-12A that the light that leaves the glass is green. When a beam of white light enters a piece of blue glass, the light leaving the glass is blue. And when a beam of white light enters a piece of red glass, the light leaving the glass is red. The color of light transmitted by the colored glass is the same color as the glass.

After completing this section, you will be able to

- **explain** what causes color.
- **compare** producing color by subtraction with producing color by addition.

The key term in this section is **filter**

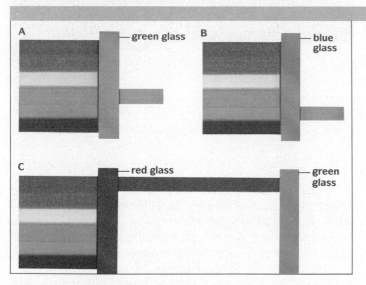

Figure 19-12

Filters absorb some colors of light and transmit others.

When light enters a transparent or translucent object, only the color of that object is transmitted. The other colors of light are absorbed. Suppose a red filter and a green filter are placed in the path of a beam of white light. Notice in Figure 19-12C that a beam of red light comes through the red filter. When the red light strikes the green filter, no light passes through. The red light is absorbed by the green filter.

OBJECTIVES
Refer to pupil page 473.

VOCABULARY
Key term: filter
Other terms: color addition, color subtraction, complementary colors, primary colors

1 MOTIVATION

Arrange to use the school stage and lighting system. Prepare various spotlights with different-colored gels, including white. Take students to the auditorium. Project the different-colored spotlights onto different areas of the stage. Have selected students move from one pool of colored light to another. Ask the other students to observe the changes in the colors of clothing as students move around the stage. Have students record their observations, and discuss them upon returning to the classroom.

2 CONCEPT DEVELOPMENT

Background   The primary light colors are green, red, and blue. The primary pigment colors are yellow, red, and blue.

Background   Light that has only one frequency or wavelength is called monochromatic. In actual practice it is virtually impossible to have only one wavelength. Therefore, light with a very narrow band of wavelengths is referred to as being monochromatic.

Teaching Tip   Colored filters are readily available from scientific supply houses. Another source of filters is a theatrical or stage supply dealer that sells colored gels. Colored overhead transparencies also serve as good filters.

Thinking Skills

predicting

Using the principles of color subtraction, have students predict the color of an opaque object when it is illuminated by a particular color of light.

Thinking Skills

inferring

Ask students why the color of the clothing they buy can appear to be different inside the store than outside the store. They should infer that the store lights may contain some coloration and may not be white light. Thus the color of the clothing appears to be different in natural light.

Demonstration   To show subtraction of certain colors, project a colored overhead transparency directly onto a screen. Hold pieces of different colored sheets of paper directly in front of the screen, and note the absorption of some colors and the reflection of others.

Enrichment   In nature, animals often change color with the seasons or according to the environment. Ask students to research this phenomenon, to identify some animals that change colors, and to explain to the class why and how these color changes take place.

Background   If a piece of green glass is finely ground, it will appear white. This appearance is due to the increase of surface area. As the surface area of the glass increases, more light is reflected than is absorbed. When the glass becomes a fine powder, all the light is reflected, and the glass appears to be white.

The color of an object that is transparent or translucent is caused by that object absorbing certain colors of light. The process of producing a color by absorbing other colors of light is called *color subtraction*. When you see a green pane of glass, the glass is absorbing all colors of light except green. Thus green is seen because all the other colors in light are subtracted.

The color of an opaque object is also caused by the process of subtraction. When white light shines upon a red rose, the rose absorbs or subtracts all the colors in the white light except red. The rose appears red because only red light is reflected.

Figure 19-13

The color of light reflected by an object is the color that is seen. All other colors are absorbed.

The subtraction of certain colors of light by an opaque object can also be shown by the following example. When white light or blue light falls on a sheet of blue paper, the paper looks blue. But if only red light or green light falls upon a sheet of blue paper, the paper looks black. Black is produced by the absence of light. The paper looks black because it absorbs the red light or green light and no light is reflected.

White objects do not subtract any colors of light. Instead, they reflect all colors of light. For example, if blue light falls upon a sheet of white paper, the paper appears blue because it reflects blue light. Similarly, if red light falls upon a sheet of white paper, the paper appears red because it reflects red light. Why does a sheet of white paper appear green under green light?[1]

[1]Only green light strikes the paper. White paper reflects this light and looks green.

Notice in Figure 19-14 that changing the color of light on a stage will cause the color of the dancer's costume to also appear to change. In white light the costume is white. In blue light, notice that the costume appears blue. In yellow light, notice that the costume appears yellow. Many other colors are possible depending on the combinations of colors of light used.

Mixing colors of light causes the colors to combine. The process of combining colors of light to produce other colors is called *color addition*. Color addition occurs when two or more separate light sources of different colors shine on the same object. If red, green, and blue beams of light are mixed, white-colored light is produced.

Figure 19-14

Changes in lighting cause the dancer's costume to appear to change color.

PROCESS SKILLS
observing, inferring

Preparation Have available plenty of newspaper color comics, and make sure they are recent enough not to have begun to fade or discolor.

Teaching Tip Students may need some assistance in finding yellow dots, as they are occasionally difficult to find on newsprint.

Answers to Procedure
1. Red dots.
2. Blue dots.
3. Yellow dots.
4. Purple.
5. Orange.
6. Green.
7. Brown.

Answers to Results and Conclusions
1. Red, yellow, or blue.
2. All others except black and white.
3. The colors are produced by subtracting some colors of light and reflecting the others.

ACTIVITY   How Are Colors Printed?

OBJECTIVE
Demonstrate how colors are combined in the printing process.

MATERIALS
newspaper color comics, illuminated pocket microscope (30×)

PROCEDURE
A. Examine a patch of red under a microscope.
   1. What do you observe?
B. Examine a patch of blue under the microscope.
   2. What do you observe?
C. Examine a patch of yellow under the microscope.
   3. What do you observe?
D. Using the microscope, find a mix of red and blue dots.
   4. What color does the mix produce?
E. Using the microscope, find a mix of red and yellow dots.
   5. What color does the mix produce?
F. Using the microscope, find a mix of blue and yellow dots.
   6. What color does the mix produce?
G. Using the microscope, find a mix of red, yellow, and blue dots.
   7. What color does the mix produce?

RESULTS AND CONCLUSIONS
1. Which colors are produced from only one ink?
2. Which colors are produced from more than one ink?
3. Explain why color printing is a color subtraction process.

Color addition is shown in Figure 19-15. A blue beam of light mixed with a green beam of light produces cyan-colored light. Similarly, addition occurs when a red beam of light is mixed with a blue beam of light, producing magenta-colored light. And when red light and green light are added, yellow-colored light is produced.

The process of addition of colors is used to produce the color in color television sets. The screens in these sets contain red, green, and blue dots. To produce different colors, three electron beams are used to light up mixtures of the different colored dots. For example, to produce white in a certain area on the screen, all the dots in that area are lit up equally. To produce blue, only the blue dots are lit up. To produce magenta, red and blue dots are lit up equally. By changing the intensity of the electron beams, various shades of colors can be produced. For example, to get pink, all the dots are lit up. But the electron beam striking the red dots is stronger than the other two electron beams.

Just as primary colors can be combined in color addition, secondary colors can be combined in color subtraction. Figure 19-16 shows how the color photographs used in this book were printed. Four inks are used—cyan, magenta, yellow, and black. Each secondary color reflects two primary colors. For example, cyan reflects blue and green. Cyan absorbs, or subtracts, red. Yellow reflects red and green, and subtracts blue. Where cyan and yellow

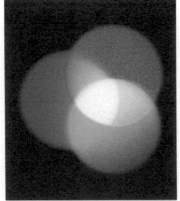

Figure 19-15

In color addition, beams of light are combined.

inks overlap you see a green color. Green is the only color that is reflected by both cyan ink and yellow ink. Magenta ink reflects red and blue, and subtracts green. What color is seen in areas where magenta ink and cyan ink overlap?[1]

[1]Blue.

By varying the proportions of the inks, it is possible to produce many different shades of color. Paints are mixed in a similar way. The more paints you put in a mixture, the darker the mixture becomes. The mixture subtracts more and more light until none is reflected. What color do you see then?[2]

[2]Black.

Figure 19-16

In the four-color printing process, inks in the colors of magenta (A), cyan (B), yellow (C), and black (D) are combined to produce a multicolored picture (E).

REVIEW

1. Where does the color in transparent, translucent, and opaque objects come from?
2. How does producing color by subtraction compare with producing color by addition?

CHALLENGE Certain pairs of colors are called *complementary colors* because they add to form white light. Each primary color has a secondary color as its complement. List the three pairs of complementary colors.

Teaching Tip Commercially prepared filmstrips, transparencies, and charts dealing with color are available from scientific supply houses and audiovisual dealers. Use these resources in class to reinforce the concepts in this chapter.

Thinking Skills

interpreting diagrams
Have students analyze Figure 19-16. Point out that as each set of colors overlays the other, more color is subtracted. Ask students why some areas show a high concentration of dots but other areas show widely spaced dots.

3 REVIEW/REINFORCEMENT

1. The color comes from the colors in light. Transparent, translucent, or opaque objects absorb certain colors; the colors not absorbed are visible to the eye.
2. Color by subtraction removes some colors while leaving others visible; color by addition is the result of combining colors of light to produce other colors.

Challenge

Primary Colors	Complements
Red	Blue
Green	Red
Blue	Green

19-5 THE WAVE NATURE OF LIGHT

pages 478–481

19-5 THE WAVE NATURE OF LIGHT

OBJECTIVES
Refer to pupil page 478.

VOCABULARY
Key terms: diffraction, interference, polarization, wave model of light

Other terms: diffraction grating, polarized light, polarizing filter

---

1 MOTIVATION

Review the properties of waves. To demonstrate the wave behavior of light, use a mirror to show reflection and a prism to show refraction. Emphasize that since all waves exhibit the properties of reflection and refraction, light can be thought of as a wave.

After completing this section, you will be able to

- **give examples** of the wave behavior of light.
- **explain** the causes of diffraction and interference of light.
- **distinguish** between polarized light and ordinary light.

The key terms in this section are
diffraction
interference
polarization
wave model of light

Most of the sun's energy that reaches the earth is in the form of visible light. From this it is known that light carries energy. But how light carries energy was not known until this century.

WAVE MODEL OF LIGHT

When Isaac Newton showed that white light is a mixture of colors, some scientists suggested that light is made up of waves. These scientists believed that each color of light is caused by a different wavelength of light. The idea that light is made up of light waves is called the **wave model of light**.

The wave model of light is supported by the fact that light is reflected and refracted. Recall that reflection and refraction are properties of waves. When light waves strike a surface, they bounce back. Light refracts, or bends, when it enters a different substance and changes speed.

In 1800, Thomas Young, an English scientist, observed that light also shows the wave property of interference. **Interference** of light occurs when two light waves meet and add or cancel each other. In his experiment Young was able to produce two identical beams of light. He passed a single light beam of one color through two narrow slits. The slits produced two identical beams of light. When the two beams of light reached a screen, they did not form a single bright line. Instead, they produced a pattern made up of bright and dark lines. The size and shape of the lines in the interference pattern depend on the light source.

Figure 19-17

The dark and bright areas are caused by interference of light.

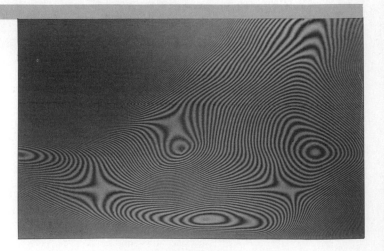

The wave model of light explains that each beam of light is made up of many tiny waves with crests and troughs. A bright line is produced where the wave crests in one beam meet the wave crests in the other beam. These waves reinforce each other. A dark line is produced where the wave crests in one beam meet the wave troughs in the other. These waves cancel each other.

The wave model of light also explains the diffraction of light. **Diffraction** of light is the spreading out of a light wave as it passes through a small opening or around a small object. A close-up photograph of the edge of a shadow is shown in Figure 19-18A. Notice that the shadow does not have a sharp edge. The wave model explains that as light waves strike the edge of an object, they bend around it. The bending of the light waves produces some light where the shadow should begin.

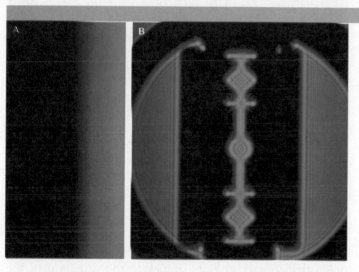

Figure 19-18

Diffraction of light can be seen at the edge of a shadow (A) or at a narrow slit (B).

Life Science Library / LIGHT AND VISION Photograph by Ken Kay © 1966 Time-Life Books, Inc.

Diffraction of light can also be shown if a beam of light is passed through a small opening. Figure 19-18B shows the diffraction of light through the center of a razor blade. The dark and light bands that you see are caused by interference between diffracted light rays. However, diffraction is best seen when the size of the opening is about the same size as the wavelength of light, about 10^{-6} m.

A piece of film containing small openings that can diffract light is called a diffraction grating. A *diffraction grating* is a transparent plate made of plastic or glass with closely spaced parallel lines cut into it. A typical diffraction grating has about 600 lines per millimeter.

Background   Diffraction can be a detriment in microscopy. If the size of an object is less than the wavelength of light, diffraction causes the object to become invisible. To compensate for this phenomenon, an electron microscope is used. The beam of electrons directed at the object has a shorter wavelength than does the visible light.

Teaching Tip   Do not touch the film portion of a diffraction grating. Always hold the grating by the frame.

Thinking Skills

comparing
Ask students to compare a diffraction grating and a prism. While both have the ability to separate white light into colors, dispersion takes place in a prism, and diffraction takes place in a diffraction grating.

Demonstration   Show diffraction gratings to the class. Pass a beam of light through the gratings, and project the light onto a screen. Emphasize the fact that the colors seen are the result of diffraction, not of dispersion as in a prism. Demonstrate that a diffraction grating can be used in a spectrometer in much the same way as a prism.

Enrichment Challenge students to solve this problem: Two apartment buildings are facing each other. Between them is a small, beautiful park. The residents of each apartment building want to be able to see the park through their windows but do not want their neighbors across the park to be able to see them through their windows. What is a possible solution? (Polarize the windows in one apartment building vertically, and polarize the windows in the other apartment building horizontally.)

Teaching Tip Polarizing filters are available from scientific supply houses, but polarized sunglasses work equally well for demonstrations. A set of polarized lenses from a local optometrist or a set of clip-on polarized sunglasses can also be used.

Tie-in/Language Arts Ask students to do a biographical study of Edwin Land, famous for inventing the Polaroid camera. Have students find out about other optical inventions that Land perfected.

When white light is passed through the slits of a diffraction grating, the light spreads out. The waves of light from one slit cross over waves from other slits, and interference takes place. Because each color of light has a different wavelength, each color has its own interference pattern. Thus a diffraction grating causes white light to separate into the colors of the spectrum.

Figure 19-19

The diffraction grating shown has separated white light into the colors of the spectrum.

POLARIZATION

Light has the properties of a transverse wave. Recall that transverse waves vibrate at right angles to the wave's direction of travel. For example, when waves travel along the surface of water, the particles of water move up and down. Like water waves, light waves also show properties of a transverse wave.

Recall that light is made up of electric and magnetic fields that vibrate at right angles to the direction of the path of the light. Unlike water waves, which vibrate in one direction, light waves vibrate in many directions. However, by passing light through certain substances, light with vibrations in only one direction can be produced.

Light that vibrates in only one direction is called *polarized light*. The process of producing light with electromagnetic vibrations in one direction is called **polarization** (poh luhr uh ZAY shuhn). A substance that causes polarization of light is called a *polarizing filter*.

Polarized light looks the same as ordinary light. However, polarized light can be blocked by a polarizing filter. Blocking polarized light can be compared to blocking a wave in a rope. Suppose a rope is put through a narrow vertical slit. As you can see in Figure 19-20A, only waves that vibrate up and down would pass through. Now suppose the rope is also put through a narrow horizontal slit. Notice that the vertical wave cannot pass through.

Polarizing filters are substances that contain long chains of molecules. These chains act like narrow slits, allowing only vibrations in one specific direction to pass through. Suppose two polarizing filters are set up so that light waves with vertical vibrations can pass through both filters. Then one polarizing filter is turned so that only light waves with horizontal vibrations can pass through. As you can see in Figure 19-20B, the vertical vibrations would not pass through. Thus no light would pass through.

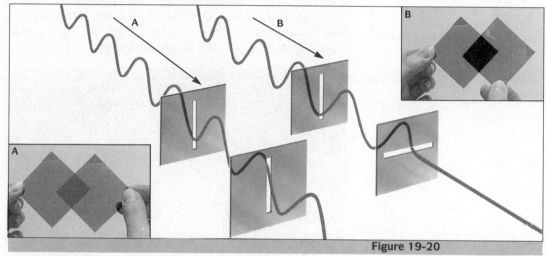

Figure 19-20

Polarized light waves vibrate in only one direction. If a polarizing filter is not lined up with the light waves, the light will be blocked.

Polarizing filters are used to reduce glare, or the light reflected from objects. The filters can reduce glare because reflected light is polarized. The filters reduce glare by removing some of the reflected light. Photographers often use polarized lenses on cameras to reduce glare. Some sunglasses use polarized lenses to reduce glare caused by reflected sunlight.

REVIEW

1. What are the wave properties of light?
2. How are interference and diffraction of light caused?
3. What is the difference between polarized light and ordinary light?

CHALLENGE Is the light from a rainbow polarized? Explain your answer.

Background   Light from the sun is not polarized. However, light reflected from the earth contains mostly horizontal waves. These horizontal waves cause glare. Polarized sunglasses block out the horizontal waves and allow the vertical waves to pass through.

3 REVIEW/REINFORCEMENT

1. Dispersion, reflection, refraction, interference, diffraction, and polarization.
2. Interference of light occurs when two light waves meet and then add to or cancel each other; diffraction of light is the spreading out of a light wave as it passes through a small opening or around a small object.
3. Polarized light vibrates in only one direction; ordinary light vibrates in many directions.

Challenge   Light from a rainbow is polarized; if a polarizing filter is lined up opposite the vibrations of the rainbow, the rainbow will not be seen.

19-6 THE PARTICLE NATURE OF LIGHT

pages 482–485

OBJECTIVES
See pupil page 482.

VOCABULARY
Key terms: particle model of light, photocell, photoelectric effect, pho-
ton

---

1 MOTIVATION

Discuss with students how something can have a dual nature or two very different uses. Ask students to list some examples from their own lives. (Some examples include a computer that can be a word processor or a database; a long piece of cloth that can be worn as a belt or as a scarf; a spoon that can be used as a cooking utensil or as an eating utensil; and a fire that can be a source of heat and warmth or a cause of destruction.) Help students recognize that many things can be described in more than one way. Ask students how this can be helpful. (Helps to give a clearer understanding of that which is being described.)

After completing this section, you will be able to

- **describe** the photoelectric effect.
- **compare** the effects of intensity and frequency on the photoelectric effect.
- **explain** the dual nature of light.

The key terms in this section are
particle model of light
photocell
photoelectric effect
photon

The wave model of light can be used to explain many of the properties of light. However, it cannot completely explain what happens when light strikes the surface of certain metals.

Look at Figure 19-21. When light strikes the knob of a negatively charged electroscope, the leaves come together. If the intensity of the light is increased, the leaves come together more quickly. If light strikes a positively charged electroscope, the leaves remain spread apart. Even when the intensity of light is increased, the leaves remain spread apart. Recall that a negatively charged electroscope loses its charge when it loses electrons. A positively charged electroscope loses its charge when it gains electrons. From this experiment it can be concluded that the light causes electrons to be lost from the metal knob.

Figure 19-21

A negatively charged electroscope (A) can lose its charge when light strikes the knob (B).

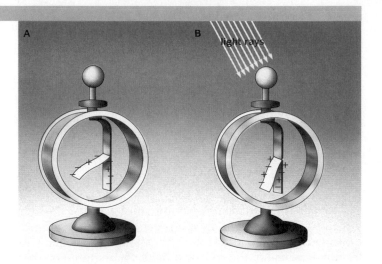

The release of electrons from a metal when light strikes it is called the **photoelectric effect**. The wave model of light explains how electrons are removed from a metal when light energy hits the metal. The greater the intensity of the light, the more energy the light waves have. Thus more electrons are released.

According to the wave model of light, the photoelectric effect can be compared with the effect of ocean waves striking a beach. The energy of striking ocean waves on the beach removes sand from it. The largest ocean waves have the most energy and, therefore, remove the most sand.

The wave model of light, however, cannot explain another effect of light striking a metal surface. It cannot explain what happens when different colors of light strike some metal surfaces. When red light strikes some metal surfaces, electrons are not released. Even when red light of high intensity is used, no electrons are released. But when blue light strikes the same metal surfaces, electrons are released.

In 1905, Albert Einstein provided an explanation. He said that light was made up of tiny particles of energy called **photons**. The idea that light is made up of particles is called the **particle model of light**.

Einstein explained that when a photon strikes an electron in a metal, the energy of the photon can be transferred to the electron. When the electron gains this energy, it escapes from the metal. However, the electron must gain a certain minimum amount of energy before it can escape from the metal. If the photon does not have this amount of energy, the electron remains on the metal.

photo- (light)
-on (particle)

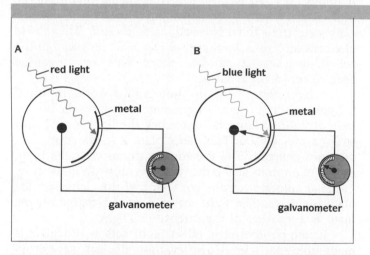

Figure 19-22

When red light strikes the metal, no current flows (*A*). When blue light strikes the metal, current flows (*B*).

Einstein also explained that the energy of the photon depended on the frequency, or color, of light. The higher the frequency of the light, the greater the energy of the photon. For example, a photon in blue light has more energy than a photon in red light. This is because blue light has a higher frequency than red light.

According to Einstein, the photons in blue light had enough energy to remove electrons from metal, but the photons in red light did not. Increasing the intensity of red light increased the number of photons. But the energy of the photons was not increased.

2 CONCEPT DEVELOPMENT

Background   A photon is a particle of electromagnetic radiation. Each photon has a quantity of energy that can be expressed as hv, where h is Planck's constant (6.63×10^{-34} J/s) and v is the frequency of the wave. As the frequency of the wave increases, the energy of the photon also increases. All photons travel at the same speed, 3×10^8 m/s (the speed of light).

Enrichment   Invite a local photographer to visit the class to demonstrate light meters. Ask him or her to show students how the meter detects different amounts of light on a subject and how this affects the finished photograph.

Tie-in/Social Studies   Have students do research and identify the areas of the world that would be well suited to the large-scale use of photocells, which convert sunlight into electricity. Have students show these areas on a map.

Thinking Skills

identifying cause and effect
After students study Figure 19-22, have them identify the photons striking the metal as the cause of the resulting electric current. Be certain that students understand how the photons that strike the metal cause a release of electrons and understand that a flow of electrons is electricity.

Teaching Tip Use a photographic light meter to show the photoelectric effect. Measure the intensity of the light in different parts of the room, both with the lights on and with the lights off. Have students chart the data to see if the room is evenly illuminated.

Teaching Tip Photocells that can be used in the classroom are available from scientific supply houses. You might also find these cells at toy or hobby stores, where they are sometimes sold as solar energy devices.

Demonstration To demonstrate the photoelectric effect, direct a beam of light at a photocell. Attach the cell to a meter to see the effect of varying colors and intensities.

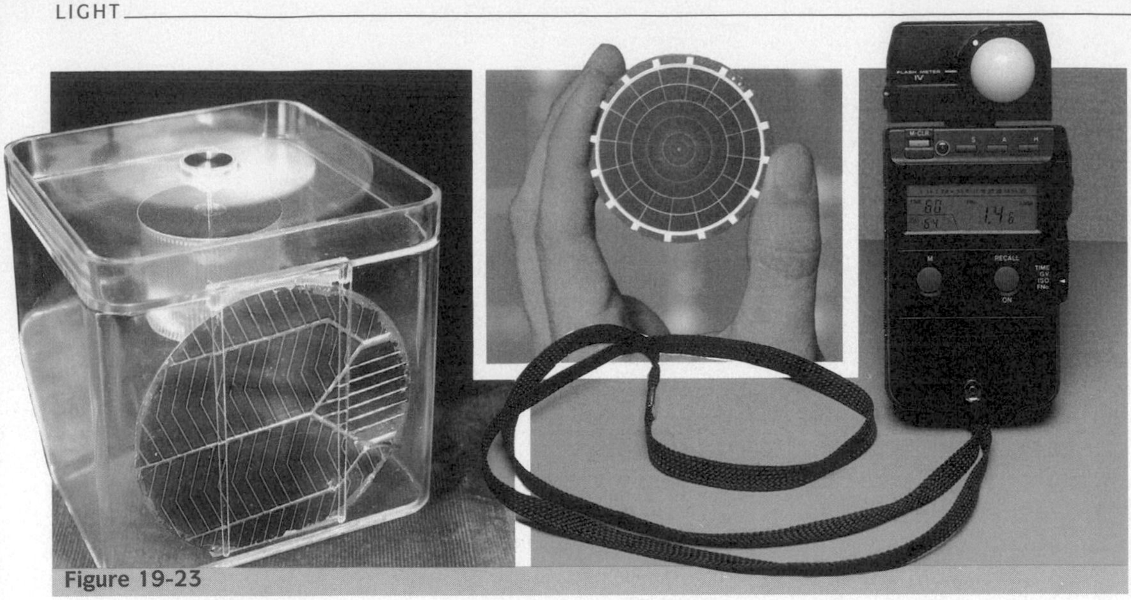

Figure 19-23

A solar cell (*inset*) can use the photoelectric effect to produce electricity, which can power a small fan (*left*). A light meter (*right*) uses the photoelectric effect to measure the intensity of light.

Today the photoelectric effect is used in photocells. A **photocell** is an electric cell that changes light energy into electrical energy. When light strikes a photocell, it causes electrons to be released inside the cell. The release of electrons causes a voltage, or electrical pressure, in the cell. Thus a current can be created. This current can be used to run many devices.

A light meter used in photography works by using the photoelectric effect. A light meter measures the brightness of light. When photons enter the light meter, they strike a metal plate. The metal plate loses electrons and becomes charged. The greater the intensity of the light, the more photons strike the plate. As more photons strike the plate, more electrons are lost, and the charge on the plate increases. The light meter uses the charge on the plate as a measure of the intensity of light.

In the photoelectric effect, light acts as though it is made up of particles. However, light also has wave properties, such as reflection, refraction, interference, and polarization. Because light has both wave properties and particle properties, it is said to have a dual nature.

The dual nature of light explains how light under certain conditions acts as a wave, and under other conditions acts like a stream of particles. The other forms of radiant energy also show this dual nature. X rays, for example, act as particles when they penetrate matter. But when X rays strike the crystals of some substances, the rays are diffracted or polarized. These effects are characteristics of waves.

REVIEW

1. What is the photoelectric effect?
2. What effects do the intensity and frequency of light have on the photoelectric effect?
3. Why is light said to have a dual nature?

CHALLENGE Light from stars has been observed to bend when passing close to the sun's surface. Does this observation support the wave model of light or the particle model of light?

CHAPTER SUMMARY

The main ideas in the chapter are listed below. Read these statements before you answer the Chapter Review questions.

- Light is part of the group of waves called the electromagnetic spectrum. (19-1)

- An object can be described as transparent, translucent, or opaque, depending on how it transmits or reflects light. (19-2)

- Evidence that light travels in a straight line includes the formation of shadows and the way light spreads out from its source. (19-2)

- Like waves, light obeys the law of reflection. (19-3)

- When light passes from one medium to another at an angle, the direction of the light changes. This change is called refraction. (19-3)

- The color of an object comes from the colors in the visible light that the object transmits or reflects. (19-4)

- Various colors are produced by subtracting or adding colors of light. (19-4)

- Evidence that light is a wave includes its properties of interference, diffraction, and polarization. (19-5)

- Evidence that light is made up of particles includes the photoelectric effect. Particles of light energy are called photons. (19-6)

- Light has properties of both waves and particles. (19-6)

The key terms in this chapter are listed below. Use each term in a sentence that shows the meaning of the term.

diffraction	law of reflection	radiant energy
electromagnetic spectrum	opaque	reflected ray
filter	particle model of light	reflection
incident ray	photocell	refraction
index of refraction	photoelectric effect	translucent
intensity	photon	transparent
interference	polarization	wave model of light

1. The release of electrons from a metal when light strikes it is called the photoelectric effect.
2. High-frequency light causes the release of electrons; low-frequency light does not cause the release of electrons. If electrons are released, the rate of release increases as the intensity of the light increases.
3. At times, light shows a wave-type behavior, and at other times, a particle-type behavior.

Challenge Wave; refraction is a wave property.

Review and Skill Masters

VOCABULARY REVIEW, page 113.
See page 459b in this book for answers.

VOCABULARY

1. radiant energy
2. intensity
3. law of reflection
4. transparent
5. incident ray
6. electromagnetic spectrum
7. interference
8. diffraction
9. translucent
10. photon

CONCEPTS

1. Radio waves, microwaves, infrared rays, visible light, ultraviolet rays, X rays, and gamma rays.
2. Transparent—air, glass, still water; translucent—wax paper, frosted glass, some plastics; opaque—bricks, wood, metal.
3. An eclipse occurs when the earth or the moon blocks the path of sunlight.
4. The intensity decreases 16 times.
5. Roemer based his computation on the time needed for light to travel from a moon of Jupiter to the earth; two measurements were made, from opposite sides of the earth's orbit.
6. The distances on the earth are generally too close together.
7. In moving water the reflected rays are scattered; in smooth water the reflected rays are parallel, so they form an image.
8. The light changes speed.
9. The raindrop acts as a prism and disperses the light.
10. Transparent and translucent objects absorb certain colors of light; the nonabsorbed colors are visible. This process is color subtraction. The color of opaque objects is also caused by color subtraction; the opaque objects absorb all colors except those reflected.

Review and Skill Masters

CHAPTER REVIEW, pages 114–115.
See page 459b in this book for answers.

VOCABULARY

Use the key terms from this chapter to complete the following sentences correctly.

1. _____ is energy that is transferred by electromagnetic waves.
2. The brightness of light is called _____.
3. The _____ states that the angle of reflection equals the angle of incidence.
4. A material that allows almost all light to pass through is described as _____.
5. A/An _____ is a light ray that strikes a surface.
6. Radio waves, infrared rays, light waves, ultraviolet rays, X rays, and gamma rays make up the _____.
7. The adding or cancelling of light waves that meet is called _____.
8. The spreading out of a light wave as it passes through a small opening is called _____.
9. A material that allows only some light to pass through is described as _____.
10. A/An _____ is a tiny particle of light energy.

CONCEPTS

1. List the parts of the electromagnetic spectrum in order of increasing frequency. (19-1)
2. Give examples of objects that are transparent, translucent, and opaque. (19-2)
3. How does an eclipse show that light travels in a straight line? (19-2)
4. What happens to the intensity of light on a surface if the distance between the light source and the surface is increased from 1 m to 4 m? (19-2)
5. How did Roemer measure the speed of light? (19-2)
6. Why is it easier to measure the speed of light between objects in space than between objects on the earth? (19-2)
7. Why can you see your reflection in still water but not in moving water? (19-3)
8. What causes light to refract when it passes between two different substances? (19-3)
9. What causes a rainbow to form? (19-3)
10. Compare how transparent, translucent, and opaque objects produce color. (19-4)

11. Compare the colors produced by mixing different paints together with those produced by mixing different colors of light. (19-4)
12. Explain why a lemon appears yellow. (19-4)
13. Distinguish between refraction and diffraction of light. (19-5)
14. Compare the interference of light waves with the interference of water waves. (19-5)
15. How could you show that reflected light is polarized? (19-5)
16. Why can light of high frequency discharge a negatively charged electroscope but not a positively charged electroscope? (19-6)
17. Blue-colored light causes electrons to be emitted from certain metal surfaces. What would be the effect of increasing the intensity of the blue light? (19-6)
18. Red-colored light does not cause electrons to be emitted from certain metal surfaces. What would be the effect of increasing the intensity of the light? What would be the effect of increasing the frequency of the light? (19-6)
19. Identify each of the following as either a wave property or a particle property of light. (19-5, 19-6)
    a. A spoon appears bent in water.
    b. Light is measured by a photometer.
    c. A rainbow forms after a rainstorm.
    d. Polarized sunglasses reduce glare.

APPLICATION/ CRITICAL THINKING

1. Is a rainbow likely to form in a desert? Explain your answer.
2. Why should photographic film be kept away from X rays?
3. Explain why black objects become hotter in the sun than do white objects.
4. Polarized sunglasses look the same as ordinary sunglasses. How could you determine if a pair of sunglasses is polarized?

EXTENSION

1. X rays are used for more than medical purposes. Do some research and make a display that shows other uses of X rays.
2. Color photography is a subtractive color process. Find out how color photographs are made.
3. The reflectors on a bicycle will always reflect light back to the light source, regardless of the angle at which the light strikes. Examine a bicycle reflector to see how this works.

READINGS

Cole, K.C. *Facets of Light, Images, and Things that Glow in the Dark.* San Francisco, Calif.: The Exploratorium, 1980.

Vandiver, Pamela. "Pigment Processing for Cave Paintings." *Science News,* June 2, 1984, p. 348.

11. Light: blue + green → cyan
             red + blue → magenta
             red + green →yellow
    Pigment: magenta + cyan → blue
             magenta + yellow → red
             cyan + yellow → green
12. Yellow is reflected; other colors are absorbed.
13. Refraction is the change in direction of a light ray as it passes from one medium to another; diffraction is the spreading out of a light wave as it passes through a small opening or around a small object.
14. Water waves—crests and troughs; light waves—bright lines and dark lines.
15. Rotate a polarizing filter in the reflected light to remove the glare.
16. A negatively charged electroscope has a surplus of electrons and loses its charge when it loses electrons; a positively charged electroscope has a shortage of electrons and loses its charge when it gains electrons.
17. The emission of electrons would increase.
18. No effect; the emissions would increase if the frequency was increased to blue light.
19. a. Wave. b. Particle c. Wave. d. Wave.

APPLICATION/CRITICAL THINKING

1. No; however, if it were to rain briefly, the abundance of sunlight could produce a rainbow.
2. X rays penetrate protective coverings on photographic film, resulting in partial exposure of the film.
3. Black objects absorb all colors of light.
4. Place a polarizing filter over one of the lenses, and rotate the filter; if the glasses are polarized, all light will be blocked out at one point of the rotation.

Test Masters

CHAPTER TEST, pages 73–76.
See page 459d in this book for answers.

USES OF LIGHT

ORGANIZER

Section	pages	Activity	pages	Reinforcement and Evaluation	pages	*Review and Skill Masters	pages	Other Components in Teacher Resource Package	pages
20—1 Mirrors	489–494	What Image Is Made by a Plane Mirror?	491	Review, Challenge	494	Challenge/Critical Thinking	123–124	Study Guide Lab Manual	100 103
20—2 Lenses	495–498	What Images Are Made by Convex Lenses?	496	Review, Challenge	498			Study Guide Lab Manual	101 105
20—3 Using Lenses	499–505	How Is a Pinhole Camera Made?	503	Puzzler Review, Challenge	499 505	Skill	122	Study Guide	102
20—4 Lasers and Holograms	506–509			Review, Challenge	509			Study Guide	103
20—5 Optical Fibers	510–513			Review, Challenge	513			Study Guide	104
CHAPTER SUMMARY	513					Vocabulary Review	119		
CHAPTER REVIEW	514–515			*Test Masters	77–80	Chapter Review	120–121		

*In the Teacher Resource Package. For answers, see pages 487b—487d in this book.

ACTIVITY MATERIALS   Quantities are based on a class of 30 students working in groups as indicated in parentheses.

What Image Is Made by a Plane Mirror? p. 491 (groups of 2)	quantity	What Images Are Made by Convex Lenses? p. 496 (groups of 2)	quantity	How Is a Pinhole Camera Made? p. 503 (groups of 2)	quantity
index card	30	convex lens or magnifying glass	15	shoebox with cover	15
small plane mirror	30	white paper	15 sheets	pie plate	15
slit rubber stopper	30	metric ruler	15	metric ruler	15
metric ruler	30			scissors	15
				clear tape	15 rolls
				waxed paper	1 box
				straight pin	15

REVIEW AND SKILL MASTERS

VOCABULARY REVIEW ———————— Chapter 20

Match the definition in Column A with the term in Column B.

Column A

Column B

_J_ 1. A copy of an object formed by light

_Q_ 2. A mirror that has a flat surface

_S_ 3. An image that does not exist where it seems to be

_C_ 4. A mirror in which the reflecting surface curves inward

_E_ 5. A mirror in which the reflecting surface curves outward

_G_ 6. The point at which light rays meets

_F_ 7. The distance from a mirror to its focal point

_R_ 8. An image that can be shown on a screen

_M_ 9. A transparent material that refracts light from an object to form an image

_D_ 10. A lens that is thicker in the center than at its edges

_N_ 11. The ability of the eye to focus on close objects, but not on distant ones

_B_ 12. A lens that is thinner in the center than at its edges

_I_ 13. The ability of the eye to focus on distant objects, but not close ones

_O_ 14. A lens located at one end of a tube that focuses incoming light

_A_ 15. Light waves of the same frequency and amplitude that are in phase

_L_ 16. A light source that produces coherent light

_H_ 17. A three-dimensional image made on a photographic plate or film

_P_ 18. A glass wire that carries light beams over long distances

_K_ 19. The reflection of light at the border between two substances

A. coherent light
B. concave lens
C. concave mirror
D. convex lens
E. convex mirror
F. focal length
G. focal point
H. hologram
I. hyperopia
J. image
K. internal reflection
L. laser
M. lens
N. myopia
O. objective lens
P. optical fiber
Q. plane mirror
R. real image
S. virtual image

© 1989 Silver, Burdett & Ginn Inc.

119

CHAPTER REVIEW ———————— Chapter 20

20-1 Mirrors

1. What kind of image does a plane mirror form? A plane mirror forms a virtual image reversed from right to left.

2. Contrast a virtual image and a real image. A real image can be shown on a screen, while a virtual image cannot be shown on a screen.

3. Compare the types of images formed by concave and convex mirrors. Concave mirrors reflect parallel light rays into either real or virtual images. Convex mirrors reflect spreading light rays into only virtual images.

20-2 Lenses

1. How do concave and convex lenses differ? A concave lens is thinner in the center than at its edges, while a convex lens is thicker in the center than at its edges.

2. What kind of image is made by a concave lens? A concave lens forms a virtual image that is erect and smaller than the object.

3. What kind of images are made by a convex lens? A convex lens forms both real and virtual images, depending on the distance of the object from the lens. The image may be inverted or erect.

20-3 Using Lenses

1. Describe how the human eye focuses light. Light is first bent by the transparent cornea. It is next focused by the convex lens onto the retina at the back of the eyeball.

2. Compare a camera to the human eye. A camera and the human eye both form images. The camera's shutter and diaphragm control the amount of light, and its lens focuses the light on the film. The human eye's eyelid and iris control the amount of light, and its lens focuses the light on the retina.

© 1989 Silver, Burdett & Ginn Inc.

120

CHAPTER REVIEW (Continued) ———————— Chapter 20

3. Describe how lenses are used in refracting telescopes and light microscopes.
Refracting telescopes use two lenses, an objective lens that focuses light into a real image, and an eyepiece lens that forms a virtual, enlarged image. Microscopes also use two lenses, an objective lens that forms a real, enlarged image, and an eyepiece lens that magnifies the image.

20-4 Lasers and Holograms

1. Contrast coherent light and ordinary light. Coherent light contains light waves of the same frequency and amplitude moving in phase. Ordinary light contains light waves of different frequencies and amplitudes moving out of phase.

2. Give two properties of a laser beam. A laser beam's light rays are almost perfectly parallel and very intense.

3. How do a hologram and an ordinary photograph differ? A hologram is a three-dimensional image, while a ordinary photograph is a two-dimensional image.

20-5 Optical Fibers

1. Describe how total internal reflection occurs. Total internal reflection occurs when light moves from a medium with a higher index of refraction to a medium with a lower index of refraction.

2. How does an optical fiber carry light? An optical fiber has two layers of glass, the core and the cladding. When light rays enter the core, they are reflected off the cladding along the length of the fiber.

3. Give two uses of optical fibers. Answers will vary. Optical fibers are used to carry telephone signals and television signals.

© 1989 Silver, Burdett & Ginn Inc.

121

SKILL/Comparing ———————— Chapter 20

Light rays travel in a straight line. Light rays bend, or refract, when they go through a curved piece of glass called a lens. A convex lens is thick in the middle and thin at the edges. Convex lenses bend light rays together toward the focus, or the center of the lens. A concave lens is thin in the middle and thick at the edges. Concave lenses spread light rays apart.

Scientists use convex and concave lenses together. For example, telescopes and microscopes use many lenses to greatly magnify very small or distant objects. Study the lenses in the drawing and answer the questions below.

Convex lens   Concave lens

1. Label each lens as concave or convex.

2. Which lens would focus rays of light into a small point?
A convex lens would focus rays toward a small point.

3. Which lens would make light rays spread apart?
A concave lens would spread out rays of light.

4. Do lenses bend rays of light toward the thicker or the thinner part of the lens?
Lenses bend rays of light towards the thicker part of the lens.

5. What is the shape of the lens of the eye?
It is a convex lens.

6. If a person is far-sighted, the blurred image on his or her retina needs to be focused. Explain which lens is used to correct this condition.
You would use convex lenses to correct far-sighted vision. Because the image falls behind the eye's retina, you need convex lenses to bring the focus of the image forward to the retina.

© 1989 Silver, Burdett & Ginn Inc.

122

CHAPTER **20** PLANNING GUIDE

Name_____ Date_____

CHALLENGE/CRITICAL THINKING _____ Chapter 20

You have two shiny ornaments, **A** and **B**, hanging by the window. You decide to use these ornaments to learn more about mirrors and the images that they form.

A   B

1. Is the light being refracted or reflected by the two ornaments?

The light is being reflected.

2. You first study ornament **A**. You notice that it forms an image of nearly the entire room. What type of mirror, concave or convex, is ornament **A**? How can you tell, using the image of the room as your guide?

It is a convex mirror. In a convex mirror, objects appear much smaller than

they actually are. A convex mirror can reflect objects in a wide area.

3. Will the image shown in ornament **A** be smaller, larger, or the same size as the original? Why?

The image will be smaller than the original. Images reflected from a convex

mirror are always smaller than the original object.

4. Would you see a larger image of yourself if you stood farther from ornament **A**? Why or why not?

No, you would see a smaller image of yourself if you stood farther away from a

convex mirror. You would see a larger image of yourself only if you stood

closer to a convex mirror.

123

Name_____ Date_____

CHALLENGE/CRITICAL THINKING (Continued) _____ Chapter 20

5. What kind of image, real or virtual, is formed by ornament **A**?

A virtual image is formed by ornament A.

6. Now you study ornament **B**. What type of mirror is ornament **B**? Why?

Ornament B is a concave mirror because its reflecting surface curves inward.

7. You can see the image of a word in ornament **B**. Is the image of the word spelled backward or forward?

The image of the word is spelled backward.

8. You notice that your image in ornament **B** is a virtual image. You also notice a real image of a spider that is hanging from the ceiling. Is the spider nearer to the ornament than you are, or farther from it? How do you know?

The spider is farther from the ornament. A concave mirror forms a virtual

image of near objects, and a real image of distant objects.

9. You stand one meter away from the window where the ornaments are hanging. You hold a plane mirror towards the window and look into it. What does the image of the room formed by ornament **A** look like in the plane mirror? Is the image of the word formed by ornament **B** spelled backward or forward in the plane mirror?

Both images should be affected in size only by the distance they are away from

the plane mirror. The image of the room should be backward from how it

appeared on ornament A. The image of the word formed by ornament B should

be spelled forward in the plane mirror.

10. You wish to tie one of the ornaments to your bike to get a panoramic view of the scenery behind you. Which ornament should you use? Why?

You should use ornament A. A convex mirror reflects objects in a wide area.

124

TEST MASTERS

Uses of Light

PART 1 _____

In the space below, write the term that each phrase defines.

Chapter Goal

1. **focal length** — The distance from a mirror to its focal point — 1

2. **objective lens** — A lens that focuses light entering a telescope or microscope — 3

3. **lens** — A transparent material that is used to refract light from an object to form an image — 2

4. **laser** — A light source that produces coherent light — 4

5. **hologram** — A three-dimensional image produced on a photographic plate or film — 4

6. **internal reflection** — The reflection of light at the boundary between two substances — 5

7. **plane mirror** — A mirror that has a flat surface — 1

8. **myopia** — The ability of the eye to focus on close objects, but not distant ones — 3

9. **optical fiber** — A glass wire that is used to carry a light signal — 5

10. **convex lens** — A lens that is thicker in the middle than at its edges — 2

PART 2 _____

Choose the term or phrase that best answers the question or completes the statement. Write the letter of that choice in the space at the left.

___d___ 1. Which part of the eye is like the shutter of a camera? — 3
  a. cornea b. lens c. retina d. eyelid

___d___ 2. Which of the following can produce an image that can be projected on a screen? — 2
  a. plane mirror c. concave lens
  b. convex mirror d. convex lens

Choose the term or phrase that best answers the question or completes the statement. Write the letter of that choice in the space at the left.

Chapter Goal

___a___ 3. A refracting telescope contains: — 3
  a. two lenses. c. one lens and one mirror.
  b. one lens. d. two mirrors.

___c___ 4. The two beams of light that produce a hologram start out: — 4
  a. with different amplitudes. c. in phase.
  b. with different frequencies. d. out of phase.

___d___ 5. Which of the following describes the image formed when an object is placed between the focal point and the surface of a concave mirror? — 1
  a. real and magnified c. virtual and magnified
  b. real and enlarged d. virtual and enlarged

___c___ 6. Which of the following describes the image formed when an object is placed between a converging lens and its focal point? — 2
  a. real and enlarged c. virtual and enlarged
  b. real and reduced d. virtual and reduced

___d___ 7. Which of the following describes a reflection of an object on the smooth surface of a lake? — 1
  a. real and inverted c. virtual and inverted
  b. real and upright d. virtual and upright

___a___ 8. Some lasers use a gas-filled tube to: — 4
  a. release photons. c. reflect photons.
  b. absorb photons. d. destroy photons.

___c___ 9. What happens if light traveling in an optical fiber does not reflect internally? — 5
  a. The light's frequency decreases.
  b. The light's frequency increases.
  c. Less light reaches the end of the fiber.
  d. More light reaches the end of the fiber.

___b___ 10. Internal reflection would most likely occur when light enters a medium of: — 5
  a. low index of refraction at a small angle.
  b. low index of refraction at a large angle.
  c. high index of refraction at a small angle.
  d. high index of refraction at a large angle.

Look at the diagram. Then read the questions that follow. Choose the term or phrase that best answers the question or completes the statement. Write the letter of that choice in the space at the left.

Chapter Goal

___d___ 1. The curved object shown in the diagram is a: — 1
  a. concave mirror. c. concave lens.
  b. convex mirror. d. convex lens.

___c___ 2. What type of image is produced in the diagram? — 1
  a. virtual image, reduced c. real image, reduced
  b. virtual image, enlarged d. real image, enlarged

___d___ 3. No image will be produced if an object is placed at: — 1
  a. B. b. C. c. D. d. F.

___c___ 4. The focal length in the diagram is the distance between F and: — 1
  a. A. b. B. c. D. d. E.

___d___ 5. If an object is placed at C, the rays of light will: — 1
  a. converge. b. reflect. c. project. d. diverge.

Read each question or direction and answer it using complete sentences.

Chapter Goal

1. Explain how a reflecting telescope works. — 3

   A reflecting telescope uses a mirror, instead of a lens, to gather and focus light. The incoming light enters a tube at one end. The light travels to the other end of the tube, where it hits a concave mirror. The real image formed by the concave mirror is reflected by a small plane mirror to the eyepiece lens on the side of the tube. As in the refracting telescope, the eyepiece lens magnifies the image.

2. Describe some uses for lasers. — 4

   Because of its intensity, a laser beam can be used to cut diamonds or metals into shapes. Very thin laser beams are used in surgery. They can be used to repair a torn retina in the eye. Laser beams can also be used to make long distance measurements accurately and to produce three-dimensional images called holograms.

3. What are the advantages of optical fibers over copper wires in sending signals? — 5

   Optical fibers have many advantages over copper wires in sending signals. One advantage is that an optical fiber can carry more signals than a copper wire. Another advantage is that optical fibers are much lighter and thinner than copper wires. Therefore, optical fibers take up less space. Also, because optical fibers do not contain metal, they are not affected by electrical interference from nearby electric power lines.

CHAPTER 20 PLANNING GUIDE

487d

20

USES OF LIGHT

The questions in the CHAPTER TEST are based on these Chapter Goals.

1. Describe the image formed by a plane mirror, distinguish between a virtual image and a real image, and compare the way a concave mirror forms an image with the way a convex mirror forms an image.
2. Distinguish between concave and convex lenses, and describe the images produced by concave and convex lenses.
3. Compare how a camera works with how the human eye works, and explain how lenses are used in light telescopes and microscopes.
4. Distinguish between coherent light and ordinary light, describe the properties of a laser beam, and compare a hologram with an ordinary photograph.
5. Explain how total internal reflection takes place, and describe the function and uses of optical fibers.

USES OF LIGHT

*The photograph shows multiple images created by a
kaleidoscope. All the images are formed by three mirrors.
Images can be formed by the reflection of light, just as echoes
are formed by the reflection of sound. Your image in a mirror is
formed by the light rays that bounce off the mirror's surface.*

- *Why does your image in a mirror look like you?*
- *How are images produced by curved mirrors?*
- *How are images formed by your eyes?*
- *How are three-dimensional images created?*

20-1 MIRRORS

A quiet pool of water may have been used as the first mirror when someone's image was reflected from the water. In 2500 B.C. the Egyptians used smooth, shiny pieces of bronze metal as mirrors. In the 1500s, glass mirrors were first widely used in Europe. Today most mirrors are made from thick plate glass coated on one side with a thin layer of metal such as aluminum. A mirror is an object that has a smooth, shiny surface. Almost all of the light striking the surface of a mirror is reflected. The reflected light forms an image. An **image** is a copy of an object formed by light.

PLANE MIRRORS

The most common type of mirror is the plane mirror. A **plane mirror** is a mirror that has a flat surface. Parallel light rays that strike the surface of a plane mirror are reflected as parallel light rays. The mirrors on bedroom doors and on medicine cabinets and the rear-view mirrors in cars are examples of plane mirrors.

Plane mirrors form images of objects. But the images made are not exactly like the objects. The image produced by a plane mirror is reversed from right to left. For example, a person with a ring on the left hand would in a mirror form an image in which the ring appears to be on the right hand.

After completing this section, you will be able to

- **describe** the image formed by a plane mirror.
- **distinguish** between a virtual image and a real image.
- **compare** the way a concave mirror forms an image with the way a convex mirror forms an image.

The key terms in this section are
concave mirror
convex mirror
focal length
focal point
image
plane mirror
real image
virtual image

planum (level surface)

CHAPTER OPENING STRATEGY

Ask students to compare the photograph with the images they would see in a handheld kaleidoscope. Explain that a kaleidoscope is simply a group of mirrors set up to form an equilateral triangle. Have students study the photograph, and ask them to try to follow the path of the light as it is reflected from one mirror to the next. Discuss with students why the mirrors reflect light.

- Why does your image in a mirror look like you? (Light bounces off you toward the mirror and then bounces straight back.)
- How are images produced by curved mirrors? (Images are reflected back at different angles.)
- How are images formed by your eyes? (Light is focused by the lens onto the retina, where an image is formed.)
- How are three-dimensional images created? (Two separate images from slightly different angles are formed. The combination of these images forms a three-dimensional image.)

20-1 MIRRORS
pages 489–494

OBJECTIVES
Refer to pupil page 489.

VOCABULARY
Key terms: concave mirror, convex mirror, focal length, focal point, image, plane mirror, real image, virtual image
Other terms: curved mirror, focused

1 MOTIVATION

Have examples of plane, concave, and convex mirrors labeled and available for the class to see. Ask students to view themselves in each mirror and to note the differences in their appearance. Ask them why concave and convex mirrors distort their image. Ask students to list uses for concave and convex mirrors.

2 CONCEPT DEVELOPMENT

Teaching Tip   Ask students if a mirror positioned in a doorway to enable you to see who is coming down the hall also allows those in the hall to see you. (Yes, because the law of reflection works in both directions.)

Background   The metal reflective coating on one-way mirrors is very thin. One-way mirrors are effective when the room on the observer's side of the mirror is darker than the room containing the reflective side of the mirror.

Demonstration   To show image reversal in a plane mirror, ask students to write their signature or the name of their school while watching their hand and pencil in a mirror. Most will have difficulty with the task. Ask a student to stand alongside a plane mirror. Direct another student to look into the same mirror. Ask both students to cover their left eye. When the image and the person are compared, image reversal will be obvious.

Thinking Skills

interpreting diagrams
Students study Figure 20-2 and follow the paths of the rays to see that the reflected light ray can be extended beyond the mirror to form a virtual image. Ask students to predict how far beyond the mirror the virtual image would appear to be if the object were 2 m in front of the mirror. (2 m.)

Figure 20-1

The image seen in a plane mirror is upright and reversed from side to side.

Notice in Figure 20-1 that the word AMBULANCE is spelled backward on the front of the ambulance. A person driving in front of the ambulance would see the word reversed in the rear-view mirror. Thus the person would see the word printed as it should be. How could you use a mirror to write a message that looks backward?[1]

The image in a plane mirror is also described as upright, or erect. The reversal of the image is only from side to side, not up and down. Notice in Figure 20-1 that the letters are upright.

The image in a plane mirror appears to be as far behind the mirror as the object is in front of the mirror. But looking behind the mirror shows that there is no image there. For this reason, the image is called a virtual image. A **virtual image** is an image that does not exist in the place it seems to be.

Figure 20-2 shows how a virtual image is formed by a plane mirror. Suppose a person stands in front of a plane mirror, as shown. Light rays leave the person and are reflected by the mirror. Notice that the light rays reflect at the same angle at which they strike the mirror. Although the light rays change direction when they are reflected, to the eye the light rays appear to travel in a straight line. They seem to come from behind the mirror at a distance equal to the distance the person is in front. Thus the image seems to be the same distance behind the mirror as the person is in front.

Figure 20-2

The image seen in a plane mirror appears to be behind the surface of the mirror.

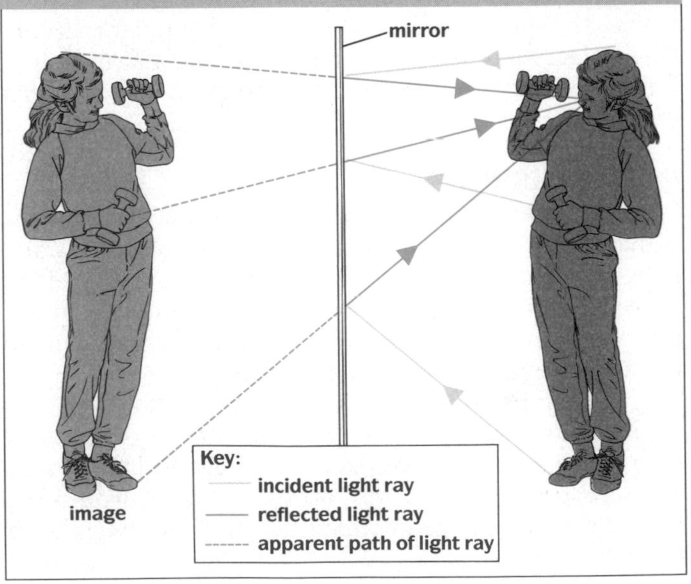

[1] Hold the mirror to one side of the paper, and look at the image formed as you write backward, from right to left.

mirror

image

Key:
incident light ray
reflected light ray
apparent path of light ray

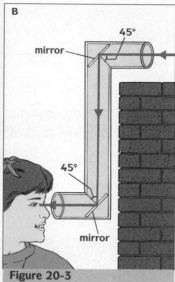

Figure 20-3

Plane mirrors have many uses.

Plane mirrors have many uses. Figure 20-3A shows how mirrors can be used to decorate a room. Why do mirrors make a room look large?[1] Figure 20-3B shows how two mirrors are used to make a periscope. With a periscope, a person can see above a wall because the light strikes each mirror at an angle of incidence of 45°.

ACTIVITY   What Image Is Made by a Plane Mirror?

OBJECTIVE

Demonstrate the properties of a plane mirror.

MATERIALS

index card, 2 small plane mirrors, 2 slit rubber stoppers, metric ruler

PROCEDURE

A. Place a plane mirror in each of two slit rubber stoppers. Set both mirrors aside.
B. Print your first name in large capital letters on an index card.
C. Place the card 5 cm in front of one mirror so that your name faces the mirror.
   1. Describe the position of the letters as seen in the mirror.
D. Move the card to a position 10 cm from the mirror. Observe the image in the mirror.
   2. How does this image compare to the image formed in step **C**?
E. Place the second mirror at right angles to the first mirror, as shown in the figure.
F. Repeat steps **C** and **D**, but make all observations in the second mirror.
   3. How did the images in the two mirrors compare?

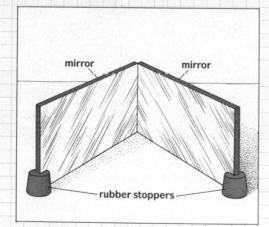

RESULTS AND CONCLUSIONS

1. Describe the image produced by a plane mirror.
2. What is the effect on an object's image in a plane mirror as the object is moved away from the mirror?
3. Why were the images formed in the first mirror virtual images?
4. Why were the images in the second mirror virtual images? Explain your answer.

[1]Because the image in a mirror seems to be behind the surface of the mirror, mirrors can reflect the depth of an entire room.

ACTIVITY   25 minutes

PROCESS SKILLS

observing, comparing, identifying cause and effect

Preparation   Slit each stopper in advance; #6 or larger one-hole or two-hole rubber stoppers will do nicely. If stoppers are not available, modeling clay will make a suitable support for the mirrors.

Teaching Tip   The mirrors should be inserted into the stoppers so that the bottom of the mirrors will sit squarely on the table. Upside-down stoppers will provide a larger base and, therefore, a more stable support.

Answers to Procedure

1. They are reversed.
2. Farther behind the mirror.
3. The image in the first mirror is reversed. The image of the image in the second mirror is doubly reversed, or normal.

Answers to Results and Conclusions

1. Virtual, erect, and reversed.
2. The image appears to be farther behind the mirror.
3. The image is not where it appears to be.
4. The object appears to be on the first mirror, but the object is actually in front of the mirror.

Thinking Skills

interpreting diagrams

Students are asked how the solar furnace shown in Figure 20-5 uses a concave mirror. The students should conclude that the light rays from a concave mirror come together and concentrate the heat at the focal point.

Teaching Tip   Tell students that a concave mirror curves inward like the mouth of a cave.

Tie-in/Social Studies   Ask students to research the making of mirrors in Italy during the Renaissance.

Teaching Tip   A shiny spoon or a polished metal bowl can serve as a curved mirror.

Enrichment   Light rays hitting the surface of a large curved mirror do not all converge at the focal point. This phenomenon, known as spherical aberration, increases as mirror size increases. Ask students to research spherical aberration and to report on methods of correcting this limitation.

CURVED MIRRORS

Mirrors can have different shapes. A mirror that is not perfectly flat but has a curved surface is called a *curved mirror*. Like a plane mirror, a curved mirror has a smooth, shiny surface that reflects light. The reflecting surface of the curved mirror can curve either inward or outward. If the reflecting surface curves inward, the mirror is called a **concave mirror**. If the reflecting surface curves outward, the mirror is called a **convex mirror**.

-cavus (hollow)
convexus (arched)

When a mirror is curved, the reflected rays of light will not be parallel to each other. Notice in Figure 20-4 that the reflected rays of light from a concave mirror come together. But the reflected rays of light from a convex mirror spread apart.

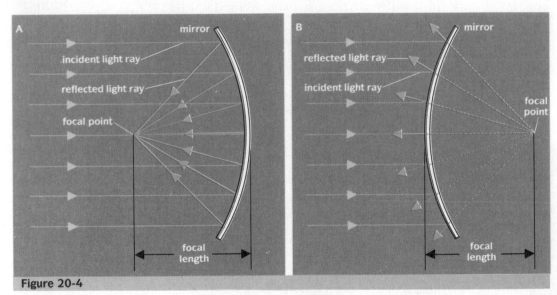

Figure 20-4

A concave mirror brings light rays together (*A*). A convex mirror spreads light rays apart (*B*).

When parallel light rays strike a concave mirror, the reflected rays come together and meet at a point. These light rays are said to be *focused*. The point at which parallel light rays meet is called the **focal point**. The distance from the mirror to the focal point is called the **focal length**.

Because concave mirrors can bring light rays together, these mirrors have many uses. Some kinds of telescopes use concave mirrors to gather and focus the light of distant stars. How does the solar stove shown in Figure 20-5 use a concave mirror to heat water?[1] Car headlights, flashlights, and spotlights also use concave mirrors. But instead of focusing light, they reflect the light given off by a light bulb placed at the focal point of the mirror.

[1]The solar stove focuses light rays from the sun on the cup of water.

Figure 20-5

This flashlight uses a concave mirror to reflect a beam of light (*left*). The image of the cup of water being heated can be seen in the concave mirror of this solar stove (*right*).

Like a plane mirror, a concave mirror can form an image that is reversed from left to right. But unlike a plane mirror, a concave mirror can also form an image that is not erect and not virtual. Under some conditions a concave mirror will form an upside-down, or inverted, image. This image is described as a real image. A **real image** is an image that can be shown on a screen. Virtual images, such as those produced by plane mirrors, cannot be shown on a screen. As you can see in Figure 20-6, the distance between an object and a concave mirror determines whether the image is virtual or real. Notice that the image of a distant object is real. As the object moves farther from the mirror, its real image becomes smaller. The image of an object that is between the mirror and the focal point is virtual and enlarged.

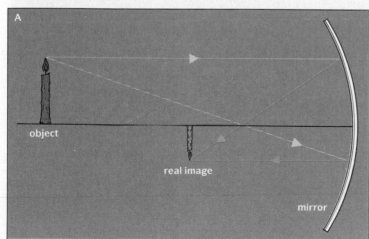
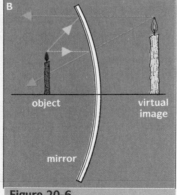

Figure 20-6

A concave mirror can form a real image (*A*) or a virtual image (*B*).

Demonstration To show that a concave mirror will form a real, inverted image, use an image box. Image boxes are available from a scientific supply house. Mount an inverted light on the top inside of the box. Then mount an empty socket on the top outside of the box. When the lamp is illuminated and directed at a concave mirror, a real image of the light will appear in the empty socket.

Thinking Skills

interpreting diagrams
Students are asked to study Figure 20-6. They follow the paths of the light rays and determine the types of images formed. Ask students what factor determines whether a concave mirror will produce a real image or a virtual image. Students should conclude that the distance between an object and a concave mirror determines whether the image is real or virtual.

Background The color of an image seen in a mirror is the same as the color of the object because the frequency of light reflected from a mirror is the same as the frequency of light that strikes the mirror.

Review and Skill Masters

CHALLENGE/CRITICAL THINKING, pages 123–124. See page 487c in this book for answers.

1. The image is reversed from left to right.
2. A virtual image does not exist in the place it seems to be; a real image can be focused on a screen.
3. A concave mirror forms an image by bringing the reflected light rays together; a convex mirror forms an image by spreading the reflected light rays apart.

Challenge   When the object is close to the mirror, the image appears to be behind the mirror, virtual, erect, and larger than the object. If the object is moved away from the mirror, the image appears to be upside down, real, and larger than the object. If the object is moved three focal lengths from the mirror, the image appears to be upside down, real, and smaller than the object.

Recall that light rays reflected from a convex mirror spread apart. Notice in Figure 20-7 that these reflected light rays seem to come from a point behind the mirror. This point is the focal point of the mirror. Because the reflected light rays appear to come from behind the mirror, the image formed appears to be behind the mirror. The image formed in a convex mirror is always virtual, upright, and smaller than the object.

Because the images seen in convex mirrors are smaller than the objects, convex mirrors are sometimes used as outside rear-view mirrors in cars and trucks. The convex mirrors give a wider view of the road than do plane mirrors. However, since the images are reduced in size, the objects seem farther away than they really are. Why must drivers be aware of this difference?[1]

[1]Drivers must learn to compensate for this distance so that they do not misjudge distances.

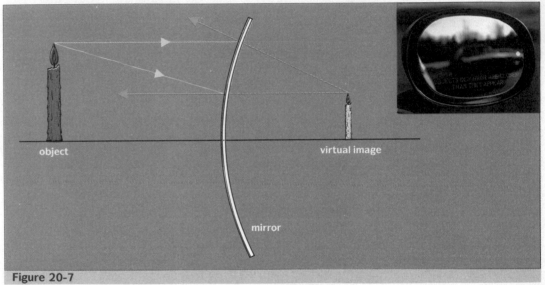

Figure 20-7

The image formed by a convex mirror is virtual, upright, and smaller than the object.

REVIEW

1. What is the appearance of an image formed by a plane mirror?
2. What are the differences between a virtual image and a real image?
3. How does the way a concave mirror forms an image compare with the way a convex mirror forms an image?

CHALLENGE Describe what happens to the image seen in a concave mirror as the object moves away from a point close to the mirror until the distance between the object and the mirror is three times the focal length.

20-2 LENSES

A piece of glass can be shaped so that light passing through it forms an image. A transparent object that is used to refract light from an object to form an image is called a **lens**. Lenses are used in microscopes, cameras, binoculars, and magnifying glasses. Each piece of glass in common eyeglasses is a lens. A good lens must be made of a good quality material. Any flaws in the lens can cause images to be unclear.

Lenses vary in size. Some glass lenses, like the ones used in microscopes, are less than one centimeter across. Very large lenses are used in telescopes. For example, the telescope at Yerkes Observatory in Wisconsin has a lens that is almost 102 cm across.

Like curved mirrors, lenses are described as convex or concave, depending on their shape. A **convex lens** is a lens that is thicker in the center than at its edges. Figure 20-8A shows three different types of convex lenses. A **concave lens** is a lens that is thinner in the center than at its edges. Figure 20-8B shows three different types of concave lenses.

> *After completing this section, you will be able to*
> - **distinguish** between concave lenses and convex lenses.
> - **describe** the images produced by concave lenses.
> - **describe** the images produced by convex lenses.
>
> *The key terms in this section are*
> concave lens
> convex lens
> lens

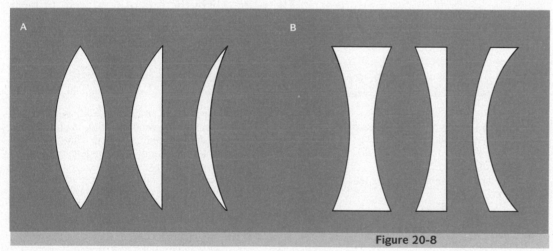

Figure 20-8

Convex lenses (A) and concave lenses (B).

Like curved mirrors, lenses can bring light rays to a point or can spread them apart. Notice in Figure 20-9A on the next page that light rays passing through a convex lens come together, or converge. For this reason, a convex lens is also called a *converging lens*. The point at which the light rays meet is called the *focal point* of the lens. The distance from the center of the lens to the focal point is the *focal length*.

> **OBJECTIVES**
> Refer to pupil page 495.
>
> **VOCABULARY**
> Key terms: concave lens, convex lens, lens
> Other terms: focal point, length

1 MOTIVATION

Have students name some uses of lenses. Write their suggestions on the chalkboard. Anticipate some of the suggestions, and have such items as binoculars, a microscope, a magnifying glass, and a telescope available for display. Ask students how mirrors and lenses are similar and how they are different.

2 CONCEPT DEVELOPMENT

Demonstration   To show the behavior of lenses, use an optical bench, which is available from most scientific supply houses. By mounting a screen, lenses, a light source, and an object on a meter stick, the characteristics of lenses, images, and relative positions can be shown. Also available is a kit that shows the paths of beams of light as they pass through different kinds of lenses.

Background   Most lenses are made of glass. Vision-correcting contact lenses are often made of plastic. Crystal quartz is used to make lenses that will withstand high temperatures.

interpreting diagrams
Students are asked to study Figure 20-9 and follow the paths of the light rays. Have students compare the pictures, noting where each focal point is in relation to the rays of light and the lens.

ACTIVITY 20 minutes

PROCESS SKILLS
observing, comparing, inferring

Preparation None required.

Teaching Tip It may be necessary to turn off the classroom lights to focus an image onto a paper screen.

Answers to Procedure
1. The size of the print appears to increase.
2. Inverted.

Answers to Results and Conclusions
1. Virtual.
2. Real.
3. A real image can be projected onto a screen; a virtual image cannot be projected.

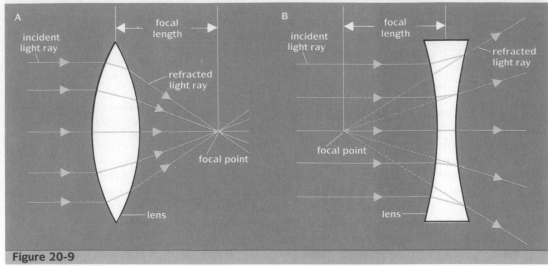

Figure 20-9

A convex lens brings light rays together (A). A concave lens spreads light rays apart (B).

Light rays passing through a concave lens spread apart, or diverge. For this reason, a concave lens is also called a *diverging lens*. Although the light rays do not meet at a point, a concave lens does have a focal point. As you can see in Figure 20-9B, the rays seem to come from behind the lens. The point where these light rays seem to meet is the focal point.

ACTIVITY   What Images Are Made by Convex Lenses?

OBJECTIVE
Demonstrate two different types of images made by convex lenses.

MATERIALS
convex lens or magnifying glass, metric ruler, white paper

PROCEDURE
A. Using your eyes only, examine the printing on this page.
B. Place a convex lens or magnifying glass directly above the printing on the page. Look through the lens at the printing. As you look at the printing, slowly raise the lens from the paper to a height of about 30 cm.
   1. What happens to the appearance of the print as the lens is slowly raised from the print?

C. Stand in front of an outside window, with your back to the window. With one hand, hold a sheet of white paper in front of you. With the other hand, hold the lens between the window and the paper.
D. Position the lens and paper so that they face some object outside. Hold the lens close to the paper. Then move the lens away from the paper until an image appears.
   2. Is the image erect or inverted?

RESULTS AND CONCLUSIONS
1. When the print was best in focus in step **B**, was this image real or virtual?
2. Compare the size of the image formed in step **D** with the size of the object. Is the image real or virtual?
3. How can you demonstrate that an image is real or virtual?

Like curved mirrors, lenses produce images that can be either real or virtual. The kind of image depends on the type of lens and the distance of an object from the lens. A convex lens produces both real and virtual images, depending on the position of the object. If the object is beyond the focal length of the lens, a real image forms. The real image is always upside down, or inverted. The image forms on the opposite side of the lens. Because it is a real image, it can be projected on a screen. Look at Figure 20-10. What happens to the size of the image as the object is moved closer to the lens?[1]

When the object is at the focal point of a convex lens, the rays of light come out of the lens parallel to each other. Because parallel light rays will not come together, or focus, no image is formed.

If an object is between a convex lens and its focal point, the lens causes light rays from the object to spread apart. The image formed is virtual. It appears to be on the same side of the lens as the object. The image is upright and larger than the object. Because it is a virtual image, this image cannot be projected on a screen.

[1]The image becomes larger.

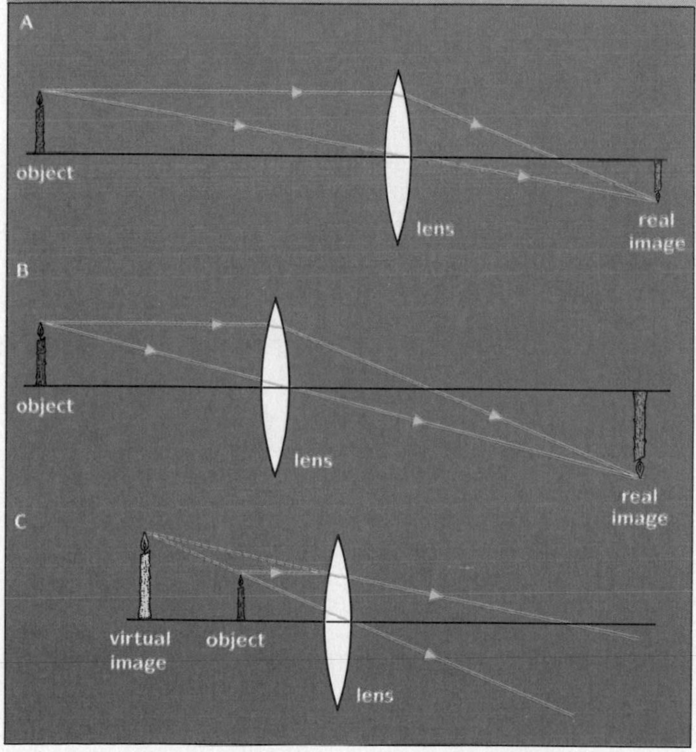

Figure 20-10

The size and type of image formed by a convex lens depends on the distance between the lens and the object.

Thinking Skills

interpreting diagrams
Students study Figure 20-10. Have them follow the paths of the light rays and determine the images formed. Then ask students what factor determines the type of image formed by a convex lens. (The position of the object.)

Thinking Skills

classifying
Ask students to classify lenses on the basis of their shape. Show students examples of different kinds of lenses, and have students classify each lens as either concave or convex.

Enrichment   A lens can act somewhat like a prism to disperse light, producing red and blue borders of projected white light. This phenomenon is known as chromatic aberration. Ask students to research this area of optics and determine if chromatic aberration is correctable.

Background   To correct chromatic aberration, a double layer consisting of two kinds of glass can be used to make a lens. Like the action of two prisms, the refracted light is refracted back to white light.

Thinking Skills

interpreting diagrams
Students study Figure 20-11 and follow the paths of the light rays to establish the formation of a virtual image. Students should be able to tell why the image is virtual, erect, and smaller than the object, using the diagram.

Teaching Tip   Use the chalkboard to show how concave and convex lenses bend light. Reproduce and emphasize the concepts shown in Figure 20-9, Figure 20-10, and Figure 20-11.

3 REVIEW/REINFORCEMENT

1. A convex lens is thick at the center and thinner at the edge, a concave lens is thinner at the center than at the edge.
2. A concave lens always produces a virtual image.
3. A convex lens can produce either a real image or a virtual image.

Challenge   The real image produced is inverted, so it must be turned upside down to appear right side up.

A single convex lens does not produce an image in perfect focus. One reason for this is that light rays passing through the edges of the lens bend more than the rays passing through the middle. This causes the light rays that pass through the lens to focus in different places.

Another reason the image is not in perfect focus is that different colors of light bend by different amounts. Recall that when white light refracts, blue is bent the most while red is bent the least. Thus when a beam of white light passes through a lens, the blue rays focus first, then the green, yellow, orange, and red. Cameras, telescopes, and microscopes often use two or more lenses together to help correct the focusing problems of a single lens.

The image produced by a concave, or diverging, lens is always virtual. Figure 20-11 shows how a concave lens forms a virtual image. As the light rays leave the lens, they spread apart. The light rays seem to come from the same side of the lens as the object. Thus the image appears to be on the same side of the lens as the object. The image formed by a concave lens is always erect and smaller than the object.

Figure 20-11

A concave lens always produces a virtual image.

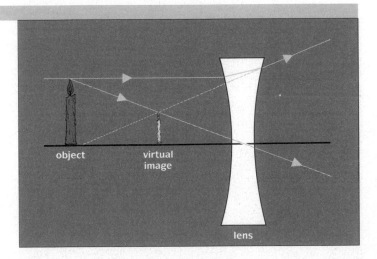

object   virtual image   lens

REVIEW

1. What is the difference between a concave lens and a convex lens?
2. What kind of images can be produced by a concave lens?
3. What kind of images can be produced by a convex lens?

CHALLENGE Why are slides upside down when they are placed in a slide projector?

20-3 USING LENSES

The ability of a lens to bend light and form images makes it useful. Lenses in telescopes make distant objects appear closer. Lenses in microscopes make small objects appear larger. In cameras, lenses focus images of objects onto film. The lens in the eye focuses light rays onto the back of the eye.

THE EYE

The process of seeing begins when light enters the eye. At the front of the eye is a curved transparent material called the *cornea* (KAWR nee uh). The cornea bends the light entering the eye. Behind the cornea is a small hole called the pupil. Surrounding the pupil is a circular muscle called the *iris* (I rihs). The iris controls the amount of light entering the eye by changing the size of the pupil. The iris has the eye's color, such as brown, blue, or green.

Behind the pupil and the iris is a lens. As you can see in Figure 20-12, this lens is convex in shape. The lens in the human eye causes light to bend, which focuses images of objects. Just as a convex lens can focus an image on a screen, the lens in the eye can focus an image on the back of the eyeball. The back of the eyeball is called the *retina* (REHT uh nuh). Nerve endings in the retina send information to the brain. The brain interprets the image that you see.

After completing this section, you will be able to

- **explain** how the human eye works.
- **compare** how a camera works with how the human eye works.
- **explain** how lenses are used in light telescopes and microscopes.

The key terms in this section are
hyperopia
myopia
objective lens

Figure 20-12

The structure of the eye.

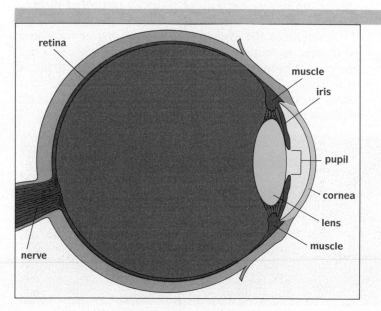

- retina
- muscle
- iris
- pupil
- cornea
- lens
- muscle
- nerve

20-3 USING LENSES
pages 499–505

OBJECTIVES
Refer to pupil page 499.

VOCABULARY
Key terms: hyperopia, myopia, objective lens
Other terms: cornea, iris, retina

1 MOTIVATION

Display an anatomical model of the eye. As students read page 499, have them find the cornea, iris, lens, and retina on the model. Ask students to compare the three-dimensional model of the eye with the two-dimensional representation in Figure 20-12.

2 CONCEPT DEVELOPMENT

Background The retina of the eye contains light sensors called rods and cones. The cones are responsible for color vision. The rods are responsible for black-and-white vision. Rods outnumber cones roughly 20 to 1 and account for night vision.

Since moonlight is reflected sunlight, it contains color frequencies; however, the only colors visible appear to be black, white, and shades of gray. Moonlight is not strong enough to fully excite the cones, which are responsible for color vision.

Demonstration To show the structures in the eye, dissect a cow or sheep's eye. Point out the major structures.

Puzzler   The object seen is conveyed to the brain as an upside-down image. The brain automatically inverts the image.

Enrichment   Ask students to research the functioning of the eye to determine why the still frames of motion-picture film appear to be in continuous movement.

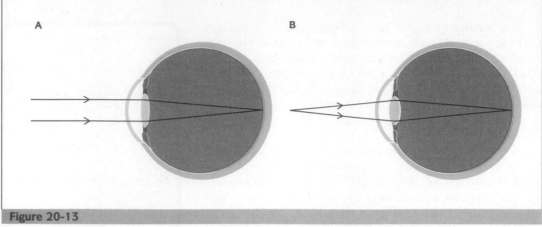

Figure 20-13

The focal length of the lens in the eye can be changed by changing the thickness of the lens.

Because the lens is flexible, the muscles in the eye can change the thickness of the lens. Changing the thickness of the lens changes the focal length of the lens. Figure 20-13 shows how changing the thickness of the lens enables the eye to focus on both nearby objects and distant objects. When the lens is made thicker, the focal length decreases. This change enables the eye to focus on nearby objects.

When the lens of the eye is made thinner, the focal length increases. This change enables the eye to focus on distant objects. In a normal eye the changes in the thickness of the lens allow the eye to focus images of objects that are near or far.

Sometimes the eyeball can be too long or too short for the eye to focus images of objects. In these cases the lens cannot become thick enough or thin enough to focus an image on the retina. Eyeglasses or contact lenses can correct these vision problems. Light that has passed through eyeglasses can be focused on the retina.

SCIENCE PUZZLER

A convex lens produces an inverted, or upside-down, image when it focuses light. You can see this by looking at distant objects through a magnifying glass. The human eye contains a convex lens that focuses light. Why don't you see objects upside down?

An eyeball that is too long from back to front causes a condition called myopia. **Myopia** (mi OH pee uh), or near-sightedness, is the eye condition in which light rays from distant objects are focused before they reach the retina. The eye can focus on close objects but not on distant ones. Notice in Figure 20-14A that this condition can be corrected by a concave lens. The concave lens causes light rays to spread apart. This change will make the light rays travel farther before they are focused.

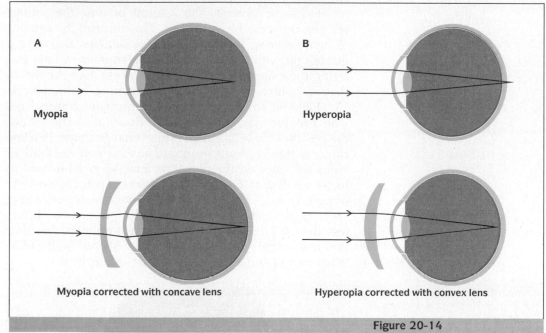

A

Myopia

B

Hyperopia

Myopia corrected with concave lens

Hyperopia corrected with convex lens

Figure 20-14

Myopia (A) can be corrected by a concave lens. Hyperopia (B) can be corrected by a convex lens.

An eyeball that is too short from back to front causes a condition called hyperopia. **Hyperopia** (hi puhr OH pee-uh), or far-sightedness, is the eye condition in which light rays from near objects are focused behind the retina. The eye can focus on distant objects but not on close ones. Look at Figure 20-14B. What type of lens is used to correct far-sightedness?[1]

As people grow older, the lens in the eye becomes harder. It cannot be adjusted as it used to. For this reason, older people often find it difficult to focus on close objects, like fine print. These people slowly become more and more farsighted. They need eyeglasses for reading. Eyeglasses like the ones in Figure 20-15 are made up of two sections with different focal lengths. How would these glasses help older people see clearly?[2]

Figure 20-15

Bifocals have lenses with two different focal lengths.

[1]A convex lens.
[2]These glasses can make two different corrections to help the lens of the eye adjust to different situations.

501

Teaching Tip   Various charts, such as the Snellen chart, are available to detect abnormalities of the eye. Use one of these charts to show how some visual problems might be detected. You may want to invite an optometrist to visit the class and discuss vision problems and their treatment and correction.

Thinking Skills

interpreting diagrams
Students study Figure 20-14A and Figure 20-14B to see how myopia and hyperopia are corrected by lenses. Ask students to identify the types of lenses used to correct hyperopia and myopia.

Review and Skill Masters

SKILL, page 122. See page 487b in this book for answers.

501

Background   Cameras use several lenses to reduce aberrations or distortions.

Teaching Tip   Some students may be amateur photographers. Ask these students, or invite a professional photographer, to speak to the class and to demonstrate the operation of the camera.

THE CAMERA

A camera is a lightproof box with a convex lens at one end and film at the opposite end. The parts of a camera are very similar to the parts of the human eye. Like the eye, the camera contains a part that controls the amount of light entering it and a part that focuses the light. A camera contains a device called the shutter, which allows light to enter the camera. The shutter works like the eyelid of the eye. When a picture is taken, the shutter is opened and closed, allowing light to enter the camera.

On some cameras the amount of time the shutter remains open can be controlled. This controls the amount of light entering the camera. These cameras also have a diaphragm, which also controls the amount of light entering the camera. The diaphragm works like the iris in the eye, controlling the size of the opening in the camera.

Light entering a camera passes through a convex lens, which focuses the light onto the film. Unlike the lens of the eye, the lens of a camera cannot change shape. In some cameras the lens can be moved inward and outward to focus an image on the film. The lens is moved inward to focus on distant objects, and outward to focus on near objects. In some cameras the lens cannot be moved. These cameras can focus on distant objects, but not on objects less than 0.5 m away. A real image forms on the film. When the film is developed, the image is fixed on the film. What part of the eye is like the film in a camera?[1]

[1]The retina.

Figure 20-16

The shutter, diaphragm, and lens of this camera can be adjusted.

502

ACTIVITY How Is a Pinhole Camera Made?

OBJECTIVE
Demonstrate the operation of a pinhole camera.

MATERIALS
cardboard shoebox with cover, metric ruler, scissors, pin, paper plate, wax paper, tape

PROCEDURE 👌
A. Find the center of each end of a shoebox by drawing diagonal lines from corner to corner. The center is where the lines meet.

B. At the center of one end, cut an opening about 1 cm by 8 cm, as shown. This is the end slot. At the other end of the box, use a pin to make a pinhole at the center.

C. On one side of the box, beginning 5 cm from the pinhole end, cut a slot 2 cm by 15 cm. This is the side slot.

D. Place the shoebox upright on one end on the center of a paper plate. Draw an outline of the end on the plate. Draw a handle on one side of the outline, as shown. Cut out the outline of the end and handle. Trim the edges of the piece so that it fits inside the box.

E. Cut a section 5 cm by 10 cm out of the center of the piece. This piece is the frame.

F. Cut a piece of wax paper to fit over the hole in the frame. Tape the wax paper over the hole. The wax paper is the screen.

G. Put the frame in the shoebox so the handle sticks out of the side slot. Cover the shoebox.

H. Point the pinhole at a distant object outdoors. Look through the end slot and move the frame back and forth until the object can be seen on the screen.

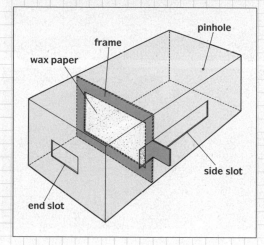

RESULTS AND CONCLUSIONS
1. In step **H**, why is the frame moved back and forth to produce an image?
2. Is the image produced in step **H** real or virtual? Explain your answer.

THE TELESCOPE

Light telescopes are instruments used to make distant objects appear closer. The largest light telescopes can be used to observe stars and planets. There are two kinds of light telescopes. They are the refracting telescope and the reflecting telescope.

A refracting telescope, like the one shown in Figure 20-17A on the next page, has two convex lenses. The lenses are called the objective lens and the eyepiece lens. The **objective lens** is a lens that focuses the light entering it. The objective lens is located at one end of a tube. The lens forms a real, inverted image.

The eyepiece lens is located at the opposite end of the tube. This is the lens you look through. The eyepiece lens acts like a magnifying glass, enlarging the real image formed by the objective lens. The eyepiece lens forms an enlarged, virtual image.

ACTIVITY 30 minutes

PROCESS SKILLS
observing, inferring, identifying cause and effect

Preparation None required.

Teaching Tip The pinhole should be quite small, so advise students that they should not wiggle the pin to enlarge the hole. The paper plate should be made of rigid material. If a flat, rigid paper plate is not available, substitute construction paper or oaktag.

Answers to Results and Conclusions
1. The pinhole has the same effect as does a lens; the frame must be moved to the focal point.
2. Real; the image is projected onto the screen.

Demonstration To show the operation of a telescope, use one of the demonstration models available from most scientific supply houses. An optical bench with interchangeable lenses can also be used to show the functioning of a telescope.

Background An additional lens is added to a terrestrial telescope to invert the already inverted image, producing an erect image. Binoculars are two attached terrestrial telescopes.

Teaching Tip   Have a compound microscope available, and demonstrate its mag-
nification power. Point out how the biological
sciences depend on the physical sciences for
many of their instruments.

Thinking Skills

comparing
Students study Figure 20-17*A* and Figure
20-17*B* to compare the refracting telescope
with the reflecting telescope. Direct students
to follow the paths of the light rays. Ask
students to identify the similarities and differences between reflecting and refracting
telescopes.

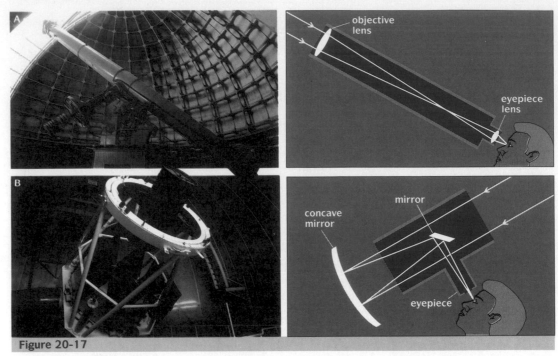

Figure 20-17

A refracting telescope (*A*) and a reflecting telescope (*B*).

A reflecting telescope does not have an objective lens.
This kind of telescope uses a concave mirror instead of a
lens to focus light. As you can see in Figure 20-17*B*, the
mirror is located at one end of a tube. Light enters the
tube at the other end. The light travels the length of the
tube and strikes the concave mirror. The concave mirror
forms a real image. A small plane mirror then reflects the
image to an eyepiece lens on the side of the tube. As in
the refracting telescope, the eyepiece lens enlarges the
image.

THE MICROSCOPE

A light microscope is an instrument used to make
small objects appear larger. A microscope usually contains
two convex lenses at opposite ends of a tube. As in a
refracting telescope, one lens is called the objective lens.
This lens is at the lower end of the tube. As you can see
in Figure 20-18, the object to be viewed is placed under
the objective lens. The objective lens forms a real, enlarged
image of the object.

The lens at the top of the tube is the eyepiece lens.
This is the lens you look through. The eyepiece further
enlarges the image.

The amount by which a lens enlarges an object is called the lens's power. For example, if a lens enlarges the image of an object 10 times, it is said to have a power of $10\times$. Many microscopes have a $10\times$ eyepiece lens. A lens that enlarges an image 40 times is said to have a power of $40\times$.

The power of both lenses together is the product of the power of each lens. Thus a $40\times$ lens and a $10\times$ lens used together will enlarge an image 400 times. Suppose a $65\times$ lens and a $10\times$ lens are used together. How much will the image be enlarged?[1]

Figure 20-18B shows how the image of an object is enlarged by a microscope. The light rays from the object first pass through the objective lens. The objective lens forms a real image. The real image is enlarged by the eyepiece lens. Notice that the image formed by the eyepiece lens is virtual and is larger than the object.

[1]650 times.

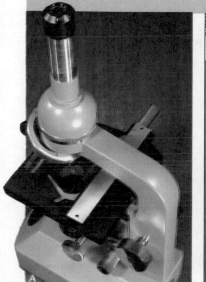
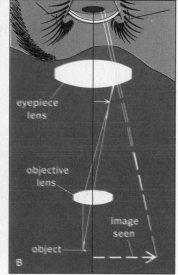

Figure 20-18

The structure of a light microscope.

REVIEW

1. How does the human eye work?
2. Compare the parts of the camera with the parts of the human eye.
3. How are lenses used in light telescopes and microscopes?

CHALLENGE An image of an object seen through a microscope moves to the right when you move the object to the left. Explain why.

Tie-in/Language Arts   No one really knows who invented the lens. However, lenses were in use in the 1500s and 1600s. Ask students to research some early pioneers in the use of lenses and to write a biographical composition about one of them.

3 REVIEW/REINFORCEMENT

1. Light enters the eye, is bent by the cornea, and passes through the pupil; behind the pupil is a lens that bends the light to focus it on the retina.
2. The shutter is like the eyelid, the diaphragm is like the iris, the lenses are similar, and the film is like the retina.
3. Lenses concentrate the light from the object to make an enlarged image.

Challenge   The light rays cross when they pass through the lens; this crossing of rays causes a reversal of image movement.

20-4 LASERS AND HOLOGRAMS

pages 506–509

20-4 LASERS AND HOLOGRAMS

OBJECTIVES
Refer to pupil page 506.

VOCABULARY
Key terms: coherent light, hologram, in-coherent light, laser

Other terms: in-phase light, flash tube, out-of-phase light

---

1 MOTIVATION

Make an overhead transparency of several Universal Product Codes (UPC's) from grocery items and a computerized cash-register tape. Ask students if they can see differences in the codes. Inform students that these differences are read by laser light and the information the code contains is transferred to a computer. The cash register can then print the name and quantity as well as the price of the item purchased.

---

2 CONCEPT DEVELOPMENT

Thinking Skills

interpreting diagrams

Students study Figure 20-19A and Figure 20-19B to note the differences in the waves in Figure 20-19A and the coherence of the light waves in Figure 20-19B. Ask students if waves with the same frequency and amplitude would always be coherent. (No; the waves would only be coherent if the crests and troughs also lined up.)

After completing this section, you will be able to

- **distinguish** between coherent light and ordinary light.
- **describe** the properties of a laser beam.
- **compare** a hologram with an ordinary photograph.

The key terms in this section are
coherent light
hologram
incoherent light
laser

A beam of light can be made so concentrated that it can burn holes in steel. A beam of light can also be made narrow enough to be used for surgery inside the human eye. How is such a light beam produced?

LASERS

Recall that ordinary white light, such as that given off by a light bulb or the sun, is made up of waves of many different frequencies, or colors. The waves in ordinary light also vary in size, or amplitude.

The different waves in ordinary light are said to be *out of phase*. Figure 20-19A shows waves that are out of phase. They have crests or troughs at different points. Waves traveling out of phase can be compared to people in a marching band stepping to different rhythms, or beats. Just as the people are marching out of step, the crests and troughs of light waves are out of step. Light that contains waves of different frequencies and amplitudes moving out of phase is called **incoherent** (ihn koh HIHR uhnt) **light**.

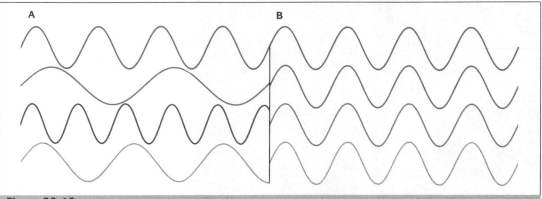

Figure 20-19

Waves that are out of phase have crests and troughs at different points (*A*). Waves that are in phase have crests and troughs at the same points (*B*).

co- (together)
-haerere (to cling)

In 1960, scientists found a way of making a beam of light that contained identical light waves. All the light waves in the beam had the same frequency and amplitude. Also, the waves moved in step. Their crests and troughs occurred at the same points. Such waves are said to be *in phase*. Waves in phase are shown in Figure 20-19B. Light that contains waves of identical frequency and amplitude that are in phase is called **coherent** (koh HIHR uhnt) **light**. Incoherent light is sometimes described as being a mixed-up form of light. Coherent light is sometimes described as being a pure form of light.

Coherent light is produced by an instrument called a **laser** (LAY zuhr). A laser produces light in much the same way that a fluorescent light produces light. A fluorescent light consists of a glass tube filled with a gas. When an electric current is sent through the gas, atoms in the gas absorb electrical energy. These atoms then release this energy in the form of photons, or light particles.

Figure 20-20 shows the parts of a laser. As you can see, the laser contains a glass tube filled with gas. Some lasers use a transparent rod instead of a gas tube. At each end of the tube is a plane mirror. Wound around the tube is a glass tube called a *flash tube*.

Figure 20-20

The structure of a laser.

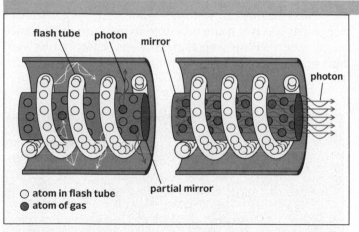

- ○ atom in flash tube
- ● atom of gas

The flash tube produces a burst of high-intensity light, much like the light from the flashbulb of a camera. Photons from the light enter the tube. Atoms in the gas absorb the photons and their energy. Some of the atoms then release this energy in the form of photons. The photons hit other atoms, causing them to release more photons. Each photon that is released has the same frequency as the photon that struck the atom. In addition, each new photon moves through the tube in phase with the other photons. The photons in the tube join, forming a coherent beam of light.

When the beam of light reaches the end of the tube, it is reflected back into the tube. Photons in the beam strike more atoms in the gas, causing more photons to be released. When the beam reaches the other end of the tube, it is reflected again. The beam is reflected back and forth many times. Each time the beam is reflected, its intensity builds up. Eventually the beam is strong enough to pass through the partially mirrored surface as a concentrated beam of coherent light.

Background   The word *laser* is an acronym that comes from putting together the initial letters of the words that describe what it is: *l*ight *a*mplification by *s*timulated *e*mission of *r*adiation.

Teaching Tip   To show coherent light-wave patterns on the chalkboard, use a staff liner, which is used by music teachers. The staff liner will hold five pieces of chalk, each of which will follow the same pattern when drawn across the board.

Enrichment   Lasers have many different uses. Ask students to research and describe one use of a laser not mentioned in this text.

Teaching Tip   Point out that a laser does not produce energy. Energy that is put into a laser is concentrated into a beam of light. The Law of Conservation of Energy applies to lasers as well as to any other energy transformation.

Background   When the atoms of laser material absorb the photons of energy, the electrons become excited, or move to a higher energy level.

Tie-in/Language Arts   Many popular periodicals contain articles about lasers and holograms. Direct students to use the *Readers' Guide to Periodical Literature* to find at least three articles in current periodicals. Have students read three articles and write a report about their readings.

Teaching Tip   Review destructive interference and constructive interference wave patterns and their meanings.

Background   While a laser can cut diamonds, gem quality diamonds are still cut and polished in the traditional manner in order to give the gems their luster.

A laser produces a powerful, thin beam of light. Notice in Figure 20-21 that the laser beam spreads out very little. This is because the light rays in a laser beam are almost parallel. The light rays in a laser beam do not spread apart, or diverge, as do those in ordinary light.

The unique properties of a laser make it very useful. Because of its intensity, a laser beam can be used to cut diamond or metals. It can also be used to produce the high temperatures necessary in nuclear fusion reactors.

Because its rays spread out very little, a laser beam is often used where accuracy is needed. For example, very thin laser beams are used in surgery. They can be used to repair a torn retina in the eye.

Laser beams can be used to measure long distances accurately. A laser beam was used to measure the distance to the moon within several centimeters. Laser beams were also used to measure the movement of rock on Mount St. Helens before it erupted.

Figure 20-21

A laser produces a thin beam of coherent light.

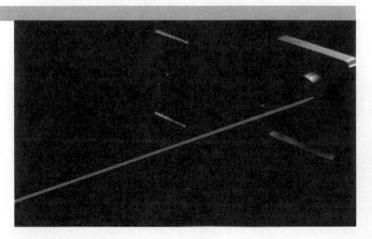

HOLOGRAMS

One of the most practical uses of laser light is its use in producing three-dimensional images called holograms (HAHL uh gramz). A **hologram** is a three-dimensional image produced on a photographic plate or sheet of film. Unlike an ordinary photograph—which shows only two dimensions, length and width—a hologram shows all three dimensions, length, width, and depth.

holo- (whole)

When a hologram of an object is made, the hologram looks like that object from any point of view. For example, by viewing the hologram from a particular angle, a side view of the object can be seen. In an ordinary photograph of an object, the front view of the object is always seen.

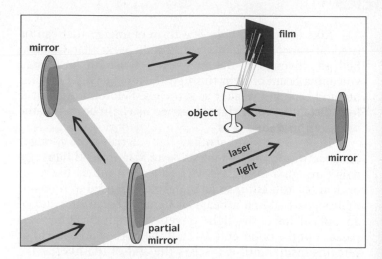

Figure 20-22

A hologram is a three-dimensional image made with a laser. This photograph shows the hologram of the top of the goblet projected on top of the stem of a real goblet.

Figure 20-22 shows how a hologram of an object is made. First a laser beam is split to produce two identical beams. One beam strikes an object. This beam is reflected by the object to a photographic plate or to a sheet of film. Notice that the distance that each reflected light ray travels depends on the shape of the object.

The other beam shines only on the plate or film. Because the two beams of light have traveled different distances they are no longer in phase. When both beams meet on the film or plate, they form patterns of bright and dark lines called interference patterns. Recall that an interference pattern is caused by light waves adding together or canceling each other. The interference patterns record the image of the object on the plate or film.

When the hologram is placed in light, the interference patterns on the film become "unscrambled." The patterns reflect the light that strikes it. The reflected light forms a three-dimensional image of the object. Holograms are being used in industry to detect defects in jet engines. Holograms are also being used in medicine to detect diseases.

REVIEW

1. How does coherent light differ from ordinary light?
2. What are the properties of a laser beam?
3. How does a hologram compare with an ordinary photograph?

CHALLENGE Explain why holograms could be used to store more information than can ordinary film.

Background A hologram produces both real and virtual images. No lens is used to make a hologram. Holography was invented in 1948 by Dennis Gabor, a Hungarian scientist. The development of the laser in the 1960s allowed the perfection of the hologram.

Demonstration To show the principles of holography, use a holography kit, available from most scientific supply houses. The kits provide materials needed to produce and view holograms.

3 REVIEW/REINFORCEMENT

1. Light that contains waves of identical frequency and amplitude that are in phase is called coherent light; ordinary light has different frequencies and amplitudes and is not in phase.
2. A laser beam is a powerful, thin beam of almost perfectly parallel light rays.
3. A hologram shows three dimensions, but an ordinary photograph shows only two.

Challenge Holograms store three dimensions of information, but photographs store only two dimensions.

20-5 OPTICAL FIBERS
pages 510–513

20-5 OPTICAL FIBERS

OBJECTIVES
Refer to pupil page 510.

VOCABULARY
Key terms: internal reflection, optical fiber
Other terms: cladding, core, light-emitting diode (LED)

1 MOTIVATION

Begin this section by demonstrating total internal reflection. Use a 45-45-90-degree prism to turn a light beam completely around. Ask students why it is possible to turn the light beam.

A total-reflection apparatus is available from some scientific supply houses. With this apparatus, a container is filled with water. At the bottom of the container is an angled mirror opposite a water outlet. When a light is directed at the mirror from above and the outlet is unplugged, the rays of light are carried down the stream of escaping water.

Point out that total internal reflection is possible when light travels from a more dense medium to a less dense medium. Ask students to read page 510 and study Figure 20-23 to develop their understanding of internal reflection.

2 CONCEPT DEVELOPMENT

Thinking Skills

interpreting diagrams
Ask students to study Figure 20-23 and to note that as the angle of incidence increases, the angle of refraction also increases until the light ray returns to the medium.

After completing this section, you will be able to

- **explain** how internal reflection takes place.
- **describe** how an optical fiber carries light.
- **describe** uses of optical fibers.

The key terms in this section are
internal reflection
optical fiber

Like electricity, light is a form of energy that can be used to carry information. In 1880, Alexander Graham Bell, the inventor of the telephone, transmitted a human voice in a beam of light through the air. But light spreads out and becomes weaker as it travels. Bell found that over long distances, voice signals carried in a light beam became too weak to understand.

In 1970 a way of sending light signals over a longer distance was found. Scientists were able to send light signals through a thin glass wire called an optical fiber. An **optical** (OP tuh kuhl) **fiber** is a glass wire used to transmit light signals. When a beam of light enters at one end of an optical fiber, the light travels through the fiber and passes out the other end. Even if the fiber bends, the light remains inside until it reaches the end of the fiber.

Figure 20-23

Light rays are bent away from the normal line as they pass from glass to air (*A,B*). If the angle of incidence is very large, a light ray will be reflected inside the glass (*C*).

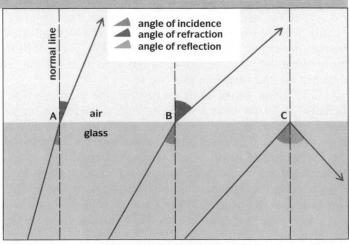

The light does not escape from the fiber; this is because of the way light behaves when it passes from a medium with a higher index of refraction to a medium with a lower index of refraction. Recall that light refracts, or bends, when it enters a new medium at an angle. When light at an angle enters a medium with a lower index of refraction, the light bends away from the normal line. As you can see in Figure 20-23A, when light enters air from glass, the light bends away from the normal line.

Figure 20-23B shows what happens when a light ray strikes the air from glass at a larger angle of incidence. Notice that the light ray is bent more strongly away from the normal line. Figure 20-23C shows what happens when the light ray strikes the surface of the air at a very large angle of incidence. The light ray is bent so much that it does not enter the air. Instead the light ray is reflected. This type of reflection is called internal reflection. **Internal reflection** is the reflection of light in one medium when it strikes another medium with a lower index of refraction.

The process of internal reflection keeps light rays from escaping through the sides of an optical fiber. The light rays do not escape because the fiber is made up of two layers of glass. The inner layer is called the *core*. The outer layer is called the *cladding*. The core has a higher index of refraction than does the cladding.

Notice in Figure 20-24 that light rays enter the core of the fiber. As the light rays travel through the core, they strike the cladding at large angles of incidence. Even where the fiber is bent, the light rays strike at large angles of incidence. Because the cladding has a lower index of refraction than does the core, these light rays are internally reflected off the cladding. They bounce back and forth inside the core, along the entire length of the fiber.

internus (within)

Teaching Tip   Many decorative lamps use optical fibers. Bring one to class for observation.

Demonstration   To show internal reflection, use a light pipe, which is available from scientific supply houses. In a light pipe a coil of glass is illuminated at one end. The light travels through the coil and emerges at the other end.

Thinking Skills

interpreting diagrams
Students study Figure 20-24 and identify the core and the cladding. Direct students to follow the path of the light down the tube and to observe that the light reflects off the cladding, even if the fiber is bent.

Demonstration   To show how optical fibers carry light, use a fiberoptics kit, which is available from most scientific supply houses. Manuals that accompany such kits describe experiments and demonstrations that show optical fibers and their characteristics.

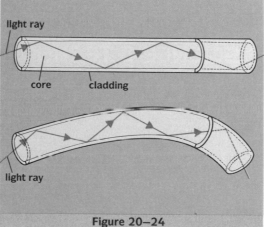

Figure 20—24

Light is internally reflected within optical fibers.

One source of light used to send signals through optical fibers is the laser. Using laser light, signals can be sent much farther than with ordinary light. Another source of light used is the *light emitting diode, or LED*. The LED is a crystal that produces light of one frequency when electric current is sent through it. The numbers in calculators and in some digital watches and clocks are produced by light from LEDs. The light produced by an LED can be sent through a fiber. This light is not as pure or as powerful as a laser beam, but it is less expensive to produce.

Enrichment   Ask students to do research to see how glass optical fibers are made.

Background   A fiber optic system illuminated by a laser beam is very useful in surgical aspects of medicine, especially in places where a normal lamp would produce heat and dry out delicate tissue.

Teaching Tip   Contact your local telephone company to find out if it is using any fiber optics. Ask if the company has a speaker who will talk to the class about present and future uses of fiber optics in communications.

Tie-in/Language Arts   Ask students to write a composition in which they predict several future uses of optical fibers.

Optical fibers have many advantages over copper wires in sending signals. One advantage is that an optical fiber can carry more signals than can a copper wire. For example, a pair of optical fibers can carry 50 times as many telephone conversations than can a pair of copper telephone wires. Another advantage is that optical fibers are much lighter and thinner than copper wires. About the thickness of a human hair, optical fibers are well suited for use in crowded cities, where space is limited.

Because optical fibers do not contain metal, they are not affected by electrical interference from nearby electric power lines. Electrical interference can sometimes be heard on the telephone as buzzing or humming sounds.

Optical fibers are already being used in telephone lines. The fibers cost less than do copper wires. The fibers are made from silica, a material found in sand. Optical fibers were used to carry television signals in the 1984 Summer Olympic Games in Los Angeles.

Optical fibers can be used to see inside the human body. One recent use of optical fibers has been in heart surgery. An optical fiber is fed through a person's vein into the heart. A laser beam is then sent through the fiber into the heart, where the beam can open clogged arteries.

SCIENCE & TECHNOLOGY

In 1880, Alexander Graham Bell invented a telephone that used sunlight instead of wires. He wrote, "I have heard a ray of sun laugh and cough and sing."

While Bell's bulky contraption never caught on, optical fibers have. Optical fibers may soon take the place of copper wires as the basic way of transmitting telephone conversations.

In laboratory tests, optical fibers have carried as many as 300,000 conversations. Scientists believe that optical fibers have the capacity to carry 300,000,000 coversations.

Major fiberoptic networks are already being installed in busy regions of the country, including Boston, New York, Chicago, and San Francisco.

The fibers can simply be placed alongside existing copper cables. This enables telephone companies to expand their service without tearing up streets to lay more cables.

In 1988 the first underwater fiberoptic cable will connect the United States with Great Britain and France. Similar systems are planned for Pacific islands.

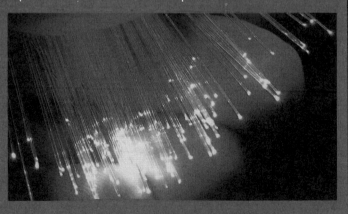

REVIEW

1. How does internal reflection take place?
2. How is light carried by an optical fiber?
3. What are some uses of optical fibers?

CHALLENGE Laser light is made up of only one wavelength of light, whereas white light is made up of many wavelengths. How does this fact explain why laser light can travel farther in an optical fiber than can white light?

CHAPTER SUMMARY

The main ideas in this chapter are listed below. Read these statements before you answer the Chapter Review questions.

- The image formed by a plane mirror is upright and reversed, and it appears to be as far behind the mirror as the object is in front. (20-1)

- Real images can be projected on a screen, whereas virtual images cannot. (20-1)

- Concave mirrors reflect parallel light rays and bring them to a point. Convex mirrors cause the reflected light rays to spread apart. (20-1)

- Convex lenses bring parallel rays of light entering them to a point called the focal point. Concave lenses cause parallel light rays entering them to spread apart. (20-2)

- Convex lenses can form either real images or virtual images, depending on the distance of the objects from the lenses. Con-

- cave lenses form only virtual images. (20-2)

- The human eye contains a convex lens that focuses light to form images. Instruments that use convex lenses include cameras, light telescopes, and microscopes. (20-3)

- Coherent light is a pure form of light that is produced by a laser. It is made up of waves with one frequency that are in phase. (20-4)

- Some of the uses of lasers include performing surgery, measuring distances accurately, and producing three-dimensional photographs called holograms. (20-4)

- Information can be sent by a light beam through a glass wire called an optical fiber. (20-5)

The key terms in this chapter are listed below. Use each term in a sentence that shows the meaning of the term.

coherent light	focal length	incoherent light	objective lens
concave lens	focal point	internal reflection	optical fiber
concave mirror	hologram	laser	plane mirror
convex lens	hyperopia	lens	real image
convex mirror	image	myopia	virtual image

3 REVIEW/REINFORCEMENT

1. For internal reflection to take place, light must pass from a dense medium to a less dense medium. If the angle of incidence is large enough for the particular material, the light will be bent so much that it will actually be reflected back into the starting material.

2. The light rays reflect off the cladding of the fiber and continue to bounce back and forth inside the core, moving along the length of the fiber.

3. Optical fibers carry communication signals and light, including laser light.

Challenge Laser light is coherent and is more powerful than white light, which is made up of many frequencies that are out of phase.

Review and Skill Masters

VOCABULARY REVIEW, page 119.
See page 487b in this book for answers.

VOCABULARY

1. plane mirror
2. real image
3. convex mirror
4. virtual image
5. concave mirror
6. lens
7. convex lens
8. hyperopia
9. focal point
10. hologram

CONCEPTS

1. On the right side.
2. A plane-mirror image is virtual and reversed; a movie-screen image is real and inverted.
3. Light rays reflected from curved mirrors can be focused.
4. A convex lens is thicker in the middle than at the edges; a concave lens is thicker at the edges than in the middle.
5. Convex; a convex lens produces a real image which can be projected on a screen.
6. A concave lens produces a virtual image.
7. They help to focus light rays onto the retina.
8. The shutter is like the eyelid, the diaphragm is like the iris, the lenses of both behave the same, and the film is like the retina.
9. A refracting telescope uses a convex lens to focus the light; a reflecting telescope uses a concave mirror to focus the light. Both telescopes have a convex eyepiece lens to enlarge the image formed by the first lens or mirror.
10. The image is formed by the objective lens and enlarged by the eyepiece lens.

Review and Skill Masters

CHAPTER REVIEW, pages 120–121.
See page 487b in this book for answers.

Chapter Review

VOCABULARY

Use the key terms from this chapter to complete the following sentences correctly.

1. A mirror that has a flat surface is called a/an _____.
2. An image that can be shown on a screen is a/an _____.
3. A/An _____ has a reflecting surface that curves outward.
4. A/An _____ is a kind of image that does not exist in the place it seems to be.
5. The reflecting surface of a/an _____ curves inward.
6. A curved piece of glass that refracts light is called a/an _____.
7. A/An _____ is a lens that is thicker in the middle than at its edges.
8. Far-sightedness is called _____.
9. The point at which light rays meet is called the _____.
10. A three-dimensional image produced on film is called a/an _____.

CONCEPTS

1. A person with hair parted on the left side stands in front of the mirror. What is the position of the hair part in the mirror? (20-1)
2. How does the image seen in a plane mirror differ from the image seen on a movie screen? (20-1)
3. How do the images formed by curved mirrors differ from those formed by plane mirrors? (20-1)
4. How can you tell if a lens is concave or convex? (20-2)
5. Is the image on a movie screen produced by a convex lens or a concave lens? Explain your answer. (20-2)
6. Which type of lens only produces a virtual image? (20-2)
7. How do convex and concave lenses correct poor eyesight? (20-3)
8. Which parts of the camera operate like the parts of the human eye? (20-3)
9. How does a refracting telescope differ from a reflecting telescope? (20-3)
10. What is the effect of using two lenses in a microscope or refracting telescope? (20-3)

11. How does a laser beam differ from the light beam produced by a flashlight? (20-4)

12. Why is a hologram produced with coherent light? (20-4)

13. Why is laser light described as being a pure form of light? (20-4)

14. Compare what happens when light strikes a hologram to what happens when light strikes an ordinary photograph. (20-4)

15. For large angles of incidence, compare what happens when light enters glass and when light leaves glass. (20-5)

16. Why does light inside an optical fiber not escape through the sides? (20-5)

17. What advantages do optical fibers have over metal wires in carrying information? (20-5)

APPLICATION/CRITICAL THINKING

1. If you walk toward a plane mirror at a speed of 1 m/sec, how fast would your image approach you?

2. With age, the lens in the human eye loses its flexibility. What effect does this have on an older person's ability to focus on nearby or distant objects? How would wearing bifocals correct this problem?

3. Lenses produce a rainbow of colors around images. Explain the cause of the colors.

4. What is the purpose of concave mirrors in flashlights and in the headlights of cars?

5. Explain why the focal length of a convex lens depends on the color of light entering it.

EXTENSION

1. Study the Greek myth of Narcissus. What part did a mirror play in this myth?

2. Visit a House of Mirrors at an amusement park. Notice how the shapes of the mirrors affect the images.

3. What is a heliograph? How is it used?

4. Find out how a lens and a lentil plant are similar.

5. Research reflecting telescopes. Make a bulletin-board display to show the different designs.

READINGS

Shuford, P.S. "An Introduction to Fiber Optics." *Byte,* January 1985, p. 197.

Thomsen, D.E. "Catching On to a Light Wave," *Science News,* February 2, 1985, p. 76.

———— "More Heroes of Optical Communications." *Science News,* March 2, 1985, p. 134.

11. A laser beam is coherent light; a flashlight beam is incoherent light.

12. A hologram is made by splitting a light beam into two identical beams; if the light were incoherent, identical beams would be impossible.

13. Laser light has waves with the same frequency and amplitude; these waves are said to be in phase. Laser light is coherent light and is sometimes called pure light.

14. When light strikes a hologram, the interference patterns on the film become unscrambled; this gives a three-dimensional image.

15. Light with a large angle of incidence enters the glass and stays inside because of internal reflection; light leaving the glass may be almost totally reflected back into the glass if the angle of incidence is large enough.

16. The light is internally reflected because of the angle at which it strikes the cladding.

17. Optical fibers can carry more signals, are much thinner and lighter, are not affected by electrical interference, and cost less than copper wires.

APPLICATION/CRITICAL THINKING

1. 1 m/s.

2. Older people find it difficult to focus on close objects; bifocals allow two lens types to be used in the same set of eyeglasses, allowing the person to focus on near objects and distant objects.

3. The rainbow of colors is the result of the lens acting like a prism.

4. The concave mirrors focus the light.

5. Each wavelength of light bends differently as it passes through a lens.

Test Masters

CHAPTER TEST, pages 77–80.
See page 487d in this book for answers.

Science in Careers

Computers can dial telephones, control assembly lines, design sweaters, and perform many other tasks. But how do computers "know" what to do?

A detailed set of instructions directs the computer. These step-by-step instructions, called a program, are written by a computer programmer.

Computer programmers work in all types of businesses where computers are used. And most businesses now require computers.

Computer Programmer

Computer programmers usually have a four-year college degree. Courses in programming are offered both at universities and at business schools. If you are interested in a career in computer programming, you should take mathematics courses and any computer courses or workshops offered at your school.■

Have you ever been to a play and noticed how the mood is affected by the lighting? Sometimes the sets do not change but each new scene looks different because the lighting has changed.

Stage-lighting electricians and designers are responsible for designing and constructing the stage lights. Besides working on plays, stage-lighting electricians are involved in television, movies, and operas.

Many stage-lighting electricians are licensed electricians.

All must understand the special requirements of stage lighting.

Some colleges offer courses in stage lighting. Many people who enter this field spend several years as an apprentice. If you would like to be a stage-lighting electrician, you should take courses in physics and get involved with any theatrical productions offered at your school.■

Stage-Lighting Electrician

People in Science

As a child, Grace Murray Hopper loved gadgets. Once she took apart a clock. When she was unable to put it back together, she took apart several more clocks until she found a solution to the problem.

Later, Ms. Hopper used this same approach to problem solving in her work with computers. In the 1940s she joined the United States Navy. There she worked with one of the first large computers.

By the 1950s, totally electronic computers were in use. These computers could process

Admiral Grace Murray Hopper, Computer Scientist

information much more quickly than the older ones could. By developing computer languages, Ms. Hopper made these new computers even easier to use.

While continuing to work with computers, Ms. Hopper advanced to the rank of rear admiral in the Navy. In 1986, Admiral Hopper retired from the Navy as the oldest officer on active duty. At the age of 79, she joined private industry, continuing an active career. Today, Admiral Hopper is recognized as one of the pioneers of computer science.■

Issues and Technology

Most people do not give much thought to the amount of personal information that is held in computers. Schools keep computer files on grades and school activities. State motor vehicle agencies collect information on everyone who has a driver's license. Credit card companies even keep records of what individuals buy, where they buy it, and how much they spend.

Generally, people do not worry about giving out information. They feel that government agencies and businesses keep their information confidential. Most people also expect that the information will be used only for the purpose for which it was collected.

It now appears that information may not always be kept confidential. More and more cases have been revealed in which personal information collected by one business or government agency is shared with others. Computers are simplifying this widespread use of personal information.

Sometimes the shared information is used for unexpected purposes. One example involves driver's license applications. Motor vehicle agencies in 49 states admit that they give information to the Selective Service System, the agency that handles the draft of young men for the armed forces. The Selective Service System then uses the information to find males 18 years of age or older who have not registered for the draft.

Some people think that it is reasonable to share information with the Selective Service, because they want people who do not register for the draft to be caught. But others feel that this is an invasion of privacy. They say that people have the right to control information about themselves or at least to know how the information will be used. Motor vehicle agencies are not alone in sharing personal information without the individual's knowledge.

Figure 1 shows a number of organizations that keep computerized records on Americans. People in several job categories were asked if they thought that the release of information by these organizations would be an invasion of privacy.

APPLYING CRITICAL THINKING SKILLS

1. A release of information by which agency was thought by most to be the greatest invasion of privacy?

The following thinking skills will be applied in answering questions.
- *Comparing* how different groups of individuals feel about sharing information.
- *Hypothesizing* why one group of individuals would have fewer objections to the selling of credit information than would other groups.
- *Evaluating* a system in which information was not shared but would only be gathered from individuals.

Answers to questions

1. Most people thought that the Internal Revenue Service's sharing of information is the most serious.

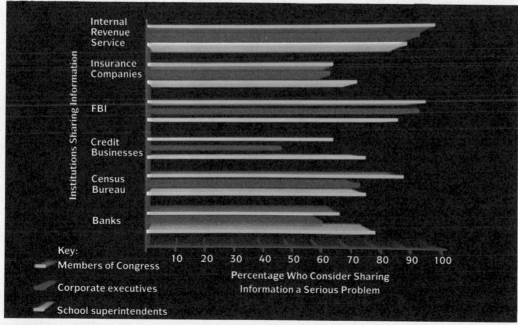

Key:
- Members of Congress
- Corporate executives
- School superintendents

Percentage Who Consider Sharing Information a Serious Problem

Institutions Sharing Information: Internal Revenue Service, Insurance Companies, FBI, Credit Businesses, Census Bureau, Banks

Figure 1

2. Answers will vary.

3. Corporate executives objected the least to selling credit information. Many businesses depend on credit information in order to make loans, to sell on credit, and for a number of other uses.

4. Some students will feel that any business or agency should only be able to get information about an individual from the individual. However, it is impractical for some organizations, such as the FBI, to rely on information given by the individual alone.

The following thinking skills will be applied in answering questions.
- *Comparing* how different groups of individuals feel about sharing information.
- *Hypothesizing* who might keep secret files on individuals.
- *Evaluating* the use of secret files on individuals.

Answers to questions

1. The percentage of people who believe secret files are being kept is going up.

2. Which organization's sharing of information would you consider to be the greatest invasion of privacy? Why?
3. Which group has the lowest percentage of people who objected to selling credit information? Why, do you think, did this group differ from the others?
4. Some people think that a business or government agency should only be able to get information about an individual from that individual. What do you think?

Privacy is a right that Americans cherish. It is protected by many laws, including the Fourth Amendment to the Constitution. The Fourth Amendment, which protects Americans against unreasonable search and seizure, was strengthened in 1974 by the Privacy Act. This act gives people control over information collected by the federal government. The act provides that there should be no secret record systems, that individuals are allowed to see and correct records about themselves, and that information collected for one purpose cannot be used for another.

The federal government alone keeps an average of 15 separate files on each American. These files include employment information kept by the Social Security Administration, financial data from the Internal Revenue Service, and personal data from the Census Bureau. Now it is known that some of these agencies share and compare information in ways that were never intended when the information was collected. And though the practice is known, it is still very hard to control.

One way of sharing information involves computer

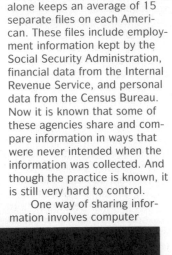

matches. In a computer match, two sets of data are compared to find people whose names are on both sets. The matches can be used to find people who should not be on two lists. For example, lists of people earning above a certain income level can be matched with lists of people receiving food stamps, thus revealing those illegally receiving food stamps.

Matches are also used to find people who should be on two lists but are not. By matching lists, the Selective Service can find males who have registered their cars but have not registered for the draft.

Many people are in favor of federal agencies locating people who cheat the government. However, many object to some of the federal government's uses of computer matching. In some instances the Internal Revenue Service, or IRS, compares reported income with computerized records of an individual's purchases. If the purchases seem more expensive than would be likely on that person's reported income, the IRS may audit the individual's taxes.

Perhaps doing computer matches to find fraud does not bother people. But is it right to examine an individual's purchases even when there is no reason to suspect that the person has done anything wrong? Where should the line be drawn? Has the computer made it impossible to draw the line at all? Figure 2 shows the percentage of people polled who thought that secret files were kept on themselves.

APPLYING CRITICAL THINKING SKILLS
1. Has the percentage of people who think that secret files are kept gone up or down? Describe the trend.

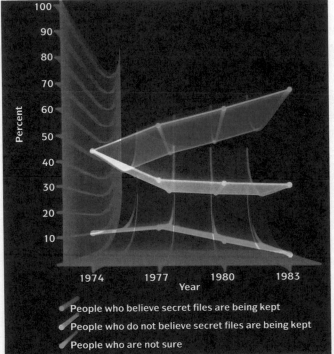

Percent

100
90
80
70
60
50
40
30
20
10

1974   1977   1980   1983

Year

People who believe secret files are being kept

People who do not believe secret files are being kept

People who are not sure

Figure 2

2. If you were polled, how would you answer?

3. If you think that secret files are kept on you or others, who would most likely keep these files, and why?

4. Do you see a problem with secret files about individuals? Are these files justified? Explain your answers.

Another problem involves people who break into computers. In 1982 a man left a computer company after not getting a pay raise. He used a home computer and telephone link-up to access his former employer's computer. He stole information. This man was caught, but many others are not.

In 1983 a group of Milwaukee teenagers made a game of using their home computers to break into a number of corporate and government computers. One of these computers

was at the Los Alamos National Laboratory, a facility that develops nuclear weapons. The teens said it was easy. They just kept guessing passwords that would access the computer. Once they typed in the right word, they could look at all the top-secret information in the files. Many people feel that more security is needed to keep computerized information out of the hands of the nosy, the mischievous, and the criminal.

Some security measures have been developed. Encryption is a security measure that codes information. A device that scrambles information into a code is put into the computer. The code can only be read by authorized individuals.

Another security measure is the call-back system. When a computer is contacted by phone, the computer calls back an authorized number. In this

way, only authorized users can access the computer by phone. Figure 3 shows some links among computer systems.

APPLYING CRITICAL THINKING SKILLS

1. What are some of the organizations from which credit bureaus collect computerized information?

2. Often, credit bureaus collect information without the knowledge of the individual. Do you think this is a problem? Explain your answer.

3. If some of these linkages were not by computer but were just exchanges of typewritten information, do you think that there would be less of a problem? Why or why not?

4. Schools share information about students. Do you see a problem with schools sharing information?

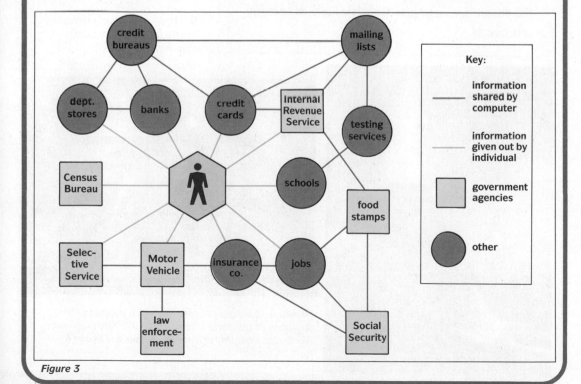

Figure 3

2. Answers will vary.

3. Many students will mention the organizations discussed earlier, such as insurance companies, credit businesses, the Internal Revenue Service, and the FBI.

4. Some students will see a problem with secret files being kept about individuals, and see it as an invasion of privacy. Others will feel that some files, such as in the case of the FBI, are not only justified but also necessary.

The following thinking skills will be applied in answering questions.
- *Tracing* the path of information.
- *Predicting* the spread of information without computers.
- *Evaluating* the practice of schools sharing information.

Answers to questions

1. Credit bureaus collect information from department stores, banks, credit card companies, and mailing lists.

2. Some students will feel that there is a problem with credit bureaus getting information from sources other than the individual. Others will feel that the credit bureaus cannot get adequate information without going to other sources. Many businesses depend on the information from credit bureaus and must get as accurate information as possible.

3. If information were all on paper, there would be less sharing of information. In part, computerized information is spread because the process is simple, quick, and inexpensive. By the time paper documents would be shared, some of the information would be out of date, and the process would be complex and expensive.

4. Answers will vary. Some of this sharing is to the student's benefit. For example, the sharing of information is necessary for colleges to make judgments on applicants.

Unit 6

ENERGY SOURCES

UNIT OVERVIEW

Chapter 21 describes the behavior and uses of radioactive substances. It also discusses the processes of nuclear fission and nuclear fusion, and how these processes can be used to produce energy.

Chapter 22 surveys sources of energy being used currently, and discusses future energy sources. The discussion includes some advantages and disadvantages of each energy source.

Unit Six

ENERGY SOURCES

*H*arnessing energy so that it can be useful is important. There are two groups of energy sources. The sun, wind, water, and internal heat of the earth make up one group. The other group includes fuels, such as oil, natural gas, coal, synthetic fuels, nuclear fuels, and plants. In this unit you will study energy sources presently being used and possible alternative sources of energy. You will also compare the advantages and disadvantages of these energy sources. ■

▲ *The sun could be an important source of energy in the future.*

▼ *These generators produce electrical energy from the energy of moving water.*

◀ *Where there are geysers, there is a potential energy source from the earth's heat. This is Andrew Geyser in North Carolina. Water from the geyser has frozen to form this cone.*

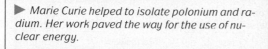

▶ *Marie Curie helped to isolate polonium and radium. Her work paved the way for the use of nuclear energy.*

▼ *Particles are given off when a proton collides with a nucleus. The positive particles are going up, and the negative particles are going down.*

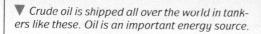

▼ *Crude oil is shipped all over the world in tankers like these. Oil is an important energy source.*

Sections appearing in red provide coverage of basic topics in this unit. See page T23.

NUCLEAR ENERGY

ORGANIZER

Section	pages	Activity	pages	Reinforcement and Evaluation	pages	*Review and Skill Masters	pages	Other Components in Teacher Resource Package	pages
21—1 Radioactivity	523–528	How Can You Make a Model of Half-Life?	527	Review, Challenge	528			*Study Guide* *Poster*	105
21—2 Isotopes and Their Uses	529–532	How Can Radioactivity Be Measured?	531	Review, Challenge	532			*Study Guide* *Lab Manual*	106 107
21—3 Nuclear Fission	533–534			Review, Challenge	534			*Study Guide* *Transparency*	107
21—4 Nuclear Power	535–538			Puzzler Review, Challenge	537 538	Skill Challenge/Critical Thinking	128 129–130	*Study Guide*	108
21—5 Nuclear Fusion	539–541			Review, Challenge	541			*Study Guide*	109
CHAPTER SUMMARY	541					Vocabulary Review	125		
CHAPTER REVIEW	542–543			*Test Masters	81–84	Chapter Review	126		

*In the Teacher Resource Package. For answers, see pages 521b–521d in this book.

ACTIVITY MATERIALS   Quantities are based on a class of 30 students working in groups as indicated in parentheses.

How Can You Make a Model of Half-Life? p. 527 (groups of 2)	quantity	How Can Radioactivity Be Measured? p. 531 (groups of 5)	quantity		quantity
shoebox pennies	15 200	Geiger counter ring stand Cobalt-60 source clamp metric ruler	6 6 6 6		

REVIEW AND SKILL MASTERS

VOCABULARY REVIEW _____ Chapter 21

Unscramble and define the following terms.

1. ytvtcdriiaoia radioactivity—the spontaneous release of energy and particles from the nucleus of an atom

2. rdtnoiaia radiation—the energy and particles released as a nucleus decays

3. paalh elcitrap alpha particle—a particle containing two protons and two neutrons

4. tabe prilecat beta particle—an electron; a particle with a negative charge

5. aammg ysar gamma rays—waves of energy with no charge or mass

6. fhal elfi half life—the time it takes for one-half of the atoms in a radioactive material to decay

7. rctaer tracer—a radioactive atom or molecule that is used to study biological, chemical, or physical processes

8. raelcun fssniio nuclear fission—the splitting of a nucleus into two smaller pieces

9. chani aeiorctn chain reaction—a reaction in which a product causes the reaction to continue

10. uearlcn rrcteao nuclear reactor—a device that is able to make use of nuclear reactions and the energy that they produce

11. ulef fuel—any substance that is used to produce energy

12. rnauecl fnuosi nuclear fusion—the joining of light nuclei to form heavier nuclei

125

CHAPTER REVIEW _____ Chapter 21

21-1 Radioactivity

1. Define radioactivity. Radioactivity is the spontaneous release of energy and particles from the nucleus of an atom.

2. How do alpha, beta, and gamma radiation differ? An alpha particle contains two protons and two neutrons. A beta particle is an electron. A gamma ray is a wave of energy.

3. Describe the decay of carbon-14. What is its half-life? Carbon-14 atoms lose two neutrons to become carbon-12. Carbon-14's half-life is 5,730 years.

21-2 Isotopes and Their Uses

1. How do scientists use radioisotopes as tracers? Scientists trace the movement of radioisotopes to study biological, chemical, or physical processes.

2. Give two examples of radioisotopes in research. Examples will vary. Radioactive carbon dioxide in plants and phosphorus-32 in fertilizer.

3. Give two examples of radioisotopes in medicine. Examples will vary. Iodine-131 in thyroid gland disorders and cobalt-60 in cancer treatments.

21-3 Nuclear Fission

1. Describe what occurs in a fission reaction. In a fission reaction, a nucleus splits into two smaller nuclei and releases energy.

2. Identify the fission fragments in this reaction.

$^{235}_{92}U + ^{1}_{0}n \rightarrow ^{141}_{56}Ba + ^{92}_{36}Kr + 3(^{1}_{0}n)$ + energy

The fission fragments are barium-141 and krypton-92.

126

CHAPTER REVIEW (Continued) _____ Chapter 21

3. Explain what happens in a fission chain reaction. Neutrons released during fission can strike other nuclei, producing more fissions in a chain reaction.

21-4 Nuclear Power

1. What are the three main parts of a nuclear reactor? The three main parts of a nuclear reactor are the core, the coolant, and the containment building.

2. Describe two safety features in a nuclear reactor. Answers will vary. Coolant flows through the core and absorbs excess heat. Control rods can slow the chain reaction.

3. Why are nuclear waste products dangerous? Nuclear waste products are dangerous because they are extremely radioactive.

21-5 Nuclear Fusion

1. Define nuclear fusion. Nuclear fusion is the joining of light nuclei to form heavier nuclei.

2. What conditions are needed for fusion reactions? Fusion takes place only if hydrogen nuclei are moving very fast and if the temperature is very high.

3. Describe the fusion reaction that occurs in the sun. Six hydrogen nuclei combine to form a helium nucleus and two hydrogen nuclei. This process releases energy.

4. Why are fusion reactors an impractical energy source? Fusion reactors require high temperature and pressure conditions. They use more energy than they produce.

127

SKILL/Interpreting a Diagram _____ Chapter 21

Unstable atoms give off energy. This energy is called radioactivity. A radioactive substance emits three kinds of radiation, shown in the diagram below. Alpha particles are heavy and have low energy. Beta particles are light and have medium energy. Gamma radiation is not a particle; it travels in waves. Gamma waves have no mass and very high energy. Study the diagram and answer the questions that follow.

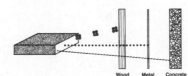

1. Name the two kinds of radiation that are particles.
   Alpha and beta particles.

2. What kind of radiation is hard to stop? Explain your answer.
   Gamma waves are hard to stop because they have very high energy.

3. Why are the large particles of the alpha radiation easy to stop and the small particles of the beta radiation harder to stop?
   Alpha particles are large and cannot pass through matter. Beta particles are smaller and slip through matter.

4. Explain why workers in nuclear power plants are not exposed to radiation.
   Workers in nuclear power plants are not exposed to radiation because nuclear reactors have concrete walls through which radiation cannot pass.

128

CHAPTER 21 PLANNING GUIDE

Name_____ Date_____

CHALLENGE/CRITICAL THINKING _____ Chapter 21

The figure below is an example of a nuclear reaction.

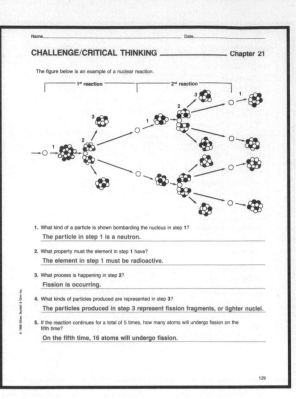

1. What kind of a particle is shown bombarding the nucleus in step 1?

The particle in step 1 is a neutron.

2. What property must the element in step 1 have?

The element in step 1 must be radioactive.

3. What process is happening in step 2?

Fission is occurring.

4. What kinds of particles produced are represented in step 3?

The particles produced in step 3 represent fission fragments, or lighter nuclei.

5. If the reaction continues for a total of 5 times, how many atoms will undergo fission on the fifth time?

On the fifth time, 16 atoms will undergo fission.

© 1989 Silver, Burdett & Ginn Inc.

129

Name_____ Date_____

CHALLENGE/CRITICAL THINKING (Continued) _____ Chapter 21

6. What is the name given to this type of reaction?

It is a chain reaction.

7. Describe one example of this type of reaction.

Answers will vary but should describe a reaction in which a product of the reaction causes the reaction to continue, for example, as in a chain of falling dominos.

8. What is meant by the term *critical mass*?

Critical mass is the minimum amount of the radioactive element needed to keep a chain reaction going.

9. Briefly describe how a nuclear power plant works.

In a nuclear power plant, water is heated and turned to steam. The steam is used to turn turbines, which produce electricity.

10. Controversy surrounds the question of the use of nuclear energy. Write a brief editorial explaining why you think we should continue or discontinue the use of nuclear energy as an energy source.

Answers will vary.

© 1989 Silver, Burdett & Ginn Inc.

130

REVIEW AND SKILL MASTERS

TEST MASTERS

Page 81

Name _____ Date _____ Score _____

Chapter 21

Radioactivity

PART 1 _____

In the space below, write the term that each phrase defines.

Chapter Goal

1. __chain reaction__ — A reaction in which a product of the reaction causes the reaction to continue — 3

2. __alpha particle__ — A form of radiation that contains two protons and two neutrons — 1

3. __nuclear reactor__ — A device that is able to make use of nuclear reactions and the energy that they produce — 4

4. __fuel__ — Any substance that is used to produce energy — 4

5. __tracer__ — A radioactive atom or molecule that is used to study biological, chemical, or physical processes — 2

6. __nuclear fusion__ — The joining of light nuclei to form heavier nuclei — 5

7. __half-life__ — The time that it takes for one half of a sample of radioactive nuclei to decay — 1

8. __nuclear fission__ — The splitting of a nucleus into two smaller nuclei — 3

PART 2 _____

Choose the term or phrase that best answers the question or completes the statement. Write the letter of that choice in the space at the left.

__c__ 1. Water is most often used in a nuclear reactor as: — 4
   a. containment.   c. both coolant and moderator.
   b. moderator.   d. both coolant and containment.

__d__ 2. Which of the following causes a chain reaction? — 3
   a. alpha particles   c. gamma rays
   b. beta particles   d. neutrons

__c__ 3. Control rods control the chain reaction in a nuclear reactor by: — 4
   a. admitting more coolant.   c. absorbing neutrons.
   b. removing fuel.   d. slowing the turbines.

Chapter 21 Radioactivity — 81

Page 82

Name _____ Date _____ Score _____

PART 2 _____

Choose the term or phrase that best answers the question or completes the statement. Write the letter of that choice in the space at the left.

Chapter Goal

__c__ 4. Radioactive iodine and stable iodine have the same: — 2
   a. number of neutrons.   c. chemical properties.
   b. mass number.   d. half-life.

__b__ 5. A Geiger counter is able to measure radiation because radiation causes the formation of: — 2
   a. heat.   c. light.
   b. ions.   d. photons.

__d__ 6. In medicine, radiosotopes that have short half-lives are most likely to be used to: — 2
   a. date materials.   c. kill cells.
   b. treat disorders.   d. detect problems.

__d__ 7. A major problem in producing fusion reactions is: — 5
   a. controlling nuclear waste.   c. keeping the core cool.
   b. obtaining fuel.   d. creating enough heat.

__a__ 8. One similarity between fission reactions and fusion reactions is that both: — 5
   a. release energy.   c. combine nuclei.
   b. produce radioactive fragments.   d. require radioactive decay.

__a__ 9. Which of the following is a fission reaction? — 3
   a. $^{235}_{92}U + ^{1}_{0}n \longrightarrow ^{137}_{53}V + ^{97}_{39}V + 2(^{1}_{0}n)$
   b. $^{15}_{7}N + ^{1}_{1}H \longrightarrow ^{12}_{6}C + ^{4}_{2}He$
   c. $^{12}_{6}C + ^{1}_{1}H \longrightarrow ^{13}_{7}N \longrightarrow ^{13}_{6}C + ^{0}_{-1}e$
   d. $^{32}_{15}P \longrightarrow ^{32}_{16}S + ^{0}_{-1}e$

__a__ 10. In the sun, nuclear reactions form: — 5
   a. helium from hydrogen.   c. barium from uranium.
   b. hydrogen from carbon.   d. uranium from krypton.

__c__ 11. By emitting an alpha particle, a nucleus reduces its mass number by: — 1
   a. 2.   b. 3.   c. 4.   d. 5.

__b__ 12. Which of the following isotopes is most likely to be radioactive? — 1
   a. $^{16}_{8}O$ b. $^{32}_{15}P$ c. $^{12}_{6}C$ d. $^{4}_{2}He$

Chapter 21 Radioactivity — 82

Page 83

Name _____ Date _____ Score _____

PART 3 _____

Look at the table. Then read the questions that follow. Choose the term or phrase that best answers the question or completes the statement. Write the letter of that choice in the space at the left.

Characteristics of Various Isotopes

Isotope	Half-life
$^{1}_{1}H$	—
$^{2}_{1}H$	—
$^{3}_{2}He$	—
$^{4}_{2}He$	—
$^{14}_{6}C$	5,570 years
$^{24}_{11}Na$	15 hours
$^{37}_{18}Ar$	35 days
$^{208}_{82}Pb$	—
$^{212}_{84}Po$	3×10^{-7} seconds
$^{238}_{92}U$	4.5×10^{9} years
$^{239}_{92}U$	23.5 minutes
$^{239}_{93}Np$	2.3 days

Chapter Goal

__b__ 1. Helium-3 can be produced by the fusion of $^{1}_{1}H$ and: — 5
   a. $^{1}_{1}H$.   b. $^{2}_{1}H$.   c. $^{3}_{2}He$.   d. $^{4}_{2}He$.

__a__ 2. Which of the following isotopes would most likely be used as a tracer in biological experiments? — 2
   a. $^{24}_{11}Na$ b. $^{212}_{84}Po$ c. $^{238}_{92}U$ d. $^{14}_{6}C$

__a__ 3. How much of a 20-g sample of $^{37}_{18}Ar$ will be left after 105 days? — 1
   a. 2.5 g   b. 5 g   c. 6.67 g   d. 10 g

__b__ 4. Which of the following is emitted when Polonium-212 decays to Lead-208? — 3
   a. $^{3}_{2}He$ b. $^{4}_{2}He$ c. $^{1}_{1}H$ d. $^{2}_{1}H$

__d__ 5. An unstable nucleus decays to produce $^{234}_{90}Th$ and $^{4}_{2}He$. The half-life of this substance is: — 3
   a. 3×10^{-7} seconds.   c. 2.3 days.
   b. 23.5 minutes.   d. 4.5×10^{9} years.

Chapter 21 Radioactivity — 83

Page 84

Name _____ Date _____ Score _____

PART 4 _____

Read each question or direction and answer it using complete sentences.

Chapter Goal

1. Describe background radiation and its sources. — 1

Small amounts of radiation are found in any environment. This radiation comes from natural sources of radiation in the earth and from cosmic rays from space. This radiation is called background radiation. Some places have more background radiation than do others. If an area has many radioactive rocks, or if a building is made of rock that contains radioactive elements, the background radiation may be high. Background radiation is greater at higher altitudes than at lower altitudes.

2. Describe the accident that took place at the nuclear reactor in Chernobyl, Soviet Union. — 4

In April 1986, an accident occurred at a nuclear reactor in Chernobyl, Soviet Union. Although the reactor was shut down, heat continued to build up in the core. The core overheated, and the graphite used as a moderator began to burn. As a result of the fire, the containment building was destroyed, and radioactive materials were released into the atmosphere.

3. What are the simple fusion reactions that take place in the sun, and the temperature conditions necessary for them? — 5

In the sun, ordinary hydrogen nuclei, $^{1}_{1}H$, combine to form helium nuclei. The process involves many steps. Six hydrogen nuclei are needed for each helium nucleus formed. Two hydrogen nuclei are also produced in the reaction. The temperature in the center of the sun is very high. This temperature is high enough to allow fusion to take place.

Chapter 21 Radioactivity — 84

21

NUCLEAR ENERGY

The questions in the CHAPTER TEST are based on these Chapter Goals.

1. Define the term *radioactivity*, and distinguish between alpha, beta, and gamma radiations; describe the decay and half-life of an unstable nucleus.

2. Describe how isotopes are used as tracers, and give examples of radioisotopes used in research and in medicine.

3. Describe fission reactions, identify fission fragments, and explain how a chain reaction occurs.

4. Identify the parts of and safety features needed in a nuclear reactor, and discuss the problems created by the wastes from a nuclear reactor.

5. Describe a fusion reactor, identify the fusion reaction that takes place in the sun, and explain why fusion reactors are not yet practical sources of energy.

NUCLEAR ENERGY

Nuclear reactors can produce large amounts of energy from small amounts of matter. The nuclear reactor shown in the photograph is an experimental reactor that can produce 100 trillion watts of electricity. Nuclear reactors generate about 10 percent of the electricity used in the United States.

- *How do nuclear reactions produce energy from matter?*
- *How is nuclear energy changed into electrical energy?*

21-1 RADIOACTIVITY

In 1896, Henri Becquerel, a French scientist, observed that a covered photographic plate became changed when placed near a uranium compound. He said that unseen rays emitted, or given off, by the uranium might cause this effect. He also said that the rays could pass through the cover and then react with the plate just as light does. He called the process that forms these rays *radioactivity* (ray dee oh ak TIHV uh tee). About the same time, Pierre and Marie Curie showed the same effect with radium compounds.

Radioactivity is the spontaneous release of energy and particles from the nucleus of an atom. Elements that give off energy and particles are said to be radioactive elements. As a radioactive atom releases particles from the nucleus, it changes into an atom of another element. This process is called *radioactive decay*. The energy and particles that are released as a nucleus decays are called **radiation** (ray dee AY shuhn).

All elements with atomic numbers greater than 83 are radioactive. Some isotopes of elements with atomic numbers less than 83 also are radioactive. Atoms whose nuclei decay spontaneously are said to be unstable. Why are some nuclei unstable while others are stable? Recall that all nuclei except those of hydrogen-1 atoms contain neutrons as well as protons. Stable nuclei tend to have a balance between protons and neutrons. If a nucleus has too many neutrons for its number of protons or too few

After completing this section, you will be able to

- **define** the term *radioactivity*.
- **distinguish** between alpha, beta, and gamma radiation.
- **describe** the decay and half-life of an unstable nucleus.

The key terms in this section are
alpha particle
beta particle
gamma rays
half-life
radiation
radioactivity

radians (beam)

CHAPTER OPENING STRATEGY

Have students make observations about the photograph. Ask students what fuel the reactor is using to produce electricity. Discuss the fact that in this reactor, atoms are being fused. Explain that the nuclear reactions occurring in the reactor are similar to the nuclear reactions taking place in the sun. Point out that even though nuclear reactors produce large amounts of energy, such reactors produce only a small percentage of the energy consumed yearly in the United states.
- How do nuclear reactions produce energy from matter? (Nuclear reactions cause atoms to split or to combine which produces energy.)
- How is nuclear energy changed into electrical energy? (The energy from nuclear reactions converts water to steam. The steam turns a turbine, which produces electrical energy.)

21-1   RADIOACTIVITY
pages 523–528

OBJECTIVES
Refer to pupil page 523.

VOCABULARY
Key terms: alpha particle, beta particle, gamma rays, half-life, radioactivity
Other terms: background radiation, decay series, radioactive decay, radioisotopes

1 MOTIVATION

Obtain a Geiger counter, and use it to detect background radiation, which comes from within the earth and from outer space. If any students have wrist watches with luminous dials, use the counter to detect the radioactivity given off by the dials. Many earth science classrooms have samples of radioactive materials that can be used. Ask students what the Gieger counter detects. Ask them to name some radioactive materials.

2 CONCEPT DEVELOPMENT

Background   In 1902, Ernest Rutherford, a British physicist, found out that radioactive elements give off electrically charged particles. Rutherford called them alpha particles and beta particles, and he stated that when the particles are given off, the process changes the atom into a different kind of atom. By 1911, Rutherford had discovered the nucleus. He stated that nearly all the mass of an atom is in its nucleus. He also stated that electrons are constantly orbiting the nucleus. Since Rutherford worked out the nuclear theory of the atom, he is called the Father of Nuclear Science.

Thinking Skills

comparing
Students compare two isotopes of carbon in Figure 21-1. They conclude that carbon-14 is unstable because it has more neutrons than protons.

Teaching Tip   Stress that radioactivity can be both useful and harmful. It is up to people to make intelligent use of their knowledge about radioactivity.

Teaching Tip   Gamma rays are like light rays but are of shorter wavelength, or higher frequency. Gamma rays move at the speed of light. Alpha particles and beta particles move at lower speeds.

Enrichment   Have students research the experiments of Ernest Rutherford and Hans Geiger. Have students report to the class how these physicists hypothesized the existence of a central nucleus in atoms.

Poster

The Teacher Resource Package includes a poster that shows the electromagnetic spectrum. You may wish to display this poster in your classroom.

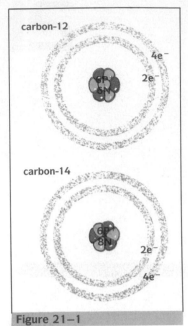

Figure 21—1

Two isotopes of carbon.

neutrons for its number of protons, the nucleus will be unstable. An unstable nucleus will be radioactive. It will give off radiation in the form of alpha (AL fuh), beta (BAY-tuh), or gamma (GAM uh) radiation.

Recall that isotopes of an element have the same number of protons but different numbers of neutrons. Figure 21-1 shows two isotopes of carbon. To be stable, small nuclei should have almost the same number of neutrons as protons. Carbon-12 is stable. Carbon-14 has too many neutrons and is unstable. Isotopes that are unstable, like carbon-14, are called *radioisotopes*.

The alpha radiation given off by radioisotopes is made up of particles. An **alpha particle** contains two protons and two neutrons. It is the same as the nucleus of a helium atom, so its symbol is ^4_2He. Because it has two protons but no electrons, an alpha particle has a 2+ charge.

The beta radiation given off by unstable nuclei also is made up of particles. A **beta particle** is an electron. Its symbol is $^0_{-1}e$. The −1 in the symbol shows that like other electrons, a beta particle has a negative charge.

Gamma rays are not made up of particles. **Gamma rays** are waves of energy. They do not have a charge, and they do not have mass. These rays are part of the electromagnetic spectrum. As you can see in Figure 21-2, gamma rays are located at the high frequency–high energy end of the spectrum.

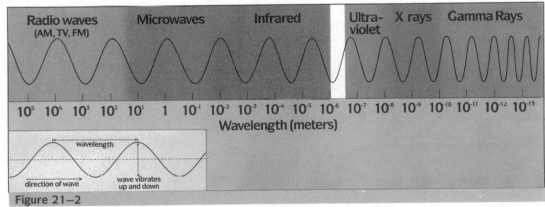

Figure 21—2

The electromagnetic spectrum.

Because gamma rays have a lot of energy, they can penetrate matter well. A thick layer of lead or concrete is needed to stop them. Beta particles do not have as much energy. A sheet of metal 1 cm thick can stop beta particles. Alpha particles have the least energy. Alpha particles can be stopped by a sheet of paper.

Small amounts of radiation are found in any environment. This radiation comes from natural sources of radiation in the earth and from cosmic rays from space. This radiation is called *background radiation*. Some places have more of it than do others. If there are many radioactive rocks in an area or if a building is made of rock that contains radioactive elements, the background radiation may be high. Background radiation is greater at higher altitudes than at lower altitudes. At higher altitudes the air is less dense, so it absorbs less cosmic radiation.

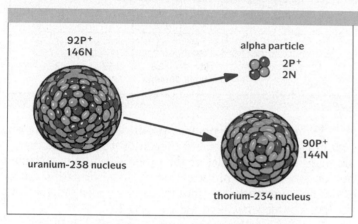

Figure 21–3

When a uranium-238 nucleus decays, it produces a thorium-234 nucleus and an alpha particle.

92P⁺
146N

alpha particle

2P⁺
2N

uranium-238 nucleus

90P⁺
144N

thorium-234 nucleus

When a radioactive nucleus emits an alpha particle or a beta particle, the atom changes to a different kind of atom. Figure 21-3 shows how a nucleus of uranium-238 decays by giving off an alpha particle. This process can be written as an equation.

$$^{238}_{92}\text{U} \rightarrow\, ^{234}_{90}\text{Th} + {}^{4}_{2}\text{He}$$

The uranium-238 nucleus contains 92 protons and 146 neutrons. Its mass number is 238. When this nucleus gives off an alpha particle, it loses 2 protons and 2 neutrons. Its mass number is now 234. The nucleus that is left has only 90 protons and is now a thorium nucleus. You can read the superscripts as a simple equation.

$$238 = 234 + 4$$

The superscripts represent mass number. This equation shows that the total number of particles stays the same. The subscripts also can be read as an equation.

$$92 = 90 + 2$$

The subscripts represent the number of protons. This equation shows that the total charge stays the same.

Thinking Skills

interpreting diagrams
Students follow the process of radioactive decay in Figure 21-3 as a nucleus of uranium-238 gives off an alpha particle. Have them relate the diagram to the equation in Figure 21-3.

Background   In one year everyone on the earth receives at least 30 millirems of radiation from cosmic rays. The atmosphere protects people and other living things from higher doses. People who travel in airplanes at heights over 9 km (about 30,000 ft) receive more intense cosmic rays. A pilot of a jet airplane receives as much radiation as many of the workers in a nuclear power plant—about 1000 millirems a year.

Teaching Tip   Discuss with students the fact that most people receive an average of 100 millirems of natural radiation a year. Some radiation enters the body along with what a person breathes, eats, and drinks.

Background   Not all natural radiation originates from cosmic rays. Some comes from within the earth. Ash from the eruption of Mount St. Helens contained the radioactive elements radon, radium, and thorium. In radiation "hot spots" on the earth, such as in the Kerala region of India, people receive at least 1500 millirems of natural radiation a year.

Background In 1932 the British physicist James Chadwick discovered that besides protons, the nucleus also contains neutrons. Later, in 1938, two German chemists, Otto Hahn and Fritz Strassmann, split uranium atoms by bombarding them with neutrons, producing barium. In 1939, Lise Meitner and Otto Frisch interpreted the work of Hahn and Strassman and calculated the energy released by nuclear fission. In 1942, Enrico Fermi produced the first atomic chain reactions.

Background Radioactive decay may take very little time, even as little as 10^{-21} seconds.

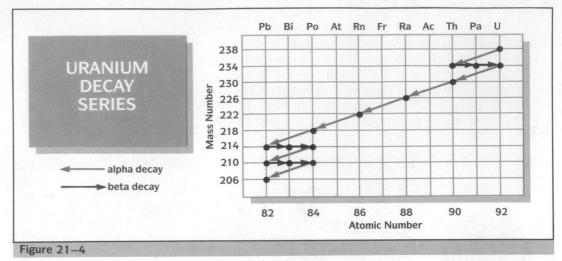

Figure 21—4

The decay series of uranium-238 includes both alpha decays and beta decays.

The thorium-234 nucleus produced by the decay of uranium-238 is also unstable. Figure 21-4 shows that there are many decay steps before the process results in a stable nucleus. For uranium, the stable nucleus formed is lead-206. The complete set of steps that show how a radioactive nucleus changes is called a *decay series*.

Figure 21-4 shows the entire uranium-238 decay series. You can see that in this series not all of the changes are alpha decays. For example, the thorium-234 formed from uranium-238 decays by giving off a beta particle. In a beta decay, one neutron changes into one proton and one electron. This electron leaves the nucleus at a high speed. This high-speed electron is a beta particle. The nucleus that remains now has one more proton and one less neutron than it had before.

Figure 21—5

When a thorium-234 nucleus decays, it produces a protactinium-235 nucleus and a beta particle.

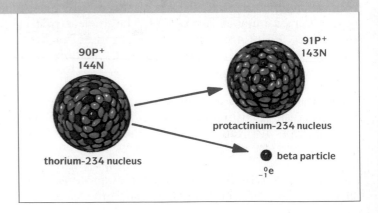

ACTIVITY How Can You Make a Model of Half-Life?

OBJECTIVE
Demonstrate the decay of a radioisotope.

MATERIALS
shoebox, 200 pennies

PROCEDURE
A. Draw a data table like the one shown.
B. Place 200 pennies tails up in a shoebox. Place the cover securely on the box.
C. Shake the box with one quick up-and-down motion.
D. Open the box and remove all pennies that are heads up. In the data table, record the number of pennies removed and the number of pennies remaining.
E. Repeat steps **C** and **D** nine more times.

Trial	Number of Pennies Removed	Number of Pennies Remaining
1		
2		
3		

RESULTS AND CONCLUSIONS
1. What do the coins in the model represent?
2. What do the coins with heads up represent?
3. How does the model demonstrate the concept of half-life?
4. Prepare a graph of your data. Put the trial numbers on the x-axis, and the number of pennies remaining on the y-axis.

ACTIVITY 30 minutes

PROCESS SKILLS
observing, recording data, graphing data, interpreting data, interpreting graphs

Preparation None required.

Answers to Results and Conclusions
1. The coins represent radioactive nuclei.
2. The coins with heads up represent the number of radioactive nuclei that decayed.
3. With each shake, the number of radioactive nuclei (tails) was reduced by one half; that is, about one half of the radioactive nuclei decayed.
4. The graph should show a curved line moving downward from the left to the right.

Figure 21-5 shows how a thorium-234 nucleus decays into a protactinium nucleus by a beta decay. This process can be written as an equation.

$$^{234}_{90}\text{Th} \rightarrow {}^{234}_{91}\text{Pa} + {}^{0}_{-1}\text{e}$$

The thorium-234 nucleus contains 90 protons and 144 neutrons. When a beta particle is lost, one neutron becomes a proton. As a result, a nucleus with 91 protons and 143 neutrons is formed. What isotope of protactinium has formed?[1]

Gamma rays are given off when some radioactive decays take place. The release of alpha or beta particles involves energy changes. The nucleus can give off some of this energy in the form of gamma rays.

Each radioactive substance decays at its own rate. The decay of a single atom cannot be predicted. However, the time it takes for many decays to take place is known. The time that it takes for one half of a sample of radioactive nuclei to decay is called the **half-life** of that substance. For example, the half-life of francium-220 is 27.5 seconds. This means that in 27.5 seconds one half of the nuclei in a sample of francium-220 will decay. In another 27.5 seconds one half of the remaining nuclei will decay, leaving only one fourth the original nuclei unchanged. Thus, three fourths of the nuclei will decay in 55 seconds. Figure 21-6 shows the way in which the process continues. How long will it take for seven eighths of the francium-220 to decay?[2]

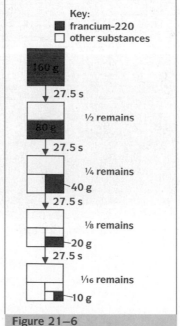

Key:
■ francium-220
□ other substances

160 g
↓ 27.5 s
½ remains
80 g
↓ 27.5 s
¼ remains
40 g
↓ 27.5 s
⅛ remains
20 g
↓ 27.5 s
1⁄16 remains
10 g

Figure 21—6
The half-life of francium-220 is 27.5 seconds. After 110 seconds, only one sixteenth of the original sample remains.

[1]Protactiniuml-234.
[2]82.5 seconds.

Thinking Skills

interpreting tables
Students use Table 21-1 to determine the age of a fossil by using the percentage of carbon-14 still left in the animal's body.

3 REVIEW/REINFORCEMENT

1. Radioactivity is the spontaneous release of energy and particles from the nucleus of an atom.
2. An atom's nucleus is unstable if there are too many protons or neutrons in the nucleus.
3. A half-life is the amount of time needed for one half of the nuclei of a radioactive substance in a sample to decay.
4. Alpha rays and beta rays are both particles, but alpha rays are positive particles, and beta rays are negative particles. Alpha particles cannot pass through matter easily, but beta particles can. It takes a piece of metal 1 cm thick to stop beta particles. Gamma rays are pure energy, have no charge or mass, and pass through matter easily. A thick layer of lead or concrete is needed to stop gamma rays.

Challenge   Because one eighth of a sample remains, three half-lives have passed; the half-life of the isotope is 36 minutes.

Some substances have very long half-lives. The half-life of uranium-238 is 4.5 billion years. The age of the earth is estimated to be 4.5 billion years. Thus one half of the uranium nuclei have decayed to other nuclei since the earth was formed.

A knowledge of half-lives can be useful in finding the age of fossils. Table 21-1 shows some radioisotopes used to find the age of different materials. As you can see the half-life of carbon-14 is 5730 years. All living things contain a constant percentage of carbon-14. Living plants and animals constantly take in carbon. This carbon replaces the decaying carbon-14. When plants and animals die, they stop taking in carbon. Thus when carbon-14 atoms decay, they are not replaced. The percentage of carbon-14 decreases. Suppose a fossil is found that has only one-eighth the carbon-14 that living animals have. That would mean three half-lives have passed since the animal died. Thus, the fossil is believed to be 17,190 years old.

Table 21-1 *Some Radioisotopes Used in Dating*

Isotope	Half-life	Objects to Be Dated	Useful Range (years)
Carbon-14	5730	Organic materials	500–50,000
Potassium-40	1.3×10^9	Earth's crust; Moon's crust	10,000 and older
Rhenium-187	4.3×10^{10}	Meteorites	40,000 and older
Uranium-238	4.5×10^9	Earth's crust	10,000,000 and older

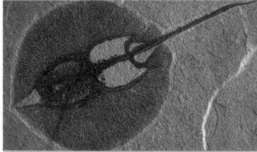

Figure 21–7

Fossils of a stingray (*left*) and a mastadon (*right*).

REVIEW

1. What is radioactivity?
2. What causes an atom's nucleus to be unstable?
3. What is a half-life?
4. How do alpha, beta, and gamma radiation differ?

CHALLENGE If one eighth of a sample of a radioisotope remains after 108 minutes, what is the half-life of this isotope?

21-2 ISOTOPES AND THEIR USES

Many radioisotopes are known to scientists. As you have seen, radioisotopes with long half-lives are used to date materials. Those with shorter half-lives are used in other kinds of research.

Some radioisotopes are used as tracers. A **tracer** is a radioactive atom or molecule that is used to study biological, chemical, or physical processes. All isotopes of an element behave the same chemically, whether they are radioactive or not. The radioactive isotopes are easy to detect, so it is easy to trace their movements. For example, a leak in a buried pipe may be difficult to locate. A small amount of radioactive material can be added to the liquid moving through the pipe. This material can be traced with a device that detects radiation. Thus workers can find the leak without digging all along the pipe.

Biologists can use tracers to follow the path of substances in living things. Food made in the leaves of plants can be traced throughout the plant. The tracer used for this is radioactive carbon dioxide, which contains carbon-14. Such molecules used as tracers are sometimes called *tagged molecules*.

Leaves will absorb the tagged carbon dioxide. The food molecules made from the tagged carbon dioxide will contain the radioactive carbon. When the leaf is placed on a piece of photographic film, the radiation from the tracer will darken, or expose, the film. The greater the amount of radioactive molecules in the leaf, the more the film will darken.

After completing this section, you will be able to

- **describe** how isotopes are used as tracers.
- **give examples** of radioisotopes used in research.
- **give examples** of isotopes used in medicine.

The key term in this section is tracer

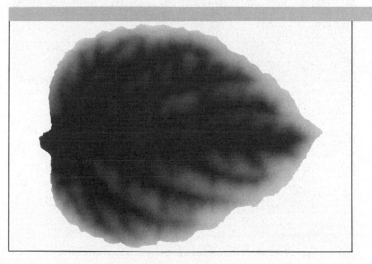

Figure 21—8

The dark areas on the film were caused by beta radiation given off by phosphorus-32 in a leaf.

21-2 ISOTOPES AND THEIR USES
pages 529–532

OBJECTIVES
Refer to pupil page 529.

VOCABULARY
Key term: tracer
Other term: tagged molecules

1 MOTIVATION

If a fossil collection is available, display a variety of fossils, and tell students the estimated age of each. Remind students how the age of a fossil is determined. Ask them why carbon-14 is used to date recent fossils. Ask students why uranium would be used to date very old fossils. Tell students that they will learn about the use of radioisotopes in this section.

2 CONCEPT DEVELOPMENT

Background   A nuclide is an atom that has a specific atomic number and atomic mass. Radioactive nuclides come predominantly from nuclear power plants and nuclear accelerators. Low intensity sources, which may be available to you, are not dangerous but should be handled with care. Students should be instructed, by words and by the way you handle these materials, to have respect for radioactivity.

Thinking Skills

interpreting diagrams
Students use Table 21-2 to find out the uses of various radioisotopes in medicine. Students may want to do research to find out why certain radioisotopes have been chosen over others for various medical uses.

Teaching Tip Students may have negative attitudes towards anything "nuclear." Stress the routine, everyday uses of radioactivity in hospitals, laboratories, and universities. Interested students might want to find out about the use of radioactivity at local facilities and then report to the class on the uses of these materials and the facilities' safety records.

Enrichment Have students list the chemical symbol, number of protons, and number of neutrons of the nuclides listed in Table 21-2.

Teaching Tip At the end of this section, review the carbon-dating technique first discussed in the *Motivation* section.

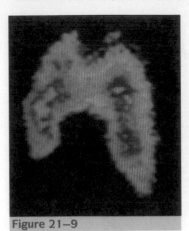

Figure 21—9

A scan of a normal thyroid gland produces an image like this.

The radioisotope phosphorus-32 was used to find out how well plants absorb fertilizer. Phosphorus-32 was added to fertilizer, and the rate at which this tracer entered plants was measured. Through these and other tests, scientists discovered that some nutrients can be absorbed directly by leaves.

In medicine, tracers can be used to detect problems with internal organs. Table 21-2 lists some radioisotopes and their medical uses. For example, thyroid gland disorders can be detected by using iodine-131 as a tracer. The thyroid gland secretes a hormone that affects the body's metabolic rate. Iodine, which is used in the production of this hormone, is absorbed by the thyroid gland. When iodine-131 tracer is injected into the body, it is absorbed by the thyroid gland. Radiation scanners can detect the tracer and produce an image like the one shown in Figure 21-9. Thus a doctor can tell if the gland is normal or enlarged.

Notice that the isotopes listed in Table 21-2 have short half-lives. Radiation can have a harmful effect on living tissues. Therefore, doctors try to use isotopes that will last long enough to help identify a problem but not long enough to harm the patient. Radiation can kill cells. It can also damage some of the chemicals that are needed for the chemical reactions that take place in cells. Radiation can cause genetic damage and cause cancer.

Table 21-2 *Some Radioisotopes Used in Medicine*

Isotope	Half-life	Uses
Arsenic-74	17.9 days	Locate brain tumors
Barium-131	11.6 days	Detect bone tumors
Chromium-51	27.8 days	Determine blood volume
Gold-198	64.8 hours	Test kidney activity
Iodine-131	8.07 days	Detect and treat thyroid problems; find blood clots
Iron-59	54.0 days	Find rate of red blood cell production
Mercury-197	65.0 hours	Find brain tumors; test spleen function
Radium-225	14.8 days	Detect skin cancer
Sodium-24	15.0 hours	Find blockage in circulatory system
Technetium-99	6.0 hours	Detect brain tumors; detect blood clots

ACTIVITY   How Can Radioactivity Be Measured?

OBJECTIVE
Determine the effect of distance on the amount of radioactivity detected by a Geiger counter.

MATERIALS
ring stand, radioactive source, forceps, Geiger counter, clamp, metric ruler, graph paper

PROCEDURE
A. Prepare a data table like the one shown.
B. Using forceps, place a radioactive source on a ring stand as shown in the figure. **Caution:** Do not pick up the source with your hands.
C. Clamp a Geiger counter tube 10 cm above the source.
D. Record the number of counts registered by the Geiger counter in 1 minute.
E. Raise the Geiger counter tube and repeat step **D** for distances of 20, 30, and 40 cm.
F. Prepare a graph of your data, showing distance on the x-axis and counts per minute on the y-axis.

Distance (cm)	Counts per Minute
10	
20	
30	
40	

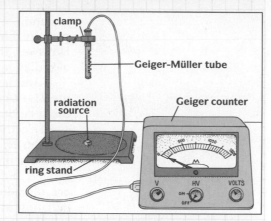

clamp

Geiger-Müller tube

radiation source

Geiger counter

ring stand

RESULTS AND CONCLUSIONS
1. Describe your graph.
2. What do the data tell you about the effect of distance on the amount of radioactivity reaching the Geiger counter?

EXTENSION
Place the Geiger counter tube 10 cm from the source, and record the number of counts in 1 minute. Place a sheet of paper on the source and repeat the count. Continue to add paper and record counts. Can you reduce the counts to zero?

Sometimes the effects of radiation can be put to use. Radiation is used to treat some kinds of tumors. Radioactive iodine can be used to treat thyroid tumors. Cobalt-60 is used to treat some kinds of cancer. Cobalt-60 is a good source of gamma rays. The cobalt-60 source can be outside the patient's body, or it can be placed inside the body. Because cobalt-60 has a half-life of 5.26 years, it is a long-lasting source of radiation.

Because radiation can be harmful, radioisotopes must be handled carefully. Radioactive substances are stored in thick containers that can absorb radiation. Radioactive substances are marked with a special label, as shown in Figure 21-10. This label is used in hospitals and laboratories all over the world so that any worker can recognize radioactive substances.

People who work with radioactive substances must be able to keep track of the amount of radiation around

Figure 21–10

Radioactive materials must be properly labeled.

ACTIVITY   30 minutes

PROCESS SKILLS
observing, measuring, recording data, graphing data, interpreting data

Preparation   Cobalt-60 is a commonly used beta emitter. Check your local, regional, and state science organizations to comply with safety regulations in the handling of radioactive materials.

Safety Tip   Tell students not to pick up a source of radioactivity with their hands.

Answers to Results and Conclusions
1. The graph should be a hyperbola, an inverse square relationship between counts per minute and distance.
2. As distance increases, the number of counts per minute decreases.

Extension   Paper is a poor shield from the radioactivity emitted by a radioactive source. The number of counts per minute should change very little until many sheets are used. It would take a very large number of sheets to reduce the counts per minute down to that of background level.

Thinking Skills

observing
In Figure 21-10, students become familiar with the special label used to mark radioactive materials. Students can discuss where they have seen this internationally recognized label.

Enrichment Have students research other radiation counters, such as the solid-state detectors that are now available. Have students discuss the advantages of these detectors over the Geiger counter.

3 REVIEW/REINFORCEMENT

1. A tracer is a radioactive atom or molecule that is needed to study biological, chemical, or physical processes.
2. Biologists use carbon-14 to follow the path of substances in living things; food made in the leaves of a plant can be traced throughout the plant.
3. Accept answers from Table 21-2.

Challenge Technetium-99 has a half-life of only 6 hours.

them. Various instruments are used to detect and measure radiation. Photographic film is one tool used to detect radiation. The badge shown in Figure 21-11B contains a piece of film. This is an inexpensive radiation detector. However, the film has to be developed before the effects of radiation can be seen.

Another radiation monitor is the Geiger counter. Figure 21-11A shows a Geiger counter. When radiation enters the tube, it ionizes the gas in the tube. The ions create a small electric current. The current is recorded by the counter and can be shown on the scale of a meter. Some Geiger counters make a clicking sound each time a current is created in the tube. The more clicks, the greater the number of radioactive decays being counted and the more radiation in the area.

The pocket radiation monitor shown in Figure 21-11C also contains gas that is ionized by radiation. If you look into the tube you can see a scale that shows the total amount of radiation it has received.

Figure 21–11

Radiation monitors include the Geiger counter (A), film badge (B), and the pocket radiation monitor (C).

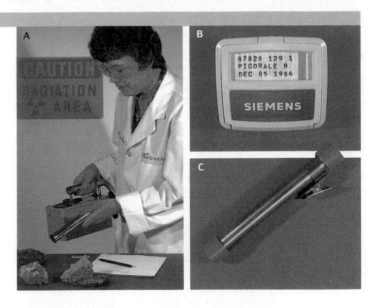

REVIEW

1. What is a tracer?
2. How is carbon-14 used in plant research?
3. Give two examples of radioisotopes used in medicine.

CHALLENGE The isotope of technetium used as a tracer is made in the laboratory where it will be used. Why can this isotope not be purchased and stored until it is used?

21-3 NUCLEAR FISSION

Albert Einstein said that energy and mass are different aspects of the same thing and that each may be converted into the other. A huge amount of energy results from the conversion of a small amount of mass. You may have heard of his equation, $E = mc^2$. In this equation, E stands for energy, m stands for mass, and c stands for the speed of light. According to the equation, one gram of matter is equivalent to 9×10^{13} joules of energy. This is enough energy to heat a house for 1000 years.

Einstein's equation was based only on thought and calculation. He did no experiments. At that time no one knew how to cause the conversion of mass into energy. In 1939, scientists experimenting with neutrons caused such a conversion. When neutrons were shot at a sample of uranium, lighter elements were produced. Some of the uranium atoms had split into smaller atoms. This change released large amounts of energy. The energy came from small amounts of mass lost from the nucleus as it split. Thus Einstein's theory had been demonstrated in the laboratory.

The splitting of a nucleus into two smaller pieces is called **nuclear fission**. This process can be written as an equation. The symbol for a neutron is ^1_0n. The subscript 0 shows that the neutron has no charge. The superscript 1 shows that the mass of one neutron is about 1 amu.

$$^{235}_{92}U + ^1_0n \rightarrow ^{141}_{56}Ba + ^{92}_{36}Kr + 3(^1_0n) + energy$$

Notice in the equation that energy is released as a result of the fission of uranium. Recall that in a chemical reaction the mass of the reactants is equal to the mass of the products. In this reaction the total mass of the uranium and the neutron is slightly greater than the total mass of the products on the right side of the equation. The "missing" mass has been changed into energy. Fission reactions, and other reactions involving the nuclei of atoms, are called *nuclear reactions*.

In this example, the uranium nucleus has split into a barium-141 nucleus and a krypton-92 nucleus. The products of a fission reaction are called *fission fragments*. Fission reactions also release 2 or 3 neutrons. How many neutrons were released in the reaction shown above? [1] This example is only one of many possible results for the fission of uranium-235. Isotopes of more than 35 elements can be produced. As a result, the fission of a sample of uranium-235 produces a mixture of elements.

[1] Three.

After completing this section, you will be able to

- **describe** fission reactions.
- **identify** fission fragments.
- **explain** how a chain reaction occurs.

The key terms in this section are
chain reaction
nuclear fission

fissio (to split)

Figure 21–12

Lise Meitner was the first scientist to publish an explanation of nuclear fission.

OBJECTIVES
Refer to pupil page 533.

VOCABULARY
Key terms: chain reaction, nuclear fission
Other terms: critical mass, fission fragments, nuclear reactions

1 MOTIVATION

Demonstrate the concept of nuclear fission by using two sets of dominoes. Set up the first set in such a way that when the first domino is tipped over, a few dominoes will fall but the majority will remain standing. Set up the other set so that when the first domino is tipped over, all the others will be tipped in chain-reaction style. Ask students why this second demonstration is analogous to a chain reaction in nuclear fission. Ask them if the chain reaction could be stopped.

Transparency

The Teacher Resource Package includes a color transparency and a black-line master of Figures 21-13B and 21-18. You may wish to use these in your discussion of fission and fusion.

2 CONCEPT DEVELOPMENT

Thinking Skills

interpreting diagrams
In Figure 21-13, students study a chain reaction. Their attention is drawn to the importance of having a critical mass if a chain reaction is desired. Students determine how many neutrons are given off by each uranium nucleus when it is split.

Teaching Tip   Point out to students that energy from nuclear chain reactions must be controlled to be useful and that the first controlled reaction took place in 1942, under the direction of the Italian scientist Enrico Fermi.

Enrichment   Have interested students research Enrico Fermi and his contribution to the understanding of nuclear fission. Have them present their findings to the class.

3 REVIEW/REINFORCEMENT

1. A nucleus is split into two smaller, nearly equal pieces.
2. Fission fragments are the products of a fission reaction.
3. $^{95}_{38}$Sr, $^{139}_{54}$Xe.
4. In a chain reaction a product of one reaction causes the reaction to continue.

Challenge $^{97}_{40}$Zr

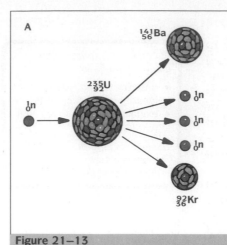
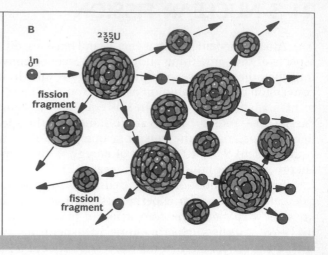

Figure 21–13

The fission of uranium-235 (*A*). A chain reaction (*B*).

What happens to the neutrons released during fission? These neutrons move quickly and can strike other nuclei, producing more fissions. This type of reaction is called a chain reaction. A **chain reaction** is one in which a product of a reaction causes the reaction to continue.

Figure 21-13B shows a chain reaction. Notice that each neutron produced splits another uranium atom. This can take place only in a large sample of uranium. In a small sample the neutrons might escape from the sample without causing another fission. The fission chain reaction might start but then quickly die out. The minimum amount of uranium that can keep the chain reaction going is called the *critical mass*. If the critical mass of uranium is present, the released neutrons will have a good chance of striking another uranium-235 nucleus. A critical mass of uranium is a source of great amounts of energy. As you will see later, the concepts of chain reaction and critical mass are put to use in nuclear power plants.

REVIEW

1. What happens in a fission reaction?
2. What are fission fragments?
3. Identify the fission fragments in this reaction.

$$^{235}_{92}\text{U} + {}^{1}_{0}\text{n} \rightarrow {}^{95}_{38}\text{Sr} + {}^{139}_{54}\text{Xe} + 2({}^{1}_{0}\text{n}) + \text{energy}$$

4. What happens in a chain reaction?

CHALLENGE   Identify x, y, and Z in the following fission reaction.

$$^{235}_{92}\text{U} + {}^{1}_{0}\text{n} \rightarrow {}^{x}_{y}\text{Z} + {}^{137}_{52}\text{Te} + 2({}^{1}_{0}\text{n})$$

21-4 NUCLEAR POWER

Recall that fission reactions release energy. A **nuclear reactor** is a device that is able to make use of nuclear reactions and the energy that they produce. Reactors can be used to generate electric power.

NUCLEAR REACTORS

In a nuclear power plant, as in some other kinds of power plants, water is heated and turned to steam. The steam is used to turn turbines, which produce electricity. In nonnuclear power plants a chemical fuel, such as coal or oil, is burned. The energy released heats the water. In a nuclear power plant, like the one shown in Figure 21-14, the heat is produced in a nuclear reactor.

The three main parts of a nuclear reactor are the core, the coolant, and the containment building. The core contains the fuel. A **fuel** is any substance that is used to produce energy. In most nuclear reactors the fuel is uranium-235. The fuel is shaped into pellets, which are packed into rods.

After completing this section, you will be able to

- **identify** the parts of a nuclear reactor.
- **describe** the safety features needed in a nuclear reactor.
- **discuss** the problems created by the wastes from a nuclear reactor.

The key terms in this section are
fuel
nuclear reactor

Figure 21-14

A nuclear power plant.

Recall that the fission of a uranium-235 nucleus releases neutrons, which can cause more fissions to take place. Thus a chain reaction can be produced. Many of these neutrons move so quickly that they cannot cause any more fissions. A substance called a *moderator* is used to slow the movement of the neutrons so that they will cause more fissions. The first moderator used was graphite. Today, water is commonly used as a moderator.

21-4 NUCLEAR POWER
pages 535–538

OBJECTIVES
Refer to pupil page 535.

VOCABULARY
Key terms: fuel, nuclear reactor
Other term: moderator

1 MOTIVATION

Have the class discuss energy use in the United States and the sources of energy available in various areas. Have students list the benefits and the problems associated with using each of these sources of energy in your area: wind, water movement, the sun, coal, oil, and nuclear reactions.

2 CONCEPT DEVELOPMENT

Background   The growth of the nuclear industry in this country has been largely curtailed by public outcry against its potential dangers. Nevertheless, nuclear fission provides about 10 percent of the nation's energy and will continue to provide us with energy for the next 50 years or more.

Teaching Tip   Have students compare what happens in a nuclear fission power plant and an oil-burning power plant.

Thinking Skills

interpreting diagrams
Students observe Figure 21-15 to find out the role of control rods in a nuclear reactor.

Enrichment Arrange for a visit to a nearby nuclear power plant or invite a power-plant spokesperson to visit the class to discuss nuclear power.

Enrichment Have students find out how many nuclear power plants there are in the United States and how much of our electrical energy is provided by nuclear power.

Review and Skill Masters

SKILL, page 128. See page 521b in this book for answers.

Notice in Figure 21-15 that the core also contains control rods. The control rods are used to absorb neutrons and slow or stop the chain reaction in the core. They are made of boron, steel, or cadmium, which can absorb neutrons easily. As the control rods are pushed into the core, neutrons are absorbed and the fission reaction slows. The reaction stops completely when the control rods are pushed all the way into the core. If the control rods are removed, the chain reaction will start again.

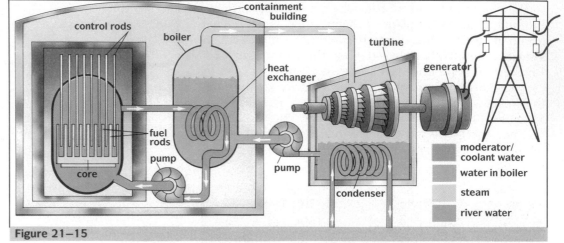

Figure 21-15

The structure of a nuclear power plant.

A chain reaction produces large amounts of heat energy. This is the energy that will be used to generate electricity. A substance called a coolant flows through the core and absorbs heat. If this heat were not carried away from the core, the core could be damaged or could even melt. Carbon dioxide, helium, and liquid sodium can be used as coolants. Water is often used because it can serve as both moderator and coolant.

As the coolant leaves the core, it flows through a device called a heat exchanger. Heat from the coolant boils water. The steam produced turns turbines, which generate electricity. Notice in Figure 21-15 that the coolant does not mix with the water that will pass through the turbine. Heat is transferred, but the fluids are kept apart.

The steam that leaves the turbines must be condensed to a liquid before it can be pumped back to the boiler. Nuclear power plants are usually built near large bodies of water so that there is water for the condenser. Water from the river is pumped through the condenser, and returned to the river. Again, note that the two fluids do not mix. Will radioactivity be released into the river?[1]

[1]No.

When the water is returned to the river, it contains more heat than it originally had. Thus it can raise the temperature of the river. Because the added heat can harm living things in the river, this heat is called thermal pollution. Thermal pollution is a problem with any power plant that uses steam turbines.

The problem of thermal pollution can be solved by using cooling towers like those shown in Figure 21-16. Water passing through the cooling tower gives off its excess heat to the atmosphere. Thus water can be returned to the river at the correct temperature.

The core of the reactor is housed in a structure called a containment building. This building is designed to prevent radiation from escaping. Thick concrete walls can absorb radioactivity. A bomblike explosion could not occur in a nuclear reactor, but problems with the coolant system could cause a dangerous build-up of heat energy in the core. If the core is allowed to overheat, it could melt down into the earth, and contaminate the soil and ground water. Nuclear reactors are equipped with many safety systems, which provide emergency cooling if the reactor must be shut down quickly.

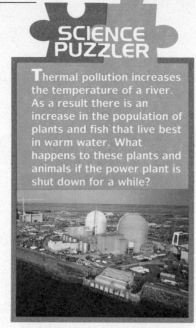

Figure 21–16
Cooling towers.

In April 1986 there was an accident at a nuclear reactor in Chernobyl, in the Soviet Union. Although the reactor was shut down, heat continued to build up in the core. The core overheated, and the graphite used as a moderator began to burn. As a result of the fire, the containment building was destroyed and radioactive materials were released into the atmosphere.

Puzzler   If the power plant is shut down for a while, the water temperature will fall, and the plants and animals may die.

Teaching Tip   Point out that waste heat is a problem at any steam-based power plant. However, nuclear power plants tend to produce more waste heat than do other power plants, so the issue of thermal pollution is frequently associated with nuclear power plants.

Enrichment   Have students research and discuss whether environmental concerns over nuclear power are justified.

Teaching Tip   Discuss the 1986 Chernobyl disaster with your students. Make available articles from newspapers and magazines that provided information about that event. Watch for articles concerning other nuclear plants' improved safety measures or changes that have resulted from the Chernobyl event.

Thinking Skills

hypothesizing
After studying Figure 21-16, students hypothesize different ways to solve the problem of thermal pollution in rivers.

Background Nuclear wastes continue to accumulate at an alarming rate, and to date there is no solution that pleases everyone regarding the problem of storage of these wastes.

3 REVIEW/REINFORCEMENT

1. Core, coolant, containment building.
2. Uranium-235.
3. The coolant flows through the core and absorbs the large amounts of heat energy there, preventing the core from being damaged or from melting.
4. Waste products from nuclear plants contain a mixture of radioisotopes, some of which decay quickly and others of which take hundreds or thousands of years to decay.

Challenge In case of an emergency, the control rods could be released, and due to the effect of gravity, would fall all the way into the core, stopping the reaction completely.

Figure 21–17

Underground storage of nuclear wastes.

NUCLEAR WASTES

Recall that fission reactions produce many different fission fragments. These fission fragments cannot be used as fuel for more fission reactions, so they do not produce useful energy. In fact they tend to absorb neutrons and make a reactor less efficient. Thus fission fragments are considered to be waste products that must be removed from the reactor.

Nuclear wastes contain a mixture of radioisotopes. Some decay very quickly. Others may take hundreds or thousands of years to decay. For example, the half-life of krypton-81 is 200,000 years.

Radioactivity is not affected by chemical reactions. Therefore nuclear wastes cannot be chemically changed into safe substances. When wastes are removed from a reactor, they must be stored in some place where they will not be a problem.

Research is being carried out to find more practical methods for the disposal of nuclear wastes. In one method that is being tested, wastes are being changed into solid form and stored deep in the earth. Another method involves adding glass-forming materials to the wastes. Such mixtures produce stable insoluble wastes that can be buried in storage containers. Nuclear wastes are often buried in formations such as salt beds, salt domes, basalt, or granite. These formations are stable. The land will not shift, or allow radioactive materials to escape.

Because of the danger that radioactive wastes present, they are stored in remote areas. Nuclear reactors are not located near these remote areas, so the wastes must be transported over long distances. Safety precautions must be taken when nuclear wastes are moved to storage areas. Wastes are carried by trucks, usually avoiding areas with large populations.

REVIEW

1. List the major parts of a nuclear reactor.
2. What is the fuel for a nuclear reactor?
3. Why is the coolant an important safety feature in a nuclear reactor?
4. Why are waste products from a nuclear power plant dangerous?

CHALLENGE In many reactors the control rods are inserted into the core from above. The control rods are held in place by electromagnets, which can release the control rods quickly. Why is this a useful safety feature?

21-5 NUCLEAR FUSION

As you have seen, fission is the splitting of a heavy nucleus to form lighter nuclei. If it is possible to split an atom, is it also possible to put one together? **Nuclear fusion** is the joining of light nuclei to form heavier nuclei. Fusion takes place in the sun and in other stars. Like fission, fusion releases large amounts of energy.

The simplest fusion reaction is the combining of hydrogen nuclei to form a helium nucleus. One kind of fusion reaction involves two isotopes of hydrogen.

$$^{2}_{1}H + ^{3}_{1}H \longrightarrow ^{4}_{2}He + ^{1}_{0}n + energy$$

As in a fission reaction, in a fusion reaction a small amount of mass is changed into energy.

In the sun, ordinary hydrogen nuclei, $^{1}_{1}H$, are combined to form helium nuclei. The process involves many steps. Six hydrogen nuclei are needed for each helium nucleus formed. Two hydrogen nuclei are also produced in the reaction.

A fusion reaction is not as simple as an equation makes it seem. Fusion does not take place spontaneously in a sample of hydrogen. It takes place only if the hydrogen nuclei are moving at a very high speed. Such a high speed is possible only in the plasma state, at temperatures in the tens of millions of degrees. That is why fusion reactions are difficult to produce in the laboratory. The temperature in the center of the sun is high enough to allow fusion to take place. In addition the energy released by fusion reactions keeps the temperature high enough for more fusion reactions to take place.

> After completing this section, you will be able to
>
> - **describe** a fusion reaction.
> - **describe** the conditions necessary for fusion reactions.
> - **identify** the fusion reaction that takes place in the sun.
>
> The key term in this section is
> **nuclear fusion**

fusio (to melt)

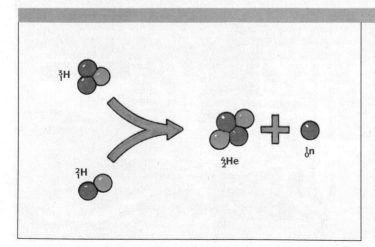

Figure 21–18

In this example of nuclear fusion two isotopes of hydrogen are combined to form a helium nucleus.

21-5 NUCLEAR FUSION
pages 539–541

1 MOTIVATION

Write in word form on the chalkboard the equation that appears on page 539: hydrogen-2 + hydrogen-3 → helium + neutron + energy. Have students interpret the equation. Ask them what was used and what was produced. Discuss whether they think this would be a viable way to produce energy. Students should conclude that the materials used are available and would be safe and clean to use. Explain that the equation students have been discussing describes what happens during fusion. Tell them the process is more difficult to control than is indicated by the equation because extreme heat is needed to make the reaction take place. Mention that many scientists are working on this fusion project, which could solve most of the world's energy problems.

2 CONCEPT DEVELOPMENT

Background In 1938 the American physicist Hans Bethe suggested that the sun and other stars are powered by nuclear fusion. Nuclear fusion may be the future power source of the world. Unlike nuclear fission, the fusion reaction is very clean, and the fuel, heavy water, is plentiful. Among the facilities working on building a functional fusion reaction are the Lawrence Livermore National Laboratory, in California, and Princeton University, in New Jersey.

comparing

In Figure 21-18, students interpret a diagram depicting nuclear fusion. Have them compare nuclear fusion with nuclear fission.

Background   The thermonuclear reaction thought to occur in the sun can be summarized as follows: Two ordinary nuclei of hydrogen fuse, forming a deuterium nucleus, a positron, and a neutrino. The neutrino escapes from the sun. The positron and an electron collide, annihilating each other, and forming gamma rays. The deuterium nucleus fuses with another nucleus of ordinary hydrogen, becoming an isotope of helium with 2 protons and 1 neutron, and releasing more gamma rays. Then two such helium isotopes fuse, producing one helium nucleus and two hydrogen nuclei. The small fraction of mass that "disappears" is converted to energy. Note that the type of thermonuclear reaction occurring in a star depends on the temperature of the star.

Teaching Tip   Point out that many nuclear agencies and/or laboratories provide information to educate the public and to promote the use of nuclear power. Have students use the information from the pamphlets and other sources to make a presentation on fusion technology.

Enrichment   Have students find out about neutrinos—what they are, where they are formed, how they are detected, and what has been learned from studying them.

At even higher temperatures the helium nuclei can fuse into carbon nuclei. At still higher temperatures, carbon nuclei can fuse into even heavier nuclei. Thus, as fusion in a star continues, the fusion of light elements into heavier ones continues. It is believed that all the naturally occurring elements were made through the process of fusion in the center of very hot stars.

Fusion reactions could provide large amounts of energy for generating electricity. Currently, fusion reactors are used only in laboratories. In these reactors, hydrogen nuclei are combined to form helium nuclei. This process releases energy.

Fusion reactors have some advantages over fission reactors. Hydrogen fuel is not radioactive. It is much more abundant on the earth than is uranium, the fuel for fission reactors. Fusion reactors do not produce fission fragments, so there is less danger from waste products.

However, there are some problems with fusion reactors. The biggest problem is the high temperature needed for fusion reactions. It takes a large amount of energy to set up the temperature and pressure conditions that make fusion possible. Until these reactors can be made to produce more energy than they use, they will not be practical energy sources.

SCIENCE & TECHNOLOGY

Controlling fusion is like trying to bottle the sun. The two biggest problems are creating a plasma at very high temperatures and then holding the plasma long enough for it to react. In a container with ordinary walls, the highly charged plasma particles would lose their energy as they touched the walls. The plasma would cool.

The solution to these problems might be a tokamak like the one shown here. The tokamak is a device that produces a powerful magnetic field around the plasma. The magnetic field confines the plasma without absorbing energy from the plasma.

In experiments with tokamaks, only a few fusion reactions have been created. Right now much more energy is put into making the reactions occur than is being produced by the fusion reactions themselves.

Scientists and engineers are designing new tokamaks. New models are expected to release more power than the amount of energy put into the reacting particles.

REVIEW

1. What is fusion?
2. What conditions are necessary for fusion to take place?
3. What type of fusion takes place in the sun?
4. Why do fusion reactors use more energy than they produce?

CHALLENGE   Write a possible fusion reaction for the formation of carbon-12 from helium-4.

CHAPTER SUMMARY

The main ideas in this chapter are listed below. Read these statements before you answer the Chapter Review questions.

- Elements that spontaneously release energy and particles from their nucleus are said to be radioactive. (21-1)

- An unstable nucleus will give off radiation in the form of alpha particles, beta particles, and gamma rays. (21-1)

- Both alpha radiation and beta radiation are made of particles. Gamma rays are waves of energy and are not made of particles. (12-1)

- The time it takes for one half of a radioactive sample to decay is called the half-life of that substance. (12-1)

- Radioisotopes are used in biological, chemical, and physical studies as tracers. Radioisotopes are used medically to treat disorders such as tumors. (12-2)

- Fission reactions occur when a nucleus is split into smaller pieces. The products of a fission reaction are called fission fragments. (12-3)

- Neutrons released from a fission reaction hit other nuclei, causing them to split. This type of reaction is called a chain reaction. (12-3)

- Nuclear reactors have three main parts: the core, the coolant, and the containment building. (12-4)

- The fuel in a nuclear reactor produces heat. This heat is used to produce steam, which turns turbines to generate electricity. (12-4)

- Fusion reactions occur when light nuclei are joined to create heavier nuclei. This type of reaction can occur only at very high temperatures, like those that occur on the sun and other stars. (12-5)

- Fusion reactions are impractical to use as an energy source on the earth because of the tremendous heat necessary for the reactions to take place. (21-5)

The key terms in this chapter are listed below. Use each term in a sentence that shows the meaning of the term.

alpha particle	fuel	nuclear fission	radiation
beta particle	gamma rays	nuclear fusion	radioactivity
chain reaction	half-life	nuclear reactor	tracer

1. Nuclear fusion is the joining of light nuclei to form heavier nuclei.
2. Fusion requires very high temperatures, and the hydrogen nuclei must be moving at a very high speed.
3. The fusion of hydrogen to helium takes place in the sun.
4. It takes large amounts of energy to set up the temperature and pressure conditions that make fusion possible.

Challenge

$$4(^{4}_{2}\text{He}) \rightarrow {}^{12}_{6}\text{C} + {}^{3}_{2}\text{He} + {}^{1}_{0}\text{N} + \text{energy}$$

Review and Skill Masters

VOCABULARY REVIEW, page 125.
See page 521b in this book for answers.

VOCABULARY

1. tracer	6. nuclear fission
2. gamma rays	7. chain reaction
3. fuel	8. alpha particle
4. nuclear fusion	9. nuclear reactor
5. radioactivity	10. beta particle

CONCEPTS

1. Alpha—helium nuclei, positive charge, low penetrating power; beta—electrons, negative charge, higher penetrating power than alpha particles.
2. Gamma rays have no charge, are pure energy, have no mass, and have the highest penetrating power.
3. Nuclei of light elements need equal numbers of protons and neutrons to be stable; carbon-12 has 6 protons and 6 neutrons, but carbon-14 has 6 protons and 8 neutrons.
4. A nucleus that emits an alpha particle is left with 2 fewer protons and 2 fewer neutrons.
5. A nucleus that emits a beta particle is left with 1 more proton and 1 less neutron than before.
6. Thirty-two days is equal to four half-lives; thus the sample divides in half four times. ($480 \times \frac{1}{2} = 240 \times \frac{1}{2} = 120 \times \frac{1}{2} = 60 \times \frac{1}{2} = 30$)
7. Phosphorous-32.
8. Radioisotopes are used as tracers to study biological, chemical, or physical processes because radioisotopes are easy to detect, making it easy to trace their movement.
9. To detect and treat thyroid problems, and to locate blood clots.
10. The striking of nuclei by fast-moving neutrons.
11. Mass is converted into energy, according to Einstein's equation $E = mc^2$.

Review and Skill Masters

CHAPTER REVIEW, pages 126–127.
See page 521b in this book for answers.

Chapter Review

Use the key terms from this chapter to complete the following sentences correctly.

1. A radioactive atom or molecule used by scientists to study a particular biological, chemical, or physical process is called a/an _____.
2. _____ are waves of energy that do not have a charge and do not have mass.
3. Any substance used to produce some type of energy is called a/an _____.
4. Light nuclei are joined to form heavy nuclei during the process of _____.
5. _____ is the spontaneous release of energy and particles from the nucleus of an atom.
6. A nuclear reaction that causes a nucleus to split into smaller pieces is called _____.
7. A/An _____ is one in which the product of a reaction causes another reaction to begin.
8. A particle that contains two protons and two neutrons is called a/an _____.
9. A device that is capable of using nuclear reactions and the energy they produce is called a/an _____.
10. A/An _____ is an electron released from a radioisotope.

CONCEPTS

1. What are the differences between alpha and beta particles? (21-1)
2. In what ways are gamma rays different from alpha particles and beta particles? (21-1)
3. Why is the carbon-12 nucleus stable while the carbon-14 nucleus is unstable? (21-1)
4. What happens to a nucleus that emits an alpha particle? (21-1)
5. What happens to a nucleus that emits a beta particle? (21-1)
6. The half-life of iodine-131 is nearly 8 days. How much of a 480-g sample of iodine-131 will remain after 32 days? (21-1)
7. Give an example of a radioisotope used in research. (21-2)
8. Why are radioisotopes used as tracers? (21-2)
9. How is radioactive iodine used in medicine? (21-2)
10. What causes a fission reaction to take place? (21-3)
11. Where does the energy released in a fission reaction come from? (21-3)

12. What are the products of a fission reaction? (21-3)

13. What is critical mass, and how is it related to a chain reaction? (21-3)

14. What is the function of a moderator in a nuclear reactor? (21-4)

15. How is a chain reaction in a nuclear reactor controlled? (21-4)

16. Why must nuclear power plants be located near large bodies of water? (21-4)

17. Why is it so important to package and store nuclear waste materials for long periods? (21-4)

18. What happens in a fusion reaction? (21-5)

19. In what ways would the use of fusion be an improvement over the use of fission? (21-5)

20. What major problem with the fusion reactor keeps fusion from being used as an energy source on the earth? (21-5)

APPLICATION/ CRITICAL THINKING

1. Tritium ($^3_1$H) is a radioisotope. Can it emit an alpha particle?

2. The half-life of carbon-14 is 5730 years, and the oldest fossils that can be dated by using carbon-14 are 40,000 years old. What fraction of the original amount of carbon-14 remains in a fossil 40,000 years old?

3. Friction in moving metallic parts is a major source of machine wear and breakdown. How might radioactive iron-59 be used as a tracer to improve petroleum products that are used to reduce friction?

4. Can fusion be called a chain reaction? Explain.

EXTENSION

1. Prepare a report that compares the advantages and disadvantages of producing electric power by using coal, nuclear fusion, and nuclear fission.

2. Find out about breeder reactors. What are they used for?

3. Do library research on the "mass defect" and its relationship to nuclear energy.

READINGS

"Deadly Meltdown." *Time,* May 12, 1986, p. 38.

Epstein S.S., and Carl Pope. *Hazardous Wastes in America.* San Francisco, Calif.: Sierra, 1982.

Ligtman, A. "Weighing the Odds." *Science 83,* December 1983, p. 10.

"Physicists Create A New Element." *Science 82,* December 1982, p. 7.

---

12. Fission fragments.

13. The minimum amount of uranium that can keep the chain reaction going.

14. To slow the movement of the neutrons so that they will cause more fissions.

15. Control rods are used to absorb neutrons and to slow or stop a chain reaction.

16. Large volumes of water are needed to condense the steam.

17. They contain a mixture of radioisotopes, and some have long half-lives and may give off dangerous radiation for hundreds or thousands of years.

18. Light nuclei join to form heavier nuclei, and small amounts of mass are changed into large amounts of energy.

19. Fusion reactors do not require radioactive fuels, nor do they produce radioactivity.

20. The problem of creating a temperature high enough to produce fusion and to produce more energy through fusion than is used to create it.

APPLICATION/CRITICAL THINKING

1. Tritium contains only 1 proton and cannot emit an alpha particle, which contains 2 protons and 2 neutrons.

2. Forty thousand years is just over seven half-lives ($\frac{1}{2} \rightarrow \frac{1}{4} \rightarrow \frac{1}{8} \rightarrow \frac{1}{16} \rightarrow \frac{1}{32} \rightarrow \frac{1}{64} \rightarrow \frac{1}{128}$); thus the fraction remaining of the original amount is $\frac{1}{128}$.

3. Make one moving part contain some radioactive iron-59. As friction occurs, tiny bits of iron will be deposited in the oil. Detecting how much radioactive iron gets into the oil will give a measure of the wear on that part of the car.

4. Fusion is not a chain reaction because a chain reaction proceeds spontaneously; fusion requires a steady source of high temperature.

Test Masters

CHAPTER TEST, pages 81–84.
See page 521d in this book for answers.

ENERGY RESOURCES

ORGANIZER

Section	pages	Activity	pages	Reinforcement and Evaluation	pages	*Review and Skill Masters	pages	Other Components in Teacher Resource Package	pages
22–1 Fuels	545–550			Review, Challenge	550			Study Guide Transparency Poster	110
22–2 Solar Energy	551–554	How Can Solar Energy Be Collected?	553	Review, Challenge	554			Study Guide Lab Manual	111 109
22–3 Hydroelectric Power	555–556			Review, Challenge	556			Study Guide	112
22–4 Other Energy Sources	557–561			Review, Challenge	561	Skill	134	Study Guide	113
22–5 Energy Conservation	562–565	Does Insulation Prevent Heat Loss?	563	Puzzler Review, Challenge	564 565	Challenge/Critical Thinking	135–136	Study Guide Lab Manual	114 113
CHAPTER SUMMARY	565					Vocabulary Review	131		
CHAPTER REVIEW	566–567			*Test Masters	85–88	Chapter Review	132–133		

*In the Teacher Resource Package. For answers, see pages 543b–543d in this book.

ACTIVITY MATERIALS
Quantities are based on a class of 30 students working in groups as indicated in parentheses.

How Can Solar Energy Be Collected? p. 553 (groups of 2)	quantity	Does Insulation Prevent Heat Loss? p. 563 (groups of 2)	quantity		quantity
shoebox	30	safety goggles	30		
dark soil	17 kg	lab apron	30		
cardboard (12 cm x 6 cm long)	15 pieces	graduate	15		
Celsius thermometer	30	250-mL beaker	30		
clear plastic wrap	1 roll	cotton	3 boxes		
masking tape	3 rolls	100-mL Florence flask	30		
		tongs	15		
		Celsius thermometer	30		
		ice water			
		hot tapwater			

REVIEW AND SKILL MASTERS

VOCABULARY REVIEW _____ Chapter 22

Use the correct words to complete the sentences below.

biomass	nonrenewable resource	solar energy
conservation	renewable resource	synthetic fuel
fossil fuels	solar cell	tidal energy
geothermal energy	solar collector	wind energy
hydroelectric power		

1. Insulating homes and driving smaller, lighter cars are examples of
   _____**conservation**_____ of energy.

2. **Biomass** _____ is any kind of organic matter that can be turned into fuel.

3. A house heated by a _____**solar collector**_____ is using active solar heating.

4. Radiant energy from the sun is called **solar energy**

5. Some areas of the world that have volcanoes and geysers can use
   _____**geothermal energy**_____ to produce electricity.

6. Using moving air to turn turbines to produce electricity is called
   wind energy

7. Coal, oil, and natural gas are _____**fossil fuels**_____ formed from the remains of ancient plants and animals.

8. Some photographic light meters use a _____**solar cell**_____ to convert the sun's radiant energy into electricity.

9. **Synthetic fuels** _____ can be made from coal, oil shale, tar sands, or living matter and are used in place of oil and natural gas.

10. A _____**renewable resource**_____, such as timber, is a natural resource that can be easily replaced.

11. **Hydroelectric power** _____ is produced by using moving water to generate electricity.

12. Like other _____**nonrenewable resources**_____, coal and uranium must be used carefully because they can run out.

13. **Tidal energy** _____ harnesses the power of the ocean's daily tides.

© 1989 Silver, Burdett & Ginn Inc.

131

CHAPTER REVIEW _____ Chapter 22

22-1 Fuels

1. How do renewable and nonrenewable resources differ? **A renewable resource is a natural resource that can be easily replaced. A nonrenewable resource is a natural resource that cannot be replaced.**

2. What are the origins and some uses of coal, oil, and natural gas? **Coal was formed from the remains of plants that lived millions of years ago and is used to produce electricity. Oil and natural gas were formed from the remains of sea life buried by mud in the ocean. Oil is used to make petroleum products, and natural gas is used to heat homes.**

3. List three sources of synthetic fuels. **Three sources of synthetic fuels are oil shale, tar sand, and biomass.**

22-2 Solar Energy

1. Define solar energy. **Solar energy is the energy given off by the sun.**

2. Contrast passive and active solar heating. **Passive solar heating needs no special equipment; active solar heating uses solar collectors.**

3. How do solar collectors and solar cells work? **Solar collectors convert solar energy into heat. Solar cells change solar energy into electricity.**

22-3 Hydroelectric Power

1. Define hydroelectric power. **Hydroelectric power is electrical energy produced by water-powered generators.**

132

CHAPTER REVIEW (Continued) _____ Chapter 22

2. How is hydroelectric power produced by moving water? **Moving water turns turbines in a generator, which produces electricity.**

22-4 Other Energy Sources

1. Define wind energy, tidal energy, and geothermal energy. **Wind energy is using moving wind to turn turbines to produce electricity. Tidal energy is the energy harnessed as the tide is used to produce electricity. Geothermal energy is energy collected from the natural heat of the earth.**

2. Give one advantage and one disadvantage to each energy source defined above. **Answers may vary. Wind energy causes no pollution, but the wind does not always blow. Tidal energy causes no pollution, but there are few good sites for plants. Geothermal energy is free, but plants must be built at the source.**

22-5 Energy Conservation

1. What is conservation? Why is it important? **Conservation is the care, wise use, and preservation of natural resources. It is important because the supply of nonrenewable resources is limited.**

2. Describe two ways to save energy for heating and transportation. **Answers will vary. You save energy for heating by building windows facing south and using storm windows. You save energy for transportation by driving smaller cars and using public transportation.**

© 1989 Silver, Burdett & Ginn Inc.

133

SKILL/Writing Persuasively _____ Chapter 22

Study the following chart that compares various forms of energy. Think about each energy source it describes and answer the questions below.

ENERGY RESOURCE	REN or N-REN	ADVANTAGES	DRAWBACKS
hydroelectric	REN	no pollution	expensive
coal	N-REN	inexpensive	pollution
passive solar	REN	clean, no pollution	expensive
biomass methane	REN	energy and fertilizer	untested
oil	N-REN	portable	pollution
tides	REN	no pollution	untested
active solar	REN	no pollution	expensive
geothermal	REN	no pollution	location
wind	REN	no pollution	reliability
gasohol	REN	portable	untested

1. Pretend you are going to write an editorial for your school newspaper. Write a paragraph that expands on one of these energy resources, discussing both the advantage and drawback listed.
   Answers will vary but should expand on the chosen energy resource and discuss the advantage and drawback listed.

2. Continue your editorial by writing a persuasive paragraph to describe why a particular renewable energy resource should be developed. This energy resource may be be the same sources as you chose for your first paragraph if the energy resource is renewable.
   Answers will vary but must deal logically and persuasively with a renewable energy resource.

© 1989 Silver, Burdett & Ginn Inc.

134

CHALLENGE/CRITICAL THINKING _____ Chapter 22

No matter where you live in the United States, it is colder in the winter than it is in the summer. In order to keep your body heat from escaping, you "winterize" yourself. You keep your skin covered and wear thicker clothing. During the winter, you want to keep heat in your house, too. This can be done in the same way. You may remove screens or regular windows and put in storm windows. You may have extra insulation placed in your walls and attic.

Two factors help you figure out how much energy you save with insulation. The first is a heating factor. This factor shows how well a furnace heats a house in that part of the country. The second factor is a savings factor. This factor shows how much is saved on energy bills by that form of winterization compared to the cost of installing it. Multiplying the heating factor by the savings factor will give you the amount of energy you will save with that one form of winterization.

A family wanted to find out how much they would save if they installed 15 storm windows. A contractor bid $48 per window to supply and install the storm windows. A savings factor of 7.9 would be gained per window. The house was gas heated and had a heating factor of $1.155.

1. How much would 15 storm windows cost?

   15 × $48 = $720

2. How would you calculate the total savings factor for all 15 windows?

   Multiplying 15 times 7.9 gives the total savings factor.

3. What was the total possible yearly savings factor?

   15 × 7.9 = 118.5

4. Total yearly savings is equal to the product of the heating factor and the savings factor. What is the yearly savings with the windows installed?

   $1.155 × 118.5 = $136.8675, round to $136.87

5. How many years would it take for the storm windows to "pay for themselves" due to heat energy savings?

   $720 ÷ $136.87 = 5.3 years

6. A discount supply company sold Brand "X" storm windows for $22 each. The discount windows would have to be installed by the owner. How long would it take for the storm windows to "pay for themselves" if the owner purchased and installed the windows?

   Cost = $22 × 15 = $330; $330 ÷ $136.87 = 2.4 years

CHALLENGE/CRITICAL THINKING (Continued) _____ Chapter 22

If the same house were heated by electricity, the savings factor would be the same. Electrical energy has a $2.73 heating factor.

7. How long would it take for the storm windows to "pay for themselves" in the electrically heated house with contractor installation?

   Yearly savings = $2.73 × 118.5 = $323.5055, round to $323.51;

   $720 ÷ $323.51 = 2.2 years

8. How long would it take for the storm windows to "pay for themselves" in the electrically heated house with "do-it-yourself" installation?

   Yearly savings = $2.73 × 118.5 = $323.5055, round to $323.51;

   $330 ÷ $323.51 = 1.02 years

9. Explain how the storm windows change the house environment to require less heating.

   Answers will vary but may include wind protection, less infiltration, and/or

   mini-solar greenhouse effect on southern windows.

10. In the space provided, explain other practical ways that this family might conserve energy.

   Answers will vary.

TEST MASTERS

Page 85

Chapter 22

Fuels

PART 1 _____

In the space below, write the term that each phrase defines.

Chapter Goal

1. **solar energy** — Energy given off by the sun — 2

2. **tidal energy** — The energy harnessed as the tide is used to produce electricity — 4

3. **solar collector** — A device for collecting solar energy and converting it into heat — 2

4. **hydroelectric power** — Electrical energy produced by water-powered generators — 3

5. **geothermal energy** — Energy collected from the natural heat from the earth — 4

6. **biomass** — Any kind of organic substance that can be turned into fuel — 1

7. **fossil fuels** — Energy sources formed from the remains of ancient plants and animals — 1

8. **conservation** — The care, wise use, or preservation of natural resources — 5

PART 2 _____

Choose the term or phrase that best answers the question or completes the statement. Write the letter of that choice in the space at the left.

a 1. Insulation, storm windows, and caulking are conservation measures designed to: — 5
   a. cut down on energy that is wasted.
   b. increase the energy that is produced.
   c. expand the ways in which energy is used.
   d. create new sources of energy.

d 2. A solar cell uses radiant energy to produce:
   a. light.   b. heat.   c. sound.   d. electricity.

a 3. Which of the following sources provides the greatest amount of energy in the United States? — 5
   a. oil   b. wind   c. tidal   d. water

Chapter 22 Fuels — 85

Page 86

PART 2 _____

Choose the term or phrase that best answers the question or completes the statement. Write the letter of that choice in the space at the left.

Chapter Goal

a 4. Which of the following is a renewable resource? — 1
   a. water   b. coal   c. oil   d. natural gas

b 5. A power plant that pumps water uphill into a reservoir until energy is needed is a type of: — 3
   a. nuclear plant.   c. tidal plant.
   b. hydroelectric plant.   d. geothermal plant.

b 6. Which of the following forms of coal usually takes the longest to form? — 1
   a. peat   c. lignite
   b. anthracite   d. bituminous coal

c 7. In a hydroelectric plant, water is used to: — 3
   a. produce steam.   c. turn a generator.
   b. cool equipment.   d. store heat.

c 8. Which of the following is an advantage of wind energy? — 4
   a. Wind is always available.
   b. Windmills are inexpensive to build.
   c. Windmills cause no pollution.
   d. Windmills take up large amounts of space.

c 9. Which of the following would most likely be a conservation measure? — 5
   a. increasing the use of coal
   b. increasing the use of oil
   c. decreasing the use of gasoline
   d. decreasing the use of solar energy

d 10. Which of the following is an example of passive solar heating? — 2
   a. using solar collectors for home heating
   b. burning wood in a wood stove
   c. using solar cells in a home heating system
   d. installing large windows that face the sun

b 11. Which of the following is a disadvantage of tidal-electric power plants? — 4
   a. The energy source is not reliable.
   b. Sites are limited.
   c. They cause pollution.
   d. Fuel is nonrenewable.

d 12. Which of the following is an advantage of hydroelectric plants? — 3
   a. There are many available sites.
   b. They are inexpensive to build.
   c. They cause no problems downstream.
   d. The fuel is free.

Chapter 22 Fuels — 86

Page 87

PART 3 _____

Look at the diagram. Then read the questions that follow. Choose the term or phrase that best answers the question or completes the statement. Write the letter of that choice in the space at the left.

Chapter Goal

d 1. In a fossil-fuel power plant, the function of the water in Power Source A would be performed by: — 1
   a. uranium.   b. steam.   c. wind.   d. coal.

c 2. Which of the following types of energy is probably not available in this area? — 4
   a. solar   b. wind   c. geothermal   d. tidal

c 3. What type of power plant is Power Source A? — 3
   a. nuclear plant   c. hydroelectric plant
   b. fossil-fuel plant   d. tidal plant

d 4. One advantage of Power Source A over Power Source B is that, with Source A: — 3
   a. fuel is free.
   b. pollution is not produced.
   c. location is not important.
   d. power can be generated constantly.

Chapter 22 Fuels — 87

Page 88

PART 4 _____

Read each question or direction and answer it using complete sentences.

Chapter Goal

1. What are the drawbacks of using coal for energy? — 1

   Burning coal releases large amounts of carbon dioxide into the air. It also releases sulfur compounds. Sulfur compounds in the air combine to form sulfuric acid. This sulfuric acid is part of the acid rain that kills aquatic life, harms plants, and destroys buildings, roads, and statues.

2. Describe and compare the kind of sites required for tidal power plants and geothermal power plants. — 4

   Tidal power plants must be located in bays in which high tide is 3.5 to 6.0 meters higher than low tide. Along most shorelines, high tide is only about 1 meter higher than low tide. Geothermal power plants must be located at the source of the energy, e.g., where hot springs, volcanoes, and geysers are found, since energy is lost if the steam or hot liquid is carried any distance by pipeline. Because of these requirements, tidal and geothermal power plants share the disadvantage of limited sites.

3. Describe some measures that can be taken to conserve energy in the home and in everyday life. — 5

   Home conservation measures include double-wall construction, windows that face south, and storm windows and doors. Energy can also be saved through the use of better insulation, weather stripping, and caulking. In daily transportation, increased use of public transportation and commuter car pools saves fuel.

Chapter 22 Fuels — 88

© Silver, Burdett & Ginn Inc.

CHAPTER 22 PLANNING GUIDE

22

ENERGY RESOURCES

The questions in the CHAPTER TEST are based on these Chapter Goals.

1. Compare renewable and nonrenewable resources, explain the origin and uses of fossil fuels, and describe some synthetic fuels.
2. Describe solar energy, compare passive and active solar heating designs, and explain how solar collectors and solar cells are used.
3. Describe hydroelectric power and how it is produced, and list advantages and drawbacks of hydroelectric power.
4. Describe and list advantages, drawbacks, and examples of wind energy, tidal energy, and geothermal energy.
5. Define the term *conservation,* explain why it is important, and describe ways to save energy.

ENERGY RESOURCES

22

Whether you are riding your bike, flying in an airplane, cooking dinner, or taking a shower, everything you do requires energy. The energy for bike riding comes from you. The energy needed to turn on the stove must come from some other source. The sun may be the source of more energy in the future. This photograph shows a solar power plant. Mirrors focus the sun's rays on the central power tower.

- *How long will fossil fuels last?*
- *What methods can be used to conserve fossil fuels?*
- *What alternative energy sources can be developed?*

22-1 FUELS

Most people have probably experienced an energy shortage. The electricity may have gone out during a storm. The lights may have dimmed during a hot summer day or during a bitterly cold winter day. A lawn mower or an automobile may have run out of gasoline. Whatever form it takes, a loss of energy can be disturbing.

RESOURCES

Recall that energy is the ability to do work. The chief sources of energy presently being used in North America are coal, oil, and natural gas. However, sunlight, flowing water, wood and other plant material, wind, synthetic fuels, tides, the earth's internal heat, and nuclear fuels like uranium also are sources of energy.

Materials found on the earth that are necessary for life or useful to humans are called *natural resources*. Water, minerals, land, wind, sunlight, and living things, such as trees, are all natural resources. Natural resources can be classified as renewable resources and nonrenewable resources. A **renewable resource** is a natural resource that can be easily replaced. Water, timber, land, sunlight, and wind are renewable resources. A **nonrenewable resource** is a resource that cannot be replaced. Coal, oil, natural gas, and uranium are nonrenewable resources.

After completing this section, you will be able to

- **compare** renewable and nonrenewable resources.
- **explain** the origin and uses of fossil fuels.
- **describe** some synthetic fuels.

The key terms in this section are
biomass
fossil fuels
nonrenewable resource
renewable resource
synthetic fuels

CHAPTER OPENING STRATEGY

Ask students what energy resource is being utilized in the photograph. (A solar energy-collecting plant.) Ask students to explain where it would be best to build such plants. Then list why such plants are likely to be more common in the future.

- How long will fossil fuels last? (Fossil fuels are nonrenewable and, therefore, will be used up. The length of time depends on how quickly we consume them.)
- What methods can be used to conserve fossil fuels? (More efficient automobiles and heating systems, better home insulation will also conserve energy.)
- What alternative energy sources can be developed? (Solar, hydroelectric, wind, tidal, and geothermal energies.)

22-1 FUELS
pages 545–550

OBJECTIVES
Refer to pupil page 545.

VOCABULARY
Key terms. biomass, fossil fuels, nonrenewable resource, renewable resource, synthetic fuels
Other terms: anthracite coal, bituminous coal, coal gasification, crude oil, gasohol, lignite, natural gas, natural resources, oil shale, peat, strip mining, tar sand

1 MOTIVATION

On the chalkboard, write the following sources of energy: *butter, wood, coal, dynamite, gasoline*. Ask students to arrange these power sources in order, starting with the substance they think will provide the most power (watts) per kilogram of matter. Students may be surprised to find out the correct order: gasoline 13.4 W/kg; butter 6.7 W/kg; coal 6.1 W/kg; wood 2.5 W/kg; dynamite 1.3 W/kg.

2 CONCEPT DEVELOPMENT

Background The amount of pressure on peat and the heat generated by this pressure determines the quality and characteristics of coal. During coal formation, 3 m of decaying vegetation become compressed into 30 cm of coal. With greater compression, more hydrogen and oxygen will be driven off, leaving a higher percentage of carbon and a lower percentage of water. The higher carbon content results in a higher quality of coal.

Thinking Skills

comparing
Students compare the products made during the four stages of coal development in Figure 22-2. Students are made aware that each successive stage involves greater pressure, which increases the quality of the coal.

Teaching Tip
Mention that peat has little commercial value when it is a soggy mass. But when peat is properly dried, it gives off about two-thirds the heat of low-quality coal, and it is cheaper than coal.

Transparency

The Teacher Resource Package includes a color transparency and a black-line master of Figures 22-1 and 22-17. You may wish to use these in your discussion of energy sources and uses.

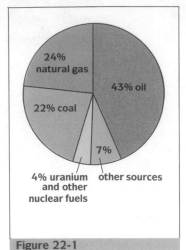

Figure 22-1

Present energy sources in the United States.

FOSSIL FUELS

About 94 percent of the energy used in the world comes from fossil fuels. **Fossil fuels** are energy sources formed from the remains of ancient plants and animals. Coal, oil, and natural gas make up the fossil fuels. Once fossil fuels are used, they cannot be replaced.

Coal is a solid organic rock made up mostly of carbon. Coal was formed from the remains of plants that lived in forests and swamps millions of years ago. Plant material is mostly cellulose, a complex organic molecule made up of carbon, hydrogen, and oxygen. The ancient plants were buried under water and layers of mud, where there was little oxygen. As these materials decayed, the percentages of hydrogen and oxygen in them decreased. This process left behind deposits with a high percentage of carbon. These deposits were compressed by heat and pressure.

Four stages in the development of coal are shown in Figure 22-2. *Peat* is young coal. It looks like rotted wood and is only about 60 percent carbon by weight. Peat buried a while longer turns into lignite (LIHG nit), which is about 70 percent carbon. *Lignite* is harder than peat, and when it is burned, lignite releases more energy than does peat. Under more heat and pressure, lignite changes into *bituminous* (bī TOO mih nuhs) *coal,* or soft coal. It is harder than lignite and is a better source of energy. Bituminous coal is between 80 and 89 percent carbon. After more heat and pressure, bituminous coal turns into *anthracite* (AN-thruh sīt) *coal.* Anthracite coal is about 95 percent carbon by weight, and it releases the most heat energy.

Figure 22-2

The four stages of coal: peat (*A*), lignite (*B*), bituminous (*C*), and anthracite (*D*).

Coal was first used as an energy source in the United States in 1830. Today, only about 20 percent of North America's energy needs are supplied by coal. However, the use of coal is expected to increase in the future. This is because coal reserves are known to be larger than the reserves of other fossil fuels.

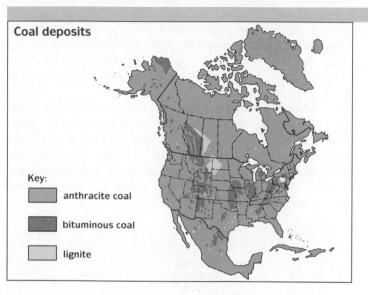

Coal deposits

Key:

▪ anthracite coal

▪ bituminous coal

▪ lignite

Figure 22-3

Coal deposits in North America.

The United States has about 28 percent of the world's known coal deposits. Most scientists agree that this is enough coal to meet the needs of this country for about 100 years. As shown in Figure 22-3, most of the coal found in the United States is bituminous coal. Which state has the largest supply of anthracite coal?[1]

More than half of the coal used in the United States is taken from strip mines. In *strip mining* the land surface above the coal is removed, as shown in Figure 22-4. Underground mining is a method of reaching coal by digging to it. The coal is then carried by railroad from the mines to power plants and other facilities.

Most of the coal used each year in the United States is burned in power plants to produce electrical energy. There are drawbacks to using coal for energy. Burning coal releases large amounts of carbon dioxide into the air. Burning coal also releases sulfur compounds, such as sulfur trioxide. Recall from Chapter 8 that sulfur trioxide and water in the air combine to form sulfuric acid. This sulfuric acid is part of the acid rain that kills aquatic life, harms plants, and damages buildings, roads, and statues.

[1]Pennsylvania.

Figure 22-4

Strip mining.

Background   Until the end of the nineteenth century, the major fuel used in the world was wood. Coal became the major energy source between 1900 and 1950. Since that time, gas and oil have been the main fuels of industrialized nations.

Thinking Skills

interpreting maps
Students use a map in Figure 22-3 to determine where large coal deposits are found in North America. Students are asked to list the five states that have the largest supply of anthracite coal. Ask students to compare the quantities of coal available in Canada and the United States.

Background   Sulfur impurities in coal are responsible for acid rain, which poses a threat to lakes, forests, and wildlife. Some coal deposits contain more sulfur than do others. Much of the coal in the eastern United States contains more than 2 percent sulfur. Coal in western states, such as Montana and Wyoming, has a sulfur content of less than 1 percent. However, the coal deposits in the West are of lower quality and must be mined by strip mining, which causes other environmental problems.

Teaching Tip   Point out that strip mining can be planned so that land is not destroyed. In Germany, for example, power companies replace all the topsoil that has been removed by strip mining. The companies then move on to another area without leaving behind a wasteland.

Teaching Tip Point out that crude oil does not form in pools that fill underground caves. It simply occupies the pore spaces of certain types of sedimentary rock, such as sandstone. Natural gas, which is lighter, occupies the spaces above the oil, and water, which is heavier, fills the spaces below the oil. Sedimentary rock is essential for the formation of oil.

Thinking Skills

identifying cause and effect
Ask students why oil that has been formed from animal remains on the ocean floor is often found inland. Students should conclude that the surface of the earth has changed many times during the oil formation period and that present inland areas may have been underwater in the past.

Background Oil not blocked by impermeable rock migrates to the surface and is lost.

Oil is another fuel that can be used to produce electricity. Oil, also called petroleum (puh TROH lee uhm), is a liquid mixture made mostly of hydrocarbons. Hydrocarbons are compounds made up of hydrogen and carbon. Oil was formed from the remains of sea life buried by mud on the ocean floor. Over centuries the animal remains and mud were buried deeper by new layers of sediment. The remains then decayed into oil. The weight of the mud forced the oil into porous rock, such as sandstone. The oil-rich rock was trapped between layers of impermeable rock. Impermeable rock allows very little liquid to pass through it. To reach the oil, drills must dig down into the rock as shown in Figure 22-5.

A fossil fuel that is commonly found with oil is natural gas. *Natural gas* is made up mostly of methane, a hydrocarbon. Notice in Figure 22-5 that natural gas is often trapped above the oil, just below the impermeable rock. Natural gas can also be found alone in gas-bearing deposits. The processes that formed natural gas are the same processes that formed oil.

Figure 22-5

Oil, natural gas, and water are usually found trapped together between layers of rock.

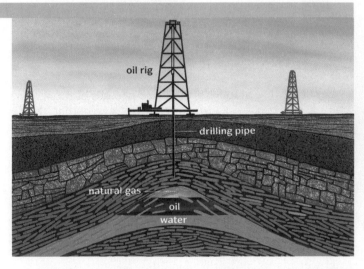

Oil and natural gas are often taken from wells drilled deep into the earth. The natural gas can be carried by pipelines to homes and factories. The gas can be used for heating and cooking, and to produce electricity.

Oil taken from the ground is a complex mixture of hydrocarbons called *crude oil*. Crude oil in its natural state has few uses. However, this complex mixture can be separated into different parts by the process known as refining. The refining process begins with distillation, as shown

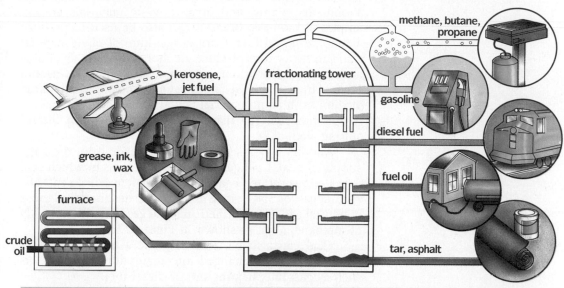

Figure 22-6

The products of oil refining.

in Figure 22-6. Distillation separates the heavy crude oil in a large tower called a fractionating column. The petroleum gases such as propane and butane, which have low boiling points, rise to the top of the column. The crude oil and tar, which have higher boiling points, remain at the bottom. Which has a higher boiling point, gasoline or kerosene?[1] Oil is used to make many products including plastics, pesticides, and synthetic fibers.

[1] Kerosene.

OTHER FUELS

Synthetic fuels are a new source of energy. **Synthetic** (sihn THEHT ihk) **fuels**, or synfuels, are fuels made by a chemical process and are used in place of oil or natural gas. Synfuels can be made from oil shale, tar sands, living matter, or coal.

Oil shale is rock that contains dark organic matter. Oil shale can be heated to remove from it a liquid similar to petroleum. Notice in Figure 22-7 that when ignited, the liquid in the rock burns. However, producing oil from rock is expensive. In addition, mining oil shale damages the land because large amounts of rock must be removed.

Tar sand is a deposit of sand coated with a tarlike substance that can be removed by heating. The process for recovering the fuel material is expensive, and the fuel is difficult to remove from the sand.

Figure 22-7

Oil shale.

Background   Coal is not convenient to handle, and it causes pollution when it is burned. To avoid these problems, coal is sometimes converted to a gas before it is used as fuel.

3 REVIEW/REINFORCEMENT

1. Renewable resources can be replaced; two examples are water and timber. Nonrenewable resources cannot be replaced; coal and oil.
2. Millions of years ago, coal was formed from the remains of plants that were buried under water and layers of mud in an area where there was little oxygen. During the process the percentage of hydrogen and oxygen in the decaying material became greatly reduced, leaving a higher percentage of carbon. Heat and pressure completed the formation of coal from this matter over millions of years.
3. Gas, coal, and oil are used to produce electricity; gas, coal, and oil are also used to heat homes and factories.
4. Synthetic fuels are made by a chemical process; two sources of synthetic fuels are coal and living matter.

Challenge   Methane vaporizes at a lower temperature, causing it to rise to the top.

Another energy source is biomass. **Biomass** is any kind of organic substance that can be turned into fuel. Wood, dry plants, and organic waste materials are examples of biomass. Biomass can also be used to produce alcohol, a liquid fuel. Corn is one kind of plant material that can be used to produce alcohol. When the alcohol is added to gasoline, the mixture is called *gasohol*. Gasohol is a fuel that can be used in cars. One problem with making alcohol from plant material is that the process for making it uses more energy than can be produced from the resulting alcohol.

Another type of synfuel can be made from the large supply of coal. *Coal gasification* is a process in which coal is heated to produce a gas. This gas is often called synthetic natural gas, or SNG, since it has properties similar to those of natural gas. This synthetic natural gas is made up mostly of methane, CH_4, as shown in Figure 22-8.

Coal can also be used to make a liquid fuel. This liquid fuel can be changed into many different products such as gasoline, heating oil, or diesel fuel.

Figure 22-8

Converting coal to natural gas, oil, and gasoline is called coal gasification.

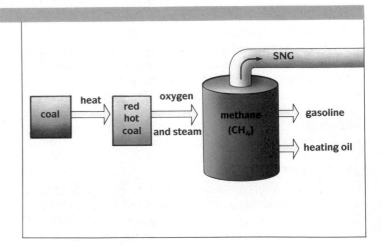

REVIEW

1. Compare renewable and nonrenewable resources, and give two examples of each.
2. Describe how coal was formed.
3. Name the major uses of coal, oil, and natural gas.
4. What are synthetic fuels? Name two sources of synthetic fuels.

CHALLENGE Look at Figure 22-8. Why is SNG leaving through the top of the vessel?

22-2 SOLAR ENERGY

The greatest single energy source for the earth is the sun. Energy given off by the sun is called **solar energy**, or radiant energy. This energy is produced by nuclear fusion reactions on the sun that convert hydrogen to helium. In the process, huge amounts of energy are given off.

Solar energy has provided almost all the sources of energy on the earth since the beginning of time. Plants use solar energy to carry out photosynthesis. Animals that eat the plants also depend on the sun for energy. Even the fossil fuels that are burned came from the sun, indirectly, since the living things that decayed into fossil fuels used solar energy.

As you can see in Figure 22-9, not all the solar energy that reaches the earth's upper atmosphere reaches the earth's surface. This means the equivalent of 700,000 trillion kW-h of power reaches the earth's surface each day. If the energy could be collected and converted into usable energy, there would be as much energy collected in 40 minutes as all the people on the earth use in a year.

After completing this section, you will be able to

- **define** the term *solar energy*.
- **compare** passive and active solar heating designs.
- **explain** how solar collectors and solar cells are used.

The key terms in this section are
solar cell
solar collector
solar energy

sol (the sun)

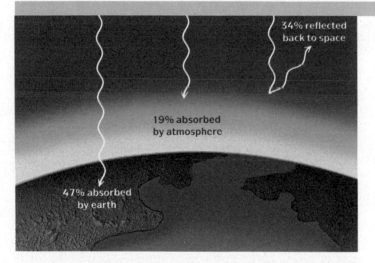

34% reflected back to space

19% absorbed by atmosphere

47% absorbed by earth

Figure 22-9

Not all the solar energy that reaches the earth is absorbed.

Solar energy has many advantages over other forms of energy. It is available everywhere, it requires no fuel, it does not pollute the environment, and its use cannot be controlled by other nations.

Capturing and using solar energy is not easy to do because the solar energy that reaches the earth is spread out over such a large area. This energy must be collected and stored in order for it to be used to make electricity.

22-2   SOLAR ENERGY
pages 551–554

OBJECTIVES
Refer to pupil page 551.

VOCABULARY
Key terms: solar cell, solar collector, solar energy
Other terms: active solar heating, passive solar heating

1 MOTIVATION

Ask students to name as many energy sources as they can. Compile on the chalkboard a list from their suggestions. Have students determine which of these energy sources owe their origin to the sun. Ask students if they can name sources of energy that do not depend on the sun. (Geothermal, nuclear, some forms of chemical energy.)

2 CONCEPT DEVELOPMENT

Thinking Skills

interpreting diagrams
Students use Figure 22-9 to find out what happens to solar energy after it enters the earth's upper atmosphere. They are made aware that more than half of the energy never reaches the earth's surface.

Background   It has been estimated that if it were possible to capture the solar energy that falls on a 200-km^2 area near the equator, there would be enough energy to supply the entire earth.

Enrichment   Ask students to design a solar collector using simple materials. Have students show and discuss their design in class.

Background   An idea being researched is the collection and concentration of the sun's energy by means of solar collectors placed in space. An orbiting solar station could generate electricity from sunlight and then transmit it by microwave antennas. These collectors would solve the problem of collecting solar energy on cloudy days or at night.

Thinking Skills

inferring
Students are told that even in cold climates, home heating requirements could be met by solar collectors. Students can infer that even where air temperatures are low, solar energy can be collected.

Other factors that limit the use of solar energy include the time of day, season of the year, latitude of the area, weather conditions, and air pollution levels. Figure 22-10 shows the extent to which areas of the United States could use solar energy for heating and hot water. What general area of the country can use solar energy the most?[1]

[1]Southwest and Florida.

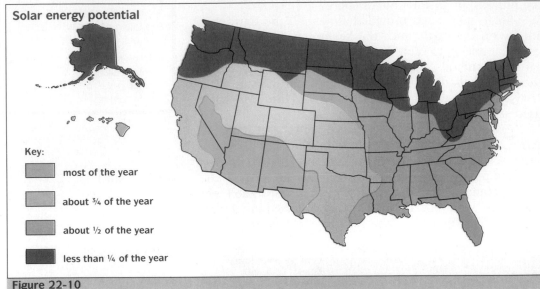

Solar energy potential

Key:

most of the year

about ¾ of the year

about ½ of the year

less than ¼ of the year

Figure 22-10

The use of solar energy for home heating and hot water is limited.

Many people are planning homes and other buildings that will make the best use of available solar energy. New houses are being designed to have windows facing the south, which causes sunlight to help warm the houses during winter months. These windows may be covered with shades or awnings to keep out the sunlight during summer months. Large glass enclosures, such as solariums or greenhouses, can be built to admit a large amount of light in winter but be shaded in summer. Such uses of the sun's radiant energy are called *passive solar heating*. Passive solar heating requires no special equipment.

Scientists are working to find ways of making greater use of solar energy in home heating. A **solar collector** is a device for collecting solar energy and converting it into heat. Using solar energy with the help of solar collectors is called *active solar heating*. A solar collector absorbs the sun's radiant energy. Heat energy is transferred from the surface to a fluid that moves through the collector tubes. The fluid carries off the heat, which can be used for heating the house or for heating water, or it can be stored for later use.

Figure 22-11

Passive solar heating (*left*) and active solar heating (*right*).

Solar heating systems must store the heat collected during sunny days for use at night and during overcast weather. Insulated tanks of water can be used for heat storage. The tanks can be placed above or below the ground. When heat is needed, the system can deliver heat from the storage tank. Even in cold climates, some home heating could be provided by solar collectors.

ACTIVITY   How Can Solar Energy Be Collected?

OBJECTIVE
Demonstrate passive solar heating.

MATERIALS
2 shoeboxes without lids, dark soil, metric ruler, 2 pieces of cardboard (12 cm × 6 cm), 2 Celsius thermometers, clear plastic wrap, tape

PROCEDURE
A. Cover the bottom of two shoeboxes with 2 cm of dark soil.

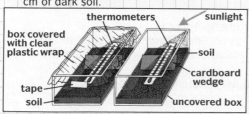

box covered with clear plastic wrap

thermometers — sunlight

tape

soil

soil

cardboard wedge

uncovered box

B. Fold two pieces of cardboard and wedge one piece into each box of soil. Place the cardboard midway in the shoebox and closer to one side, as shown in the figure.

C. Prop up a thermometer on the cardboard inside each box.

D. Carefully tape a sheet of plastic wrap over the top of one of the boxes.

E. Record the temperature of each box.

F. Place both boxes out of doors in sunlight for 40 minutes. The sun must not fall directly on the thermometers.

G. Record the temperature of both boxes after 20 minutes and after 40 minutes.

RESULTS AND CONCLUSIONS
1. Which box showed the greatest temperature increase? Why?
2. Use your results to explain how a passive solar heating system works.

ACTIVITY 45 minutes

PROCESS SKILLS
interpreting data, comparing, identifying cause and effect

Preparation   Collect the soil beforehand so that it is at room temperature.

Answers to Results and Conclusions
1. The box that was covered; the plastic prevented the heat that was absorbed by the dark soil from escaping into the air.
2. The thermometer readings of the covered box showed that although the same amount of sunlight fell on both thermometers, the readings on the thermometer in the covered box were higher. This shows that in a passive solar heating system, heat can be stored if it is not allowed to escape.

Teaching Tip   Explain to the class that a solar cell consists of two separate layers. A semiconductor, like silicon or germanium, is used as one layer. A metal conductor, like aluminum or silver, is used as the second layer. Electrons flow between the layers when light strikes the cell.

3 REVIEW/REINFORCEMENT

1. Solar energy is energy given off by the sun.
2. Advantages—it is available everywhere; it requires no fuel; it does not pollute the environment; and its use cannot be controlled by other nations. Disadvantages— capturing and using solar energy is not easy to do; it is limited by time of day, season, latitude, weather, and air pollution levels; and at present, it is expensive to install for heating.
3. Passive solar heating requires no special equipment; active solar heating is achieved with the help of solar collectors and other devices.
4. A solar cell is made of thin layers of silicon that are sensitive to sunlight; an electric current is created when light falls on the cell. These solar cells are being used in calculators, light meters, light buoys, two-way radios, and space vehicles.

Challenge   A home that uses passive solar heating has windows facing south; these let in the sunlight and provide warmth in winter but are shaded in summer to keep the home cool. A home that uses active solar heating has solar collectors with water pipes that collect heat from the sun during the day and heat water; the heated water is stored or pumped to the rest of the house for use as needed.

Solar energy also can be used to produce electricity. A **solar cell** is a device that converts radiant energy from the sun into electrical energy. Solar cells are made of thin layers of silicon that are sensitive to sunlight. When light hits these materials, an electric current is created. Since solar cells are very sensitive to sunlight, they work even when the sun's rays are not strong.

Figure 22-12

Solar cells can be used to produce electricity in small devices, like this music box (*left*). Many solar cells are needed to produce electricity for this solar-powered car (*right*).

Notice in Figure 22-12 that solar cells can be small. Therefore they can be used in small electronic devices, such as calculators and photographic light meters. Solar cells can also be connected to each other to create a larger electrical supply. The United States Coast Guard uses solar cells to light buoys, and the Forest Service uses solar-powered two-way radios. Solar cells are also widely used in the space program, where they have provided most of the electricity for space vehicles in orbit. Solar cells may one day generate electricity in power plants or for individual homes or cars.

REVIEW

1. What is solar energy?
2. List advantages and disadvantages of solar energy?
3. How does passive solar heating differ from active solar heating?
4. Describe and list some uses of a solar cell.

CHALLENGE   Describe the features of a home that uses solar energy.

22-3 HYDROELECTRIC POWER

Moving water has been a useful source of energy for many centuries. Water wheels have been used to change the energy of moving water to mechanical energy since the first century B.C. The invention of the generator made it possible for people to make even greater use of moving water. A generator produces electricity from mechanical energy. The first water-powered generator was built on the Fox River in Wisconsin in 1882.

Electrical energy produced by water-powered generators is called **hydroelectric** (hī droh ih LEHK trihk) **power**. Hydroelectric power plants built along rivers convert the energy of moving water into electricity. Water passes through a turbine which is connected to a generator, which produces the electrical energy.

About 4 percent of the electrical energy used in North America today is produced by hydroelectric power plants. In a modern hydroelectric power plant, water is held behind a concrete dam, as shown in Figure 22-13. The dam causes a reservoir to form. Water from the reservoir is gradually released to turn the turbines. What happens to the water after it passes through the turbines?[1]

hydro- (water)

[1] It flows downriver.

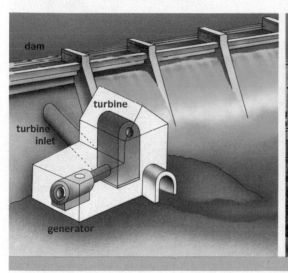

Figure 22-13

A hydroelectric power plant.

There are advantages to hydroelectric power plants. They do not produce water pollution or air pollution. They do not use up the water that passes through them, and the water that runs them is free. Also, the water behind many dams is used for recreation, irrigation, and flood

22-3 HYDROELECTRIC POWER
pages 555–556

OBJECTIVES
Refer to pupil page 555.

VOCABULARY
Key term: hydroelectric power

1 MOTIVATION

If there is a hydroelectric power plant in the vicinity, a field trip to the plant is well worth the effort. If there is no such plant nearby, show students one of the excellent films available on hydroelectric power.

2 CONCEPT DEVELOPMENT

Background   The potential energy in water at a high elevation is one of the purest forms of energy available. It provides energy without wastes and is relatively easy to control. From 80 to 90 percent of controlled water energy can be converted to work. This far exceeds the efficiencies of solar and thermal energy systems, 25 to 45 percent of which can be converted to work.

Background
Early settlements and towns were built near water sources so that water could be used to turn the paddle wheels of mills.

Teaching Tip
Discuss with students the fact that water power is essentially a form of solar energy. Review the water cycle with them: the sun evaporates water from oceans, lakes, and rivers. Warm air rises, carrying moisture. The moisture falls as precipitation on the land, filling the lakes and rivers. Dams store this water for hydroelectric power plants and then release it to flow back into the ocean to begin the cycle again. Emphasize that the cycle begins with energy from the sun.

3 REVIEW/REINFORCEMENT

1. Hydroelectric power is electrical energy produced by water-powered generators.
2. Moving water passes through a turbine that is connected to a generator; the water moves the turbine blades, which causes the generator to move and to produce electrical energy.
3. In a standard hydroelectric power plant, water is held behind a concrete dam to form a reservoir; water from the reservoir is gradually released through pipes that run downward to turn the turbine blades. In a water storage plant, water is pumped uphill during non-peak hours, using cheaper electricity; the water is released during peak hours, when more electricity is needed.

Challenge
A large amount of water in a dam increases the reliability and power available from a stream; the amount of power at a site depends on the rate of water flow multiplied by the vertical distance the water drops.

control. Why, then, is so little of the total amount of electric power used in North America produced by hydroelectric power plants? One of the reasons is that these plants are expensive to build. Investment costs per kilowatt are higher for hydroelectric plants than for nuclear or fossil-fueled projects. Also, most of the best sites in the United States are already in use. Building new dams would be possible, but it would mean flooding valuable cropland, scenic rivers, or recreational areas. There are also dangers related to dams. Dams sometimes break, releasing vast amounts of water that flood large areas. In addition, problems may occur downstream from dams. A large, flowing river may be changed into a small stream, causing an environmental change for the river's wildlife.

Some hydroelectric power plants are pumped storage power plants. In these power plants water is pumped uphill and stored in a reservoir or a storage pool until the energy is needed. Notice in Figure 22-14 that a pumped storage power plant also contains a turbine and a generator.

Figure 22-14

A pumped storage hydroelectric power plant.

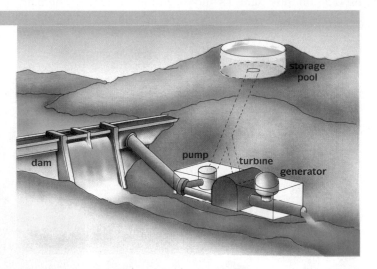

REVIEW

1. What is hydroelectric power?
2. Explain how the energy of moving water can be used to produce hydroelectric power.
3. How does a standard hydroelectric power plant differ from a pumped storage plant?

CHALLENGE How is the amount of water that flows through a dam related to the amount of electric power produced?

22-4 OTHER ENERGY SOURCES

Some energy sources make use of the earth's renewable resources. These energy sources include wind energy, tidal energy, and geothermal energy.

WIND ENERGY

For centuries, windmills have performed mechanical work, such as pumping water and grinding grain into flour. Wind power was probably first used by the Persians in A.D. 600. Many windmills were used in Europe and North America during the nineteenth century. However, by the end of the century, electric motors began to replace windmills as a source of mechanical energy. Today, windmills are being used as a source of electricity.

Just as moving water can turn turbines to produce electricity, wind can turn turbines. Using the wind to turn turbines to produce electricity is called **wind energy**. The energy of the wind moves the blades of the windmill to produce mechanical energy, which turns the turbines to produce electrical energy.

In the last 15 years, many new kinds of wind generators have been developed. As you can see in Figure 22-15, windmills can be quite large. Large windmills are more efficient than are small ones. When the blades are doubled in size, nearly four times as much electricity can be produced. Someday, windmills may even be built on platforms out at sea, where the wind blows steadily.

After completing this section, you will be able to

- **describe** wind energy, tidal energy, and geothermal energy.
- **list** advantages, drawbacks, and examples of wind energy, tidal energy, and geothermal energy.

The key terms in this section are
geothermal energy
tidal energy
wind energy

Figure 22-15

Modern windmills can vary in shape.

OBJECTIVES
Refer to pupil page 557.

VOCABULARY
Key terms: geothermal energy, tidal energy, wind energy

1 MOTIVATION

Have students look at the picture of the windmills in Figure 22-15. Ask students what causes the wind that spins the blades on the wind generators. Discuss with students the interaction of high and low pressure systems that causes uneven heating and results in winds.

2 CONCEPT DEVELOPMENT

Thinking Skills

comparing
Students compare the efficiency of large windmills with that of smaller ones. Students are made aware that as the size of the blade increases, there is a twofold increase in the amount of electricity produced.

Background   The actual power available from the wind is proportional to the cube of the wind speed. If the wind speed is doubled, eight times as much power is available. However, it is theoretically impossible in an open-air wind plant to recover more than 59 percent of the kinetic energy in wind. If the prop itself is 75 percent efficient and the generator is 75 percent efficient, only 33 percent of the energy in wind is actually converted to electricity.

Teaching Tip   Mention that all the forms of energy discussed so far can be traced back to the sun. In contrast, tidal energy depends mostly on the moon, with some effect from the sun and the spinning earth.

Thinking Skills

comparing
Students are provided with the minimum requirements for the ratio between high and low tides. When given a ratio, students can determine if the tidal energy available is sufficient to produce electric power.

Wind energy has several advantages. The wind is free, and it causes no pollution. However, there are disadvantages. The wind does not always blow, wind direction may vary, and freezing rain affects windmill efficiency. Many windmills are needed to generate electricity, and they take up a lot of space. The cost of constructing a wind-powered generating plant is very high. Another disadvantage is that windmills interfere with television reception. Also, many unattractive overhead wires would be needed to transport the electrical energy.

TIDAL ENERGY

The power of the earth's regular ocean tides is another potential source of energy. The tides are the daily rise and fall of the earth's ocean waters. Tides are caused by gravitational forces between the moon, the earth, and the sun, and by the spinning of the earth. The size of the tides varies from place to place, depending on the shape of the shoreline. **Tidal energy** is the energy harnessed as the tide is used to produce electricity. In a bay or inlet at high tide, water can be trapped behind a dam. At low tide the water can be released to turn turbine generators.

Figure 22-16

Low tide (*left*) and high tide (*right*) in the Bay of Fundy, Canada.

Although the tides contain great amounts of energy, there are few useful sites for tidal power plants. These power plants must be located in bays in which high tide is 3.5 m to 6.0 m higher than low tide. Along most shorelines, high tide is only about 1 m higher than low tide. One possible site is in the Bay of Fundy, which is located between Canada and Maine. Here the difference between high tide and low tide averages 15 m.

A typical tidal power plant has three main parts. First, there is a dam that holds back ocean water in a lake area called a tidal basin. Second, the dam has gates that control the level of the water in the basin. The third part is the powerhouse that contains the generators. As the tide rises, water enters the basin through the gates, and the water level in the basin rises. When the water level in the basin equals that of the ocean, the gates are closed. When the tide goes down, the gates are opened to allow the water to pass through the turbines, producing electric power.

Figure 22-17

A 240,000-kW tidal power plant on the Rance River, France.

Today, tidal power plants are operating in only a few nations. The 240,000-kW plant on the Rance River in France is shown in Figure 22-17. This dam across the Rance River makes use of one of the highest tides in the world, about 13.5 meters. When the tide moves up the river, the rising water is trapped by the dam and directed through 24 huge turbines to produce electricity. A 400-kW plant operates along a bay in the Soviet Union. The People's Republic of China has about 40 small tidal power plants producing about 8000 kW of electricity. In 1985 an experimental 850-kW tidal power plant opened in Norway. The benefits of tidal power are similar to those of solar energy. Tides are a reliable power source, and they do not cause pollution. However, building dams and emptying bays and estuaries can hurt fishing, shipping, and recreational use of the water.

Tie-in/Social Studies   Have students locate on a world map the countries mentioned in the text as having tidal power plants. Have students hypothesize where the plants might be located, taking into consideration the fact that tidal energy is best harnessed where there is a bay that can be easily dammed.

Background   The gravitational force exerted by the moon tends to pull the oceans facing the moon into a bulge. On the side of the earth opposite the moon, another tidal bulge is caused by centrifugal force. This force is caused by the earth and the moon rotating around a common center of mass, the center of gravity of the earth-moon system. This center is 4500 km from the center of the earth, on a line directed toward the moon. The motion of the earth as it revolves around the center of mass of the earth-moon system causes a large centrifugal force, which forms the second tidal bulge. Because of the earth's rotation every 24 hours, the tides rise and fall twice during that period.

Background   Geothermal energy is concentrated along active plate margins or in mantle plumes. It is also likely to occur in regions where magma is relatively close to the surface because of imperfections in the earth's crust. In areas of recent volcanic activity, rocks associated with old magma chambers may remain hot for hundreds of thousands of years.

Teaching Tip   Tell students that a geothermal area need not be marked by surface features such as hot springs and geysers. Point out that oil fields are not usually marked by surface oil either.

Enrichment   Ask students to research the difference between hot springs and geysers.

Review and Skill Masters

SKILL, page 134. See page 543b in this book for answers.

GEOTHERMAL ENERGY

geo- (earth)
-therme (heat)

Geothermal (jee uh THER muhl) **energy** is energy collected from the natural heat of the earth. The temperature of the earth gradually increases with depth. The temperature of the center of the earth has been estimated to be about 3500–4500°C. Most of this vast amount of energy is too far under the surface to be recovered. However, in some places on the earth, the heat is closer to the surface. It is in these places that scientists have been trying to use geothermal energy to produce electricity.

The places where the earth's heat is near the surface are areas where hot springs, volcanoes, and geysers are found. In some of these places, heated rock formations are saturated with water. There geothermal energy can be obtained by drilling wells into the rock and bringing the fluid to the surface as steam or as pressurized hot water. The steam or water can be piped directly to a power plant. Geologists do not always know where to drill for sources of underground hot water. That is why many geothermal power plants are located near hot springs.

SCIENCE & TECHNOLOGY

Nearly 75 percent of the solar energy that strikes the earth is absorbed by the ocean's upper layers. Ocean Thermal Energy Conversion, or OTEC, is a way to tap this energy by making use of the difference in temperatures between the sun-warmed upper layers and the cold deeper layers of the ocean.

The system works best in tropical areas where the water is very warm. The top, warm layers of the ocean run in currents toward the North and South Poles. Meanwhile, the deep, cold layers slide from the two poles along the ocean's bottom toward the equator.

An OTEC plant situated offshore simply draws in the warm surface water. This water is used to heat ammonia, propane, or any other liquid that boils at a relatively low temperature. The vapor produced from the liquid drives a turbine, producing electricity. Cold water from the ocean's bottom layers is used to condense the vapor back to a liquid. The cycle then begins again.

The electricity generated by an OTEC plant can be carried by a cable to the shore. Or an OTEC plant could be a self-sufficient factory. The oceans contain many minerals and chemicals. An OTEC plant can extract these minerals and chemicals from seawater.

Geothermal energy is used in Italy, Iceland, and New Zealand. Hot springs have been used to heat homes in Boise, Idaho, since the 1890s. Geothermal energy is also being used in California to make electricity. Scientists think that geothermal energy could produce 20 million kilowatts of power in the United States over the next 20 years. That amount of energy is about the same as the use of 700,000 barrels of crude oil per day.

One drawback of geothermal energy use is that power plants must be built at the source. Too much heat and pressure are lost if steam or hot liquid is carried more than a kilometer by pipeline. Another problem is that the water contains corrosive salts, which could cause pollution. There is also the problem of unstable land. When large amounts of water are removed from beneath the ground, the land could cave in.

Figure 22-18

A geothermal power plant (*left*). A hot spring (*right*) is a good site for geothermal power.

REVIEW

1. How can wind energy be used to generate electricity?
2. Explain how a simple tidal power plant works.
3. What is geothermal energy?
4. Name one drawback each of wind energy, tidal energy, and geothermal energy.

CHALLENGE Which of the three forms of energy generation discussed in this section would be best for your community?

Teaching Tip　Tell students that the first geothermal electric power plant was built in 1905 in Larderello, Italy. The first in the United States was built in 1960 at The Geysers in California. Ask students why Italy and California are likely places for geothermal power plants.

3 REVIEW/REINFORCEMENT

1. The energy of the wind moves the blades of a windmill to produce mechanical energy, which turns turbines to produce electrical energy.
2. Water is trapped behind a dam across a bay or inlet at high tide; at low tide the water is released to turn turbine generators.
3. Geothermal energy is energy collected from the natural heat of the earth.
4. The windmills take up a great deal of space and are expensive to construct; building tidal dams and emptying bays and estuaries can hurt fishing, shipping, and recreational use of the water; water from a geothermal source contains corrosive salts, which can cause pollution.

Challenge　Answers will depend on your location.

22-5 ENERGY CONSERVATION
pages 562–565

After completing this section, you will be able to

- **define** the term *conservation*.
- **explain** why *conservation* is important.
- **describe** ways to save energy.

The key term in this section is
conservation

1 MOTIVATION

Ask students how their life would change if the supply of energy resources was depleted. Ask them to name ways in which they could cut down on energy use at home. Write these suggestions on the chalkboard. Discuss with the class some ways in which people could conserve energy for transportation.

2 CONCEPT DEVELOPMENT

Thinking Skills

inferring
Students use the diagram in Figure 22-19 to infer what industries have developed, expanded, or been modified since we have become aware of a need for energy conservation. Students should be able to infer that the automotive industry, the field of architectural design, and industries that deal with building supplies have been affected by energy conservation.

Background   Scientists have tried to determine how long domestic oil supplies will last. One estimate of proven and potential reserves is that they will last about 40 years. Even now, about 30 percent of the oil used in the United States is imported. This percentage is an improvement over previous years. Until recently, we imported about 55 percent of our oil.

North America will probably use more energy in the next 25 years than it has used in its entire history to date. At the same time the world demand for energy will probably triple. Will the world demand for energy be supplied? Where will this energy come from?

Recall that most of the energy needs today are met by nonrenewable resources. Figure 22-19 shows the United States' energy use. Where is the most energy used?[1] Remember that once a barrel of oil is burned, it is gone forever. The question is not whether energy resources will run out but when will they run out.

Figure 22-19

Energy use in the United States.

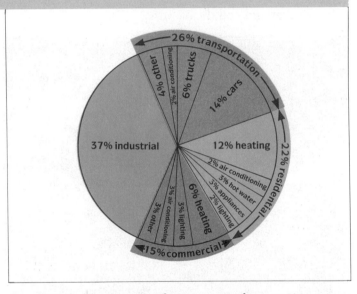

[1]Industry uses the most energy.

Renewable sources of energy may have an important impact. The Department of Energy has estimated that by the year 2000, about 20 percent of the needed energy will come from renewable resources. Other scientists have estimated that from 15 to 50 percent of the energy needs could be met by solar, wind, hydroelectric, tidal, geothermal, and biomass energy sources. But other sources of energy will be needed. Many people think that new technology can supply new energy sources. But such technology takes time to develop and is expensive.

Nonrenewable energy resources can be made to last longer by conservation. **Conservation** is the care, wise use, or preservation of natural resources. Conservation can be practiced in the home, school, and workplace.

con- (with)
-servare (to preserve)

ACTIVITY Does Insulation Prevent Heat Loss?

OBJECTIVE
Determine the effect of insulation on heat flow into and out of a system.

MATERIALS
safety goggles, lab apron, four 250-mL beakers, two 100-mL Florence flasks, cotton, graduate, tongs, 2 Celsius thermometers, ice water, clock or watch

  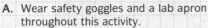

PROCEDURE
A. Wear safety goggles and a lab apron throughout this activity.
B. Draw a data table like the one shown.
C. Place each Florence flask into a beaker. Add cotton around one of the flasks.
D. Measure 50 mL of hot tap water into each flask. Add the thermometers.
E. Measure the temperature each minute for 10 minutes, and record the temperatures.
F. Repeat steps **D** through **E** with ice water. Use only the cold water. Be careful that no pieces of ice get into the flasks.

	Minutes					
	1	2	3	4	5	6–10
Hot water temperature (°C)						
Ice water temperature (°C)						

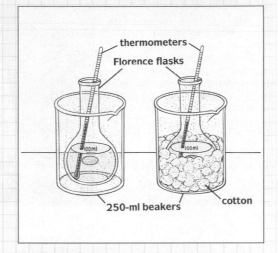
thermometers
Florence flasks
250-ml beakers
cotton

RESULTS AND CONCLUSIONS
1. Which flask of hot water showed a smaller change in temperature?
2. Which flask of cold water showed a smaller change in temperature?
3. Relate the results of this activity to building insulation.

EXTENSION
Repeat the activity using different materials, such as wool or foam rubber, as insulators, and compare results.

ACTIVITY 30 minutes

PROCESS SKILLS
observing, comparing, measuring, interpreting data, inferring

Preparation None required.

Answers to Results and Conclusions
1. The one with the cotton around it.
2. The one with the cotton around it.
3. In this activity, cotton provided insulation that made the hot water lose heat more slowly and the cold water gain heat more slowly; similarly, if proper insulation is used in a building, there will be less of a heat loss during winter and less need for a cooling system during summer.

Enrichment Have students investigate how well their homes are insulated. They should decide where heat loss is most likely to occur.

One third of the energy used in the United States is used for heating and cooling buildings. Therefore, designing buildings with energy-saving improvements can cut the use of energy. Such improvements include double-wall construction, windows that face south, and storm windows and doors. If all the people in North America conserved energy in their homes, half a million barrels of fuel oil could be saved each day. This energy could be saved through the use of better insulation, weather stripping, caulking, and using storm windows. Notice the house in Figure 22-20. The white areas by the windows show the loss of heat. The black and purple areas show where heat loss is the least. If this family used better insulation, caulking, and storm doors and windows, not only would they be conserving energy but their home fuel bills would be less.

Figure 22-20
Infrared photograph of a house at night shows heat loss.

Review and Skill Masters

CHALLENGE/CRITICAL THINKING, pages 135–136. See page 543c in this book for answers.

Puzzler   The radiation that is reflected from the Bonaventure Hotel may strike other buildings in the vicinity and increase the cost of cooling these buildings.

Tie-in/Social Studies   Have students investigate world-wide production and use of energy. Ask them to report on other industrialized nations and their energy use in comparison with that of the United States. Ask students to provide explanations for the information they find.

Tie-in/Language Arts   Ask students to write a newspaper article on energy conservation. Discuss the use of an interesting twist to encourage a reader to read the entire article. At the same time the article should provide arguments about the need for energy conservation. Students should include facts and figures to support their ideas.

SCIENCE PUZZLER

The building shown in the photograph is of the Los Angeles Bonaventure Hotel. It was built with mirrored windows, which reflect the radiation from the sun. This helps to keep the building cool in the summer. How do you think this building affects the surrounding buildings?

Transportation uses large amounts of energy. Of this amount, private passenger cars use about 50 percent. Smaller and lighter cars would help cut fuel use. Increased use of public transportation and car pools also saves fuel.

Conservation is just part of the solution to prolong our present energy resources. Even with conservation, about 5–10 million more barrels of fuel will be needed per day in 1990 than are needed today. Along with conservation, new ways of increasing the efficiency of our energy sources must be found. Alternative energy sources will also have to be developed. Solving energy problems will be a challenge, but with everyone's effort and cooperation, it can be accomplished.

Figure 22-21

Turning down the thermostat (*top left*), insulating your home (*bottom left*), and using public transportation (*right*) are ways to conserve energy.

REVIEW

1. What percent of the total energy usage is provided by non-renewable resources? What percent is supplied by renewable resources?
2. What is conservation?
3. Name three ways to conserve energy used for heating and three ways to conserve energy used for transportation.

CHALLENGE Make and describe a personal plan for energy conservation.

1. About 94 percent; 6 percent.
2. Conservation is the care, wise use, or preservation of natural resources.
3. By using better insulation, weather stripping, caulking, and storm doors and windows; by using smaller and lighter cars, and by taking advantage of public transportation and commuter car pools.

Challenge Plans will vary, depending on your location and local situations.

CHAPTER SUMMARY

The main ideas in this chapter are listed below. Read these statements before you answer the Chapter Review questions.

- The chief sources of energy in use today are fossil fuels, which include oil, natural gas, and coal. (22-1)

- Natural resources are materials found on the earth that are necessary for life or useful to humans. These resources can be renewable or nonrenewable. (22-1)

- There are four stages in the development of coal: peat, lignite, bituminous coal, and anthracite coal. (22-1)

- Oil and natural gas are commonly found together, trapped below layers of impermeable rock. (22-1)

- Synthetic fuels, or synfuels, are fuels made by a chemical process and used in place of oil or natural gas. (22-1)

- Biomass is any kind of organic substance that can be turned into fuel. (22-1)

- The greatest single potential energy source for the earth is the sun. Energy given off by the sun is called solar energy. (22-2)

- A solar collector is a device for collecting solar energy and converting it into heat. A solar cell is a device that converts solar energy into electrical energy. (22-2)

- A hydroelectric power plant uses moving water to turn the turbines in a generator to produce electricity. (22-3)

- Using moving wind to turn the turbines in a generator to produce electricity is wind energy. (22-4)

- Tidal energy is the energy harnessed as the tide is used to produce electricity. (22-4)

- Geothermal energy is energy collected from the natural heat of the earth. (22-4)

- Conservation is the care, wise use, or preservation of natural resources. (22-5)

The key terms in this chapter are listed below. Use each term in a sentence that shows the meaning of the term.

biomass	nonrenewable resource	solar energy
conservation	renewable resource	synthetic fuels
fossil fuels	solar cell	tidal energy
geothermal energy	solar collector	wind energy
hydroelectric power		

Review and Skill Masters

VOCABULARY REVIEW, page 131.
See page 543b in this book for answers.

VOCABULARY

1. b 2. i 3. c 4. d 5. h 6. a 7. g 8. k 9. e
10. j

CONCEPTS

1. Materials found on the earth that are necessary for life or useful to humans.
2. Renewable resources can be replaced; water, timber, wind. Nonrenewable resources cannot be replaced; coal, oil, natural gas, uranium.
3. Remains of sea life were buried by mud on the ocean floor, then were buried deeper by new layers of sediment. The remains changed to oil.
4. Compounds made of hydrogen and carbon.
5. Stage 1—Peat or young coal is formed; stage 2—lignite develops when peat is buried for a longer time; stage 3—more heat and pressure turns lignite into bituminous coal; stage 4—added heat and pressure turn bituminous coal into anthracite coal.
6. The energy released is directly proportional to the amount of carbon it contains.
7. Propane, butane, gasoline, kerosene.
8. Produced by nuclear fusion on the sun, 34 percent of the energy is reflected, 19 percent is absorbed by the air, 47 percent is absorbed by the ground.
9. Device that converts radiant energy from the sun into electrical energy.
10. A device for collecting solar energy and converting it into heat.
11. Passive—building design allows maximum amount of heat to enter in winter least amount in summer; active—solar collectors collect solar energy and convert it to heat.

Review and Skill Masters

CHAPTER REVIEW, pages 131–132.
See page 543b in this book for answers.

Chapter Review

VOCABULARY

Write the letter of the term that best matches the definition. Not all the terms will be used.

1. The care and wise use of natural resources
2. A device for collecting solar energy to convert it to heat
3. Fuels formed from the remains of ancient plants and animals
4. Energy collected from the natural heat from the earth
5. A device that converts radiant energy into electrical energy
6. An organic substance that can be turned into fuel
7. A natural resource that can be easily replaced
8. Fuels made by a chemical process
9. Electrical energy produced by water-powered generators
10. Energy given off by the sun

a. biomass
b. conservation
c. fossil fuels
d. geothermal energy
e. hydroelectric power
f. nonrenewable resource
g. renewable resource
h. solar cell
i. solar collector
j. solar energy
k. synthetic fuels
l. tidal energy
m. wind energy

CONCEPTS

1. What are natural resources? (22-1)
2. Explain the difference between renewable and nonrenewable resources. List three examples of each. (22-1)
3. Describe how scientists think oil was formed. (22-1)
4. What are hydrocarbons? (22-1)
5. Name four stages in the development of coal. (22-1)
6. How is the percentage of carbon in coal related to the amount of energy coal releases when it is burned? (22-1)
7. Name three products of the refining process. (22-1)
8. Explain how solar energy is produced and what happens to it when it reaches the earth. (22-2)
9. What is a solar cell? (22-2)
10. What is a solar collector? (22-2)
11. Explain the difference between active solar heating and passive solar heating. (22-2)
12. List two advantages and two disadvantages of using solar energy. (22-2)

13. Explain how a hydroelectric power plant generates electricity. (22-3)

14. Why does hydroelectric power make up less than 5 percent of the electricity used in the United States today? (22-3)

15. How is a pumped storage power plant different from other hydroelectric power plants? (22-4)

16. What do wind energy, tidal energy, and geothermal energy have in common? (22-4)

17. List two advantages and two disadvantages each to the use of wind power, geothermal power, and tidal power. (22-4)

18. Why are geothermal power plants usually located near geysers and hot springs? (22-4)

19. What is conservation, and why is it important? (22-5)

20. How can energy be conserved in your home? (22-5)

21. How can energy be conserved in terms of transportation? (22-5)

---

1. Which is the best source of energy for heating your home? Why?
   a. natural gas   **d.** oil
   b. electricity   **e.** wood
   c. coal

2. Explain how solar energy has provided almost all the sources of energy on the earth.

3. Why is conservation such an important issue?

4. What disadvantages might there be when a dam is built on a river?

APPLICATION/ CRITICAL THINKING

---

1. Do library research to explore the reasons why coal, the most abundant fossil fuel, has faded from use.

2. Do library research to investigate the role of lead as an additive to gasoline.

3. Do library research to investigate the role of sulfur in fossil fuels and air pollution.

EXTENSION

Energy Resources. "A Special Report." *National Geographic,* February 1981.

Gadler, Steve J., and Wendy Adamson. *Sun Power: Facts About Solar Energy.* Minneapolis, Minn.: Lerner, 1978.

Naar, John. *The New Wind Power.* New York: Penguin, 1982.

Smith, Norman F. *Energy Isn't Easy.* New York: Putnam's, 1984.

READINGS

12. Available everywhere, and requires no fuel; is not easy to capture, and depends on the time of day, season, and latitude.

13. Water moves a turbine that is connected to a generator.

14. Costs more to build than nuclear or fossil-fueled projects; best sites already in use.

15. A pumped storage plant during slack periods pumps water uphill to be released during peak periods; in a standard plant, water flows continuously.

16. They are all renewable resources.

17. Wind—is free, causes no pollution; does not always blow, changes direction. Tidal—does not cause pollution, is reliable; few sites can be used, shipping and fishing can be hurt. Geothermal—free, is easy to transport; is available in few places, contains corrosive salts.

18. Heat is closer to the surface there.

19. The care, wise use, or preservation of natural resources.

20. By adding insulation, caulking, weather stripping, and storm windows and doors.

21. By using smaller and lighter cars, public transportation, and car pools.

APPLICATION/CRITICAL THINKING

1. Answers will vary.

2. Because of photosynthesis, solar energy is stored in biomass and fossil fuels; heat from the sun causes wind, and it also powers the water cycle, which is the basis of hydroelectric power.

3. Conservation will help to prolong our present energy resources.

4. Dams sometimes break, causing floods; downstream from dams, a large flowing river may be changed to a small stream, affecting wildlife environments.

Test Masters

CHAPTER TEST, pages 85–88.
See page 543d in this book for answers.

Science in Careers

Petroleum chemists are scientists who study the chemical properties of oil and oil products. The chemicals that make up petroleum are not always the same. Various oil wells and deposits contain different chemicals. By testing for different chemicals, petroleum chemists can tell the quality of the oil.

The kinds of chemicals in a particular deposit also affect the way in which the oil is drilled. Using information from petroleum chemists, an oil company determines whether or not to drill for oil in a particular area.

Petroleum chemists work in refineries, for oil-drilling companies, and for companies that clean up oil spills. Others work in research or in companies that use oil products. The top positions in petroleum chemistry require a master's degree or Ph.D. If you are interested in this career, you should take courses in chemistry and geology in high school.■

Petroleum Chemist

Heating and Air-conditioning Technician

Heating and air-conditioning systems are necessary for our comfort, health, and way of life. But these systems are expensive and use a great amount of energy. Making sure that these systems work efficiently is the job of heating and air-conditioning technicians. They install, repair, and service heating and cooling systems.

Heating and air-conditioning technicians may work for construction companies and con-tractors or in large office buildings. They may also work in companies that sell heating and air-conditioning systems.

Heating and air-conditioning technicians often graduate from technical and trade schools. They also receive on-the-job training. If you are interested in this occupation, you should take vocational or technical courses in your high school, as well as courses in physical science and mathematics.■

People in Science

Dr. Enrico Fermi, Physicist

Dr. Enrico Fermi was an Italian physicist who won the Nobel Prize for his work with uranium fission. He had discovered that slowly moving neutrons were easily absorbed by the nucleus of uranium atoms. This bombardment of the uranium atom resulted in nuclear fission.

In 1938, Dr. Fermi was forced to flee Fascist Italy, and he came to the United States. Here he directed the building of what turned out to be the first nuclear reactor. This reactor consisted of blocks of uranium and graphite piled on top of each other. The graphite served to slow the neutrons. The slowly moving neutrons were absorbed by the uranium and started nuclear fission. This reactor produced the first controlled nuclear chain reaction.

Dr. Fermi's work in Italy and in the United States led to the development of other, more-advanced nuclear reactors. The careful use of nuclear fission still has great potential.■

Issues and Technology

Nuclear power is a controversial subject, and one of the biggest issues is the problem of nuclear wastes. Using nuclear power to make electricity or nuclear weapons produces radioactive wastes. All radioactive substances, including radioactive wastes, decay, or break down into other substances. In the process, energy and particles known as radiation are given off.

Radioactive wastes can be very dangerous. Exposure to radioactive substances can damage body tissues. It can lead to cancer or genetic damage. Exposure to large amounts of radiation can be fatal.

Radioactive wastes can remain dangerous for thousands of years. Right now there is no simple way to safely get rid of the wastes. Does using nuclear power make sense when there is no way to safely dispose of its by-products?

Different radioactive substances emit radiation for different lengths of time. The length of time depends on the half-life of the substance. The half-life is the amount of time it takes for one half of the radioactive nuclei in a sample to decay.

Some radioactive substances have short half-lives. Their radioactivity disappears in a few days. Others have long half-lives. Plutonium-239 has a half-life of 240,000 years. Uranium-238 has a half-life of 4.5 million years. Radioactive wastes containing these substances would have to be kept away from living things for hundreds of thousands or, in some cases, millions of years. The radiation level of one element found in nuclear wastes is shown in Figure 1.

APPLYING CRITICAL THINKING SKILLS

1. How long does it take for one half of this radioactive substance to decay? How long does it take for three fourths to decay?
2. Do you see any problem with creating wastes that remain dangerous for so long? Why or why not?
3. Wastes that are produced today must be safely contained for hundreds, and sometimes thousands, of years. Do you think that it is all right to produce wastes that must be safeguarded by future generations? Explain.
4. No one has yet found a satisfactory way to permanently and safely deal with radioactive wastes. Should that fact be taken into account when deciding to use nuclear power? Why or why not?

The following thinking skills will be applied in answering questions.
- *Identifying* the half-life of a radioactive substance.
- *Hypothesizing* whether nuclear wastes produced today will cause problems in the future.
- *Evaluating* the wisdom of using nuclear power before having proper disposal of nuclear wastes.

Answers to questions
1. It takes 240 years for one half of the radioactive substance to decay. Three fourths decays in 480 years.
2. Students will probably see a problem. Their reasons may vary but will probably center on the difficulty of controlling substances that remain harmful for so long.
3. The moral question centers on whether people who are alive today have the right to make decisions that may create problems for future generations. Some students will feel that we do not have this right. Others may feel that many current decisions affect future generations. This response may start a discussion of other political and ecological decisions of today that will have important consequences many years from now.
4. Answers will vary. Some students may say that they feel nuclear power should not be used until there is a safe way to deal with the wastes. Others may feel that nuclear energy is truly necessary now and must be used while a solution to the problem of waste disposal is sought.

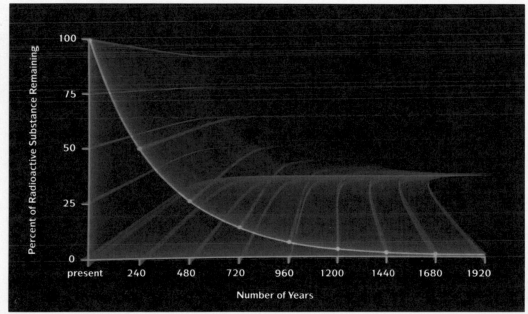

Figure 1

The following thinking skills will be applied in answering questions.
- *Identifying* the location of proposed nuclear waste sites.
- *Evaluating* the merits and problems of locating nuclear waste sites in the East.
- *Hypothesizing* what might happen in trying to determine the site for a permanent high-level waste site.

Answers to questions

1. Most of the proposed dump sites are located in the East.
2. The dump sites that were eliminated were located in the East. Students' answers may depend on where the students live. Some may think that the sparse population in the West justifies putting the dumps there. Others will feel that locating all the dumps in the West is an unfair burden on just one part of the country.
3. Since most of the nuclear reactors are located in the East, there is good reason to locate the waste sites there. Since the East is the most densely populated, it is also a poor site for the location of the waste sites. There are, therefore, strong arguments both for and against locating waste sites in the East. Students may view the problem differently according to the part of the country in which they live.
4. Although any community should be able to refuse a permanent high-level dump being located within its borders, there are problems with this refusal. If all potential communities reject the waste site, more time would be needed to propose other sites. This series of events could be repeated several times, losing valuable time. If no community wanted the dump site, the community weakest in political terms would probably get the waste site.

The United States has 100 licensed nuclear power plants. These plants produce about 3 million to 4 million kg of radioactive wastes each year. Millions of kilograms of wastes also result from the military's production of nuclear weapons. Additional wastes are produced by research laboratories and hospitals that use radioisotopes for medical treatment.

Facilities that produce nuclear wastes are located in all parts of the nation. But there are few places where these wastes can legally be stored. Therefore, highly radioactive waste must be moved thousands of kilometers across the country, from the place where it is produced to the place where it is to be buried.

So far there have been no transport-related accidents in which radioactive materials have been released. Nuclear materials are shipped in special containers. The containers are made to withstand impacts, falls, fire, and submersion in water without breaking open and releasing their contents. However, some people worry that no system is foolproof. Just because there have been no accidents to date does not mean that there will be no accidents in the future.

The spent fuel from nuclear reactors is a high-level waste. Currently this fuel is stored in pools of water at the site of nuclear power plants. This waste cannot be moved because there is no permanent storage facility for high-level nuclear waste in the United States. There is no such storage anywhere in the world.

There are plans for the United States to have a permanent site ready to accept this waste by 1998. Figure 2 shows the location of several possible nuclear waste dumps.

APPLYING CRITICAL THINKING SKILLS

1. In what part of the country are most of the proposed dump sites located?

2. In 1986 the Department of Energy withdrew from consideration all of the dump sites shown in red on the map. Where were these proposed dump sites located? Many people in the West were upset about this change. What do you think about eliminating these possible dump sites?

3. Most of the nation's nuclear reactors are located in the East. This area of the country is also the most densely populated. Taking both of these facts into consideration, how would you choose a site for the storage of nuclear wastes?

4. When the decision about a permanent dump for all of the nation's nuclear wastes is made, the government will pick the site. Should the people in the proposed area have the right to refuse? If every place chosen votes against the dump, how will the site of the nuclear waste facility be decided?

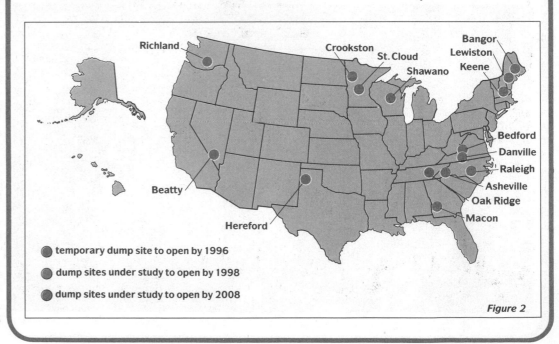

Richland
Crookston
St. Cloud
Shawano
Bangor
Lewiston
Keene
Bedford
Danville
Raleigh
Asheville
Oak Ridge
Macon
Beatty
Hereford

● temporary dump site to open by 1996

● dump sites under study to open by 1998

● dump sites under study to open by 2008

Figure 2

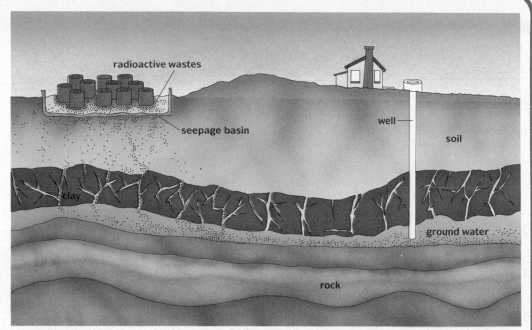

radioactive wastes

seepage basin

well

soil

clay

ground water

rock

Figure 3

The final decision on the location of the permanent high-level nuclear waste storage facility will not be made until 1991. However, the people in the three most likely sites are getting ready to fight the decision.

There are some people in each location who would like the nuclear waste facility to be located in their community. The facility would bring jobs. With guarantees that it will be safe, these people see no reason why they should turn down such a large employer.

However, there are environmental concerns. One possible dump site is in Deaf Smith County, Texas. The wastes would be buried in salt caverns almost 1 km underground. Some scientists believe that the wastes would remain sealed and safe there for many years. But the people of Deaf Smith County point out that the world's largest single source of

fresh ground water lies under their land. The ground water here is used for drinking as well as for crop irrigation in Texas and many other states. An accidental leak into the ground here would be disastrous.

People in the nuclear industry say that there is no need to worry. The wastes would be placed in huge leakproof steel canisters. These canisters would be monitored and guarded; no one would be able to disturb their contents.

However, people on the other side of the argument point out that there have already been problems with leakage at waste storage sites now in use. Almost 2 million L of radioactive wastes have seeped into the soil near the government's temporary site in Hanford, Washington. Some people are worried that the wastes could get into the ground water there and travel to the nearby Columbia River. This river is

used by millions for shipping, fishing, and recreation.

What can happen if an unsuitable storage site is chosen? Figure 3 is a diagram of a waste site that had leakage problems.

APPLYING CRITICAL THINKING SKILLS

1. A special seepage basin was constructed to catch possible leakage from the waste containers. Into what other areas have radioactive wastes spread?

2. The clay layer below the soil was thought to be a barrier that would trap water or toxins. However, the clay was not an effective barrier. What has happened here?

3. What is the probable effect of the leakage on the nearby well?

4. Do you think the leakage could affect areas in addition to those places close to the storage site? Explain your answer.

The following thinking skills will be applied in answering questions.
- *Stating* the areas in which radioactive wastes have spread.
- *Describing* the effects of the spread of radioactive wastes.
- *Hypothesizing* the effects of rdioactive wastes spreading outside their protective basin.

Answers to questions

1. Radioactive wastes spread to the soil layers. In addition, some wastes penetrated the clay layer and seeped into the ground water.

2. Radioactive substances leaked through small cracks and holes in the clay layer.

3. Radioactive wastes have probably contaminated the nearby well. This well water could injure anyone drinking it and could contaminate crops watered by it.

4. Leakage could affect any areas that are exposed to this underground water source. Therefore, large areas could be contaminated. Since there is no way to insure that a leak will never occur, ideally these wastes should never be stored near underground water supplies. This leaves out most parts of the country, reverting back to the question of using nuclear products without proper means of waste disposal.

APPENDIX 1 *Periodic Table of Elements*

IA 1								
1 1.0 **H** Hydrogen	IIA 2							
3 6.9 **Li** Lithium	**4** 9.0 **Be** Beryllium	IIIB	IVB	VB	VIB	VIIB	← VIIIB →	Transition Elements
11 22.9 **Na** Sodium	**12** 24.3 **Mg** Magnesium	3	4	5	6	7	8	9
19 39.1 **K** Potassium	**20** 40.0 **Ca** Calcium	**21** 44.9 **Sc** Scandium	**22** 47.9 **Ti** Titanium	**23** 50.9 **V** Vanadium	**24** 51.9 **Cr** Chromium	**25** 54.9 **Mn** Manganese	**26** 55.8 **Fe** Iron	**27** 58.9 **Co** Cobalt
37 85.4 **Rb** Rubidium	**38** 87.6 **Sr** Strontium	**39** 88.9 **Y** Yttrium	**40** 91.2 **Zr** Zirconium	**41** 92.9 **Nb** Niobium	**42** 95.9 **Mo** Molybdenum	**43** (99)* **Tc** Technetium	**44** 101.0 **Ru** Ruthenium	**45** 102.9 **Rh** Rhodium
55 132.9 **Cs** Cesium	**56** 137.3 **Ba** Barium	Lanthanide Series†	**72** 178.4 **Hf** Hafnium	**73** 180.9 **Ta** Tantalum	**74** 183.8 **W** Tungsten	**75** 186.2 **Re** Rhenium	**76** 190.2 **Os** Osmium	**77** 192.2 **Ir** Iridium
87 (223)* **Fr** Francium	**88** (226)* **Ra** Radium	Actinide Series‡	**104** (259)* **Unq** Unnilquadium	**105** **Unp** Unnilpentium	**106** **Unh** Unnilhexium	**107** * *	**108** * *	**109** * *

Periods 1–7 shown in the left column.

† Lanthanide Series Lanthanoid Series	**57** 138.9 **La** Lanthanum	**58** 140.1 **Ce** Cerium	**59** 140.9 **Pr** Praseodymium	**60** 144.2 **Nd** Neodymium	**61** (147)* **Pm** Promethium	**62** 150.3 **Sm** Samarium	**63** 151.9 **Eu** Europium
‡ Actinide Series Actinoid Series	**89** (227)* **Ac** Actinium	**90** 232.0 **Th** Thorium	**91** (231)* **Pa** Protactinium	**92** 238.0 **U** Uranium	**93** (237)* **Np** Neptunium	**94** (242)* **Pu** Plutonium	**95** (243)* **Am** Americium

*Atomic masses appearing in parentheses are those of the most stable known isotopes.

▢ These elements occur in nature, and are solids at room temperature (20°C).

▢ These elements occur in nature, and are liquids at room temperature (20°C).

▢ These elements occur in nature, and are gases at room temperature (20°C).

▢ These elements do not occur in nature, and have been produced in laboratories.

			IIIA	IVA	VA	VIA	VIIA	18
IB	IIB		13	14	15	16	17	2 4.0 **He** Helium

10	11	12	5 10.8 **B** Boron	6 12.0 **C** Carbon	7 14.0 **N** Nitrogen	8 15.9 **O** Oxygen	9 18.9 **F** Fluorine	10 20.1 **Ne** Neon
			13 26.9 **Al** Aluminum	14 28.0 **Si** Silicon	15 30.9 **P** Phosphorus	16 32.0 **S** Sulfur	17 35.4 **Cl** Chlorine	18 39.9 **Ar** Argon
28 58.7 **Ni** Nickel	29 63.5 **Cu** Copper	30 65.3 **Zn** Zinc	31 69.7 **Ga** Gallium	32 72.5 **Ge** Germanium	33 74.9 **As** Arsenic	34 78.9 **Se** Selenium	35 79.9 **Br** Bromine	36 83.8 **Kr** Krypton
46 106.4 **Pd** Palladium	47 107.8 **Ag** Silver	48 112.4 **Cd** Cadmium	49 114.8 **In** Indium	50 118.6 **Sn** Tin	51 121.7 **Sb** Antimony	52 127.6 **Te** Tellurium	53 126.9 **I** Iodine	54 131.3 **Xe** Xenon
78 195.0 **Pt** Platinum	79 196.9 **Au** Gold	80 200.5 **Hg** Mercury	81 204.3 **Tl** Thallium	82 207.1 **Pb** Lead	83 208.9 **Bi** Bismuth	84 (210)* **Po** Polonium	85 (210)* **At** Astatine	86 (222)* **Rn** Radon

64 157.2 **Gd** Gadolinium	65 158.9 **Tb** Terbium	66 162.5 **Dy** Dysprosium	67 164.9 **Ho** Holmium	68 167.2 **Er** Erbium	69 168.9 **Tm** Thulium	70 173.0 **Yb** Ytterbium	71 174.9 **Lu** Lutetium
96 (247)* **Cm** Curium	97 (247)* **Bk** Berkelium	98 (251)* **Cf** Californium	99 (254)* **Es** Einsteinium	100 (257)* **Fm** Fermium	101 (258)* **Md** Mendelevium	102 (255)* **No** Nobelium	103 (256)* **Lr** Lawrencium

* *No names have been given and no mass data is available.

Atomic masses based on C-12 = 12.0000

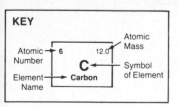

KEY

Atomic Number → 6   12.0 ← Atomic Mass

C Carbon

Element Name →

Symbol of Element →

APPENDIX 2 *Advances in Science and Technology*

B.C.

300 Democritus proposes an atomic theory of matter.

250 Archimedes proposes the principle of buoyancy.

A.D.

271 The first compass is used in China.

410 Alchemy begins.

1596 Galileo invents the thermometer.

1608 Galileo is the first to use the refracting telescope to study the heavens.

1616 Snell discovers the law of refraction.

1662 Boyle states the relationship between pressure and volume of a gas.

1643 Torricelli invents the barometer.

1665 Newton discovers that sunlight is made up of different colors.

1668 Newton invents the reflecting telescope.

1676 Roemer calculates the speed of light.

1687 Newton proposes his three laws of motion.

1714 Fahrenheit constructs a mercury thermometer.

1738 Bernoulli states the relationship between the speed of moving air and its pressure.

1742 Celsius invents the Celsius scale for temperature.

1752 Franklin shows that lightning is electricity.

1772 Rutherford and Priestly discover nitrogen.

1777 Lavoisier shows that air is made up mostly of nitrogen and oxygen.

1787 Charles states the relationship between volume and temperature of a gas.

1800 Volta produces the first electric cell.

1802 Dalton proposes the atomic theory.

1819 Oersted shows that an electric current produces a magnetic field.

1821 Faraday discovers electromagnetic induction.

1826 Nobili invents the galvanometer.

1827 Ohm states the relationship between current, voltage, and resistance.

1829 Henry invents an electric motor.

1831 Maxwell proposes the electromagnetic theory of light.

1839 Steinheil builds the first electric clock.

1839 Goodyear vulcanizes rubber.

1843 Joule determines the relationship between work and heat.

1858 Von Stradonitz develops a system for writing chemical formulas.

1857 Tyndall discovers the scattering of light by particles in a gas or liquid.

1859 Plante invents the first storage battery.

1869 Mendeleev proposes the periodic law for elements.

1876	Bell invents the telephone.
1877	Edison invents the phonograph.
1878	Hughes invents the microphone.
1880	Edison invents the electric light.
1884	Chardonnet invents rayon, the first synthetic fiber.
1887	Michelson measures the speed of light.
1895	Roentgen discovers X rays.
1896	Becquerel discovers radioactivity.
1897	Thomson discovers the electron.
1898	The Curies isolate radium and polonium.
1899	Rutherford discovers alpha and beta rays.
1903	The Wrights make the first powered flight.
1904	Elster invents the first photocell.
1905	Einstein proposes the equivalence of mass and energy and explains the photoelectric effect.
1911	Rutherford proposes a theory of atomic structure.
1913	Bohr proposes a theory of atomic structure.
1913	The Geiger counter is invented.
1914	Moseley proposes the idea of atomic number.
1932	Chadwick discovers the neutron.
1937	Whittle builds the first jet engine.
1938	The first cyclotron is built.
1939	Meitner publishes the first report on nuclear fission.
1942	The first electronic computer is built.
1947	An airplane breaks the sound barrier.
1947	The transistor is invented.
1951	Electric power is produced from nuclear energy.
1957	The first artificial satellite, Sputnik, orbits the earth.
1958	The first American artificial satellite orbits the earth.
1958	The microchip is invented.
1960	The laser is invented.
1961	A human orbits the earth.
1966	A spacecraft makes a soft landing on the moon.
1969	Humans land on the moon.
1970	The optical fiber is invented.
1975	Microchip-based products become commonly used.
1976	The Viking space probe lands on Mars.
1986	Voyager airplane circles the earth without refueling.

APPENDIX 3 *Safety in the Laboratory*

An important part of your study of science will be working on activities. Most of the activity work you will do is quite safe. Yet some equipment and chemicals can cause you or a classmate injury if you do not handle them properly.

Within certain activities, safety symbols are included next to the heading PROCEDURE. These safety symbols alert you to specific hazards in the procedure and to safety measures that should be taken to prevent accidents. Read the following guidelines and safety symbol explanations.

Safety Guidelines

- Prepare for every activity by reading through the entire activity before starting.
- Follow all written directions exactly unless your teacher gives you other directions.
- Read all labels before using a chemical.
- Work in a careful, organized manner. Do not play or fool around.
- Report all spills, accidents, or injuries to your teacher immediately.
- Use only tongs, test-tube holders, or hot pads to hold or move hot glassware.
- Make sure your working area is dry and clutter free. Do not handle electrical equipment with wet hands.
- Do not allow cords from hot plates or electrical equipment to dangle from work tables.
- Do not use any electrical equipment with frayed cords, loose connections, or exposed wires. Report such equipment to your teacher.
- Do not use glassware that is cracked. If glassware is broken, tell your teacher. Do not pick up broken glass yourself.
- Put away any books or notebooks that you will not be using during an activity.
- At the end of every activity, clean up your work area, put everything away, and wash your hands.
- Your teacher may have additional safety guidelines for you to follow.

Safety Symbols

 This symbol will be used when there is a danger of cuts caused by glassware, scissors, or other possibly sharp laboratory tools.

 This symbol will be used when chemicals or combinations of chemicals can possibly cause noxious fumes.

 This symbol will be used to remind you to exhibit care in handling electrical equipment.

 This symbol will be used whenever a lab apron should be worn to prevent damage to clothes by chemicals, acids, or stains.

 This symbol will be used to remind you to exhibit caution when working with the Bunsen burner and to be careful not to get burned when handling hot equipment.

 This symbol will be used to remind you to follow directions when working with chemicals that could be explosive if misused.

 This symbol will be used when safety goggles should be worn and when there is a possibility of danger to eyes.

 This symbol will be used when radioactive materials are present.

 This symbol will be used to remind you to be careful when using the Bunsen burner and to check that the gas outlet is turned off when not in use.

 This symbol will be used when substances in an investigation could be poisonous if ingested.

APPENDIX 4 *Units of Measurement*

The modern metric system is called the International System of Units, abbreviated SI in all languages. In SI there are seven fundamental units called base units. They are the meter (m), kilogram (kg), second (s), ampere (A), Kelvin (K), candela (cd), and mole (mol).

The meter is a unit of length; the kilogram, a unit of mass; the second, a unit of time; the ampere, a unit of electric current; the Kelvin, a unit of temperature; the candela, a unit of brightness; and the mole, a unit of amount of substance.

Metric to English Conversions

1 cm = 0.394 in.
1 m = 39.372 in.
1 m = 3.281 ft
1 km = 0.621 mi
1 g = .0353 oz
1 kg = 2.205 lb
1 L = 1.057 qt

English to Metric Conversions

1 in. = 2.540 cm
1 yd = 91.440 cm
1 mi = 1.609 km
1 lb = .454 kg
1 oz = 28.350 g
1 qt = .943 L

Approximate Equivalents

1 km	ten football fields
1 cm	width of a fingernail
1 mm	thickness of a dime
1 g	mass of a dollar bill
1 mg	mass of a human hair
1 L	volume of a quart of milk
20°C	room temperature

Commonly Used Metric Units

Length

Unit	Symbol	Equal to
meter	m	—
kilometer	km	1000 m
centimeter	cm	1/100 m
millimeter	mm	1/1000 m

Mass

Unit	Symbol	Equal to
gram	g	—
kilogram	kg	1000 g
milligram	mg	1/1000 g
tonne	t	1000 kg

Volume

Unit	Symbol	Equal to
liter	L	—
milliliter	mL	1/1000 L

Temperature

$°F = 9/5 \, °C + 32$
$°C = 5/9 \, (°F - 32)$
$K = °C + 273$

APPENDIX 5 *Significant Figures and Scientific Notation*

Significant Figures

Some estimation is required whenever measurements are made. Numbers in a measurement that are certain or reasonably certain are called significant figures. The following rules will help you determine which digits in a number are significant.

1. All nonzero digits are significant. For example, 35.684 has five significant digits, and 2.97 has three significant digits.
2. All zeros between nonzero digits are significant. For example, in the number 306.92 the zero is significant. Thus 306.92 has five significant digits.
3. Zeros to the left of the first nonzero digit are not significant. For example, in the number 0.00349 the three zeros are not significant; they are merely placeholders. Thus 0.00349 has only three significant digits.
4. Zeros at the end of a number that includes a decimal point, and zeros to the right of a decimal point, are significant. For example, in the number 480.0 the two zeros are significant. Thus 480.0 has four significant digits.
5. Zeros at the end of a number and to the left of a decimal point that is not shown may or may not be significant. For example, when a broadcaster says that there are 50,000 people at a football game, you cannot tell if this number is from an actual count or if it is an estimate.
6. The number of significant digits in a measurement is independent of the unit. The measurement of the length of an object could be given as 10.6 cm, 106 mm, 0.106 m, or 0.000106 km. In each case there are three significant digits.
7. In calculations, an answer should not contain more significant digits than the numbers you start with. In addition and subtraction the answer should not contain more digits to the right of the decimal point than does the number with the fewest number of digits to the right of the decimal point.
8. In multiplication and division the answer should not contain more significant digits than does the number with the fewest significant digits. For example, when multiplying 3.54 by 3.2, the answer can contain only two significant digits. This is because the number with the fewest significant digits, 3.2, has only two significant digits.

Scientific Notation

Scientists use a method known as scientific notation in writing very large or very small numbers to make them easier to understand and use. In **scientific notation** a number is written as a product of two numbers. The first number is a number between 1 and 10. The second number is written as the number 10 to some power. The power is a whole number that can be positive or negative. For example, the number 5000 written in scientific notation is 5×10^3.

To write a number greater than 1 in scientific notation, do the following:

1. Move the decimal point to the left until a number between 1 and 10 is obtained.
$$6,400,000 = 6.4$$
Moving the decimal point six places to the left gives 6.4.

2. Write the second number as the number 10 to a positive power. The power is determined by the number of places the decimal point is moved. In the example the decimal place is moved six places to the left. Therefore the power is 6.

The second number is written as 10^6.
The first and second numbers written together gives 6.4×10^6.

To write a number that is less than 1 in scientific notation, do the following:

1. Move the decimal point to the right until a number between 1 and 10 is obtained.
$$0.00017 = 1.7$$
Moving the decimal point four places to the right gives 1.7.

2. Write the second number as 10 to a negative power. The power is determined by the number of places the decimal point is moved. In the example the decimal point is moved four places to the right. Therefore, the power is -4.

The second number is written as 10^{-4}.
The first and second numbers written together gives 1.7×10^{-4}.

Silver Burdett & Ginn
PHYSICAL SCIENCE SKILLS HANDBOOK

The Physical Science Skills Handbook provides an opportunity to develop and apply skills that are useful in physical science. Each of the six lessons relates to a specific unit in the text. A given lesson may provide a fresh look at a familiar topic, or it may introduce an entirely new topic.

The theme of this handbook is "science in unexpected places." As you work through the lessons, you will find out how scientific measurement can "enhance" a day at the beach, how chemistry and common sense can solve a crime, and how even a dancer is involved with physics. You also will learn about some new and exciting applications of physical science, such as voice-prints and solar heating.

Each lesson consists of a visual display, a brief story or explanation, and a series of questions. As you interact with the pictures and the text, you will sharpen your ability to observe, compare, predict, infer, identify cause and effect, interpret diagrams, use math, and hypothesize.

CONTENTS

POWERS OF TEN

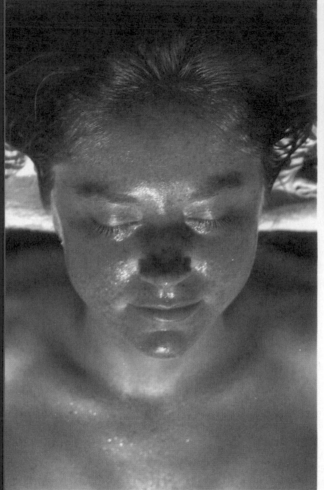

Figure A   1 m (1.0×10^0 m)

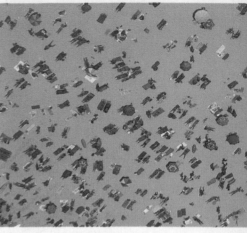

Figure B   100 m (1.0×10^2 m)

Figure E   1 cm (0.01 m)

It is a perfect day at the beach. The girl in Figure A stretches out on her blanket. In school she has just finished studying about measurement of very large and very small distances.

The picture of the girl was taken from only one meter away. However, Figure B, which shows much more of the beach area, was taken from about 100 meters away. Figure C, in which the beach appears as part of the shoreline, was taken from a satellite about 100 kilometers above the earth.

The view in Figure D, which was taken from

100,000 kilometers, is even more amazing. The entire shoreline appears as a grain of sand on the planet Earth!

Now turn your attention for a moment in the other direction. What might be the view of the girl from less than a meter away? Figure E, for example, was taken from one centimeter away. You can probably get this view of your skin with a hand lens or magnifying glass. You now begin to see smaller areas in greater detail.

The next photo, Figure F, was taken through a microscope. You can "see" the skin as if you

Figure C   100 km (100,000 m)

Figure D   100,000 km (100,000,000 m)

Figure F   1 mm (0.001 m)

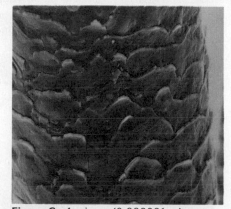

Figure G   1 micron (0.000001 m)

were one millimeter away. Skin cells and hair follicles now become visible. With the aid of an electron microscope, the view in Figure G shows an image as if you were a micron away!

Questions

1. Scientific notation, which is useful in expressing very large and very small numbers, is based on powers of ten. For example, Figure A shows a sunbather from a distance of 1 m, or 1.0×10^0 m. Figure B is from 100 m away. Express this as a power of ten.

2. Express the measurements in Figures C and D as powers of ten using the meter as your base unit.

3. How much farther from Figure A is Figure D than Figure C?

4. Suppose you took a photo of the beach from a plane flying at an altitude of 10,000 meters. Express this as a power of ten. What objects or details might you see?

5. Express the measurements in Figures E, F, and G, in meters, as powers of ten.

6. How many times larger does Figure G appear than Figure F?

Answers
FORENSIC SCIENCE
(Correlates with Unit 2: THE NATURE OF MATTER)

1. To examine for paint marks left by the red sports car.
2. A wad of chewing gum: It might show telltale teeth marks.
3. The red paint found on the green sedan did not match the red paint on these cars.
4. The saliva left on the chewing gum can be matched to the blood type of the suspect.
5. Possibly. The tooth specialist at the crime lab determined that the tooth marks in the gum were made by someone with missing teeth. A normal set of teeth might not have been distinctive enough to separate the two suspects.
6. Observation: Car seen speeding away from the scene; gum tossed out the window. Hypothesis: Red sports car believed to have sideswiped green sedan. Experiment: Paint and gum analyzed. Data: Dental exams and blood tests. Conclusion: Police piece the information together and accuse one of the drivers.

FORENSIC SCIENCE

Figure A

Figure B

Figure C

Forensic science is science applied to law enforcement. The following story shows how physical and chemical evidence can be the key to the conviction of an offender—and the pardon, of innocent persons. See if you can piece the puzzle together.

The scene of the crime (Figure A): A green sedan has been sideswiped by a careless driver swerving from side to side. The damaged car is taken to the crime lab.

The witness (Figure B): A bystander down the road noticed a red, late-model sports car speeding from the scene of the accident toward the tollway. Also, the driver was seen tossing something out the window onto the pavement (Figure D).

The alert (Figure C): Toll booth attendants are alerted, and five red sports cars are detained. An analyst from the crime lab is dispatched to the toll booths. Three drivers are released and two are asked to remain. Both have the same year and model car.

The suspects: Both of the remaining drivers are taken for dental exams and blood tests.

Figure D

Figure E

Figure F

The crime lab (Figures E and F): Physical and chemical evidence collected at the scene of the accident are examined.

The result: One of the drivers is accused of sideswiping the green sedan and fleeing the scene of the accident. Police congratulate the forensic scientists on a job well done.

Questions

1. Why was the damaged car brought to the crime lab?
2. What clue is shown in Figure D? How might it be important?
3. How were three out of five cars eliminated as suspects?
4. Blood type can be determined from saliva. How do you suppose this fact is relevant to the evidence?
5. The guilty driver has two teeth missing on the right side of the mouth. Might the suspect have escaped suspicion if he or she had normal teeth? Explain.
6. How does this story illustrate the steps of the scientific method?

584

Answers
COMPUTER MOLECULES
(Correlates with Unit 3: CHANGES IN MATTER)

1. By colored circles. Chains of amino acids are attached to each other at various points to form the protein molecule.
2. Doctors could analyze the shape of the naturally-produced molecule and try to find or produce a molecule with a similar shape to induce production of insulin.
3. One set of chains is yellow and the other set is red. The computer model shows tubelike structures, spheres, and fibers that make up the chains. It also shows a hollow space in the middle.
4. Both show the presence of intertwining chains and a molecular shape that resembles a sideways "Y." The drawing gives the impression of a straight-line angular molecule while the computer model shows more curves and twists. Also, the computer model gives more detail in that it shows each chain made up of tiny spheres. There are many possible reasons for these differences. The drawing is flat, and is done in straight lines for the sake of simplicity. The computer model is three-dimensional and seems to include more detail. Also, the molecule can probably exist in many different positions, which can be captured on the computer screen just by manipulating the model. The drawing is fixed in one position in only two dimensions.
5. Twenty. Pentons, because they are surrounded by five other molecules. Hexons, because they are surrounded by six other molecules.
6. They can show three dimensions; they can be manipulated easily into different positions; they can show more detail; they can represent shape and structure more accurately; they can be drawn quickly and changed easily. They can be constructed more easily; they can be displayed or printed on a flat surface while still showing three dimensions; they can be manipulated more easily; they can be stored easily on a disk.

COMPUTER MOLECULES

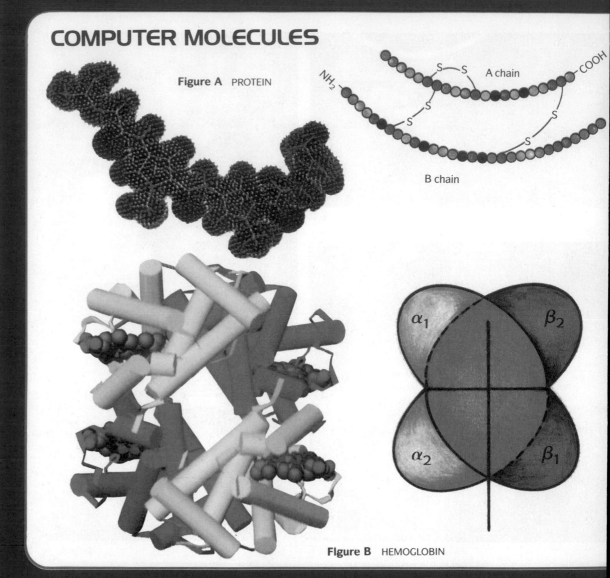

Figure A PROTEIN

A chain

B chain

Figure B HEMOGLOBIN

A colorful array of circles and lines rapidly fills the computer screen. An intriguing object shaped like a space satellite appears.

A new video game? No, it's just a biochemical researcher using a computer to generate a three-dimensional model of the adenovirus, the cause of the common cold.

Before the use of computer graphics, scientists had to rely on drawings and solid models to represent organic molecules and structures. These models were hard to construct and use. Now, a researcher can sketch an image in just minutes, then move it easily with a joystick.

The photographs above show examples of computer-generated models. Next to each is a drawing of the structure.

Questions

1. A typical protein molecule (Figure A) is made up of various kinds of amino acids. How are the amino acids represented in the computer graphic and in the drawing? Describe the structure of the protein molecule based on the photo and the drawing.
2. The function of an organic molecule is usually

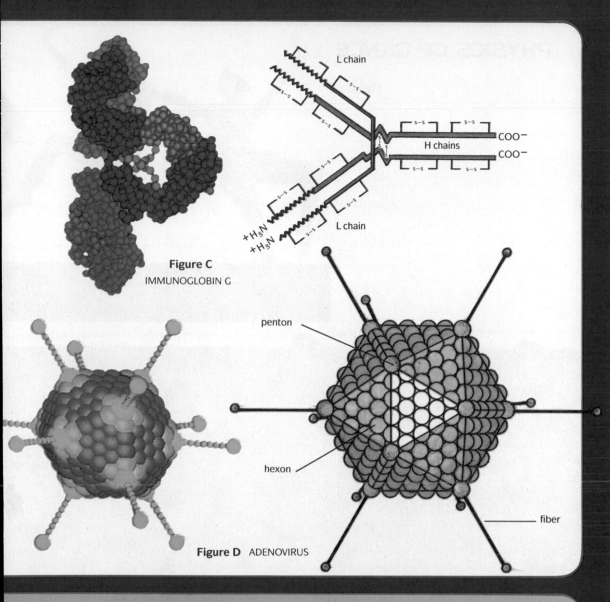

Figure C
IMMUNOGLOBIN G

penton

hexon

fiber

Figure D ADENOVIRUS

dependent upon its shape. Suppose the molecule in Figure A was responsible for insulin production in the human body. How might the ability to generate molecules via computer be helpful in finding a cure for people whose bodies cannot make insulin?

3. A hemoglobin molecule (Figure B) consists of two sets of protein chains, labeled α (alpha) and β (beta). How can you identify these chains in the computer-generated model? What details are visible in the computer model that are not visible in the drawing?

4. Study the drawing and computer model of immunoglobin G (Figure C). How are the two models similar? How are they different? Give possible reasons for these differences.

5. The body of the adenovirus (Figure D) forms a geometric solid called an icosahedron. How many triangular faces make up this solid? Why do you think the molecules called pentons and hexons are so named?

6. What advantages do computer-generated models have over drawings made on paper? Over solid ball-and-stick models?

Answers
PHYSICS OF DANCE
(Correlates with Unit 4: FORCES AND ENERGY)

1. Both dancers are the same height from the floor. The larger dancer must exert more force than the smaller dancer. The smaller dancer is jumping the greater proportion of her own weight.
2. The tallest dancers must be the first and third from the left. The shortest must be the dancer second from the left. The dancers first and third from the left must be the same height, and the last three dancers on the right must be the same height.
3. The first and third dancers from the left.
4. Student answers may vary. In terms of the force and energy expended, yes — but perhaps a larger dancer has more strength and endurance and does not feel this extra physical exertion.
5. It would be much easier to achieve a uniform look with dancers of similar size. For example, the dancers would probably jump to about the same height naturally, without the need for a lot of adjustment in timing. This would cut down on rehearsal time.
6. In Figure C, the skater is doing a barrel turn. He must be concerned about using enough force to get high enough off the ground to complete the turn before he lands. He must also generate enough angular momentum to make a full turn in a nearly-horizontal position. In Figure D, the skater is performing a movement, probably a turn, close to the ground. She must be concerned about balancing with her center of gravity lower than usual. She is leaning slightly forward to balance against the leg that is thrust forward. In Figure E, the skater is using the principle of equal and opposite forces to maintain her balance. The arm reaching forward, the leg reaching backward, the vertical force of her skate on the ice, plus the upward reach of her head act as four vectors that have a resultant force of zero.

PHYSICS OF DANCE

Figure A

Figure B

One interesting relationship between physics and dance involves how the size of a dancer's body affects the movements he or she performs. You know that it takes more force to accelerate a larger mass than a smaller one. So it is not too surprising that a 183-cm (six-foot) dancer needs about 75 percent more force to jump the same height as a 153-cm (five-foot) dancer.

The amount of force required by the larger dancer is even greater if both dancers jump to a height equally proportional to their own heights. For example, suppose a 183-cm and a 153-cm dancer want to jump to a height that is one-fourth their own heights. For the 183-cm dancer this is a jump of 46 cm (eighteen inches), while for the 153-cm dancer this is a jump of only 38 cm (fifteen inches). Thus, the larger dancer will go higher and be in the air longer than the smaller dancer.

Questions

1. Observe the dancers in Figure A. Compare the relative distance from the floor to the feet of the two dancers. Describe the amount of

Figure C

Figure D

Figure E

force exerted by both dancers. Which dancer is jumping the greater proportion of his or her own height?

2. Observe the dancers in Figure B. If each dancer is jumping to a height one-fourth his own weight, which dancer(s) must be the tallest? The shortest? Which dancers must be the same height?

3. In Figure B, which dancer(s) will remain in the air the longest?

4. Do you agree with the statement, "Dance is harder for a 183-cm person than it is for a 153-cm person"? Why?

5. Directors of shows that require a chorus of dancers often try to select dancers of approximately the same size. Why might they do this?

6. Ice dancers and skaters must use the principles of physics in much the same way as dancers do. Study Figures C, D, and E. What principles of force and motion do you think these skaters must be concerned with as they perform the skating or dancing movements you see?

VISUALIZING SOUND

Figure A

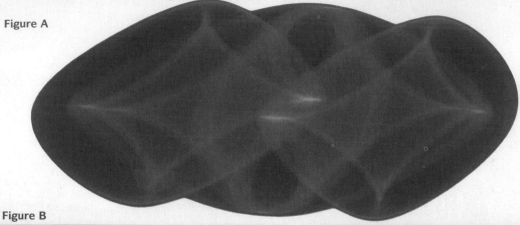

Figure B

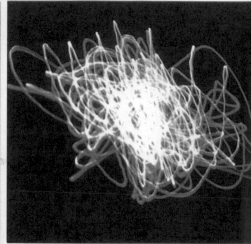

Figure C

Have you ever answered the phone and known who was calling—even if the person did not immediately give his or her name? You were able to do this because you recognized the person's voice. Some of the qualities that make each person's voice unique can be seen in a visualization of sound waves called a voiceprint.

Voiceprints, as well as other sound patterns, can be recorded by a device called a sound analyzer. Sounds are picked up by a microphone and shown on a screen or a printout called a spectrogram. For example, the sounds shown in Figures A, B, and C were made by a tuning fork, cough, and a hand hitting a microphone. Sound analyzers are used in forensic science, speech and hearing therapy, language study, bird songs, and machine noise analysis.

A voiceprint is also called a speech spectrogram. Figures D, E, and F all show speech spectrograms.

Figure D shows a spectrogram of the word "baby." The first part of the wave pattern is the "bay" sound, and the last part is the "ee" sound. In this type of spectrogram, vowel

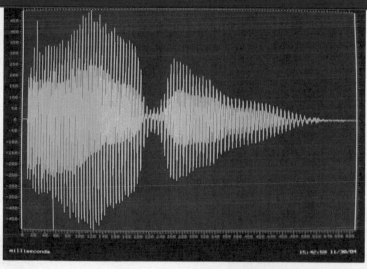

Figure D

Figure E

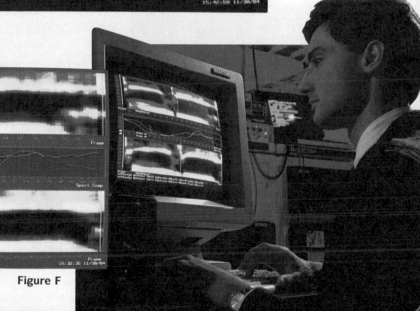

Figure F

sounds show a larger amplitude than consonant sounds because vowels cause the greatest amount of vibration in the vocal chords.

Questions

1. Observe Figure A. How does this visual representation correlate with the sound produced by a tuning fork?
2. How do the visualizations in Figures B and C resemble the sounds they represent?
3. In Figure D, which vowel sound in the word "baby" shows the greatest amplitude? Why?
4. What are some words that might produce a spectrogram similar to Figure D?
5. Figures E and F show another type of spectrogram of the word "baby," this time with two different voices saying the word. The horizontal axis measures time and the vertical axis measures intensity. How do the two voices differ in timing and intensity?
6. The Italian word for help is "aiuto" (ī u toh). Describe the sound pattern you think this word would make. Which would be a more "effective" call for assistance—the English or the Italian word? Why?

Answers

SOLAR HEATING
(Correlates with Unit 6: ENERGY SOURCES)

1. The glassed-in area at the left side of the house and the green thermal wall at the right. The awning.
2. It is larger and more spread out.
3. Glass panels.
4. Water in the solar collector absorbs radiant energy from the sun. The heated water from the collector moves to a storage tank, then moves through pipes to heat the house. Once the water has given up its heat, it is pumped back into the storage tank and finally into the solar collector to be heated and circulated once again.
5. If pump 1 broke down, cold water would back up in the storage tank. The water could not be reheated in the solar collector, which means that the system would soon be filled with cold water. If pump 2 broke down, cold water would back up in the pipes. The water level in the storage tank would go down, and no water would reach the solar collector to be reheated.
6. The solar collector in Figure G is at ground level, and it is not attached directly to the house. This could be an advantage since the water would not have to be pumped up to the solar collector the way it is in the diagram. A disadvantage might be that the water has to travel farther, and additional devices would be needed to make this happen. This could make the system prone to malfunction. Also, it is more likely that a collector nearer the ground would be shielded from the sun by trees or plants.
7. To act as insulation to hold the heat obtained from the sun during the day. Water.

SOLAR HEATING

Figure B

Figure C

Figure D

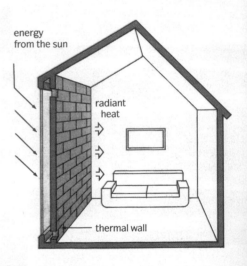

Figure A PASSIVE SOLAR HEATING

energy from the sun

radiant heat

thermal wall

The idea of using solar energy to heat a building is not new. What is new are the ways in which scientists are learning to collect and store solar energy. These methods make solar heating more effective and reliable.

Solar heating systems can be either active or passive. In a passive system, windows and glass panels are positioned to let in the maximum amount of sunlight. The sunlight is absorbed by special materials in the walls or floors of the house. These materials then warm the house by radiating heat, as shown in Figure A. Figures B, C, and D are examples of passive solar houses.

In an active system, solar collectors are used to absorb energy from the sun. The energy may be transferred and stored by circulating water. A pump, fan, heat exchanger, and pipes are often used in combination to transfer and store the energy. Figure E shows a typical active solar heating system, and Figures F, G, and H show examples of active solar houses.

Questions

1. Study the house in Figure B. Where is the sunlight absorbed? What device is used to

Figure F

Figure G

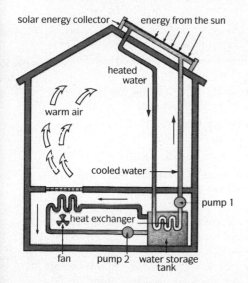

solar energy collector — energy from the sun

heated water

warm air

cooled water

pump 1

heat exchanger

fan   pump 2   water storage tank

ACTIVE SOLAR HEATING   **Figure E**

Figure H

help control the amount of sunlight absorbed?
2. Why do you suppose the house in Figure C has proportionately more solar energy absorbing areas than the house in Figure B?
3. What is the main source of entry of solar energy in Figure D?
4. Figure F shows a house heated by a system very similar to that shown in Figure E. Use both the photograph and the diagram to describe the process by which sunlight heats the house.

5. What would happen to an active system if pump 1 were to break down? If pump 2 were to break down?
6. In what way is the solar collector shown in Figure G different from the solar collector shown in the diagram or in Figure F? What advantages might this have? What disadvantages might this have?
7. The panels shown in Figure H are folded up against the house during the night. Why? What do you suppose is inside the circular drums?

Glossary

acceleration (ak sehl uh RAY shuhn)   A change in velocity over time.   *p. 332*

accuracy   The degree of closeness between a measured value and a true value.   *p. 37*

acid   A substance that releases hydrogen ions when it dissociates in water.   *p. 185*

acid anhydride (an HĪ drīd)   An oxide of a nonmetal that forms an acid when the oxide is mixed with water.   *p. 199*

acoustics (uh KOOS tihks)   The study of sound.   *p. 455*

actinide (AK tuh nīd) **series**   The elements beginning with actinium in the seventh row of the Periodic Table.   *p. 222*

activation energy   The amount of energy needed to start a chemical reaction.   *p. 174*

alcohol   A hydrocarbon in which a hydrogen atom is replaced by a hydroxyl group.   *p. 263*

alkali (AL kuh lī) **metals**   The elements in Group 1 of the Periodic Table.   *p. 209*

alkaline (AL kuh līn) **earth metals**   The elements of Group 2 of the Periodic Table.   *p. 212*

alkanes (AL kaynz)   Hydrocarbons that have only single bonds between the carbon atoms.   *p. 256*

alkenes (AL keenz)   Hydrocarbons that contain one double bond between carbon atoms.   *p. 258*

alkynes (AL kīnz)   Hydrocarbons that have one triple bond between carbon atoms.   *p. 258*

allotropes (AL uh trohps)   Different structural forms of the same element.   *p. 231*

alloys   Mixtures of metals.   *p. 216*

alpha (AL fuh) **particle**   A particle that contains two protons and two neutrons, given off by a radioisotope.   *p. 524*

alternating current (ac)   A type of electric current that changes direction at regular intervals in a circuit.   *p. 420*

amorphous (uh MOR fuhs) **solid**   A solid whose particles lack a regular, repeating order.   *p. 60*

amplifier   A device used to increase the strength of a current.   *p. 424*

amplitude (AM pluh tood)   A measure of the greatest displacement of matter from its normal resting position.   *p. 436*

anode (AN ohd)   The electrode through which electrons leave an electric cell.   *p. 392*

aromatic hydrocarbons   Organic molecules that have alternate single and double bonds in six-carbon ring structures.   *p. 260*

atom   The smallest particle of an element that has the properties of that element.   *p. 81*

atomic mass   The mass of an atom in relation to the mass of the carbon-12 atom.   *p. 93*

atomic mass unit (amu) A unit of mass defined as one-twelfth the mass of a carbon-12 atom. *p. 92*

atomic number The number of protons in the nucleus of an atom of an element. *p. 90*

base A substance that releases hydroxide ions in solution. *p. 190*

basic anhydride An oxide of a metal that forms a base when added to water. *p. 200*

beta (BAY tuh) **particle** An electron given off by a radioisotope. *p. 524*

biomass Any kind of organic substance that can be turned into fuel. *p. 550*

boiling point The temperature at which a liquid boils at sea level. *p. 65*

Boyle's law A law which states that the volume of a gas decreases as its pressure increases if the temperature stays the same. *p. 371*

buoyant (BOY uhnt) **force** An upward force exerted on an object by a fluid in which the object is immersed. *p. 290*

carbohydrates (kahr boh HĪ drayts) Organic compounds that contain carbon, hydrogen, and oxygen, and that are the body's main source of energy. *p. 268*

carboxyl (kahr BAHK suhl) **group** A group of atoms made up of one carbon atom, two oxygen atoms, and one hydrogen atom, found in organic acids. *p. 264*

catalyst (KAT uh lihst) A substance that changes the rate of a chemical reaction. *p. 179*

cathode (KATH ohd) The electrode through which electrons enter an electric cell. *p. 392*

cathode-ray tube A tube in which an electron beam is directed to a small area on a screen to form a picture. *p. 424*

center of gravity The point at which all of an object's mass appears to be located. *p. 286*

centripetal acceleration (sehn TRIHP un tuhl ak sehl uh RAY shuhn) The acceleration of an object moving in a curved path or circle at constant speed. *p. 346*

centripetal force The force that causes an object moving at constant speed to move in a curved path or circle. *p. 347*

chain reaction A type of reaction in which a product of a reaction causes the reaction to continue. *p. 534*

Charles's law A law which states that the volume of gas increases as its temperature increases if the pressure stays the same. *p. 372*

chemical bonds The forces that hold particles of matter together. *p. 115*

chemical change A change that produces one or more kinds of matter that are different from those present before the change. *p. 74*

chemical equation A shorthand method used by scientists to show the changes that take place in a chemical reaction. *p. 160*

chemical formula A group of symbols that shows the makeup of a compound. *p. 11*

chemical property The ability of a substance to undergo or resist chemical changes. *p. 74*

chemical reaction A process in which one or more substances are changed into one or more different substances. *p. 159*

chemical symbol A notation of one or two letters that represent an element. *p. 95*

coefficient (koh uh FIHSH unht) A whole number placed in front of a symbol or formula to show the number of atoms or molecules involved. *p. 162*

coherent (koh HIHR uhnt) **light** Light that contains waves of identical frequency and amplitude that are in phase. *p. 506*

colloid (KAHL oid) A mixture whose properties are in between those of a solution and a suspension. *p. 148*

compound A pure substance made up of two or more elements that are chemically combined. *pp. 58, 107*

compound machine A machine that is a combination of two or more simple machines. *p. 323*

compression The part of a compressional wave where particles of matter are pushed close together. *p. 435*

compressional wave A wave that displaces particles of matter back and forth parallel to the direction of the wave. *p. 435*

computer A device that follows a set of instructions to process information. *p. 426*

concave lens A lens that is thinner in the center than at its edges. *p. 495*

concave mirror A mirror in which the reflecting surface curves inward. *p. 492*

concentration (kahn sehn TRAY shuhn) The amount of any ion or substance present in a solution. *p. 193*

conclusion A statement that tells if the data from an experiment support the hypothesis. *p. 9*

condensation point The temperature at which a gas changes to a liquid. *p. 66*

conduction The transfer of heat energy by direct contact between particles. *p. 373*

conductor A substance that allows electric charges to flow through easily. *p. 384*

conservation The care, wise use, or preservation of natural resources. *p. 562*

convection Heat transfer that occurs in moving fluids. *p. 373*

convex lens A lens that is thicker in the center than at its edges. *p. 495*

convex mirror A mirror in which the reflecting surface curves outward. *p. 492*

corrosion (kuh ROH zhuhn) A chemical change that takes place when a metal combines with substances around it, such as oxygen. *p. 76*

covalent (koh VAY lehnt) **bond** A bond in which electrons are shared between atoms. *p. 122*

covalent compound A compound that contains covalent bonds. *p. 123*

crystalline (KRIHS tuh lihn) **solid** A solid whose particles are arranged in a regular, repeating, three-dimensional pattern. *p. 60*

cyclic hydrocarbon An organic compound that has a round, or ring-type structure. *p. 260*

decibel (dB) The unit used to measure sound intensity. *p. 447*

decomposition reaction A chemical reaction in which a compound breaks down into two or more substances. *p. 168*

degree Celsius (°C) A unit of temperature used in science. *p. 18*

density (DEHN suh tee) The mass per unit volume of a substance. *p. 68*

diatomic molecule A molecule made up of two atoms of a single element. *p. 236*

diffraction (dih FRAK shuhn) The spreading out of waves past the edge of a barrier or through a small opening. *pp. 440, 479*

direct current (dc) A type of electric current that travels in one direction in a circuit. *p. 420*

distance The length of the actual path traveled by an object. *p. 329*

Doppler effect The change in pitch that occurs when a source of sound and a listener are moving in relation to each other. *p. 449*

double replacement reaction A chemical reaction that takes place when the compounds in a reaction exchange ions. *p. 171*

dry cell An electric cell in which the electrolyte is a paste. *p. 393*

ductile (DUHK tuhl) A property of metals which means that they can be drawn out into a wire. *p. 205*

efficiency The ratio of the work output to the work input of a machine. *p. 313*

effort arm The distance from the effort force to the fulcrum of a lever. *p. 316*

effort distance The distance that an effort force moves. *p. 309*

effort force The force that is applied to do work. *p. 303*

electric cell A device that changes chemical energy into electrical energy. *p. 391*

electric circuit (SER kiht) A system through which an electric current can travel. *p. 397*

electric current The flow of electrons or flow of charge. *p. 391*

electric motor A device that changes electrical energy into mechanical energy. *p. 418*

electric power The amount of electrical energy used each second. *p. 401*

electrical force A force between electric charges. *p. 283*

electricity A form of energy called electrical energy. *p. 383*

electromagnet (ih lehk troh MAG niht)   An iron core placed in a current-carrying coil of wire.   *p. 414*

electromagnetic induction   The act of producing an electric current by moving a wire at a right angle through a magnetic field.   *p. 419*

electromagnetic spectrum   The different forms of electromagnetic waves.   *p. 461*

electron (ih LEHK trahn)   A negatively charged particle in an atom.   *p. 87*

electronics (ih lehk TRAHN ihks)   The study of the behavior of electrons in electric curcuits.   *p. 423*

electroscope (ih LEHK truh skohp)   A device that can detect the presence of electric charges.   *p. 388*

element   A substance that cannot be made into simpler substances by ordinary means.   *p. 58*

endothermic (ehn doh THER mihk) **reaction**   A chemical reaction that absorbs energy.   *p. 175*

energy   The ability to do work.   *pp. 28, 295*

ester (EHS tuhr)   A product of the reaction between an organic acid and an alcohol.   *p. 264*

exothermic (ehk soh THER mihk) **reaction**   A chemical reaction that gives off energy.   *p. 175*

experiment   A controlled procedure designed to test a hypothesis.   *p. 8*

extrapolation (ehk strap uh LAY shuhn)   A way of using a graph to obtain values for quantities beyond those that are known.   *p. 34*

filter   A transparent or translucent substance that allows only certain colors of light to pass through it.   *p. 473*

fixed pulley   A pulley that is attached to something that does not move.   *p. 320*

focal length   The distance from a mirror to its focal point.   *p. 492*

focal point   The point at which a mirror or a lens causes parallel light rays to meet.   *p. 492*

force   A push or a pull.   *pp. 28, 281*

formula mass   The sum of the atomic masses of the atoms present in a unit of ions.   *p. 126*

fossil fuels   Energy sources formed from the remains of ancient plants and animals.   *p. 546*

freezing point   The temperature at which a liquid freezes.   *p. 65*

frequency   The number of waves that pass a given point each second.   *p. 437*

friction   A force between surfaces that opposes motion.   *p. 283*

fuel   Any substance that is used to produce energy.   *p. 535*

fulcrum (FUL kruhm)   The fixed point of a lever.   *p. 316*

gamma (GAM uh) **rays**   Waves of energy given off by a radioisotope.   *p. 524*

gas   The state of matter that does not have a definite shape or volume.   *p. 60*

gears   Interlocking toothed wheels.   *p. 322*

generator (jehn un RAY tuhr)   A device that changes mechanical energy into electrical energy.   *p. 419*

geothermal (jee uh THER muhl) **energy**   Energy collected from the natural heat of the earth.   *p. 560*

glass   A supercooled liquid that is so viscous that it appears to be solid.   *p. 233*

graph   A display of data.   *p. 30*

gravitational force   An attraction between any two objects that have mass.   *p. 282*

grounding   The process of removing the charge on a charged object by connecting it to the earth.   *p. 390*

group   Vertical columns in the Periodic Table, made up of elements that have similar chemical properties.   *p. 99*

half-life   The time it takes for one half of a sample of radioactive nuclei to decay.   *p. 527*

halogenation (hal uh juh NAY shuhn)   A process in which halogens combine with covalent compounds.   *p. 242*

halogens (HAL uh juhns)   The elements in Group 17 of the Periodic Table.   *p. 242*

harmony (HAHR muh nee)   A pleasing sound that results when two or more different tones are played at the same time.   *p. 451*

heat   The total energy of all the particles in a sample of matter.   *p. 361*

heat engine   A device that changes the heat energy from burning fuel into mechanical energy.   *p. 377*

heat of fusion   The amount of heat energy that will change a solid at its melting point to a liquid at the same temperature.   *p. 366*

heat of vaporization   The amount of heat energy that will change a liquid at its boiling point to a gas at the same temperature.   *p. 368*

heterogeneous (heht uhr uh JEE nee uhs) **mixture**   A mixture whose makeup differs from point to point.   *p. 132.*

hologram (HAHL uh gram)   A three dimensional image produced on a photographic plate or sheet of film.   *p. 508*

homogeneous (hoh muh JEE nee uhs) **mixture**   A mixture whose makeup is the same throughout.   *p. 132*

hydrocarbons (HĪ droh kahr buhnz)   Organic compounds made of only carbon and hydrogen.   *p. 256*

hydroelectric (hī droh ih LEHK trihk) **power**   Electrical energy produced by water-powered generators.   *p. 555*

hydrogenation (hī druh jeh NAY shuhn)   The addition of hydrogen to a compound.   *p. 248*

hydronium (hi DROH nee uhm) **ions** H_3O^+ ions.   *p. 185*

hydroxide (hī DRAHK sīd) **ion**   An ion, OH^-, that contains one oxygen atom and one hydrogen atom.   *p. 190*

hyperopia (hī puhr OH pee uh)   The eye condition in which light rays from near objects are focused behind the retina.   *p. 501*

hypothesis (hī PAHTH uh sihs)   A possible answer to a question.   *p. 8*

image   A copy of an object formed by light.   *p. 489*

incident ray   A light ray that strikes a surface.   *p. 468*

inclined plane   A simple machine that has a sloping surface that is longer than its vertical side.   *p. 311*

incoherent (ihn koh HIHR uhnt) **light**   Light that contains waves of different frequencies and amplitudes moving out of phase.   *p. 506*

index of refraction   A measure of the refraction of light in a medium as the light enters from air or a vacuum.   *p. 471*

indicator   A compound that changes color as the concentration of H^+ or OH^- ions in a solution changes.   *p. 195*

induction (ihn DUHK shuhn)   The process of charging an object by the presence of a nearby charged object.   *p. 387*

inertia (ihn ER shuh)   The tendency of an object to remain at rest or in motion.   *p. 336*

inhibitors (ihn HIHB uh tuhrz)   Catalysts that slow down chemical reactions.   *p. 179*

inner transition elements   The elements in the sixth and seventh rows of the Periodic Table.   *p. 221*

insulator (IHN suh lay tuhr)   A substance that does not allow electric charges to flow through easily.   *p. 385*

integrated circuit   A circuit in which transistors and other electronic components have been engraved on a chip.   *p. 427*

intensity   The amplitude of a sound wave, or the loudness of a sound.   *p. 446*   The brightness of light.   *p. 465.*

interference   The adding or cancelling of two or more waves passing through a medium at the same time.   *pp. 442, 478*

internal reflection   The reflection of light in one medium when it strikes another medium with a lower index of refraction.   *p. 511*

interpolation (in ter puh LAY shuhn)   A way of finding information between two values that are known.   *p. 34*

ion   A charged particle.   *p. 115*

ionic bond   A force of attraction between oppositely charged ions.   *p. 118*

ionic compound   A compound that contains ionic bonds.   *p. 119*

isomers (Ī suh muhrz)   Compounds that have the same chemical formula but different structural formulas.   *p. 254*

isotopes (Ī soh tohps)   Atoms of the same element with different numbers of neutrons.   *p. 91*

joule J (jool)   A unit of work equal to one newton-meter.   *p. 305*

kilogram (kg)   The SI unit of mass.   *p. 16*

kilowatt (kW)   A unit of power equal to 1000 watts, or 1000 joules per second.   *p. 401*

kilowatt-hour (kW-h)   The amount of electrical energy used when one kilowatt of power is used for one hour.   *p. 404*

kinetic energy   Energy of motion.   *p. 28, p. 295*

kinetic theory   A theory that says that all matter is made of particles that are in constant motion.   *p. 359*

lanthanide (LAN thuh nīd) **series**   The 15 elements beginning with lanthanum in the sixth row of the Periodic Table.   *p. 221*

laser (LAY zuhr)   An instrument that produces coherent light.   *p. 507*

Law of Conservation of Energy   A scientific law that states that energy can neither be created nor destroyed but can be changed from one form to another.   *pp. 29, 298*

Law of Conservation of Mass   A scientific law which states that mass cannot be created or destroyed.   *p. 28*   A law which states that in a chemical reaction the total mass of the reactants equals the total mass of the products.   *p. 164*

Law of Conservation of Momentum   A law which states that momentum can be transferred between objects but the total momentum is never lost.   *p. 338*

law of reflection   A law which states that when a ray of light is reflected from a smooth surface, the angle of reflection is equal to the angle of incidence.   *p. 468*

lens   A transparent object that is used to refract light from an object to form an image.   *p. 495*

lever (LEHV uhr)   A simple machine that consists of a bar that turns, or pivots, around a fixed point.   *p. 316*

lipids (LIHP ihdz)   Organic compounds that contain carbon, hydrogen, and oxygen, and that are mostly used to store energy.   *p. 269*

liquid   The state of matter that has a definite volume but not a definite shape.   *p. 60*

liter (L)   A unit of volume used in science.   *p. 14*

luster (LUHS tuhr)   The property of having a shiny appearance.   *p. 205*

magnet   Any substance that can attract iron or other magnetic materials.   *p. 409*

magnetic domain   In a magnetic substance, a region in which atoms are arranged so that their magnetic fields line up to form a larger magnetic field.   *p. 411*

magnetic field   The area around the magnet where the magnetic force acts.   *p. 410*

magnetic force   A force caused by moving electric charges.   *p. 283*

magnetism (MAG nuh tihz uhm)   The attraction that magnets have for magnetic materials, and the attraction and repulsion between magnetic poles; also called magnetic force.   *p. 410*

malleable (MAL ee uh buhl)   A property of metals which means that they can be pounded into many shapes including thin sheets.   *p. 205*

mass   A measure of the amount of matter in an object.   *p. 27*

mass number   The sum of the protons and neutrons in an atom.   *p. 91*

matter   Anything that has mass and takes up space.   *p. 57*

measurement   An observation that has a numerical value.   *p. 37*

mechanical advantage   The number of times a machine multiplies an effort force.   *p. 308*

melting point   The temperature at which a solid becomes a liquid.   *p. 65*

metallic bond   The force of attraction that holds the network of metal ions together.   *p. 206*

metalloids   Elements that have properties of both metals and nonmetals.   *p. 228*

metals   Elements that are shiny, that are good conductors of heat and electricity, and that can be pounded into various shapes.   *p. 205*

meter (M)   The SI unit of length.   *p. 12*

mixture   A combination of two or more kinds of matter that can be separated by physical means.   *pp. 58, 131*

model   A means by which scientists try to explain something that they cannot see or understand by relating it to something that they do see or understand.   *p. 81*

molecular mass   The sum of the atomic masses of all atoms in a molecule.   *p. 125*

molecule The smallest unit of any covalent substance that can exist alone and still show the properties of that substance. *p. 122*

momentum (moh MEHN tuhm) An object's mass multiplied by its velocity. *p. 337*

motion The change in the position of an object as compared with a reference point. *p. 329*

movable pulley A pulley that moves with the resistance. *p. 320*

myopia (mī OH pee uh) The eye condition in which light rays from distant objects are focused before they reach the retina. *p. 501*

neutralization (noo truh luh ZAY shuhn) The reaction between an acid and a base. *p. 197*

neutron (NOO trahn) A particle with no charge, found in the nucleus of an atom. *p. 88*

newton (N) The SI unit of force. *pp. 17, 286*

Newton's First Law of Motion A law that states that an object at rest remains at rest until an unbalanced force acts on it. *p. 334*

Newton's Second Law of Motion A law that states that an unbalanced force on an object causes it to accelerate in the direction of the force. *p. 339*

Newton's Third Law of Motion A law that states that for every action by a force, there is an equal and opposite reaction by another force. *p. 342*

noble gases The elements in Group 18 of the Periodic Table. *p. 245*

nonmetals Elements that lack luster, that generally do not conduct electricity or heat, and that are not ductile or malleable. *p. 227*

nonrenewable resource A resource that cannot be replaced. *p. 545*

nuclear fission The splitting of a nucleus into two smaller pieces. *p. 533*

nuclear force An attractive force that holds the nucleus of an atom together. *p. 282*

nuclear fusion The joining of light nuclei to form heavier nuclei. *p. 539*

nuclear reactor A device that is able to make use of nuclear reactions and the energy that they produce. *p. 535*

nucleic acids (noo KLEE ihk AS ihdz) Organic compounds that control the functions of cells. *p. 270*

nucleus (NOO klee uhs) The part of the atom that has most of the mass of the atom, and that has a positive charge. *p. 87*

objective lens A lens that focuses the light entering it. *p. 503*

observation An examination of something in nature. *p. 7*

Ohm's law The relationship of resistance, voltage, and current written as $R = V/I$. *p. 396*

opaque (oh PAYK) A property of a material that does not allow light to pass through. *p. 463*

optical (OP tuh kuhl) **fiber** A glass wire used to transmit light signals. *p. 510*

ores Mixtures of compounds of metals, found in the earth. *p. 207*

organic acid An organic compound formed when one hydrogen of a hydrocarbon molecule is replaced by a carboxyl group. *p. 264*

organic compounds Compounds that contain carbon. *p. 253*

oxidation The combination of oxygen with any element or compound. *p. 239*

parallel circuit An electric circuit in which there is more than one path for the current. *p. 399*

particle model of light The idea that light is made up of particles. *p. 483*

period A horizontal row in the Periodic Table, made up of elements that have different properties. *p. 102*

periodic law A law which states that the properties of the elements repeat in a regular way if the elements are arranged by increasing atomic number. *p. 99*

Periodic Table A table in which elements are arranged in order of increasing atomic number. *p. 99*

pH scale A measure of the H^+ ion concentration of a solution. *p. 194*

photocell An electric cell that changes light energy into electrical energy. *p. 484*

photoelectric (foh toh ih LEHK trihk) **effect** The release of electrons from a metal when light strikes it. *p. 482*

photons Tiny particles of energy. *p. 483*

physical change A change in which the appearance of matter changes but its properties and makeup remain the same. *p. 73*

physical properties Characteristics of matter that can be measured and observed without changing the makeup of the substance. *p. 62*

physical science The study of matter and energy. *p. 4*

pitch How high or low a sound is. *p. 448*

plane mirror A mirror that has a flat surface. *p. 489*

plasma The state of matter that is a hot gas of electrically charged particles. *p. 61*

polarization (poh luhr uh ZAY shuhn) The process of producing light with electromagnetic vibrations in one direction. *p. 480*

polymer (PAHL ih muhr) A molecule made up of simple units that form a repeating structure. *p. 266*

potential energy Stored energy. *pp. 28, 295*

power The amount of work done in a period of time. *p. 305*

precipitate (prih SIHP uh tayt) A solid material that is formed in a chemical reaction and that separates from the solution. *p. 172*

pressure Force acting on a unit area. *pp. 292, 371*

products The new substances that are formed in a chemical reaction. *p. 160*

proteins (PROH teenz) Organic compounds that are made up of carbon, oxygen, hydrogen, and nitrogen. *p. 269*

proton (PROH tahn) A positively charged particle in the nucleus of an atom. *p. 87*

pulley A machine that is made up of a rope that turns around a wheel. *p. 320*

quality The distinct sound of a tone. *p. 450*

radiant energy Energy that is transferred by electromagnetic waves. *p. 461*

radiation (ray dee AY shuhn) The transfer of energy by waves. *p. 373* The energy and particles that are released as a nucleus decays. *p. 523*

radioactivity (ray dee oh ak TIHV uh tee) The spontaneous release of energy and particles from the nucleus of an atom. *p. 523*

rarefaction (rair uh FAK shuhn) The part of a compressional wave where particles of matter are spread apart. *p. 435*

reactants The starting substances in a chemical reaction. *p. 160*

real image An image that can be shown on a screen. *p. 493*

reflected ray The light ray that is reflected from a surface. *p. 468*

reflection The bouncing back of waves or light rays from a surface. *pp. 439, 468*

refraction (rih FRAK shuhn) The change in direction of a wave or a light ray as it passes from one medium to another. *pp. 441, 470*

renewable resource A natural resource that can be easily replaced. *p. 545*

resistance (rih ZIHS tuhns) The opposition to the flow of charges in a substance. *p. 395*

resistance arm The distance from the resistance force to the fulcrum of a lever. *p. 316*

resistance distance The distance that a resistance force moves. *p. 309*

resistance force A force that opposes motion. *p. 303*

resonance (REHZ uh nuhns) The response that an object makes to vibrations that match its natural frequency. *p. 444*

reverberation (rih ver buh RAY shuhn) A mixture of repeating echoes. *p. 455*

salt A compound formed from the positive metal ions of a base and the negative nonmetal ions of an acid. *p. 197*

saturated hydrocarbon A hydrocarbon molecule in which all bonds between carbon atoms are single bonds. *p. 256*

saturated solution A solution in which all the solute that the solution can hold at a given temperature has been dissolved. *p. 143*

science A method of obtaining knowledge about nature. *p. 3*

scientific law A general statement that describes some pattern in nature. *p. 11*

scientific method The way that scientists gather information and test ideas. *p. 7*

scientific notation   A number written as the product of a coefficient between 1 and 10 and a power of ten.   *p. 40*

screw   A simple machine that is an inclined plane wound around a cylinder.   *p. 315*

semiconductor   A substance that conducts electricity at some temperatures but not at other temperatures.   *p. 228*

series circuit   An electric circuit in which there is only one path for the current.   *p. 399*

significant digits   The numbers in a measurement that a scientist reads and estimates on a scale. *p. 37*

simple machine   A device that changes the size or direction of a force being used to do work.   *p. 307*

single replacement reaction   A chemical reaction that takes place when one element replaces another element in a compound, forming a new compound.   *p. 170*

solar cell   A device that converts radiant energy from the sun into electrical energy.   *p. 554*

solar collector   A device for collecting solar energy and converting it into heat.   *p. 552*

solar energy   Energy given off by the sun.   *p. 551*

solid   The state of matter that has a definite shape and a definite volume.   *p. 60*

solubility (sahl yuh BIHL uh tee)   The amount of solute that will dissolve in a given amount of solvent at a given temperature.   *p. 141*

solute   The substance present in the smaller amount in a solution.   *p. 136*

solution   A homogeneous mixture of two or more substances.   *p. 136*

solvent   The substance that is present in the greater amount in a solution.   *p. 136*

specific gravity   A ratio between the density of a substance and the density of water.   *p. 70*

specific heat   The amount of heat energy needed to raise the temperature of 1 g of a substance by 1°C.   *p. 362*

spectroscope (SPEHK truh skohp)   A tool that separates light into different colors.   *p. 22*

speed   The distance an object moves in a given amount of time.   *p. 330*

spontaneous (spahn TAY nee uhs) **reaction**   A reaction that takes places with so little energy added to start the reaction that it seems as if no activation energy is needed.   *p. 174*

static electricity   The effects caused by electric charges at rest.   *p. 384*

structural formula   A model that shows the arrangement of atoms in a molecule.   *p. 254*

sublimation (suhb luh MAY shuhn)   The direct change in state from solid to gas without melting.   *p. 73*

subscript   A small lowered number that shows the proportion of elements in a compound.   *p. 110*

substituted hydrocarbon   A hydrocarbon in which one or more of the hydrogen atoms has been replaced by a different atom or a group of atoms. *p. 262*

supersaturated solution   A solution that has more dissolved solute than is normal for a given temperature.   *p. 144*

surface tension   The tendency of a liquid to form a skin at the surface.   *p. 63*

suspension   A heterogeneous mixture in which particles of a substance are temporarily mixed in a liquid.   *p. 147*

synthesis reaction   A chemical reaction in which two or more substances combine to form a new compound.   *p. 167*

synthetic (sihn THEHT ihk) **fuels**   Fuels that are made by a chemical process and that are used in place of oil or natural gas.   *p. 549*

technology (tehk NAHL uh jee)   The application of scientific knowledge in an effort to improve the quality of human life.   *p. 5*

temperature   A measure of the average kinetic energy in a sample of matter.   *p. 359*

theory (THEE uh ree)   A hypothesis that has been tested and supported many times.   *p. 10*

tidal energy   The energy harnessed as the tide is used to produce electricity.   *p. 558*

tracer   A radioactive atom or molecule that is used to study biological, chemical, or physical processes.   *p. 529*

transistor (tran ZIHS tuhr)   A solid electronic component that amplifies and controls the flow of electric current in a circuit.   *p. 425*

transition elements   The elements located between Groups 2 and 13 in the Periodic Table.   *p. 215*

translucent (trans LOO suhnt)   A property of a material that allows only some light to pass through.   *p. 463*

transparent (trans PAIR uhnt)   A property of a material that allows almost all light to pass through.   *p. 463*

transverse wave   A wave in which matter vibrates up and down at right angles to the direction in which the wave travels.   *p. 434*

triatomic molecule   A molecule made up of three atoms of a single element.   *p. 239*

unsaturated hydrocarbon   A molecule that has double bonds between carbon atoms.   *p. 258*

unsaturated solution   A solution in which more solute can be dissolved.   *p. 143*

vacuum tubes   Electronic components that change alternating current to direct current and amplify, or increase, the current.   *p. 423*

velocity (vuh LAHS uh tee)   Speed in a definite direction.   *p. 331*

virtual image   An image that does not exist in the place it seems to be.   *p. 490*

vitamins   Complex organic compounds used in small amounts to control chemical reactions in the body.   *p. 270*

voltage   A measure of the energy available to move charges in a circuit.   *p. 394*

watt (W)   The SI unit of power, equal to one joule per second.   *pp. 306, 401*

wave   A disturbance that travels through space or matter in a regular pattern.   *p. 433*

wave model of light   The idea that light is made up of light waves.   *p. 478*

wavelength   The distance from any point on a wave to the corresponding point on the next wave.   *p. 436*

weak interactions   Forces believed to cause the nuclei of some atoms to break apart.   *p. 283*

wedge   A type of modified inclined plane that has a thick end and a thinner or sharper end.   *p. 314*

weight   The amount of gravitational force between two objects.   *p. 286*

wet cell   An electric cell that contains an electrolyte in liquid solution.   *p. 392*

wheel and axle   A simple machine that consists of two wheels that turn around the same pivot.   *p. 321*

wind energy   Using the wind to turn turbines to produce electricity.   *p. 557*

work   Using force to move an object through a distance.   *p. 303*

Index

CREDITS

dett & Ginn. 192: l. Avtex Fibers; r. E.I. du Pont de Nemours. 194: t. Silver Burdett & Ginn; b. Patti Murray/Earth Scenes. 195: Yoav/Phototake. 199: t. © Dr. Jeremy Burgess/Science Photo Library/Photo Researchers, Inc.; inset. © Eric Grave/Photo Researchers, Inc.; b. Katharine Thomas/Taurus Photos. 200: Lou Jacobs Jr./Grant Heilman Photography.

Chapter 9 204: Michael Holford, Photo: Ruth Eng. 206: t.l. Marvin E. Newman/The Image Bank; b.l. © 1988 Marc & Evelyne Bernheim/Woodfin Camp & Associates; r. Steve Dunwell/The Image Bank. 207: E.R. Degginger. 209–211: Yoav/Phototake. 213: t. Larry Lefever/Grant Heilman Photography; b. © Biophoto Associates/Photo Researchers, Inc. 214: t. E.R. Degginger; b. © Michael Abbey/Science Source/Photo Researchers, Inc. 216: Yoav/Phototake. 218: Atlas Foundry Co. 219: t. © David Taylor/Science Photo Library/Photo Researchers, Inc.; b. IMAGERY. 220: t. International Gold Corporation; b. Eric Kroll/Taurus Photos. 221: l. Susan van Etten/Taurus Photos; r. Wes Thompson/Stock Market. 222: Gabe Palmer/Stock Market.

Chapter 10 226: Christopher Morris/Black Star. 228: l., m. E.R. Degginger; r. Tino Hammid. 229: E.R. Degginger. 230: l. Peter Brouillet; r. Eric Kroll/Taurus Photos. 231: E.R. Degginger. 232: Tino Hammid. 233: l., r. E.R. Degginger; m. William E. Ferguson. 235: t. Dan McCoy/Rainbow; b. Roger Ressmeyer/Wheeler Pictures. 236, 237: E.R. Degginger. 238: Runk-Schoenberger/Grant Heilman Photography. 239: Neal & Molly Jansen/Shostal Associates. 241: l. D. Cavagnaro/Peter Arnold, Inc.; r. William E. Ferguson. 242: E.R. Degginger. 243: James H. Carmichael Jr./Bruce Coleman. 244: Silver Burdett & Ginn. 245: Peter Menzel/Wheeler Pictures. 246: l. E.R. Degginger; r. Jawitz/The Image Bank.

Chapter 11 252: © Craig Hammell/Stock Market. 254: Silver Burdett & Ginn. 255: Focus on Sports. 256: Richard Gross/Stock Market. 258: Ray Shaw/Stock Market. 261: l. E.R. Degginger; r. William Rivelli/The Image Bank. 262: IMAGERY. 264: t. © 1988 Jonathan Blair/Woodfin Camp & Associates; b. Silver Burdett & Ginn. 266: Silver Burdett & Ginn. 267: t. Courtesy ICI Americas, Inc.; b. Barry L. Runk/Grant Heilman Photography. 268, 269: Barry L. Runk/Grant Heilman Photography. 274: l. Yona Schley/Phototake; r. Gary Gladstone/The Image Bank. 278: t. The Granger Collection; b. Wide World. 279: t., inset Ben Rose/The Image Bank; b. Focus on Sports.

Chapter 12 280: © 1988 Jim Tuten/Woodfin Camp & Associates. 282: l. E.R. Degginger; t.r. Linda & David Phillips; b.r. E.R. Degginger. 283: Steven Goldblatt. 284: t. Tom Tracy; b. J. Allan Cash Ltd./Shostal Associates. 285: Jan Langlois Photographic Services. 286–288: Silver Burdett & Ginn. 289: NASA. 292: Stock Market. 293: Louis van Camp/Shostal Associates. 294: James A. Sugar/Black Star. 295: R. Glander/Shostal Associates. 296: l. Michael Milford/Wheeler Pictures; r. Ted Horowitz/Stock Shop. 297: Peter Menzel/Wheeler Pictures. 298: t.l. E.R. Degginger; t.r. J. Barry O'Rourke/Stock Market; b. Alan Felix/Shostal Associates.

Chapter 13 302: Courtesy of Mitsubishi. 304: Silver Burdett & Ginn. 306: Al Henderson/Click, Chicago. 307: t.l. Michal Heron; b.l. Christopher Morrow/Click, Boston; r. Cary Wolinsky/Stock, Boston. 311: © Russ Kinne/Photo Researchers, Inc. 315: l. Jim Trotter/Shostal Associates; r. Shostal Associates. 316: IMAGERY. 318: t.l. Peter Vandermark/Stock, Boston; t.r. Erika Stone/Peter Arnold, Inc.; b. Silver Burdett & Ginn. 319: l. Silver Burdett & Ginn; r. Don & Pat Valenti/Tom Stack & Associates. 320: Silver Burdett & Ginn. 322: l. Jim Harris/Stock, Boston; r. IMAGERY. 323: © 1988 Dick Durrance/Woodfin Camp & Associates. 324: Silver Burdett & Ginn.

Chapter 14 328: E.R. Degginger. 330: Focus on Sports. 331: Ray Pfortner/Peter Arnold, Inc. 332: Silver Burdett & Ginn. 333: Southern Stock. 334: Silver Burdett & Ginn. 335: t. © G. Aschendorf/Photo Researchers, Inc.; b. Kryn Taconis/Magnum. 336: t. Fritz Prenzel/Peter Arnold, Inc.; b. Courtesy of General Motors. 338: Silver Burdett & Ginn. 339: Alvis Upitis/Shostal Associates. 341: Focus on Sports. 342: NASA. 347: Silver Burdett & Ginn. 348: NASA. 352: l. Silver Burdett & Ginn; r. Ralph Lucel/Shostal Associates. 356: t. © John Hesiltine/Science Photo Library/Photo Researchers, Inc.; b. The Granger Collection. 357: t.l. © Dr. R. Clark & M. Goff/Photo Researchers Inc.; t.r. Henry Ford Museum; b. The Granger Collection. 357: © David Parker/Science Photo Library/Photo Researchers, Inc.

Chapter 15 359: © 1988 Howard Sochurek/Woodfin Camp & Associates. 361: E.R. Degginger. 362–364: IMAGERY. 365: Peter Arnold, Inc. 366, 369: E.R. Degginger. 370: Richard Choy/Peter Arnold, Inc. 370: Click/Chicago. 371: IMAGERY. 372: l. Vaughn E. Winslow/Click/Chicago; R. Galen Rowell/Peter Arnold, Inc. 375: © NASA/Science Source/Photo Researchers, Inc. 376: t. E.R. Degginger; b.l. Silver Burdett & Ginn; b.r. courtesy American Down Association. 377: Werner H. Miller/Peter Arnold, Inc.

Chapter 16 382: D.C. Lowe/Shostal Associates. 384: IMAGERY. 388: t. Shostal Associates; b. IMAGERY. 390, 393: IMAGERY. 394: t. Ellis Herwig/Taurus Photos. 395: IMAGERY. 396: Raffaello Faval/Shostal Associates. 397: IMAGERY. 398: t. Courtesy Alupower; b. IMAGERY. 400: Imagery. 401: l. Taurus Photos; r. Dan McCoy/Rainbow. 402: E.R. Degginger. 403: Silver Burdett & Ginn. 404: r. Ray Pfortner/Peter Arnold, Inc.; l. Silver Burdett & Ginn.

Chapter 17 408: © Stanford Linear Accelerator Center/Science Photo Library/Photo Researchers, Inc. 410: Imagery. 411–412: Silver Burdett & Ginn. 417: Silver Burdett & Ginn. 418: Imagery. 421: L.L.T. Rhodes/Taurus Photos. 424: Imagery. 425: b.l. inset & b.r. Imagery. 426: I.B.M. Archives. 427: © Hank Morgan/Science Source/Photo Researchers, Inc. 428: t.l. Silver Burdett & Ginn; b.l. Martin M. Rotker/Taurus Photos; r. E.R. Degginger.

Chapter 18 432: T. Adams. 434–435: Silver Burdett & Ginn. 439: l. Ken Kerbs/Omni Photo Communications; t.r., b.r. E.R. Degginger. 440: t.l. Grant Heilman Photography; b. Runk-Schoenberger/Grant Heilman Photography. 442: E.R. Degginger. 443: r. Imagery; l. courtesy Memorex Corporation. 444: Wide World Photos. 446: Woods Hole Oceanographic Institution. 448: E.R. Degginger. 451: Silver Burdett & Ginn. 452: Bettmann Archives. 453: l. E.R. Degginger; r. Victoria Beller-Smith/Photo Trends. 454: © 1988 David Burnett/Contact Press Images/Woodfin Camp & Associates. 455: l. © Junebug Clark/Photo Researchers, Inc.; r. Silver Burdett & Ginn. 456: t. Kurt Scholz/Shostal Associates; b. Jeff Smith/The Image Bank.

Chapter 19 460: © David Parker/Science Photo Library/Photo Researchers, Inc. 463: H. Armstrong Roberts. 464: l. E.R. Degginger; r. © John J. Dommers/Photo Researchers, Inc. 470: E.R. Degginger. 471: t. Niki Mareschal/The Image Bank; b. E.R. Degginger. 475: t. David M. Campion; b. Martha Swope. 476: Nancy Rodger/The Exploratorium. 477: © Margaret Durrance/Photo Researchers, Inc. 478: The Exploratorium. 479: l. E.R. Degginger; r. Ken Kay/Time-Life Books. 480: Bausch & Lomb. 481: Silver Burdett & Ginn. 484: l. Barry L. Runk/Grant Heilman Photography; m. © 1988 Wally NcNamee/Woodfin Camp & Associates; b. Silver Burdett & Ginn.

Chapter 20 488: Schwartzenling/The Exploratorium. 490: © Grace Moore. 491: Shostal Associates. 493: l. Imagery; r. E.R. Degginger. 494: Imagery. 500: Bill Stanton/Magnum. 501–502: Silver Burdett & Ginn. 504: l.t. E.R. Degginger; l.b. Phil Degginger; l. E.R. Degginger. 508: E.R. Degginger. 509: © Jerry Mason/Science Photo Library/Photo Researchers, Inc. 511: Imagery. 512: © John Walsh/Science Photo Library/Photo Researchers, Inc. 516: l. © Joseph Nettis/Photo Researchers, Inc.; r. courtesy of The Metropolitan Opera. 520: t. E.R. Degginger; b.l. © Jim Burgin/Science Source/Photo Researchers, Inc.;